Cover image: *Courtesy of Photodisc/Getty Images.*

Excerpts taken from:

Prentice Hall Mathematics, Algebra 1
by Allan E. Bellman, Sadie Chavis Bragg, Randall I. Charles, Basia Hall, William G. Handlin, Sr. and Dan Kennedy
Copyright © 2009 by Pearson Education, Inc.
Published by Prentice Hall
Upper Saddle River, New Jersey 07458

Prentice Hall Mathematics, Pre-Algebra
by Randall I. Charles, Bonnie McNemar and Alma Ramirez
Copyright © 2009 by Pearson Education, Inc.
Published by Prentice Hall

This special edition published in cooperation with Pearson Custom Publishing.

All trademarks, service marks, registered trademarks, and registered service marks are the property of their respective owners and are used herein for identification purposes only.

Printed in the United States of America

9 8 7 6 5 4 3 2 1

60542

www.pearsonhighered.com

ISBN 10: 0-555-01845-8
ISBN 13: 978-0-555-01845-3

MINNESOTA MATH

MEETING THE 8TH GRADE STANDARDS

CUSTOM EDITION

Taken from:

Prentice Hall Mathematics Algebra 1
by Allan E. Bellman, Sadie Chavis Bragg, Randall I. Charles, Basia Ha
William G. Handlin, Sr. and Dan Kennedy

and

Prentice Hall Mathematics Pre-Algebra
by Randall I. Charles, Bonnie McNemar and Alma Ran

Custom Publishing

New York   Boston   San Fra
London   Toronto   Sydney   Tokyo
Mexico City   Munich   Paris   Cape Tow

Pearson
Custom Publishing
is a division of

PEARSON

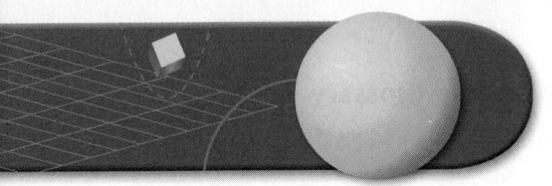

Contents in Brief

Chapter 1

Algebraic Expressions and Integers

Assessment and Test Prep

The content in this chapter was derived from *Prentice Hall Mathematics, Pre-Algebra,* by Randall I Charles, Bonnie McNemar, and Alma Ramirez.

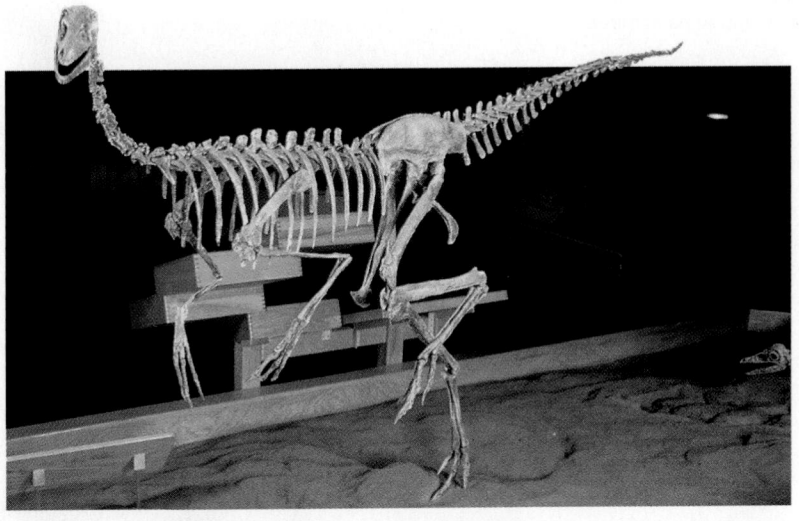

Chapter **2**

Solving One-Step Equations and Inequalities

The content in this chapter was derived from *Prentice Hall Mathematics, Pre-Algebra,* by Randall I Charles, Bonnie McNemar, and Alma Ramirez.

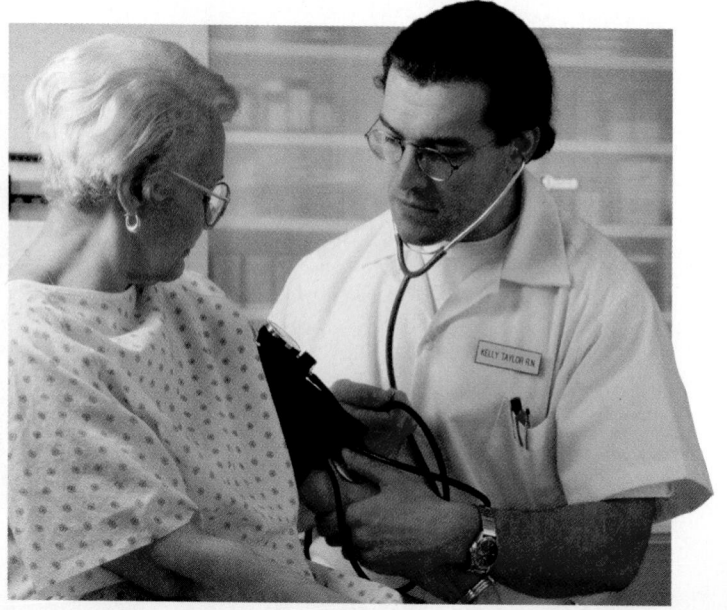

Chapter 3

Decimals and Equations

Assessment and Test Prep

The content in this chapter was derived from *Prentice Hall Mathematics, Pre-Algebra,* by Randall I Charles, Bonnie McNemar, and Alma Ramirez.

Variables, Function Patterns, and Graphs

Student Support

☑ Instant Check System

Vocabulary

GO Online

The content in this chapter was derived from chapter one of *Prentice Hall Mathematics, Algebra I,* by Allan E. Bellman, Sadie Chavis Bragg, Randall I. Charles, Basia Hall, William G. Handlin, Sr., and Dan Kennedy.

Rational Numbers

The content in this chapter was derived from chapter two of *Prentice Hall Mathematics, Algebra I,* by Allan E. Bellman, Sadie Chavis Bragg, Randall I. Charles, Basia Hall, William G. Handlin, Sr., and Dan Kennedy.

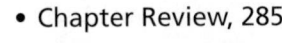

Chapter 6

Solving Equations

The content in this chapter was derived from chapter three of *Prentice Hall Mathematics, Algebra I,* by Allan E. Bellman, Sadie Chavis Bragg, Randall I. Charles, Basia Hall, William G. Handlin, Sr., and Dan Kennedy.

Chapter 7

Solving Inequalities

The content in this chapter was derived from chapter four of *Prentice Hall Mathematics, Algebra I*, by Allan E. Bellman, Sadie Chavis Bragg, Randall I. Charles, Basia Hall, William G. Handlin, Sr., and Dan Kennedy.

Chapter 8

Graphs and Functions

Assessment and Test Prep
  • **Test-Taking Strategies:** Using a Variable, 474
  • Chapter Review, 475
  • Chapter Test, 478
  • **Standardized Test Prep:** Reading Comprehension, 479

The content in this chapter was derived from chapter five of *Prentice Hall Mathematics, Algebra I,* by Allan E. Bellman, Sadie Chavis Bragg, Randall I. Charles, Basia Hall, William G. Handlin, Sr., and Dan Kennedy.

Chapter 9

Linear Equations and Their Graphs

The content in this chapter was derived from chapter six of *Prentice Hall Mathematics, Algebra I,* by Allan E. Bellman, Sadie Chavis Bragg, Randall I. Charles, Basia Hall, William G. Handlin, Sr., and Dan Kennedy.

Chapter 10

Systems of Equations and Inequalities

Assessment and Test Prep

The content in this chapter was derived from chapter seven of *Prentice Hall Mathematics, Algebra I,* by Allan E. Bellman, Sadie Chavis Bragg, Randall I. Charles, Basia Hall, William G. Handlin, Sr., and Dan Kennedy.

Chapter 11

Exponents and Exponential Functions

The content in this chapter was derived from chapter eight of *Prentice Hall Mathematics, Algebra I,* by Allan E. Bellman, Sadie Chavis Bragg, Randall I. Charles, Basia Hall, William G. Handlin, Sr., and Dan Kennedy.

Assessment and Test Prep

Chapter 12

Nonlinear Functions and Polynomials

Assessment and Test Prep

The content in this chapter was derived from *Prentice Hall Mathematics, Pre-Algebra,* by Randall I Charles, Bonnie McNemar, and Alma Ramirez.

What You've Learned

In previous courses you learned:

- How to evaluate expressions using the order of operations.
- How to add, subtract, multiply, and divide whole numbers.
- How to compare whole numbers.
- How to relate numbers to points on a number line.

 Check Your Readiness    for Help to the Lesson in green.

Multiplying and Dividing Whole Numbers (Skills Handbook, pp. 763, 764)

Find each product or quotient.

1. $7 \div 7$ **2.** $99 \div 9$ **3.** $44 \div 4$ **4.** $57 \div 3$

5. $65 \div 5$ **6.** 5×8 **7.** $68 \div 4$ **8.** 11×4

9. 22×8 **10.** 2×14 **11.** 83×2 **12.** 5×15

Comparing Whole Numbers (Skills Handbook, p. 761)

Compare. Use $>$, $<$, or $=$ to complete each statement.

13. $5 \blacksquare 2$ **14.** $1 \blacksquare 0$ **15.** $14 \blacksquare 17$

16. $6 + 12 \blacksquare 7 + 13$ **17.** $10 - 2 \blacksquare 27 - 18$ **18.** $4 \times 7 \blacksquare 2 \times 14$

Multiplying and Dividing Whole Numbers (Skills Handbook, pp. 763, 764)

Find each product or quotient.

19. $36 \div 3$ **20.** 10×3 **21.** $7(4)$ **22.** $25 \div 5$

23. $12 \cdot 8$ **24.** $7\overline{)35}$ **25.** $20 \cdot 10$ **26.** $9\overline{)720}$

27. $124 \div 4$ **28.** $12\overline{)156}$ **29.** $4 \cdot 12 \cdot 10$ **30.** $132 \div 11$

Reading Numbers on a Number Line (Skills Handbook, p. 761)

What is the distance of each point from zero on the number line?

31. A **32.** B

33. C **34.** D

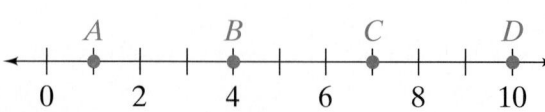

Algebraic Expressions and Integers

◄)) Key Vocabulary

- absolute value (p. 19)
- conjecture (p. 35)
- coordinate plane (p. 52)
- counterexample (p. 37)
- evaluate (p. 14)
- inductive reasoning (p. 35)
- integers (p. 19)
- opposites (p. 19)
- order of operations (p. 8)
- ordered pair (p. 52)
- origin (p. 52)
- quadrants (p. 52)
- variable (p. 4)
- variable expression (p. 4)
- x-axis (p. 52)
- x-coordinate (p. 52)
- y-axis (p. 52)
- y-coordinate (p. 52)

What You'll Learn Next

In this chapter, you will learn how to

- Use variables and variable expressions.

- Perform operations with integers.

- Graph points in the coordinate plane.

- Solve a problem by looking for a pattern.

Activity Lab Applying what you learn, on pages 64–65 you will solve problems about sunken ships.

1-1 Variables and Expressions

What You'll Learn
- To identify variables, numerical expressions, and variable expressions
- To write variable expressions for word phrases

... And Why
To use the language of algebra to model real-world problems

✓ Check Skills You'll Need
Complete each equation.

1. 1 week = ■ days

2. 1 foot = ■ inches

3. 1 nickel = ■ cents

4. 1 gallon = ■ quarts

5. 1 yard = ■ feet

 **for Help**
Table 1, p. 818

🔊 New Vocabulary
- variable
- variable expression

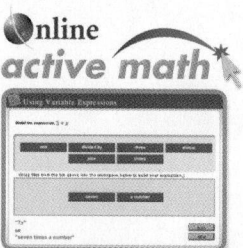

For: Variable Expressions Activity
Use: Interactive Textbook, 1-1

1 Identifying Numerical and Variable Expressions

Gas Mileage How many miles can you drive on ten gallons of gas? The answer depends on the type of vehicle you drive. The table shows some typical data.

Vehicle Type	Miles	Gallons	Miles per Gallon
Subcompact	330	10	$330 \div 10$
Compact	300	10	$300 \div 10$
Mid-size sedan	245	10	$245 \div 10$
Sport utility vehicle	175	10	$175 \div 10$
Pickup truck	160	10	$160 \div 10$

The last column gives a *numerical expression*
for each vehicle's miles per gallon.

If you don't know the number of miles, you can use a *variable* to stand for the number. Then you can write a *variable expression* for miles per gallon.

variable → m ← miles on 10 gallons

variable expression → $m \div 10$ ← miles per gallon

A **variable** is a letter that stands for a number.
A **variable expression** is a mathematical phrase that uses variables, numerals, and operation symbols.

1 EXAMPLE Identifying Expressions

Identify each expression as a *numerical expression* or a *variable expression*. For a variable expression, name the variable.

a. $5 - 5$
numerical expression

b. $c - 5$
Variable expression; c is the variable.

1. Identify each expression as a *numerical expression* or a *variable expression*. For a variable expression, name the variable.

a. $8 \div x$ **b.** 100×6 **c.** $d + 43 - 9$

2 Writing Variable Expressions

You can translate word phrases into variable expressions.

Word Phrase	Variable Expression
Nine more than a number y	$y + 9$
4 less than a number n	$n - 4$
A number z times three	$z \cdot 3$ or $3z$ or $3(z)$
A number a divided by 12	$a \div 12$ or $\frac{a}{12}$
5 times the quantity 4 plus a number c	$5 \cdot (4 + c)$ or $5(4 + c)$

Writing in Math

You can translate many words for operations into operation symbols.

total	$+$
more than	$+$
increased by	$+$
difference	$-$
fewer than	$-$
less than	$-$
decreased by	$-$
product	$\times$ or $\cdot$ or ( )
times	$\times$ or $\cdot$ or ( )
quotient	$\div$ or —
divided by	$\div$ or —

A variable expression is an efficient way to express a mathematical relationship.

2 EXAMPLE   Real-World 🌐 Problem Solving

Science The fastest dinosaur may have been *Ornithomimus,* which could run about 60 ft in a second. Write a variable expression for the distance Ornithomimus could run in a given time.

Words	60	times	number of seconds

Let s = number of seconds.

Expression	60	$\cdot$	s

The variable expression $60 \cdot s$, or $60s$, describes the distance in feet Ornithomimus could run in s seconds.

Real-World 🌐 Connection

Ornithomimus was an ostrich-like oviraptor about 7 ft tall. Its long tail acted as a counterbalance and as a stabilizer during fast turns.

✓ **Quick Check**

2. a. Bagels cost $.50 each. Write a variable expression for the cost of b bagels.

  b. Measurement Write a variable expression for the number of hours in m minutes.

EXERCISES

For more exercises, see *Extra Skill and Word Problem Practice.*

Practice and Problem Solving

A Practice by Example

Example 1
(page 4)

GO for Help

Identify each expression as a *numerical expression* or a *variable expression*. For a variable expression, name the variable.

1. $b + 6$ **2.** $80 \div 8$ **3.** $14 - n$

4. 14×14 **5.** $100x$ **6.** $8 + 8 + 8 + 8$

Example 2
(page 5)

Write a variable expression for each word phrase.

7. 16 more than m **8.** 6 divided by z

9. the product of c and 3   **10.** 2 less than p

11. b times 3   **12.** 4 fewer than j

13. n divided by 3   **14.** 3 divided by n

15. x less than 2   **16.** 8 less than z

Write a numerical or variable expression for each quantity.

17. two dozen eggs   **18.** d dozen eggs

19. the value in cents of 7 nickels   **20.** the value in cents of n nickels

21. number of quarts in 3 gallons   **22.** number of quarts in g gallons

B Apply Your Skills

Identify each expression as a *numerical expression* or a *variable expression*. For a variable expression, name the variable.

23. $d + 53$ **24.** $12 - 7$ **25.** $\frac{g}{9}$ **26.** $4(5)$

Measurement Write an expression for each quantity.

27. the number of days in 4 weeks

28. the number of days in w weeks

29. number of pounds in 160 ounces

30. number of pounds in z ounces

31. the number of feet in 100 inches

32. the number of feet in i inches

33. Mia has $20 less than Brandi. Brandi has d dollars. Write a variable expression for the amount of money Mia has.

Use the calorie chart at the left for Exercises 34 and 35.

34. Write a variable expression for the number of calories in e eggs and one slice of bread.

35. Write a variable expression for the number of calories in a fruit salad made from a apples and b bananas.

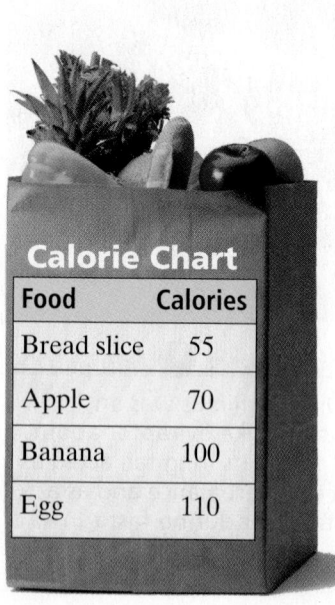

Calorie Chart

Food	Calories
Bread slice	55
Apple	70
Banana	100
Egg	110

GO Online

Homework Video Tutor

Visit: PHSchool.com
Web Code: ade-0101

Modeling In each model, the red line represents a variable expression. Match each model with its expression.

A. $\frac{x}{4}$ **B.** $4 + x$ **C.** $4x$ **D.** $x - 4$

36.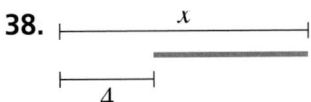

37.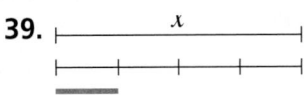

38.

39.

C Challenge

40. Writing in Math How are numerical expressions and variable expressions similar? How are they different?

41. Error Analysis A student wrote the variable expression $n - 5$ for the word phrase *n less than five*. Explain the student's error.

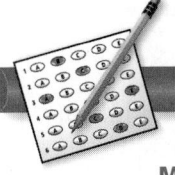

Test Prep

Multiple Choice

A hot-air balloon is at an altitude of m meters. In Exercises 42–44, which expression matches the given word phrase?

42. the balloon's new altitude after rising 34 meters
 A. $m - 34$ **B.** $m + 34$ **C.** $3m$ **D.** $34m$

43. the balloon's new altitude after falling 2,000 meters
 F. $m + 2{,}000$ **G.** $2{,}000 - m$ **H.** $2{,}000m$ **J.** $m - 2{,}000$

44. the balloon's new altitude after tripling its altitude
 A. $m - 34$ **B.** $m + 34$ **C.** $3m$ **D.** $34m$

45. Pam is 15 years old. Which expression gives Pam's age p years ago?
 F. $p - 15$ **G.** $p + 15$ **H.** $15 - p$ **J.** $\frac{p}{15}$

Mixed Review

Skills Handbook

GO for Help

Compute.

46. 9×25 **47.** $3 \times 6 \times 4$ **48.** 8×1

49. $225 \div 3$ **50.** $169 \div 13$ **51.** $25{,}942 \div 12{,}971$

52. Purchasing A customer buys orange juice for \$.95 and two apples for \$.55 each. She gives the cashier a five-dollar bill. How much change should the cashier give the customer?

53. Nutrition There are seven servings in a box of pita chips. The box weighs 16 oz. About how many ounces are in each serving? Round your answer to the nearest tenth.

1-2 The Order of Operations

What You'll Learn

- To use the order of operations
- To use grouping symbols

. . . And Why

To find the value of an expression with more than one operation

 **Check Skills You'll Need**

Find each quotient.

1. $164 \div 2$ **2.** $344 \div 8$

3. $284 \div 4$ **4.** $133 \div 7$

5. $182 \div 13$ **6.** $650 \div 25$

 **for Help**

Skills Handbook, p. 764

🔊 **New Vocabulary**

- order of operations

 **Using the Order of Operations**

Activity

Experimenting With Order

In most languages, the meaning of words depends on their order. For example, "sign the check" is not the same as "check the sign."

Similarly, order is important in the language of mathematics.

1. **Mental Math** Find the value of the expression $3 + 5 \times 2$.

2. **Analyze** What answer do you get to Question 1 if you multiply before adding? If you add before multiplying?

3. **Reasoning** How does the order in which you do the operations affect your answer?

The order in which you perform operations can affect the value of an expression. To avoid confusion, mathematicians have agreed on an **order of operations.** Multiply and divide first. Then add and subtract.

To *simplify* a numerical expression, you use the order of operations and replace the expression with the simplest name for its value.

1 EXAMPLE **Simplifying Expressions**

Simplify $4 + 15 \div 3$.

$$4 + 15 \div 3$$

$$4 + 5 \qquad \text{First divide.}$$

$$9 \qquad \text{Then add.}$$

☑ **Quick Check**

1. Simplify each expression.

   a. $2 + 5 \times 3$ **b.** $12 \div 3 - 1$ **c.** $10 - 1 \cdot 7$

When operations have the same rank in the order of operations, do them from left to right.

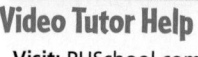 **nline**

Video Tutor Help

Visit: PHSchool.com
Web Code: ada-0775

2 EXAMPLE   Using the Order of Operations

Simplify $3 \cdot 5 - 8 \div 4 + 6$.

$3 \cdot 5 - 8 \div 4 + 6$

$15 \quad - \quad 2 \quad + \quad 6$ **Multiply and divide from left to right.**

$13 + 6$ **Add and subtract from left to right.**

19 **Add.**

✓ Quick Check

2. Simplify each expression.

   a. $4 - 1 \cdot 2 + 6 \div 3$ **b.** $5 + 6 \cdot 4 \div 3 - 1$

Calculator Hint

Many calculators use the order of operations. To test yours, enter $10 - 4 \div 2$. If the answer is 8, then your calculator uses the order of operations.

If the answer is 3, then your calculator does not use the order of operations.

2 Using Grouping Symbols

Grouping symbols, such as parentheses, ( ), and brackets, [ ], indicate order. A fraction bar also is a grouping symbol, since $\frac{4 + 2}{3} = (4 + 2) \div 3$. Always work inside grouping symbols first.

Key Concepts   Order of Operations

1. Work inside grouping symbols.

2. Multiply and divide in order from left to right.

3. Add and subtract in order from left to right.

3 EXAMPLE   Simplifying With Grouping Symbols

Multiple Choice Which procedure is correct for simplifying $24 \div [6 - (2 \cdot 2)]$?

  Ⓐ $24 \div [6 - (2 \cdot 2)] = 4 - 2 \cdot 2 = 4 - 4 = 0$
  Ⓑ $24 \div [6 - (2 \cdot 2)] = 24 \div 4 \cdot 2 = 24 \div 8 = 3$
  Ⓒ $24 \div [6 - (2 \cdot 2)] = 4 - 2 \cdot 2 = 2 \cdot 2 = 4$
  Ⓓ $24 \div [6 - (2 \cdot 2)] = 24 \div (6 - 4) = 24 \div 2 = 12$

Choice D follows the order of operations by working inside the grouping symbols first. Choice D is correct.

✓ Quick Check

3. Simplify the expression $1 + \frac{10 - 2}{4}$.

To do Example 3 with a graphing calculator, see page 746.

Test-Taking Tip

Grouping symbols say "do this first." Inside grouping symbols, multiply and divide before adding and subtracting.

You can use the order of operations to find the area of an irregular figure by more than one method.

More Than One Way

Urban Planning Some urban planners specialize in planning entire new towns. These towns are designed for livability, with plenty of open space. The sketch shows the dimensions for a new town called Panorama. Find Panorama's area.

Kevin's Method

Divide the figure into rectangles. Then add their areas.

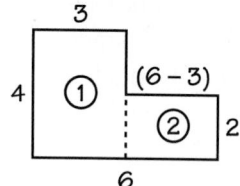

$$Area = Area \, ① + Area \, ②$$
$$= 4 \cdot 3 + (6 - 3) \cdot 2$$
$$= 4 \cdot 3 + 3 \cdot 2$$
$$= 12 + 6$$
$$= 18$$

Panorama's area is 18 km².

Tina's Method

Visualize attaching a small rectangle to complete a large rectangle. Then subtract the small area from the large area.

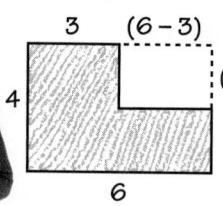

$$Area = \begin{matrix} \text{Area of large} \\ \text{rectangle} \end{matrix} - \begin{matrix} \text{Area of small} \\ \text{rectangle} \end{matrix}$$
$$= 6 \cdot 4 - (6 - 3) \cdot (4 - 2)$$
$$= 6 \cdot 4 - 3 \cdot 2$$
$$= 24 - 6$$
$$= 18$$

Panorama's area is 18 km².

Choose a Method

1. Which method would you use to find the town's area? Explain.

2. Can you think of another way to solve the problem? Explain.

EXERCISES

For more exercises, see *Extra Skill and Word Problem Practice.*

Practice and Problem Solving

A Practice by Example

Examples 1 and 2
(pages 8 and 9)

GO for Help

Example 3
(page 9)

Simplify each expression.

1. $3 + 6 \times 4$ **2.** $35 \div 7 - 2$ **3.** $8 - 2 \cdot 3$

4. $6 - 6 \div 3$ **5.** $21 - 13 + 8$ **6.** $6 \cdot 2 + 4$

7. $12 - 8 \div 2 + 3$ **8.** $21 \div 7 + 14 \times 2$ **9.** $2 \cdot 2 + 0 \cdot 4$

10. $4(4) - 2(5)$ **11.** $2 + 3 \cdot 24 \div 6$ **12.** $4 \div 4 \cdot 4 + 4 - 4$

13. $7 + 3 \cdot (8 \div 4)$ **14.** $2(15 - 9) \cdot 9$ **15.** $[2 + (6 \cdot 8)] - 1$

16. $2(6) + \dfrac{7 + 8}{3}$ **17.** $3(7 + 4)$ **18.** $12 \div (3 - 2) + 1$

19. $6 + \dfrac{6 + 2}{4}$ **20.** $\dfrac{21 + 15}{3 + 6}$ **21.** $(21 + 3) \div 4 \div 2$

B Apply Your Skills

22. Error Analysis A student found the value of the expression $30 \div 6 - 1$ to be 6. Explain the student's error.

23. Writing in Math Why do we need to agree on an order of operations?

Simplify each expression. Justify your work.

24. $(56 - 5) \div 17$ **25.** $60 \div 4 + 9$ **26.** $2[8 + (5 - 3)] - 8$

27. $12 \div 3 \times 4$ **28.** $36 - 27 \div 9 \div 1$ **29.** $6(4 + 1) - 5$

30. $14 + 5 \times 2$ **31.** $440 \div (2 + 18)$ **32.** $16 \div 8 \times 2$

GO for Help

For a guide to solving
Exercise 26, see
page 13.

Compare. Use >, <, or = to complete each statement.

33. $15 \cdot 3 - 2 \ \blacksquare \ 15 \cdot (3 - 2)$ **34.** $18 - 6 \div 3 \ \blacksquare \ (18 - 6) \div 3$

35. $8 + 12 \div 4 \ \blacksquare \ (8 + 12) \div 4$ **36.** $22 - 7 \cdot 2 \ \blacksquare \ (22 - 7) \cdot 2$

37. $12 \div 3 + 9 \cdot 4 \ \blacksquare \ 12 \div (3 + 9) \cdot 4$

38. $(19 - 15) \div (3 + 1) \ \blacksquare \ 19 - 15 \div 3 + 1$

Insert grouping symbols to make each number sentence true.

39. $7 + 4 \cdot 6 = 66$ **40.** $7 \cdot 8 - 6 + 3 = 17$ **41.** $3 + 8 - 2 \cdot 5 = 45$

42. Multiple Choice Insert grouping symbols to make the number sentence $3 + 8 - 2 \cdot 5 = 45$ correct.

    A $(3 + 8) - 2 \cdot 5 = 45$ **B** $3 + (8 - 2) \cdot 5 = 45$

    C $[3 + (8 - 2)] \cdot 5 = 45$ **D** $3 + [8 - (2 \cdot 5)] = 45$

Write a numerical expression for each phrase. Then simplify.

43. five added to the product of four and nine

44. twenty-one minus the sum of fifteen and five

45. seventeen minus the quotient of twenty-five and five

GO Online
Homework Video Tutor

Visit: PHSchool.com
Web Code: ade-0102

46. On the Job A part-time employee worked 4 hours on Monday and 7 hours each day for the next 3 days. Write and simplify an expression that shows the total number of hours worked.

C Challenge **Write two expressions you could use to find the area of each shaded figure. Find the area.**

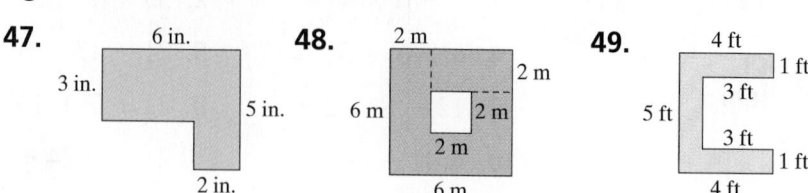

47. 6 in.   3 in.   5 in.   2 in.

48. 2 m   2 m   6 m   2 m   2 m   6 m

49. 4 ft   1 ft   3 ft   5 ft   3 ft   1 ft   4 ft

50. Open-Ended Write a word problem for the numerical expression $3(4 + 3) + 2$. Then simplify the expression.

51. Number Sense Use the digits 1–9 in order. Insert operation signs and grouping symbols to get a value of 100.

Test Prep

Multiple Choice

52. Which expression has a value of 18?
  A. $3 \cdot 2 + 4$
  B. $(18 - 10) \div 4 + 15$
  C. $4 \cdot 2 + 3 - 2$
  D. $27 - 13 \cdot 2 + 17(6 - 5)$

53. Which expression gives the area of the garden?
  F. $4(2 + 5) + 5 \cdot 5$
  G. $(2 + 5 + 2) \cdot (2 + 5 + 2) - 4(2 \cdot 2)$
  H. $(2 + 5 + 2) - (2 \cdot 2)$
  J. $4(2 \cdot 2) + 4(5 \cdot 2) + 5 \cdot 5$

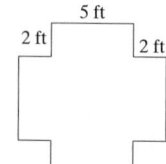

5 ft   2 ft   2 ft

54. Which set of grouping symbols makes the equation true? $2 \cdot 3 + 5 - 2 \cdot 2 = 12$
  A. $(2 \cdot 3) + 5 - (2 \cdot 2)$
  B. $2 \cdot [3 + (5 - 2)] \cdot 2$
  C. $2 \cdot [3 + (5 - 2 \cdot 2)]$
  D. $2 \cdot (3 + 5) - 2 \cdot 2$

55. What is the value of $8 \cdot 5 - 3(24 \div 6)$?
  F. 28
  G. 64
  H. 111
  J. 148

Mixed Review

 **GO for Help**

Lesson 1-1 **Write a variable expression for each word phrase.**

56. the product of a number n and 8

57. k divided by 20

58. six less than a number h

59. the value, in cents, of d dimes

60. A telephone call costs c cents per minute. Write a variable expression for the cost of a 15-minute call.

Understanding Math Problems Read the problem below. Then let Daria's thinking guide you through the solution. Check your understanding with the exercises at the bottom of the page.

Simplify $2[8 + (5 - 3)] - 8$.

What Daria Thinks | ### What Daria Writes

There are two sets of grouping symbols, square brackets and parentheses: $[8 + (5 - 3)]$.

$$2[8 + (5 - 3)] - 8$$

I need to begin by working inside the innermost grouping symbols, the parentheses: $(5 - 3)$.

$$2[8 + (2)] - 8$$

Now I need to work inside the next pair of grouping symbols, the square brackets, to find $[8 + 2]$.

$$2[10] - 8$$

Multiply before subtracting.

$$20 - 8$$

Now subtract.

$$12$$

The simplified expression is 12.

EXERCISES

Simplify each expression.

1. $2[(13 - 4) \div 3]$

2. $1 + \frac{10 - 2}{4}$

3. $3[(8 + 4) \div 6]$

4. $\frac{6 + 9}{3} - 2$

5. $4[3 + (2 \cdot 3)]$

6. $16 \div (8 - 4) - 2$

7. $3(8 - 2) + 12$

8. $2[4(7 - 2) + 3]$

9. $6 - \frac{4 - 10}{2}$

10. $25 \div (15 \div 3) \cdot 2$

11. $\frac{17 - 12}{5} + (4 - 2)$

12. $7(12 \div 3 - 3)$

1-3

Writing and Evaluating Expressions

What You'll Learn

- To evaluate variable expressions
- To solve problems by evaluating expressions

. . . And Why

To solve real-world problems involving packaging and shopping

☑ **Check Skills You'll Need**

Simplify each expression.

1. $6(9 + 1)$

2. $17 - 2 + 3$

3. $9 + 8 \cdot 2 + 4$

4. $[3(5) + 1] \cdot 2$

 **for Help**

Lesson 1-2

🔊 **New Vocabulary**

- evaluate

1 Evaluating Variable Expressions

To **evaluate** a variable expression, you first replace each variable with a number. Then, you use the order of operations to simplify.

1 EXAMPLE

Evaluate $4y - 15$ for $y = 9$.

$$
\begin{aligned}
4y - 15 &= 4(9) - 15 \quad &\text{Replace } y \text{ with 9.} \\
&= 36 - 15 \quad &\text{Multiply.} \\
&= 21 \quad &\text{Subtract.}
\end{aligned}
$$

☑ Quick Check

1. Evaluate each expression.

a. $63 - 5x$, for $x = 7$ **b.** $4(t + 3) + 1$, for $t = 8$

Sometimes expressions have more than one variable.

2 EXAMPLE   Replacing More Than One Variable

Evaluate $3ab + \dfrac{c}{2}$ for $a = 2$, $b = 5$, and $c = 10$.

$$
\begin{aligned}
3ab + \frac{c}{2} &= 3 \cdot 2 \cdot 5 + \frac{10}{2} \quad &\text{Replace the variables.} \\
&= 3 \cdot 2 \cdot 5 + 5 \quad &\text{Work within grouping symbols.} \\
&= 6 \cdot 5 + 5 \quad &\text{Multiply from left to right.} \\
&= 30 + 5 \quad &\text{Multiply.} \\
&= 35 \quad &\text{Add.}
\end{aligned}
$$

☑ Quick Check

2. Evaluate each expression.

a. $6(g + h)$, for $g = 8$ and $h = 7$

b. $2xy - z$, for $x = 4$, $y = 3$, and $z = 1$

c. $\dfrac{r + s}{2}$, for $r = 13$ and $s = 11$

2 Solving Problems by Evaluating Expressions

You can write and evaluate variable expressions to solve problems.

3 EXAMPLE   Real-World 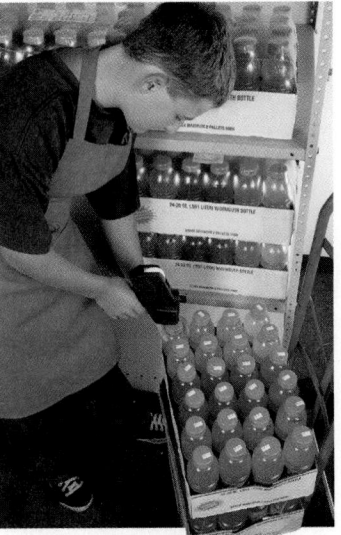 Problem Solving

Purchasing Energy drinks come in cases of 24 bottles.
a. Write a variable expression for the number of cases a store should order to get *b* bottles of energy drinks.
b. Evaluate the expression for 120 bottles.

a. *b* bottles

$\dfrac{b}{24}$ ← bottles wanted
       ← number in case

b. 120 bottles

$\dfrac{b}{24} = \dfrac{120}{24}$ **Evaluate for *b* = 120.**

$= 5$ **Divide.**

The store should order five cases to get 120 bottles.

✓ Quick Check

3. The store pays $29 for each case of drinks. Write a variable expression for the cost of *c* cases. Find the cost of five cases.

Real-World 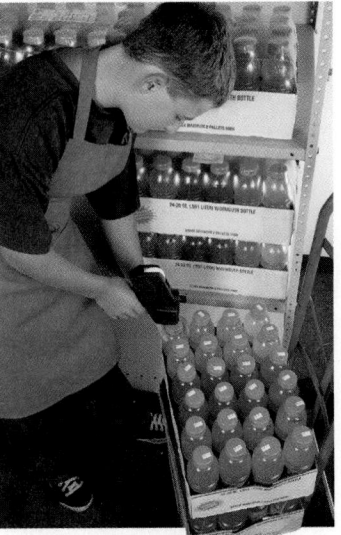 Connection

In a case, bottles are often arranged in 4 rows of 6 (or 6 rows of 4).

4 EXAMPLE   Real-World 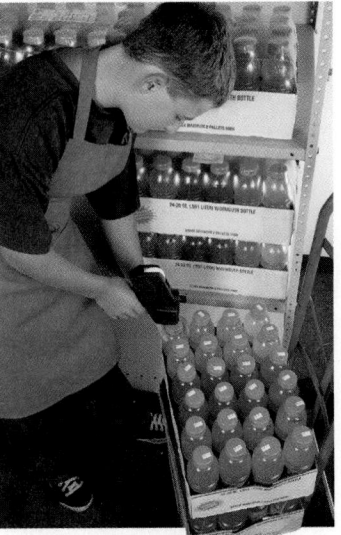 Problem Solving

Online Shopping An online music store charges $14 for each CD. Shipping costs $6 per order. Write a variable expression for the cost of ordering CDs. Find the cost of ordering eight CDs.

Table

Number of CDs	Cost of CDs	Shipping ($)	Total Cost ($)
1	$1 \cdot 14$	6	$1 \cdot 14 + 6 = 20$
2	$2 \cdot 14$	6	$2 \cdot 14 + 6 = 34$
4	$4 \cdot 14$	6	$4 \cdot 14 + 6 = 62$

Let *n* = number of CDs.

Expression   14   ·   *n*   +   6

Evaluate the expression for *n* = 8.

$14 \cdot n + 6 = 14 \cdot 8 + 6$ **Replace *n* with 8.**

$= 112 + 6 = 118$ **Multiply. Then add.**

It costs $118 to order eight CDs.

Problem Solving Hint
In Example 4, the phrase *for each* implies multiplication. So *$14 for each CD* means "$14 times the number of CDs."

✓ Quick Check

4. Find the cost of ordering ten CDs.

EXERCISES

For more exercises, see *Extra Skill and Word Problem Practice*.

Practice and Problem Solving

A Practice by Example

Example 1
(page 14)

GO for Help

Evaluate each expression.

1. $7b$, for $b = 5$ **2.** $5 - c$, for $c = 3$ **3.** $x \div 8$, for $x = 40$

4. $3n + 2$, for $n = 7$ **5.** $41 - 4h$, for $h = 10$ **6.** $5a + 7$, for $a = 20$

Example 2
(page 14)

Evaluate each expression for $x = 2$, $y = 3$, and $z = 10$.

7. xyz **8.** $8y \div x$ **9.** $\frac{z}{5} + 2$ **10.** $4y - x$

11. $2z + xy$ **12.** $\frac{9 + y}{x}$ **13.** $4xy - z$ **14.** $5(y + z)$

Examples 3 and 4
(page 15)

15. Word Processing An office assistant types 55 words per minute.
   a. Write a variable expression for the number of words the office assistant types in m minutes.
   b. Evaluate the expression for 20 minutes.

16. Online Purchasing An online video store charges $24 for each DVD. Shipping costs $4 per order.
   a. Write a variable expression for the cost of ordering DVDs.
   b. Find the cost of ordering 3 DVDs.

B Apply Your Skills

Evaluate each expression.

17. $2a + 5$, for $a = 5$ **18.** $105z$, for $z = 7$

19. $6 \div a + 8$, for $a = 2$ **20.** $19 - (a - 4)$, for $a = 8$

21. $13ab$, for $a = 1$ and $b = 7$ **22.** $16 - 4mn$, for $m = 0$ and $n = 3$

23. $j(5 + k)$, for $j = 11$ and $k = 4$ **24.** rst, for $r = 5$, $s = 5$, and $t = 5$

25. $\frac{150}{z + y}$, for $y = 25$ and $z = 50$ **26.** $\frac{x - y}{4}$, for $x = 52$ and $y = 12$

27. Marine Biology Write an expression for the number of kilometers a dolphin travels in d hours swimming at 8 km/h. Then find the number of kilometers the dolphin travels in 3 hours.

28. Data Analysis Use the chart to find how many calories a 100-lb person uses in an hour of moderate walking.
   a. Write an expression for the number of calories a 100-lb person uses in moderate walking for w hours.
   b. Evaluate the expression to find the number of calories a 100-lb person uses in moderate walking for 2 hours.

Calories per Hour Used by a 100-lb Walker

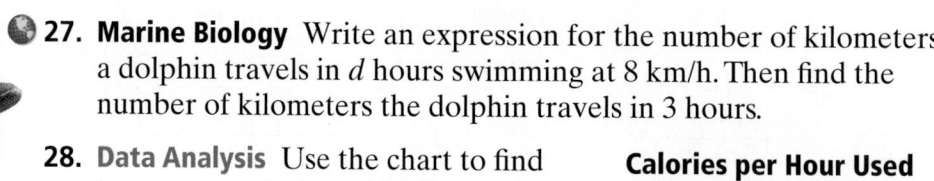

Type of Walking	Calories
Slow	110
Moderate	153
Brisk	175
Racing	295

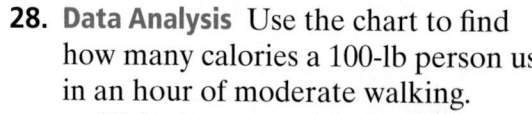

Source: www.nutristrategy.com

Real-World Connection

By *porpoising* (jumping clear of the water), dolphins can travel as fast as 26 km/h.

29. Error Analysis Your friend evaluates $(10 - k) \div 5$ for $k = 5$ and gets 9 for an answer. Explain your friend's error.

Homework Video Tutor
Visit: PHSchool.com
Web Code: ade-0103

30. Evaluate $4a - b + \frac{b}{2}$, for $a = 3$ and $b = 4$.

31. A fitness club requires a \$100 initiation fee and dues of \$25 each month. Write an expression for the cost of membership for n months. Then find the cost of membership for one year.

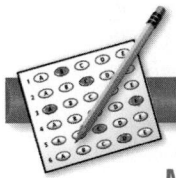 **Challenge**

32. A carnival charges \$5 for admission plus \$2 per ride.
  a. Write an expression for the cost of admission plus r rides.
  b. Find the cost of admission plus six rides.
  c. How many rides can you afford if you have \$15 to spend?

33. **Writing in Math** Write a word problem that could be solved by evaluating the expression $3x - 5$ for $x = 5$.

Test Prep

Multiple Choice

In Exercises 34–37, use the following fact to answer the questions:
Every minute, about 145 babies are born in the world.

34. Which expression shows how many babies are born in the world in m minutes?
  A. $60m$
  B. $145m + 60$
  C. $60m + 145$
  D. $145m$

35. How many babies are born in the world in 6 minutes?
  F. 360 babies
  G. 505 babies
  H. 870 babies
  J. 930 babies

36. How many babies are born in the world in one day?
  A. 3,480 babies
  B. 86,400 babies
  C. 104,400 babies
  D. 208,800 babies

37. How many babies are born in the world in one week?
  F. 1,461,600 babies
  G. 522,000 babies
  H. 60,900 babies
  J. 10,080 babies

Mixed Review

 **for Help**

Lesson 1-2   **Simplify each expression.**

38. $(60 - 6) \div 9$ **39.** $80 \div 2 + 13$ **40.** $5 \div 5 \cdot 5 - 5$

Lesson 1-1   **Write a variable expression for each word phrase.**

41. t fewer than 19   **42.** d divided by 20   **43.** the sum of 8 and n

Skills Handbook

44. **Error Analysis** Valerie has test grades of 96, 82, 78, and 76. Using a calculator, she found her average grade to be 275. Is Valerie's answer reasonable? Explain Valerie's error.

Integers and Absolute Value

What You'll Learn

- To represent, graph, and order integers
- To find opposites and absolute values

... And Why

To represent real-world quantities that are less than zero, such as cold temperatures

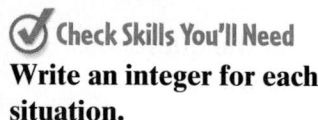 **Check Skills You'll Need**

Write an integer for each situation.

1. lose $7

2. find $9

3. 8 steps forward

4. 3 yards gained

5. 5 floors down

GO for Help

Skills Handbook, p. 779

🔊 **New Vocabulary**

- **opposites**
- **integers**
- **absolute value**

1 Comparing Integers

Antifreeze is mixed with the water in a car's radiator to prevent the water from freezing. Pure water freezes at about 32 degrees Fahrenheit (°F) *above* zero. A mixture of equal parts water and antifreeze freezes at about 32 degrees *below* zero.

Freezing Points

Substance	Freezing Temperature (°F)
Water	32
Antifreeze and water	−32
Seawater	28
Gasoline	−36

You can write 32 degrees above zero as +32°F or 32°F. You can write 32 degrees below zero as −32°F. Read the numbers 32 and −32 as "*positive* 32" and "*negative* 32," respectively.

1 EXAMPLE Representing Negative Numbers

Temperature Write a number to represent the temperature shown by the thermometer.

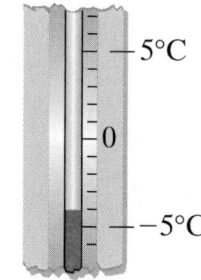

The temperature of the liquid in the thermometer is 4 degrees Celsius below zero, or −4°C.

✓ Quick Check

1. **Temperature** Seawater freezes at about 28°F, or about 2 degrees Celsius below zero. Write a number to represent the Celsius temperature.

You can graph positive and negative numbers on a number line. A number line helps you compare numbers and arrange them in order.

Numbers increase in value from left to right.

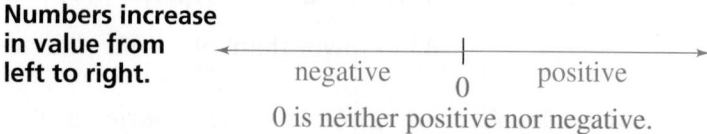

0 is neither positive nor negative.

To compare and order numbers, you can use symbols for "is less than" (<), "is less than or equal to" (≤), "is greater than" (>), and "is greater than or equal to" (≥).

2 EXAMPLE   **Graphing on a Number Line**

Graph −1, 4, and −5 on a number line. Compare the numbers and order them from least to greatest.

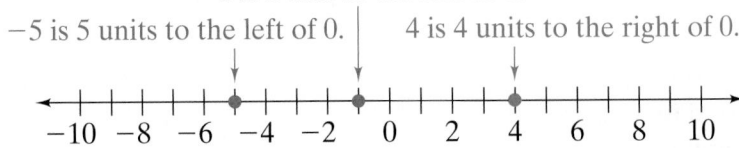

−1 is 1 unit to the left of 0.
−5 is 5 units to the left of 0.
4 is 4 units to the right of 0.

−5 is to the left of −1, and −1 is to the left of 4, so $-5 < -1 < 4$. From least to greatest, the numbers are −5, −1, 4.

✓ Quick Check

2. Graph 0, 2, and −6. Compare the numbers and order the numbers from least to greatest.

---

2   Finding Absolute Value

Numbers that are the same distance from zero on a number line but in opposite directions are called **opposites.**

4 units   4 units

−4 and 4 are opposites.

Integers are the whole numbers and their opposites. A number's distance from zero on the number line is called its **absolute value.** You write *the absolute value of 3* as $|3|$.

Vocabulary Tip

Recall: The <u>whole numbers</u>, 0, 1, 2, 3, 4, . . . , are the counting numbers and zero.

3 EXAMPLE   **Finding Absolute Value**

Use a number line to find $|-3|$ and $|3|$.

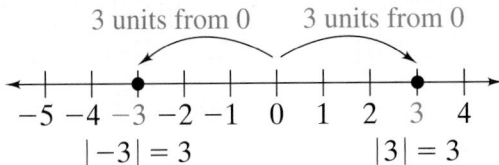

3 units from 0   3 units from 0

$|-3| = 3$ $|3| = 3$

✓ Quick Check

3. Write $|-10|$ in words. Then find $|-10|$.

EXERCISES

For more exercises, see *Extra Skill and Word Problem Practice*.

Practice and Problem Solving

A Practice by Example

Example 1
(page 18)

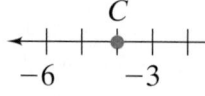

Write a number to represent each quantity.

1. a profit of $250   **2.** 18°C below zero   **3.** 45 s before launch

4. a deposit of $110   **5.** a debt of $50   **6.** win by 7 points

7. 300 ft below sea level   **8.** a loss of 8 yd   **9.** an elevation of 3,400 ft

Example 2
(page 19)

Write the number represented by each point on the number line.

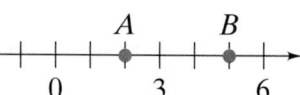

10. *A*   **11.** *B*   **12.** *C*

Graph each set of numbers on a number line. Then order the numbers from least to greatest.

13. −2, 8, −9   **14.** −3, −12, −9   **15.** 0, 6, −6

Example 3
(page 19)

Use a number line to find the absolute values of the integers in each pair.

16. 1, −1   **17.** −2, 2   **18.** −8, 8   **19.** −7, 7   **20.** 6, −6   **21.** −4, 4

Simplify each expression.

22. $|18|$ **23.** the absolute value of −9

24. $|-3|$ **25.** the absolute value of 6

26. $|-7|$ **27.** the absolute value of −2

B Apply Your Skills

Open-Ended **Describe a quantity each integer could represent.**

28. −1,000   **29.** 28   **30.** −126

Write the integer represented by each point.

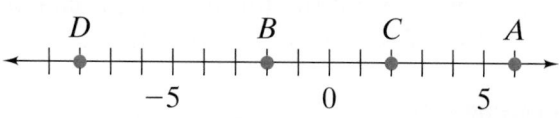

31. *A*   **32.** *B*   **33.** *C*   **34.** *D*

Simplify each expression.

35. $|0|$ **36.** $|-1,000|$ **37.** $-|-13|$

38. $|-56|$ **39.** $-|-23|$ **40.** $-|12|$

Compare. Use >, <, or = to complete each statement.

41. −8 ▨ 0   **42.** 4 ▨ −25   **43.** −9 ▨ −2

44. $|-1|$ ▨ $|50|$ **45.** $|-6|$ ▨ $|-12|$ **46.** $|10|$ ▨ $|-10|$

Visit: PHSchool.com
Web Code: ade-0104

47. Multiple Choice Which expression would you use to represent 10 times your height h in inches?

Ⓐ $10 + h$ Ⓑ $10 - h$ Ⓒ $10h$ Ⓓ $10 \div h$

Write an expression to represent each quantity.

48. a loss of $\frac{1}{3}$ of an investment of d dollars

49. n degrees Fahrenheit above $r°$F room temperature

Read the passage below before doing Exercises 50 and 51.

Finding Famous Ships

Scientist-explorer Robert D. Ballard led the expeditions that found two famous ships deep in the North Atlantic Ocean.

In 1912, the luxury passenger liner *Titanic* struck an iceberg. It came to rest 12,500 ft below sea level. *Titanic* was 882 ft long and 92 ft wide.

In 1941, the mighty warship *Bismarck* sank in battle. *Bismarck* was 823 ft long and 118 ft wide.

Star Hercules, only 269 ft long, towed the underwater camera sled that found *Bismarck* under 15,617 ft of water.

50. Write integers to represent the positions of *Titanic* and *Bismarck*.

51. A friend says that *Bismarck*'s resting place is higher than *Titanic*'s since 15,617 is higher than 12,500. Explain your friend's error.

Complete each sentence with a word that makes it true.

52. An integer is negative, positive, or _?_.

53. All _?_ integers are less than zero.

54. The opposite of a _?_ number is negative.

55. The absolute value of an integer is never _?_.

Ⓒ Challenge

Open-Ended Name two consecutive integers between the given integers.

56. $-6, 2$ **57.** $0, -4$ **58.** $-8, -12$

Record Low Temperatures for Three States

State	Temperature (°C)
California	-45
Nevada	-50
Georgia	-17

Source: *U.S. National Climatic Data Center*

59. a. Data Analysis Use a number line to graph the temperatures in the chart at the left. Label each temperature with the name of the state where it was recorded.
b. Which state recorded the lowest temperature?

60. Writing in Math  How can you use integers to describe elevations above and below sea level?

61. Reasoning Explain why $|x + y|$ and $|x| + |y|$ are not the same. Give examples to show that $|x + y| = |x| + |y|$ for some values of x and y, and $|x + y| \neq |x| + |y|$ for other values of x and y.

Multiple Choice

62. Which list shows the values in order from least to greatest?
- **A.** 0, 3, −17, −25
- **B.** −25, −17, 0, 3
- **C.** 0, −17, −25, 3
- **D.** −25, 0, 3, −27

63. Which expression has the value −90?
- **F.** $|-90|$
- **G.** 90
- **H.** $|90|$
- **J.** $-|90|$

64. Which list shows the values in order from least to greatest?
- **A.** $|-6|$, 6, $|-3|$, 3
- **B.** -6, $-|-3|$, 3, $|-6|$
- **C.** $|-6|$, $|-3|$, $|3|$, $|6|$
- **D.** -3, $-|-6|$, $-|3|$, 6

65. Which two integers are between −5 and 2?
- **F.** −4, 1
- **G.** −3, 3
- **H.** −6, 1
- **J.** 0, 4

Mixed Review

GO for Help

Lesson 1-3

Evaluate each expression.

66. $p - 5$, for $p = 19$ **67.** $3d + 3$, for $d = 7$ **68.** $55y$, for $y = 8$

Lesson 1-2

Compare. Use >, <, or = to complete each statement.

69. $5 + 10 \div 5 \blacksquare (5 + 10) \div 5$

70. $(9 - 6) \div (2 + 1) \blacksquare 9 - 6 \div 2 + 1$

Lesson 1-1

71. Suppose you have c CDs. Your friend has 6 more CDs than you do. Write an expression for the number of CDs your friend has.

✓ Checkpoint Quiz 1   **Lessons 1-1 through 1-4**

Write a variable expression for each word phrase.

1. 23 more than f **2.** g divided by 34   **3.** product of 9 and p

Simplify each expression.

4. $17 + 16 - 13$ **5.** $70 \div [5(3 + 4)]$ **6.** $9 \times 6 \div 3 + 1$

Evaluate each expression for $x = 4$, $y = 6$, and $z = 12$.

7. $2x - 8$ **8.** $3(z + y)$ **9.** $4y - z + \frac{z}{x}$

🌐 **10. Temperature** On Monday the average temperature was −10°F. On Tuesday it was −15°F. On Wednesday it was −13°F. On Thursday it was 0°F.
- **a.** Graph the temperatures on a number line.
- **b.** Write the days in order from coldest to warmest.

You can use models, such as colored tiles, to represent integers.
Use a yellow tile ☐ to represent a positive integer.
Use a red tile ■ to represent a negative integer.

1 ACTIVITY

Use models to represent the integers 3, −1, and −4.

☐☐☐ 3   ■ −1   ■■■■ −4

An equal number of yellow tiles and red tiles combine to make zero.

These tiles make a zero pair. ⟶ ☐■ represents zero, or ☐ + ■ = 0.

You can remove zero pairs in sets of mixed tiles.

2 ACTIVITY

Write the integer that is represented by ■■■■■☐☐.

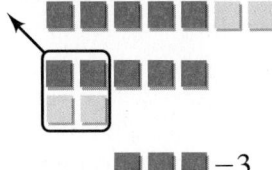

**Group the zero pairs.
Then remove them.**

**Write the integer that the
remaining tiles represent.**

■■■ −3

EXERCISES

Use tiles to model each integer.

1. −3   **2.** 5   **3.** −2   **4.** 7

5. 0   **6.** −6   **7.** 2   **8.** −8

Write an integer for each model.

9. ☐☐   **10.** ■■■■■   **11.** ■■   **12.** ☐☐☐☐☐☐

13. ■■☐☐
   ☐☐■■   **14.** ■■☐■☐☐
   ☐   **15.** ☐■☐☐☐☐
   ☐☐■■   **16.** ■■☐☐☐■■

17. a. Describe how you would model the integers −15 and 25.
    b. Reasoning Suppose you combine the models from part (a).
    How many zero pairs could you make? How many tiles
    would be left after you removed the zero pairs?

1-5 Adding Integers

Multiple Representations

What You'll Learn

- To use models to add integers

- To use rules to add integers

... And Why

To use integers to solve real-world problems in sports and Earth science

✓ Check Skills You'll Need

Compare. Use >, <, or = to complete each statement.

1. $-6 \ \blacksquare \ -3$

2. $2 \ \blacksquare \ -15$

3. $-5 \ \blacksquare \ |5|$

4. $|10| \ \blacksquare \ |-10|$

5. $|9| \ \blacksquare \ |-2|$

6. $|-8| \ \blacksquare \ |0|$

GO for Help
Lesson 1-4

1 Using Models to Add Integers

If a car goes forward 20 ft and then backs up 20 ft, it ends where it started. Using opposite integers, you can represent this situation as $20 + (-20) = 0$.

When you add opposites, the sum is zero. So, opposites are also called *additive inverses*.

Key Concepts   Addition of Opposites

The sum of an integer and its opposite is zero.

Arithmetic	Algebra
$1 + (-1) = 0$	$x + (-x) = 0$
$-1 + 1 = 0$	$-x + x = 0$

You can use tiles to add integers. One positive tile and one negative tile combine to make a zero pair since $\square + \blacksquare = 0$.

To add integers using tiles, combine tiles and remove the zero pairs.

1 EXAMPLE   Using Tiles to Add Integers

Modeling Use tiles to find $2 + (-5)$.

$2 + (-5)$    Model the sum.

-3 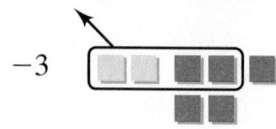   Group and remove zero pairs. There are three negative tiles left.

$2 + (-5) = -3$

✓ Quick Check

1. Use tiles to find each sum.

   a. $-1 + 4$ **b.** $7 + (-3)$ **c.** $-2 + (-2)$

---

24   **Chapter 1** Algebraic Expressions and Integers

A number line provides another model that you can use to add integers, as shown in Example 2.

GO **Online**

Video Tutor Help
Visit: PHSchool.com
Web Code: ada-0775

2 EXAMPLE Using a Number Line

Football On two plays, a football team first loses 8 yd and then gains 3 yd. Find −8 + 3 to find the result of the two plays.

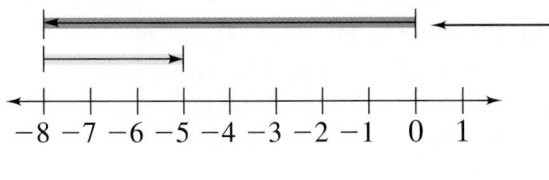

Start at 0. To represent −8, move left 8 units. To add positive 3, move right 3 units to −5.

−8 + 3 = −5

The result of the two plays is a loss of 5 yd.

✓ Quick Check

2. Use a number line to find each sum.

   a. 2 + (−6)   **b.** −4 + 9   **c.** −5 + (−1)

2 Using Rules to Add Integers

You can also use rules to find the sum of two integers.

Key Concepts **Adding Integers**

Same Sign The sum of two positive integers is positive. The sum of two negative integers is negative.

Different Signs To add two integers with different signs, find the difference of their absolute values. The sum has the sign of the integer with the greater absolute value.

---

3 EXAMPLE Applying Rules to Add Integers

Find each sum.

a. **−12 + (−31)**

   $-12 + (-31) = -43$ Since both integers are negative, the sum is negative.

b. **7 + (−18)**

   $|-18| - |7| = 18 - 7$ Find the difference of the absolute values.

   $= 11$ Simplify.

   $7 + (-18) = -11$ Since −18 has the greater absolute value, the sum is negative.

✅ **Quick Check**

3. Find each sum.

   a. $-22 + (-16)$　　**b.** $60 + (-13)$　　**c.** $-125 + 35$

4 **EXAMPLE**　**Real-World 🌐 Problem Solving**

Earth Science The earthquake monitor in Hockley, Texas, is located in a salt mine at an elevation of -416 m. The elevation of the monitor in Albuquerque, New Mexico, is 2,156 m higher than the one in Hockley. Find the elevation of the monitor in Albuquerque.

$-416 + 2,156$	**Write an expression.**
$\|2,156\| - \|-416\| = 2,156 - 416$	**Find the difference of the absolute values.**
$= 1,740$	**Simplify.**
$-416 + 2,156 = 1,740$	**Since 2,156 has the greater absolute value, the sum is positive.**

The elevation of the monitor in Albuquerque is 1,740 m.

Real-World 🌐 Connection

A worldwide network of monitors keeps track of earthquake activity. Here technicians check the monitor in Albuquerque.

✅ **Quick Check**

4. The elevation of a monitor in Piñon Flat, California, is 1,696 m higher than the monitor in Hockley, Texas. Find the elevation of the monitor in Piñon Flat.

To add several integers, use the order of operations.

5 **EXAMPLE**　**Using the Order of Operations**

Find $-12 + (-6) + 15 + (-2)$.

$-12 + (-6) + 15 + (-2)$	**Add from left to right.**
$-18 \quad + \quad 15 + (-2)$	**The sum of two negative integers is negative.**
$-3 \quad + \quad (-2)$	$\|-18\| - \|15\| = 3.$ **Since -18 has the greater absolute value, the sum is negative.**
-5	**The sum of two negative integers is negative.**

$-12 + (-6) + 15 + (-2) = -5$

✅ **Quick Check**

5. Find each sum.

   a. $1 + (-3) + 2 + (-10)$　　**b.** $-250 + 200 + (-100) + 220$

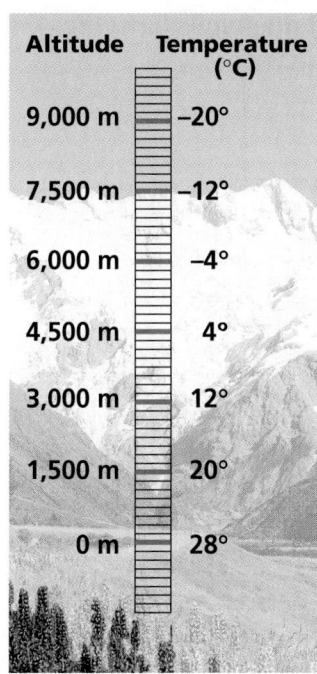

Altitude	Temperature (°C)
9,000 m	−20°
7,500 m	−12°
6,000 m	−4°
4,500 m	4°
3,000 m	12°
1,500 m	20°
0 m	28°

🌐 **Meteorology** The graph at the left shows how temperature changes with altitude. Use this graph for Exercises 51–53.

51. As the altitude increases, what happens to the temperature?

52. What is the change in temperature from 1,500 m to 6,000 m?

53. Multiple Choice Find the change in temperature for every 1,500-meter increase in altitude.
Ⓐ 12°C   Ⓑ 8°C   Ⓒ −8°C   Ⓓ −12°C

Mental Math Simplify each expression.

54. $-6 - (-8)$ **55.** $-45 - 15$ **56.** $-7 - (-7) + (-7)$

57. $100 - (-50)$ **58.** $20 - (-10) - 20$ **59.** $-11 + 22 - (-55)$

60. $3 - (-3) + 6$ **61.** $-32 + 2 + (-10)$ **62.** $-87 + (-3) + 90$

63. $6 - (-6) + 6$ **64.** $0 + (-15) - 15$ **65.** $-13 - 17 + 10$

Write a numerical expression for each phrase. Then simplify and answer the question.

66. You are $2 in debt. You borrow $4 more. What is the total amount of your debt?

67. An airplane takes off, climbs 3,000 ft, and then descends 600 ft. What is the airplane's current height?

68. From 0°F, the temperature increases 15 degrees and then drops 25 degrees. What is the current temperature?

C Challenge

Estimation Round each number. Then estimate the sum or difference.

SAMPLE $-2,216 - 488 \approx -2,200 - 500 = -2,700$

69. $-41 - (-86)$ **70.** $-227 - 49$ **71.** $-398 - 67$

72. $-86 - 22$ **73.** $288 - 59$ **74.** $63 - (-21)$

75. a. Writing in Math A thermometer is like a vertical number line. Use the one at the right to write a subtraction problem.
    b. Write and simplify a numerical expression for your problem.

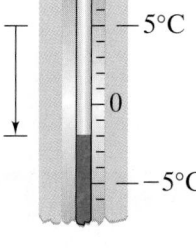

76. a. Patterns Copy and complete. The first one is done for you.
    $8 - (-4) = 12$
    $12 - (-4) = ■$
    $16 - (-4) = ■$
    $20 - (-4) = ■$
    $24 - (-4) = ■$
    b. If you begin at 8 and subtract −4 five times, the result is ■.
    c. Begin at 0 and subtract −4 six times. What is the result?

77. Reasoning For what values of a is each statement true? Give an example, if possible.
    a. $|a - 5| = |a| - 5$ **b.** $|a - 5| > |a| - 5$ **c.** $|a - 5| < |a| - 5$

In each number square, the rows, columns, and diagonals have the same sum. Copy and complete each number square.

78.

5	−9	▩
▩	−1	▩
−3	▩	−7

sum = ▩

79.

−2	▩	▩
−9	−5	▩
−4	▩	▩

sum = ▩

80.

▩	−5	▩	6
▩	4	3	▩
2	0	▩	5
−3	▩	▩	−6

sum = ▩

81.

−6	4	5	−9
2	▩	−1	−3
−5	1	▩	0
▩	−7	−8	▩

sum = ▩

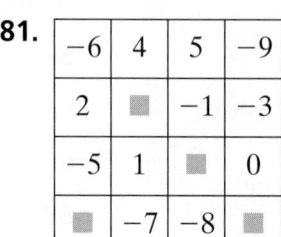

Test Prep

Multiple Choice

82. Three of the four expressions have the same value. Which one has a different value?
A. $6 + (−4)$ **B.** $6 − 4$ **C.** $|4 − 6|$ **D.** $−6 − 4$

83. Suppose you have a score of 25 in a game. You get a penalty that lowers your score by 60 points. What is your new score?
F. $−85$ **G.** $−40$ **H.** $−35$ **J.** 15

84. How many degrees warmer is a temperature of 20°C than a temperature of −7°C?
A. $−27°C$ **B.** $−13°C$ **C.** $13°C$ **D.** $27°C$

85. What is the value of $−23 + −(−15) + |−17| + (−35)$?
F. $−56$ **G.** $−26$ **H.** $|−26|$ **J.** 56

Mixed Review

for Help

Lesson 1-5   **Find each sum.**

86. $−17 + 12$ **87.** $−8 + 15$ **88.** $−9 + (−4) + 7$

Lesson 1-4   **Open-Ended Complete each statement with an integer.**

89. $−5 > $ ▩   **90.** ▩ < 6 **91.** $|−1| > $ ▩   **92.** $|$▩$| < 8$

Lesson 1-1   **93.** Write an expression for the phrase *one hundred plus the product of six and nine*. Simplify the expression.

Inductive Reasoning

1 Writing Rules for Patterns

Inductive reasoning is making conclusions based on patterns you observe. A conclusion you reach by inductive reasoning is a **conjecture.**

1 EXAMPLE Reasoning Inductively

Visual Patterns Use inductive reasoning. Make a conjecture about the next figure in the pattern. Then draw the figure.

 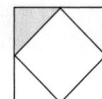 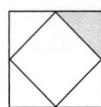

Observation: The shaded triangle is rotating clockwise around the square.

Conjecture: The next figure will have a shaded triangle in the bottom-right corner.

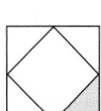

✓ Quick Check

1. Make a conjecture about the next figure in the pattern at the right. Then draw the figure.

For a number pattern, a conjecture can be a rule that explains how to make the pattern. The three dots in a pattern tell you that the pattern continues.

2 EXAMPLE Writing Rules for Patterns

Number Patterns Write a rule for each number pattern.

a. 30, 25, 20, 15, . . .   Start with 30 and subtract 5 repeatedly.

b. 2, −2, 2, −2, . . .   Alternate 2 and its opposite.

c. 1, 3, 4, 12, 13, . . .   Start with 1. Alternate multiplying by 3 and adding 1.

✓ Quick Check

2. Write a rule for each pattern.

   a. 4, 9, 14, 19, . . .   **b.** 3, 9, 27, 81, . . .   **c.** 1, 1, 2, 3, 5, 8, . . .

What You'll Learn

• To write rules for patterns

• To make predictions and test conjectures

. . . And Why

To use inductive reasoning in finding patterns and in making conjectures about economic data

✓ Check Skills You'll Need

Find each difference.

1. $-3 - 4$ 2. $-7 - 4$

3. $-11 - 4$ 4. $-15 - 4$

GO for Help
Lesson 1-6

🔊 New Vocabulary

• inductive reasoning

• conjecture

• counterexample

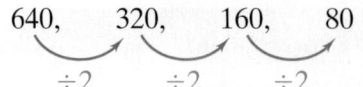

3 EXAMPLE **Extending a Pattern**

Number Patterns Write a rule for the number pattern
640, 320, 160, 80, . . . Find the next two numbers in the pattern.

640,   320,   160,   80   The first number is 640. The next
  ÷2   ÷2   ÷2   numbers are found by dividing by 2.

The rule is *Start with 640 and divide by 2.* The next two numbers
in the pattern are 80 ÷ 2 = 40 and 40 ÷ 2 = 20.

✓ Quick Check

3. Write a rule for the pattern 1, 3, 5, 7, . . . Find the next two
numbers in the pattern.

2 Predictions and Counterexamples

With sufficient information, you can make predictions based on
reasonable conjectures. Such predictions will probably—but not
necessarily—turn out to be accurate.

4 EXAMPLE **Real-World 🌐 Problem Solving**

Statistics See the graph below. Is a conjecture that average hourly
earnings in the year 2005 will be about $15.75 reasonable?

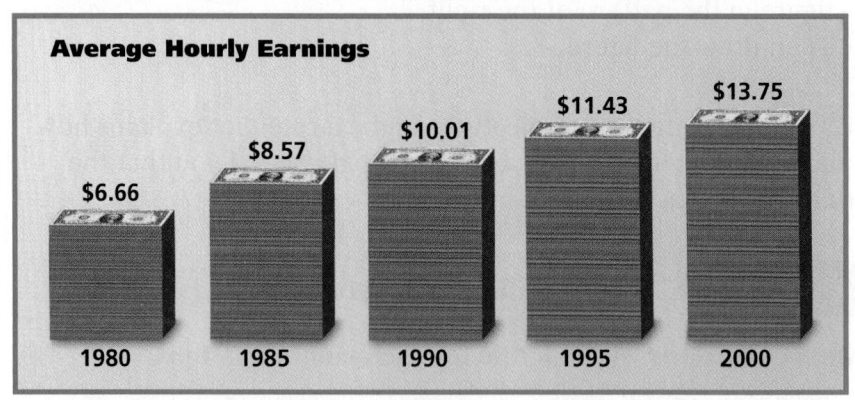

Average Hourly Earnings

				$13.75
			$11.43	
		$10.01		
	$8.57			
$6.66				
1980	1985	1990	1995	2000

Average hourly earnings appear to increase by $1.50 to $2.50
every five years. The conjecture of $15.75 in 2005 is reasonable,
since it is about $2.00 more than the earnings for 2000.

✓ Quick Check

4. You toss a coin four times, and it comes up heads each time. Is
the conjecture *The coin will come up heads on every toss*
reasonable? Explain.

An example that proves a statement false is a **counterexample.** You need only one counterexample to prove that a conjecture is incorrect.

5 EXAMPLE **Analyzing Conjectures**

Inductive Reasoning Is each conjecture correct or incorrect? If it is incorrect, give a counterexample.

a. **Every four-sided figure is a rectangle.**
The conjecture is incorrect. The figure below has four sides, but it is not a rectangle.

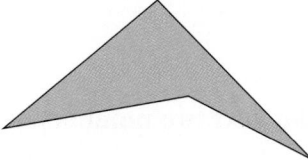

b. **The absolute value of any integer is positive.**
The conjecture is incorrect. The absolute value of zero is zero, which is neither positive nor negative.

c. **The next figure in the pattern below has 15 dots.**

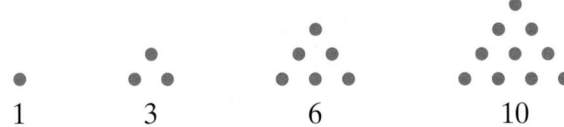

| 1 | 3 | 6 | 10 |

The conjecture is correct. The diagram below shows the next figure in the pattern.

Quick Check

5. Is each conjecture correct or incorrect? If it is incorrect, give a counterexample.

   a. The last digit of the product of 5 and a whole number is either 0 or 5.
   b. A number and its absolute value are always opposites.
   c. The next figure in the pattern has 25 dots.

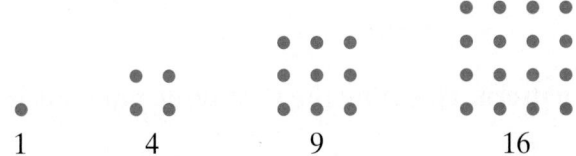

| 1 | 4 | 9 | 16 |

EXERCISES

For more exercises, see *Extra Skill and Word Problem Practice*.

Practice and Problem Solving

A Practice by Example

Example 1
(page 35)

for Help

Visual Patterns Describe the next figure in each pattern. Then draw the figure.

1.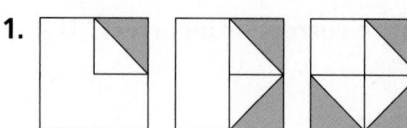

2.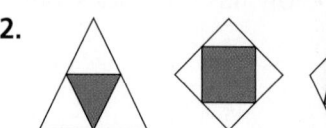

Examples 2 and 3
(pages 35 and 36)

Write a rule for each pattern. Then find the next two numbers in each pattern.

3. $100, 85, 70, 55, \ldots$ 4. $5, 20, 80, 320, \ldots$ 5. $2, 7, 12, 17, \ldots$

6. $-10, -4, 2, 8, \ldots$ 7. $1, 4, 7, 10, \ldots$ 8. $1, 2, 5, 6, 9, \ldots$

Example 4
(page 36)

9. Mario caught a cold on each of his last three visits with his cousin. Is it reasonable for Mario to conclude that his catching a cold is the result of visiting his cousin? Explain.

Example 5
(page 37)

Is each conjecture correct or incorrect? If it is incorrect, give a counterexample.

10. All birds can fly.

11. Every square is a rectangle.

12. The product of two numbers is never less than either of the numbers.

B Apply Your Skills

Visual Patterns Describe the next figure in each pattern. Then draw the figure.

13.

14.

GO Online
Homework Video Tutor
Visit: PHSchool.com
Web Code: ade-0107

Write a rule for each pattern. Then find the next three numbers in each pattern.

15. $1, 1.5, 2, 2.5, 3, \ldots$ 16. $-1, 1, -2, 2, -3, 3, \ldots$ 17. $6, 4, 2, 0, \ldots$

Reasoning **Is each conjecture correct? If incorrect, give a counterexample.**

18. Every clover has three leaves.

19. The sum of two numbers is always greater than either of the two numbers.

20. A whole number is divisible by 3 if the sum of its digits is divisible by 3.

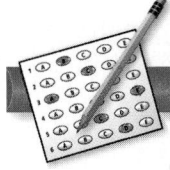 **Challenge** **Write a rule for each pattern. Then find the next three numbers.**

21. $1, 4, 10, 22, 46, 94, \ldots$ **22.** $1, -2, 4, -5, 7, -8, \ldots$

23. a. Writing in Math Use the graph at the right. Write a conjecture about the unemployment rate in 2001. Justify your reasoning.
    b. How could you test your conjecture?

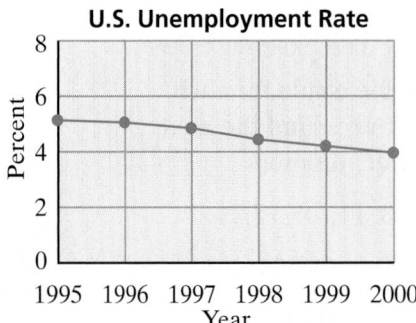

Test Prep

Multiple Choice

24. What are the next three numbers in this pattern? 11, 22, 12, 23, . . .
    A. 13, 23, 14   **B.** 13, 24, 15   **C.** 13, 24, 14   **D.** 32, 43, 33

25. Which best describes the rule for this pattern?
    1, −12, 12, −1, . . .
    F. subtract 24, then add 13   **G.** subtract 13, then add 24
    H. subtract −24, then add 13   **J.** subtract −13, then add 24

26. Which letter continues this pattern of letters in the alphabet?
    B, E, I, N, ▪
    A. R   **B.** S   **C.** T   **D.** U

Mixed Review

 **GO for Help**

Lesson 1-6 **Find each difference.**

27. $1 - 8$ **28.** $-4 - (-9)$ **29.** $86 - (-17)$

Lessons 1-3, 1-5 **Evaluate each expression for $x = -1$ and $y = -3$.**

30. $x + y$ **31.** $y + x + 2$ **32.** $24 + x + y$

Lesson 1-3 **33. Science** The water in a stream flows at the rate of 1,500 gal/h. Write a variable expression for the amount of water that flows in n hours. Evaluate your expression for $n = 24$.

Look for a Pattern

1 Finding Number Patterns

Math Strategies in Action
What do songs on the radio, computer code, and your body's DNA have in common?

All are based on patterns. Radio uses patterns of electromagnetic waves. Computer code consists of patterns of numbers. Your DNA is made up of molecules that repeat in special patterns.

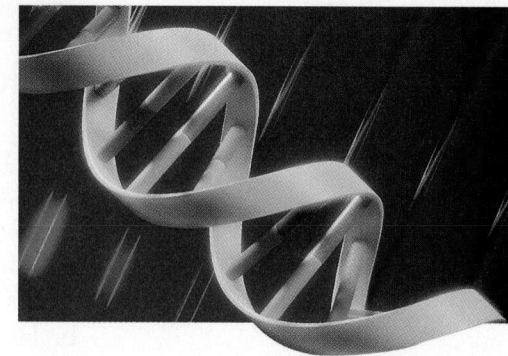

You can solve many types of problems by finding and using patterns. Making predictions from patterns is a form of inductive reasoning.

1 EXAMPLE   Real-World Problem Solving

Information News spreads quickly at Riverdell High. Each student who hears a story repeats it 15 minutes later to two students who have not yet heard it and then tells no one else.

Suppose one student hears some news at 8:00 A.M. How many students will know the news at 9:00 A.M.?

Understand the Problem

1. How many students does each student tell?

2. How long does the news take to reach the second and third students?

Make a Plan

Make a table to organize the numbers. Then look for a pattern.

3. How many *new* students will hear the news at 8:15 A.M.?

4. How many 15-minute periods are there between 8:00 A.M. and 9:00 A.M.?

The pattern is to add the number of new students to the number who already know.

$1 + 2 = 3$ **the number who know at 8:15**
(One student talks to 2.)

$3 + 4 = 7$ **the number who know at 8:30**
(Two students talk to 4.)

Make a table and extend the pattern to 9:00.

Time	8:00	8:15	8:30	8:45	9:00
Number of new students told	1	2	4	8	16
Number of students who know	1	$1 + 2 =$ 3	$3 + 4 =$ 7	$7 + 8 =$ 15	$15 + 16 =$ 31

By 9:00 A.M., 31 students will know the news.

One way to check whether a solution is reasonable is to solve the problem by another method. You can use a *tree diagram* to show the pattern visually.

	Time	New Students	Students Who Know
	8:00	1	1
	8:15	2	3
	8:30	4	7
	8:45	8	15
	9:00	16	31

5. Describe two ways to find the number of students who will know the news at 9:15 A.M.

6. Suppose you want to continue the pattern beyond 9:15. Which would work better, a table or a tree diagram? Explain.

7. There are 251 students at Riverdell High. By what time will every student know the news?

✓ Quick Check

8. Suppose each student who hears the story repeats it in 10 minutes. How many students will know the news at 9:00 A.M.?

EXERCISES

For more exercises, see *Extra Skill and Word Problem Practice*.

Practice and Problem Solving

A Practice by Example

Example 1
(page 40)

***Look for a Pattern* to help you solve each problem.**

1. **Data Analysis** Caroline is training for a swim meet. The graph shows the number of laps per day she swims each week. If she stays with this training pattern, how many laps per day will Caroline swim in week 8?

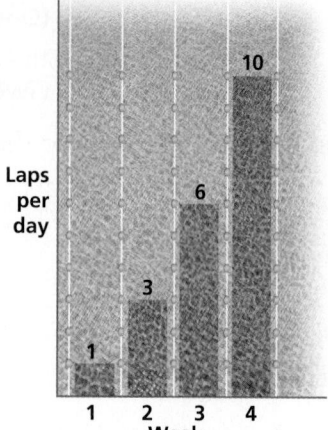

2. Students are to march in a parade. There will be one first grader, two second graders, three third graders, and so on, through the twelfth grade. How many students will march in the parade?

 3. **Savings** Suppose that every day you save twice as many pennies as you saved the day before. You start by saving one penny on January 1. How much money will you have in all on January 10?

4. An old clock started to lose one minute each day. It was too fragile to fix, but too beloved to stop. How slow was the clock after one year of this? After two years?

B Apply Your Skills

Solve using any strategy.

5. **Geometry** You can cut a pizza into two pieces with one straight cut. With two cuts you can get four pieces. Three cuts give a maximum of seven pieces. What is the maximum number of pieces with four cuts? With five cuts?

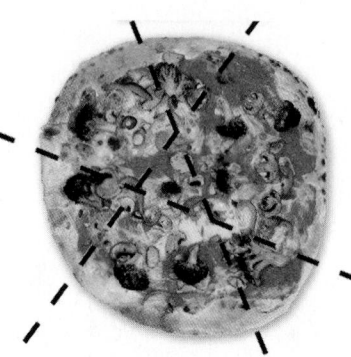

Strategies

- Act It Out
- Draw a Diagram
- Guess, Check, Revise
- Look for a Pattern
- Make a Model
- Make a Table
- Simulate the Problem
- Solve by Graphing
- Use Multiple Strategies
- Work a Simpler Problem
- Work Backward
- Write an Equation
- Write a Proportion

6. **a. Number Sense** Complete. Then look for a pattern.

$2 \cdot 2 = \blacksquare$ $3 \cdot 3 = \blacksquare$
$1 \cdot 3 = \blacksquare$ $2 \cdot 4 = \blacksquare$
Difference $= \blacksquare$ Difference $= \blacksquare$

$4 \cdot 4 = \blacksquare$ $5 \cdot 5 = \blacksquare$
$3 \cdot 5 = \blacksquare$ $4 \cdot 6 = \blacksquare$
Difference $= \blacksquare$ Difference $= \blacksquare$

b. Which is greater, $10 \cdot 12$ or $11 \cdot 11$? What is the difference?

c. **Reasoning** Suppose you know that $47 \cdot 47 = 2,209$. Use this to find $46 \cdot 48$.

d. Suppose you know that $64 \cdot 66 = 4,224$. Use this to find $65 \cdot 65$.

42   **Chapter 1** Algebraic Expressions and Integers

GO **nline**
Homework Video Tutor
Visit: PHSchool.com
Web Code: ade-0108

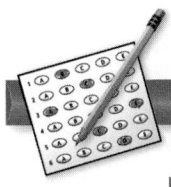
Challenge

7. For a buffet dinner, a restaurant charges $10 for one person, $20 for two, $29 for three, $37 for four, $44 for five, and so on.
  a. How much does a buffet dinner for 8 cost? How much does a group of 8 save by eating together rather than separately?
  b. The buffet costs the restaurant $6 per person. How large a group can the restaurant serve without losing money?

8. A woman jogging at 6 mi/h passes a man biking in the opposite direction at 12 mi/h. If they maintain their speeds, how far from each other will they be 10 minutes after passing?

Test Prep

Multiple Choice

9. One edition of *Alice's Adventures in Wonderland* has 352 pages. How many 4s were used in its page numbers?
  A. 38   **B.** 52   **C.** 75   **D.** 88

10. Jayne has 3 quarters, 2 dimes, a nickel, and 2 pennies in her pocket. How many different amounts of money can she make using three of these coins?
  F. 24   **G.** 20   **H.** 17   **J.** 14

11. Assuming one yeast cell "buds" into two cells (the original cell and one new cell) at a rate of once every hour, how many yeast cells will be present from one yeast cell after 8 hours?
  A. 128   **B.** 256   **C.** 512   **D.** 1,024

Mixed Review

GO **for Help**

Lesson 1-7

Visual Patterns Describe the next figure in each pattern. Then draw the figure.

12.

13.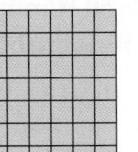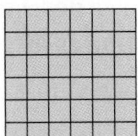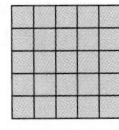

Lesson 1-5 **14. Weather** At midnight, the temperature was −5°F. By dawn, the temperature had risen 14°. What was the temperature at dawn?

Lesson 1-3 **Evaluate each expression for $m = 1$ and $n = 4$.**

  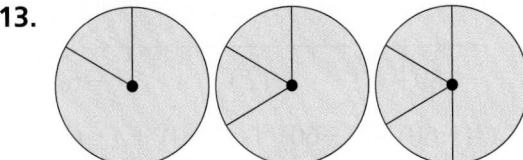

  15. $4m - n$ **16.** $mn + 13$ **17.** $4(n + 2) + m$

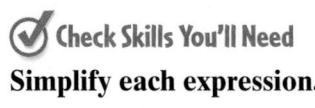
Multiplying and Dividing Integers

What You'll Learn

- To multiply integers using repeated addition, patterns, and rules
- To divide integers using rules

. . . And Why

To solve real-world problems involving deep-sea exploration and currency

✓ **Check Skills You'll Need**

Simplify each expression.

1. $5 \cdot 4$ **2.** $3 \cdot 8$

3. $5 \cdot 5$ **4.** $14 \cdot 2$

5. $6 \cdot 5$ **6.** $20 \cdot 7$

GO for Help

Skills Handbook, p. 763

1   **Multiplying Integers**

Activity

Preparing to Multiply Integers

1. Copy and complete the table. The first row is done for you.

Multiplication	Repeated Addition	Sum
$3 \cdot (-5)$	$-5 + (-5) + (-5)$	-15
$5 \cdot (-4)$	▪	▪
$2 \cdot (-8)$	▪	▪
$4 \cdot (-10)$	▪	▪

2. What do you notice about the signs of the sums?

3. **Inductive Reasoning** What does the pattern suggest about the product of a positive integer and a negative integer?

You can think of multiplication as repeated addition.

1 **EXAMPLE**   **Real-World** 🌐 **Problem Solving**

Deep-Sea Exploration **After it is launched from a boat, *Deep Rover* descends 60 ft/min. Where is it in relation to sea level 3 minutes after its launch?**

Use a number line to show repeated addition.

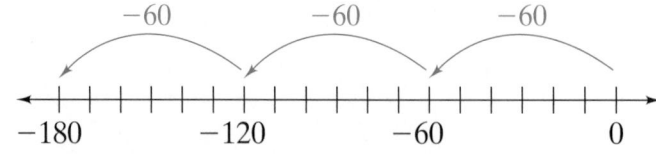

$3(-60) = (-60) + (-60) + (-60) = -180$

Deep Rover is at -180 feet, or 180 feet below sea level.

✓ **Quick Check**

1. Simplify each product.

   a. $2(-6)$ **b.** $4(-3)$ **c.** $7(-2)$

Real-World 🌐 **Connection**

Scientists explore the deep waters of the Pacific Ocean in *Deep Rover,* a submersible designed for research.

You can use patterns to simplify the product of a negative number and a positive number, or the product of two negative numbers.

2 EXAMPLE Using Patterns to Multiply Integers

Patterns Use a pattern to find each product.

a. −2(5)

2(5) = 10	**Start with products you know.**
1(5) = 5	
0(5) = 0	
−1(5) = −5	**Continue the pattern.**
−2(5) = −10	

b. −2(−5)

2(−5) = −10
1(−5) = −5
0(−5) = 0
−1(−5) = 5
−2(−5) = 10

Vocabulary Tip

Symbols for multiplication:

×	−2 × 2
·	−2 · 2
( )	−2(3)
*	−2 * 3

✓ Quick Check

2. Patterns Use a pattern to simplify −3(−4).

By inductive reasoning, the patterns from Example 2 suggest rules for multiplying integers.

Key Concepts Multiplying Integers

The product of two integers with the same sign is positive.
The product of two integers with different signs is negative.
The product of zero and any integer is zero.

Examples	3(4) = 12	3(−4) = −12
	−3(−4) = 12	−3(4) = −12
	3(0) = 0	−4(0) = 0

3 EXAMPLE Using Rules to Multiply Integers

Multiple Choice Which procedure is correct for multiplying
−3 · 5(−4)?

Ⓐ −3 · 5(−4) = 15(−4) = −60
Ⓑ −3 · 5(−4) = −3(1) = −3
Ⓒ −3 · 5(−4) = −3(−1) = 3
Ⓓ −3 · 5(−4) = −15(−4) = 60

Multiply from left to right. The product of a negative integer and a positive integer is negative. The product of two negative integers is positive. The product is 60. The answer is D.

Test-Taking Tip

Eliminate any choices that cannot be correct. Since 3 · 5 · 4 > 3, you can eliminate choices B and C.

✓ Quick Check

3. Simplify each product.

a. −4 · 8(−2)   **b.** 6(−3)(5)   **c.** −7 · (−14) · 0

Dividing Integers

The rules for dividing integers are similar to those for multiplying.

Key Concepts **Dividing Integers**

The quotient of two integers with the same sign is positive.
The quotient of two integers with different signs is negative.
Remember that division by zero is undefined.

Examples

$$12 \div 3 = 4 \qquad 12 \div (-3) = -4$$
$$-12 \div (-3) = 4 \qquad -12 \div 3 = -4$$

---

4 **EXAMPLE** **Real-World** **Problem Solving**

Currency **Find the average of the differences in the values of a Canadian dollar and a U.S. dollar for 1999–2003.**

Value of Dollars (U.S. Cents)

Year	Canadian Dollar	U.S. Dollar	Difference
1999	67	100	−33
2000	67	100	−33
2001	65	100	−35
2002	64	100	−36
2003	71	100	−29

SOURCES: Bank of Canada; *The World Almanac*

$$\frac{-33 + (-33) + (-35) + (-36) + (-29)}{5}$$ **Write an expression for the average.**

$$= \frac{-166}{5}$$ **Use the order of operations. The fraction bar acts as a grouping symbol.**

$$= -33.2$$ **The quotient of a negative integer and a positive integer is negative.**

For 1999–2003, the average difference was −33¢. The Canadian dollar was worth an average of 33¢ less than the U.S. dollar.

✓ Quick Check

4. Simplify each quotient.

    a. $-32 \div 8$ **b.** $-48 \div (-6)$ **c.** $-56 \div (-4)$

    d. Find the average of 4, −3, −5, 2, and −8.

EXERCISES

For more exercises, see *Extra Skill and Word Problem Practice*.

Practice and Problem Solving

A Practice by Example

Example 1
(page 44)

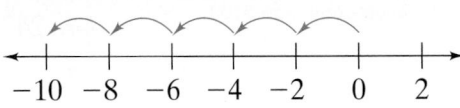

GO for Help

1. Write a number sentence for the product shown on the number line.

Write each sum as a product. Simplify the product.

2. $(-9) + (-9) + (-9) + (-9)$

3. $(-5) + (-5) + (-5) + (-5) + (-5)$

4. **Weather** The temperature dropped 5 degrees each hour for 7 h. Use an integer to represent the total change in temperature.

Simplify each product.

5. $3(-3)$ 6. $4(-11)$ 7. $3(-8)$

8. $5(-10)$ 9. $6(-3)$ 10. $2(-15)$

11. $9(-9)$ 12. $3(-24)$ 13. $8(-6)$

Examples 2 and 3
(page 45)

14. $-5(-3)$ 15. $-6 \cdot 10$ 16. $-10 \cdot 0$

17. $-9(-8)(-5)$ 18. $0(-12) \cdot 4$ 19. $8 \cdot 3(-4)$

Example 4
(page 46)

Find each quotient.

20. $24 \div (-24)$ 21. $18 \div (-1)$ 22. $-120 \div 12$

23. $56 \div (-8)$ 24. $-72 \div 12$ 25. $-100 \div (-10)$

26. $-38 \div (-2)$ 27. $-72 \div 6$ 28. $-33 \div 11$

For each group, find the average.

29. temperatures: $-9°C, -12°C, 9°C, 4°C, -2°C$

30. football yardage: 10 yd, -5 yd, 7 yd, 9 yd, -11 yd

31. golf scores: $-3, 4, 2, 1, -4, -1, 3, -2$

32. bank balances: $325, -\$150, \$130, \$200, -\$45$

B Apply Your Skills

Mental Math Without computing, tell whether each product or quotient is *positive* or *negative*. Explain your reasoning.

33. $-6(-20)$ 34. $7(-83)$ 35. $39 \div (-3)$ 36. $-3(8)(-24)$

Name the point on the number line that is the graph of each product.

37. $-2 \cdot 0$ 38. $4(-2)$ 39. $2(-2)$ 40. $|-2| \cdot |-2|$

Homework Video Tutor
Visit: PHSchool.com
Web Code: ade-0109

Use repeated addition, patterns, or rules to simplify each product or quotient.

41. $225 \div (-15)$ **42.** $|-2| \cdot (-7)$ **43.** $-59(-79)$

44. $243(-88)$ **45.** $-200 \div -25$ **46.** $-18(-12)$

47. $38(-2)$ **48.** $1{,}000 \div (-50)$ **49.** $24(-16)(-32)$

50. Investing The price of one share of a stock fell \$3 each day for 12 days.
  a. Write an integer to represent the total change in price of a share of the stock.
  b. The original stock price was \$76 per share. What was the price after the drop?

Compare. Use >, <, or = to complete each statement.

51. $(-9)(-6) \blacksquare 8(-10)$ **52.** $5(-2) \blacksquare (-6)(-1)$

53. $-10 \div (-2) \blacksquare 25 \div (-5)$ **54.** $-|-28| \div 7 \blacksquare -28 \div (-7)$

55. $|-25| \div |-5| \blacksquare |-25 \div (-5)|$ **56.** $-(-15 \div 5) \blacksquare -100 \div (-20)$

Number Sense **Use integer rules and other math facts to answer each question.**

57. What integer and -8 have the product -96?

58. What integer and 9 have the product -135?

59. What integer and -3 have the quotient 9?

60. What two integers have a sum of negative ten and a product of negative seventy-five?

C Challenge   **Open-Ended** **Simplify each pair of expressions. Then write an integer that is between the values of the expressions.**

61. $-2 \cdot (-2)$ and $2 \cdot 4$ **62.** $10 + (-7)$ and $10 \div (-5)$

63. $50 + (-48)$ and $80 \div (-20)$ **64.** $121 \div (-11)$ and $|-7| - |7|$

65. a. Inductive Reasoning Will the sign be positive or negative for the product of three negative integers? Of four negative integers? Of five negative integers?
  b.  **Writing in Math** Use inductive reasoning to write a rule for the sign of the product of more than two negative integers.

66. Reasoning If a and b are positive integers, and x and y are negative integers, what is the sign of $\frac{a + b}{x + y}$? Explain.

67. Investing Jerry owns 20 shares of stock valued at \$23 each. One day, the price of the stock rose \$2. It fell \$1 on each of the next three days. The stock price rose \$4 on the next day. What was the average daily gain or loss for a share of the stock over this time period? What was the total value of Jerry's stock at the end of this time period?

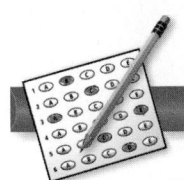

Test Prep

Multiple Choice

68. A scuba diver descended to a depth of 50 feet in 25 seconds. Which integer indicates the average number of feet per second the diver traveled?

   A. -50 **B.** -25 **C.** -2 **D.** -1

69. Which of the following is the simplest form of $\frac{-1,225}{35}$?

   F. -35 **G.** -25 **H.** -25 **J.** 35

In Exercises 70 and 71, what is the average for each group of data?

70. bank balances: $200, -\$85, \$120, \$200, \$280$

   A. $\$97$ **B.** $\$119$ **C.** $\$143$ **D.** $\$177$

71. feet above and below sea level:

   135 ft, -56 ft, 92 ft, -29 ft, -88 ft, -60 ft

   F. -31 ft   **G.** -1 ft   **H.** 19 ft   **J.** 76 ft

Mixed Review

Lesson 1-8

72. Reasoning How many whole numbers from 10 to 200 have exactly two identical digits?

Lessons 1-5 and 1-6

Compare. Use >, <, or = to complete each statement.

73. $-3 + (-8) \blacksquare 12 - (-6)$

74. $-9 + 13 \blacksquare 24 - 30$

75. $|-6| - |12| \blacksquare -8 + |-12|$

Lesson 1-1

Write a variable expression for each word phrase.

76. 50 decreased by a number n **77.** the product of y and 60

78. the sum of x and y **79.** the quotient of d divided by 5

Checkpoint Quiz 2   **Lessons 1-5 through 1-9**

Simplify each expression.

1. $3 + (-11)$ **2.** $12 - (-8)$ **3.** $-9 \cdot 5$

4. $-64 \div (-8)$ **5.** $|3| \cdot 8 \div (-2)$ **6.** $-8(-3)(3)$

Open-Ended Use integers to complete each equation.

7. $\blacksquare + \blacksquare = -7$ **8.** $\blacksquare - (-20) = \blacksquare$ **9.** $\blacksquare \cdot \blacksquare = -40$

Patterns Find the next three numbers in each pattern.

10. $-7, -2, 3, 8, \ldots$ **11.** $1, 3, 9, 27, \ldots$

Studying Math Definitions

You can learn new vocabulary by building your own index-card word list.
- Write the term. Then write the definition.
- Include any math symbols related to the term.
- Give an example that shows how the term is used.
- Give a nonexample showing how the term might *not* apply.

EXAMPLE

Make an index card for the vocabulary term *variable expression*.

Variable Expression

Definition: A variable expression is a mathematical phrase that uses variables, numerals, and operation symbols.

Example: $h + 5$ $f - 7$ $3a$ $\frac{x}{2}$

Nonexamples: 5 $25 - 4$ 13 -21

Write the term.

Write the definition.

Give examples.

Give nonexamples.

EXERCISES

Make an index card like the one shown above for each vocabulary term. Include any helpful everyday meanings.

1. variable
2. order of operations
3. evaluate
4. opposites
5. integers
6. absolute value
7. conjecture
8. inductive reasoning
9. counterexample

10. **Error Analysis** A student wrote the definition of *integers* at the right. Which parts are correct? Which parts are incorrect? Explain.

Integers

Definition: Integers are all the counting numbers and their opposites.

Examples: $-8, 4, -1, 5, 10, -12$

Nonexamples: $\frac{1}{2}, 0, -\frac{3}{4}, -1.5$

Reading Bar and Line Graphs

You can analyze data presented in a graph. A bar graph usually compares quantities. The bar graph below shows boys' participation in high school baseball in several states for a recent year.

1 ACTIVITY

Use the bar graph.

1. About how many boys played high school baseball in Texas?

2. About how many boys played high school baseball in Illinois?

3. About how many more boys played high school baseball in Texas than in Illinois?

4. In which two states is the combined number of boys who played high school baseball about equal to the number who played in Pennsylvania?

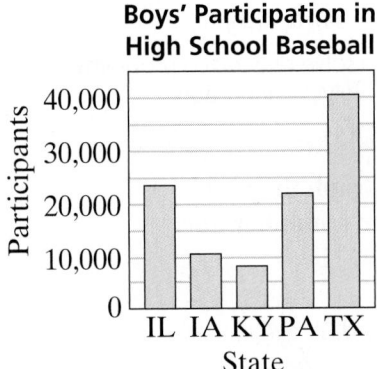

Boys' Participation in High School Baseball

A line graph usually shows change over time. The line graph shows girls' participation in high school baseball over several years.

2 ACTIVITY

Use the line graph.

5. Between what two school years did girls' participation in high school baseball increase the most?

6. In what two school years was girls' participation in high school baseball about the same?

7. Between what two school years did girls' participation in high school baseball decrease by about 500?

8. In what school year was girls' participation in high school baseball about 1,275?

9. a. Estimate the change in participation from 1994–1995 to 2003–2004.
   b. If the trend continues, how many girls will participate in high school baseball in 2014–2015?

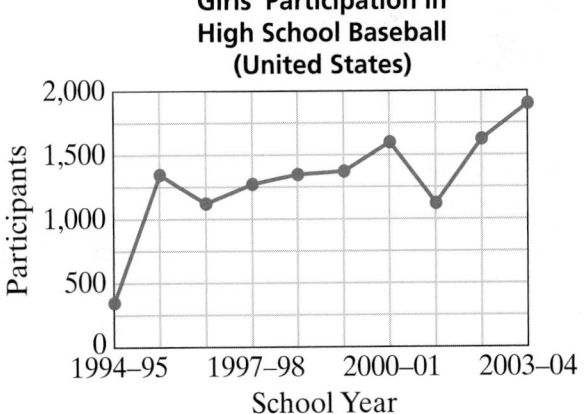

Girls' Participation in High School Baseball (United States)

1-10 The Coordinate Plane

What You'll Learn

- To name coordinates and quadrants in the coordinate plane
- To graph points in the coordinate plane

. . . And Why

To solve real-world problems involving geography

 **Check Skills You'll Need**

Graph the numbers on a number line.

1. $-2, 1, -5$

2. $0, 2, -4$

3. $-3, 3, -2$

4. $-1, -5, -8$

GO for Help
Lesson 1-4

🔊 **New Vocabulary**

- coordinate plane
- *x*-axis
- *y*-axis
- quadrants
- origin
- ordered pair
- *x*-coordinate
- *y*-coordinate

---

1 Naming Coordinates and Quadrants

A **coordinate plane** is formed by the intersection of two number lines. The horizontal number line is called the **x-axis** and the vertical number line is called the **y-axis.**

The *x*- and *y*-axes divide the coordinate plane into four **quadrants.**

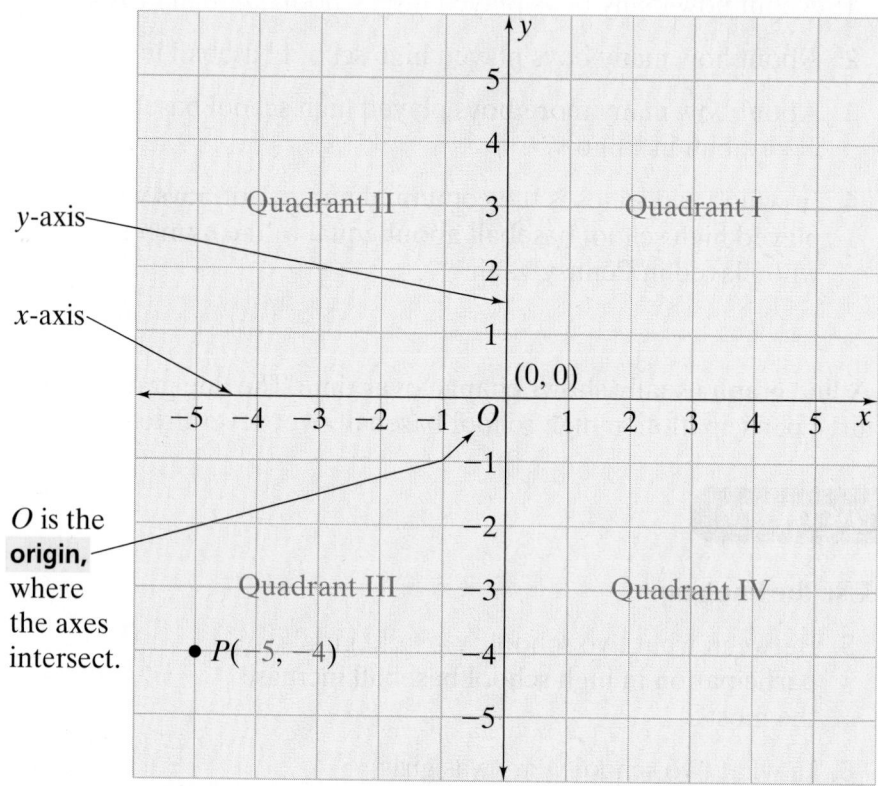

An **ordered pair** gives the coordinates and location of a point. The ordered pair $(-5, -4)$ identifies point P in Quadrant III above.

$$(-5, -4)$$

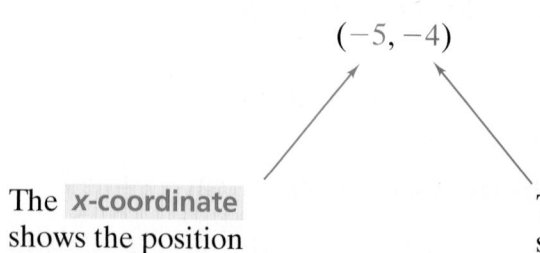

The **x-coordinate** shows the position right or left of the *y*-axis.

The **y-coordinate** shows the position above or below the *x*-axis.

Online active math

For: Coordinate Plane Activity
Use: Interactive Textbook, 1-10

---

1 EXAMPLE — Naming Coordinates and Quadrants

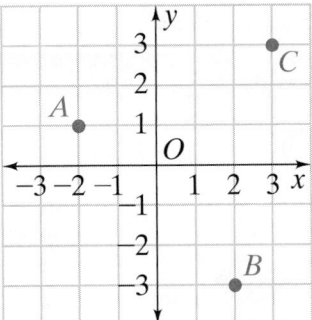

Write the coordinates of point *A*. In which quadrant is point *A* located?

Point *A* is located 2 units to the left of the *y*-axis. So the *x*-coordinate is −2. The point is 1 unit above the *x*-axis. So the *y*-coordinate is 1.

The coordinates of point *A* are (−2, 1). Point *A* is located in Quadrant II.

✓ Quick Check

1. **a.** Use the graph in Example 1. Write the coordinates of *B* and *C*.
   b. Identify the quadrants in which *B* and *C* are located.

2 Graphing Points

To graph a point *A*(*x*, *y*) in a coordinate plane, you graph the ordered pair (*x*, *y*).

2 EXAMPLE — Graphing Points

Graph point $R(3, -4\frac{1}{2})$.

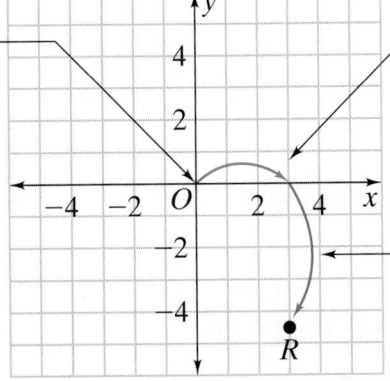

Step 1
Start at the origin.

Step 2
For 3 in $R(3, -4\frac{1}{2})$, move 3 units to the right.

Step 3
For $-4\frac{1}{2}$ in $R(3, -4\frac{1}{2})$, move $4\frac{1}{2}$ units down. Draw a dot. Label it *R*.

✓ Quick Check

2. **a.** Graph these points on one coordinate plane: $K(3, 1)$, $L(-2\frac{1}{2}, 1)$, and $M(-2, -4)$.
   b. **Geometry** Draw lines to connect points *K*, *L*, and *M*. Describe the figure that results.

North Pole

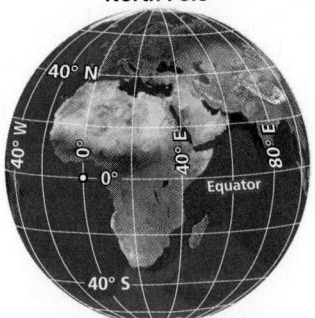

South Pole

Real-World Connection

Latitude and longitude are measurements in a coordinate system that locate every point on Earth's surface.

EXERCISES

Practice and Problem Solving

For more exercises, see *Extra Skill and Word Problem Practice.*

A Practice by Example

Example 1
(page 53)

GO for Help

In which quadrant does each point lie?

1. *J*　　2. *V*　　3. *M*

4. *K*　　5. *P*　　6. *Q*

Write the coordinates of each point.

7. *T*　　8. *G*　　9. *R*

10. *Q*　　11. *P*　　12. *M*

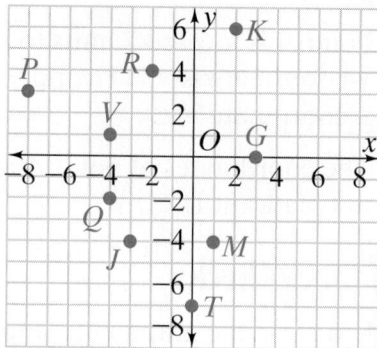

Example 2
(page 53)

Draw a coordinate plane. Then graph each point.

13. $A(-1, 3)$　　14. $B(-4, -1)$　　15. $C(2, 5)$　　16. $D(2, -2)$

17. $E(0, 6)$　　18. $F(-3, 2)$　　19. $G(6, 0)$　　20. $H(1, 7)$

21. $K(5, -6)$　　22. $L(0, 0)$　　23. $M(-5, -2)$　　24. $N(7, 0)$

25. $P(-1, -3)$　　26. $Q(1, 1)$　　27. $R(0, -4)$　　28. $S(-3, 4)$

B Apply Your Skills

29. What ordered pair names the origin?

Name the point with the given coordinates.

30. $(3, 2)$　　31. $(0, -5)$

32. $(2, 3)$　　33. $(-2, -3)$

Write the coordinates of each point.

34. *A*　　35. *B*

36. *C*　　37. *D*

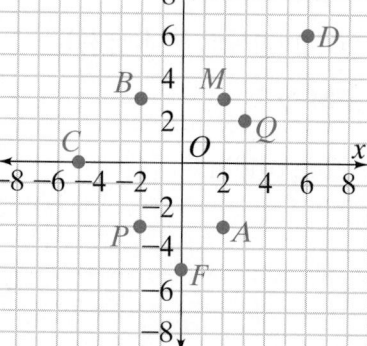

Test-Taking Tip

You can tell in which quadrant to graph an ordered pair by looking at the signs of the coordinates.
$(+, +)$ goes in Q I.
$(-, +)$ goes in Q II.
$(-, -)$ goes in Q III.
$(+, -)$ goes in Q IV.

Mental Math Write the coordinates of each point.

38. the point 5 units to the left of the *y*-axis and 2 units below the *x*-axis

39. the point on the *y*-axis 4 units below the *x*-axis

40. **Multiple Choice** Which coordinates describe the point on the *x*-axis 3 units to the right of the origin?
   Ⓐ $(0, 3)$　　Ⓑ $(3, 0)$　　Ⓒ $(3, -3)$　　Ⓓ $(3, 3)$

GO Online

Homework Video Tutor

Visit: PHSchool.com
Web Code: ade-0110

Mental Math In which quadrant does $P(x, y)$ lie?

41. *x* is positive, *y* is negative.　　42. *x* is positive, *y* is positive.

43. *x* is negative, *y* is positive.　　44. *x* is negative, *y* is negative.

54　Chapter 1　Algebraic Expressions and Integers

In which quadrant or on which axis does each point lie?

45. $V(13, 25)$

46. $W(x, y)$ if $x = 0, y > 0$

47. $X(-17, -2)$

48. $Z(x, y)$ if $x > 0, y < 0$

49. $B(0, |-2|)$

50. $R(x, y)$ if $x < 0, y > 0$

Geometry **Graph and connect the points in the order given. Connect the last point to the first. Name the figure.**

51. $(-4, 1), (1, 1), (-3, -1)$

52. $(2\frac{1}{2}, 2), (2\frac{1}{2}, -1), (-5, -1), (-5, 2)$

53. $(-1, 2), (1, 5), (7, 5), (5, 2)$

54. $(2, -4), (7, -1), (4, 4), (-1, 1)$

Geometry *PQRS* **is a square. Find the coordinates of** *S*.

55. $P(-5, 0), Q(0, 5), R(5, 0), S(\blacksquare, \blacksquare)$

56. $P(-1, 3), Q(4, 3), R(4, -2), S(\blacksquare, \blacksquare)$

🌐 **Geography** **On a map, coordinates are given in degrees of longitude and latitude. Use the map below for Exercises 57–60.**

SAMPLE
Austin, Texas:
Longitude:
  about 98° W
Latitude:
  about 30° N

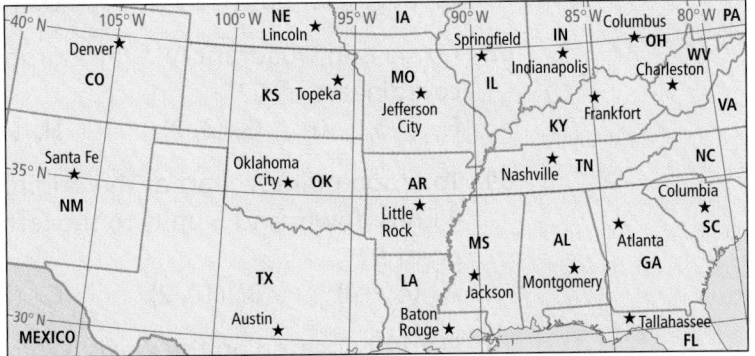

57. Find the longitude and latitude of Jackson, Mississippi.

58. Find the longitude and latitude of Topeka, Kansas.

59. What city is located near 85° W, 38° N?

60. What city is located near 106° W, 35° N?

Geometry **Use one coordinate plane for Exercises 61–63.**

61. Graph the points $(-2, 1), (-2, 3), (1, 3),$ and $(1, 1)$. Connect them in the order given. Connect the last point to the first.

62. Change the coordinates of Exercise 61 as described below. Graph and connect the points for each new set of coordinates. Use a different color for each set.
  a. Multiply each x-coordinate by -1.
  b. Multiply each y-coordinate by -1.
  c. Multiply each coordinate by -1.
  d. Multiply each coordinate by 2.

63. **Writing in Math** Compare each figure in Exercise 62 to the figure in Exercise 61. Write a short paragraph describing your results.

 Challenge

Writing in Math

Describe how to graph
$Q(4, 23)$ and four other
points, each 1 unit
from Q.

64. Open-Ended Draw a dot-to-dot picture on a coordinate
grid. Write the coordinates of the points in order.
Exchange coordinates with a classmate and draw the
other's picture.

65. Reasoning Assume that $a \neq b$. Do (a, b) and (b, a) describe the
same point? Explain.

66. Write the coordinates of four points in the coordinate plane that
are 3 units from the origin. Graph the points.

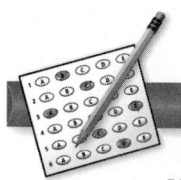

Test Prep

Multiple Choice

67. $P(a, b)$ is in Quadrant III. Which word pair makes the following
sentence true?

The value of a must be __?__ and the value of
b must be __?__.

A. positive; positive   B. positive; negative
C. negative; positive   D. negative; negative

68. $C(x, y)$ is in Quadrant IV. Which ordered pair could be the
coordinates of C?

F. $(-3, -7)$ G. $(0, 2)$ H. $(-8, 0)$ J. $(5, -6)$

69. To graph point R, start at the origin, move 10 units to the right,
4 units down, and 6 units to the left. What are the coordinates of
point R?

A. $(4, -4)$ B. $(10, 2)$ C. $(6, 10)$ D. $(-4, -6)$

70. $P(a, b)$ is located on the x-axis. Which statement is true for all
nonzero values of a?

F. $a > b$ G. $b > a$ H. $|a| > b$ J. $|b| > a$

71. $T(a, b)$ is located in Quadrant II. Which statement is *never* true?

A. $a > b$ B. $b > a$ C. $|a| > b$ D. $|b| > a$

Mixed Review

 **GO for Help**

Lesson 1-9   **Find each product or quotient.**

72. $-11 \cdot 11$ **73.** $-432 \div 48$ **74.** $\dfrac{0}{-56}$

Lesson 1-5 🌐 **75. Submarines** A submarine at sea level dives 800 ft and then
another 125 ft. Find the submarine's final depth.

Lesson 1-4   **Write the value of each expression.**

76. $|-8|$ **77.** $-|-95|$ **78.** the opposite of 12

79. $|16| + 4$ **80.** $|-6| - 2$ **81.** the opposite of -3

You can use a graphing calculator to display ordered pairs on a coordinate plane.

ACTIVITY

Graph these ordered pairs: $(-6, 2)$, $(-5, 6)$, $(-4, -1)$, $(-3, -5)$, $(-2, 4)$, $(0, 9)$, $(1, 5)$, $(2, -4)$, $(2, 0)$, $(3, 6)$, $(5, 2)$, $(7, -5)$, $(8, 4)$.

Step 1 Enter the ordered pairs into list L_1 for the x-coordinates and list L_2 for the y-coordinates.

Press LIST . To clear old entries in L_1, select L_1 and press CLEAR ENTER . (Clear old entries in other columns in a similar way.) Enter all the x-coordinates into list L_1. Enter all y-coordinates into list L_2. Check L_1 and L_2 to make sure the coordinates align as they should.

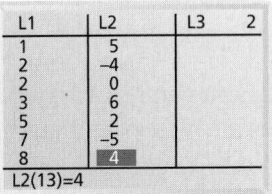

Step 2 In **PLOT**, enter 1 and select **On**. Select the **Type** as shown below, and check that **Xlist** and **Ylist** show L_1 and L_2, respectively.

Step 3 Press ZOOM 6 to graph the data with the standard viewing window. Then press GRAPH .

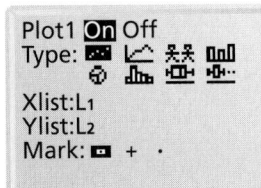

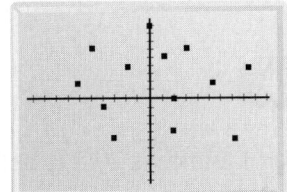

EXERCISES

Graph each group of ordered pairs.

1. $(-5, -1)$, $(-2, 4)$, $(-1, 3)$, $(0, 4)$, $(1, 6)$, $(3, 0)$, $(4, 2)$, $(5, -3)$

2. $(-5, 7)$, $(4, 6)$, $(9, 2)$, $(-2, -8)$, $(0, 3)$, $(-3, -1)$, $(-6, 1)$, $(5, 5)$, $(1, -6)$, $(-1, -3)$, $(3, -2)$, $(-4, 9)$, $(-8, 4)$, $(2, -5)$, $(6, 0)$, $(7, -4)$

Graph the ordered pairs. Adjust the window settings to see all the points.

3. $(-5, 2)$, $(-6\frac{1}{2}, 5)$, $(-5, -5\frac{1}{2})$, $(3, -5)$, $(-5\frac{1}{2}, -4)$, $(-4, -3\frac{1}{2})$, $(4, 5)$, $(-5\frac{1}{2}, -5)$

4. $(-10, -5)$, $(-8, -9)$, $(-6, 2)$, $(-5, 8)$, $(7, -3)$, $(9, -6)$, $(10, 4)$, $(12, 9)$

Graph the ordered pairs. Describe the pattern you see.

5. $(7, 3)$, $(-3, -2)$, $(1, 0)$, $(-5, -3)$, $(9, 4)$, $(3, 1)$, $(5, 2)$, $(-7, -4)$

6. $(0, -5)$, $(-2, -3)$, $(4, -5)$, $(0, -1)$, $(2, -3)$, $(-4, -5)$

Writing Gridded Responses

Some tests require you to enter a number answer on a grid. You must find the answer and also show it in a form that you can fit on the grid. For example, you can enter an improper fraction on the grid, but not a mixed number.

1 EXAMPLE

What is the sum of -0.5 and 2?

$-0.5 + 2 = 1.5, \frac{3}{2},$ or $1\frac{1}{2}.$

For the grid, you can use 1.5 or $\frac{3}{2}$, but not $1\frac{1}{2}$. You write the answer in the spaces at the top of the grid and fill in the corresponding bubbles below.

● The grids at the right are correct for 1.5 and $\frac{3}{2}$, respectively.

Here are things to remember as you grid your responses:

- You must begin in the left column OR end in the right column.
- You cannot have blanks in the middle of a response.
- Always write a mixed number as an improper fraction or a decimal.
- You do not have to simplify fractions.

2 EXAMPLE

The surface of a lake is 29.8 ft below sea level. What is the elevation in feet of a street that is 35 ft above the surface of the lake?

$(-29.8) + 35$ **Write an expression.**

$|35| - |-29.8|$ **Find the difference of the absolute values.**

5.2   **Simplify. Since 35 has the greater absolute value, the sum is positive.**

The street is 5.2 feet above sea level. Enter 5.2 on the grid as shown.
● You do not enter the units.

EXERCISES

Write what you would grid for each answer.

1. Simplify $12 \div [12 - (4 \cdot 2)]$.

2. What is the next number in the pattern $0.4, 0.8, 1.3, 1.9, 2.6, \ldots$?

3. What is the next number in the pattern $0, \frac{1}{2}, 1, 1\frac{1}{2}, 2, \ldots$?

Chapter Review

Vocabulary Review

absolute value (p. 19)
conjecture (p. 35)
coordinate plane (p. 52)
counterexample (p. 37)
evaluate (p. 14)
inductive reasoning (p. 35)

integers (p. 19)
opposites (p. 19)
order of operations (p. 8)
ordered pair (p. 52)
origin (p. 52)
quadrants (p. 52)

variable (p. 4)
variable expression (p. 4)
x-axis (p. 52)
x-coordinate (p. 52)
y-axis (p. 52)
y-coordinate (p. 52)

Go Online
PHSchool.com

For: Vocabulary quiz
Web Code: adj-0151

Choose the vocabulary term that correctly completes the sentence.

1. The ordered pair $(0, 0)$ represents the location of the __?__ .

2. A letter that stands for a number in an expression is a(n) __?__ .

3. The vertical axis in the coordinate plane is known as the __?__ .

4. The coordinate plane is divided into four __?__ .

5. All whole numbers and their opposites are __?__ .

6. In the ordered pair $(-5, 2)$, the number -5 is the __?__ .

7. The distance that a number is from zero on a number line is the __?__ of the number.

Skills and Concepts

1-1 Objectives

▼ To identify variables, numerical expressions, and variable expressions (p. 4)

▼ To write variable expressions for word phrases (p. 5)

A **variable** is a letter that stands for a number. A **variable expression** uses variables, numerals, and operation symbols.

Write a variable expression for each word phrase.

8. twenty-five less than x

9. the product of n and 3

10. ten decreased by t

11. a number x divided by 4

12. a number n increased by 5

13. two more than y

1-2 Objectives

▼ To use the order of operations (p. 8)

▼ To use grouping symbols (p. 9)

To simplify a numerical expression, follow the **order of operations.**

1. Work inside grouping symbols.

2. Multiply and divide in order from left to right.

3. Add and subtract in order from left to right.

Simplify each expression.

14. $3 \cdot 7 + 6 \div 2$ 15. $(4 + 8) \div 2 \cdot 2$ 16. $9 \cdot 5 - 4(12 \div 6)$

1-3 Objectives

▼ To evaluate variable expressions (p. 14)

▼ To solve problems by evaluating expressions (p. 15)

To **evaluate** a variable expression, substitute a number for each variable. Use the order of operations to simplify.

Evaluate each expression.

17. $3x + 4$, for $x = 5$

18. $15 + 10 \div n$, for $n = 5$

19. $(y - 6)2$, for $y = 16$

20. $4(4 + m)$, for $m = 6$

21. $15t \cdot 10$, for $t = 3$

22. $z + [15 - (z - 1)]$, for $z = 4$

1-4 Objectives

▼ To represent, graph, and order integers (p. 18)

▼ To find opposites and absolute values (p. 19)

Integers are the set of whole numbers and their **opposites**. The **absolute value** of an integer is its distance from zero on a number line. On a number line, the integer farther to the right is the greater integer.

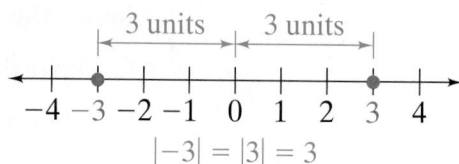

$|-3| = |3| = 3$

Simplify each expression.

23. the opposite of 17

24. $|-1{,}000|$

25. the absolute value of negative 9

26. the opposite of the absolute value of 12

Compare. Use >, <, or = to complete each statement.

27. $-7 \blacksquare -9$ **28.** $0 \blacksquare -3$ **29.** $-6 \blacksquare 2$ **30.** $|-5| \blacksquare |5|$

🌐 **31. Water Slides** A slide at a water park is 30 ft high. What integer represents your change in elevation when you go down the slide?

1-5 and 1-6 Objectives

▼ To use models to add integers (p. 24)

▼ To use rules to add integers (p. 25)

▼ To use models to subtract integers (p. 30)

▼ To use a rule to subtract integers (p. 31)

To add integers with the *same* sign, add their absolute values. The sum has the same sign. To add integers with *different* signs, find the difference of their absolute values. The sum has the sign of the integer with the greater absolute value. To subtract an integer, add its opposite.

Simplify each expression.

32. $8 + (-15)$

33. $-9 + 21$

34. $9 - (-5)$

35. $14 + (-9) + (-20)$

36. $-62 - (-59) - 24$

37. $-7 - 4$

38. $-4 + 12 + (-3) + (-6)$

🌐 **39. Wildlife** An eagle leaves her nest on the side of a cliff. She soars upward 60 ft and then dives 80 ft. What is her change in elevation after leaving the nest?

1-7 Objectives

▼ To write rules for patterns (p. 35)

▼ To make predictions and test conjectures (p. 36)

Inductive reasoning is making conclusions based on patterns you observe. A conclusion reached by inductive reasoning is a **conjecture.**

Write a rule for each pattern. Find the next three numbers in the pattern.

40. $0, 6, 12, 18, \ldots$ **41.** $-18, -9, 0, 9, \ldots$ **42.** $\frac{1}{2}, 1, 1\frac{1}{2}, 2, \ldots$

1-8 Objectives

▼ To find number patterns (p. 40)

You can use patterns to solve problems.

43. Suppose you plan to save $12 per week. You have already saved $7.50. In how many weeks will you have saved at least $100?

44. A four-line classified ad costs $28 for a week. Each additional line costs $10.50. What is the weekly cost of a 12-line ad?

1-9 Objectives

▼ To multiply integers using repeated addition, patterns, and rules (p. 44)

▼ To divide integers using rules (p. 46)

To multiply or divide integers, multiply or divide the absolute values of the integers. If the integers have the same sign, the product or quotient is positive. If the integers have different signs, the product or quotient is negative.

Multiply or divide.

45. $7(-6)$ **46.** $250 \div (-50)$ **47.** $(-9)(-8)$

48. $-56 \div (-8)$ **49.** $-120 \div 40$ **50.** $-15(11)$

51. $\frac{-64}{8}$ **52.** $(-5)(-7)$ **53.** $(-6)(-17)$

1-10 Objectives

▼ To name coordinates and quadrants in the coordinate plane (p. 52)

▼ To graph points in the coordinate plane (p. 53)

A **coordinate plane** is formed by the intersection of two number lines. The *x*-axis and the *y*-axis divide the coordinate plane into four **quadrants.** An **ordered pair** gives the coordinates of a point. The *x*-coordinate shows the position right or left of the *y*-axis. The *y*-coordinate shows the position above or below the *x*-axis.

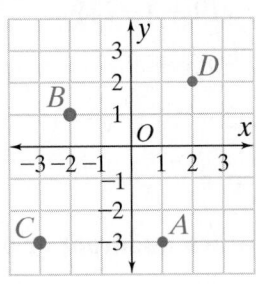

Write the coordinates of each point.

54. A **55.** B **56.** C **57.** D

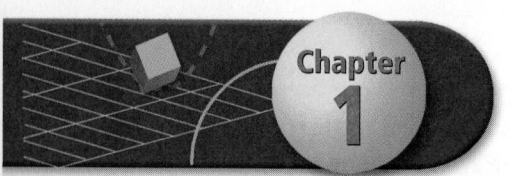

Chapter Test

Go Online
PHSchool.com
For: Online chapter test
Web Code: ada-0152

Write an expression for each phrase.

1. a number n increased by nineteen

2. ten less than negative three

3. the product of x and negative five

4. 5 more than the opposite of y

Evaluate each expression for the given values of the variables.

5. $3a + 5$, for $a = -5$

6. $5m + 9 + 7n$, for $m = 8$ and $n = 1$

7. $3|x - y| + x$, for $x = 1$ and $y = 8$

8. $20 - 2(a - b)$, for $a = 3$ and $b = 2$

Simplify each expression.

9. $|-5|$

10. opposite of -9

11. opposite of 7

12. $|15|$

Use >, <, or = to complete each sentence.

13. $-6 \blacksquare -5$

14. $8 \blacksquare -10$

15. $-3 \blacksquare 3$

16. $0 \blacksquare -7$

Simplify each expression.

17. $15 + (-7)$

18. $-8 - (-12)$

19. $-9(-7)$

20. $54 \div (-6)$

21. $-6 \cdot 48$

22. $\frac{-56}{-7}$

23. $119 - (-24)$

24. $-47 + (-21)$

25. $-83 + 17$

26. $5(-12)(-3)(-1)$

27. $2 \cdot |14 - (-9)|$

28. $8 \cdot 6 \div (2 + 1)$

29. $4 + 7 \cdot 2 + 8$

30. $16 - 2 \cdot (5 + 3)$

In which quadrant or on which axis does each point lie?

31. $(-5, 7)$

32. $(0, -4)$

33. $(-8, -6)$

Write the coordinates of each point.

34. F

35. G

36. H

37. J

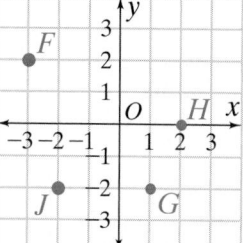

38. A shirt costs \$15 and jeans cost \$25.
   a. Write an expression for the cost of j jeans and s shirts.
   b. Evaluate the expression to find the cost of three pairs of jeans and five shirts.
   c. How many pairs of jeans can you buy for \$60?

39. Which statement is *always* true?
   A. The absolute value of an integer is equal to the opposite of the integer.
   B. The absolute value of an integer is greater than zero.
   C. An integer is greater than its opposite.
   D. A positive integer is greater than a negative integer.

40. A submarine was 250 m below sea level. It rose 75 m. Use an integer to describe the new depth of the submarine.

41. Write a rule for the pattern below. Find the next three numbers in the pattern.
   100, 90, 85, 75, 70, 60, . . .

42. You are in an elevator on the seventh floor. You go down 4 floors and then up 8 floors. Then you go down 3 floors and up 9 floors. The elevator goes down again 2 floors, and you get off. According to the pattern, on which floor are you now?

43. **Writing in Math** Describe how to order the integers $2, -6, 9, 0,$ and -13 from least to greatest.

Test Prep

Reading Comprehension Read each passage below. Then answer the questions on the basis of what is *stated* or *implied* in the passage.

Numbers in Nature Numbers appear everywhere in the patterns of nature. For example, the numbers of petals on flowers form patterns. Find some flowers and count their petals. You will find, with few exceptions, the number of petals to be one of 3, 5, 8, 13, 21, 34, and so forth. Also, although all snowflakes are different, each one has 6-fold symmetry. Put 20 pennies on a table and push them as close together as you can. Notice that all the pennies in the middle are surrounded by 6 others. This is an example of 6-fold symmetry.

1. What is true about the pattern for numbers of petals on flowers?
   - Ⓐ The numbers are all odd.
   - Ⓑ The increases from one to the next are always the same.
   - Ⓒ The increases from one to the next suggest a pattern you've seen before.
   - Ⓓ The number of petals on any flower has to be a number in the pattern.

2. Describe the pattern for the numbers of petals in flowers.

3. What number would follow 34 in the pattern for the numbers of petals on flowers?
   - Ⓔ 34   Ⓕ 35   Ⓖ 55   Ⓗ 68

4. What do patterns in snowflakes and pennies pushed close together have in common?

Wings or Wheels? The Arctic tern, a small sea bird, is the animal that migrates the longest distance each year. It can fly from a latitude of 84°N in the Arctic to 78°S in the Antarctic, and back. For some terns, this journey may be about 25,000 mi, which is about the distance around Earth at the equator. By contrast, the average number of miles a vehicle in the United States travels each year is about 14,000. Some Arctic terns live 25 years, which means they pile up an impressive number of miles traveled in a lifetime.

5. About how far does an Arctic tern fly in one migration south?
   - Ⓐ 162 mi   Ⓑ 14,000 mi
   - Ⓒ 12,500 mi   Ⓓ 25,000 mi

6. On average, how far does a vehicle in the United States travel each year?
   - Ⓔ 14,000 mi   Ⓕ 14,000 km
   - Ⓖ 25,000 mi   Ⓗ 25,000 km

7. Which travels farther in a year, an Arctic tern in its annual migration or a vehicle that's driven the average number of miles? About how much farther?

8. About how far could an Arctic tern fly in its migrations over 25 years? Justify your answer.

Activity Lab

Locating Sunken Ships

Applying Integers Marine archeologists are scientists who study sunken ships. They use scanning devices to locate objects on the ocean floor. When they find a "hot spot," divers take a closer look. If they find a sunken ship, the divers take underwater photographs and record the ship's latitude and longitude, identifying a specific point on Earth's surface.

Ancient World
This globe includes latitude (lines that run east–west) and longitude (lines that run north–south) rings.

Activity

Which part of Earth's coordinate globe corresponds to the indicated part of a coordinate plane?

1. the *x*-axis　　**2.** the *y*-axis　　**3.** the origin

Write and simplify an expression to show how the depth of a submersible robot changes.

4. from the *Edmund Fitzgerald* to the *Andrea Doria*

5. from the *Titanic* to the *Atocha*

6. from the water's surface to the *Atocha*

7. Estimation About how many times the depth of the *Atocha* is the depth of the *Andrea Doria*? Write an equation to model this relationship.

8. Research Pick one of the ships discussed here or another sunken ship. What factors led to its sinking? Explain.

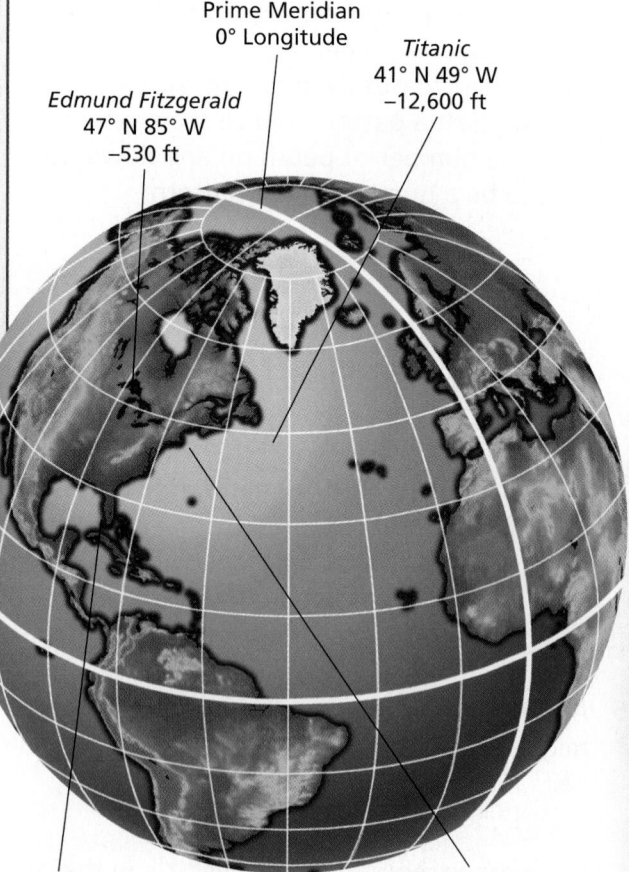

Prime Meridian
0° Longitude

Titanic
41° N 49° W
−12,600 ft

Edmund Fitzgerald
47° N 85° W
−530 ft

Equator
0° Latitude

Atocha
24° N 82° W
−55 ft

Andrea Doria
40° N 69° W
−240 ft

Embedded Treasure
Time and water pressure pushed these coins into a piece of wood.

Sunken World

Scientists explore shipwrecks in submersible vehicles such as Alvin (above) when the ship is too deep for scuba gear (worn by the diver).

Go Online
PHSchool.com

For: Information about sunken ships
Web Code: ade-0153

What You've Learned

In Chapter 1, you learned:

● How to apply the order of operations to evaluate numerical expressions.

● How to evaluate expressions with variables.

● How to add, subtract, multiply, and divide integers.

 **Check Your Readiness**  **for Help** to the Lesson in green.

Related Equations (Skills Handbook, pp. 768–773)

Complete the related equations.

1. $2.0 - \blacksquare = 0.9$ $0.9 + \blacksquare = 2.0$ **2.** $2 + \blacksquare = 2.3$ $2.3 - \blacksquare = 2$

3. $2.0 - \blacksquare = 1.3$ $1.3 + \blacksquare = 2.0$ **4.** $\blacksquare + 1.2 = 7$ $7 - \blacksquare = 1.2$

5. $3 \cdot \blacksquare = 7.5$ $7.5 \div \blacksquare = 3$ **6.** $7.2 \div \blacksquare = 1.2$ $1.2 \cdot \blacksquare = 7.2$

7. $3.6 \div \blacksquare = 6$ $6 \cdot \blacksquare = 3.6$ **8.** $\blacksquare \cdot (10) = 0.7$ $0.7 \div \blacksquare = 10$

Comparing Numbers (Lessons 1-5, 1-6, and 1-9)

Compare. Use $>$, $<$, or $=$ to complete each statement.

9. $6 \blacksquare 16$

10. $5 \blacksquare -5$

11. $-52 \blacksquare -21$

12. $0 \blacksquare -8$

13. $-7 \blacksquare 3$

14. $12 + 3 \blacksquare 19 - 4$

15. $-2 \cdot 6 \blacksquare 4 \cdot (-3)$

16. $27 \div 9 \blacksquare 6 \cdot 2$

17. $18 - 27 \blacksquare -34 + 12$

18. $8(-5) \blacksquare 100 - 65$

19. $6 \div (10 - 8) \blacksquare 1 + 5$

20. $3(-2)(-4) \blacksquare 4(-3)(2)$

Order of Operations With Integers (Lesson 1-2)

Simplify each expression.

21. $5 \cdot 2 + 5 \cdot 3$

22. $7(6 - 2)$

23. $10 \cdot 3 - 5 \cdot 3$

24. $-(34 + 76)$

25. $4(6) + 4(3)$

26. $-4(12 - 16)$

27. $7(8) - 10(8)$

28. $11 \cdot 9 - 6 \cdot 9$

29. $-2 \cdot 3 - 2 \cdot 7$

30. $6 \cdot (-9) - 3(-9)$

31. $-5(3) - (-5)(2)$

32. $(72 - 81)(5)$

Solving One-Step Equations and Inequalities

What You'll Learn Next

In this chapter, you will learn how to

● Use the Distributive Property.

● Write and solve equations.

● Write, solve, and graph inequalities.

● Solve a problem by Try, Test, Revise.

Activity Lab Applying what you learn, on pages 124–125 you will solve problems about a school fair.

◀))Key Vocabulary

● coefficient (p. 78)

● constant (p. 78)

● deductive reasoning (p. 79)

● equation (p. 82)

● inequality (p. 104)

● inverse operations (p. 88)

● like terms (p. 78)

● open sentence (p. 82)

● solution of an equation (p. 83)

● solution of an inequality (p. 104)

● term (p. 78)

2-1 Properties of Numbers

What You'll Learn

- To identify properties of addition and multiplication
- To use properties to solve problems

. . . And Why

To solve real-world problems involving purchases

✓ Check Skills You'll Need

Simplify.

1. $-18 + (-7)$

2. $32 - (-3)$

3. $(-13) + 6$

4. $2 - 48$

 for Help

Lessons 1-5 and 1-6

🔊 New Vocabulary

- **Commutative Properties**
- **Associative Properties**
- **additive identity**
- **multiplicative identity**
- **Identity Properties**

1 Identifying Properties

The sum of 6 and 4 is the same as the sum of 4 and 6. Similarly, the product of 9 and 5 is the same as the product of 5 and 9. These suggest the following properties.

> **Key Concepts** **Commutative Properties of Addition and Multiplication**
>
> Changing the order of the values you are adding or multiplying does not change the sum or product.
>
> | Arithmetic | Algebra |
> |---|---|
> | $6 + 4 = 4 + 6$ | $a + b = b + a$ |
> | $9 \cdot 5 = 5 \cdot 9$ | $a \cdot b = b \cdot a$ |

You can also change the grouping of the values before you add or multiply them.

> **Key Concepts** **Associative Properties of Addition and Multiplication**
>
> Changing the grouping of the values you are adding or multiplying does not change the sum or product.
>
> | Arithmetic | Algebra |
> |---|---|
> | $(2 + 7) + 3 = 2 + (7 + 3)$ | $(a + b) + c = a + (b + c)$ |
> | $(9 \cdot 4)5 = 9(4 \cdot 5)$ | $(ab)c = a(bc)$ |

1 EXAMPLE   Real-World Problem Solving

Golf Carlos rented a set of golf clubs for $7 and a golf cart for $12. He paid a greens fee of $23. Find his total cost.

You can use the Associative Property of Addition to find the total cost in two different ways.

$(7 + 12) + 23 = 19 + 23 = 42$ **Add 7 and 12 first.**

$7 + (12 + 23) = 7 + 35 = 42$ **Add 12 and 23 first.**

Carlos's total cost was $42.

✓ Quick Check

1. You spend $6 for dinner, $8 for a movie, and $4 for popcorn. Find your total cost. Explain which property or properties you used.

When you add a number and 0, the sum equals the original number. The **additive identity** is 0. When you multiply a number and 1, the product equals the original number. The **multiplicative identity** is 1.

Vocabulary Tip

In mathematics, an <u>identity</u> leaves the value of other numbers unchanged.

Key Concepts | Identity Properties of Addition and Multiplication

The sum of any number and zero is the original number. The product of any number and 1 is the original number.

Arithmetic	Algebra
$12 + 0 = 12; 10 \cdot 1 = 10$	$a + 0 = a; a \cdot 1 = a$

---

2 EXAMPLE **Identifying Properties**

Name each property shown.

a. $5 \cdot 7 = 7 \cdot 5$ Commutative Property of Multiplication

b. $c \cdot 1 = c$ Identity Property of Multiplication

c. $7 + a = a + 7$ Commutative Property of Addition

d. $5(xy) = (5x)y$ Associative Property of Multiplication

✓ Quick Check

2. Name each property shown.

    a. $3 + 6 = 6 + 3$ **b.** $8 = 1 \cdot 8$ **c.** $(3z)m = 3(zm)$

---

2 Using Properties

When numbers are easy to compute mentally, you can use properties and mental math to find sums.

3 EXAMPLE **Using Mental Math With Addition**

Use mental math to simplify $(81 + 6) + 9$.

$(81 + 6) + 9$

$= (6 + 81) + 9$ **Use the Commutative Property of Addition.**

$= 6 + (81 + 9)$ **Use the Associative Property of Addition.**

$= 6 + 90$ **Add within parentheses.**

$= 96$ **Add.**

Test-Taking Tip

Look for combinations that equal 10 or a multiple of 10, since they are easier to use in calculating mentally.

✓ Quick Check

3. Use mental math to simplify each expression.

    a. $6 + 7 + 14$ **b.** $8 + 0 + 2 + (-7)$

    c. $5 + 12 + 18 + 5$ **d.** $19 + (-30) + 21$

$.85

$.35

$1.65

4 EXAMPLE   <u>Real-World</u> 🌐 **Problem Solving**

School Supplies **Suppose you buy the school supplies shown at the left. Use mental math to find the cost of the supplies.**

$1.65 + 0.85 + 0.35$

$= 0.85 + 1.65 + 0.35$	**Use the Commutative Property of Addition.**
$= 0.85 + (1.65 + 0.35)$	**Use the Associative Property of Addition.**
$= 0.85 + 2.00$	**Add within parentheses.**
$= 2.85$	**Add.**

The cost of the school supplies is $2.85.

✓ Quick Check

4. Use the supermarket receipt and mental math to find the cost of the groceries.

```
    SOUTH STREET
       MARKET

DATE 08.03.03   THU
1 GALLON MILK  $2.30
BREAD          $1.80
APPLES         $2.20
```

GO for Help

For a guide to adding decimals, see Skills Handbook, page 768.

You can also use mental math to help you find products.

5 EXAMPLE   **Using Mental Math With Multiplication**

Use mental math to simplify $(4 \cdot 9) \cdot 5$.

$(4 \cdot 9) \cdot 5 = (9 \cdot 4) \cdot 5$	**Use the Commutative Property of Multiplication.**
$= 9 \cdot (4 \cdot 5)$	**Use the Associative Property of Multiplication.**
$= 9 \cdot 20$	**Multiply within parentheses.**
$= 180$	**Multiply.**

✓ Quick Check

5. Use mental math to simplify each expression.

    a. $25 \cdot (3 \cdot 4)$ **b.** $3 \cdot 1 \cdot -5 \cdot 8$

    c. $2(-8)(-15)$ **d.** $5 \cdot 9 \cdot 6 \cdot (-2) \cdot (-1)$

EXERCISES

For more exercises, see *Extra Skill and Word Problem Practice*.

Practice and Problem Solving

A Practice by Example

Example 1
(page 68)

GO for Help

Use the Associative Property to write two different expressions that you could use to find each sum.

1. Add 1, 3, and 25.   **2.** Add 5, 91, and 11.

3. Travel On a road trip, your family spends $120 for gas, $15 for bottled water, and $80 for food. Find your family's total cost. Explain which property or properties you used.

Example 2
(page 69)

Name each property shown.

4. $7 + 6 = 6 + 7$ **5.** $0 + 8 = 8$ **6.** $(6 \cdot 15)2 = 6(15 \cdot 2)$

7. $(12r)s = 12(rs)$ **8.** $999 \cdot 1 = 999$ **9.** $ab = ba$

Example 3
(page 69)

Mental Math **Use mental math to simplify each expression.**

10. $(5 + 23) + 65$ **11.** $(3 + 62) + 7$ **12.** $9 + (14 + 1)$

13. $-8 + 35 + 15$ **14.** $31 + 0 + (-2)$ **15.** $15 + 13 + (-25)$

Example 4
(page 70)

16. $(0.50 + 34) + 3.50$ **17.** $(4.55 + 27) + 5.45$

18. $1.50 + (3.17 + 6.50)$ **19.** $-0.25 + 4.88 + 3.25$

20. $7.02 + 3.40 + 1.98$ **21.** $8.39 + (-2.00) + 1.61$

22. Mental Math Loryn is flying roundtrip from Dallas, Texas, to Minneapolis, Minnesota. The fare for her ticket is $308. Each airport charges a $16 airport fee. There is also a tax of $12 on the fare. What is the total cost of Loryn's ticket?

Example 5
(page 70)

Mental Math **Use mental math to simplify each expression.**

23. $6 \cdot 3 \cdot 5$ **24.** $5 \cdot 7 \cdot (-2)$ **25.** $25 \cdot 4 \cdot 8$ **26.** $8 \cdot 4 \cdot (-10)$

B Apply Your Skills

GO Online
Homework Video Tutor
Visit: PHSchool.com
Web Code: ade-0201

Name each property shown.

27. $8(3 \cdot 2) = (8 \cdot 3)2$ **28.** $5 + 8 = 8 + 5$ **29.** $(6x)y = 6(xy)$

30. $6 \cdot 1 = 6$ **31.** $999 + 0 = 999$ **32.** $a \cdot 1 = 1 \cdot a$

Simplify each expression.

33. $25 + 157 + (-75)$ **34.** $140 + 17 + (-60)$

35. $5 \cdot 50 \cdot 20 \cdot (-2)$ **36.** $125 + 18 + 75 + 162$

$15.20

$7.65

$1.35

37. Gardening Lance has purchased some supplies to start his new garden. Use the prices shown at the left and mental math to find the cost of the supplies.

38. Writing in Math Which two numbers would you combine first to simplify $3 + 6 + 27$? Explain.

2-1 Properties of Numbers   **71**

C Challenge

Mental Math Evaluate each expression.

39. $x(y \cdot z)$, for $x = 4, y = 27,$ and $z = 5$

40. $t(u)(-v)$, for $t = 3, u = 20,$ and $v = 8$

41. $a + b + c$, for $a = 14, b = 252,$ and $c = 26$

42. $d(v)(d)$, for $d = 5$ and $v = 24$

43. Reasoning Can you use $4 + 2 = 6$ as your first step in simplifying $3 \cdot 4 + 2 \div (-2)$? Explain.

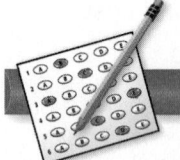

Test Prep

Multiple Choice

44. Which equation shows the Associative Property of Addition?
A. $8 + 6 + 7 = 8 + 7 + 6$ **B.** $(10 + 5) + 15 = 10 + (5 + 15)$
C. $9 + 0 + (-1) = 9 + (-1)$ **D.** $(-2) \cdot 1 \cdot 9 = (-2) \cdot 9$

Read the passage below before doing Exercises 45 and 46.

A Fair Fare in Alaska

Railroads are a popular means of transportation in Alaska. One scenic train route travels 356 miles from Anchorage to Fairbanks. It includes a stop in Denali Park, where you can see the tallest mountain in the United States, Mount McKinley. A one-way fare for the 12-hour trip is $154 in the summer and $120 in the spring and fall. A one-way fare for the 7.5-hour trip from Anchorage to Denali Park is $102 in the summer, and $84 in the spring and fall. Children's fares are half the fares for adults.

45. Two adults and two children plan to travel round trip from Anchorage to Fairbanks. How much will the trip cost in the summer?
F. $360   **G.** $462   **H.** $720   **J.** $924

46. Three adults and two children plan to travel round trip from Anchorage to Denali Park. How much will the trip cost in the fall?
A. $672   **B.** $504   **C.** $336   **D.** $252

Mixed Review

Lesson 1-10

In which quadrant does the graph of each ordered pair lie?

47. $(-6, -3)$ **48.** $(8, -1)$ **49.** $(-4, 17)$ **50.** $(-1, 4)$

Lesson 1-9 **51. Recreation** Lin worked 4 hours per day for 3 days to build a model bridge. How many hours did she spend on the project?

Lesson 1-2

Simplify each expression.

52. $3 \cdot 5 + 3 \cdot 15$ **53.** $4 \cdot 7 + 4 \cdot 11$ **54.** $5 \cdot 22 - 5 \cdot 2$

The Distributive Property

1 | Numerical Expressions

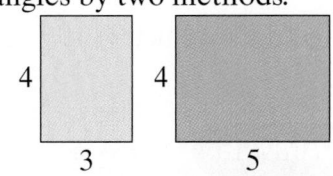

Exploring the Distributive Property

You can find the total area of two rectangles by two methods.

1. **Method 1:** Find the area of each rectangle. Then find the sum of the areas.

    4   4

    3   5

2. **Method 2:** Combine the two rectangles into one large rectangle. Find its length. Find its width. Then find its area.

    4

    3   5

3. On a piece of paper, draw two rectangles with the same width, and lengths different from those above. Label the dimensions. Repeat Method 1 and Method 2 with your pair of rectangles. What do you notice about your results?

What You'll Learn

- To use the Distributive Property with numerical expressions
- To use the Distributive Property with algebraic expressions

. . . And Why

To solve real-world problems involving fundraising

☑ **Check Skills You'll Need**

Simplify each expression.

1. $3 \cdot 7 - 9$

2. $(9 - 5)6$

3. $8 + 2 \cdot 6$

4. $2(6 - 3)$

5. $4 \cdot 5 - 4 \cdot 3$

6. $3 \cdot 2 - 1 \cdot 2$

GO for Help
Lesson 1-2

🔊 **New Vocabulary**
- Distributive Property

The Activity above shows different ways to find the sum of the areas of two rectangles. It suggests the *Distributive Property,* which combines multiplication with addition and subtraction.

Key Concepts | **Distributive Property**

To multiply a sum or difference, multiply each number within the parentheses by the number outside the parentheses.

Arithmetic	Algebra
$3(2 + 6) = 3(2) + 3(6)$	$a(b + c) = ab + ac$
$(2 + 6)3 = 2(3) + 6(3)$	$(b + c)a = ba + ca$
$6(7 - 4) = 6(7) - 6(4)$	$a(b - c) = ab - ac$
$(7 - 4)6 = 7(6) - 4(6)$	$(b - c)a = ba - ca$

You can use the Distributive Property to multiply mentally.

1 EXAMPLE **Using the Distributive Property I**

Use the Distributive Property to find 20(102) mentally.

$$20(102) = 20(100 + 2) \qquad \text{Write 102 as (100 + 2).}$$

$$20(100 + 2) = 20 \cdot 100 + 20 \cdot 2 \quad \text{Use the Distributive Property.}$$

$$= 2{,}000 + 40 \qquad \text{Multiply.}$$

$$= 2{,}040 \qquad \text{Add.}$$

✓ Quick Check

1. Find the product $9 \cdot 199$ mentally.

2 EXAMPLE Real-World 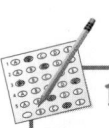 Problem Solving

Multiple Choice At the annual Pancake Breakfast, 397 people ate 4 pancakes each. How many pancakes were served?

Ⓐ 1,600   Ⓑ 1,588   Ⓒ 401   Ⓓ 397

$$(397)4 = (400 - 3)4 \qquad \text{Write 397 as (400 − 3).}$$

$$= 400 \cdot 4 - 3 \cdot 4 \quad \text{Use the Distributive Property.}$$

$$= 1{,}600 - 12 \qquad \text{Multiply.}$$

$$= 1{,}588 \qquad \text{Subtract.}$$

1,588 pancakes were served. The answer is B.

✓ Quick Check

2. Your club sold calendars for $7. Club members sold 204 calendars. How much money did they raise?

3 EXAMPLE **Using the Distributive Property II**

Simplify 8(15) − 8(5).

$$8(15) - 8(5) = 8(15 - 5) \quad \text{Use the Distributive Property.}$$

$$= 8(10) \qquad \text{Subtract within parentheses.}$$

$$= 80 \qquad \text{Multiply.}$$

✓ Quick Check

3. Simplify each expression.

a. $7(21) + 7(9)$ **b.** $12(52) - 12(62)$ **c.** $(16)7 - (11)7$

Test-Taking Tip

You can use the Distributive Property with mental math.

99×2
$= (100 - 1) \times 2$
$= (100 \times 2) - (1 \times 2)$
$= 200 - 2$
$= 198$

You can use algebra tiles to model the Distributive Property with variable expressions.

4 EXAMPLE Using Tiles to Multiply

Use algebra tiles to multiply 3(2x + 5).

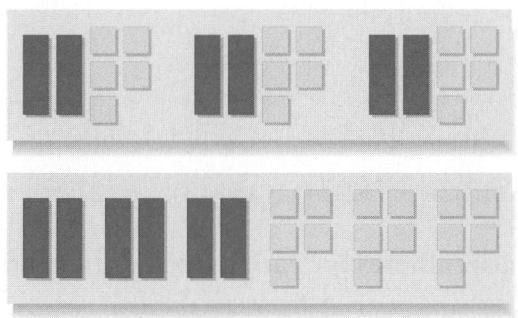

Model three groups of 2x + 5.

Group like tiles.

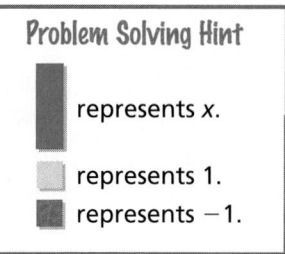

Problem Solving Hint

█ represents x.

▢ represents 1.

▨ represents -1.

So, $3(2x + 5) = 6x + 15$.

✓ Quick Check

4. Use algebra tiles to multiply.

   a. $4(2x - 3)$ **b.** $3(x + 4)$ **c.** $(3x + 1)2$

In Example 4, notice that 3 multiplies both $2x$ and 5.
That is, $3(2x + 5) = 3(2x) + 3(5)$.

5 EXAMPLE Using the Distributive Property III

Multiply.

a. $-5(4x - 3)$

$-5(4x - 3) = -5(4x) - (-5)(3)$ **Use the Distributive Property.**

$\qquad\qquad\quad = -20x - (-15)$ **Multiply.**

$\qquad\qquad\quad = -20x + 15$ **Simplify.**

b. $(2x + 5)7$

$(2x + 5)7 = (2x)7 + (5)7$ **Use the Distributive Property.**

$\qquad\qquad = 14x + 35$ **Multiply.**

Vocabulary Tip

When you distribute papers in class, you give some to each classmate. Similarly, when you <u>distribute</u> a number over a sum or difference, you multiply each value within the parentheses by that number.

✓ Quick Check

5. Multiply.

   a. $2(7 - 3d)$ **b.** $(6m + 1)(3)$ **c.** $-3(5t - 2)$

EXERCISES

For more exercises, see *Extra Skill and Word Problem Practice*.

Practice and Problem Solving

A Practice by Example

Examples 1 and 2
(page 74)

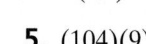
for Help

Mental Math Use the Distributive Property to simplify.

1. 6(23) **2.** 5(18) **3.** 7(48) **4.** 13(101)

5. (104)(9) **6.** 6(52) **7.** 8(98) **8.** (208)4

9. Ticket Sales A theater sold out its evening performances four nights in a row. The theater has 294 seats. How many people attended the theater in the four nights?

Example 3
(page 74)

Simplify each expression.

10. 7(3) + 7(5) **11.** 2(9) − 3(9) **12.** 6(4) + 6(8)

13. 9(3) − 2(3) **14.** (12)27 − (12)24 **15.** (3)5 + (27)5

Example 4
(page 75)

Write an expression using parentheses for each model. Then multiply.

16.

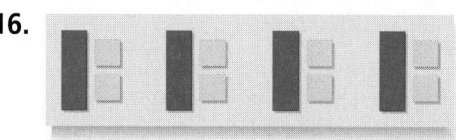

17.

Multiply. Use algebra tiles as needed.

18. 2(t − 5) **19.** (v − 3)4 **20.** 3(2h − 1) **21.** −2(7z + 3)

Example 5
(page 75)

Multiply.

22. 7(b − 3) **23.** 12(a + 3) **24.** (2 + 3d)5 **25.** −5(m + 6)

26. 3(5 − 3w) **27.** −7(t − 4) **28.** 4(b + 5) **29.** (y − 6)2

B Apply Your Skills

Mental Math Use the Distributive Property to simplify.

30. 5(1,005) **31.** (8) · 11 + (−13) · 11

32. 13 · (−3) − 7 · (−3) **33.** −32 · 6 + 29 · 6

34. 4 · 19 − 4 · (11) **35.** (−8) · 10 + 3 · (−8)

Mental Math Solve using mental math.

36. Every day, Lila eats a bowl of cereal that has 193 calories. What is the total number of calories from cereal that Lila eats in a week?

37. The trip from Roberto's house to his aunt's house is 896 miles. How long is the round trip?

Use the Distributive Property to multiply.

38. $-3(2t + 6)$ **39.** $-7(-3n + 2)$ **40.** $(4 - t)(-7)$

41. $-5(-m + 6)$ **42.** $-8(6 - c)$ **43.** $(5y + 8)(-3)$

44.  **Writing in Math** Explain how to use the Distributive Property to multiply $6(3r + 4s)$.

45. Error Analysis Suppose your friend wrote $7(2m + t) = 14m + t$. What error did your friend make?

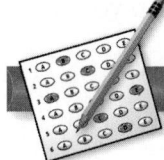 **Challenge**

Mental Math Use the Distributive Property to simplify.

46. $(-4)(70) + (-4)(-90)$ **47.** $3(9) - 3(5) + 3(6)$

Name each property shown.

48. $m[t + (-t)] = mt + m(-t)$ **49.** $m[t + (-t)] = m(-t + t)$

50. $m[t + (-t)] = [t + (-t)]m$ **51.** $m + [t + (-t)] = (m + t) + (-t)$

Test Prep

Multiple Choice

52. According to the map, if you drive from Atlanta to Los Angeles (L.A.) and back, how many miles would you travel?
A. 7,776 mi   **B.** 3,888 mi
C. 1,944 mi   **D.** 1,888 mi

53. Which equation correctly illustrates the Distributive Property?
F. $18(100 + 4) = (18 \cdot 100) + 4$
G. $18(100 + 4) = (18 + 100) \cdot (18 + 4)$
H. $18(100 + 4) = (18 + 100) \cdot 4$
J. $18(100 + 4) = (18 \cdot 100) + (18 \cdot 4)$

54. You rent three videos for $2.95 each. What do you pay?
A. $6.95   **B.** $8.85   **C.** $9.00   **D.** $9.15

Mixed Review

GO for Help

Lesson 2-1

Name the property shown.

55. $3(6 \cdot 2) = 3(2 \cdot 6)$ **56.** $8 = 8 + 0$ **57.** $4(8 \cdot 3) = (4 \cdot 8)3$

Lessons 1-5 and 1-6

58. You have $120 in your checking account. In one month, you deposit $30, write a check for $21, withdraw $20, and deposit $45. Find your balance at the end of the month.

Lesson 1-3

Evaluate each expression.

59. $7 - m$, for $m = 6$ **60.** $6t + 1$, for $t = -2$ **61.** $c \div 3 - 5$, for $c = 6$

2-3 Simplifying Variable Expressions

What You'll Learn

- To identify parts of a variable expression
- To simplify expressions

. . . And Why

To extend addition and subtraction skills to include variables

☑ **Check Skills You'll Need**

Simplify each expression.

1. $5(b + 4)$

2. $-3(2x + 5)$

3. $4(-8 - 3q)$

4. $-6(2b - 7)$

 **for Help**
Lesson 2-2

🔊 **New Vocabulary**

- term
- constant
- like terms
- coefficient
- simplify a variable expression
- deductive reasoning

1 Identifying Parts of a Variable Expression

The diagram shows the possible parts of a variable expression.

A **term** is a number or the product of a number and variable(s).

$$7a + 4a + 3b - 6 \leftarrow \text{A \textbf{constant} is a term that has no variable.}$$

Like terms have identical variables.

A **coefficient** is a number that multiplies a variable.

When you have a variable expression that includes subtraction, you can rewrite the expression using only addition. This will help you find the coefficient(s) and constant(s).

$$5x - 3y + z - 2$$
$$= 5x + (-3y) + z + (-2) \quad \textbf{Rewrite subtraction as adding opposites.}$$
$$= 5x + (-3y) + 1z + (-2) \quad \textbf{Identity Property of Multiplication}$$

Rewriting the expression using addition shows that the coefficients are 5, −3, and 1. The constant is −2. Notice that the sign between terms in the original expression determines whether a coefficient or constant is positive or negative.

1 EXAMPLE   Identifying Parts of an Expression

Name the coefficients, the like terms, and the constants in $3m - 2n + n - 4$.

Coefficients: $3, -2, 1$ Like terms: $-2n$ and n Constant: -4

☑ **Quick Check**

1. Name the coefficients, the like terms, and the constants.

   a. $6 + 2s + 4s$ **b.** $-4x$ **c.** $9m + 2r - 2m + r$

2 Simplifying Variable Expressions

You **simplify a variable expression** by replacing it with an equivalent expression that has as few terms as possible. Algebra tiles can help you model this process.

2 EXAMPLE · Using Tiles to Simplify

Simplify $2x + 4 + 3x$.

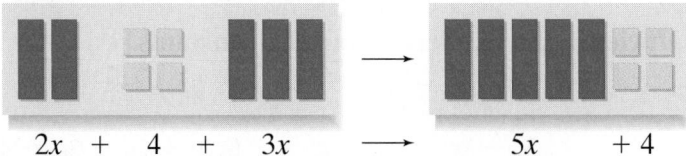

$$2x \quad + \quad 4 \quad + \quad 3x \quad \longrightarrow \quad 5x \quad + 4$$

✓ Quick Check

● **2.** Use tiles to simplify $3a + 2 + 4a - 1$.

You can also use the Distributive Property to combine like terms.

3 EXAMPLE · Combining Like Terms

Simplify $5y + y$.

$$
\begin{aligned}
5y + y &= 5y + 1y & & \textbf{Use the Identity Property of Multiplication.} \\
&= (5 + 1)y & & \textbf{Use the Distributive Property.} \\
&= 6y & & \textbf{Simplify.}
\end{aligned}
$$

GO **online**

Video Tutor Help
Visit: PHSchool.com
Web Code: ada-0775

✓ Quick Check

3. Simplify each expression.

   a. $3b - b$ **b.** $-4m - 9m$ **c.** $p + 6p - 4p$

Deductive reasoning is the process of reasoning logically from given facts to a conclusion. As you use properties, rules, and definitions to justify the steps in a problem, you are using deductive reasoning.

4 EXAMPLE · Using Deductive Reasoning

Simplify $4g + 3(3 + g)$. **Justify each step.**

$$
\begin{aligned}
4g + 3(3 + g) &= 4g + 9 + 3g & & \textbf{Use the Distributive Property.} \\
&= 4g + 3g + 9 & & \textbf{Use the Commutative Property} \\
& & & \textbf{of Addition.} \\
&= (4 + 3)g + 9 & & \textbf{Use the Distributive Property to} \\
& & & \textbf{combine like terms.} \\
&= 7g + 9 & & \textbf{Simplify.}
\end{aligned}
$$

✓ Quick Check

4. Simplify each expression. Justify each step.

   a. $6y + 4m - 7y + m$ **b.** $4x + 3 - 2(5 + x)$

Practice and Problem Solving

 Practice by Example

Example 1
(page 78)

Name the coefficients, the like terms, and the constants.

1. $3x + 5y - 3$ **2.** $2x - 7$ **3.** $4x - 7x + 3x$

4. $6xy - 5xy$ **5.** $-3x$ **6.** $a + 2a + 3a - 4a$

Example 2
(page 79)

Use tiles to simplify each expression.

7. $x + 2 + 3x + 5 + x + 3 + 2x$

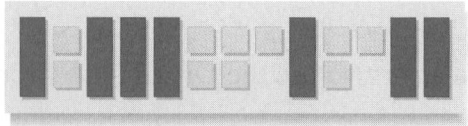

8. $2x + 1 + x - 4 + 4x + 1$

9. $x + 2 + 3x$ **10.** $2x + 1 + 6x - 4$

Example 3
(page 79)

Simplify each expression.

11. $12a + a$ **12.** $5a + 8a$ **13.** $-2b + b$

14. $7w - w$ **15.** $2r - 5 + 6r$ **16.** $4a - 3 + 5a$

Example 4
(page 79)

Simplify each expression. Justify each step.

17. $2g + 3(g + 5)$ **18.** $-3z + 8(z + y)$

19. $4m + 3d - 5m + d$ **20.** $t - 3 + 2(t + 2)$

 **Apply Your Skills**

Simplify each expression.

21. $8z + 8y + 3z$ **22.** $t - 3t + 2t + 4$ **23.** $18 + 6(9k - 13)$

24. $r + 3 - 6r + r$ **25.** $-4(a + 3) - a$ **26.** $4m + 3 - 5m + m$

27. $3(g + 5) + 2g$ **28.** $2b - 6 + 3b - b$ **29.** $-5 + 3x + 3 + 2$

30. $4(w + 2x) + 9(-4w)$ **31.** $3(2n + 4) - 2(3n + 6)$

32. Pet Supplies Juan bought supplies for his new gecko. He bought four plants for p dollars each. He also bought a 10-gallon tank for $10 and a water dish for $3. Write an expression Juan could use to find the total cost of the supplies.

33. Error Analysis Your friend simplified $x + y + xy$ to $2xy$. What error did your friend make?

34. Open-Ended Use the variables r and s to write a variable expression. Evaluate your expression for $r = 2$ and $s = -5$.

 **Online**
Homework Video Tutor
Visit: PHSchool.com
Web Code: ade-0203

35. <u>Writing in Math</u> The expression $10bc$ has two variables. Explain why $10bc$ is not two terms.

 **Challenge**   **Simplify each expression. Justify each step.**

36. $12 - 4(-8v + 17)$ **37.** $6(2x + y) + 2y - 12x$

38. $(2t + 4)3 + 6(-5t) - (-8)$ **39.** $-12(5x) + 3(-7x) - x$

40. $w + 3w + 4(5 + w - 3w)$ **41.** $18u - 6(9k - 7 - 10u) + 4k$

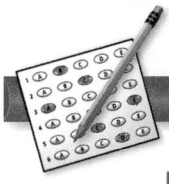

Test Prep

Multiple Choice

42. Which expression has exactly two like terms?
  A. $3t + 1 - t$ **B.** $7 + 2m$ **C.** $8q + 3p$ **D.** $6r + r - 9r$

43. Which expression simplifies to $3x + 4z + 6$?
  F. $3(x + 6) + 4z$ **G.** $7(x + z) + 6$
  H. $7z + 3(x + 2) - 3z$ **J.** $3 + x + 4 + z + 6$

44. Jaleesa bought three folders for b cents each and two report covers for c cents each. She also bought a binder for $1.89. Which expression could Jaleesa use to find the total cost?
  A. $b + c + 189$ **B.** $3b + 189$
  C. $3b + 2c + 189$ **D.** $189 - 2b - 3c$

Mixed Review

Lesson 2-2   **Mental Math Use the Distributive Property to find each product.**

45. $8(102)$ **46.** $54 \cdot 6$ **47.** $19(30)$ **48.** $(41)(9)$

Lesson 1-8 🌐 **49. Rock Climbing** A pair of rock climbers start up a 1,000-ft cliff. After one hour, they have gone up 160 ft. After two hours, they have gone up 320 ft. If they continue at this rate, how far up will they have gone after five hours?

 **Checkpoint Quiz 1**   **Lessons 2-1 through 2-3**

Name each property shown.

  1. $3 \cdot (-6) = -6 \cdot 3$ **2.** $(3a)b = 3(ab)$

  3. $17 \cdot 1 = 17$ **4.** $6 + 0 = 0 + 6$

  5. $(3 + 2)(4) = (4)(3 + 2)$ **6.** $4(3 - 2) = 4(3) - 4(2)$

Simplify each expression.

  7. $3(a + 2a)$ **8.** $9y - 3y + 12y$ **9.** $7(2w) + 2(w - 3)$

Variables and Equations

What You'll Learn

- To classify types of equations
- To check equations using substitution

. . . And Why

To check solutions of real-world equations involving weights

✔ Check Skills You'll Need

Write a variable expression for each phrase.

1. the sum of x and 46

2. four less than g

3. t decreased by five

4. the quotient of z and 26

 **for Help**
Lesson 1-1

🔊 New Vocabulary

- equation
- open sentence
- solution of an equation

---

1 Classifying Types of Equations

An **equation** is a mathematical sentence with an equal sign. Here are three of the ways you will see equations in this book.

$9 + 2 = 11$	a numerical expression equal to a numerical expression
$x + 7 = 37$	a variable expression equal to a numerical expression
$a + (-3) = 2a + 5$	a variable expression equal to a variable expression

An equation with a numerical expression equal to another numerical expression is either *true* or *false*. An equation with one or more variables is an **open sentence.**

1 EXAMPLE Classifying Equations

State whether each equation is *true, false,* or an *open sentence.*

a. **6 + 12 = 18**   true, because $18 = 18$

b. **6 = 4 + 3**   false, because $6 \neq 7$

c. **6y = −3 + 5y**   an open sentence, because there is a variable

✔ Quick Check

1. State whether each equation is *true, false,* or an *open sentence.* Explain.

   a. $9 - 7 = 3$ b. $8 + x = 2$ c. $4 \cdot 5 = 20$

You can write a mathematical word sentence as an equation.

2 EXAMPLE Writing an Equation

Write an equation for
Nine times the opposite of five is forty-five.
State whether the equation is *true, false,* or an *open sentence.*

Vocabulary Tip

The verb <u>is</u> between two quantities suggests writing the equal sign.

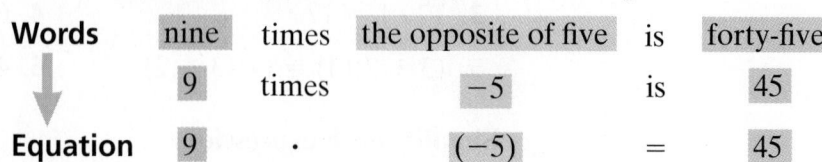

Words	nine	times	the opposite of five	is	forty-five
	9	times	−5	is	45
Equation	9	·	(−5)	=	45

The equation is false. $9 \cdot (-5) = -45$, and $-45 \neq 45$.

Sometimes you cannot remove the same number of tiles from each side. You may need to add tiles to form zero pairs. Here's how to solve $x + 2 = -4$.

$x + 2 = -4$

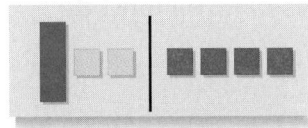 **Model the equation.**

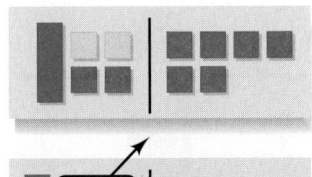 **Add −2 to each side.**

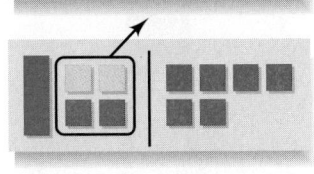 **Remove zero pairs.**

 $x = -6$

Check $x + 2 = -4$

$-6 + 2 \stackrel{?}{=} -4$ **Replace x with −6.**

$-4 = -4$ ✔

Model and solve each equation. Check your result.

16. $y + 2 = -2$ **17.** $x + 5 = 2$ **18.** $n + 7 = 1$

19. $-1 = k + 3$ **20.** $x - 4 = 5$ **21.** $2 = z - 3$

Modeling Write and solve the equation for each model.

22. 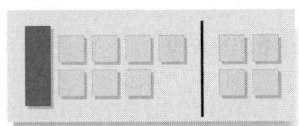 **23.** 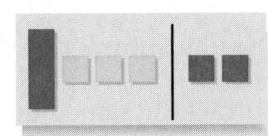 **24.**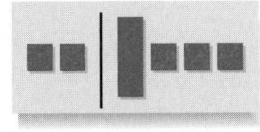

25. Open-Ended Write two different equations that have the solution modeled at the right.

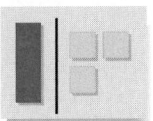

26. Number Sense Give an example of an equation model that has the same color unit squares on each side but still requires zero pairs to solve. Explain why zero pairs are needed.

2-5

Solving Equations by Adding or Subtracting

What You'll Learn

- To solve one-step equations using subtraction
- To solve one-step equations using addition

. . . And Why

To solve real-world problems involving health

 **Check Skills You'll Need**

Simplify each expression.

1. $3 + 4 - 4$

2. $7 + 9 - 7$

3. $8 - 2 + 2$

4. $6 + 2 - 2$

GO for Help
Lesson 2-1

🔊 **New Vocabulary**

- inverse operations

1 ▶ **Using Subtraction to Solve Equations**

Solving an equation is like keeping a barbell balanced. If you add weight to or subtract weight from one side of the bar, you must do the same on the other side.

Subtract 5 lb from each side.

As you can see in the photos, you keep the barbell balanced when you remove the same weight from each side.

In previous math courses, you used related equations like $3 + 5 = 8$ and $8 - 3 = 5$. These equations show that addition and subtraction undo each other.

When you solve an equation, your goal is to get the variable alone on one side of the equation. The value on the other side tells you the solution of the original equation. You use **inverse operations,** which undo each other, to get the variable alone.

Key Concepts | **Subtraction Property of Equality**

You can subtract the same number from each side of an equation.

Arithmetic	Algebra
$10 = 2(5)$	If $a = b$,
$10 - 5 = 2(5) - 5$	then $a - c = b - c$.

After you solve an equation, use your result in the original equation (as shown in Example 1) to check that your solution is correct.

1 EXAMPLE Subtracting to Solve an Equation

Solve $x + 6 = 4$.

Method 1

$x + 6 = 4$

$x + 6 - 6 = 4 - 6$ **Subtract 6 from each side.**

$x = -2$ **Simplify.**

Method 2

$x + 6 = 4$

$\underline{\quad -6 \quad -6}$

$x = -2$

Check $x + 6 = 4$

$-2 + 6 \overset{?}{=} 4$ **Replace x with −2.**

$4 = 4 \checkmark$

✓ Quick Check

1. Solve each equation.

 a. $x + 8 = 3$ **b.** $5 = d + 1$ **c.** $c + (-4) = -5$

You can write and solve equations describing real-world situations. To help check, decide whether your solution is correct using the original problem.

2 EXAMPLE Real-World 🌐 Problem Solving

Health Fred's target heart rate is 130 beats/min. This is 58 beats/min more than his resting heart rate. Find his resting heart rate.

Words   target rate   is   58   more than   resting rate

   ⬇   Let r = resting heart rate.

Equation   130   =   58   + r

$130 = 58 + r$

$130 = r + 58$ **Use the Commutative Property of Addition.**

$130 - 58 = r + 58 - 58$ **Subtract 58 from each side.**

$72 = r$ **Simplify.**

Fred's resting heart rate is 72 beats per minute.

Check The resting heart rate plus 58 beats per minute should be 130 beats per minute.
$72 + 58 = 130 \checkmark$

Real-World 🌐 Connection

Here is one method for estimating your target heart-rate range: Begin by subtracting your age from 220. Then multiply the result by 0.6 and 0.8 to find the lower and upper limits of your heart-rate range.

✓ Quick Check

2. Cora measures her heart rate at 123 beats per minute. This is 55 beats per minute more than her resting heart rate r. Write and solve an equation to find Cora's resting heart rate.

2 Using Addition to Solve Equations

When you solve an equation involving subtraction, *add* the same number to each side of the equation.

Key Concepts | **Addition Property of Equality**

You can add the same number to each side of an equation.

Arithmetic	Algebra
$8 = 2(4)$	If $a = b$,
$8 + 3 = 2(4) + 3$	then $a + c = b + c$.

Online active math

For: Equations Activity
Use: Interactive Textbook, 2-5

3 EXAMPLE   **Adding to Solve an Equation**

Solve $b - 12 = -49$.

$$b - 12 = -49$$
$$b - 12 + 12 = -49 + 12 \qquad \text{Add 12 to each side.}$$
$$b = -37 \qquad \text{Simplify.}$$

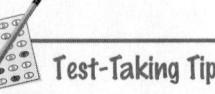 **Quick Check**

3. Solve each equation.

   a. $y - 5 = 8$ **b.** $p - 30 = 42$ **c.** $98 = x - 14$

---

4 EXAMPLE   **Real-World** 🌐 **Problem Solving**

Purchasing **Your friend's VCR cost $328 less than her TV. Her VCR cost $179. About how much did her TV cost?**

   Ⓐ about $175   Ⓑ about $300
   Ⓒ about $325   Ⓓ about $500

$$\$328 \approx \$325$$
$$\$179 \approx \$175 \qquad \text{Round to numbers that are easy to compute.}$$
$$175 \approx t - 325 \qquad \text{Write an equation.}$$
$$175 + 325 \approx t - 325 + 325 \qquad \text{Add 325 to each side.}$$
$$500 \approx t \qquad \text{Simplify.}$$

Your friend's TV cost about $500. The answer is D.

Quick Check

4. A used book costs $17 less than the same book new. The used book costs $9. About how much does the new book cost?

Test-Taking Tip

When you go from words to an equation, the order of the math symbols may be different from the order of the words:

• ten fewer than n ➜ $n - 10$

• eight less than r ➜ $r - 8$

• n times 5 ➜ $5n$

EXERCISES

For more exercises, see *Extra Skill and Word Problem Practice*.

Practice and Problem Solving

A Practice by Example

Example 1
(page 89)

 **for Help**

Solve each equation.

1. $a + 8 = 12$ **2.** $t + (-3) = 8$ **3.** $3 = n + 4$

4. $d + (-4) = -7$ **5.** $c + 9 = 37$ **6.** $q + (-10) = -25$

7. $b + 24 = 19$ **8.** $65 = n + 24$ **9.** $40 = w + (-5)$

Example 2
(page 89)

10. Astronomy The average distance from the sun to Jupiter is 778 million km. This distance is 550 million km greater than the average distance from the sun to Mars. Write and solve an equation to find the average distance d that Mars is from the sun.

GO for Help

For a guide to reading and solving Exercise 11, see page 93.

11. Physics The speed of sound through steel is 5,200 meters per second (m/s). This is 2,520 m/s faster than the speed of sound through silver. Write and solve an equation to find the speed of sound s through silver.

Example 3
(page 90)

Solve each equation.

12. $d - 4 = -7$ **13.** $c - 34 = 20$ **14.** $a - 4 = -18$

15. $r - 3 = 8$ **16.** $z - 100 = 100$ **17.** $5 = d - 1$

18. $40 = g - 20$ **19.** $34 = c - 19$ **20.** $-54 = q - 9$

Example 4
(page 90)

21. Astronomy Venus's average distance from the sun is 108 million km. This distance is 42 million km less than the average distance from the sun to Earth. Write and solve an equation to find Earth's average distance d from the sun.

B Apply Your Skills

Copy and complete the steps for solving each equation.

22. $35 + b = -90$
$35 - \blacksquare + b = -90 - \blacksquare$
$b = \blacksquare$

23. $y - 86 = -322$
$y - 86 + \blacksquare = -322 + \blacksquare$
$y = \blacksquare$

Solve each equation.

24. $54 + x = 98$ **25.** $e - 43 = -45$ **26.** $47 = 7 + y$

27. $450 = a - 325$ **28.** $h + 35 = 15$ **29.** $298 + n = 294$

30. $x - 366 = -415$ **31.** $89 + y = 112$ **32.** $-27 = w - 14$

33. Multiple Choice In 1996, 487 million people across the world spoke English. This was 512 million people fewer than the number who spoke Mandarin Chinese. Which equation could you use to find the number of people n who spoke Mandarin Chinese?

  Ⓐ $487 = n - 512$ Ⓑ $487 = n \times 512$
  Ⓒ $487 = 512 - n$ Ⓓ $487 = 512 \div n$

34. Open-Ended Write a word problem that can be solved using the equation $x + 15 = 18$.

35. This year, the Tigers won six more games than the Panthers. What other fact would you need to know in order to use the equation $p + 6 = 22$ to find the number of games, p, that the Panthers won?

 **Mental Math** Use mental math to solve each equation.

36. $b + 15 = -5$ **37.** $130 = 30 + s$ **38.** $x + 800 = 500$

39. Error Analysis A student solved the equation $x - 6 = -6$. His solution was -12. What error did the student make?

40. Writing in Math To solve $x + 25 = -22$, one student subtracted 25 from each side. Another student added -25 to each side. Will both methods work? Explain.

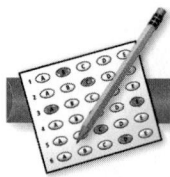 **Challenge**   **Solve each equation.**

41. $-45 = x + (-3) + 50$ **42.** $-215 + e + (-43) = -145$

43. $n - 29 - 16 = 246$ **44.** $34 + p + 112 = 78 - 7$

45. $183 + k - 20 = -15$ **46.** $328 = z - 31 + 219$

Test Prep

Gridded Response   Solve the equation given by each sentence.

47. Negative six plus y equals eighteen.

48. Twelve equals 23 subtracted from n.

49. Negative five equals x minus eight.

50. The number a plus 5 is 18.

51. Negative 8 plus y equals 13.

52. Negative seventeen is 32 less than y.

Mixed Review

Lesson 2-4   **State whether each equation is** *true, false,* **or an** *open sentence.* **Explain.**

53. $x + 2 = 4$ **54.** $4 = 6 - 2$ **55.** $5 - 3 = 7 - 4$

Lesson 1-8   **56. Patterns** Deric studied 30 min for his first math test. He studied 45 min for the second test and 60 min for the third test. If he continues this pattern, how long will he study for the fifth test?

Understanding Word Problems Read the problem below. Then let Tom's thinking guide you through the solution. Check your understanding with the exercise at the bottom of the page.

Physics The speed of sound through steel is 5,200 meters per second (m/s). This is 2,520 m/s faster than the speed of sound through silver. Write and solve an equation to find the speed of sound s through silver.

What Tom Thinks	What Tom Writes
I'll read the problem and write down the important information.	Speed of sound through steel = 5,200 m/s. The speed through steel is 2,520 m/s faster than the speed through silver.
Where to start? Well, it's always helpful to look for a relationship in the problem.	The speed through steel is 2,520 m/s faster than the speed through silver.
The speed is greater through steel. I will either have to subtract from the speed through steel to get the speed through silver, or add to the speed through silver to get the speed through steel. I'll add.	Steel speed = silver speed + 2,520
Since I know the speed through steel, I have to name only one variable.	Let s = speed of sound through silver.
Now I can write the equation.	$5,200 = s + 2,520$
I can solve the equation by using the Subtraction Property of Equality.	$5,200 - 2,520 = s + 2,520 - 2,520$ $2,680 = s$
I have to state what was asked for in the problem.	The speed of sound through silver is 2,680 m/s.

EXERCISE

1. Pamela can run the 300-m hurdles in 52.3 s. Elaine takes 2.8 s more than Pamela to make the same run. How long does it take Elaine to run the 300-m hurdles?

Solving Equations by Multiplying or Dividing

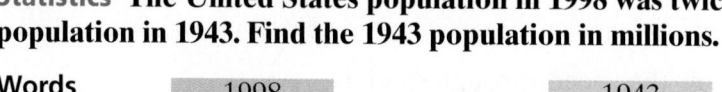

1 **Using Division to Solve Equations**

Division and multiplication are inverse operations. You can solve an equation that involves multiplication by using the Division Property of Equality.

Key Concepts **Division Property of Equality**

If you divide each side of an equation by the same nonzero number, the two sides remain equal.

Arithmetic	Algebra
$6 = 3(2)$	If $a = b$ and $c \neq 0$,
$\dfrac{6}{3} = \dfrac{3\,(2)}{3}$	then $\dfrac{a}{c} = \dfrac{b}{c}$.

Test-Taking Tip

When gridding an answer, be sure to grid the units digit, 5, in the column to the left of the decimal point.

1 **EXAMPLE** **Real-World Problem Solving**

Statistics The United States population in 1998 was twice the population in 1943. Find the 1943 population in millions.

Words

1998 population	was	twice	1943 population

Let p = population in 1943.

Equation $\quad$ 270 $\quad$ = $\quad$ 2 · $\quad$ p

$$270 = 2p$$

$$\dfrac{270}{2} = \dfrac{2p}{2} \quad \textbf{Divide each side by 2.}$$

$$135 = p \quad \textbf{Simplify.}$$

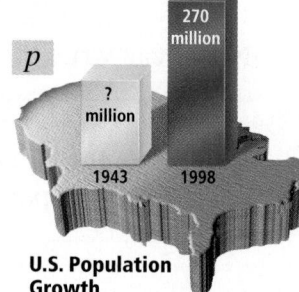

U.S. Population Growth

The United States population in 1943 was 135 million people.

Check Is the answer reasonable? Twice the 1943 population should be the 1998 population. Since $135 \cdot 2 = 270$, the answer is reasonable.

✓ **Quick Check**

1. Solve each equation.

  a. $4x = 84$ **b.** $91 = 7y$ **c.** $12w = 108$

Solve $5r = -20$.

$$5r = -20$$

$$\frac{5r}{5} = \frac{-20}{5} \quad \textbf{Divide each side by 5.}$$

$$r = -4 \quad \textbf{Simplify.}$$

Check $\quad\quad 5r = -20$

$$5 \cdot (-4) \stackrel{?}{=} -20 \quad \textbf{Replace } r \textbf{ with } -4.$$

$$-20 = -20 ✔$$

Video Tutor Help

Visit: PHSchool.com
Web Code: ada-0775

☑ **Quick Check**

2. Solve each equation.

    a. $-3b = 24$ **b.** $96 = -8n$ **c.** $-4d = -56$

2   Using Multiplication to Solve Equations

When you multiply each side of an equation by the same number, the two sides remain equal.

Key Concepts   **Multiplication Property of Equality**

You can multiply each side of an equation by the same number.

         Arithmetic   **Algebra**

          $12 = 3(4)$ If $a = b$,

      $12 \cdot 2 = 3(4) \cdot 2$ then $ac = bc$.

---

③ **EXAMPLE**   Multiplying to Solve an Equation

Solve $\frac{x}{-9} = -3$.

$$\frac{x}{-9} = -3$$

$$-9\left(\frac{x}{-9}\right) = -9(-3) \quad \textbf{Multiply each side by } -9.$$

$$x = 27 \quad \textbf{Simplify.}$$

☑ **Quick Check**

3. Solve each equation.

    a. $\frac{r}{-5} = 10$ **b.** $\frac{s}{6} = 54$ **c.** $-30 = \frac{t}{20}$

EXERCISES

Practice and Problem Solving

A Practice by Example

Examples 1 and 2
(pages 94 and 95)

GO for Help

Solve each equation.

1. $6x = 96$

2. $108 = 9x$

3. $8y = 112$

4. $45 = 9a$

5. $5w = 95$

6. $15c = 90$

7. $125 = 25d$

8. $180 = 45s$

9. $20b = 2{,}000$

10. $8x = -48$

11. $4a = 28$

12. $-60 = 12m$

13. $-2b = 30$

14. $-10d = 100$

15. $162 = -18t$

16. $-75 = -15x$

17. $-5x = -115$

18. $-60y = -360$

19. Earnings Carol earns \$8/h. How many hours must she work to earn \$288?

20. Savings Raul saves \$15 each month. At this rate, how many months will he take to save \$135?

Example 3
(page 95)

Solve each equation.

21. $6 = \frac{a}{7}$

22. $\frac{w}{12} = 2$

23. $\frac{n}{15} = 7$

24. $\frac{b}{-6} = 20$

25. $-2 = \frac{d}{8}$

26. $\frac{v}{3} = -4$

27. $-\frac{m}{20} = -2$

28. $\frac{r}{-5} = -4$

B Apply Your Skills

Solve each equation.

29. $39 = c \cdot 3$

30. $25x = -125$

31. $\frac{v}{3} = 14$

32. $\frac{m}{-4} = 13$

33. $-50 = \frac{n}{-6}$

34. $72 = 8n$

35. $22p = 110$

36. $\frac{r}{-9} = -18$

37. Reasoning You can divide each side of an equation by the same nonzero value. Explain what would result from the equation $4 \cdot 0 = 5 \cdot 0$ if you could divide each side by zero, and if $\frac{0}{0} = 1$.

Mental Math Is -3 a solution of each equation? Explain.

38. $\frac{b}{-3} = 1$

39. $\frac{-18}{k} = -6$

40. $3t = 9$

Write an equation for each sentence. Solve the equation.

41. The product of negative twenty and y is one hundred.

42. The value n divided by ten is one hundred.

43. Seven multiplied by k is negative one hundred sixty-eight.

GO Online
Homework Video Tutor
Visit: PHSchool.com
Web Code: ade-0206

44. Multiple Choice One of the world's tallest office buildings is in Malaysia. The building has 88 stories. The height of the 88 stories is 1,232 ft. What is the height of one story?

Ⓐ 9 ft high   Ⓑ 11 ft high   Ⓒ 14 ft high   Ⓓ 88 ft high

U.S. School Enrollment

Grades	Millions of Students
Kindergarten	■
1–8	30
9–12	14

SOURCE: U.S. Department of Education.
Go to **www.PHSchool. com** for a
data update. Web Code: adg-9041

45. Use the table at the left. The number of students in grades 9–12 is 4.7 times the number of students in kindergarten. Write and solve an equation to find the number of students s in kindergarten. Round to the nearest million.

46. **Writing in Math**  How are the procedures to solve $3x = 9$ and $x + 3 = 9$ alike? How are they different?

47. **Open-Ended** Write a question that can be solved using the equation $5x = 45$.

Mental Math Solve each equation.

48. $75m = -7,500$

49. $\frac{v}{-50} = 300$

50. $3,823 = \frac{s}{100}$

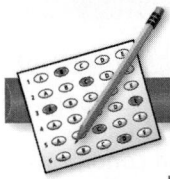 **Challenge**

For what values of x is each equation true?

51. $|x| = 7$

52. $-3|x| = -9$

53. $\frac{|x|}{3} = 2$

54. $x - a = b$

55. $a + x = b$

56. $ax = b$

Test Prep

Multiple Choice In Exercises 57–60, which equation matches the given sentence?

57. Negative six multiplied by q equals one hundred eight.
   A. $-6 + q = 108$
   B. $-6q = 108$
   C. $108q = -6$
   D. $q = -6 + 108$

58. Thirteen equals the quotient of x divided by three.
   F. $13 = \frac{x}{3}$
   G. $\frac{x}{13}$
   H. $13 = 3x$
   J. $\frac{13}{3} = x$

59. Forty-two is the product of some number and 6.
   A. $6(42) = x$
   B. $\frac{6}{x} = 42$
   C. $\frac{x}{42} = 6$
   D. $42 = 6x$

60. Some number divided by eight equals four.
   F. $\frac{8}{x} = 4$
   G. $\frac{8}{4} = x$
   H. $\frac{x}{8} = 4$
   J. $\frac{4}{8} = x$

Mixed Review

Lesson 2-5

Solve each equation.

61. $-4 = a + 7$
62. $n - 5 = 12$
63. $t - (-4) = -15$
64. $y + 10 = 12$

Lesson 1-5 🌐 65. **Hiking** Suppose you start hiking from a point 92 ft below sea level and break for lunch on a hilltop that is 1,673 ft above sea level. What is your change in elevation?

Lesson 1-1

Write a variable expression for each phrase.

66. three less than a

67. 7 times a number n

Guess, Check, Revise

What You'll Learn

- To solve a problem using the Guess, Check, Revise strategy

. . . And Why

To solve real-world problems involving money

 **Check Skills You'll Need**

Simplify.

1. $158 + 20$

2. $158 + 30$

3. $158 + 25$

4. $158 + 22$

5. In Exercises 1–4, which result came closest to 181?

GO for Help
Lesson 1-5

Math Strategies in Action Did you know that meteorologists use weather balloons to collect data? They use the temperature, humidity, and other data in mathematical models to bring you the daily weather forecast. As more data become available—from weather balloons and satellites, for example—the models, and therefore the weather reports, become more accurate.

Similarly, in math problems, you can make an initial conjecture. You can test your conjecture. If it is not the right answer, you can use what you learn from your first conjecture to make a better, second conjecture.

Real-World Connection

Each day, weather balloons make more than 1,000 measurements of conditions in the upper atmosphere around the world.

1 EXAMPLE **Real-World Problem Solving**

Ticket Sales The theater club at school put on a play. For one performance, the club sold 133 tickets and raised $471. Tickets cost $4 for adults and $3 for students. How many student tickets and how many adult tickets did the club sell?

Understand the Problem

Look at the given information to make an informed conjecture.

1. How much does each type of ticket cost?

2. How many tickets did the club sell for the performance?

3. How much money did the club raise from ticket sales for this performance?

Make a Plan

Make a conjecture, and then test it. Use what you learn from your conjecture to make a better, second conjecture.

4. When you make a conjecture for how many adult tickets were sold, how can you use your conjecture to find how many student tickets could have been sold?

5. By what number do you multiply your conjecture of adult tickets sold to find how much money was made on adult tickets?

Carry Out the Plan

You can organize conjectures in a table. As a first conjecture, try making about half the tickets adult tickets.

Adult Tickets	Student Tickets	Total Money (in dollars)	
60	$133 - 60 = 73$	$60(4) + 73(3) = 240 + 219$ $= 459$	**The total is too low. Increase the number of adult tickets.**
80	$133 - 80 = 53$	$80(4) + 53(3) = 320 + 159$ $= 479$	**The total is too high. Decrease the number of adult tickets.**
70	$133 - 70 = 63$	$70(4) + 63(3) = 280 + 189$ $= 469$	**The total is very close. Increase the number of adult tickets.**
72	$133 - 72 = 61$	$72(4) + 61(3) = 288 + 183$ $= 471$	**The total is correct.**

There were 72 adult tickets and 61 student tickets sold.

Check the Answer

To check the answer for reasonableness, solve the problem another way. Consider using logical reasoning.

- The less expensive ticket is $3. So the theater club would get $133 \cdot \$3 = \$399$ if all the tickets sold were student tickets.
- $\$471 - \$399 = \$72$. The theater club actually raised $72 more than if they had sold only student tickets.
- Since adult tickets are $1 more than student tickets, there must have been 72 adult tickets sold.
- $133 - 72 = 61$. There were 61 student tickets sold.
- Since $72 \cdot 4 + 61 \cdot 3 = 471$, the solution 72 adult tickets and 61 student tickets is correct.

✓ Quick Check

6. Suppose the club sold the same number of tickets, but raised $452. How many tickets of each type did the theater club sell?

EXERCISES

For more exercises, see *Extra Skill and Word Problem Practice*.

Practice and Problem Solving

A Practice by Example

Example 1
(page 98)

GO for Help

Use the *Guess, Check, Revise* strategy to solve each problem.

1. **Coin Collections** Bonnie has 16 coins in her pocket worth $1.50. What are two different combinations of coins she could have in her pocket?

2. **Currency** A cashier's drawer has some $5 bills, some $10 bills, and some $20 bills. There are 15 bills worth a total of $185. How many $5 bills, $10 bills, and $20 bills are there?

3. The Smiths have two children. The sum of their ages is 23. The product of their ages is 132. How old are the children?

4. The sum of Mr. and Mrs. Bergen's ages is 100. The difference between their ages is 10. How old are Mr. and Mrs. Bergen?

B Apply Your Skills

Strategies

- Act It Out
- Draw a Diagram
- Guess, Check, Revise
- Look for a Pattern
- Make a Model
- Make a Table
- Simulate the Problem
- Solve by Graphing
- Use Multiple Strategies
- Work a Simpler Problem
- Work Backward
- Write an Equation
- Write a Proportion

GO Online
Homework Video Tutor
Visit: PHSchool.com
Web Code: ade-0207

C Challenge

Solve using any strategy.

5. **Geometry** A rectangular vegetable garden has a length of 5 ft and a width of 8 ft. The length is increased by 2 ft. By how many square feet does the area increase?

6. Trains leave New York for Boston every 40 min. The first train leaves at 5:20 A.M. What departure time is closest to 12:55 P.M.?

7. Lovell is 16 years old. Lovell's age is the same as Rafi's age divided by three. How old is Rafi?

8. **Number Theory** A number multiplied by itself and then by itself again gives −1,000. What is the number?

9. **Coin Collections** In a group of quarters and nickels, there are four more nickels than quarters. How many nickels and quarters are there if the coins are worth $2.30?

10. The sum of the page numbers on two facing pages is 245. The product of the numbers is 15,006. What are the page numbers?

11. **Shopping** A student bought some compact discs for $12 each and some books for $5 each. She spent $39 in all on five items. How many of each item did she buy?

12. **Relay Races** Two runners ran as a team in a 5,000-m relay race. The first runner ran 500 m farther than the second runner. How many meters did each run?

13. **Savings** Ron puts three pennies in a jar. His father offers to triple the total amount of money in Ron's jar at the end of each day. How much is in the jar at the end of one week?

14. **Biology** A certain bacteria doubles the number of its cells every 20 min. A scientist puts 50 cells in a culture dish. How many cells will be in the culture dish after 2 h?

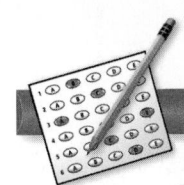

Multiple Choice

15. A photograph is 6 in. × 4 in. If you make a copy of the photograph with double the length and width, what is the area of the copy?

A. 96 in.^{2} **B.** 48 in.^{2} **C.** 24 in.^{2} **D.** 20 in.^{2}

16. Cara's age is 4 times Laura's age. If Cara is 16, how old is Laura?

F. 4 years   **G.** 12 years   **H.** 20 years   **J.** 64 years

17. On a recent test, the lowest score was one fourth the highest score. If the lowest score was 25, how much higher was the highest score?

A. 4   **B.** 25   **C.** 75   **D.** 100

Mixed Review

Lesson 2-6

GO for Help

(Algebra) **Solve each equation.**

18. $\frac{m}{4} = 52$ **19.** $3x = -18$ **20.** $63 = \frac{t}{-3}$ **21.** $-32 = -16y$

Lessons 2-1 and 2-2

Identify each property shown.

22. $8 + (6 + 17) = (8 + 6) + 17$ **23.** $1{,}879 \cdot 1 = 1{,}879$

24. $8(5 - 3) = 8(5) - 8(3)$ **25.** $-1 + 7 - 3 = -1 - 3 + 7$

Lesson 1-9   **26. Weather** The sound of thunder travels about one mile in five seconds. Suppose a bolt of lightning strikes 3 mi away. How long does it take for the sound of the thunder to reach you?

Math at Work

Nurse

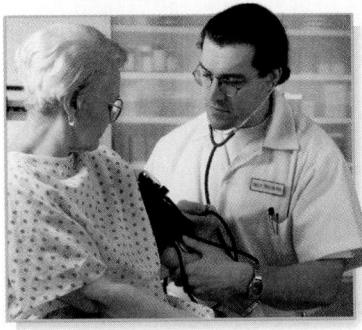

Anyone who has been in a hospital knows that nurses are patients' principal caregivers. Nurses dispense medication, monitor patients' progress, and tend to patients' daily medical needs.

Mathematics is important in a nurse's duties. Nurses compare a patient's blood pressure reading against established norms and make a conclusion about the result. They also solve math problems when they convert one unit of measure of medication to another, and then calculate the total amount of various medications needed for a patient in their care.

Go Online
PHSchool.com **For:** Information about nurses
Web Code: adb-2031

Sometimes a graph will help you analyze data. You can use a spreadsheet program to create different types of graphs. First, enter the data in a spreadsheet. Then use a graphing tool to draw an appropriate graph.

1 EXAMPLE

The spreadsheet gives the voting-age populations in thousands for two states. Graph the data in the spreadsheet.

	A	B	C
1	Year	Arizona	Georgia
2	1992	2,812	5,006
3	1994	2,923	5,159
4	1996	3,245	5,420
5	1998	3,405	5,620
6	2000	3,764	6,017

Row 3 contains voting-age populations of both states in 1994.

Cell B3 contains the voting-age population of Arizona in 1994.

Column B contains the voting-age population of Arizona.

Choose an appropriate type of graph from your spreadsheet program. Line graphs are often useful to display changes in data over a period of time. Since the data show changes over time for two states, use a double line graph.

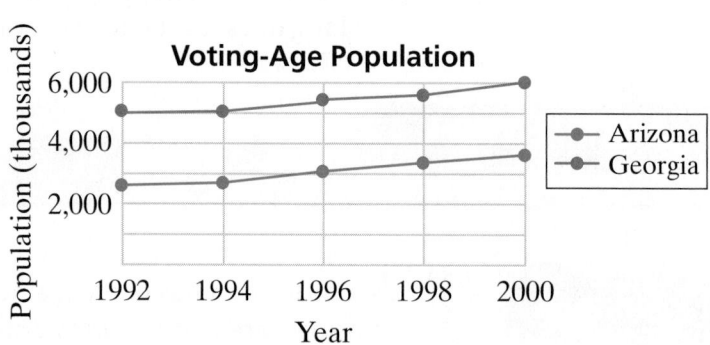

1. Use a spreadsheet to graph the data below.

Average Prices Farmers Received

Year	1996	1997	1998	1999	2000	2001	2002	2003
Price for Turkey (¢/lb)	43.3	39.9	38.0	40.8	40.6	39.0	36.5	36.0
Price for Chicken (¢/lb)	38.1	37.7	39.3	37.1	33.6	39.3	30.5	34.6

SOURCE: U.S. Department of Agriculture.
Go to **www.PHSchool.com** for a data update.
Web Code: adg-9041

The spreadsheet gives population data (in thousands) for five states. Graph the data in the spreadsheet.

	A	B	C
1		Age 25 to 34	Age 75 to 84
2	California	5,297	1,357
3	Florida	2,112	1,068
4	Illinois	1,805	544
5	New York	2,671	896
6	Texas	3,284	741

Bar graphs are often useful in comparing amounts. Since the data in the spreadsheet show populations for two age ranges, use a double bar graph.

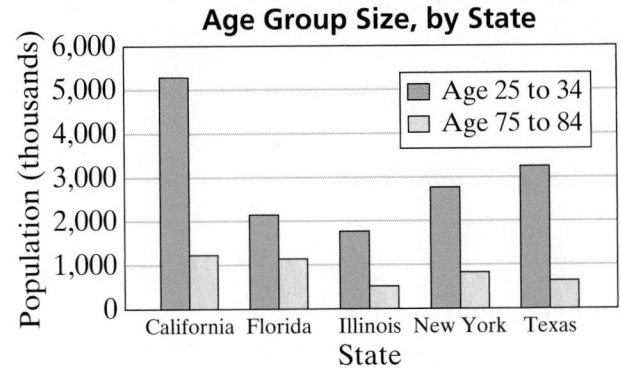

2. **a.** Use a spreadsheet to make a double bar graph of the postage rate data below.

Postage Rates

Sent From the United States to	First Class 1-oz Letter (¢)	Postcard (¢)
United States	39	24
Canada	60	50
Mexico	60	50
All other countries	80	70

SOURCE: U.S. Postal Service. Go to **www.PHSchool.com** for a data update. Web Code: adg-9041

   b. Data Analysis Use the graph you made in part (a). Which bar is tallest? Explain.

3. **Writing in Math** Explain when you would use a line graph and when you would use a bar graph to display a data set.

Inequalities and Their Graphs

1 Graphing Inequalities

An **inequality** is a mathematical sentence that contains $>$, $<$, $\geq$, $\leq$, or $\neq$. Some inequalities contain a variable. Any number that makes an inequality true is a **solution of the inequality.** For example, -4 is a solution of $y \geq -5$ because $-4 \geq -5$.

You can graph the solutions of an inequality on a number line.

1 EXAMPLE Graphing Solutions of Inequalities

Graph the solutions of each inequality on a number line.

a. $y < 3$

An open dot shows that 3 is *not* a solution.

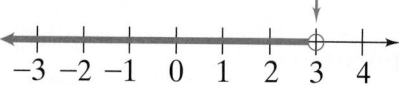

Shade all the points to the left of 3.

b. $x > -1$

An open dot shows that -1 is *not* a solution.

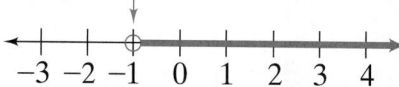

Shade all the points to the right of -1.

c. $a \leq -2$

A closed dot shows that -2 *is* a solution.

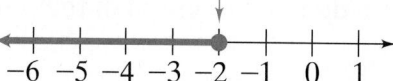

Shade all the points to the left of -2.

d. $-6 \leq g$

A closed dot shows that -6 *is* a solution.

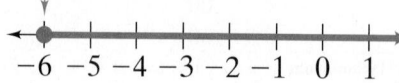

Shade all the points to the right of -6.

✔ **Quick Check**

1. Graph the solutions of each inequality.
  a. $z < -2$ **b.** $4 > t$ **c.** $a \geq -5$ **d.** $2 \geq c$

You can write an inequality for a graph.

2 EXAMPLE Writing Inequalities to Describe Graphs

Write the inequality shown in each graph.

a.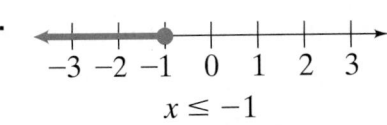

$x > 0$

b.

$x \le -1$

<blockquote>
Vocabulary Tip

Read $>$ as "is greater than."

Read $<$ as "is less than."

Read $\ge$ as "is greater than or equal to."

Read $\le$ as "is less than or equal to."
</blockquote>

✓ Quick Check

2. Write an inequality for the graph below.

You can write an inequality to describe a real-world situation. Keep in mind that *at most* means "no more than," and hence, "less than or equal to." *At least* means "no less than," and hence, "greater than or equal to."

3 EXAMPLE <u>Real-World</u> Problem Solving

Nutrition Food can be labeled *low sodium* only if it meets the requirement established by the federal government. Use the table to write an inequality for this requirement.

Label	Definition
Sodium-free food	Less than 5 mg per serving
Very low sodium food	At most 35 mg per serving
Low-sodium food	At most 140 mg per serving

Words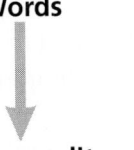

a serving of low-sodium food | has at most | 140 mg sodium

Let s = number of milligrams of sodium in a serving of low-sodium food.

Inequality s $\le$ 140

✓ Quick Check

3. Use the table in Example 3. A certain food is labeled *sodium free*. Write an inequality for *n*, the number of milligrams of sodium in a serving of this sodium-free food.

EXERCISES

For more exercises, see *Extra Skill and Word Problem Practice*.

Practice and Problem Solving

A Practice by Example

Example 1
(page 104)

GO for Help

Graph the solutions of each inequality on a number line.

1. $x < 7$ **2.** $y > 2$ **3.** $a < 3$ **4.** $c < 1$

5. $-3 < z$ **6.** $x > 1$ **7.** $m \leq -4$ **8.** $b \geq 6$

9. $4 \leq p$ **10.** $a \geq -2$ **11.** $j \geq -1$ **12.** $-5 < w$

Example 2
(page 105)

Write an inequality for each graph.

13. number line with closed dot at -2 shading left; marks $-3\ -2\ -1\ 0\ 1\ 2\ 3$

14. number line with closed dot at 2 shading right; marks $-1\ 0\ 1\ 2\ 3\ 4$

15. number line with open dot at 0 shading left; marks $-3\ -2\ -1\ 0\ 1\ 2$

16. number line with open dot at -4 shading right; marks $-5\ -4\ -3\ -2\ -1\ 0$

Example 3
(page 105)

Write an inequality for each situation. Use the variable given.

17. Let t be truck weight in tons.   **18.** Let s be speed in mi/h.

B Apply Your Skills

Write an inequality for each sentence. Graph the solutions of each inequality on a number line.

19. x is less than 5.   **20.** y is greater than -3.

21. A number c is at least 12.   **22.** r is not greater than five.

23. The total t is greater than 7.   **24.** p is not more than 30.

25. b is less than or equal to 8.   **26.** A number n is positive.

27. Reasoning Explain how you know whether the endpoint of the graph of an inequality should be a closed dot or an open dot.

28. The sign at the amusement park (left) tells you how tall you must be to ride. Write an inequality for this situation. Let h be height in feet.

Write an inequality for each graph.

29. number line with closed dot at -10 shading right; marks $-20\ -10\ 0\ 10$

30. number line with open dot at 300 shading left; marks $100\ 200\ 300\ 400\ 500$

31. number line with open dot at $-\frac{1}{2}$ shading right; marks $-1\ -\frac{3}{4}\ -\frac{1}{2}\ -\frac{1}{4}\ 0\ \frac{1}{4}\ \frac{1}{2}$

32. number line with closed dot at 1 shading right; marks $0\ \frac{1}{3}\ \frac{2}{3}\ 1\ 1\frac{1}{3}\ 1\frac{2}{3}$

Real-World Connection

Amusement parks make rules for safety.

33. Reasoning Explain why graphing the solutions of an inequality is more efficient than listing all the solutions of the inequality.

34. Writing in Math Describe a situation that you could represent with an inequality. Then write the inequality.

35. Movie Tickets Write an inequality to describe this situation. A student pays for three movie tickets with a twenty-dollar bill and gets change back. Let t be the cost of a movie ticket.

36. Nutrition High-fiber foods have at least 5 g of fiber per serving. Write an inequality to represent this situation. Let f be the number of grams of fiber per serving of high-fiber food.

C Challenge

37. Compare. Use $>$ or $<$ to complete each statement.
   a. If $a < b$, then $b \blacksquare a$.
   b. If $x > y$ and $y > z$, then $x \blacksquare z$.

38. Number Sense No more than 50 students walked in a walkathon. Let s be the number of students. Determine which numbers are reasonable values for s: $40, 45\frac{1}{2}, 50,$ and 55.

Test Prep

Multiple Choice

39. Which inequality best represents the following sentence?
   A number t is greater than or equal to -8.
   A. $-8 \leq t$ **B.** $t > -8$ **C.** $t \leq -8$ **D.** $-8 \geq t$

40. Which graph matches the inequality $x < -4$?
   F.
   $-5 \; -4 \; -3 \; -2 \; -1 \quad 0$
   G.
   $-5 \; -4 \; -3 \; -2 \; -1 \quad 0$
   H.
   $-5 \; -4 \; -3 \; -2 \; -1 \quad 0$
   J.
   $-5 \; -4 \; -3 \; -2 \; -1 \quad 0$

41. A game-board designer has to design a board that is at least 5 feet wide. Let w be the width of the board. Which inequality describes this situation?
   A. $w < 5$ **B.** $w > 5$ **C.** $w \leq 5$ **D.** $w \geq 5$

Mixed Review

GO for **Help**

Lessons 2-5 and 2-6

Solve each equation.

42. $x - 5 = 29$ **43.** $7y = 35$ **44.** $t \div 12 = 6$

Lesson 2-3

Simplify each expression.

45. $6 - 5s + 4s + 3$ **46.** $n + (n + 2) + (n + 4)$

Lesson 1-1

47. Write a variable expression for the number of weeks in y years.

Solving One-Step Inequalities by Adding or Subtracting

What You'll Learn

- To solve one-step inequalities using subtraction
- To solve one-step inequalities using addition

. . . And Why

To solve real-world problems involving computer memory

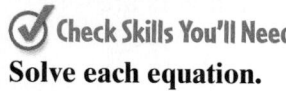 **Check Skills You'll Need**

Solve each equation.

1. $m + 7 = 5$

2. $k - 8 = 11$

3. $12 + h = 21$

4. $6 = n - 23$

 **for Help**
Lesson 2-5

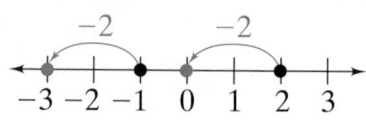

1 Solving Inequalities by Subtracting

Solving an inequality is similar to solving an equation. You want to get the variable alone on one side of the inequality.

You can see from the number line that if you subtract 2 from each side of the inequality $-1 < 2$, the resulting inequality $-3 < 0$ is still true.

Key Concepts **Subtraction Property of Inequality**

You can subtract the same number from each side of an inequality.

Arithmetic	Algebra
$7 > 4$, so $7 - 3 > 4 - 3$	If $a > b$, then $a - c > b - c$.
$6 < 9$, so $6 - 2 < 9 - 2$	If $a < b$, then $a - c < b - c$.

1 EXAMPLE **Subtracting to Solve an Inequality**

Solve each inequality. Graph the solutions.

a. $n + 8 \geq 19$

$$n + 8 \geq 19$$
$$n + 8 - 8 \geq 19 - 8 \quad \textbf{Subtract 8 from each side.}$$
$$n \geq 11 \qquad\qquad \textbf{Simplify.}$$

b. $-26 > y + 14$

$$-26 > y + 14$$
$$-26 - 14 > y + 14 - 14 \quad \textbf{Subtract 14 from each side.}$$
$$-40 > y \text{ or } y < -40 \quad \textbf{Simplify.}$$

✓ Quick Check

1. Solve each inequality. Graph the solutions.

   a. $m + 3 > 6$ **b.** $8 + t < 15$ **c.** $-3 \leq x + 7$

2 EXAMPLE <u>Real-World</u> 🌐 <u>Problem Solving</u>

Computers Nearly 768 megabytes (MB) of memory are available for running your computer. If its basic systems require 512 MB, how much memory is available for other programs?

Words

| memory for basic systems | plus | memory for other programs | is less than | total memory |

Let m = memory available for other programs.

Inequality   512   + m <   768

$$512 + m < 768$$
$$512 - 512 + m < 768 - 512 \qquad \textbf{Subtract 512 from each side.}$$
$$m < 256 \qquad \textbf{Simplify.}$$

Less than 256 MB of memory is available for other programs.

Real-World 🌐 **Connection**

You can increase the memory of a computer by adding more memory chips. These chips have extra memory in multiples of 128 megabytes.

✓ **Quick Check**

2. An airline lets you check up to 65 lb of luggage. One suitcase weighs 37 lb. How much can another suitcase weigh?

2   Using Addition to Solve Inequalities

To solve an inequality involving subtraction, use addition.

Key Concepts   **Addition Property of Inequality**

You can add the same number to each side of an inequality.

    Arithmetic   **Algebra**

$7 > 3$, so $7 + 4 > 3 + 4$ If $a > b$, then $a + c > b + c$.

$2 < 5$, so $2 + 6 < 5 + 6$ If $a < b$, then $a + c < b + c$.

3 EXAMPLE   **Adding to Solve an Inequality**

Solve $n - 15 < 3$.

$$n - 15 < 3$$
$$n - 15 + 15 < 3 + 15 \qquad \textbf{Add 15 to each side.}$$
$$n < 18 \qquad \textbf{Simplify.}$$

✓ **Quick Check**

3. Solve each inequality.

    a. $m - 13 > 29$ **b.** $v - 4 \leq 7$ **c.** $t - 5 \geq 11$

Online
active math

For: Inequalities Activity
Use: Interactive Textbook, 2-9

EXERCISES

For more exercises, see *Extra Skill and Word Problem Practice*.

Practice and Problem Solving

A Practice by Example

Example 1
(page 108)

GO for Help

Solve each inequality. Graph the solutions.

1. $w + 5 < 12$ **2.** $2 > 9 + a$ **3.** $x + 6 \geq 7$ **4.** $2 + m \leq 2$

5. $18 \leq 20 + w$ **6.** $-7 < 5 + x$ **7.** $30 \geq t + 45$ **8.** $p + 22 \geq -10$

Example 2
(page 109)

9. Transportation The total weight limit for a truck is 100,000 lb. The truck weighs 36,000 lb empty. What is the most that the truck's load can weigh?

10. Budgeting You are saving to buy a bicycle that will cost at least $120. Your parents give you $45 toward the bicycle. How much money will you have to save?

Example 3
(page 109)

Solve each inequality.

11. $x - 5 \geq 6$ **12.** $n - 12 \leq 3$ **13.** $r - 4 \leq 3$

14. $x - 7 < 15$ **15.** $c - 9 > 5$ **16.** $h - 10 \geq 6$

17. $w - 8 < 3$ **18.** $12 \geq y - 5$ **19.** $4 \geq y - 4$

B Apply Your Skills

What do you do to the first inequality to get the second inequality?

20. $x + 8 \leq 11; x \leq 3$ **21.** $x - 3 > 9; x > 12$

Solve each inequality. Graph the solutions.

22. $x - 8 > -2$ **23.** $6 < y + 19$ **24.** $3 \leq y - 5$

25. $-8 \geq k - 3$ **26.** $-3 + y > 4$ **27.** $a - 0.5 < 2.5$

28. $7 + r > 11$ **29.** $9 < b + 4$ **30.** $u - 3 \geq 9$

GO Online
Homework Video Tutor
Visit: PHSchool.com
Web Code: ade-0209

Write an inequality for each sentence. Then solve the inequality.

31. Thirteen plus a number n is greater than fifteen.

32. The sum of a number w and 3 is less than or equal to ten.

33. Shopping Jim has $87. He spends $6 for socks and at least $32 for shoes. How much does he have left to spend for shirts?

34. A store's dressing room has a limit of 10 garments per customer. If Carol has at least 3 garments below the limit, how many garments does she have in her dressing room?

C Challenge

Reasoning Justify each step.

35. $4 + a + 3 > 16$
$4 + 3 + a > 16$
$7 + a > 16$
$7 - 7 + a > 16 - 7$
$a > 9$

36. $m - 2(8 - 5) \leq -9$
$m - 2(3) \leq -9$
$m - 6 \leq -9$
$m - 6 + 6 \leq -9 + 6$
$m \leq -3$

37. Writing in Math Which of the inequalities $m > -2$, $m < -2$, $-2 < m$, and $-2 > m$ are solutions to $m + 4 > 2$? Explain.

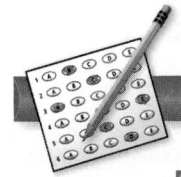
Multiple Choice

38. If x and y are positive, and $x > y$, which is true?

A. $x > \frac{x + y}{2}$ **B.** $y > \frac{x + y}{2}$ **C.** $x = \frac{x + y}{2}$ **D.** $x < \frac{x + y}{2}$

For Exercises 39 and 40, use the table at the left. Assume that your computer's basic systems use at least 12 MB of memory.

Computer Memory

Application	Memory Requirement
Word processor	11 MB
Spreadsheet	5 MB
Web browser	9 MB
E-mail	4 MB

39. You want to have your e-mail active while you work on a paper with your word processor. How much memory must your computer have?

F. at most 13 MB **G.** at least 14 MB
H. at least 27 MB **J.** at most 32 MB

40. If you search the Web for data at the same time that you have your e-mail active, how much memory must your computer have?

A. at most 41 MB **B.** at least 25 MB
C. at most 20 MB **D.** at least 15 MB

Mixed Review

GO for Help

Lesson 2-8

Graph the solutions of each inequality.

41. $x < 2$ **42.** $x \geq -5$ **43.** $y \leq 4$ **44.** $m > 0$

Lesson 2-3

Simplify each expression.

45. $4x + 6 - 2x + 6$ **46.** $-4 - 5t + t - 10$

Lesson 1-4

47. Write an integer to represent a debt of $35.

✓ Checkpoint Quiz 2 **Lessons 2-4 through 2-9**

State whether the equation is *true*, *false*, or an *open sentence*. Explain.

1. $4 + 15 = 27 - 8$ **2.** $-30 = 9w$ **3.** $|9 - 10| = 8 - 9$

Solve each equation or inequality.

4. $y - 3 = -7$ **5.** $x + 4 = 8$ **6.** $7t = 42$ **7.** $m \div 8 = -4$

8. $-90 = 10f$ **9.** $9 \leq 3 + a$ **10.** $r - 12 < 7$ **11.** $m + 15 > -4$

12. You have some quarters, dimes, and pennies—eight coins worth $.77 altogether. How many of each type of coin do you have?

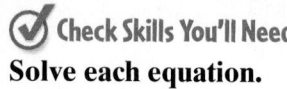

2-10 Solving One-Step Inequalities by Multiplying or Dividing

What You'll Learn

- To solve one-step inequalities using division
- To solve one-step inequalities using multiplication

. . . And Why

To solve real-world problems involving weight limits

 **Check Skills You'll Need**

Solve each equation.

1. $6x = 24$

2. $63 = -7v$

3. $\frac{x}{-2} = 10$

4. $\frac{t}{6} = 48$

GO for Help
Lesson 2-6

1 Solving Inequalities Using Division

Activity

Solving Inequalities

Explore what happens when you divide each side of an inequality by a number.

1. Simplify each expression at the right. Replace each ■ with > or <.

2. **Patterns** Does the direction of the inequality symbol stay the same as you divide each side of an inequality by the given numbers? Explain your reasoning.

$6 \div 3 \; \blacksquare \; 12 \div 3$
$6 \div 2 \; \blacksquare \; 12 \div 2$
$6 \div 1 \; \blacksquare \; 12 \div 1$
$6 \div (-1) \; \blacksquare \; 12 \div (-1)$
$6 \div (-2) \; \blacksquare \; 12 \div (-2)$
$6 \div (-3) \; \blacksquare \; 12 \div (-3)$

You can solve an inequality that involves multiplication by dividing each side of the inequality by a nonzero number.

Key Concepts **Division Properties of Inequality**

If you divide each side of an inequality by a positive number, you leave the inequality symbol unchanged.

Arithmetic	Algebra
$3 < 6$, so $\frac{3}{3} < \frac{6}{3}$	If $a < b$ and c is positive, then $\frac{a}{c} < \frac{b}{c}$.
$8 > 2$, so $\frac{8}{2} > \frac{2}{2}$	If $a > b$ and c is positive, then $\frac{a}{c} > \frac{b}{c}$.

If you divide each side of an inequality by a negative number, *you reverse the inequality symbol.*

Arithmetic	Algebra
$6 < 12$, so $\frac{6}{-3} > \frac{12}{-3}$	If $a < b$ and c is negative, then $\frac{a}{c} > \frac{b}{c}$.
$16 > 8$, so $\frac{16}{-4} < \frac{8}{-4}$	If $a > b$ and c is negative, then $\frac{a}{c} < \frac{b}{c}$.

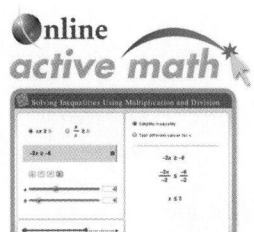
Engineering An elevator can carry up to 2,500 lb. Suppose the weight of an average adult is 150 lb. At most how many average-sized adults can safely ride the elevator at the same time?

Words	the number of adults	times	150 lb	is less than or equal to	2,500 lb

Let x = the number of adults.

| **Inequality** | x | · | 150 lb | ≤ | 2,500 |

$$150x \leq 2,500$$

$$\frac{150x}{150} \leq \frac{2,500}{150}$$ **Divide each side by 150.**

$$x \leq 16.\overline{6}$$ **Simplify. Round the answer down to find a whole number of people.**

At most 16 average adults can safely ride the elevator at one time.

Check Is the answer reasonable? The total weight of 16 average adults is 16(150) = 2,400 lb. This is less than 2,500 lb but so close that another adult could not ride. The answer is reasonable.

✅ Quick Check

1. Solve each inequality.

   a. $4x > 40$ **b.** $-21 > 3m$ **c.** $36 > -9t$

 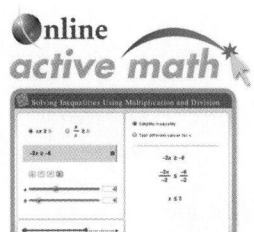
---

2 **Solving Inequalities Using Multiplication**

You can solve inequalities that involve division.

Key Concepts **Multiplication Properties of Inequality**

If you multiply each side of an inequality by a positive number, you leave the inequality symbol unchanged.

Arithmetic	**Algebra**
3 < 4, so 3(5) < 4(5)	If $a < b$ and c is positive, then $ac < bc$.
7 > 2, so 7(6) > 2(6)	If $a > b$ and c is positive, then $ac > bc$.

If you multiply each side of an inequality by a negative number, *you reverse the inequality symbol.*

Arithmetic	**Algebra**
6 < 9, so 6(−2) > 9(−2)	If $a < b$ and c is negative, then $ac > bc$.
7 > 5, so 7(−3) < 5(−3)	If $a > b$ and c is negative, then $ac < bc$.

🌐nline
active math

For: Inequalities Activity
Use: Interactive Textbook, 2-10

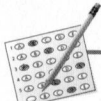

Test-Taking Tip

You can check whether the inequality symbol in your solution is correct. For example, for the inequality $\frac{t}{-4} \geq 7$, choose a number that is less than -28, such as -32. Substitute -32 into the original inequality. Since $\frac{-32}{-4} = 8$ and 8 is greater than 7, the inequality symbol in the solution is correct.

2 EXAMPLE   **Multiplying to Solve an Inequality**

Solve $\frac{t}{-4} \geq 7$.

$$\frac{t}{-4} \geq 7$$

$$-4\left(\frac{t}{-4}\right) \leq -4(7)$$ **Multiply each side by −4 and reverse the inequality symbol.**

$$t \leq -28$$ **Simplify.**

✓ Quick Check

2. Solve each inequality.

   a. $\frac{m}{4} \geq 2$ b. $\frac{t}{-3} < 7$ c. $5 < \frac{r}{7}$

More Than One Way

Solve $-3x < 12$.

Roberto's Method

Divide each side by -3 and reverse the inequality symbol.

$$-3x < 12$$
$$\frac{-3x}{-3} > \frac{12}{-3}$$
$$x > -4$$

Michelle's Method

Rewrite the inequality so the coefficient of the variable is positive.

$$-3x < 12$$
$$-3x + 3x < 12 + 3x$$
$$0 < 12 + 3x$$
$$0 - 12 < 3x + 12 - 12$$
$$-12 < 3x$$
$$\frac{-12}{3} < \frac{3x}{3}$$
$$-4 < x, \text{ or } x > -4$$

Choose a Method

1. Which method would you use to solve this inequality? Explain.

2. Solve $18 < -6x$ using Roberto's Method or Michelle's Method.

EXERCISES

For more exercises, see *Extra Skill and Word Problem Practice*.

Practice and Problem Solving

A Practice by Example

Example 1
(page 113)

GO for Help

Solve each inequality.

1. $3t > 21$ **2.** $-2x < 14$ **3.** $8 > -4x$ **4.** $6m > 24$

5. $9x \leq 27$ **6.** $18 < -2m$ **7.** $64 \leq -8k$ **8.** $7m > 28$

9. $3x < 21$ **10.** $81 > -9y$ **11.** $5f \geq -15$ **12.** $-3x < 0$

13. Earnings Paul earns $9 per hour. How many hours must Paul work to earn at least $645?

Example 2
(page 114)

Solve each inequality.

14. $\frac{x}{-6} > 3$ **15.** $\frac{m}{6} \leq -18$ **16.** $\frac{x}{3} \geq 5$ **17.** $\frac{y}{4} > 3$

18. $\frac{r}{-4} > 2$ **19.** $6 > \frac{q}{-3}$ **20.** $20 < \frac{v}{6}$ **21.** $\frac{b}{4} \geq 3$

22. $\frac{v}{-5} < 9$ **23.** $\frac{x}{4} \leq 12$ **24.** $\frac{x}{-3} < 0$ **25.** $8 > \frac{h}{10}$

B Apply Your Skills

What happens to the inequality symbol when you do the following to each side of an inequality?

26. subtract a negative number   **27.** multiply by a positive number

28. divide by a negative number   **29.** multiply by a negative number

Solve each inequality.

30. $-4x < -16$ **31.** $-r \geq 21$ **32.** $\frac{1}{2}x \geq -3$ **33.** $\frac{b}{3} \geq -31$

34. $-3 \geq \frac{g}{-7}$ **35.** $3 > \frac{b}{-6}$ **36.** $4x > -8$ **37.** $-6x \leq -24$

38. Budgeting Marnie pays $.06 per kilowatt-hour for electricity. She has budgeted $72 for her electricity. What is the greatest number of kilowatt-hours Marnie can use and stay within her budget?

$3x > -12$
$\frac{3x}{3} < \frac{-12}{3}$
$x < -4$

39. Error Analysis Your friend solved $3x > -12$ as shown at the left. What error did your friend make?

40. Multiple Choice Sue worked at least 13 hours last week. She earns $5.75 per hour. What is the least amount she earned?
    Ⓐ $75   Ⓑ $74.75   Ⓒ $65   Ⓓ $7.50

Write an inequality for each sentence. Then solve the inequality.

41. A number t multiplied by seven is less than or equal to 21.

42. A number b divided by 4 is greater than or equal to 3.

43. The quotient of a number v divided by -5 is less than 9.

44. Reasoning The rules for multiplying and dividing both sides of an inequality do not mention zero. Discuss why.

GO Online
Homework Video Tutor
Visit: PHSchool.com
Web Code: ade-0210

45. Writing in Math Explain how solving $-4t < 32$ is different from solving $4t < -32$.

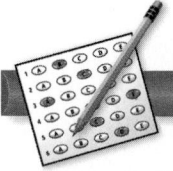 **Challenge**

Reasoning Justify each step.

46. $2g \geq -18$
$\dfrac{2g}{2} \geq \dfrac{-18}{2}$
$g \geq -9$

47. $-7m \leq -28$
$\dfrac{-7m}{-7} \geq \dfrac{-28}{-7}$
$m \geq 4$

48. $\dfrac{a}{3} > 12$
$\left(\dfrac{a}{3}\right)(3) > 12(3)$
$a > 36$

49. Open-Ended Write a problem that you would solve using the inequality $5m \leq 15$.

50. Day Care In Georgia, for every 18 four-year-old children in day care there must be at least one teacher. At one day-care center, 56 four-year-olds are signed up for next year. At least how many teachers must the center have to teach four-year-olds next year?

Test Prep

Multiple Choice

51. What is done to $\frac{1}{3}x \leq 18$ to get $x \leq 54$?
A. Multiply each side by 3.   **B.** Divide each side by 3.
C. Multiply each side by $\frac{1}{3}$.   **D.** Multiply each side by $3x$.

52. Which number is a solution of $-2x \leq -4$?
F. -2 **G.** 0   **H.** 1   **J.** 10

53. Which inequality has the same solutions as $\frac{a}{4} < -20$?
A. $4d > 80$ **B.** $\frac{m}{-4} < -40$ **C.** $-2r < -40$ **D.** $\frac{z}{-2} > 40$

54. Which inequality best represents the following sentence?
A number x divided by 7 is greater than -13.
F. $\frac{7}{x} > -13$ **G.** $\frac{x}{7} > -13$ **H.** $\frac{7}{x} < -13$ **J.** $\frac{x}{7} < -13$

Mixed Review

 **GO for Help**

Lesson 2-9

Solve each inequality.

55. $6 + t > 17$ **56.** $-9 \geq r + 5$ **57.** $11 > v - 12$

Lessons 2-1 and 2-2

Name each property shown.

58. $-12\,(100 - 3) = -12\,(100) - (-12)\,(3)$

59. $102 + 34 + 98 = 102 + 98 + 34$

60. $(80 + 321) + 109 = 80 + (321 + 109)$

Lesson 1-6   **61. Weather** The high temperature one day in January was 34°F, and the low temperature was 27°F. What was the difference between the high and the low temperatures that day?

High-use academic words are words that you will see often in textbooks and on tests. These words are not math vocabulary terms, but they are important for you to know to be successful in mathematics.

Words to Learn: Direction Words

Some words tell you what to do in a problem. You need to understand what these words are asking so that you give the correct answer.

Word	Meaning
Determine	Find out by investigating or calculating
Explain	Give facts and details to make an idea easy to understand
Identify	Tell the name of or describe the characteristics of something

EXERCISES

Determine whether each statement is *true* or *false*.

1. The owner's manual for a car explains how to drive.

2. The weatherman determines what kind of storm will arrive.

3. This week's supermarket flyer identifies items that are on sale.

Identify each property shown.

4. $7 + a = a + 7$

5. $3(x - 4) = 3x - 12$

Explain how to use zero pairs to solve each equation.

6.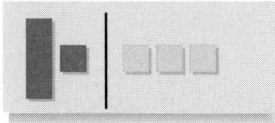

7.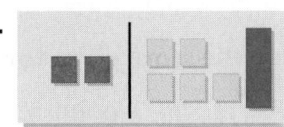

8. **a.** **Word Knowledge** Think about the word **justify**. Choose the letter for how well you know the word.
   A. I know its meaning.
   B. I have seen it, but I do not know its meaning.
   C. I do not know it.
   b. Look up **justify** in a dictionary or online. Write its definition.
   c. Write a sentence involving mathematics and using the word **justify**.

Writing Short Responses

Short-response questions are often worth 2 points. To get full credit you need to give the correct answer and either give a good explanation, justify your thinking, or show your work.

EXAMPLE

Jenna had a coupon for $15 off the price of a graphing calculator. She used it to buy a calculator for $89 before tax. **(a)** Write an equation to find the original price. **(b)** Solve your equation.

Here is a *scoring rubric* to help assess different types of answers.

Scoring Rubric

[2] The original price of the calculator is correct. The equation and the solution are correct with all work shown.

[1] The original price is correct, but no work is shown, OR the original price is incorrect, but the work shown has minimal errors.

Here are three responses with the points each received.

2 points	1 point	0 points
x is the original price. $$x - 15 = 89$$ $$x - 15 + 15 = 89 + 15$$ $$x = 104$$ The original price was $104.	x is the original price. $$x + 15 = 89$$ $$x + 15 - 15 = 89 - 15$$ $$x = 74$$ The original price was $74.	The original price was $74.

EXERCISES

Use the scoring rubric to explain the score given for each response.

1. the 2-point response   **2.** the 1-point response   **3.** the 0-point response

Write and solve an equation to solve each problem. Then score your answer using the scoring rubric above.

4. Your grandfather gives you a share of stock that is currently worth $62. He tells you that it has increased in value by $17 since he purchased it. How much did he pay for the stock?

5. The height of a multistory building is 135 ft. It has 15 stories. What is the height of each story?

Chapter Review

Vocabulary Review

🔊 additive identity (p. 69)
Associative Properties of Addition
and Multiplication (p. 68)
coefficient (p. 78)
Commutative Properties of
Addition and Multiplication
(p. 68)
constant (p. 78)

deductive reasoning (p. 79)
Distributive Property (p. 73)
equation (p. 82)
Identity Properties of Addition
and Multiplication (p. 69)
inequality (p. 104)
inverse operations (p. 88)
like terms (p. 78)

multiplicative identity (p. 69)
open sentence (p. 82)
simplify a variable expression
(p. 78)
solution of an equation (p. 83)
solution of an inequality (p. 104)
term (p. 78)

For each numbered definition given below, write the letter of the word or phrase being defined.

1. a value that makes an equation true
2. a term that has no variable
3. a number or the product of a number and variable(s)
4. the number that multiplies a variable
5. the number zero
6. terms with identical variables
7. an equation with one or more variables
8. a mathematical sentence with an equal sign
9. the number one
10. a mathematical sentence with $>, <, \geq, \leq,$ or $\neq$

a. coefficient
b. constant
c. additive identity
d. solution of an equation
e. term
f. equation
g. multiplicative identity
h. like terms
i. inequality
j. open sentence

Go Online
PHSchool.com
For: Online vocabulary quiz
Web Code: adj-0251

Skills and Concepts

2-1 Objectives

▼ To identify properties of addition and multiplication (p. 68)

▼ To use properties to solve problems (p. 69)

Use the **Commutative Property** to change order. Use the **Associative Property** to change grouping. Adding zero to an expression does not change its value. Multiplying an expression by 1 does not change its value.

Simplify each expression. Justify each step.

11. $58 + 16 + 2 + 4$ **12.** $4 \cdot 7 \cdot 25 \cdot 1$ **13.** $125 + 347 + 75$

14. $(20 \cdot 65) \cdot 5$ **15.** $10 \cdot 15 \cdot 2$ **16.** $37 + 0 + (5 + 63)$

2-2 Objectives

▼ To use the Distributive Property with numerical expressions (p. 73)

▼ To use the Distributive Property with algebraic expressions (p. 75)

Use the **Distributive Property** to multiply a number outside parentheses by each term of a sum or difference.

Mental Math **Use the Distributive Property to simplify.**

17. $9(96)$ **18.** $8(62)$ **19.** $(43)(9)$

Use the Distributive Property to multiply.

20. $4(w + 9)$ **21.** $(2 + 4a)12$ **22.** $-7(6 - 2m)$

23. Explain why $5x + 15 = 5(x + 3)$.

2-3 Objectives

▼ To identify parts of a variable expression (p. 78)

▼ To simplify expressions (p. 78)

To **simplify** a variable expression, replace it with an equivalent expression with as few terms as possible.

Simplify each expression.

24. $8a + 7 - 11a$ **25.** $3(w + 3) + 4w$

26. $6 + x - 4x + 3$ **27.** $19 - 4(5n + 1) - 4n$

28. $10 + 7k - 2(3k + 5)$ **29.** $-7(2r - 1) + 3(8 - r)$

30. Explain how to determine whether terms are like terms.

2-4 Objectives

▼ To classify types of equations (p. 82)

▼ To check equations using substitution (p. 83)

You can write an **equation** to model a situation. An equation with numerical expressions is true or false. An equation with at least one variable is an **open sentence**. A **solution** of an open-sentence equation is a value of a variable that makes the equation true.

Write an equation for each sentence. Is each equation *true, false,* or an *open sentence?*

31. Thirty-two plus five equals the product of six and six.

32. A number t divided by seventeen equals the opposite of three.

33. The product of four and twenty equals eighty.

34. **Culture** The admission price to an art museum increased by $1.75 to $6.50. Let p be the original admission price. Write an equation to model the situation.

▼ To solve one-step equations using subtraction (p. 88)

▼ To solve one-step equations using addition (p. 90)

▼ To solve one-step equations using division (p. 94)

▼ To solve one-step equations using multiplication (p. 95)

To solve an equation, use an **inverse operation** and the **properties of equality** to get the variable alone on one side of the equation.

Solve each equation.

35. $6 + y = 17$ **36.** $-2 = a - 10$ **37.** $3x = -15$

38. $\frac{m}{9} = 3$ **39.** $\frac{w}{4} = 32$ **40.** $40 = -5b$

2-7 Objectives

▼ To solve a problem using the Guess, Check, Revise strategy (p. 98)

You can solve some problems by trying an answer. Use each incorrect conjecture to make a better conjecture.

🌐 **41. School Supplies** Marcella and Danilo went to a bookstore. Marcella bought 2 notebooks and 3 pens for $14.50. Danilo bought 1 notebook and 2 pens for $7.50. How much does 1 notebook cost?

2-8 Objectives

▼ To graph inequalities (p. 104)

▼ To write inequalities (p. 105)

To graph an **inequality,** use a number line. Use an open dot for $>$ and $<$. Use a closed dot for $\geq$ and $\leq$.

Graph the solutions of each inequality.

42. $m > -13$ **43.** $t \geq -2$ **44.** $0 < r$ **45.** $w \leq 6$

Write an inequality for each sentence.

46. The temperature t is less than zero degrees.

47. The height h is greater than twelve feet.

2-9 and 2-10 Objectives

▼ To solve one-step inequalities using subtraction (p. 108)

▼ To solve one-step inequalities using addition (p. 109)

▼ To solve one-step inequalities using division (p. 112)

▼ To solve one-step inequalities using multiplication (p. 113)

To solve a one-step inequality, use inverse operations and the **properties of inequality** to get the variable alone on one side of the inequality. When multiplying or dividing each side of an inequality by a negative number, *reverse* the direction of the inequality symbol.

Solve each inequality.

48. $n - 4 > 10$ **49.** $-5 \leq k - 7$ **50.** $6s \leq 18$

51. $\frac{m}{3} < -2$ **52.** $-d > 14$ **53.** $\frac{c}{-4} \geq -9$

Go Online
PHSchool.com
For: Online chapter test
Web Code: ada-0252

Is each equation *true, false,* or an *open sentence?* Explain.

1. $24 = 3(-8)$

2. $5x + 28 = 153$

3. $18(-7 \div 7) = (-2)(9)$

4. $-6 + 15 = (120 \div 20) - (5 - 8)$

Simplify. Use the Commutative and the Associative Properties.

5. $50 \cdot 38 \cdot 2$

6. $45 + 62 + 55$

7. $2 \cdot 27 \cdot 5$

8. $99 + (-7) + 101$

9. **Open-Ended** Write a number sentence that illustrates the Associative Property of Addition.

Simplify each expression.

10. $2(x + y) - 2y$

11. $5a + 2b + 3a - 7b$

12. $3(2r - 5) + 8(r + 2)$

13. $(-2c + 3d)(-5) + 3(-2c) - (-8d)$

Solve each equation.

14. $k - 23 = 17$

15. $\frac{t}{-5} = 15$

16. $y \div 12 = -3$

17. $7w = -217$

18. $-9 + a = 11$

19. $n - 2 = 13$

20. $120 = 38 + p$

21. $w \cdot (-2) = 14$

22. $r + 6 = 30$

23. $m - 7 = -3$

24. $9t = 18$

25. $-3f = -42$

26. $5 = \frac{s}{-7}$

27. $\frac{h}{12} = 12$

For Exercises 28 and 29, write and solve an equation.

28. **Fencing** Thirty-six sections of fencing, all the same length, are joined to form a fence 180 m long. How long is each section of fencing?

29. Brian bought a used bike for $25 less than its original price. He paid a total of $88 for the bike. What was the original price of the bike?

30. **Writing in Math** How are the rules for solving inequalities similar to those for solving equations? How are they different?

Write an inequality for each situation. Graph the solutions.

31. The total t is greater than 5.

32. The perimeter p is less than 64.

33. The number of passengers p on the bus is no more than 45.

34. The number of students s that ran in the road race was not less than 55.

35. The number of questions q answered correctly is at most 49.

Solve each inequality.

36. $5 \le x + 1$

37. $\frac{a}{3} > 4$

38. $y - 6 < 9$

39. $-2n \le 10$

40. $3b \ge 3$

41. $\frac{p}{-2} < -5$

42. $r + 8 > 12$

43. $j - 7 \le 24$

44. $h - 5 \ge -16$

45. $8 + b < -3$

46. $3k \le -27$

47. $\frac{h}{4} > 16$

48. $9 < \frac{a}{6}$

49. $-7z < 21$

Decimals and Equations

◀)) Key Vocabulary

- compatible numbers (p. 135)
- formula (p. 145)
- mean (p. 139)
- measures of central tendency (p. 139)
- median (p. 139)
- mode (p. 139)
- outlier (p. 140)
- perimeter (p. 146)
- range (p. 139)

What You'll Learn Next

In this chapter, you will learn how to

- Estimate with decimals.
- Solve equations with decimals.
- Convert metric units of measure.
- Solve a problem by simplifying the problem.

Activity Lab. Applying what you learn, on pages 176–177 you will solve problems about price comparisons.

Review   Writing and Comparing Decimals

For Use With Lesson 3-1

Each digit in a decimal has both a place and a value. The value of any place is one-tenth the value of the place to its left. A place-value chart like the one at the right can help you read and write decimals.

ones	.	tenths	hundredths	thousandths	ten thousandths
0	.	4	2	6	

1 EXAMPLE

a. Express 0.426 using words.

The last digit, 6, is in the thousandths place. So, 0.426 ends with the word *thousandths*.

0.426 is four hundred twenty-six thousandths.

b. Write *two and three hundredths* as a decimal.

And represents the decimal point. The hundredths place is the second place to the right of the decimal point.

Two and three hundredths is 2.03.

You can use decimal squares to model and compare decimals.

2 EXAMPLE

a. Model 0.6.

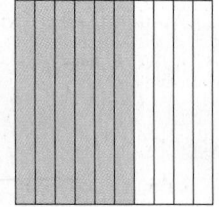

b. Model 0.58.

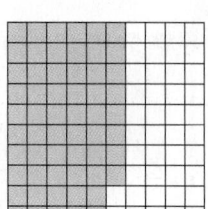

c. Model 1.05.

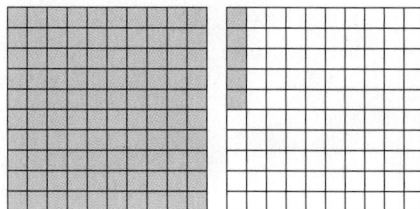

d. Compare 0.6 and 0.58. The models show that 0.6 > 0.58.

EXERCISES

Express each decimal using words.

1. 0.23   **2.** 0.624   **3.** 3.081   **4.** 58.36

Write each as a decimal.

5. three and two tenths   **6.** five and forty-one hundredths   **7.** fourteen ten-thousandths

Model and compare each pair of decimals.

8. 0.2 and 0.12   **9.** 0.89 and 0.9   **10.** 0.53 and 0.5   **11.** 1.35 and 1.4

128   Review   Writing and Comparing Decimals

Rounding and Estimating

1   Rounding Decimals

ctivity

Estimating in the Real World

Some real-world problems require only an estimate for an answer. Others require an exact answer. Decide whether each situation needs an estimate or an exact answer. Explain your reasoning.

1. a headline noting the number of people living in China

2. the amount of money a baby sitter charges per hour

3. the width of a window screen

4. the distance from Earth to the moon

5. the hours at soccer practice in one month

6. the number of tickets to sell for a play

You can round decimal numbers when you don't need exact values.

What You'll Learn

- To round decimals
- To estimate sums and differences

. . . And Why

To understand and apply appropriate estimation strategies in real-world situations such as grocery shopping

✓ Check Skills You'll Need

Use the number 27.3865. Write the value of the given digit.

1. 2   **2.** 3

3. 8   **4.** 6

GO for Help

Skills Handbook, p. 818

1   EXAMPLE   Rounding Decimals

a. Round 4.2683 to the nearest tenth.

⌐ tenths place

4.2683

⌐ 5 or greater

⌐ Round up to 3.

4.3

b. Round 4.2683 to the nearest one.

⌐ ones place

4.2683

⌐ less than 5

⌐ Do not change.

4

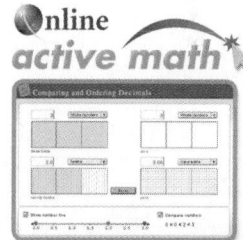

Online active math

For: Comparing Decimals Activity
Use: Interactive Textbook, 3-1

✓ Quick Check

1. Identify the underlined place. Then round each number to that place.

    a. 38.<u>4</u>1   **b.** <u>0</u>.7772   **c.** 7,098.<u>5</u>6

    d. 274.94<u>3</u>4   **e.** 5.<u>0</u>25   **f.** 9.8<u>5</u>1

Estimating Sums and Differences

Read the symbol ≈ as "is approximately equal to."

You can estimate a result before you calculate. Then, if your answer is close to your estimate, you know that it probably is correct.

Write $126   ≈ $130

Read $126 is approximately equal to $130.

One way to estimate is to round all numbers to the same place.

2 EXAMPLE   Rounding to Estimate

Problem Solving Hint

After you have rounded to a place greater than the ones place, write zeros from that place to the decimal point. Do not write zeros after the decimal point.

Estimate to find whether each answer is reasonable.

a. Calculation   Estimate

$$
\begin{array}{rcr}
\$135.95 & \approx & \$140 \\
\$15.90 & \approx & \$20 \\
+ \ \$24.05 & \approx & + \ \$20 \\
\hline
\$275.90 \ \textbf{✗} & & \$180
\end{array}
$$

The answer is not close to the estimate. It is *not* reasonable.

b. Calculation   Estimate

$$
\begin{array}{rcr}
464.90 & \approx & 460 \\
- \ 125.73 & \approx & - \ 130 \\
\hline
339.17 \ \textbf{✔} & & 330
\end{array}
$$

The answer is close to the estimate. It is reasonable.

✓ Quick Check

2. Estimate by rounding.

   a. $355.302 + 204.889$ **b.** $453.56 - 230.07$

A *front-end estimate* is often closer to the exact sum than an estimate you find by rounding. First add the front-end digits. Round to estimate the sum of the remaining digits. Then combine estimates.

3 EXAMPLE   Real-World 🌐 Problem Solving

$1.73

$1.10

$2.71

Grocery Shopping Carrots cost **$2.71**, peppers cost **$1.73**, and broccoli costs **$1.10**. Estimate the total cost of the vegetables.

$$
\begin{array}{l}
\text{Add the} \\
\text{front-end digits.} \longrightarrow
\end{array}
\quad
\begin{array}{r}
2.71 \longrightarrow \\
1.73 \longrightarrow \\
+ \ 1.10 \longrightarrow \\
\hline
4 \quad +
\end{array}
\quad
\left.
\begin{array}{r}
.70 \\
.70 \\
+ \ .10 \\
\hline
1.50 = 5.50
\end{array}
\right\}
\begin{array}{l}
\textbf{Estimate by} \\
\textbf{rounding.}
\end{array}
$$

The total cost is about $5.50.

✓ Quick Check

3. Estimate using front-end estimation.

   a. $6.75 + 2.2 + 9.58$ **b.** $\$1.07 + \$2.49 + \$7.40$

You can also use *clustering* to estimate the sum of several numbers that are all close to the same value.

4 EXAMPLE <u>Real-World</u> 🌐 <u>Problem Solving</u>

Telephone Service Estimate the total long-distance charge for the months of May, June, July, and August shown at the right.

four months
↓

The values cluster around $15. ⟶ 15 · 4 = 60

The total long-distance charge is about $60.00.

☑ **Quick Check**

4. Estimate using clustering.

   a. $4.50 + $5.20 + $5.55
   b. 26.7 + 26.2 + 24.52 + 25.25 + 23.9

In this lesson, you have seen several methods for finding a reasonable estimate. Here are two methods used for the same situation.

More Than One Way

Estimate the total cost of four items priced at $4.39, $3.75, $4.96, and $2.40.

Nicole's Method

Round each price to the nearest dollar. Then add.

$4.39 + $3.75 + $4.96 + $2.40
$4   + $4   + $5   + $2   = $15

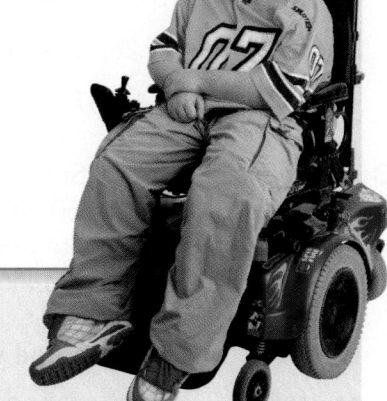

Eric's Method

Use front-end estimation.

$4.39	⟶	$.40
3.75	⟶	.80
4.96	⟶	1.00
+2.40	⟶	+.40
$13	+	$2.60 = $15.60

Choose a Method

1. Which method would you use to estimate the cost of the items? Explain.

2. Find the exact cost. Which estimate is nearer the exact cost?

EXERCISES

For more exercises, see *Extra Skill and Word Problem Practice*.

Practice and Problem Solving

A Practice by Example

Example 1
(page 129)

GO for Help

Identify the underlined place. Then round each number to that place.

1. 27.3856 **2.** 0.9122 **3.** 1,045.98 **4.** 74.879

Round to the underlined place.

5. 345.678 **6.** 3.14159 **7.** 214.76 **8.** 2.9437

Example 2
(page 130)

Estimate by rounding.

9. $37.99 − $27.32 **10.** 1.58 + 17.0244 **11.** 172.98 − 128.301

12. $4.89 + $3.87 **13.** $16.81 + $11.49 **14.** $565 − $225

Example 3
(page 130)

Estimate using front-end estimation.

15. $6.04 + $3.45 + $4.43 **16.** $5.92 + $4.07

17. 9.89 + 2.43 + 8.37 **18.** 14.39 + 79.12

19. Fitness Kim ran 2.76 miles on Monday, 2.34 miles on Tuesday, and 1.97 miles on Wednesday. Use front-end estimation to estimate the total distance Kim ran.

Example 4
(page 131)

Estimate using clustering.

20. 44.87 + 42.712 + 43.5 **21.** $9.50 + $8.45 + $9.08

22. $21.37 + $22.99 + $22.15 **23.** 15.4 + 16 + 15.9 + 16.25 + 15.7

24. Pets Rico's dog has a litter of four puppies. The puppies weigh 2.33 lb, 2.70 lb, 2.27 lb, and 2.64 lb. Use clustering to estimate the total weight of the puppies.

B Apply Your Skills

Estimate. Use a method of your choice.

25. 8.974 + 2.154 **26.** 102.44 + 48.35 **27.** 600 − 209.52

28. $38.59 + $15.28 **29.** $50.00 − $28.89 **30.** $412.44 + $72.23

31. 800 + 810.5 + 807.3 + 791.1 **32.** 54.23 + 56.12 + 57.98 + 55.55

Lake Erie

Lake Superior

33. Geography Lake Superior, the largest of the Great Lakes, has an area of about 31,760 mi². Lake Erie, the smallest of the Great Lakes, has an area of about 9,920 mi². About how much larger is Lake Superior than Lake Erie?

Estimate. State the method you used.

34. $8.99 + $8.01 **35.** 2.3 + 2.3 + 4.56 **36.** $89.90 − $49.29

37. 102.54 − 74.75 **38.** 20.55 − 1.48 **39.** 78.87 + 11.49

132 Chapter 3 Decimals and Equations

Go Online
Homework Video Tutor
Visit: PHSchool.com
Web Code: ade-0301

40. Weather Mobile, Alabama, has an average annual rainfall of 63.96 in. The average annual rainfall in San Francisco, California, is 19.70 in. About how much more rain falls each year in Mobile than in San Francisco?

41. Open-Ended Describe a situation in which a rounded answer is appropriate. Describe one in which an exact answer is necessary.

 **Challenge**

42. Writing in Math You have $11.50 to buy two presents. You find one item that costs $7.43. Another item costs $4.41. What estimation strategy will help you decide whether you have enough money to buy both? Explain.

43. Error Analysis You used a calculator to find $383.8 - 21.9$. Your estimate was 360, but your display reads 164.8. How could you have gotten 164.8 on your calculator?

Test Prep

Multiple Choice

44. Which phrase best completes the statement?
The sum of $12.75 and $7.65 is __?__.
A. less than $20.00
B. greater than $20.00
C. an integer
D. greater than $25.00

45. When you estimate $320.18 + 46 + 8.68$ by rounding to tens, what value do you get?
F. 370
G. 374.9
H. 375
J. 380

Short Response

46. In 2000, the population of the state of Georgia was about 8.19 million. In 1950, the population was about 3.44 million.
a. About how much greater was Georgia's population in 2000 than in 1950?
b. Explain how you found your answer for part (a).

Mixed Review

Go for Help

Lesson 2-10 **Solve each inequality.**

47. $9x \le 27$ **48.** $4x < 16$ **49.** $-3y \le 0$ **50.** $-6k > -24$

Lesson 2-7 **51. Collections** Ming's model vehicle collection contains 4-wheeled trucks and 2-wheeled bikes. She owns an even number of vehicles, and they have 26 wheels in all. If Ming has a little more than twice as many bikes as trucks, how many of each does she own?

Lesson 1-9 **Simplify.**

52. $(-2)(-2)$ **53.** $4(-3)$ **54.** $-8 \div 2$ **55.** $6(-5)$

3-1 Rounding and Estimating   **133**

Estimating Decimal Products and Quotients

• To estimate products

• To estimate quotients

. . . And Why

To determine the reasonableness of answers to real-world problems involving mass

☑ **Check Skills You'll Need**

Round to the nearest one.

1. 145.89   **2.** 199.27

3. 101.06   **4.** 28.45

 **for Help**

Lesson 3-1

🔊 **New Vocabulary**

• compatible numbers

---

1 | **Estimating Products**

You can use mental math to estimate products and quotients. It is a good idea to estimate answers to check your calculations.

1 EXAMPLE   **Estimating the Product**

Estimate 7.65 · 3.2.

$7.65 \approx 8$ $3.2 \approx 3$ **Round to the nearest one.**
$\quad 8 \cdot 3 = 24$ **Multiply.**
$7.65 \cdot 3.2 \approx 24$

☑ **Quick Check**

1. Estimate each product.

   a. 4.72 · 1.8   **b.** 17.02 · 3.78   **c.** 8.25 · 19.8

2 EXAMPLE   **Real-World** 🌐 **Problem Solving**

Quilting Arlene bought 6 yd of fabric to make this Lone Star quilt. The fabric cost \$6.75/yd. The sales clerk charged Arlene \$45.90 before tax. Did the clerk make a mistake? Explain.

$6.75 \approx 7$ **Round to the nearest dollar.**

$7 \cdot 6 = 42$ **Multiply 7 times 6, the number of yards of fabric.**

The sales clerk made a mistake. Since $6.75 < 7$, the actual cost should be less than the estimate. The clerk should have charged Arlene less than \$42.00 before tax.

☑ **Quick Check**

2. Photography You buy 8 rolls of film for your camera. Each roll costs \$4.79. Estimate the cost of the film before tax.

2 Estimating Quotients

When dividing, remember these names for the parts of a division sentence.

dividend

$6 \div 3 = 2$ ← quotient

divisor

When dividing, you can use *compatible numbers* to estimate quotients. **Compatible numbers** are numbers that are easy to divide mentally. When you estimate a quotient, first round the divisor, and then round the dividend to a compatible number.

3 EXAMPLE   Real-World 🌎 Problem Solving

Measurement A bowling ball has a mass of 5.61 kg. Each bowling pin has a mass of 1.57 kg. How many bowling pins are about equal to the bowling ball in mass? Estimate 5.61 ÷ 1.57.

$1.57 \approx 2$ **Round the divisor.**

$5.61 \approx 6$ **Round the dividend to a multiple of 2 that is close to 5.61.**

$6 \div 2 = 3$ **Divide.**

The mass of three bowling pins is about equal to that of the bowling ball.

✓ Quick Check

3. Estimate each quotient.

    a. $38.9 \div 1.79$ **b.** $11.95 \div 2.1$ **c.** $82.52 \div 4.25$

5.61 kg

1.57 kg

Real-World 🌎 Connection

The masses of ten-pin bowling balls range from 3.63 kg to 7.26 kg.

You can estimate to determine the reasonableness of results.

4 EXAMPLE   Estimating to Determine Reasonableness

Number Sense Is 2.15 a reasonable quotient for 17.931 ÷ 8.34?

$8.34 \approx 8$ **Round the divisor.**

$17.931 \approx 16$ **Round the dividend to a multiple of 8 that is close to 17.931.**

$16 \div 8 = 2$ **Divide.**

Since 2.15 is close to the estimate 2, it is reasonable.

✓ Quick Check

4. Use estimation. Is each quotient reasonable? Explain.

    a. $1.564 \div 2.3 = 0.68$ **b.** $26.0454 \div 4.98 = 52.3$

Test-Taking Tip

You can sometimes use estimation to eliminate answer choices on a multiple choice test.

What is 8.19 ÷ 2.1?

Ⓐ 39   Ⓑ 4.1

Ⓒ 3.9   Ⓓ 0.41

If you estimate $8 \div 2 \approx 4$, then you know you can eliminate choices A and D.

EXERCISES

For more exercises, see *Extra Skill and Word Problem Practice*.

Practice and Problem Solving

A Practice by Example

Example 1
(page 134)

Estimate each product.

1. $4.56 \cdot 7.02$ **2.** $11.15 \cdot 4.44$ **3.** $6.3 \cdot 9.2$

4. $24.5 \cdot 4.2$ **5.** $3.29 \cdot 58$ **6.** $0.08 \cdot 40.05$

Example 2
(page 134)

Estimate the cost of each purchase.

7. Food Tom bought 6 hamburgers for $2.89 each.

8. Sports Equipment The athletic director bought 5 soccer balls for $12.29 each.

Example 3
(page 135)

Estimate each quotient using compatible numbers.

9. $3.9 \div 2.1$ **10.** $3.86 \div 1.95$ **11.** $19.56 \div 0.71$

12. $585 \div 11.75$ **13.** $18.2 \div 3.4$ **14.** $57.1 \div 7.2$

15. Unit Pricing Marshall buys a sack of peaches for $5.98. If the peaches weigh 2.77 pounds, about what price per pound did Marshall pay?

Example 4
(page 135)

Use estimation. Is each quotient reasonable? Explain.

16. $102.6 \div 22.5 = 45.6$ **17.** $\$32.40 \div 4.80 = \$67.50$

18. Number Sense Explain how you would find a reasonable estimate for $14.90 \div 4.56$.

B Apply Your Skills

Estimate each product or quotient.

19. $193.7 \cdot 1.78$ **20.** $7.95 \div 2.1$ **21.** $9.392 \div 2.9$

22. $876.66 \cdot 39.64$ **23.** $\$75.45 \div 12.48$ **24.** $16.33 \cdot 3.5$

Data Analysis Use the table below for Exercises 25–27.

Selected Wages (40-h week)

Occupation	Detroit, MI	Lincoln, NE
Elementary School Teacher	$1,820.80	$1,298.00
Secretary	$723.20	$508.00
Truck Driver	$685.20	$636.80

Source: U.S. Department of Labor

25. Estimate the hourly wage for each staff position.

26. Estimate the yearly (52 weeks) salary for each staff position.

27. How much more per hour does a secretary in Detroit, Michigan, make than a secretary in Lincoln, Nebraska?

Homework Video Tutor

Visit: PHSchool.com
Web Code: ade-0302

Use estimation. Is each product or quotient reasonable? Explain.

28. $-46.82(-1.5) = 702.3$ **29.** $-71.5071 \div (-11.9) = 6.009$

 **30. Gas Mileage** Shari is planning a 450-mi car trip. Her car can travel about 39 mi on a gallon of gasoline. Gasoline costs $1.89/gal. About how much will the gas cost for her trip?

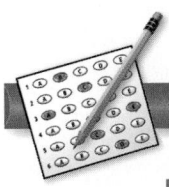 Challenge

Estimate each quotient.

31. $-483.09 \div 7.29$ **32.** $-362,400 \div (-4.2)$

33. Health Humans breathe about 15 breaths in a minute. The average breath at rest contains 0.76 liter of air. About how many liters of air will you breathe while at rest for 25 minutes?

34. Writing in Math You estimate $21.2 \div 3.75$ to be 5. Your friend estimates the quotient to be 7. Explain how the two estimates can be different and yet both be reasonable.

Test Prep

Multiple Choice

35. Greta ran the 400-m dash in 49.07 s. If Greta ran at a constant rate, how many meters did she run in one second?
   A. between 8 m and 9 m   **B.** between 9 m and 10 m
   C. between 10 m and 11 m   **D.** between 11 m and 12 m

36. A shrew, the world's smallest mammal, has a heart rate of 790 beats per minute. About how many times does a shrew's heart beat in 5 minutes?
   F. 3,500   **G.** 4,000   **H.** 4,500   **J.** 4,790

Short Response

37. Two people estimate the product $1.99 · 8.5.
   a. Will they necessarily get the same estimate?
   b. Explain your answer.

38. You review your sales slip after buying 4 CDs that cost $14.95 each. Before tax, the total was $77.80. Is this total correct? Explain.

Mixed Review

Lesson 3-1

Estimate each sum or difference.

39. $2.99 + $6.01   **40.** $25.90 − $5.79   **41.** $12.3 + 12.3 + 14.56$

42. $1,242.24 − 24.05$ **43.** $18.95 − 7.48$ **44.** $7.47 − $5.50

Lesson 1-10

In which quadrant or on which axis of a coordinate plane does each point lie?

45. $(2, 4)$ **46.** $(-5, 0)$ **47.** $(8, -6)$ **48.** $(0, 8)$ **49.** $(-5, -3)$

Lesson 1-8 **50. Travel** A bus trip from Sacramento to Los Angeles takes 7 h 40 min. You depart at 11:40 A.M. At what time will you arrive in Los Angeles?

Read the exercise below and then read how the needed data are found in the table. Follow along as the problem is solved. Check your understanding by solving the exercise at the bottom of the page.

Use the table. How much more per hour does a registered nurse in Washington, D.C., make than a registered nurse in Dallas, Texas?

The title of the table tells you that the table entries are wages for a 40-h week.

Occupations: Look down for registered nurse.

Cities: Look across for Dallas and Washington.

The table tells you that in a 40-h week:

A registered nurse in Dallas makes $997.60.

A registered nurse in Washington makes $1,114.00.

Selected Wages (40-h week)

Occupation	Dallas, TX	Washington, DC
Registered Nurse	$997.60	$1,114.00
Radiology Technician	$909.60	$1,025.20
Orderly	$381.60	$452.00

SOURCE: U.S. Department of Labor

Estimate:

A Washington registered nurse makes about $1,120 − $1,000 = $120 more in a 40-h week.

That's about $120 ÷ 40 = $3 more per hour.

Calculate — Method 1

1,114.00 − 997.60 = 116.40   **Subtract to find the difference in weekly wages.**

116.40 ÷ 40 = 2.91   **Divide to find the difference in hourly wages.**

Calculate — Method 2

1,114.00 ÷ 40 = 27.85   **Divide to find the Washington hourly wage.**

997.60 ÷ 40 = 24.94   **Divide to find the Dallas hourly wage.**

27.85 − 24.94 = 2.91   **Subtract to find the difference in hourly wages.**

A Washington registered nurse makes $2.91/h more than one in Dallas.

This is close to the estimate of $3/h.

EXERCISES

1. How much less per hour does an orderly in Dallas make than an orderly in Washington?

2. How much less per hour does a radiology technician in Dallas make than a nurse in Dallas?

Mean, Median, and Mode

1 Finding Mean, Median, Mode, and Range

Mean, *median*, and *mode* are **measures of central tendency** of a collection of data. Consider the data 2, 3, 4, 5, 8, 8, and 12.

The **mean** is the sum of the data values divided by the number of data values.

$$\text{mean} = \frac{2 + 3 + 4 + 5 + 8 + 8 + 12}{7}$$
$$= \frac{42}{7} = 6 \quad \underset{\text{number of data values}}{\underline{}}$$

The **median** is the middle number when data values are written in order and there is an odd number of data values. For an even number of data values, the median is the mean of the two middle numbers.

$$2 \quad 3 \quad 4 \quad \underset{\uparrow}{5} \quad 8 \quad 8 \quad 12$$
$$\text{median}$$

The **mode** is the data item that occurs most often. There can be one mode, more than one mode, or no mode.

$$2 \quad 3 \quad 4 \quad 5 \quad \underbrace{8 \quad 8}_{\text{mode}} \quad 12$$

The **range** of a set of data is the difference between the greatest and least values in the data set.

$$\text{range} = \underset{\underset{\text{greatest value}}{\uparrow}}{12} - \underset{\underset{\text{least value}}{\uparrow}}{2} = 10$$

1 EXAMPLE Real-World Problem Solving

Fundraising Use the **Readathon** graph. Find the (a) mean, (b) median, (c) mode, and (d) range.

a. Mean: $\dfrac{\text{sum of data values}}{\text{number of data values}}$

$$= \frac{40 + 45 + 48 + 50 + 50 + 59}{6}$$

$$= \frac{292}{6}$$

$$= 48.666\ldots \approx 48.7$$

b. Median: 40 45 48 50 50 59 **Write the data in order.**

$\dfrac{48 + 50}{2} = 49$ **Find the mean of the two middle numbers.**

c. Mode: Find the data value that occurs most often. The mode is 50.

d. Range: Greatest value − least value = 59 − 40 = 19.

READATHON
(PAGES READ
IN 1 WEEK)

Nick 40 Bettina 45 Kyle 48 Larry 50 Marita 50 Latana 59

What You'll Learn

- To find mean, median, mode, and range of a set of data
- To choose the best measure of central tendency

. . . And Why

To solve real-world problems involving consumer issues

✔ **Check Skills You'll Need**

Write the numbers from least to greatest.

1. 8, 6, 4, 9, 3, 5, 6
2. 72, 68, 69, 71, 72
3. 112, 101, 98, 120, 101
4. 3.74, 3, 3.7, 3.3, 37

GO for Help
Skills Handbook, p. 761

🔊 New Vocabulary

- measures of central tendency
- mean • median
- mode • outlier
- range

To do Example 1 with a graphing calculator, see page 747.

GO Online

Video Tutor Help
Visit: PHSchool.com
Web Code: ada-0775

✓ Quick Check

● **1.** Find the mean, median, mode, and range: 2.3 4.3 3.2 2.9 2.7 2.3

② EXAMPLE   **Identifying Modes**

For: Central Tendency Activity
Use: Interactive Textbook, 3-3

How many modes, if any, does each have?

a. $1.50 $2.00 $2.25 $2.40 $3.50 $4.00

No values are the same, so there is no mode.

b. 2 3 6 **8** **8** 10 11 12 **14** **14** 18 20

Both 8 and 14 appear the same number of times, and most often. There are two modes.

c. grape, grape, banana, nectarine, <u>strawberry</u>, <u>strawberry</u>, <u>strawberry</u>, orange, watermelon

Strawberry appears most often. There is one mode.

✓ Quick Check

2. Find the number of modes.

●   **a.** 11 9 7 7 8 8 13 11   **b.** 38.5 55.4 45.3 38.5 68.4

An **outlier** is a data value that is much greater or less than the other data values. An outlier can affect the mean of a group of data.

③ EXAMPLE   <u>Real-World</u> 🌐 <u>Problem Solving</u>

Approximate Land Areas That Can Be Farmed in Central American Countries

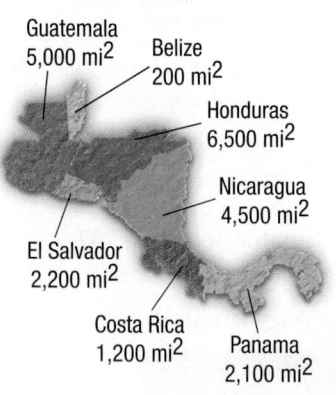

Guatemala
5,000 mi²

Belize
200 mi²

Honduras
6,500 mi²

Nicaragua
4,500 mi²

El Salvador
2,200 mi²

Costa Rica
1,200 mi²

Panama
2,100 mi²

SOURCE: *The New York Times Almanac*

Geography Use the map of Central America at the left.

a. Which data value is an outlier?

The data value for Honduras, 6,500 mi², is an outlier. It is an outlier because it is 1,500 mi² away from the closest data value.

b. How does the outlier affect the mean?

$\dfrac{21,700}{7} = 3,100$ **Find the mean with the outlier.**

$\dfrac{15,200}{6} \approx 2,500$ **Find the mean without the outlier.**

$3,100 - 2,500 = 600$

The outlier raises the mean by about 600 mi².

✓ Quick Check

3. Find an outlier in each group of data below and tell how it affects the mean. Round to the nearest tenth.

●   **a.** 9 10 12 13 8 9 31 9   **b.** 1 17.5 18 19.5 16 17.5

2 Choosing the Best Measure

One measure of central tendency may be better than another to describe data. For example, consider the eight hourly wage rates shown at the right. Here are the measures of central tendency.

Employees' Hourly Wages	
$5.50	$6.20
$5.50	$6.30
$5.50	$8.00
$6.00	$17.00

Mode: $5.50
Mean: $7.50
Median: $6.10

The mode is the lowest wage listed. So the mode does not describe the data well.

The mean is above the hourly wage of all but two workers. The mean is influenced by the outlier, $17.

The median is the best measure of central tendency here since it is not influenced by the size of the outlier.

4 EXAMPLE Identifying the Best Measure

Which measure of central tendency best describes each situation? Explain.

a. the favorite movies of students in the eighth grade

Mode; since the data are not numerical, the mode is the appropriate measure. When determining the most frequently chosen item, or when the data are not numerical, use the mode.

b. the daily high temperatures during a week in July

Mean; since daily high temperatures in July are not likely to have an outlier, mean is the appropriate measure. When the data have no outliers, use the mean.

c. the distances students in your class travel to school

Median; since one student may live much farther from school than the majority of students, the median is the appropriate measure. When an outlier may significantly influence the mean, use the median.

> **Vocabulary Tip**
>
> To help you recall that <u>median</u> means "middle number," think of the green, grassy median strip in the middle of a divided highway.

✓ Quick Check

4. a. Comparison Shopping Toshio found the following prices for sport shirts:
$20, $26, $27, $28, $21, $42, $18, and $20.
Find the mean, median, and mode for the shirt prices.
   b. Reasoning Which measure of central tendency best describes the data? Justify your reasoning.

EXERCISES

For more exercises, see *Extra Skill and Word Problem Practice.*

Practice and Problem Solving

A Practice by Example

Example 1
(page 139)

GO for Help

Find the mean, median, mode, and range of each group of data. If an answer is not a whole number, round to the nearest tenth.

1. 47 56 57 63 89 44 56
2. 4 5 2 3 2 3 3 3 1 1 3

3. 1 2 4 5 5 6 9
4. 2.8 3.6 3.8 4.1 2.8 3.7 4.3

5. Fitness Mia's workouts lasted 1.0 h, 1.5 h, 2.25 h, 1.5 h, 2.4 h, and 2.1 h. Find the mean, median, and mode of these times. If the answer is not an integer, round to the nearest tenth.

Example 2
(page 140)

How many modes, if any, does each group of data have?

6. 31 44 44 31 38
7. 4.3 4.9 4.9 5.2

8. 64 68 64 65 68 65 72 61
9. Bob, Ana, Ron, Bob, Kay

Example 3
(page 140)

Find the outlier in each group of data and tell how it affects the mean.

10. 37 4 7 3 11 9 13 5
11. 126 123 115 125 123

12. Grades Rita's quiz scores are 72, 96, 74, 80, and 79. Find the outlier and tell how it affects Rita's mean quiz score.

Example 4
(page 141)

Which measure of central tendency best describes each situation? Explain.

13. numbers of apples in 2-lb bags
14. favorite brands of jeans of 14-year-olds
15. ages of students in a fifth-grade classroom

Which measure of central tendency best describes each group of data? Explain.

16. minutes on the Internet
50 63 59 85 367 48
17. heights of students in inches
51 45 47 48 50 50 50 52

B Apply Your Skills

For Exercises 18–22, find mean, median, mode, and range. Which measure of central tendency best describes each group of data? Explain.

18. 3,456 560 435 456
19. 5.6 6.8 1.2 6.5 7.9 6.5

20. 33 76 86 92 86
21. 8 2 4 9 16

22. resting heart rate in beats per minute: 79 72 80 81 40 72

Which measure of central tendency best describes each situation? Explain.

GO Online
Homework Video Tutor
Visit: PHSchool.com
Web Code: ade-0303

23. shoe colors in a classroom
24. widths of computer screens at a bank
25. numbers of pets owned by classmates

142 Chapter 3 Decimals and Equations

 Challenge

For Exercises 26–28, use the table at the left. Round answers to the nearest tenth.

Fat and Calorie Content
(per 2-tablespoon serving)

Seed or Nut	Fat (g)	Calories
Peanut	8.9	104
Pecan	9.1	90
Pistachio	7.9	92
Pumpkin	7.9	93
Sunflower	8.9	102
Walnut	7.7	80

26. Data Analysis You make a mixture using the same amount of each kind of seed and nut.
  a. What is the mean number of grams of fat in a 2-tablespoon serving of the mixture?
  b. What is the mean number of Calories in a 2-tablespoon serving of the mixture?

27. Writing in Math Describe two mixtures that each use a total of 8 tablespoons. Do the two parts of Exercise 26 for your mixtures.

28. Nutrition A mixture of equal amounts of pumpkin seeds, sunflower seeds, and pistachios contains 12 tablespoons in all. How many grams of fat and how many Calories does the mixture have?

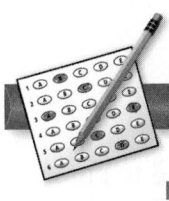

Test Prep

Multiple Choice

29. The average cost of a meal at the Grand Plaza is $20. Which one of the following statements *cannot* be true?
  A. The cost of four meals is greater than $20.
  B. Some meals cost less than $10.
  C. Each meal costs exactly $20.
  D. Each meal costs more than $20.

30. Kayla's first three quiz scores are 90, 85, and 88. Which score on her next quiz will raise Kayla's mean quiz score to 90?
  F. 97　　**G.** 95　　**H.** 92　　**J.** 90

31. Ten out of 20 students score a perfect 100 on a math test. Which of the following describes the score of 100 for the 20 students?
  A. mean　　**B.** median　　**C.** mode　　**D.** outlier

Short Response

32. In a neighborhood with 46 homes, two are more than 6,000 ft² in area, and the rest are less than 2,500 ft² in area.
  a. Would the mean or the median provide a better measure of the typical home size?
  b. Explain your reasoning.

Mixed Review

 **GO for Help**

Lesson 3-2 **Estimate each product or quotient.**

33. $9.01 ÷ $1.42　　**34.** 7.5 · 89.1　　**35.** 12.6 · $2.99

Lesson 2-7 **36. Retail Sales** Karen sells children's hats for $4 and adults' hats for $7. On Saturday, she sold 120 hats, and she collected $720. How many adults' hats did she sell?

Lesson 2-3 **Simplify each expression.**

37. $6x + 8 + 2$　　**38.** $5z + 4x + 3z$　　**39.** $x - 4t + 2t + 5$

Mean and Median on a Graphing Calculator

For Use With Lesson 3-3

You can use a graphing calculator to find means and medians.

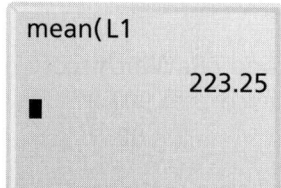

ACTIVITY

Find (a) the mean and (b) the median number of acres in Ohio zoos.

Zoos in Ohio

Zoo	Number of Acres	Number of Species
Cincinnati Zoo	75	3,500
Cleveland Metroparks Zoo	168	579
Columbus Zoo and Aquarium	588	758
Toledo Zoo	62	700

SOURCE: *The World Almanac*

a. Use the mean function. Use LIST to enter 75, 168, 588, and 62 for **L1**. In **STAT**, select **MATH** and **mean**, then ENTER. Using **STAT** again, select **L1**. Press ENTER twice to find the mean.

```
mean(L1
           223.25
■
```

The mean is about 223 acres.

b. Use the median function. Use LIST to enter 75, 168, 588, and 62 for **L1**. In **STAT**, select **MATH** and **median**, then ENTER. Using **STAT** again, select **L1**. Press ENTER twice to find the median.

```
median(L1
             121.5
■
```

The median is 121.5 acres.

EXERCISES

Use a calculator to find the mean and median.

1. number of species in Ohio zoos

2. 85°F, 79°F, 80°F, 75°F, 82°F

3. $3.75, $4.50, $9.25, $4.70, $5.90

4. 100, 95, 82, 102, 78, 76

5. **Miles of Atlantic Coastline by State**

State	DE	FL	GA	ME	MD	MA	NH	NJ	NY	NC	RI	SC	VA
Miles	28	580	100	228	31	192	13	130	127	301	40	187	112

SOURCE: National Oceanic and Atmospheric Administration, U.S. Dept. of Commerce

Using Formulas

1 Substituting Into Formulas

What You'll Learn
- To substitute into formulas
- To use the formula for the perimeter of a rectangle

...And Why

To use formulas to solve real-world problems involving distances, temperatures, and perimeters

✓ **Check Skills You'll Need**

Evaluate each expression for $x = 3$ and $y = 4$.

1. $2x + 2y$ **2.** $2x + y$

3. $2(x + y)$ **4.** $\frac{x + y}{2}$

GO for Help

Lesson 1-3

🔊 **New Vocabulary**
- formula
- perimeter

A **formula** is an equation that shows a relationship between quantities that are represented by variables.

An important formula in math and science is $d = rt$, where d is the distance, r is the rate or speed, and t is the time spent traveling.

1 EXAMPLE   Real-World Problem Solving

Travel Suppose you travel 162 miles in 3 hours. Use the formula $d = rt$ to find your average speed.

$d = rt$	Write the formula.
$162 = (r)(3)$	Substitute 162 for d and 3 for t.
$\dfrac{162}{3} = \dfrac{3r}{3}$	Divide each side by 3.
$54 = r$	Simplify.

Your average speed is 54 mi/h.

✓ Quick Check

1. Use the formula $d = rt$. Find d, r, or t.

   a. $d = 273$ mi, $t = 9.75$ h   **b.** $d = 540.75$ in., $r = 10.5$ in./yr

2 EXAMPLE   Real-World Problem Solving

Insects You can estimate the temperature outside using the chirps of a cricket. Use the formula $F = \frac{n}{4} + 37$, where n is the number of times a cricket chirps in one minute, and F is the temperature in degrees Fahrenheit. Estimate the temperature when a cricket chirps 100 times in a minute.

$F = \dfrac{n}{4} + 37$	Write the formula.
$F = \dfrac{100}{4} + 37$	Replace n with 100.
$F = 25 + 37$	Divide.
$F = 62$	Add.

The temperature is about 62°F.

✅ Quick Check

2. Use the formula $F = \frac{n}{4} + 37$ to estimate the temperature in degrees Fahrenheit for each situation.

a. 96 chirps/min   **b.** 88 chirps/min   **c.** 66 chirps/min

2   Using a Perimeter Formula

The **perimeter** of a figure is the distance around the figure. You can find the perimeter of a rectangle by adding the lengths of the four sides, or by using the formula $P = 2\ell + 2w$, where ℓ is the length, and w is the width. For rectangles, it does not matter which dimension you choose to be the length or the width.

3   EXAMPLE   Finding Perimeter

Multiple Choice Use the formula for the perimeter of a rectangle, $P = 2\ell + 2w$. What is the perimeter of the rectangle?

   Ⓐ   60 ft   Ⓑ   61 ft   Ⓒ   62 ft   Ⓓ   64 ft

12.5 ft

18.5 ft

$$P = 2\ell + 2w \qquad \text{Write the formula.}$$
$$P = 2(18.5) + 2(12.5) \quad \text{Replace } \ell \text{ with 18.5 and } w \text{ with 12.5.}$$
$$P = 37 + 25 \qquad \text{Multiply.}$$
$$P = 62 \qquad \text{Add.}$$

The perimeter of the rectangle is 62 ft.

✅ Quick Check

3. Find the perimeter of each rectangle.

a.

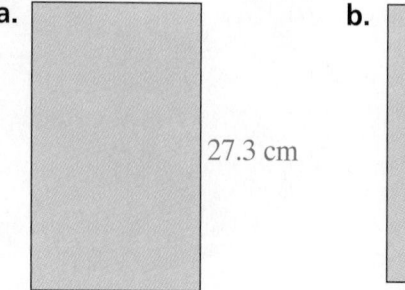

27.3 cm

16.8 cm

b.

17.4 in.

8.6 in.

EXERCISES

For more exercises, see *Extra Skill and Word Problem Practice.*

Practice and Problem Solving

 Practice by Example

Example 1
(page 145)

 **for Help**

Use the formula $d = rt$. Find d, r, or t.

1. $r = 38.5$ m/h, $t = 12.5$ h

2. $d = 2{,}730$ mi, $t = 9.75$ h

3. $d = 596.39$ cm, $r = 2.3$ cm/s

4. $d = 10.2$ ft, $r = 0.5$ ft/h

Example 2
(page 145)

Use the formula $F = \frac{n}{4} + 37$ to estimate each temperature.

5. 120 chirps/min

6. 80 chirps/min

7. 92 chirps/min

8. 64 chirps/min

Example 3
(page 146)

Use the formula $P = 2\ell + 2w$. Find the perimeter of each rectangle.

9.
11.2 mm
16.5 mm

10.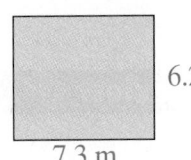
6.2 m
7.3 m

B **Apply Your Skills**

Given that C is the temperature in degrees Celsius, use the formula $F = 1.8C + 32$ to find each temperature F in degrees Fahrenheit.

11. $C = 58$ **12.** $C = -4$ **13.** $C = 72$ **14.** $C = 56$ **15.** $C = -89$

Go Online
Homework Video Tutor
Visit: PHSchool.com
Web Code: ade-0304

Geometry **Use the formula $P = 2\ell + 2w$. Find the perimeter of each rectangle. Then use the formula $A = \ell w$ to find each area.**

16.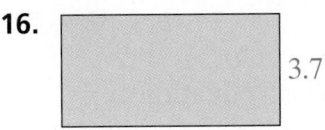
3.7 m
7.3 m

17.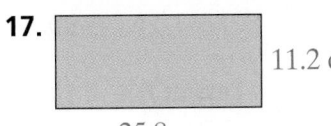
11.2 cm
25.8 cm

18. **Multiple Choice** **The area of the rectangle is 27.8 square feet. Which is the best estimate of the length of the rectangle?**

4 ft

Ⓐ 5 ft   Ⓑ 6 ft
Ⓒ 7 ft   Ⓓ 8 ft

C **Challenge**

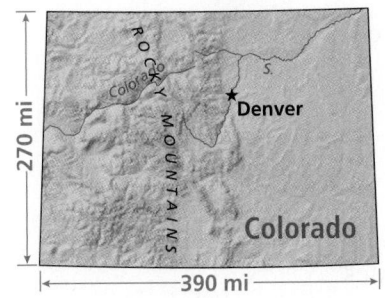
270 mi
390 mi
Denver
Colorado

19. The top surface of a world-record rectangular strawberry shortcake was 175.33 ft long and 48 in. wide. Use the formula for perimeter. Find the approximate perimeter of the cake.

20. Find the approximate area of the top of the cake in Exercise 19.

21. The state of Colorado is nearly rectangular in shape. Use the formula for area. Find the approximate area of Colorado.

22. Use the formula for perimeter. Find the approximate perimeter of Colorado.

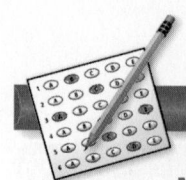

Test Prep

Multiple Choice

23. What is the perimeter of a rectangle that measures 32 cm by 11 cm?
    A. 352 cm   **B.** 86 cm   **C.** 54 cm   **D.** 43 cm

24. Suppose you travel 320 mi in 5 h. What is your average speed?
    F. 58 mi/h   **G.** 60 mi/h   **H.** 64 mi/h   **J.** 75 mi/h

25. A giant tortoise travels about 0.17 mi/h on land. If a tortoise travels at a constant speed, how far can it travel in 2.5 h?
    A. 0.0425 mi   **B.** 0.267 mi   **C.** 0.425 mi   **D.** 4.25 mi

Short Response

26. A rectangular yard has width w and length ℓ. **(a)** What is a formula for its perimeter, P? **(b)** Find P when w is 16.4 m and ℓ is 28.2 m.

27. The pronghorn antelope can run 0.73 mi/min. **(a)** At this speed, how far can this animal travel in 30 seconds? **(b)** In 1.5 minutes?

Mixed Review

Lesson 3-3

Find the mean, median, and mode. Round to the nearest whole number where necessary. Which measure of central tendency best describes the data?

28. minutes of homework
8 125 154 120 105 125

29. milliliters per container
250 250 355 355 375 250

Lesson 2-5

Solve each equation.

30. $c + 8 = 41$ **31.** $b + 32 = 19$ **32.** $98 = n + 42$

Lesson 1-7

33. Patterns Which equation, $n = 2t$ or $t = n \cdot 2$, describes the relationship between the variables in the table? Explain.

n	14	16	18	20
t	7	8	9	10

✓ Checkpoint Quiz 1   Lessons 3-1 through 3-4

Round each number to the underlined place value.

1. 15.6<u>5</u>71   **2.** 0.89<u>1</u>4   **3.** 7,02<u>2</u>.56   **4.** 345.<u>6</u>78

Estimate.

5. $3.7 \cdot 8.06$ **6.** $17.25 + 6.66$ **7.** $8.7 - 9.6$ **8.** $11.7 \div 1.8$

Find the mean, median, and mode.

9. 47, 56, 58, 63   **10.** 1, 4, 1, 3, 1, 2, 3, 2, 1, 2

11. Jennifer drives at an average speed of 54 mi/h. At this rate, how long does it take Jennifer to drive 459 miles?

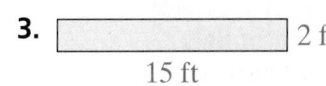

Understanding Math Problems Read the problem below. Then let Joe's thinking guide you through the solution. Check your understanding with the exercises at the bottom of the page.

Geometry Use the formula $P = 2\ell + 2w$. Find the perimeter of the rectangle. Then use the formula $A = \ell w$ to find each area.

4 ft

What Joe Thinks

First I need to use the formula for perimeter.

Substitute 7.3 for ℓ and 3.7 for w.

I can use the Distributive Property to make the work easier.

Add within parentheses.

Now multiply.

Next, I need to use the formula for area.

Substitute 7.3 for ℓ and 3.7 for w and multiply.

Now I need to write the units. Don't forget that area is in square units.

What Joe Writes

$P = 2\ell + 2w$

$P = 2(7.3) + 2(3.7)$

$P = 2(7.3 + 3.7)$

$P = 2(11)$

$P = 22$

$A = \ell w$

$A = 7.3(3.7) = 27.01$

Perimeter is 22 m. Area is 27.01 m^2.

EXERCISES

Geometry Use the formula $P = 2\ell + 2w$. Find the perimeter of the rectangle. Then use the formula $A = \ell w$ to find each area.

1.

2.4 cm

4 cm

2.

$1\frac{1}{2}$ in.

9 in.

3.

2 ft

15 ft

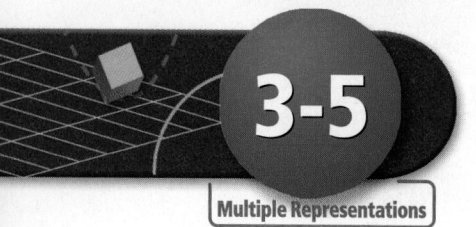

3-5

Multiple Representations

Solving Equations by Adding or Subtracting Decimals

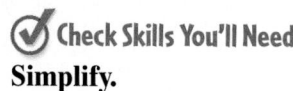 **Check Skills You'll Need**

Simplify.

1. $2.8 + 7.06$

2. $0.65 + 1.8$

3. $4.52 - 2.48$

4. $3.7 - 0.62$

 **for Help**

Skills Handbook, 768

---

1 Using Subtraction to Solve Equations

In Lesson 2-5, you used the Subtraction Property of Equality to solve equations involving integers. You can also use this property to solve equations with decimals. Remember to subtract the same number from each side of the equation.

1 EXAMPLE   Subtracting to Solve an Equation

Solve $n + 4.5 = -9.7$.

$$n + 4.5 = -9.7$$
$$n + 4.5 - 4.5 = -9.7 - 4.5 \quad \text{Subtract 4.5 from each side.}$$
$$n = -14.2 \quad \text{Simplify.}$$

Check $\quad n + 4.5 = -9.7$
$$-14.2 + 4.5 \overset{?}{=} -9.7 \quad \text{Replace } n \text{ with } -14.2.$$
$$-9.7 = -9.7 ✔$$

Quick Check

1. Solve each equation.

a. $x + 4.9 = 18.8$

b. $14.73 = -24.23 + b$

2 EXAMPLE   Real-World Problem Solving

Astronomy Use the diagram below. A communications satellite is circling Earth. About how far is the satellite from the moon?

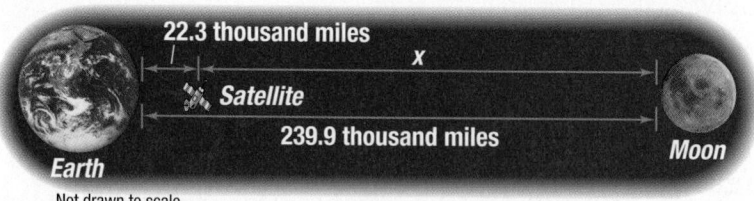

22.3 thousand miles

x

Satellite

239.9 thousand miles

Earth

Moon

Not drawn to scale

$$22.3 \approx 22 \quad \text{Round to numbers that are}$$
$$239.9 \approx 240 \quad \text{easy to compute.}$$

$$22 + x \approx 240$$
$$22 + x - 22 \approx 240 - 22 \quad \text{Subtract 22 from each side.}$$
$$x \approx 218 \quad \text{Simplify.}$$

The satellite is about 218 thousand miles from the moon.

 **nline**

Video Tutor Help

Visit: PHSchool.com
Web Code: ada-0775

✓ Quick Check

2. **Analyzing Markup** A store's cost plus markup is the price you pay for an item. Suppose a pair of shoes costs a store $35.48. You pay $70. Write and solve an equation to find the store's markup.

GO for Help

For help with adding and subtracting decimals, see Skills Handbook, page 768.

2 Using Addition to Solve Equations

You can also use the Addition Property of Equality to solve an equation involving decimals. Remember to add the same number to each side of the equation.

3 EXAMPLE Adding to Solve an Equation

Solve $k - 14.4 = -18.39$.

$$k - 14.4 = -18.39$$
$$k - 14.4 + 14.4 = -18.39 + 14.4 \quad \textbf{Add 14.4 to each side.}$$
$$k = -3.99 \quad \textbf{Simplify.}$$

Online active math

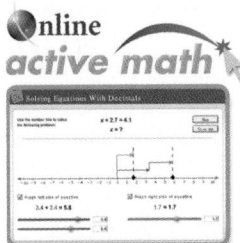

For: Decimal Equations Activity
Use: Interactive Textbook, 3-5

✓ Quick Check

3. Solve each equation.

   a. $n - 5.85 = 15.25$ b. $-10 = c - 2.6$

4 EXAMPLE Real-World Problem Solving

Gridded Response Danzel wrote a check for $76.85. His new account balance is $235.15. What was his previous balance?

Words   previous balance minus check is new balance

Let p = previous balance.

Equation p −   76.85   =   235.15

$$p - 76.85 = 235.15$$
$$p - 76.85 + 76.85 = 235.15 + 76.85 \quad \textbf{Add 76.85 to each side.}$$
$$p = 312 \quad \textbf{Simplify.}$$

Danzel's previous balance was $312.

Test-Taking Tip

On gridded items, you cannot grid the units. Here, the correct number to grid is 312.

✓ Quick Check

4. **Shopping** You spent $14.95 for a new shirt. You now have $12.48. Write and solve an equation to find how much money you had before you bought the shirt.

EXERCISES

For more exercises, see *Extra Skill and Word Problem Practice*.

Practice and Problem Solving

A Practice by Example

Examples 1 and 2
(page 150)

GO for Help

Solve each equation.

1. $c + 9 = 3.7$ **2.** $b + 7.6 = 23$ **3.** $43.6 = n + 17.5$

4. $6.35 + b = 9.89$ **5.** $12.13 = n + 1.4$ **6.** $x + 0.35 = 9.15$

7. Astronomy The planet Mars takes 599.01 days longer than Mercury to orbit the sun. In all, the Mars orbit takes 686.98 days. Write and solve an equation to find about how long it takes Mercury to orbit the sun.

8. Car Sales Julia trades in her small car for a large pickup truck that weighs 1,855.3 lb more than the car. If the truck weighs 4,360.3 lb, what is the weight of the car?

Examples 3 and 4
(page 151)

Solve each equation.

9. $d - 4.9 = 18.8$ **10.** $c - 19.2 = 24$ **11.** $-2.5 = q - 1.7$

12. $-5.6 = y - 8$ **13.** $4.3 = g - 1$ **14.** $a - 108.8 = -203$

15. Personal Finance You spent $13.50 for movie tickets. You now have $26.50. Write and solve an equation to find out how much money you had before buying the tickets.

16. Rachel wrote a check for $161.15. Her new account balance is $423.28. What was her previous account balance?

B Apply Your Skills

GO Online
Homework Video Tutor
Visit: PHSchool.com
Web Code: ade-0305

Complete the steps for each equation. Justify each step.

17. $x + 1.2 = 15$ **18.** $y - 3.33 = 12.42$
    $x + 1.2 - ■ = 15 - ■$ $y - 3.33 + ■ = 12.42 + ■$
            $x = ■$ $y = ■$

19. Running Michael Johnson's world record in the 200-m sprint is 19.32 s. His 400-m world record is 23.86 s slower than his 200-m record. Write and solve an equation to find Johnson's 400-m record.

20. Biology A hare travels about 17.83 mi/h faster on land than a giant tortoise. A hare can hop at about 18 mi/h. Write and solve an equation to find about how fast a giant tortoise can travel on land.

Real-World Connection

Giant tortoises can weigh up to 500 lb.

Solve each equation.

21. $4.035 = a - 3.25$ **22.** $h - (-1.5) = 1.5$ **23.** $e + (-7.8) = -6.7$

24. $r - 0.832 = 8.67$ **25.** $b - (-1.5) = -9$ **26.** $-32 = x + (-8.05)$

Mental Math Use mental math to solve each equation.

27. $1.60 = 0.40 + s$ **28.** $x + 8.8 = 9.9$ **29.** $5.5 = x - 5.5$

$$x - 1.6 = -6$$
$$x - 1.6 + 1.6 = -6 - 1.6$$
$$x = -7.6$$

30. Error Analysis A student solved an equation as shown at the left. Explain the student's error.

31. Writing in Math Explain how you would use the Addition (not Subtraction) Property of Equality to solve $x + 1.8 = -4.7$.

C Challenge

Solve each equation.

32. $143.587 + x - 22.96 = 156.4$ **33.** $-924.87 - 1{,}237 + b = 86.125$

34. Reasoning Without solving, tell how the solutions of the equations $x + 14 = 15, x + 1.4 = 1.5,$ and $x + 0.14 = 0.15$ compare. Explain.

Test Prep

Multiple Choice

35. Which statement describes how to solve $x + 0.042 = 0.826$?
  A. Add 0.042 to each side. **B.** Subtract 0.042 from each side.
  C. Add 0.826 to each side. **D.** Subtract 0.826 from each side.

Short Response

Read the cartoon below before doing Exercises 36 and 37.

Dilbert by Scott Adams

Source: ©1993 United Features Syndicate, Inc.

36. How much money does the clerk owe Dilbert?

37. Dilbert does not want any pennies. What other amount of money could Dilbert have given the cashier? Justify your answer.

Mixed Review

Lesson 3-4

Use the formula $A = \ell w$. Find A.

38. $\ell = 23.4$ in., $w = 15.8$ in. **39.** $\ell = 5.5$ cm, $w = 7$ cm

Lesson 2-6

Solve each equation.

40. $6a = 24$ **41.** $-2b = 60$ **42.** $-81 = 9a$

Lesson 2-2

43. A large juice costs $.83. A small juice costs $.57. Ida buys one juice each school day. If Ida buys small juices instead of large juices, how much money will she save each week?

Solving Equations by Multiplying or Dividing Decimals

What You'll Learn

- To solve one-step decimal equations involving multiplication
- To solve one-step decimal equations involving division

. . . And Why

To solve real-world problems in oil production

✓ **Check Skills You'll Need**

Find each product.

1. 2.6(4.5)

2. 3.2(0.15)

3. 11.03(0.6)

4. 8.003(0.6)

GO for Help

Skills Handbook, p. 769

1 Using Division to Solve Equations

In Lesson 2-6, you used the Division Property of Equality to solve equations involving integers. You can also use this property to solve equations with decimals. Remember to divide each side of the equation by the same nonzero number.

1 EXAMPLE Dividing to Solve an Equation

Solve $0.9r = -5.4$.

$$0.9r = -5.4$$

$$\frac{0.9r}{0.9} = \frac{-5.4}{0.9} \qquad \text{Divide each side by 0.9.}$$

$$r = -6 \qquad \text{Simplify.}$$

Check $\qquad 0.9r = -5.4$

$$0.9(-6) \stackrel{?}{=} -5.4 \qquad \text{Replace } r \text{ with } -6.$$

$$-5.4 = -5.4 ✓$$

✓ **Quick Check**

1. Solve each equation.

a. $0.8x = -1.6$ **b.** $1.15 = 2.3x$ **c.** $-81.81 = -0.9n$

2 EXAMPLE Real-World 🌐 Problem Solving

GO for Help

For help with dividing decimals, see Skills Handbook, page 773.

Petroleum An oil field produces an average of 16.8 thousand barrels of crude oil per day. About how many days will it take to produce 200 thousand barrels?

Words	daily barrel production	times	number of days	equals	200 thousand barrels

Let d = number of days.

Equation	16.8	·	d	=	200

$$16.8d = 200$$

$$\frac{16.8d}{16.8} = \frac{200}{16.8} \qquad \text{Divide each side by 16.8.}$$

$$d = 11.904\ldots \qquad \text{Simplify.}$$

$$d \approx 12 \qquad \text{Round to the nearest whole number.}$$

It will take about 12 days to produce 200 thousand barrels.

✅ Quick Check

2. **Postage** You paid $7.70 to mail a package that weighed 5.5 lb. Write and solve an equation to find the cost per pound.

2 | Using Multiplication to Solve Equations

To solve an equation involving division, multiply each side by the same nonzero number.

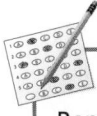

Test-Taking Tip

Remember to maintain the balance: Whatever you do to one side of an equation you must do to the other side.

3 EXAMPLE | Multiplying to Solve an Equation

Solve $\frac{m}{-7.2} = -12.5$.

$$\frac{m}{-7.2} = -12.5$$

$$\frac{m}{-7.2}(-7.2) = -12.5(-7.2) \quad \textbf{Multiply each side by } -7.2.$$

$$m = 90 \qquad\qquad \textbf{Simplify}.$$

✅ Quick Check

3. Solve each equation.

   a. $\frac{r}{-6.0} = 0.5$ **b.** $\frac{s}{2.5} = 5$ **c.** $-80 = \frac{t}{4.5}$

4 EXAMPLE | Real-World 🌐 Problem Solving

Multiple Choice The 1923 baseball season was one of Babe Ruth's best. He was at bat 522 times and had a batting average of 0.393, rounded to the nearest thousandth. The batting average formula is $a = \frac{h}{n}$, where a is the batting average, h is the number of hits, and n is the number of times at bat. How many hits did Babe Ruth make?

  Ⓐ 522 hits   Ⓑ 393 hits   Ⓒ 206 hits   Ⓓ 205 hits

$$a = \frac{h}{n}$$

$$0.393 = \frac{h}{522} \qquad \textbf{Replace } a \textbf{ with 0.393 and } n \textbf{ with 522.}$$

$$(0.393)(522) = \frac{h}{522}(522) \qquad \textbf{Multiply each side by 522.}$$

$$h = 205.146 \qquad \textbf{Simplify.}$$

$$h \approx 205 \qquad \begin{array}{l}\textbf{Since } h \textbf{ (hits) represents an integer,}\\ \textbf{round to the nearest integer.}\end{array}$$

Babe Ruth made 205 hits. The answer is D.

✅ Quick Check

4. Suppose your batting average is 0.222. You have batted 54 times. How many hits do you have?

Real-World 🌐 Connection

During his professional career, Babe Ruth was at bat 8,399 times and had a batting average of 0.342.

EXERCISES

For more exercises, see *Extra Skill and Word Problem Practice*.

Practice and Problem Solving

Ⓐ Practice by Example

Examples 1 and 2
(page 154)

GO for Help

Solve each equation.

1. $0.8s = -6.4$ **2.** $0.8x = 0.48$ **3.** $-0.5y = -0.73$

4. $2x = -4.88$ **5.** $-0.3y = 7.53$ **6.** $2.21 = 1.7w$

7. $1.92 = 1.6s$ **8.** $3.2n = 27.52$ **9.** $0.7x = 2.8$

10. Manufacturing A factory produces an average of seven thousand televisions per day. About how many days will it take to produce 63.5 thousand televisions?

11. Postage You paid $5.30 to mail a package that weighed 2.5 lb. Write and solve an equation to find the mailing cost per pound.

Examples 3 and 4
(page 155)

Solve each equation.

12. $\frac{n}{2.3} = -4.8$ **13.** $0.97 = \frac{c}{-2}$ **14.** $\frac{h}{7} = -8$

15. $\frac{n}{1.7} = 0.22$ **16.** $\frac{k}{2.01} = 0.04$ **17.** $120 = \frac{v}{3.8}$

18. $9 = \frac{a}{1.5}$ **19.** $\frac{m}{7.08} = -100$ **20.** $-200 = \frac{f}{4}$

21. Batting Averages During the 1954 baseball season with the New York Yankees, Yogi Berra was at bat 584 times and had a batting average of 0.307. Use the batting-average formula in Example 4 to find the number of hits Berra made.

Ⓑ Apply Your Skills

Solve each equation.

22. $6.4x = 0.2816$ **23.** $-5.1z = -11.73$

24. $0.004m = 0.12$ **25.** $4.5 = m \div (-3.3)$

26. $-33.04 = \frac{z}{-0.03}$ **27.** $-0.45 = x \div 12$

28. a. Error Analysis Harry found 324.8 as a solution for the equation $4x = 81.2$. What was Harry's error?
   b. Estimation How could Harry have used estimation to check whether his answer was reasonable?

Write an equation for each sentence. Solve for the variable.

29. The product of a number n and -7.3 is 30.66.

30. The quotient of a number n divided by -4.5 equals 200.6.

31. A number n divided by -2.35 equals 400.9.

GO Online
Homework Video Tutor
Visit: PHSchool.com
Web Code: ade-0306

32. a. Batting Averages Your batting average is 0.244, and you have been at bat 82 times. How many hits do you have?
   b. Writing in Math Why is it necessary to round your answer in part (a) to the nearest integer?

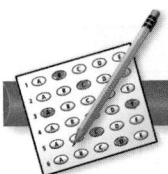 33. **Utilities** Jan pays $.08 per kilowatt-hour for electricity. Her electric bill is $59.22. Write and solve an equation to find how many kilowatt-hours of electricity Jan used.

34. **Number Sense** The weight of a record-setting onion was 12.25 lb. An average-sized onion weighs 0.5 lb. About how many average-sized onions have a total weight equal to the record-setting onion?

C Challenge

35. **Measurement** If you know a length ℓ in meters, you can multiply the length by 3.28 to find the length in feet f.
   a. Write an equation to model this situation.
   b. A tree is 7.5 m tall. Use your equation to find this height in feet.
   c. A bookshelf is 6 ft tall. What is this height in meters?
   d. A room is 12 ft long and 15 ft wide. Use your equation and the formula for the area of a rectangle to find the area of the room in square meters. Round to the nearest tenth.

36. **Reasoning** Find values for x and y that satisfy $xy = 0.42$ and $x + y = 1.3$.

37. **Batting Averages** About how many hits did Babe Ruth have during his professional career? (*Hint:* See page 155.)

Test Prep

Multiple Choice

38. A group of friends goes out for dinner. The bill is $36.81. If they share the cost equally and each person's share is about $7.35, how many people are in the group?
   A. 4   **B.** 5   **C.** 6   **D.** 7

39. Which equation has 3.2 as its solution?
   F. $20x = 6.4$ **G.** $6.4 = 2x$ **H.** $\frac{x}{2} = 6.4$ **J.** $\frac{x}{6.4} = 2$

Short Response

40. A barber gave enough haircuts in one day to earn $337.50. Each haircut cost $12.50. **(a)** How many haircuts did the barber give that day? **(b)** Estimate the amount of money the barber can make in a week.

Mixed Review

GO for Help

Lesson 3-5

Solve each equation.

41. $c + 9 = 3.7$ 42. $-5.6 = y - 8$ 43. $4.035 = a - 3.25$

Lesson 2-4

Is the given number a solution of the equation? Show why.

44. $20 - c = 12; c = 8$ 45. $8 = 2a + 3; a = 0$

Lesson 1-7

46. **a. Patterns** Multiply $99 \cdot 24, 99 \cdot 25$, and $99 \cdot 26$.
   b. Describe the pattern you found in part (a).
   c. Use the pattern to evaluate $99 \cdot 27$.

3-7 Using the Metric System

What You'll Learn

• To identify appropriate metric measures

• To convert metric units

. . . And Why

To solve real-world problems involving metric measures

✓ **Check Skills You'll Need**

Find each product or quotient.

1. 5×100

2. $14.06 \div 1,000$

3. 0.294×10

4. $0.9 \div 100$

GO for Help

Skills Handbook, p. 772

1 Identifying Appropriate Metric Measures

Knowing the approximate size of each metric unit of measure will allow you to choose an appropriate unit.

Key Concepts   **Metric Units of Measurement**

	Unit	Reference Example
Length	millimeter (mm)	about the thickness of a dime
	centimeter (cm)	about the width of a thumbnail
	meter (m)	about the distance from a doorknob to the floor
	kilometer (km)	a little more than one half mile
Capacity	milliliter (mL)	about 5 drops of water
	liter (L)	a little more than a quart of milk
Mass	milligram (mg)	about the mass of a speck of sawdust
	gram(g)	about the mass of a paper clip
	kilogram (kg)	about one half the mass of this math book

1 EXAMPLE   **Choosing an Appropriate Unit**

Choose an appropriate metric unit. Explain your choice.

a. height of a classroom chalkboard

Meter; the height of a chalkboard is about twice the distance from the floor to a doorknob.

b. mass of a backpack filled with books

Kilogram; the mass of a backpack filled with books is many times the mass of this textbook.

c. capacity of a birdbath

Liter; several quart bottles of water would fill a birdbath.

✓ **Quick Check**

1. Choose an appropriate metric unit. Explain your choice.

   a. length of a broom   **b.** the mass of an energy bar

   c. mass of a horse   **d.** capacity of a car's gas tank

2 EXAMPLE Estimating With Metric Units

Estimation Choose a reasonable estimate. Explain your choice.

a. capacity of a juice box: 200 mL or 200 L

200 mL; the juice box holds less than a quart of milk.

b. length of a new pencil: 15 cm or 15 m

15 cm; the length of a pencil would be about 15 widths of a thumbnail.

c. mass of a small tube of toothpaste: 100 g or 100 kg

100 g; the mass is about the same as a box of paper clips.

✔ Quick Check

2. Choose a reasonable estimate. Explain your choice.

a. distance between two cities: 50 mm or 50 km
b. amount of liquid that an eyedropper holds: 10 mL or 10 L

2 Converting Metric Units

The metric system uses a decimal system to relate different units to each other. Look at the metric-units chart below. The units highlighted in yellow are the units most often used. From left to right, each unit is 10 times the size of the unit before it.

	milli-	centi-	deci-	UNIT	deka-	hecto-	kilo-
Length	millimeter (mm)	centimeter (cm)	decimeter (dm)	meter (m)	dekameter (dam)	hectometer (hm)	kilometer (km)
Capacity	milliliter (mL)	centiliter (cL)	deciliter (dL)	liter (L)	dekaliter (daL)	hectoliter (hL)	kiloliter (kL)
Mass	milligram (mg)	centigram (cg)	decigram (dg)	gram (g)	dekagram (dag)	hectogram (hg)	kilogram (kg)

You can convert from one unit to another by multiplying or dividing by 10; 100; 1,000; and so on.

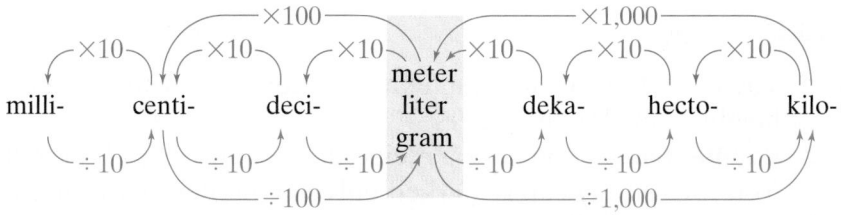

Vocabulary Tip

The prefixes, such as *milli*, *centi*, and *deci*, denote the relative sizes of the units.

To convert from one unit to another in the metric system, find the relationship between the two units.

Remember:

• Multiply if you are going from a larger unit to a smaller unit since there will be more of the smaller units.

• Divide if you are going from a smaller unit to a larger unit since there will be fewer of the larger units.

GO▶for Help

For a guide to multiplying and dividing decimals by powers of ten, see Skills Handbook, page 772.

3 EXAMPLE   **Converting Between Metric Units**

Mental Math   **Complete each statement.**

a. 4.35 L = ■ mL

$4.35 \cdot 1{,}000 = 4{,}350$ **To convert liters to milliliters, multiply by 1,000.**

$4.35 \text{ L} = 4{,}350 \text{ mL}$

b. 914 cm = ■ m

$914 \div 100 = 9.14$ **To convert centimeters to meters, divide by 100.**

$914 \text{ cm} = 9.14 \text{ m}$

✓ Quick Check

3. Complete each statement.

  a. 35 mL = ■ L   **b.** ■ g = 250 kg   **c.** ■ cm = 60 m

Real-World 🌐 Connection

The ancient city of Machu Picchu (c. 1450–1550) is located in Peru's Andes Mountains. It is one of the few major pre-Columbian sites found nearly intact.

4 EXAMPLE   **Real-World 🌐 Problem Solving**

Geography   **The ancient Incan city of Machu Picchu is located in Peru. Its altitude is about 2,300 m above sea level. What is Machu Picchu's altitude in kilometers?**

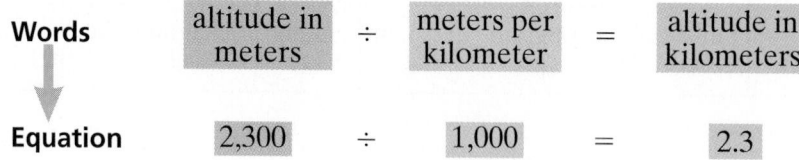

Words	altitude in meters	÷	meters per kilometer	=	altitude in kilometers
Equation	2,300	÷	1,000	=	2.3

Machu Picchu is about 2.3 km above sea level.

✓ Quick Check

4. a. The record for the highest a kite has flown is 3.8 km. Find the height of the kite in meters.

  b. Number Sense   You have a recipe that requires 0.25 L of milk. Your measuring cup is marked only in milliliters. How many milliliters of milk do you need?

EXERCISES

For more exercises, see *Extra Skill and Word Problem Practice*.

Practice and Problem Solving

A Practice by Example

Example 1
(page 158)

GO for Help

Match each quantity with an appropriate metric unit. Explain your choice.

1. length of your thumb
2. mass of a book
3. length of a soccer field
4. amount of water in a fishbowl
5. mass of an eraser
6. amount of fluid in a straw

A. gram
B. meter
C. centimeter
D. milliliter
E. liter
F. kilogram

Example 2
(page 159)

Choose a reasonable estimate. Explain your choice.

7. the mass of a small dog: 5 g or 5 kg
8. amount of liquid you should drink daily: 2,000 mL or 2,000 L
9. the mass of a box of cereal: 350 mg or 350 g

Example 3
(page 160)

Mental Math Complete each statement.

10. $54 \text{ m} = \blacksquare \text{ cm}$
11. $\blacksquare \text{ L} = 234 \text{ mL}$
12. $12 \text{ g} = \blacksquare \text{ kg}$
13. $\blacksquare \text{ m} = 3.01 \text{ km}$
14. $0.25 \text{ m} = \blacksquare \text{ cm}$
15. $\blacksquare \text{ mL} = 7.3 \text{ L}$
16. $595 \text{ g} = \blacksquare \text{ kg}$
17. $35 \text{ m} = \blacksquare \text{ km}$
18. $\blacksquare \text{ mg} = 0.27 \text{ g}$

Example 4
(page 160)

19. **Geography** Elgin Street, in Bacup, England, is the shortest street in the world. It is 518 cm long. How many meters long is it?

20. **Biology** A shrew, the mammal with the fastest metabolism, has a mass of only 0.004 kg. What is its mass in grams?

B Apply Your Skills

Choose an appropriate metric unit of measure. Explain your choice.

21. mass of a banana
22. depth of Lake Michigan
23. length of a small calculator
24. mass of a car
25. width of a highway
26. quantity of water in a spoon

27. **Error Analysis** One of the world's largest pearls had a mass of 6,392 g. Camille wrote in her report that the pearl had a mass of 6,392,000 kg. What was her error?

28. **Multiple Choice** The world's longest model train has 650 cars and is 0.695 km long. Which expression could you use to find how many meters long the train is?
    Ⓐ $650 \div 0.695$
    Ⓑ $0.695 \div 650$
    Ⓒ $0.695 \times 1,000$
    Ⓓ $695 \times 1,000$

Write the metric unit that makes each statement true.

29. $9.03 \text{ m} = 9,030 \blacksquare$
30. $890 \text{ cm} = 8.9 \blacksquare$
31. $130,000 \blacksquare = 1.3 \text{ km}$

32. Earth Science The flow of water over Niagara Falls averages 6,008,835,000 mL/s.
   a. On the average, about how many liters of water flow over Niagara Falls each second?
   b. About how many liters flow over the falls in a minute?

Estimation **Choose a reasonable estimate. Explain your choice.**

33. the width of a sidewalk: 150 cm or 150 m

34. the length of 24 city blocks: 2 m or 2 km

35. the mass of a thumbtack: 1 mg or 1 g

Mental Math **Complete each statement.**

36. $90,050 \text{ mL} = \blacksquare \text{ L}$ **37.** $\blacksquare \text{ m} = 875 \text{ cm}$ **38.** $620 \text{ m} = \blacksquare \text{ km}$

39. $9,120 \text{ mg} = \blacksquare \text{ g}$ **40.** $900 \text{ km} = \blacksquare \text{ m}$ **41.** $5 \text{ g} = \blacksquare \text{ kg}$

42. $\blacksquare \text{ cm} = 13 \text{ km}$ **43.** $301 \text{ kg} = \blacksquare \text{ mg}$ **44.** $\blacksquare \text{ km} = 562,300 \text{ cm}$

45. Nutrition A world-record grapefruit had a mass of 3,068 g. What was its mass in kilograms?

46. Zoology A hippopotamus is so large that it has a stomach 304.8 cm long, yet it is agile enough to outrun a human. How long is the stomach of a hippopotamus in meters?

Number Sense **Match each measurement with its equivalent measurement from the table.**

47. 0.015 km   **48.** 1,500 cm   **49.** 150,000 mg

50. 0.15 L   **51.** 15 L   **52.** 1,500 g

A. 15,000 mL	**B.** 150 cm	**C.** 150 g
D. 1.5 kg	**E.** 15 m	**F.** 150 mL
G. 150 kg	**H.** 0.15 mL	**I.** 1,500 mm

53. Marine Biology The blue whale is the largest of all known animals. The largest known blue whale measured 33.58 meters in length.
   a. How many millimeters long was this whale?
   b. How many kilometers long was this whale?

Challenge **54. Writing in Math** The prefix kilo- means "one thousand," and the prefix milli- means "one thousandth." What do the prefixes tell you about kilometer and kilogram, and milliliter and milligram?

55. Physical Fitness You walk about 3 mi/h.
   a. Approximately how many kilometers can you walk in an hour?
   b. How many meters can you walk in an hour?

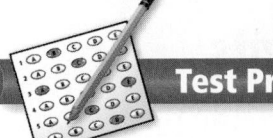

Gridded Reponse

56. The albatross has a wingspan of 3,350 mm, the largest wingspan of any bird. What is the wingspan of an albatross in meters?

57. How many milliseconds are in one second?

58. A worm is about 143 mm long. What is the length of the worm in centimeters?

59. A pitcher threw a baseball 95 mi/h at a baseball game. Rounded to the nearest foot, how many feet per second is this?

60. Sean tries to drink $2\frac{1}{2}$ qt of water every day. How many gallons does he average in a week?

Mixed Review

for Help

Lesson 3-6 **61. Knot Tying** Clinton Bailey, Sr., holds the record for knot tying. He tied six different rope knots in 8.1 s. Write and solve an equation to find his average time per knot.

Lesson 3-2 **Estimate each product or quotient.**

62. $28.134 \div 3.75$ **63.** $8.517 \cdot 9.82$ **64.** $101.49 \div 9.51$

Lessons 2-9 and 2-10 **Solve each inequality.**

65. $a - 5 \geq 16$ **66.** $n + 8 < -7$ **67.** $-3r \leq 21$

✓ Checkpoint Quiz 2   Lessons 3-5 through 3-7

Solve each equation.

1. $0.5m = 0.125$ **2.** $d \div 0.3 = 28.5$ **3.** $y - 135.43 = -5.43$

4. $12.2 = 4x$ **5.** $29.25 = 4.5w$ **6.** $k + 870.9 = 1{,}000.5$

Choose the most reasonable estimate. Explain your choice.

7. height of a standard house window: 1.5 cm or 1.5 m

8. capacity of a shampoo bottle: 500 mL or 500 L

Complete each statement.

9. 95 mL = ■ L   **10.** ■ cm = 76.5 km

11. ■ km = 675 m   **12.** 7.1 kg = ■ g

13. Horses The world's smallest horse had a mass of only 9.1 kg. What was the mass of the horse in grams?

Extension

Precision and Significant Digits

For Use With Lesson 3-7

The pin at the right measures about 5 cm. A more precise measurement is 4.5 cm. An even more precise measurement is 46 mm. The smaller the units on the scale of a measuring instrument, the more precise the measurement is.

1 EXAMPLE

Choose the more precise measurement.

a. 5 g or 8 mg
Since a milligram is a smaller unit of measure than a gram, 8 mg is more precise than 5 g.

b. 2.72 m or 3.5 m
A hundredth of a meter is a smaller unit of measure than a tenth of a meter. So 2.72 m is more precise than 3.5 m.

A calculation will be only as precise as the least precise measurement used in the calculation. So, round your results to match the precision of the least precise measurement.

2 EXAMPLE

Add the lengths 6.31 m, 5.447 m, and 2.8 m.

$6.31 + 5.447 + 2.8 = 14.557$ **The least precise measurement**
is 2.8 m. Round the sum to the
Rounded to tenths ≈ 14.6 m   **nearest tenth of a meter.**

Digits that represent an actual measurement are *significant digits*. Nonzero digits (1–9) are always significant. The rules below will help you decide whether a zero is a significant digit.

Type of Number	Which Zeros Are Significant	Example
decimal numbers between 0 and 1	Zeros to the left of *all* the nonzero digits are not significant. All other zeros are significant.	significant digits 0.006040 not significant digits
positive integers	Zeros to the right of *all* the nonzero digits are not significant (unless specifically known to be). Zeros between nonzero digits are significant.	significant digits 203,400 not significant digits
noninteger decimal numbers greater than 1	All zeros are significant.	significant digits 350.07050

164 Extension Precision and Significant Digits

3 EXAMPLE

How many significant digits are in 0.0504 m?

The 5 and the 4 are significant. The zero between them is significant.
The other zeros are not significant. There are three significant digits.

When you multiply or divide measurements, round your answer to match the least number of significant digits in the problem.

4 EXAMPLE

A plot for a new house measures 152.6 m by 121 m. What is the area of the plot? Use significant digits.

$\boxed{}$ **3 significant digits**

$152.6 \cdot 121 = 18{,}464.6$ ⟵ **Multiply.**

$\boxed{}$ **4 significant digits**

The area is $18{,}500 \text{ m}^2$. ⟵ **Round the area to 3 significant digits.**

EXERCISES

Choose the more precise measurement.

1. 3 m or 5.2 m   **2.** 8 mL or 9.5 L   **3.** 1.89 km or 8.7 cm   **4.** 1.9 kg or 1.87 kg

5. Error Analysis Your friend says that 4.35 km is more precise than 5.2 cm because a hundredths unit is a smaller unit than a tenths unit. What mistake did your friend make?

Find each sum or difference. Round to the place value of the less precise measurement.

6. 5.6 g + 8 g   **7.** 8.35 kg + 6.2 kg   **8.** 8.2 km − 1.75 km   **9.** 9 cm − 2.3 cm

Determine the number of significant digits in each measurement.

10. 0.069 m   **11.** 100.5 L   **12.** 3,400 kL   **13.** 5.2100 km

Find each product or quotient. Use significant digits.

14. 1,234 in. · 31 in.   **15.** 0.0702 ft · 227 ft   **16.** 16,250 m ÷ 14.5 s   **17.** 132.5 cm · 43.2 cm

Act It Out

What You'll Learn

• To solve problems by acting them out

. . . And Why

To solve real-world problems involving motion

 **Check Skills You'll Need**

Write a rule for each number pattern. Find the next three numbers in the pattern.

1. $0, 6, 12, 18, \ldots$

2. $-18, -9, 0, 9, \ldots$

3. $0, 2, 1, 3, 2, 4, 3, \ldots$

4. $7, 6, 8, 7, 9, 8, 10, \ldots$

GO for Help
Lesson 1-7

Math Strategies in Action
Have you ever wondered how public speakers manage to talk to large audiences in a relaxed manner? Many public speakers brainstorm their topic ahead of time. Then they act out their speech by practicing in front of a mirror. You can *Act It Out* to solve math problems. Here is a well-known problem that can be solved by acting it out.

1 EXAMPLE **Real-World Problem Solving**

A snail is trying to escape from a well 10 ft deep. The snail can climb 2 ft each day, but each night it slides back 1 ft. How many days will the snail take to climb out of the well?

Understand the Problem

A snail needs to climb 10 ft to escape from a well. It can climb 2 ft per day. At night the snail slides back 1 ft.

1. How far up the well will the snail be after the first day and the first night?

2. How far up the well will the snail be after the second day?

3. How far up the well will the snail be after the second day and the second night?

Make a Plan

At first you might think that the snail progresses 1 ft each day and will therefore take 10 days to escape. This answer is wrong, however, because it leaves out an important part of the problem.

To act out the problem, stand up and follow these steps:

- Move forward two steps to *simulate*, or model, the snail's climb during the day.
- Then move backward one step to simulate the snail's slide back during the night.

Carry Out the Plan

Act out the problem, keeping track of your progress in a table like the one below.

Time	Progress
Day 1	Up 2 ft from bottom
Night 1	Up 1 ft from bottom
Day 2	Up 3 ft from bottom

4. Copy and complete the table, acting out the rest of the problem. How many days will it take for the snail to make it out of the 10-ft well?

Check the Answer

You can check whether your answer is reasonable by drawing a diagram.

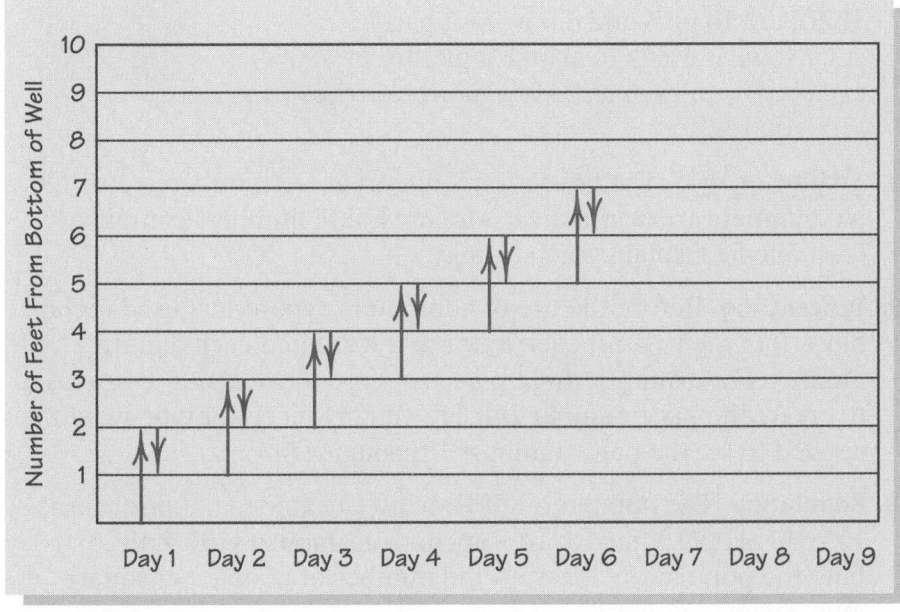

✓ Quick Check

5. Copy and complete the diagram to check your answer.

EXERCISES

For more exercises, see *Extra Skill and Word Problem Practice*.

Practice and Problem Solving

A Practice by Example

Example 1
(page 166)

GO for Help

Solve by acting out each problem.

1. **Sports** In a tennis tournament, each athlete plays one match against each of the other athletes. There are 12 athletes scheduled to play in the tournament. How many matches will be played?

2. **Fencing** A rancher wants to build a fence for a square lot with dimensions of 50 yd by 50 yd. He wants to install a fence post every 5 yd with a post at each corner. How many fence posts will he need?

3. **Elections** Four candidates run for president of the student council. Three other candidates run for vice-president. In how many different ways can the two offices be filled?

B Apply Your Skills

Strategies

- Act It Out
- Draw a Diagram
- Guess, Check, Revise
- Look for a Pattern
- Make a Model
- Make a Table
- Simulate the Problem
- Solve by Graphing
- Use Multiple Strategies
- Work a Simpler Problem
- Work Backward
- Write an Equation
- Write a Proportion

Solve using any strategy.

4. The school store buys pencils for $.20 each. It sells the pencils for $.25 each. How much profit does the store make if it sells five dozen pencils?

5. **Construction** To accommodate a wheelchair, a builder installed countertops that are 0.75 ft lower than the original ones. The new countertops are 2.5 ft high. How high were the original countertops?

6. What is the total number of squares in the figure at the right?

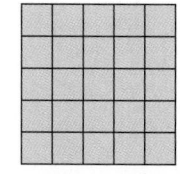

7. There are 10 girls and 8 boys at a party. A cartoonist wants to sketch a picture of each boy with each girl. How many sketches are required?

8. **Writing in Math** The houses on your street are numbered 1 to 120. No numbers are skipped. How many house numbers contain at least one 5? Explain your strategy.

9. **Typesetting** Before the use of computers, typesetters used metal pieces of type to print each letter in a word and each digit in a number. For example, three pieces of type—1, 4, and 8—were used to create the page number 148. How many pieces of type would be needed to set the page numbers 1 through 476?

C Challenge

10. **Population** The population of Rancho Cucamonga, California, is 151,640 people. The area of Rancho Cucamonga is 37.4 mi^2. Find the population density—the number of people per square mile. Show your work.

11. **Seating Arrangements** Ana, Brian, Carla, David, and Eric are friends. They go to a movie but cannot find five seats together. They have to split up into a group of three and a group of two. How many different ways can the friends organize themselves into these two groups?

GO Online

Homework Video Tutor

Visit: PHSchool.com
Web Code: ade-0308

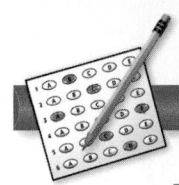

Test Prep

Multiple Choice What is the solution of each equation?

12. $x - 8 = -4.8$

  A. −12.8   **B.** −3.2   **C.** 3.2   **D.** 12.8

13. $8 + c = -2.3$

  F. −10.3   **G.** −5.7   **H.** 5.7   **J.** 10.3

14. $7.53 = -0.3y$

  A. 25.1   **B.** 2.26   **C.** −2.26   **D.** −25.1

Short Response **15.** A corral is ringed by 60 ft of fencing with posts every 4 ft. How many fence posts are there? Show your work.

Mixed Review

Lesson 3-7 **Measurement** **Complete each statement.**

16. 27 cm = ■ m   **17.** 5,200 km = ■ m   **18.** 2,000 mg = ■ g

19. 0.5 L = ■ mL   **20.** 3 m = ■ cm   **21.** 6 kg = ■ mg

Lesson 3-3 **22.** **Test Scores** Your test scores so far this semester are 100, 90, 82, 96, and 78. You have one more 100-point test to take. Including the last test, what is your highest possible average?

Lesson 3-1 **Estimate using front-end estimation.**

23. $9.54 + $1.25   **24.** $6.72 + $5.28   **25.** $12.19 + $5.66

Math at Work

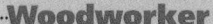

Woodworker

Woodworkers cut, shape, assemble, and finish wood to create tables, chairs, and other types of furniture. To create these items, woodworkers must plan and carry out many individual steps in sequence.

Machines used in professional woodworking shops cut and shape wood with great precision. The most sophisticated machines are controlled by computer programs. Woodworkers can enhance their skills by taking mathematics and computer courses that develop their ability to think three-dimensionally.

Go Online
PHSchool.com **For:** Information about woodworkers
Web Code: adb-2031

An extended-response question can be worth as many as four points. It often has multiple parts. To get full credit, you need to answer each part and show all of your work or justify your thinking.

EXAMPLE

To get a 90 for this grading period, Jerilyn needs a test average of 94.5. She had a 93.2 average on her first three tests and scored 97 on the fourth test. **(a)** Explain in words how to find the next score she needs. **(b)** Write an equation to find the fifth test score. **(c)** Solve your equation.

Here are three responses with the points each received.

4 points	3 points	1 point
There are 5 tests. For a test average of 94.5, the sum of the test scores must be 5 times 94.5, or 472.5 points.	There are 5 tests. For a test average of 94.5, the sum of the test scores must be 5 times 94.5, or 472.5 points.	Let g = grade on fifth test. $93.2 + 97 + g = 90$
Let g = grade on fifth test.	Let g = grade on fifth test.	$190.2 + g = 90$
$3(93.2) + 97 + g = 472.5$	$3(93.2) + 97 + g = 472.5$	$g = 90 - 190.2$
$376.6 + g = 472.5$	$276.9 + 97 + g = 472.5$	$g = 100.2$
$g = 472.5 - 376.6$	$373.9 + g = 472.5$	
$g = 95.9$	$g = 472.5 - 373.9$	
Jerilyn must score 95.9 or higher on her fifth test.	$g = 98.6$	
	Jerilyn must score 98.6.	

The 4-point response shows the work and gives a written answer to the problem. Note that it identifies the variable before writing the equation. The 3-point response contains a computational error, but the student completed all parts. The 1-point response shows an incorrect equation, and it does not explain the process.

EXERCISES

Use the Example above to do each exercise.

1. **Error Analysis** What is the error in the 3-point response?

2. Write a possible 2-point response for the problem. Explain why it is worth 2 points.

Chapter Review

Vocabulary Review

compatible numbers (p. 135)
formula (p. 145)

mean (p. 139)
measures of central tendency (p. 139)

median (p. 139)
mode (p. 139)
outlier (p. 140)

perimeter (p. 146)
range (p. 139)

Choose the vocabulary word that completes each sentence.

1. The sum of a group of data items divided by the number of data items is the   ? .

2. Numbers that are easy to divide are called   ? .

3. The data item that occurs most often in a group is the   ? .

4. A data item that is much greater or much less than the rest of the data items in a group is a(n)   ? .

5. When an odd number of data items are written in order, the middle item is the   ? .

6. An equation that shows a relationship between quantities that are represented by variables is a(n)   ? .

7. Numbers that describe groups of data items are called   ? .

8. The distance around a figure is the   ? .

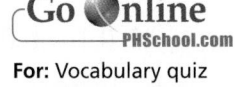

Go Online
PHSchool.com

For: Vocabulary quiz
Web Code: adj-0351

Skills and Concepts

3-1 Objectives

▼ To round decimals (p. 129)

▼ To estimate sums and differences (p. 130)

You can estimate the sum of decimals by rounding, front-end estimating, or clustering.

You can estimate the difference of decimals by rounding.

Estimate each sum or difference. State which method you used.

9. $3.14 + 6.952$

10. $10.2538 - 6.095$

11. $14.451 + 9.736$

12. $14.27 - 4.268$

13. $20.681 + 19.39 + 20.56$

14. $12.814 - 6.3791$

15. $9.0426 + 2.7182$

16. $21.9384 - 15.639$

17. $6.257 + 6.129 + 6.34$

18. $19.83 - 14.268$

19. Explain when you would use each estimation method named above to estimate a sum of decimals. Use examples.

20. **Weather** Last year Lake Jones rose to 672.42 feet during the spring floods. This year Lake Jones rose to 711.36 feet. About how much higher did the lake rise this year?

3-2 Objectives

▼ To estimate products (p. 134)

▼ To estimate quotients (p. 135)

You can estimate a product by rounding. You can estimate a quotient of two decimals by using **compatible numbers.**

Estimate each product or quotient.

21. 8.15(6.04) **22.** 19.28 ÷ 5.439 **23.** 1.9 · 4.92

24. 25.1 ÷ 4.87 **25.** 12.497 · 0.894 **26.** 59.3581 ÷ 11.5304

27. 3.59(−2.3291) **28.** −17.45 ÷ 3.059 **29.** (−2.0936)(−5.6892)

3-3 Objectives

▼ To find mean, median, mode, and range of a set of data (p. 139)

▼ To choose the best measure of central tendency (p. 141)

You can use a **measure of central tendency** to describe a collection of data. The **mean** is the sum of the data items divided by the number of data items. The **median** is the middle value or the mean of the two middle values when the data are written in order. The **mode** is the data item that occurs most often. The **range** is the difference between the greatest and least values in a data set. An **outlier** is a data item that is much greater or much less than the rest of the data items.

Find the mean, median, and mode. When an answer is not an integer, round to the nearest tenth. Identify any outliers.

30. 2, 3, 6, 2, 8, 9, 5, 10, 4, 5 **31.** 16.1, 16.3, 15.9, 16.2, 16.3, 16.3, 15.8

32. 32, 35, 31, 57, 33, 30, 34 **33.** 0.1, 7.9, 0.2, 0.3, 0.1, 0.2, 0.1, 0.1, 0.3

Which measure of central tendency best describes each situation? Explain.

34. the favorite radio stations of teenagers in your neighborhood

35. the numbers of videos owned by students in your class

36. the prices of 8-oz containers of yogurt at six local grocery stores

3-4 Objectives

▼ To substitute into formulas (p. 145)

▼ To use the formula for the perimeter of a rectangle (p. 146)

A **formula** is an equation that shows a relationship between quantities that are represented by variables. You can use formulas to find such things as **perimeter,** area, and distance.

Evaluate each formula for the values given.

37. distance: $d = rt$
when $r = 35$ mi/h and
$t = 2$ h

38. area of a rectangle: $A = \ell w$
when $\ell = 16$ mm and
$w = 24$ mm

39. Circumference: $C = 2\pi r$
when $r = 6$ in. Use 3.14 for π.

40. perimeter of a square: $P = 4s$
when $s = 13$ cm

3-5 and 3-6 Objectives

▼ To solve one-step decimal equations involving subtraction (p. 150)

▼ To solve one-step decimal equations involving addition (p. 151)

▼ To solve one-step decimal equations involving division (p. 154)

▼ To solve one-step decimal equations involving multiplication (p. 155)

To solve a one-step equation, use an inverse operation and a property of equality to get the variable alone on one side of the equation.

Solve each equation.

41. $n + 3.8 = 10.9$ **42.** $y - 6.72 = 2.53$ **43.** $h + 0.67 = -1.34$

44. $t - 2.7 = 23.5$ **45.** $12.9 + x = 3.8$ **46.** $5.7 = b - 4.9$

47. $6.3m = 15.75$ **48.** $a \div 4.9 = 8.33$ **49.** $v \cdot 7.1 = 80.23$

50. $c \div 12.5 = 77.5$ **51.** $-5.7z = 110.58$ **52.** $d \div 4.75 = -38.95$

53. Finance On Monday a stock is worth $3.20 per share. By Friday the stock is worth $2.64 per share.
   a. Write an equation to model the change in price.
   b. Solve the equation to find the amount by which the price changed.

3-7 Objectives

▼ To identify appropriate metric measures (p. 158)

▼ To convert metric units (p. 159)

The **metric system** of measurement uses a decimal system to relate units to one another. To measure, you must choose an appropriate unit of measure.

Choose an appropriate metric unit of measure. Explain each choice.

54. height of a building **55.** mass of a bicycle **56.** amount of milk in a glass

Mental Math Complete each statement.

57. $0.85 \text{ m} = \blacksquare \text{ cm}$ **58.** $160 \text{ mL} = \blacksquare \text{ L}$ **59.** $2.3 \text{ m} = \blacksquare \text{ cm}$

60. $1.6 \text{ kg} = \blacksquare \text{ g}$ **61.** $0.62 \text{ L} = \blacksquare \text{ mL}$ **62.** $80 \text{ g} = \blacksquare \text{ kg}$

63. Explain why centimeters would be an inappropriate unit to measure the height of a mature oak tree.

3-8 Objectives

▼ To solve problems by acting them out (p. 166)

You can solve some problems by acting them out.

64. School Mike, Don, Tameka, and Rosa sit in the four desks in the last row of desks. Each day they sit in a different order. How many days can they do this before they repeat a seating pattern?

65. Recreation You are hiking with three friends. You pass a group of six hikers going the other way. Each person in one group greets each person in the other group. How many greetings are there? Explain.

Chapter Test

Go Online
PHSchool.com
For: Chapter test
Web Code: ada-0352

Estimate each value.

1. $6.43 - 4.079$ 2. $2.06 + 3.91$

3. $5.97 - 1.674$ 4. $6.025 + 0.35$

5. $8.54 + 2.3$ 6. $6.25 \cdot 9.87$

7. $12.89 \div 3.04$ 8. $1.76 \cdot 3.93$

9. $4.96 \div 2.49$ 10. $3.2 \cdot 14.69$

Find the mean, median, mode, and range. When an answer is not an integer, round to the nearest tenth. Identify any outliers.

11. $11, 12, 9, 13, 10, 12, 11, 14, 12$

12. $5.3, 5.6, 5.2, 5.0, 5.4, 5.6, 5.1, 5.0$

13. $10.6, 9.8, 11.6, 29.1, 3.4, 11.4, 12.7$

14. $8.7, 8.5, 8.7, 8.5, 8.6, 8.5, 8.7, 8.6$

Evaluate each formula for the given values.

15. area of a rectangle: $A = \ell w$
    when $\ell = 3.8$ in. and $w = 1.5$ in.

16. perimeter of a square: $P = 4s$
    when $s = 4.7$ cm

17. perimeter of a rectangle: $P = 2\ell + 2w$
    when $\ell = 2.9$ m and $w = 6.05$ m

Solve each equation.

18. $x + 7.8 = 12.5$

19. $n - 5.9 = 0.5$

20. $4.1 + c = -1.2$

21. $d - 6.3 = 11$

22. $-9.7 + h = 10.3$

23. $m \div 2.7 = 14.58$

24. $h \cdot 4.7 = 30.55$

25. $b \div (-7.8) = -79.56$

26. $-3.4t = 30.94$

Write an appropriate metric unit of measure for each quantity.

27. the height of a truck

28. the capacity of a standard shampoo bottle

29. the mass of a pineapple

30. the width of a paperback book

Complete.

31. 4.5 m = ▪ cm   32. 68 mL = ▪ L

33. 90 kg = ▪ g   34. $6,700$ cm = ▪ m

35. 4 L = ▪ mL   36. 50.2 g = ▪ kg

For Exercises 37 and 38, write an equation, and then solve.

37. **Shopping** You spend $6.50 on a pair of gloves. You now have $7.00. How much money did you have originally?

38. **Reptiles** The fastest speed recorded for a reptile on land is 9.7 m/s for a spiny-tailed iguana. At this rate, how long would it take this iguana to travel 116.4 m?

39. **Geography** Madrid and Barcelona are cities in Spain. The distance between them is 636,000 m. What is this in kilometers?

40. **Mechanics** A mechanical toy on a circular track goes forward 3 in. and then backward 2 in. How many moves does the toy take to complete one 15-in. revolution of the track?

41. **Data Analysis** Which measure of central tendency best describes the weights of the dogs in one neighborhood?

    15 lb, 20 lb, 18 lb, 27 lb, 15 lb, 70 lb

    A. mean   B. median
    C. mode   D. all of the above

42. **Writing in Math** Explain how the outlier in the data set affects the mean.

    $3, 2, 6, 3, 5, 4, 15, 4, 3$

Variables, Function Patterns, and Graphs

◀》 Key Vocabulary

- absolute value (p. 196)
- coordinates (p. 200)
- domain (p. 205)
- equation (p. 181)
- exponent (p. 185)
- function (p. 203)
- independent variable (p. 204)
- integers (p. 193)
- irrational numbers (p. 194)
- mean (p. 216)
- order of operations (p. 186)
- ordered pair (p. 200)
- origin (p. 200)
- positive correlation (p. 210)
- rational numbers (p. 193)
- real numbers (p. 194)
- scatter plot (p. 209)
- stem-and-leaf plot (p. 218)
- variable (p. 180)

What You'll Learn Next

- In this chapter, you will use variables to transform English phrases into mathematical expressions.

- You will use the order of operations to simplify expressions.

- You will explore function rules and learn to identify relationships within functions.

Data Analysis   **Activity Lab** You will use box-and-whisker plots to analyze and display data, on pages 228–229.

Using Variables

✓ Check Skills You'll Need

GO for Help Skills Handbook page 789

Estimate to find whether each answer is reasonable.

1.	**2.**	**3.**	**4.**
$154.38	478.23	76.425	$316.24
22.45	−199.30	18.94	− 48.76
276.12	378.93	182.6	$267.48
+28.98		+54.769	
$481.93		232.729	

◄))) New Vocabulary • variable • algebraic expression • equation • open sentence

---

1 Modeling Relationships With Variables

Vocabulary Tip

Each expression below means 6.50 multiplied by h.

$6.50 \times h$

$6.50 \cdot h$

$6.50(h)$

$(6.50)h$

$6.50h$

$(6.50)(h)$

If you earn an hourly wage of $6.50, your pay is the number of hours you work multiplied by 6.50.

In the table at the right, the variable h stands for the number of hours you worked. A **variable** is a symbol, usually a letter, that represents one or more numbers. The expression $6.50h$ is an algebraic expression. An **algebraic expression** is a mathematical phrase that can include numbers, variables, and operation symbols. Algebraic expressions are sometimes called variable expressions.

Hours Worked	Pay (dollars)
1	6.50×1
2	6.50×2
3	6.50×3
h	$6.50 \times h$

1 EXAMPLE   Writing an Algebraic Expression

Write an algebraic expression for each phrase.

a. seven more than n

$n + 7$ "More than" indicates addition. Add the first number 7 to the second number n.

b. the difference of n and 7

$n - 7$ "Difference" indicates subtraction. Begin with the first number n. Then subtract the second number 7.

c. the product of seven and n

$7n$ "Product" indicates multiplication. Multiply the first number 7 by the second number n.

d. the quotient of n and seven

$\frac{n}{7}$ "Quotient" indicates division. Divide the first number n by the second number 7.

✓ **Quick Check** ❶ Write an algebraic expression for each phrase.
   a. the quotient of 4.2 and c **b.** t minus 15

To translate an English phrase into an algebraic expression, you may need to define one or more variables first.

 **EXAMPLE** **Writing an Algebraic Expression**

Define a variable and write an algebraic expression for each phrase.
a. two times a number plus 5

| **Relate** | two times | a number | plus 5 |

| **Define** | Let n = the number. |

| **Write** | 2 | · | n | + | 5 |

$2n + 5$

Problem Solving Hint

In math, you write the phrase "seven less than twelve" as $12 - 7$. The order of the numbers in the math phrase is different than the order of the numbers in the English phrase.

b. 7 less than three times a number

| **Relate** | 7 | less than | three times | a number |

| **Define** | Let a = the number. |

| **Write** | 3 | · | a | − | 7 |

$3a - 7$

 **Quick Check** ❷ Define a variable and write an algebraic expression for each phrase.
a. 9 less than a number   **b.** the sum of twice a number and 31

---

2 | **Modeling Relationships With Equations**

An **equation** is a mathematical sentence that uses an equal sign. If an equation is true, then the two expressions on either side of the equal sign represent the same value. An equation that contains one or more variables is an **open sentence.** In everyday language, the word "is" suggests an equal sign in the associated equation.

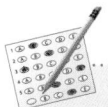

Test-Taking Tip

When choosing the best equation, test your answer. In Example 3, three CDs cost $36. Only answer D gives $36 when $n = 3$.

❸ EXAMPLE **Writing an Equation**

Multiple Choice Track One Media sells all CDs for $12 each. Which equation best represents the cost c of a given number n of CDs?

Ⓐ $12 + c = n$ Ⓑ $n + 12 = c$ Ⓒ $12c = n$ Ⓓ $c = 12n$

| **Relate** | The total cost | is | $12 | times | the number of CDs bought. |

| **Define** | Let n = the number of CDs bought. |
| | Let c = the total cost. |

| **Write** | c | = | 12 | · | n |

The equation is $c = 12n$, so D is the correct answer.

 **Quick Check** ❸ **a.** Suppose the manager at Track One Media raises the price of each CD to $15. Write an equation to find the cost of n CDs.
b. **Critical Thinking** Suppose the manager at Track One Media uses the equation $c = 10.99n$. What could this mean?

When you write an equation for data in a table, it may help to write a short sentence describing the relationship between the data. Then translate the sentence into an equation. Be sure to tell what each variable represents.

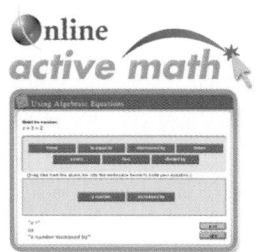

For: Equation Activity
Use: Interactive Textbook, 1-1

4 EXAMPLE Real-World Problem Solving

Sales Write an equation for the data in the table.

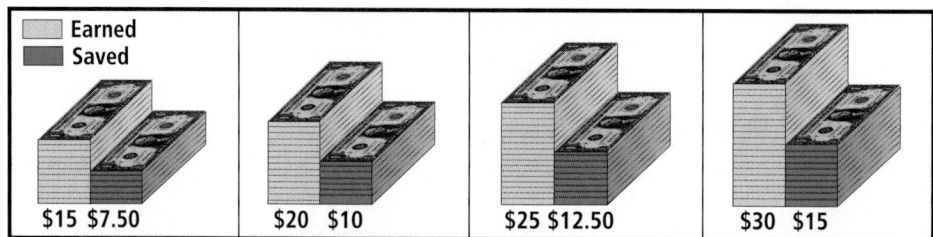

Relate   change   equals $20.00 minus   cost.

Define   Let c = cost of item purchased.

Let a = amount of change.

Write a =   20   − c

• $a = 20 - c$

Cost of Purchase	Change From $20
$20.00	$0
$19.00	$1.00
$17.50	$2.50
$11.59	$8.41

✓ **Quick Check**   4 Write an equation for the data in the table.

Amounts Earned and Saved

☐ Earned
■ Saved

$15 $7.50 $20 $10 $25 $12.50 $30 $15

EXERCISES

For more exercises, see *Extra Skill and Word Problem Practice.*

Practice and Problem Solving

 Practice by Example

Example 1
(page 180)

GO for Help

Write an algebraic expression for each phrase.

1. 4 more than p

2. y minus 12

3. 12 minus m

4. the product of 15 and c

5. the quotient of n and 8

6. the quotient of 17 and k

7. 23 less than x

8. the sum of v and 3

Example 2
(page 181)

Define a variable and write an expression for each phrase.

9. 2 more than twice a number

10. a number minus 11

11. 9 minus a number

12. a number divided by 82

13. the product of 5 and a number

14. the sum of 13 and twice a number

15. the quotient of a number and 6

16. the quotient of 11 and a number

Example 3
(page 181)

Define variables and write an equation to model each situation.

17. The total cost is the number of cans times $.70.

18. The perimeter of a square equals 4 times the length of a side.

19. The total length of rope, in feet, used to put up tents is 60 times the number of tents.

20. What is the number of slices of pizza left from an 8-slice pizza after you have eaten some slices?

Example 4
(page 182)

Define variables and write an equation to model the relationship in each table.

21.

Number of Workers	Number of Radios Built
1	13
2	26
3	39
4	52

22.

Number of Tapes	Cost
1	$8.50
2	$17.00
3	$25.50
4	$34.00

23.

Number of Sales	Total Earnings
5	$2.00
10	$4.00
15	$6.00
20	$8.00

24.

Number of Hours	Total Pay
4	$32
6	$48
8	$64
10	$80

Ⓑ Apply Your Skills

Write an expression for each phrase.

25. the sum of 9 and k minus 17

26. 6.7 more than 5 times n

27. 9.85 less than the product of 37 and t

28. the quotient of $3b$ and 4.5

29. 15 plus the quotient of 60 and w

30. 7 minus the product of v and 3

31. the product of 5 and m, minus the quotient of t and 7

32. the sum of the quotient of p and 14, and the quotient of q and 3

33. 8 minus the product of 9 and r

GO ⬤nline
Homework Video Tutor
Visit: PHSchool.com
Web Code: ate-0101

Write a phrase for each expression.

34. $q + 5$ **35.** $3 - t$ **36.** $9n + 1$ **37.** $\frac{y}{5}$ **38.** $7hb$

Define variables and write an equation to model the relationship in each table.

39.

Number of Days	Change in Height (meters)
1	0.165
2	0.330
3	0.495
4	0.660

40.

Time (months)	Length (inches)
1	4.1
2	8.2
3	12.3
4	16.4

41. Use the table at the right.
  a. Does each statement fit the data in the table? Explain.
    i. hours worked = lawns mowed · 2
    ii. hours worked = lawns mowed + 3
  b. **Writing** Which statement in part (a) better describes the relationship between hours worked and lawns mowed? Explain.

Lawns Mowed	Hours
1	
2	
3	6

42. Multiple Choice Which equation best describes the relationship between the amount of money a in a bag of quarters and the number of quarters q?

Ⓐ $a = 0.25q$ Ⓑ $a = 0.25 + q$ Ⓒ $q = 0.25a$ Ⓓ $q = 0.25 + q$

Real-World 🌎 Connection

People in the United States have spent more than $8.5 billion annually on lawn care.

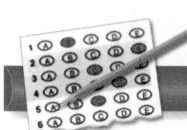

Drop Height (ft)	Height of First Bounce (ft)
1	$\frac{1}{2}$
2	1
3	$1\frac{1}{2}$
4	2
5	$2\frac{1}{2}$

43. a. Write an equation to describe the relationship between the height of the first bounce and the drop height.
  b. Suppose you drop the ball from a window 20 ft above the ground. Predict how high the ball will bounce.

44. Suppose the second bounce is $\frac{1}{4}$ of the original drop height. Write an equation to relate the height of the second bounce to the drop height.

Open-Ended Describe a real-world situation that each equation could represent. Include a definition for each variable.

45. $d = 5t$ **46.** $a = b + 3$ **47.** $c = \frac{40}{h}$

Test Prep

Multiple Choice

48. Which is an algebraic expression for "six less than k"?
  A. $\frac{6}{k}$ **B.** $\frac{k}{6}$ **C.** $6 - k$ **D.** $k - 6$

49. Which is an algebraic expression for "the product of 10 and a"?
  F. $a + 10$ **G.** $a - 10$ **H.** $10a$ **J.** $\frac{a}{10}$

50. Which is an algebraic expression for "9 more than v"?
  A. $v + 9$ **B.** $v - 9$ **C.** $9 - v$ **D.** $9v$

51. A container of milk contains 64 ounces. Which equation models the number n of ounces remaining after you have drunk m ounces?
  F. $m - 64 = n$ **G.** $64 - m = n$ **H.** $n - 64 = m$ **J.** $n - m = 64$

52. Which equation models the relationship in the table if r represents the row number and t represents the number of tulips?
  A. $r = 3t$ **B.** $\frac{r}{t} = 3$
  C. $t = r + 3$ **D.** $t = 3r$

Row Number	Number of Tulips
1	3
2	6
3	9
4	12

53. Which is an algebraic expression for "the quotient of $r + 5$ and b"?
  F. $\frac{r + 5}{b}$ **G.** $\frac{r}{b + 5}$
  H. $\frac{b}{r + 5}$ **J.** $\frac{b}{r} + 5$

Mixed Review

Skills Handbook

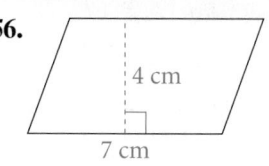 **for Help**

Find the area of each figure. For Exercises 54 and 55, find the perimeter of each figure.

54. 3 cm, 5 cm

55. 9 in., 15 in., 12 in.

56. 4 cm, 7 cm

4-2

Exponents and Order of Operations

What You'll Learn

- To simplify and evaluate expressions and formulas
- To simplify and evaluate expressions containing grouping symbols

. . . And Why

To find the total cost of sneakers including sales tax, as in Example 3

Check Skills You'll Need

GO for Help Skills Handbook page 787

Find the greatest common factor of each set of numbers.

1. 4 and 8   **2.** 12 and 15   **3.** 5 and 7

4. 8 and 12   **5.** 14 and 21   **6.** 12 and 20

Find the least common multiple of each set of numbers.

7. 4 and 8   **8.** 12 and 15   **9.** 5 and 7

10. 3 and 9   **11.** 6 and 9   **12.** 9 and 12

◀)) **New Vocabulary**   • simplify • exponent • base • power
                          • order of operations • evaluate

1 Simplifying and Evaluating Expressions and Formulas

Problem Solving Hint

Drawing a diagram may help you understand the problem.

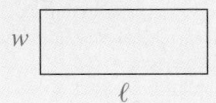

Activity: Order of Operations

⬡ **Geometry** Two formulas for the perimeter of a rectangle are
$P = 2\ell + 2w$ and $P = 2(\ell + w)$.

1. The length ℓ of a rectangle is 8 in. and its width w is 3 in. Find the perimeter of the rectangle using each of the formulas.

2. When you used $P = 2\ell + 2w$, did you add first or multiply first?

3. When you used $P = 2(\ell + w)$, did you add first or multiply first?

4. Which formula do you prefer to use? Why?

To **simplify** a numerical expression, you replace it with its simplest name. The simplest name for $2 \cdot 8 + 2 \cdot 3$ and for $2(8 + 3)$ is 22.

Expressions may include exponents. Using an exponent provides a shorthand way to show a product of equal factors.

$$\text{base} \rightarrow 2^{\overset{\textstyle\downarrow\ \text{exponent}}{4}} = \underbrace{2 \cdot 2 \cdot 2 \cdot 2}_{\text{power}}$$

An **exponent** tells how many times a number, the **base,** is used as a factor. A **power** has two parts, a base and an exponent.

You read the expression 2^4 as "two to the fourth power." To simplify 2^4, you replace it with its simplest name, 16. There are special names for 2^3, "two cubed," and 2^2, "two squared."

Look at the expression below. It is simplified in two ways.

$$3 + 5 - 6 \div 2 \qquad 3 + 5 - 6 \div 2$$
$$8 \quad - 6 \div 2 \qquad 3 + 5 - \quad 3$$
$$2 \quad \div 2 \qquad 8 \quad - \quad 3$$
$$1 \,\text{✗} \qquad \qquad 5 \,\text{✓}$$

← Different results! →

To avoid having two different results when simplifying the same expression, mathematicians have agreed on an order for doing operations.

 Key Concepts

Summary	**Order of Operations**

1. Perform any operation(s) inside grouping symbols.
2. Simplify powers.
3. Multiply and divide in order from left to right.
4. Add and subtract in order from left to right.

Video Tutor Help

Visit: PHSchool.com
Web Code: ate-0775

1 EXAMPLE **Simplifying a Numerical Expression**

Simplify $25 - 8 \cdot 2 + 3^2$.

$25 - 8 \cdot 2 + 3^2 = 25 - \underbrace{8 \cdot 2} + 9$ **Simplify the power: $3^2 = 3 \cdot 3 = 9$.**

$= \underbrace{25 - 16} + 9$ **Multiply 8 and 2.**

$= \quad 9 \quad + 9$ **Add and subtract in order from left to right.**

$= 18$ **Add.**

 **Quick Check** **1** Simplify each expression.
    a. $6 - 10 \div 5$ **b.** $3 \cdot 6 - 4^2 \div 2$ **c.** $4 \cdot 7 + 4 \div 2^2$ **d.** $5^3 + 90 \div 10$

You **evaluate** an algebraic expression by substituting a given number for each variable. Then simplify the numerical expression using the order of operations.

2 EXAMPLE **Evaluating an Algebraic Expression**

Evaluate $3a - 2^3 \div b$ for $a = 7$ and $b = 4$.

$3a - 2^3 \div b = 3 \cdot 7 - 2^3 \div 4$ **Substitute 7 for a and 4 for b.**

$= 3 \cdot 7 - 8 \div 4$ **Simplify the power.**

$= 21 - 2$ **Multiply and divide from left to right.**

$= 19$ **Subtract.**

Quick Check **2** Evaluate each expression for $c = 2$ and $d = 5$.
    a. $4c - 2d \div c$ **b.** $d + 6c \div 4$ **c.** $c^4 - d \cdot 2$ **d.** $40 - d^2 + cd \cdot 3$

You can use expressions with variables to model many real-world situations.

3 EXAMPLE <u>Real-World</u> Problem Solving

Sales The equation $c = p + 0.06p$ represents the cost c of a pair of sneakers with price p and sales tax of 6%. Use a table to find the cost for $20, $30, $45, and $59 pairs of sneakers.

Price p	$p + 0.06p$	Cost c
$20	$20 + 0.06(20)$	$21.20
$30	$30 + 0.06(30)$	$31.80
$45	$45 + 0.06(45)$	$47.70
$59	$59 + 0.06(59)$	$62.54

 **Quick Check** **3** The equation $c = p + 0.05p$ represents the cost c of an item with a price p and a 5% sales tax. Make a table to find the cost of items with prices $5, $10, $15, and $20.

2 Simplifying and Evaluating Expressions With Grouping Symbols

When you simplify expressions with parentheses, work within the parentheses first. Inside parentheses, use the order of operations.

4 EXAMPLE Simplifying an Expression With Parentheses

Simplify $15(13 - 7) \div (8 - 5)$.

$15(13 - 7) \div (8 - 5) = 15(6) \div 3$ **Simplify within parentheses first.**
$\qquad\qquad\qquad\qquad = 90 \div 3$ **Multiply and divide from left to right.**
$\qquad\qquad\qquad\qquad = 30$ **Divide.**

Quick Check **4** Simplify each expression.
a. $(5 + 3) \div 2 + (5^2 - 3)$ 　　　　　　**b.** $8 \div (9 - 7) + (13 \div 2)$

The base for an exponent is the number, variable, or expression directly to the left of the exponent. For $(cd)^2$, cd is the base. For cd^2, d is the base. Grouping symbols show which part of the expression is the base of the power.

5 EXAMPLE Evaluating Expressions With Exponents

Evaluate each expression for $c = 15$ and $d = 12$.
a. $(cd)^2$ 　　　　　　　　　　　　　　　　　　　**b.** cd^2
$(cd)^2 = (15 \cdot 12)^2$ ← Substitute 15 for c and 12 for d. → $cd^2 = 15 \cdot 12^2$
$\qquad\quad = (180)^2$ ← Simplify within parentheses. $\qquad\quad = 15 \cdot 144$
$\qquad\quad = 32{,}400$ ← Simplify. → $\qquad\quad = 2160$

 **Quick Check** **5** Evaluate each expression for $r = 9$ and $t = 14$.
a. rt^2 　　　　　　**b.** r^2t 　　　　　　**c.** $(rt)^2$

You can also use brackets [ ] as grouping symbols. When an expression has several grouping symbols, simplify the innermost expression first.

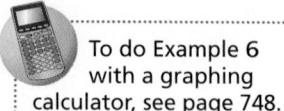
To do Example 6 with a graphing calculator, see page 748.

6 **EXAMPLE** Simplifying an Expression

Simplify $2[(13 - 7)^2 \div 3]$.

$$\begin{aligned}
2[(13 - 7)^2 \div 3] &= 2[(6)^2 \div 3] & \text{First simplify } (13 - 7).\\
&= 2[36 \div 3] & \text{Simplify the power.}\\
&= 2[12] & \text{Divide within the brackets.}\\
&= 24 & \text{Multiply.}
\end{aligned}$$

 **Quick Check** **6** Simplify each expression.
 a. $5[4 + 3(2^2 + 1)]$ **b.** $12 + 3[18 - 5(16 - 13)]$ **c.** $5 + [(2 + 1)^3 - 3]$

Calculator Hint

To simplify a power such as 6^3, press 6 y^x 3. On a graphing calculator, use 6 $\wedge$ 3. There is a special key for squares, so you can simplify 6^2 by pressing 6 x^2.

A fraction bar is also a grouping symbol. For an expression like $\frac{2 + 8}{5 - 3}$, do the calculations above and below the fraction bar before simplifying the fraction.

7 **EXAMPLE** Real-World Problem Solving

Urban Planning A neighborhood association turned a vacant lot into a park. The park is shaped like the trapezoid below. Use the formula $A = h\left(\dfrac{b_1 + b_2}{2}\right)$ to find the area of the lot.

$$\begin{aligned}
A &= h\left(\frac{b_1 + b_2}{2}\right)\\
&= 130\left(\frac{100 + 200}{2}\right) & \begin{array}{l}\text{Substitute 130 for } h,\\ \text{100 for } b_1, \text{ and 200 for } b_2.\end{array}\\
&= 130\left(\frac{300}{2}\right) & \text{Simplify the numerator.}\\
&= 130(150) & \text{Simplify the fraction.}\\
&= 19{,}500 & \text{Multiply.}
\end{aligned}$$

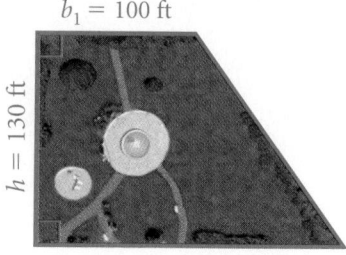

$b_1 = 100$ ft

$h = 130$ ft

$b_2 = 200$ ft

The area of the park is 19,500 ft^2.

 **Quick Check** **7** Find the area of a trapezoid with height $h = 300$ ft and bases $b_1 = 250$ ft and $b_2 = 170$ ft.

EXERCISES
For more exercises, see *Extra Skill and Word Problem Practice.*

Practice and Problem Solving

A **Practice by Example**

Example 1
(page 186)

GO for Help

Simplify each expression.

1. $5 + 6 \cdot 9$ **2.** $40 - 2 \cdot 3^2$ **3.** $8 + 12 \div 6 - 3$

4. $8 \cdot 4 + 9^2$ **5.** $5 \cdot 3^2 - 13$ **6.** $21 + 49 \div 7 + 1$

Example 2
(page 186)

Evaluate each expression for $a = 5$, $b = 12$, and $c = 2$.

7. $a + b + 2c$ **8.** $2b \div c + 3a$ **9.** $b^2 - 4a$

10. $ca + a$ **11.** $abc + ab$ **12.** $5a + 12b$

Example 3
(page 187)

13. The equation $s = p - 0.15p$ represents the sale price s of an item with an original price p, after a 15% discount. Make a table to find the discount prices for items with original prices of $12, $16, $20, and $25.

14. The equation $a = \frac{1}{2}(8)h$ represents the area a of a triangle with base of 8 cm and a height of h cm. Make a table to find the areas of triangles with heights of 6 cm, 7 cm, 8 cm, and 9 cm.

Example 4
(page 187)

Simplify each expression.

15. $2(5 + 9) - 6$ **16.** $(17 - 7) \div 5 + 1$ **17.** $(2 + 9) \cdot (8 - 4)$

18. $(7^2 - 3^2) \div 8$ **19.** $17 - 5^2 \div (2^4 + 3^2)$ **20.** $(10^2 - 4 \cdot 8) \div (8 + 9)$

Example 5
(page 187)

Evaluate each expression for $s = 11$ and $v = 8$.

21. sv^2 **22.** $(sv)^2$ **23.** $s^2 + v^2$ **24.** $(s + v)^2$

25. $s^2 - v^2$ **26.** $(s - v)^2$ **27.** $2s^2v$ **28.** $(2s)^2v$

Example 6
(page 188)

Simplify each expression.

29. $6[13 - 2(4 + 1)]$ **30.** $[3(7 + 4) - 2]6$ **31.** $20 - [4(3 + 2)]$

32. $1^{11} + 3\left[\left(\frac{22}{11} + 8\right) \div 5\right]$ **33.** $27[5^2 \div (4^2 + 3^2) + 2]$ **34.** $9 + [4 - (10 - 9)^2]^3$

Example 7
(page 188)

Evaluate the formula $V = \frac{Bh}{3}$ for each pair of values.

35. $B = 4 \text{ cm}^2, h = 6 \text{ cm}$ **36.** $B = 21 \text{ in.}^2, h = 13 \text{ in.}$

37. $B = 7 \text{ ft}^2, h = 9 \text{ ft}$ **38.** $B = 8.4 \text{ cm}^2, h = 10 \text{ cm}$

39. $B = 500 \text{ ft}^2, h = 90 \text{ ft}$ **40.** $B = 118 \text{ m}^2, h = 66 \text{ m}$

B Apply Your Skills

Simplify each expression.

41. $(2 + 3)^2 - 10$ **42.** $2^3 + 3^2 - 10$ **43.** $(2^3 + 3)^2 - 10$

44. $(2^3 + 3^2) - 16$ **45.** $3 + 6 \cdot 8$ **46.** $(5.2 - 1) \cdot 12$

47. $1 + 2(3 + 4) \div (5 \cdot 6)$ **48.** $4^3 \div 8 - 1 + 5 \div 8$

Homework Video Tutor

Visit: PHSchool.com
Web Code: ate-0102

49. A student wrote that $(a + b)^2 = a^2 + b^2$.
  a. Evaluate each side of the equation for $a = 0$ and $b = 1$.
  b. Evaluate each side of the equation for $a = 1$ and $b = 1$.
  c. Open-Ended Choose another pair of values for a and b. Evaluate each side of the equation for those values.
  d. Writing An equation is true if each side of the equation simplifies to the same value or expression. Is the equation $(a + b)^2 = a^2 + b^2$ true? Explain.

50. Multiple Choice The frame at the left is 2 in. wide. The outer height h is 17 in., and the outer width w is 14 in. Use the formula $A = (h - 4)(w - 4)$ to find the area of the picture.

  Ⓐ 130 in.^{2} Ⓑ 169 in.^{2} Ⓒ 180 in.^{2} Ⓓ 238 in.^{2}

2 in.

2 in.

Evaluate each expression for $m = 3, p = 7,$ and $q = 4$.

51. $mp - q$ **52.** $m(p - q)$ **53.** $mp^2 - q$ **54.** $m(p^2 - q)$

55. $(mp^2) - q$ **56.** $m(p - q)^2$ **57.** $m \div q + 2p$ **58.** $qp^2 + pq^2$

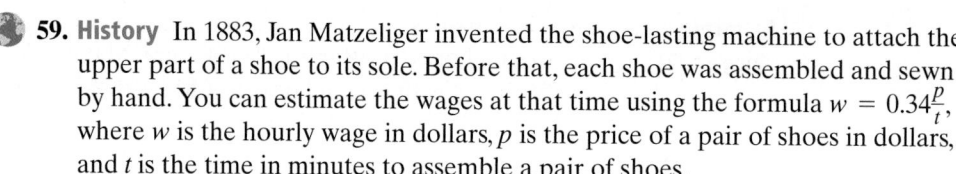

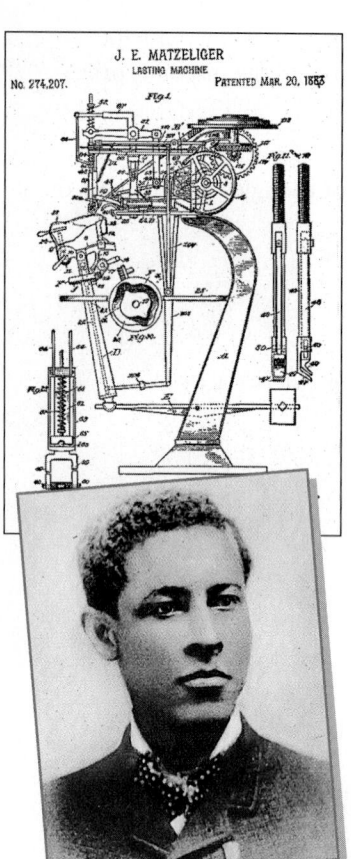

59. History In 1883, Jan Matzeliger invented the shoe-lasting machine to attach the upper part of a shoe to its sole. Before that, each shoe was assembled and sewn by hand. You can estimate the wages at that time using the formula $w = 0.34\frac{p}{t}$, where w is the hourly wage in dollars, p is the price of a pair of shoes in dollars, and t is the time in minutes to assemble a pair of shoes.

In 1891, a worker who used the shoe-lasting machine could assemble one pair of shoes in two minutes. A pair of shoes cost about $.94. Estimate the worker's hourly wage to the nearest cent.

60. a. Food The formula for the volume of a sphere with radius r is $V = \frac{4\pi r^3}{3}$. Find the volume of a seedless orange with radius 5 cm.
  b. Suppose the peel of the orange is 0.5 cm thick. What volume of the orange is edible?
  c. Express the edible part of the orange as a percent of the whole orange. Round your answer to the nearest percent.

Complete each table.

61.

h	$(5h^2 - 4)$
3	■
7	■
8	■
10	■

62.

a	$(5 \cdot 2 - a + 4)$ 10
2	■
5	■
9	■
12	■

Real-World  **Connection**

Jan Matzeliger (1852–1889) immigrated to the United States and worked in a shoe factory in Lynn, Massachusetts.

63. a. Geometry The formula for the volume of a cylinder is $V = \pi r^2 h$. What is the volume of the cylinder at the right? Round your answer to the nearest hundredth of a cubic inch.

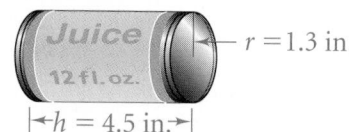

  b. Critical Thinking About how many cubic inches does an ounce of juice fill? Round your answer to the nearest tenth of a cubic inch.
  c. The formula for the surface area of a cylinder is $SA = 2\pi r(r + h)$. What is the surface area of the cylinder? Round your answer to the nearest hundredth of a square inch.

 **for Help**

For a guide to solving Exercise 64, see p. 192.

64. Sports The formula for the volume of a sphere with radius r is $V = \frac{4\pi r^3}{3}$. Find the volume of a croquet ball that has radius 4.6 cm. Round your answer to the nearest hundredth.

65. Writing Suppose you have a numerical expression. Is there only one number that is the simplest form of the expression? Explain.

C Challenge

Use grouping symbols to make each equation true.

66. $10 + 6 \div 2 - 3 = 5$ **67.** $14 - 2 + 5 - 3 = 4$

68. $3^2 + 9 \div 9 = 2$ **69.** $6 - 4 \div 2 = 1$

70. a. Simplify $12 + (3 + 7)$ and $(12 + 3) + 7$.
  b. Does it seem that the placement of the parentheses affects the value of an expression when only addition is involved? Explain.

71. a. Simplify $(12 - 3) + 7$ and $12 - (3 + 7)$.
  b. Does it seem that the placement of the parentheses affects the value of the expression when both addition and subtraction are involved? Explain.

72. Open-Ended Use the numbers 1, 2, 4, and 5 in any order to write expressions to equal each integer from 1 to 20. Examples:

$$(2 \cdot 4) + 1^5 = 9 \qquad 4(5 - 2) + 1 = 13$$

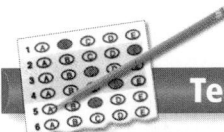 **73. a. Geometry** A trapezoid has height $h = 8$ ft, and bases $b_1 = 4$ ft and $b_2 = 5.5$ ft. Use the formula $A = h\left(\dfrac{b_1 + b_2}{2}\right)$ to find the area of the trapezoid.

b. Critical Thinking Does the area of the trapezoid double if the height doubles? If one base doubles? If both bases double? Explain your answers.

Multiple Choice

74. Simplify $5^3 - 15 \div 2 + 2$.
    A. 2   **B.** 57   **C.** 112   **D.** 119.5

75. Simplify $8(5 - 3)^3 + 9$.
    F. 73   **G.** 57   **H.** 40   **J.** 22

76. Evaluate $2ab + c$ for $a = 3.3$, $b = 4.5$ and $c = 2$.
    A. 18.4   **B.** 31.7   **C.** 32.8   **D.** 41.6

77. Evaluate $(r - s)^2$ for $r = 9$ and $s = 6.5$.
    F. 2.5   **G.** 3.5   **H.** 6.25   **J.** 12.25

78. A shirt is on sale for $25 at the local department store. There is also a 4% sales tax. What is the total cost of the shirt, including the sales tax?
    A. $25   **B.** $26   **C.** $29   **D.** $35

79. You can find the distance d an object falls in feet for time t in seconds using the formula $d = 16t^2$. Suppose a ball is dropped out of a window of a tall building. How far will the ball fall in 3 seconds?
    F. 144 ft   **G.** 96 ft   **H.** 48 ft   **J.** 16 ft

Mixed Review

 **Lesson 4-1**
GO for Help

Write an expression for each phrase.

80. 2 more than c **81.** the product of 36 and m

82. the difference of t and 21   **83.** the quotient of y and 5

Skills Handbook

Write each decimal as a percent.

84. 0.5   **85.** 0.34   **86.** 0.95   **87.** 1.45   **88.** 0.06

Find each answer.

89. What is 50% of 86?   **90.** What is 18% of 105?

Add or subtract. Write each answer in simplest form.

91. $\dfrac{3}{10} + \dfrac{1}{5}$ **92.** $\dfrac{3}{8} - \dfrac{1}{4}$ **93.** $\dfrac{5}{12} + \dfrac{2}{3}$

94. $\dfrac{3}{4} - \dfrac{1}{3}$ **95.** $\dfrac{5}{8} + \dfrac{5}{12}$ **96.** $\dfrac{7}{8} - \dfrac{2}{3}$

Understanding Word Problems Read through the problem below.
Then follow along with what Alana thinks as she solves the problem. Check
your understanding with the exercise at the bottom of the page.

The formula for the volume of a sphere with radius r is $V = \frac{4\pi r^3}{3}$.
Find the volume of a croquet ball that has a radius of 4.6 cm.
Round your answer to the nearest hundredth.

What Alana Thinks

I need to read the problem carefully so that I can
understand it. I'll write down the important
information. I need to know what each variable
stands for; r is radius and V is volume.

Now I should substitute 4.6 for r, so that I can
find the volume.

I can use a calculator to evaluate the formula. I
enter 4 $\boxed{\pi}$ $\boxed{\times}$ 4.6 $\boxed{\wedge}$ 3 $\boxed{/}$ 3 in my calculator.

I should round the calculator answer
407.7200834 to the nearest hundredth.

I need to remember to include the unit in my
final answer. For volume, I must use cubic units.

What Alana Writes

Formula for volume: $V = \frac{4\pi r^3}{3}$

Radius of the croquet ball: 4.6 cm

$V = \frac{4\pi(4.6)^3}{3}$

≈ 407.72

407.72 cm^3

EXERCISES

1. The formula $t = m + 0.06m + 0.15m$ gives the total cost t for a meal that has a
   menu price m dollars and has 6% tax and 15% tip. Use the formula to find the total
   cost for a meal with a menu price $14.20.

2. The formula $A = h\left(\frac{b_1 + b_2}{2}\right)$ gives the area A of trapezoid with height h and bases
   b_1 and b_2. Use the formula to find the area of a trapezoid with height 5 cm
   and bases of 7 cm and 12 cm.

3. The formula S.A. $= 4\pi r^2$ gives the surface area S.A. of a sphere with radius r. Find
   the surface area of a ball that has a radius of 5 in. Round to the nearest hundredth.

Example 4
(page 195)

Use <, =, or > to compare.

24. $\frac{2}{3}$ ■ $\frac{1}{6}$ **25.** $-\frac{2}{3}$ ■ $-\frac{1}{6}$ **26.** $\frac{15}{8}$ ■ $1\frac{6}{8}$ **27.** $\frac{3}{5}$ ■ 0.6

Order the numbers in each group from least to greatest.

28. $2.01, 2.1, 2.001$ **29.** $-9\frac{2}{3}, -9\frac{7}{12}, -9\frac{3}{4}$ **30.** $-\frac{5}{6}, -\frac{1}{2}, \frac{2}{3}$

31. $-1.01, -1.001, -1.0009$ **32.** $\frac{7}{11}, 0.63, 0.636$ **33.** $\frac{22}{25}, \frac{8}{9}, 0.8888$

Example 5
(page 196)

Find each absolute value.

34. $|4|$ **35.** $|-9|$ **36.** $\left|\frac{-9}{14}\right|$ **37.** $|-0.5|$

38. $\left|\frac{3}{5}\right|$ **39.** $|0|$ **40.** $|-1295|$ **41.** $\left|-\frac{4}{5}\right|$

B **Apply Your Skills**

Write each number in the form $\frac{a}{b}$ using integers to show that it is a rational number.

42. 0.2 **43.** 5 **44.** 21.3 **45.** 1.034 **46.** -4

Name the set(s) of numbers to which each number belongs.

47. $\left|\frac{93}{3}\right|$ **48.** $|-782|$ **49.** $|-1.93|$ **50.** $\left|\frac{37}{59}\right|$

Use <, =, or > to compare.

51. $|19|$ ■ $|-19|$ **52.** $|-18|$ ■ $|-17|$ **53.** $\left|\frac{1}{2}\right|$ ■ $|-0.51|$

54. $|-3.121|$ ■ $|3.12|$ **55.** $\left|\frac{-8}{10}\right|$ ■ $\left|\frac{-16}{20}\right|$ **56.** $\left|\frac{1}{3}\right|$ ■ $|-0.333|$

Simplify each expression. (Hint: Absolute value symbols are grouping symbols.)

57. $4 + |3 - 1|$ **58.** $|41 - 38| + 6$ **59.** $|a - a| + a$

60. $|24| + |-4|$ **61.** $|12 \cdot |-4|$ **62.** $|-6 + 4| + |3|$

63. a. Math in the Media In the cartoon below, what type of number is pi (π)?
   b. Will the football ever be hiked? Explain.

Real-World **Connection**

Careers Cartoonists may draw syndicated cartoons, such as the one at the right, that appear daily in newspapers.

64. Multiple Choice Use the number line. If R and T are opposites, what is the value of Q?

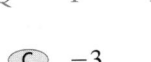

(A) 7   (B) 0   (C) -3 (D) -7

Homework Video Tutor

Visit: PHSchool.com
Web Code: ate-0103

65. Writing Are natural numbers, whole numbers, and integers also rational numbers? Explain.

Determine whether each statement is *sometimes*, *always*, or *never* true.

66. The difference of two rational numbers is an integer.

67. The product of two numbers is greater than either number.

68. The opposite of a number is less than the number.

69. The quotient of two nonzero integers is a rational number.

Evaluate each expression for $c = 5, d = 1,$ and $e = 6$.

70. $-|c + d|$ **71.** $2e + \left|\dfrac{c}{d}\right|$ **72.** $\dfrac{|e - d|}{c}$ **73.** $|d + 2| + |-7|$

 **Challenge** **74. a. Science** Use the formula $d = \dfrac{m}{v}$ to find the density d of each substance in the table below.

Densities of Some Substances

	Mass (*m*)	Volume (*v*)	Density (*d*)
Aluminum	38.5 g	14 cm³	■
Gold	38.6 g	2 cm³	■
Silver	42 g	4 cm³	■
Diamond	1.75 g	0.5 cm³	■

b. List the substances from least to greatest density.

75. a. Open-Ended Find a number between -2 and -3 on a number line.
  b. Find a number between -2.8 and -2.9.
  c. Find a number between $-2\frac{1}{16}$ and $-2\frac{3}{8}$.
  d. Make a Conjecture On a number line, is it possible to find a number between any two different given numbers? Explain.

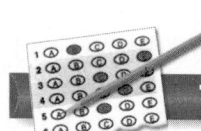

Test Prep

Multiple Choice

76. Which number has the same value as $-\left|-\frac{3}{4}\right|$?
  A. -0.75 **B.** -0.34 **C.** 0.34 **D.** 0.75

77. Which group of numbers is ordered from least to greatest?
  F. $-0.7, -\frac{3}{4}, -1$ **G.** $-1, -\frac{3}{4}, -0.7$ **H.** $-1, -0.7, -\frac{3}{4}$ **J.** $-\frac{3}{4}, -0.7, -1$

78. Suppose a is a nonzero integer. Which statement is never true?
  A. $a > -a$ **B.** $a < -a$ **C.** $|a| = -a$ **D.** $|a| = -|a|$

79. Which number is NOT an integer?
  F. -10 **G.** $-\frac{2}{3}$ **H.** 0 **J.** 5

80. Which set of numbers is most reasonable to use to describe the area of your kitchen floor?
  A. whole numbers   **B.** integers
  C. rational numbers   **D.** real numbers

81. Use the double-bar graph. In which year was there the least difference between the numbers of metal workers and of textile workers?
   F. 1970
   G. 1980
   H. 1990
   J. 2000

Metal and Textile Workers

SOURCE: U.S. Bureau of Labor Statistics

82. Suppose your brother says that fractions are rational numbers, but fractions are not integers. Which number is a counterexample for this statement?

A. $\frac{10}{3}$ B. $\frac{5}{3}$ C. $-\frac{5}{3}$ D. $-\frac{9}{3}$

Mixed Review

Lesson 4-2

Simplify each expression.

83. $3 + 5 \cdot 6$

84. $(3 + 5)6$

85. $3 + 52 \cdot 6$

86. $(33 + 9) \div 6$

87. $\frac{12 - 4 \cdot 3}{7 + 13 \cdot 15}$

88. $8 - 3 \div 6$

Lesson 4-1

Define variables and write an equation to model the relationship in each table.

89.

Number of Hours	Distance Traveled
1	7 mi
2	14 mi
3	21 mi
4	28 mi

90.

Number of Books	Total Cost
1	$3.50
2	$7.00
3	$10.50
4	$14.00

✓ Checkpoint Quiz 1

Lessons 4-1 through 4-3

Write a variable expression for each phrase.

1. the sum of b and 4

2. the quotient of c and 2

3. the product of a and 4.3

4. b plus c plus twice a

Evaluate each expression for $a = 3$ and $b = 7$.

5. $(b - a)b$

6. $a^2 + b^2$

7. $ba^2 - a$

8. $(2a)^2 b$

9. Is it true that a number is always greater than its opposite? Explain.

10. What set of numbers is reasonable to use for the number of loaves of bread a bakery bakes in one day?

Graphing on the Coordinate Plane

Two number lines that intersect at right angles form a **coordinate plane.**
The horizontal axis is the **x-axis** and the vertical axis is the **y-axis.**
The axes intersect at the **origin** and divide the coordinate plane into
four sections called **quadrants.**

An **ordered pair** of numbers identifies the location of a point. These numbers are the **coordinates** of the
point on the graph. Point B has coordinates $(-2, 4)$.

$$(-2, 4)$$

x-coordinate	**y-coordinate**
or abscissa	or ordinate

The x-coordinate tells you how far to move right (positive) or left (negative)
from the origin. The y-coordinate tells you how far to move up (positive) or down
(negative) from the origin.

1 EXAMPLE Identifying Coordinates

a. Name the coordinates of point Z in the graph.

Move 2 units to the left of the origin. Then move
3 units down. The coordinates of Z are $(-2, -3)$.

b. Name the coordinates of point Q in the graph.

Since Q is directly above the origin, the
x-coordinate is 0. Move 2 units up from the origin.
The coordinates of Q are $(0, 2)$.

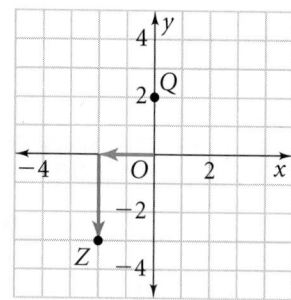

2 EXAMPLE Graphing Points

a. Graph the point $A\left(-2\frac{1}{2}, 3\right)$ on the coordinate plane.

Move $2\frac{1}{2}$ units to the left of the origin.
Then move 3 units up.

b. Graph the point $B(3, 0)$ on the coordinate plane.

Since the y-coordinate is 0, point B is on the x-axis.
Move 3 units to the right of the origin.

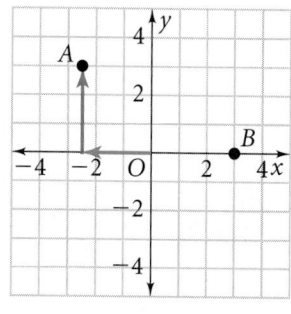

You can determine which quadrant a point is in by graphing the point or by considering the signs of the x- and y-coordinates. A point on an axis is not considered to be in a quadrant.

3 EXAMPLE Identifying Quadrants

In which quadrant or on which axis would you find each point?

a. $(-1, 5)$

Since the x-coordinate is negative and the y-coordinate is positive, the point is in Quadrant II.

b. $(0, 3)$

Since the x-coordinate is 0, the point is on the y-axis.

The **midpoint** of a segment is the point halfway between the endpoints. You can use the coordinates of the endpoints to find the midpoint of a segment.

Given a segment with endpoints $A(x_1, y_1)$ and $B(x_2, y_2)$, the midpoint M is $\left(\dfrac{x_1 + x_2}{2}, \dfrac{y_1 + y_2}{2}\right)$.

4 EXAMPLE Midpoint of a Line Segment

Find the midpoint of $\overline{GH}$.

$\left(\dfrac{x_1 + x_2}{2}, \dfrac{y_1 + y_2}{2}\right)$ **Use the midpoint formula.**

$= \left(\dfrac{-2 + 6}{2}, \dfrac{4 + (-3)}{2}\right)$ **Replace (x_1, y_1) with $(-2, 4)$ and (x_2, y_2) with $(6, -3)$.**

$= \left(\dfrac{4}{2}, \dfrac{1}{2}\right) = \left(2, \dfrac{1}{2}\right)$ **Simplify.**

The midpoint of $\overline{GH}$ is $\left(2, \dfrac{1}{2}\right)$.

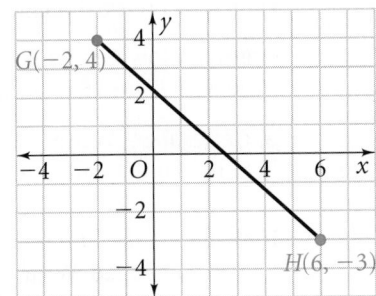

EXERCISES

Name the coordinates of each point on the graph at the right.

1. S **2.** T **3.** U **4.** V

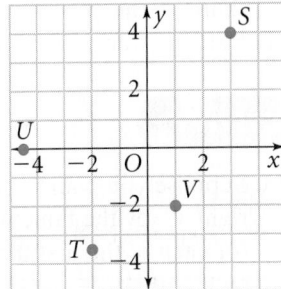

Graph the points on the same coordinate plane.

5. $(3, 0)$ **6.** $\left(-1\frac{1}{2}, 2\right)$ **7.** $(-2, -3)$ **8.** $\left(4, -2\frac{1}{2}\right)$

In which quadrant or on which axis would you find each point?

9. $\left(-10\frac{1}{2}, 6\right)$ **10.** $(-12, 0)$ **11.** $(8, -18)$ **12.** $(0, 5)$

Find the midpoint of the segment with the given endpoints.

13. $C(8, 1)$ and $D(-4, 3)$ **14.** $S(6, -9)$ and $T(0, 2)$

15. $A(-2, 4)$ and $B(-6, -2)$ **16.** $P(5, -6)$ and $Q(-3, 5)$

Complete each statement.

17. If the x-coordinate and the y-coordinate of an ordered pair are positive, the ordered pair is in Quadrant ___?___.

18. The x-coordinate is 0 and the y-coordinate is negative. Is the point in Quadrant III? Explain.

Patterns and Expressions

Activity Lab

Hands-On

FOR USE WITH LESSON 4-4

In Lesson 4-1, you wrote variable expressions for word phrases. You can also write variable expressions to represent patterns.

1 ACTIVITY

Use the figures below to answer the following questions.

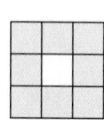

Figure 1

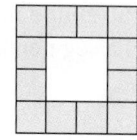

Figure 2

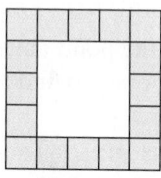

Figure 3

1. Copy the table at the right. Write the number of tiles you would need for each of the first three figures.

2. **Predict** How many tiles would you need to make Figure 4? Make a sketch of Figure 4 on graph paper. Write your results in the table.

3. **Predict** How many tiles would you need to make Figure 5? Make a sketch of Figure 5 on graph paper. Write your results in the table.

4. **a. Generalize** Write a sentence that describes the relationship between the figure number and the number of tiles needed to build it.
   b. Write an algebraic expression using n that tells the total number of tiles needed. Write your expression in the table.
   c. Use your expression. How many tiles would be needed for Figure 40?

5. **a.** Graph the data for Figures 4–5. Use the horizontal axis for the figure number and the vertical axis for the number of tiles. What do you notice about the shape of the graph?
   b. Extend your graph to find how many tiles would be needed for Figure 8.

Figure	Total Number of Tiles Needed
1	■
2	■
3	■
4	■
5	■
n	■

2 ACTIVITY

6. **a.** Suppose you plan to build a patio in a design like the ones shown at the right. Copy the table below. Write the total number of bricks needed for each of the first three figures.

Figure	1	2	3	4	5	n
Total Number of Bricks Needed	■	■	■	■	■	■

   b. Predict How many bricks will you need to make Figures 4 and 5? Make sketches and write your results in the table.

7. **a. Generalize** Write a sentence that describes the relationship in the table.
   b. Write an algebraic expression using n that tells the total number of bricks needed. Write your expression in the table.
   c. Suppose you have at most 50 bricks to use. Can you use them all to make a figure like those above? Explain.

202 Activity Lab Patterns and Expressions

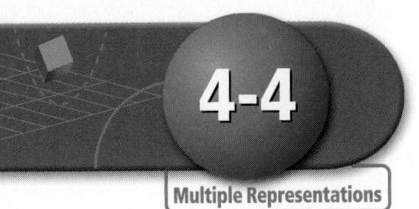

4-4

Patterns and Functions

What You'll Learn

• To write a function rule
• To understand relationships of quantities in a function

...And Why

To find reasonable domain and range for real-world situations, as in Example 4

✓ **Check Skills You'll Need**

Write an algebraic expression for each phrase.

1. 10 more than twice a number
2. a number divided by 4
3. 8 minus six times a number
4. twice a number subtracted from 7

GO for Help Lesson 4-1

◄)) **New Vocabulary** • function • function rule • dependent variable • independent variable • domain • range

---

1 ▸ Writing a Function Rule

In Lesson 4-2, the equation $C = p + 0.06p$ shows the relationship between the original price p of a pair of sneakers and the total cost C after the 6% sales tax is included. The relationship between these quantities is a function.

A **function** is a relationship that assigns exactly one output value for each input value. For each input there is only one corresponding output. A **function rule,** such as $C = p + 0.06p$, is an equation that describes a functional relationship.

1 EXAMPLE Writing a Function Rule

Laundry Suppose you are washing and drying clothes at a self-service laundry. The relationship between the number of loads (input) and the cost (output) is a function. Use the table to write a function rule.

Number of Loads	1	2	3	4
Cost	$2.75	$5.50	$8.25	$11.00

Relate Total cost is 2.75 · number of loads   Describe how the quantities relate.

Define Let n = the number of loads.   **The number of loads is the input.**

Let c = the total cost.   **The total cost is the output.**

Write c = 2.75 · n **Translate this relationship to a function rule.**

● The function rule is $c = 2.75n$.

✓ **Quick Check** ❶ Write a function rule for the relationship between the number of hours (input) and the number of miles (output).

Hours	1	2	3	4
Total Miles	60	120	180	240

---

2 EXAMPLE Writing a Function Rule

One
House

Two
Houses

Three Houses

The relationship between the number of houses (input) and the number of toothpicks (output) is a function. Use the table to write a function rule.

Number of Houses	1	2	3	4
Total Number of Toothpicks	6	11	16	21

Relate Total number of toothpicks is one more than five times the number of houses.

Describe how the quantities relate.

Define Let n = the number of houses.
Let t = the total number of toothpicks.

The number of houses is the input.
The total number of toothpicks is the output.

Write $t = 5n + 1$ **Translate this relationship to a function rule.**

● The function rule is $t = 5n + 1$.

✔ **Quick Check** ❷ **a.** How many toothpicks are needed to make seven houses?
b. Reasoning Could a set of houses be built with exactly 12 toothpicks? Explain.
c. Write a rule for the function represented by the data in the table.

Input x	1	2	3	4
Output y	5	8	11	14

2 Relationships in a Function

In Example 2, the total number of toothpicks t depends on the number of houses n. The value of the **dependent variable** t depends on the value of the **independent variable** n. In real-world situations, you must determine which varying quantity is dependent and which is independent.

3 EXAMPLE Identifying Independent and Dependent Quantities

Memory Stick The table and graph model a function relating the storage capacity of a memory stick and its cost. Identify the independent and dependent quantities.

Memory (mb)	Cost ($)
32	19
64	29
128	39
256	49

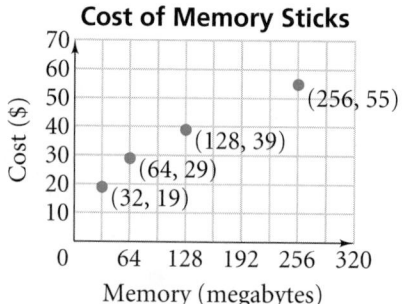

Cost of Memory Sticks

The cost is the *dependent* quantity because it *depends* on the storage capacity of
● the memory stick. Memory is the *independent* quantity.

✔ **Quick Check** ❸ The cooking time for an unstuffed turkey is about 20 minutes per pound. What are the independent quantity and dependent quantity for this situation?

The possible values for the input, or the independent variable, of a function are the **domain** of the function. The possible values of the output, or the dependent variable, are the **range** of the function.

4 EXAMPLE Reasonable Domain and Range

Maria earns $7 per hour for baby-sitting after school and on Saturday. She works no more than 16 hours a week.

a. Identify the independent and dependent quantities for this situation.

The amount Maria earns depends on the number of hours she works in a week. So the amount Maria earns is the dependent variable. The number of hours she works is the independent variable.

b. Find reasonable domain and range values for this situation.

A reasonable domain is from 0 to 16 hours. If Maria works 0 hours, she earns $0. If she works 16 hours, she earns 7 · $16, or $112. So, a reasonable range is from $0 to $112.

✓ Quick Check ❹ Charlie downloads songs for $.75 each. He has between $3.00 and $6.00 to spend on songs. Identify the independent and dependent quantities for this situation and find reasonable domain and range values.

EXERCISES

For more exercises, see *Extra Skill and Word Problem Practice.*

Practice and Problem Solving

A Practice by Example

Example 1
(page 203)

The relationships in the tables below are functions. Write a function rule for each.

1.

Cans of Soup	Number of Servings
1	4
2	8
3	12
4	16

2.

Number of Cans of Frozen Orange Juice	Total Cost
1	$1.25
2	$2.50
3	$3.75
4	$5.00

Example 2
(page 204)

3.

Number of Hours a Plumber Works	Cost to Home Owner
1	$65
2	$90
3	$115
4	$140

4.

Time (hours)	Cost of Bike Rental
1	$10
2	$16
3	$22
4	$28

Example 3
(page 204)

Identify the independent and dependent quantity in each situation.

5. The cost of a long-distance telephone call increases, with the number of minutes of the call.

6. Water pressure increases 0.44 pounds per square inch (0.44 psi) with each increase of one foot in depth below sea level.

Example 4
(page 205)

Identify the independent and dependent quantities for each situation, and find reasonable domain and range values.

7. Tara's car travels about 25 miles on one gallon of gas. She has between 10 and 12 gallons of gas in the tank.

8. Sal and three friends plan to bowl one or two games each. Each game costs $2.50.

B **Apply Your Skills**

Copy and complete each table. Then write a function rule for each relationship.

9.

Number of Minutes Reading	Number of Words Read
1	125
2	250
3	375
4	■
5	■

10.

Number of Hours of Yoga Lessons	Total Cost
1	$15
2	$27
3	$39
4	■
5	■

11. The graph shows the average size of a school's ninth-grade class over several years.
   a. Does this graph represent a function? Explain.
   b. If the graph represents a function, identify the independent and dependent quantities.

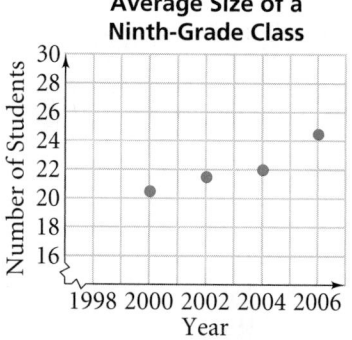
Average Size of a Ninth-Grade Class

Online
Homework Video Tutor
Visit: PHSchool.com
Web Code: ate-0104

12. a. The weight of the books carried in a backpack depends on the number of books in the backpack. Susan's books weigh from 1 pound up to 3.5 pounds each and she carries at most 4 books. Find a reasonable domain and range for the situation.
   b. **Critical Thinking** Can noninteger numbers be part of the domain? of the range? Explain.

13. Each side of the first figure is one unit. Copy and complete the table. Then find a function rule for the relationship between a figure's number and its perimeter.

Figure Number	Perimeter
1	■
2	■
3	■
4	■

Figure 1   Figure 2

Figure 3   Figure 4

14. **Motorcycles** The table below shows the price of several motorcycles and the size of their engines. Identify the independent and dependent quantities. Explain.

Engine (cc)	249	398	645	996
Price ($)	3199	6099	6699	8599

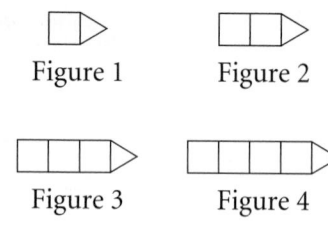

15. a. Copy the table at the right. Evaluate the expression $x^2 + 1$ for $x = 1, 2, 3,$ and 4. Record your results in the second column.

b. Critical Thinking Do the numbers in the table represent a function? Explain.

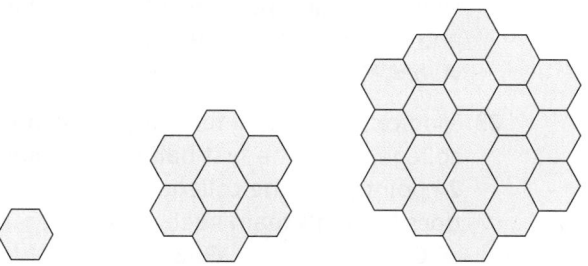

x	$x^2 + 1$
1	■
2	■
3	■
4	■

C Challenge

16. a. Look at the pattern below. Make a table that relates the figure number n to the number of hexagons h.

Figure 1   Figure 2   Figure 3

b. Predict What will be the number of hexagons in Figure 4?

c. Does your table represent a function? Explain.

17. a. Complete the table for the side lengths and areas of squares.

b. Identify the independent and the dependent quantities.

Side length	1	1.5	2	2.5	3
Area	■	■	■	■	■

c. Graph the data. Show the data for the independent quantity on the horizontal axis and the data for the dependent quantity on the vertical axis.

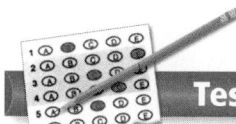

Test Prep

Multiple Choice

18. The graph at the right represents the temperature of water that was boiled and then left to cool. Which statement is true?

A. Time depends on the water temperature.

B. The water temperature depends on time.

C. The cooling time depends on how long the water boils.

D. The water temperature depends on the boiling time.

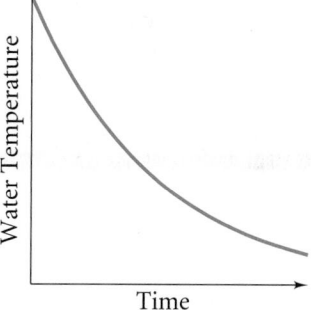

19. The function $c = 23(n - 1) + 37$ represents the cost c in cents for mailing a letter weighing n ounces. Which statement is true?

F. The weight of a letter depends on its cost.

G. The number of letters mailed depends on the total number of ounces of the letters.

H. The cost to mail a letter depends on its weight.

J. Each letter costs 37¢ an ounce.

20. Evaluate the expression $3x - 5$ for $x = -2, 0, 1,$ and 5. Which value of x produces the greatest value from the expression?

A. –2   **B.** 0   **C.** 1   **D.** 5

21. Simplify $|-7 + 8| + |-9|$.
    F. 26   **G.** 10   **H.** −26   **J.** 8

22. Jacob recorded the height of a sunflower each week for 5 weeks.

Week	1	2	3	4	5
Height (cm)	15	30	45	60	75

Which function best describes the relationship, if *w* represents the week and *h* represents the height?
    A. $h = 15w$ **B.** $w = 15h$ **C.** $h = w + 15$ **D.** $w = h + 15$

23. Monica's basketball team is playing an exhibition game against a local college. After the first half of the game, Monica sees that her team has 24 points, and the college team has 32 points. How many more points does Monica's team need to tie the game?
    F. 6   **G.** 8   **H.** 12   **J.** 56

24. A collection of quarters and nickels is worth $3.40. There are 24 coins. How many of the coins are quarters?
    A. 9   **B.** 11   **C.** 13   **D.** 15

Mixed Review

GO for Help

Lesson 4-3

Are whole numbers, integers, or rational numbers the most reasonable for each situation?

25. your height

26. the number of pages in your math text

27. the overnight low temperature in degrees Celsius for Barrow, Alaska, on January 15

Lesson 4-2

Evaluate each expression for $c = 5$ and $d = 8$.

28. $d^2 - c^3$ **29.** cd^2 **30.** dc^2

31. $(3cd)^2$ **32.** $cd - c^2$ **33.** $(4c)^2d$

Algebra at Work

Cartographer

A cartographer, or mapmaker, makes measurements of an area being mapped. The cartographer uses these measurements to create the scale of the map showing the ratio of map distance to actual distance. Knowing the scale of a map means that you can use a proportion to calculate any distance on the map.

Go Online
PHSchool.com
For: Information about cartographers
Web Code: atb-2031

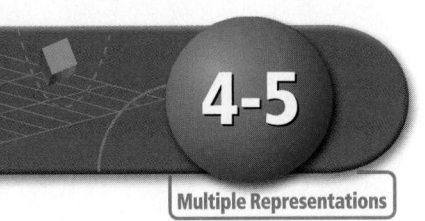

Scatter Plots

What You'll Learn

• To analyze data using scatter plots

. . . And Why

In Example 2, you will analyze data to find the relationship between the age and the asking price of a car.

Check Skills You'll Need

GO for Help Review page 200

Graph each point on the same coordinate grid.

1. $(6, 4)$ **2.** $(-5, 1)$ **3.** $\left(2\frac{1}{2}, -5\right)$ **4.** $(0, -1)$

◀ᴗ)) **New Vocabulary**   • scatter plot   • positive correlation   • negative correlation
      • no correlation   • trend line

---

1   Analyzing Data Using Scatter Plots

A **scatter plot** is a graph that relates two groups of data. To make a scatter plot, plot the two groups of data as ordered pairs. Most scatter plots are in the first quadrant of a coordinate plane, because the data are usually positive numbers.

1 EXAMPLE   **Making a Scatter Plot**

Data Collection The table at the left shows data students collected on their test scores and the number of hours they watched television the previous day. Make a scatter plot of the data.

For 2 hours of television watched and a test score of 80, plot (2, 80).

The highest score is 100. So a reasonable scale on the vertical axis is 0 to 100 with every 20 points labeled.

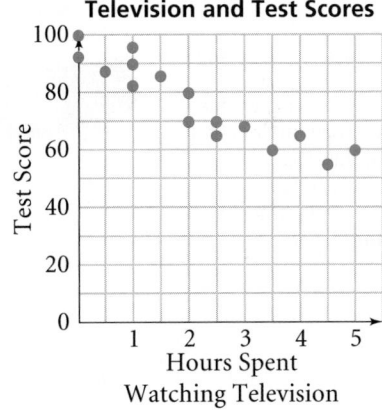

✓ **Quick Check**   ❶ Use the data in the table below. Make a scatter plot of newspaper circulation and the number of households with television.

Year	1950	1960	1970	1980	1990	2000
Daily Newspaper Circulation (millions)	54	59	62	62	62	55
Households With Television (millions)	4	46	59	76	92	101

Lesson 4-5   Scatter Plots   **209**

You can use scatter plots to find trends in data. The scatter plots below show the three types of relationships that two sets of data may have.

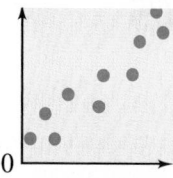

Positive correlation
In general, both sets of data increase together.

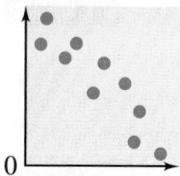

Negative correlation
In general, one set of data decreases as the other set increases.

No correlation
Sometimes data sets are not related.

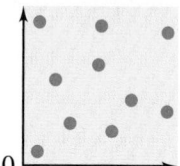

A   **trend line**   on a scatter plot shows a correlation more clearly.

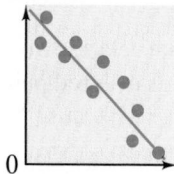

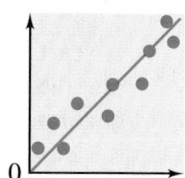

2 **EXAMPLE**   Real-World 🌐 Problem Solving

Multiple Choice The scatter plot shows the age and asking price of several used mid-sized cars. What type of relationship does the scatter plot show?

Prices of Mid-Sized Used Cars

Sketch a trend line to approximate the data. About as many points should be above the line as below the line.

Ⓐ a negative correlation   Ⓑ no correlation
Ⓒ an undefined correlation   Ⓓ a positive correlation

As the age of a car increases, the asking price generally decreases. There is a negative correlation, so the correct answer is A.

✓ **Quick Check** ❷ **a.** **Critical Thinking** In the graph above, what does the data point at (4, 14,900) represent?
b. Use the graph to predict the asking price of a 7-year-old car.

EXERCISES

For more exercises, see *Extra Skill and Word Problem Practice*.

Practice and Problem Solving

Practice by Example

Example 1
(page 209)

GO for Help

Make a scatter plot for each set of data below.

1. **Gasoline Purchases**

Dollars Spent	10	11	9	10	13	5	8	4
Gallons Bought	6.3	6.1	5.6	5.5	8.3	2.9	5.2	2.7

2. **Jeans Sales**

Average Price	$21	$28	$36	$40
Number Sold	130	112	82	65

Example 2
(page 210)

Describe the trend in each scatter plot below.

3. 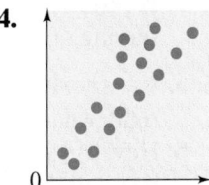 4. 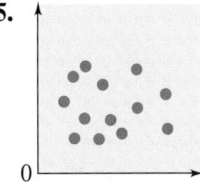 5.

Apply Your Skills

Critical Thinking Would you expect a *positive correlation*, a *negative correlation*, or *no correlation* between the two data sets? Explain why.

6. the amount of free time you have and the number of classes you take

7. the sales of snow shovels and the amount of snowfall

8. the air pollution levels for a city and the number of cars registered in that city

9. length of a baby at birth and the month in which the baby was born

10. the number of calories burned and the time spent exercising

11. a high-school sprinter's age and the time it takes to finish a 100-meter race

12. **Open-Ended** Describe three situations: one that shows a positive correlation, one that shows a negative correlation, and one that shows no correlation.

13. During one month at a local deli, the number of pounds of ham sold decreased as the number of pounds of turkey sold increased.
    a. Is this an example of a *positive correlation, negative correlation,* or *no correlation*?
    b. **Reasoning** Is it reasonable to conclude that the change in turkey sales caused the decrease in ham sales? Explain.

14. a. Think about the weather and its effect on voters. What correlation would you expect between the amount of precipitation and voter turnout? Explain.
    b. **Reasoning** Should candidates in an election be concerned about the weather forecast? Explain.

ay supplement with complete guide to ballot questions.

Daily Tribune

RAIN, HEAVY AT TIMES
CHANCE OF SNOW
HIGH: 38 LOW: 30
FULL REPORT ON PAGE 20

Tuesday, November 3, 2005

Election process

Lesson 4-5   Scatter Plots   **211**

15. a. Nutrition Draw a scatter plot of the data below. Graph the grams of fat on the *x*-axis and the number of Calories on the *y*-axis.

Calories Per Serving of Some Common Foods

Food	Grams of Fat	Number of Calories	Food	Grams of Fat	Number of Calories
Whole Milk	8	150	Eggs	6	80
Chicken	4	90	Ham	19	245
Corn	1	70	Broccoli	1	45
Ground Beef	10	185	Cheese	9	115

b. Draw a trend line on the scatter plot. Describe the correlation, if any, between Calories and grams of fat.

c. Writing Write a statement describing the relationship between calories and grams of fat.

d. A serving of ice cream has 14 grams of fat. Predict the number of calories a serving of ice cream has.

16. a. Transportation In the scatter plot at the right, what does a point represent?

b. How can you tell if some vehicles traveled the same distance?

c. How can you tell which vehicles paid the same toll charge?

d. Is there a correlation between distance traveled and toll charges? Explain.

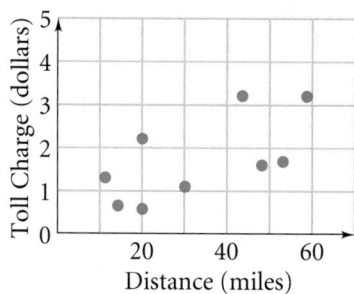

Toll Charges for 9 Vehicles on the Indiana Toll Road

Source: Indiana Department of Highways

17. Open-Ended Describe a situation in which the correlation of two sets of data is undefined.

GO Online

Homework Video Tutor

Visit: PHSchool.com
Web Code: ate-0105

C Challenge

If change in one quantity *causes* change in a second quantity, then the quantities have a *causal relationship*. Quantities can be correlated but not have a causal relationship. Is there a causal relationship in the following situations? Explain.

18. the number of cavities and the size of an elementary student's vocabulary

19. the depth of a snowfall and the amount of time spent clearing the driveway

20. the time of sunrise and the daily high temperature

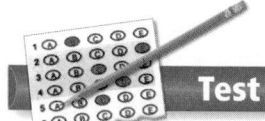

Test Prep

Multiple Choice

21. Suppose you take a survey of all the schools in your state. What would you expect the relationship between the number of students and the number of teachers in each school to be?
  A. positive correlation **B.** negative correlation
  C. no correlation **D.** none of the above

22. When 18 gallons of water are pumped into an empty tank, the tank is filled to three fourths of its capacity. How many gallons of water will the tank hold?
  F. 12 **G.** 13.5 **H.** 18.5 **J.** 24

23. Which sets of data would most likely have a negative correlation?
- **A.** the population of Detroit over a 10-year period and the population of Kansas City over the same 10-year period
- **B.** the height of a person and that person's shoe size
- **C.** the number of times a car stops to fill its gas tank and the amount of gas the tank can hold
- **D.** the size of an animal and the amount of food it needs each day

24. Evaluate $(2m^2 + 5) - (m + 1)$ for $m = 3$.
  - **F.** 13 **G.** 19 **H.** 22 **J.** 37

25. Evaluate $\frac{(p + 3t)}{6} \div (p \div 6)$ for $p = 6$ and $t = 4$.
  - **A.** $\frac{1}{4}$ **B.** $\frac{1}{2}$ **C.** 3 **D.** 4

Mixed Review

GO for Help

Lesson 4-4

26. Jillian's scooter can travel about 60 miles on one gallon of gas. The gas tank holds as much as 1.5 gallons. Identify the independent and dependent quantities for this situation, and reasonable domain and range values.

Lesson 4-3

Decide whether each statement is *true* or *false*. If the statement is false, give a counterexample.

27. All positive integers are natural numbers.

28. A number cannot have a value equal to its square.

29. All integers are rational numbers.

✓ Checkpoint Quiz 2   Lessons 4-4 through 4-5

1. Write a function rule for the relationship between the number of minutes and the number of words.

Minutes	1	2	3	4
Words Typed	35	70	105	140

Identify the independent and the dependent quantity in each situation.

2. increase in pressure with depth below sea level

3. time in a cell phone account and amount of money in the account

4. the number of papers delivered and the amount of money earned

5. a. Make a scatter plot of the data below.

Weeks Web Site Has Been Online	1	2	5	6	8
Visits to Web Site (thousands)	5.5	5.6	4.1	3.4	3.5

b. Does the scatter plot show a *positive correlation*, a *negative correlation*, or *no correlation*?

c. What values are in the domain?

Activity Lab

Interpreting Graphs

Bar graphs, line graphs, and circle graphs are three of the most common ways to represent data. Venn diagrams are another way to show relationships among data.

Bar graphs are used to compare amounts. One axis shows the categories and the other axis shows the amounts.

1 ACTIVITY

The bar graph shows the number of hours per week that Central High School students study.

1. How many hours per week do juniors study?

2. **Writing** How can you identify which class spends the *least* amount of time studying, without determining the actual value? Explain.

3. Do seniors study twice as long as freshmen?

4. **Critical Thinking** Suppose you saw the same data in a bar graph where the *y*-axis was labeled from 0 to 20. Explain how the new bar graph might convey a different impression from the one above.

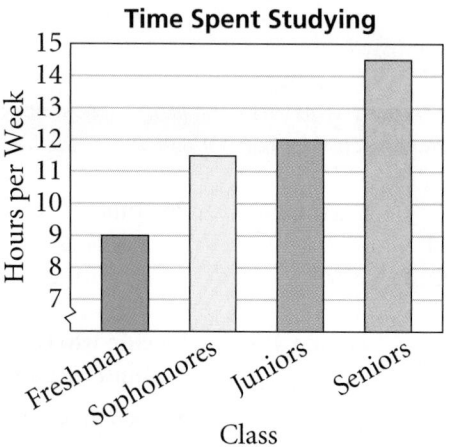

Line graphs are used to show the change in a set of data over a period of time. You can use a line graph to look for trends and make predictions.

2 ACTIVITY

The line graph shows the profits of a small company over several years.

5. **Multiple Choice** Choose the statement that best describes the profits for this company.
   - A Profits generally decreased from 1998 to 2006.
   - B Profits showed no general trend.
   - C Profits generally increased from 1998 to 2006.
   - D Profits showed no change from 1998 to 2006.

6. What were the company's profits in 2002?

7. **Estimate** Based on the data shown in the graph, estimate the company's profits in 2005.

8. **Predict** Based on the data shown in the graph, predict the company's profits in 2008.

Interpolation is estimating a value among existing data. *Extrapolation* is predicting a value outside the existing data.

9. **Critical Thinking** In Question 7 you interpolated and in Question 8 you extrapolated. Why are interpolated values generally more reliable than extrapolated values?

Circle graphs show data as percents or fractions of a whole. The total must be 100% or 1. Circle graphs show the parts of the whole. The angles at the center are central angles, and each angle is proportional to the percent or fraction of the total.

3 ACTIVITY

The circle graph shows grades earned by 60 students on their first science test.

10. Estimate the number of students who earned a C on their science test.

11. Multiple Choice Based on the graph, which of the following statements is NOT true?

Science Grades

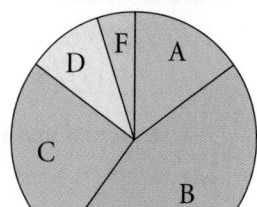

   Ⓐ Less than half of students earned a B on the test.
   Ⓑ More than one fourth of students earned an A.
   Ⓒ More than half of the students earned a B or higher.
   Ⓓ Less than one fourth of students scored below a C.

12. Writing Would a circle graph showing how many students scored 70, 71, 72, 73, and so on, be helpful in representing the results of the science test? Explain.

13. Multiple Choice Which circle graph best represents the sales of CDs for one store?

Music Category	Rock	Country	Rap	Other
Percent of CDs Sold	47%	33%	13%	7%

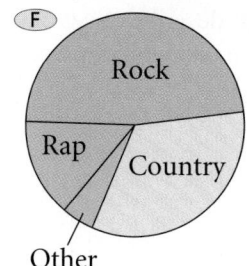

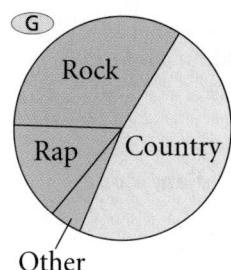

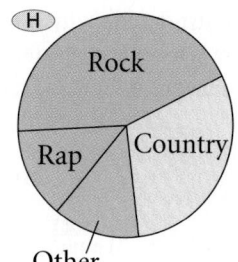

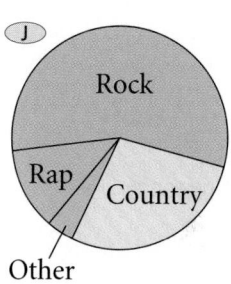

A Venn diagram shows the relationships among collections of objects or numbers. The intersection, or overlap, of two circles indicates what is common to both collections.

4 ACTIVITY

The Venn diagram shows the results of a survey of students who are in either band or chorus or both.

14. Multiple Choice Based on the diagram, which of the following statements is true?

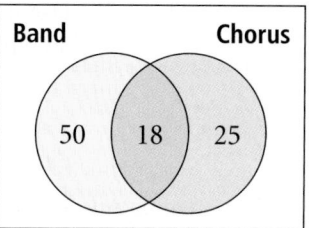

   Ⓐ Twice as many students are in band than are in chorus.
   Ⓑ There are 18 more students in band than in chorus.
   Ⓒ There are 68 students in band.
   Ⓓ Seventy-five students were surveyed.

15. What does the number 18 in the intersection represent?

Mean, Median, Mode, and Range

What You'll Learn

- To find mean, median, mode, and range
- To make and use stem-and-leaf plots

. . . And Why

To analyze real-world employment data, as in Example 1

Write the numbers in each group in order from least to greatest.

1. 2.4, 9.8, 3.6, 7.5, 1.9

2. 144, 235, 98, 72, 58, 195

3. $-12, 14, -3, -8, 7, 0$

4. $2\frac{1}{2}, -3\frac{2}{3}, -4\frac{3}{8}, 6\frac{1}{4}, -2\frac{5}{8}, 4\frac{1}{2}$

Use mental math to simplify.

5. $\dfrac{3 + 4 + 5 + 6 + 7}{5}$

6. $\dfrac{5 + 6 + 8 + 9}{4}$

 New Vocabulary • measures of central tendency • mean • outlier • median • mode • range • stem-and-leaf plot

---

1 Finding Mean, Median, and Mode

To understand a set of data, you need to organize and summarize the data using a measure of central tendency. Mean, median, and mode are all **measures of central tendency.**

You must decide which measure of central tendency best describes a set of data. Below is a review of mean, median, and mode, and where you would use each as the measure of central tendency.

 Key Concepts

Review	Mean, Median, Mode

Mean $= \dfrac{\text{sum of the data items}}{\text{total number of data items}}$

Use the mean to describe the middle of a set of data that *does not* have an outlier. An **outlier** is a data value that is much higher or lower than the other data values in the set. The mean is often referred to as the average.

The **median** is the middle value in the set when the numbers are arranged in order. For a set containing an even number of data items, the median is the mean of the two middle data values.

Use the median to describe the middle of a set of data that *does* have an outlier.

The **mode** is the data item that occurs the most times. It is possible for a set of data to have no mode, one mode, or more than one mode.

Use the mode when the data are nonnumeric or when choosing the most popular item.

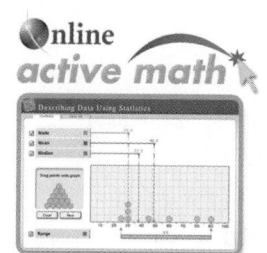
1 EXAMPLE <u>Real-World</u> Problem Solving

Wages Find the mean, median, and mode of the data in the line plot below. Which measure of central tendency best describes the data?

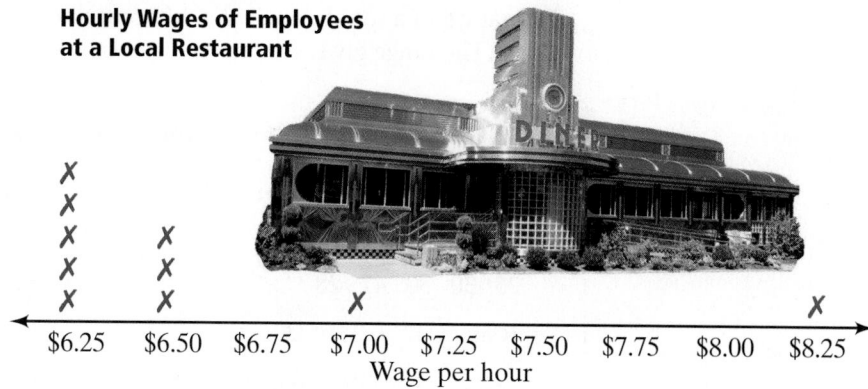

Hourly Wages of Employees at a Local Restaurant

X								
X								
X	X							
X	X							
X	X		X					X

$6.25 $6.50 $6.75 $7.00 $7.25 $7.50 $7.75 $8.00 $8.25
Wage per hour

↓ 5(6.25) is a shortcut for adding 6.25 + 6.25 + 6.25 + 6.25 + 6.25.

Mean: $\dfrac{5(6.25) + 3(6.50) + 7.00 + 8.25}{10} = 6.6$

↑ total number of employees

Median: 6.25 6.25 6.25 6.25 6.25 6.50 6.50 6.50 7.00 8.25

List data in order. 6.25 and 6.50 are the two middle data values.

$\dfrac{6.25 + 6.50}{2} = 6.375$ The median of an even number of data items is the mean of the two middle data values.

Mode: 6.25   the data item that occurs most often

The mean is $6.60, the median is about $6.38, and the mode is $6.25. The mean is greater than the salary of 8 workers. The mode is the salary of the 5 workers with the lowest salary. The median best describes the data.

✓ Quick Check **1** **a.** **Wages** The employee who earns $8.25 per hour resigns. She is replaced by an employee earning $7.50 per hour. Find the mean, median, and mode of the data.
b. **Critical Thinking** Which measure best describes the data? Explain why.

Students often ask, "What grade do I need on the next test to bring up my average?" The example below shows you how to solve this kind of problem.

2 EXAMPLE **Solving an Equation**

Suppose your grades on three history exams are 80, 93, and 91. What grade do you need on your next exam to have a 90 average on the four exams?

$\dfrac{80 + 93 + 91 + x}{4} = 90$ Use the formula for mean. Let x = the grade on the fourth exam.

$\dfrac{264 + x}{4} = 90$ Simplify the numerator.

$4\left(\dfrac{264 + x}{4}\right) = 4(90)$ Multiply each side by 4.

$264 + x = 360$ Simplify.

$264 + x - 264 = 360 - 264$ Subtract 264 from each side.

$x = 96$ Simplify.

Your grade on the next exam must be 96 for you to have an average of 90.

 **Quick Check** ② **Critical Thinking** If 100 is the highest possible score on the fourth exam, is it possible to raise your average to 92? Explain.

The **range** of a set of data is the difference between the greatest and least data values. The range gives you a measure of the spread of the data.

③ EXAMPLE Finding the Range and Mean of Data

Find the range and mean of each set of data. Use the range to compare the spread of the two sets of data.

25 30 30 47 28

Range: $47 - 25 = 22$

Mean: $\dfrac{25 + 30 + 30 + 47 + 28}{5}$

$\dfrac{160}{5} = 32$

34 28 31 36 31

Range: $36 - 28 = 8$

Mean: $\dfrac{34 + 28 + 31 + 36 + 31}{5}$

$\dfrac{160}{5} = 32$

Both sets of data have a mean of 32. The range of the first set of data is 22, and the range of the second set of data is 8. The second set of data is less spread out.

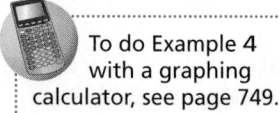 **Quick Check** ③ For the first five days in February, the low temperatures in northern Maine were 7°F, 4°F, −3°F, −6°F, and 0°F. During the same time period, the low temperatures in northern Michigan were 24°F, 15°F, −2°F, −10°F, and −5°F. Find the mean and range of each set of data. Compare the spreads of the temperature data.

2 Stem-and-Leaf Plots

> To do Example 4 with a graphing calculator, see page 749.

You can use a stem-and-leaf plot to organize data. A **stem-and-leaf plot** is a display of data made by using the digits of the values. To make a stem-and-leaf plot, separate each number into a stem and a leaf. This is the stem and leaf for the number 2.39.

all digits
to the left of   last
last digit   digit
└──▶ 2.3 | 9 ◀
       ↑   ↑
      stem leaf

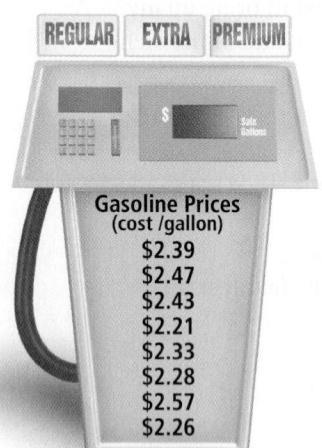

REGULAR   EXTRA   PREMIUM

Gasoline Prices
(cost /gallon)
$2.39
$2.47
$2.43
$2.21
$2.33
$2.28
$2.57
$2.26

④ EXAMPLE Making a Stem-and-Leaf Plot

Make a stem-and-leaf plot for the data at the left.

Use the first two digits for the "stems."

$$\begin{array}{c|ccc} 2.2 & 1 & 6 & 8 \\ 2.3 & 3 & 9 \\ 2.4 & 3 & 7 \\ 2.5 & 7 \end{array}$$

Use the corresponding last digits for the "leaves." Arrange the numbers in order.

2.5 | 7 means 2.57

 **Quick Check** ④ Make a stem-and-leaf plot for the data below.
4.5 4.3 0.8 3.5 2.6 1.4 0.2 0.8 4.3 6.0

You can find the measures of central tendency of data displayed in a stem-and-leaf plot. The stem-and-leaf plot in the next example is a back-to-back stem-and-leaf plot. The stem is between the two bars, and the leaves are on each side. Leaves are in increasing order from the stems.

 **EXAMPLE** Using a Stem-and-Leaf Plot

Find the mean of the city mileage and highway mileage for nine new cars.

New Car Mileage (mi/gal)

City		Highway
	9	1	
9 8 3 3 0	2	7 8
4 1 1	3	0 2 2 7 8 8
	4	1

means 20 mi/gal ← 0 | 2 | 7 → means 27 mi/gal

Mean City Mileage: $\dfrac{19 + 20 + 23 + 23 + 28 + 29 + 31 + 31 + 34}{9} = 26.\overline{4}$ mi/gal

Mean Highway Mileage: $\dfrac{27 + 28 + 30 + 32 + 32 + 37 + 38 + 38 + 41}{9} = 33.\overline{6}$ mi/gal

 Quick Check ⑤ **a.** Find the median of the city mileage and of the highway mileage.
b. Find the mode(s) of the city mileage and of the highway mileage.
c. Find the range of the city mileage and of the highway mileage.

EXERCISES

For more exercises, see *Extra Skill and Word Problem Practice*.

Practice and Problem Solving

Ⓐ Practice by Example

Example 1
(page 217)

Find the mean, median, and mode. Which measure of central tendency best describes the data?

1. weights of textbooks in ounces
    12 10 9 15 16 10

2. ages of students on math team
    14 14 15 15 16 15 15 16

3. time spent on Internet in min/day
    75 38 43 120 65 48 52

4. weights of channel catfish in pounds
    4.8 5 2.3 4.4 4.8 5.1

Example 2
(page 217)

Write and solve an equation to find the value of *x*.

5. 3.8, 4.2, 5.3, *x*; mean 4.8

6. 99, 86, 76, 95, *x*; mean 91

7. 100, 121, 105, 113, 108, *x*; mean 112

8. 31.7, 42.8, 26.4, *x*; mean 35

Example 3
(page 218)

Find the range.

9. 12 15 17 28 30

10. 5.3 6.2 3.1 4.8 7.3

11. −12 −15 5 3 −2 0 −7

12. $2\frac{1}{2}$ $3\frac{1}{3}$ $-5\frac{3}{4}$ $\frac{3}{8}$ $3\frac{5}{8}$

13. For each list of data, find the range and the mean.
    Use the range to compare the spread of the data.

List 1	List 2
64 43 55 28 71	48 53 61 47 52

Example 4
(page 218)

Make a stem-and-leaf plot for each set of data.

14. 18 35 28 15 36 10 25 22 15

15. 18.6 18.4 17.6 15.7 15.3 17.5

16. 785 776 788 761 768 768 785

17. 0.8 0.2 1.4 3.5 4.3 4.5 2.6 2.2

Example 5
(page 219)

Find the mean, median, mode, and range of each side of the stem-and-leaf plot.

18.

Time Spent on Homework (minutes/day)

Class A		Class B
6 6 4 3	4	1 1 4 5 7
9 8 6 4 4 4	5	0 2 2 2 4
5 2 1 0	6	4 5 8 9
8 7 6 6 4 2	7	3 6 7 9 9 9

means 43 ← 3 | 4 | 1 → means 41

19.

Growth of Two Varieties of Tulip Plants (inches/day)

Type A		Type B
6 3 3	2	
3 2 1 1	3	1 1 2
1	4	3 5 8
	5	2 4

means 0.33 ← 3 | 3 | 1 → means 0.31

B Apply Your Skills

Find the mean, median, mode, and range.

20. 9.8 7.2 6.3 8.7 5.8 9.4 5.1 6.2

21. 3 −12 −1 −7 −2 0 −5 −1 −4 −2

22. 42.1 46.4 58.2 67.3 49.1 40.2 22.3 46.6

23. Critical Thinking The mean of a set of data is 7.8, the mode is 6.6, and the median is 6.8. What is the least possible number of data values? Explain.

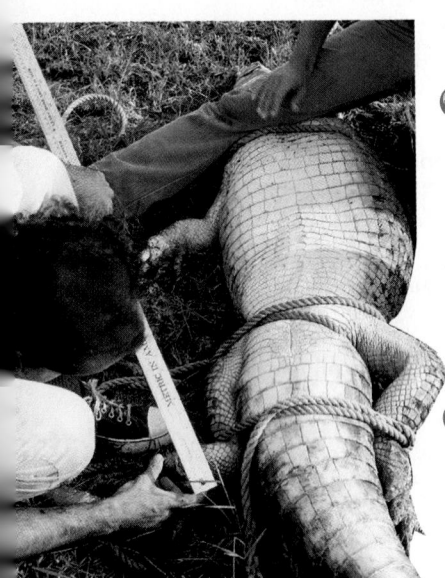

24. Wildlife Management A wildlife manager working at the Everglades National Park in Florida measured and tagged adult male crocodiles. The data he collected are at the right.
  a. What are the mean and median lengths of the crocodiles?
  b. The wildlife manager captured another crocodile. Its length was 3.3 m. What is the mean with this new piece of data? What is the median? Round to the nearest tenth.

Crocodile Lengths (meters)

2.4	2.5	2.5	2.3
2.8	2.4	2.3	2.4
2.1	2.2	2.5	2.7

25. Manufacturing Two manufacturing plants create sheets of steel for medical instruments. The back-to-back stem-and-leaf plot at the right shows data collected from the two plants.
  a. Find the mean, median, mode, and range of each set of data.
  b. Which measure of central tendency best describes each set of data? Explain.
  c. Reasoning Which plant has the better quality control? Explain.

Width of Steel (millimeters)

Manufacturing Plant A		Manufacturing Plant B
	4	3 5 9
8 7 4 4 2	5	2 7
4 3 1	6	3 4
	7	2

means 6.1 ← 1 | 6 | 3 → means 6.3

26. Open-Ended Give an example of a set of data for which the mode best represents the data. Explain.

27. Sports The median height of the 21 players on a girls' soccer team is 5 ft 7 in. What is the greatest possible number of girls who are less than 5 ft 7 in. tall?

Go Online
Homework Video Tutor
Visit: PHSchool.com
Web Code: ate-0106

28. Writing How does an outlier affect the mean of a set of data?

220 Chapter 4 Variables, Function Patterns, and Graphs

 **Challenge**

29. Make a back-to-back stem-and-leaf plot of the data below.

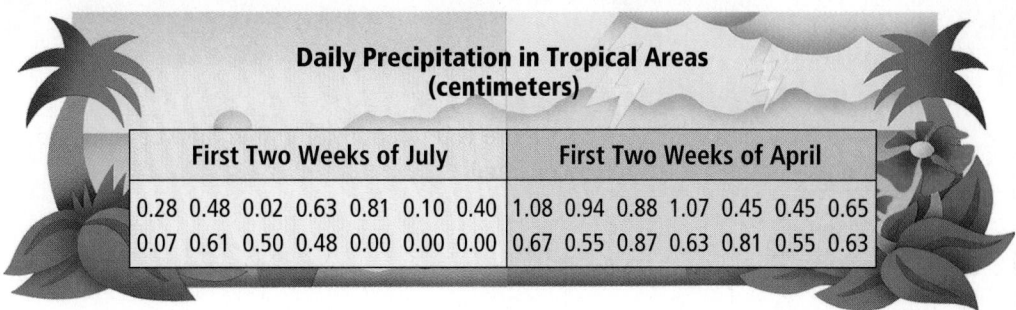

Daily Precipitation in Tropical Areas (centimeters)

First Two Weeks of July	First Two Weeks of April
0.28 0.48 0.02 0.63 0.81 0.10 0.40	1.08 0.94 0.88 1.07 0.45 0.45 0.65
0.07 0.61 0.50 0.48 0.00 0.00 0.00	0.67 0.55 0.87 0.63 0.81 0.55 0.63

30. Data Collection Record the high and low temperatures in your town for one week. Make a back-to-back stem-and-leaf plot with the data you collect.

31. During the first 6 hours of a trip, you average 44 mi/h. During the last 4 hours of your trip, you average 50 mi/h. What is your average speed for the whole trip? (*Hint:* First find the total number of miles traveled.)

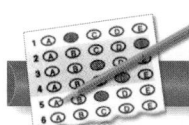

Test Prep

Multiple Choice

32. You have a mean score of 84 after taking five 100-point tests. What do you need to score on the sixth 100-point test to have a mean score of 85?
A. 85 **B.** 89 **C.** 90 **D.** 92

33. The average speeds of the winners of the Daytona 500 from 1999 to 2004 are listed at the right. What is the mean of the given speeds, rounded to the nearest tenth?
F. 158.6 mi/h **G.** 153.4 mi/h
H. 156.1 mi/h **J.** 151.9 mi/h

Daytona 500

Year	Average Speed
1999	161.6 mi/h
2000	155.9 mi/h
2001	161.7 mi/h
2002	142.0 mi/h
2003	133.9 mi/h
2004	156.3 mi/h

Source: *2005 Sports Almanac*

34. Find the sum of the mean, the median, and the mode of the following data: 22, 18, 17, 18, 25, 24, 24, 18, 29, 23.
A. 58.75 **C.** 60.25
B. 59.5 **D.** 62.3

35. The average low temperature for a 4-day period in January for the city of Orlando, Florida, was 58°F. After the fifth day, the 5-day average was 59°F. What was the low temperature on the fifth day?
F. 59°F **G.** 60°F **H.** 61.5°F **J.** 63°F

Mixed Review

Lesson 4-6

Find the mean, median, mode, and range for each set of data.

36. 1.1, 1.4, 2.2, 1.3, 2.5 **37.** 73, 68, 79, 86, 98, 92

Lesson 4-2

Evaluate each expression. Use $a = 4$, $b = 2$, and $c = 1$.

38. $3a^2 + (b - c)$ **39.** $-\dfrac{4a + b}{2}$

Lesson 4-6 Mean, Median, Mode, and Range **221**

Writing Gridded Responses

Some standardized test questions require you to enter a number answer on a grid. The number can be a fraction or a decimal.

1 EXAMPLE

What is $\frac{1}{2} + \frac{3}{4}$?

The sum can be written as $\frac{10}{8}$, $\frac{5}{4}$, or 1.25. Write your answer in the spaces at the top, and fill in the corresponding bubbles below. These three forms of the answer are shown at the right.

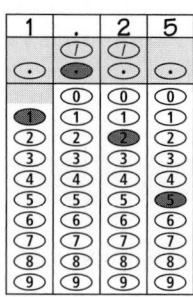

Note:

- Write a mixed number as an improper fraction. For example, do not put the mixed number $1\frac{1}{4}$ in the grid because the test-scoring computer will read "1 1/4" as $\frac{11}{4}$.
- Fractions do not have to be simplified unless specifically asked for in the question.

2 EXAMPLE

How many feet are in $\frac{1}{7}$ mile? Round to the nearest foot.

There are 5280 feet in a mile, so there are $5280 \div 7 \approx 754.3$ feet in $\frac{1}{7}$ mile. Rounded to the nearest foot, the answer is 754 feet. Enter 754 on the grid.

Do not enter the units.

EXERCISES

What number should you grid for each answer?

1. What is 14% of 0.4?

2. What part of a mile is 2200 feet? Round to the nearest hundredth of a mile.

3. What is the value of $\frac{(x + 2)^2}{x + 3}$ when $x = 1$?

4. What is the value of x^2 when $x = 0.2$?

5. Suppose you buy five yards of fabric for a banner. You use 152 inches of material. How many inches of material are left over?

Chapter Review

Vocabulary Review

absolute value (p. 196)
algebraic expression (p. 180)
base (p. 185)
coordinate plane (p. 200)
coordinates (p. 200)
counterexample (p. 194)
dependent variable (p. 204)
domain (p. 205)
equation (p. 181)
evaluate (p. 186)
exponent (p. 185)
function (p. 203)
function rule (p. 203)
independent variable (p. 204)
inequality (p. 195)
integers (p. 193)

irrational numbers (p. 194)
mean (p. 216)
measures of central tendency (p. 216)
median (p. 216)
midpoint (p. 201)
mode (p. 216)
natural numbers (p. 193)
negative correlation (p. 210)
no correlation (p. 210)
open sentence (p. 181)
opposites (p. 196)
order of operations (p. 186)
ordered pair (p. 200)
origin (p. 200)
outlier (p. 216)
positive correlation (p. 210)

power (p. 185)
quadrants (p. 200)
range (p. 218)
range of a function (p. 205)
rational numbers (p. 193)
real numbers (p. 194)
scatter plot (p. 209)
simplify (p. 185)
stem-and-leaf plot (p. 218)
trend line (p. 210)
variable (p. 180)
whole numbers (p. 193)
x-axis (p. 200)
x-coordinate (p. 200)
y-axis (p. 200)
y-coordinate (p. 200)

For: Vocabulary quiz
Web Code: atj-0151

Choose the term that correctly completes each sentence.

1. The (median, mode) is the middle value in the set when the numbers are arranged in order.

2. (Evaluate, Simplify) an algebraic expression by substituting a given number for each variable.

3. A mathematical phrase that uses numbers, variables, and operation symbols is an (algebraic expression, equation).

4. The number $-\frac{5}{8}$ belongs to the set of (irrational, rational) numbers.

5. The (absolute value, opposite) of a number is its distance from 0 on a number line.

6. You express the fraction of a pizza you have eaten by using a(n) (rational number, integer).

7. In an ordered pair, the first number is the (*x*-coordinate, *y*-coordinate), which tells how far to move to the left or right of the origin as you graph the point represented by the ordered pair.

8. A (coordinate plane, scatter plot) is a graph that relates data from two different sets.

9. When one set of data increases while another set of data decreases, there is a (positive correlation, negative correlation) between the two sets of data.

10. Simplify a (power, exponent) by multiplying the base by itself the indicated number of times.

11. The (quadrant, origin) is the point where the *x*- and *y*-axes intersect.

12. A (function, variable) is a relationship that assigns exactly one output value for each input value.

Skills and Concepts

▼ To model relationships with variables (p. 180)

▼ To model relationships with equations and formulas (p. 181)

▼ To simplify and evaluate expressions and formulas (p. 185)

▼ To evaluate expressions containing grouping symbols (p. 187)

A **variable** represents one or more numbers. To **evaluate** a variable expression, you substitute a given number for each variable. Then you **simplify** the expression using the **order of operations.**

Order of Operations

1. Perform any operation(s) inside grouping symbols.

2. Simplify powers.

3. Multiply and divide in order from left to right.

4. Add and subtract in order from left to right.

Define a variable and write an expression for each phrase.

13. the sum of 5 and three times a number

14. 30 minus a number

15. the quotient of 7 and a number

16. the product of a number and 12

Evaluate each expression. Use $a = 3$, $b = 2$, and $c = 1$.

17. $2a^2 - (4b + c)$ **18.** $9(a + 2b) + c$ **19.** $\dfrac{2a + b}{2}$ **20.** $4a - b^2$

4-3 Objectives

▼ To classify numbers (p. 193)

▼ To compare numbers (p. 195)

Real numbers can be classified as either rational numbers or irrational numbers. A **rational number,** like $\frac{5}{8}$, is a ratio of two integers. An **irrational number,** like π or $\sqrt{2}$, cannot be written as ratio of integers. Rational numbers include **natural numbers** $(1, 2, 3, \dots)$, **whole numbers** $(0, 1, 2, 3, \dots)$, and **integers** $(\dots, -2, -1, 0, 1, 2, \dots)$.

Name the set(s) of numbers to which each number belongs.

21. -3.21 **22.** $\sqrt{7}$ **23.** $-\frac{1}{2}$ **24.** 18 **25.** $\frac{35}{5}$

4-4 Objectives

▼ To write a function rule (p. 203)

▼ To recognize relationships in functions (p. 204)

A **function** is a relationship that assigns exactly one output value for each input value. A **function rule** is an equation that describes a functional relationship.

In a functional relationship, the output value depends on the input value. The variable that describes the input is the **independent variable.** The variable that describes the output is the **dependent variable.**

The possible values for the input, or independent variable, of a function are the **domain** of the function. The possible values of the output, or dependent variable, are the **range** of the function.

Identify independent and dependent quantities for each situation and find reasonable domain and range values.

26. Tom has $8.00. He wants to buy oranges which cost $.75 a piece.

27. Anna earns $6.50 per hour at her job. She can work up to 18 hours per week.

The relationships in the tables below are functions. Write a function rule for each table.

28.

x	y
1	7
2	14
3	21
4	28

29.

x	y
1	6
2	9
3	12
4	15

30.

x	y
1	20
2	16
3	12
4	8

4-5 Objective

▼ To analyze data using scatter plots (p. 209)

A **scatter plot** is a graph that relates two sets of data. There are four kinds of relationships that the data may have.

positive correlation: In general, both sets of data increase together.

negative correlation: In general, one set of data decreases as the other set increases.

no correlation: The data sets are not related.

31. a. Make a scatter plot of the data below.

Height (meters)	1.5	1.8	1.7	2.0	1.7	2.1	1.6	1.9	1.9
Arm Span (meters)	1.4	1.7	1.7	1.9	1.6	2.0	1.6	1.8	1.9

b. Is there a *positive correlation,* a *negative correlation,* or *no correlation* between the sets of data?

4-6 Objectives

▼ To use mean, median, mode, and range (p. 216)

▼ To make and use stem-and-leaf plots (p. 218)

Mean, median, and **mode** are three measures of central tendency. The **range** of a data set is the difference between the greatest and least items. A **stem-and-leaf plot** is a display that organizes the data by showing each item in order.

Find the mean, median, and mode for each set of data.

32. 85, 87, 81, 92, 87, 80, 83

33. 24, 45, 33, 27, 24

34. 2.4, 2.3, 2.1, 2.5, 2.3, 2.2

35. 42, 18, 55, 37, 57, 37, 48, 47, 37

The stem-and-leaf plot at the right shows kilometers walked during a benefit walk. Use it for Exercises 36–38.

36. Find the mean, median, mode, and range.

37. How many people walked more than 19 km?

38. How many people walked less than 17.1 km?

Benefit Walk (km)

16	1 1 2 3 5 5
17	0 2 2
18	4 5 8 9
19	3 6 7 9 9 9

19 | 3 means 19.3

Chapter Test

Go Online
PHSchool.com
For: Chapter Test
Web Code: ata-0152

Define variables and write an equation to model the relationship in each table.

1.
Number	Cost
1	$2.30
2	$4.60
3	$6.90

2.
Payment	Change
$1	$9
$2	$8
$3	$7

Simplify each expression.

3. $3 + 5 - 4$

4. $8 - 2^4 \div 2$

5. $\dfrac{2 \cdot 3 - 1}{3^2}$

6. $36 - (4 + 5 \cdot 4)$

Explain why each statement is true or false.

7. All rational numbers are integers.

8. The absolute value of a number is always positive.

Write an expression for each phrase.

9. ten times the result of eleven minus two

10. the quantity p minus five eighths times the result of one fourth plus p

11. **Open-Ended** Write four rational numbers. Use a number line to order them from least to greatest.

12. **Sales** The price p of a CD is $17.95. The sales tax rate r is 7.5%. Use the formula $C = p + rp$ to find the total cost C of the CD.

Use the scatter plot below for Exercises 13–15.

13. Is there a *positive correlation, negative correlation,* or *no correlation* between daily mean temperature and latitude?

Climate Data

14. What is the daily mean temperature for the location at latitude 58° N?

15. What is the range of daily mean temperatures?

16. **Writing** Explain why $\left|\dfrac{a}{b}\right| = \dfrac{a}{b}$ is *not* always true.

Use the table below for Exercises 17–18.

Percent of People Who Speak a Language Other Than English at Home

State	Percent
Connecticut	15
Massachusetts	15
Maine	9
New Hampshire	9
New Jersey	20
New York	23
Pennsylvania	7
Rhode Island	17
Vermont	6

SOURCE: U.S. Census Bureau
Go to **www.PHSchool.com** for a data update.
Web Code: atg-9041

17. Make a stem-and-leaf plot for the data.

18. Find the mean, median, mode, and range of the data.

19. **Purchasing** The price of a turkey depends on its weight. This week, whole turkeys sell for $1.59 per lb.
a. Write a rule to describe the function.
b. What is the price of a 14-lb turkey?
c. If you had $10 to buy a turkey, how big a turkey could you buy?

Identify the independent and dependent variables and write a function rule to describe each situation.

20. the amount of money you earn mowing lawns at $15 per lawn

21. the profit you make by selling flowers at $1.50 each when each flower costs you $.80

22. a. Write a function rule for the relationship shown in the table.

b. Use the function to find the total savings after 7 weeks.

Number of Weeks	Total Savings
1	$52
2	$64
3	$76
4	$88

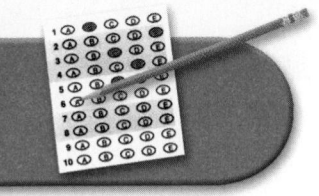

Standardized Test Prep

Reading Comprehension Read the passage below, and then answer the questions on the basis of what is *stated* or *implied* in the passage.

> **Travel Math** Often one of the biggest complications of visiting a foreign country is doing the math. Things that would cause no problem at home are suddenly challenging because the units are different. Consider a quarter-pound hamburger. At 2.2 pounds (lbs) per kilogram (kg), what is the mass of a quarter-pound hamburger in the metric system?
>
> Once you have ordered lunch, you have to pay for it. Let's see . . . one U.S. dollar is worth 1.53 Canadian dollars, 0.70 British pounds, or 1.07 European euros. So how much does a quarter-pound hamburger cost in other countries?
>
> Then there is figuring out the temperature. Even if you can remember the formula Fahrenheit $= \frac{9}{5} \cdot$ Celsius $+ 32$, you must do some work to find whether 20°C is a beach day or a ski day.
>
> Fortunately, it doesn't have to be quite so hard. If you look for some simple approximations, you can usually get around foreign countries without having to pack a calculator. As with many other aspects of travel, the trick is to think ahead, anticipate what might be coming, and have a plan for dealing with it. Before you go, figure out which formulas you will be using and come up with some simple approximations. Then you can leave your calculator home.

1. About how many kilograms are there in 10 lb?

 A 25 kg B 20 kg
 C 11 kg D 5 kg

2. About how many kilograms correspond to a quarter pound?

 F 0.1 kg G 0.5 kg
 H 5 kg J 8.8 kg

3. Based on the article above, which could you use to estimate an exchange of Canadian dollars and United States dollars?

 A 1 U.S. Dollar = ___ Canadian Dollar
 B 1 U.S. Dollar = ___ Canadian Dollar
 C 2 U.S. Dollars = 3 Canadian Dollars
 D 3 U.S. Dollars = 2 Canadian Dollars

4. Suppose you pay $3.00 for a hamburger in Canada. How much is this in United States currency?

 A $1.95 B $3.00
 C $4.53 D $4.59

5. According to the article, about how many euros could you get for 5 U.S. dollars?

 A 0.20 euros B 1.50 euros
 C 4.20 euros D 5.50 euros

6. Suppose you are traveling in France. You see a T-shirt for 40 euros. Is this a reasonable price? Justify your answer.

7. A taxicab ride in London costs you 15 pounds. How much is this in United States currency?

8. The formula Fahrenheit = 2 · Celsius + 30 gives a good estimate of the temperature in degrees Fahrenheit when you know the temperature in degrees Celsius. Is 20°C a beach day? Justify your answer.

9. A foreign exchange student could use the formula Celsius = (Fahrenheit − 32) to find the temperature in degrees Celsius when he knows the temperature in degrees Fahrenheit. Write a formula the student could use to get a good estimate of the Celsius temperature.

Box-and-Whisker Plots

A box-and-whisker plot is a graph that summarizes a data set along a number line. There is a box in the middle and whiskers at either side.

The least value of the data set determines the left whisker. The greatest value of the data set determines the right whisker.

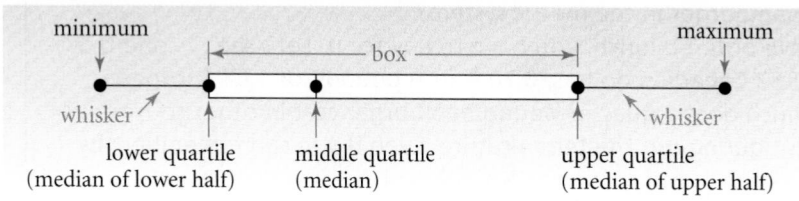

minimum ↓ ↓ maximum

whisker / box \ whisker

lower quartile (median of lower half)   middle quartile (median)   upper quartile (median of upper half)

1 ACTIVITY

You can use a parallel box-and-whisker plot to compare two sets of data. The box-and-whisker plot shows average monthly rainfall for Miami and New Orleans.

1. a. Which city shows a greater range in average monthly rainfall?

   b. Explain how the parallel box-and-whisker plot makes it easy to compare the ranges in this case.

2. How do the maximums, minimums, and the medians of the two data sets compare?

Average Monthly Rainfall (millimeters)

20 40 60 80 100 120 140 160 180 200 220

Miami, Fla.

New Orleans, La.

The widths of the boxes in the box-and-whisker plot are different. The width of the box is the difference between the upper and lower quartiles. This is called interquartile range.

3. a. Find the interquartile range for the average monthly rainfall for Miami and New Orleans.

   b. Reasoning What does the interquartile range indicate about the average monthly rainfall for New Orleans and Miami?

4. Writing What does the interquartile range tell you about how data clusters around the median of the data?

2 ACTIVITY

The data at the right show the prices of snowboards sold at two different shops.

Snowboard Prices

Middletown Snowboards	Snowboard Central
$345	$386
$375	$343
$356	$402
$360	$395
$405	$370
$350	$392

5. Use the prices from Middletown Snowboards. Order the data from least to greatest.

6. Find the middle, lower, and upper quartiles for the prices from Middletown Snowboards.

7. Draw the box-and-whisker plot. Leave space for a second box-and-whisker plot.

8. **Critical Thinking** Is the middle quartile in the middle of the box? Explain.

9. **a.** Find the middle, lower, and upper quartiles for the prices from Snowboard Central.
   b. Draw a box-and-whisker plot for the Snowboard Central data above the plot for the Middletown Snowboards data.

10. **Writing** How do prices of snowboards from each store compare? Use the terms *range, interquartile range*, and *median* in your answer.

EXERCISES

11. **Writing** Describe similarities and differences between stem-and-leaf plots and box-and-whisker plots.

12. **a. Data Collection** Gather data on a topic of your choice.
    b. Make a box-and-whisker plot to display your data.
    c. Write a paragraph interpreting the data.

What You've Learned

- In Chapter 4, you used variables to write expressions and equations that represent real-world situations.

- In Chapter 4, you completed patterns in tables.

- Also in Chapter 4, you wrote functions for data in tables.

 **Check Your Readiness**

 for Help to the Lesson in green.

Writing an Equation (Lesson 4-1)

Write an equation to model each situation.

1. The total cost of n cartons of milk is \$3.60. Each carton costs \$.45.

2. The perimeter of an equilateral triangle is 3 times the length of a side s. The perimeter is 124 in.

Using the Order of Operations (Lesson 4-2)

Evaluate each expression for $a = 4, b = 13,$ and $c = 2.$

3. $2a + cb$ **4.** $cb - a^2$ **5.** $5c + 2a - b$ **6.** $38 - a^2 \div c$

Simplify each expression.

7. $5 + 4 \cdot 7$ **8.** $(5 + 4)(7)$ **9.** $5(4)(7)$

10. $\dfrac{15 - 3 \cdot 2}{3^2}$ **11.** $(42 - 6) \div 2$ **12.** $42 - (6 \div 2)$

Use $<, =,$ or $>$ to compare.

13. $\dfrac{5}{8} \blacksquare \dfrac{10}{15}$ **14.** $-\dfrac{2}{5} \blacksquare -\dfrac{3}{10}$ **15.** $\dfrac{16}{9} \blacksquare \dfrac{4}{3}$ **16.** $\dfrac{4}{5} \blacksquare 0.8$

Writing a Function Rule (Lesson 4-4)

Write a function rule for the relationship in each table.

17.

Hours	Miles Traveled
1	55
2	110
3	165
4	220

18.

Color Copies	Total Cost ($)
1	1.20
2	2.00
3	2.80
4	3.60

19.

Weight on Spring (lb)	Length of Spring (in.)
1	4
2	6
3	8
4	10

Rational Numbers

Key Vocabulary

- additive inverse (p. 232)
- coefficient (p. 257)
- complement of an event (p. 270)
- constant (p. 257)
- deductive reasoning (p. 264)
- dependent events (p. 279)
- element (p. 235)
- event (p. 269)
- experimental probability (p. 271)
- independent events (p. 278)
- like terms (p. 257)
- matrix (p. 235)
- multiplicative inverse (p. 248)
- outcome (p. 269)
- probability (p. 269)
- reciprocal (p. 249)
- sample space (p. 269)
- term (p. 257)
- theoretical probability (p. 269)

What You'll Learn Next

- In this chapter, you will extend your ability to calculate with whole numbers, decimals, and fractions to include integers.

- You will use the Order of Operations and the Distributive Property to simplify expressions.

- You will learn how to calculate theoretical and experimental probability.

Activity Lab Applying what you learn, you will do activities related to baseball, on pages 290–291.

231

Adding Rational Numbers

What You'll Learn

• To add rational numbers using models and rules
• To apply addition

. . . And Why

To use integers to represent yards gained and lost in a football game, as in Example 3

 Check Skills You'll Need

GO for Help Skills Handbook page 792

Find each sum.

1. 4 + 2
2. 10 + 7
3. 9 + 5
4. 27 + 32
5. 0.4 + 0.9
6. 5.2 + 0
7. 4.1 + 6.8
8. 7.6 + 9.5
9. $\frac{1}{5} + \frac{3}{5}$
10. $\frac{4}{9} + \frac{7}{9}$
11. $\frac{1}{2} + \frac{3}{4}$
12. $\frac{3}{8} + \frac{1}{4}$

New Vocabulary • Identity Property of Addition • additive inverse
• Inverse Property of Addition • matrix • element

---

1 Adding Rational Numbers

In previous math courses, you learned that the sum of a number and 0 is the original number. This is true for any number, whether it is positive or negative.

Key Concepts

Property	Identity Property of Addition

For every real number n, $n + 0 = n$ and $0 + n = n$

Examples $-5 + 0 = -5$ $\quad$ $0 + 5 = 5$

The opposite of a number is its **additive inverse.** The number line shows the sum of $4 + (-4)$.

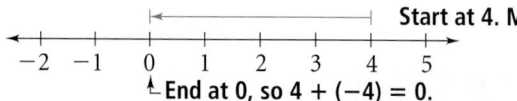

Start at 4. Move left 4 units.

End at 0, so $4 + (-4) = 0$.

The additive inverse of a negative number is a positive number. The number line below shows the sum of $-5 + 5$.

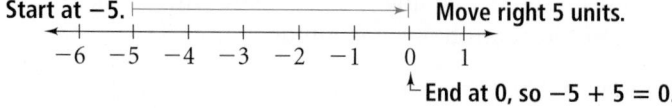

Start at -5.

Move right 5 units.

End at 0, so $-5 + 5 = 0$.

Key Concepts

Property	Inverse Property of Addition

For every real number n, there is an additive inverse $-n$ such that $n + (-n) = 0$.

Examples $17 + (-17) = 0$ $\quad$ $-17 + 17 = 0$

You can use number lines as models to add integers.

1 EXAMPLE Using a Number Line Model

For: Addition Activity
Use: Interactive Textbook, 2-1

Simplify each expression.

a. 2 + 6   Start at 2. ⟶ Move right 6 units.   2 + 6 = 8

0   2   4   6   8   10

b. 2 + (−6)   Start at 2. Move left 6 units.   2 + (−6) = −4

−8   −6   −4   −2   0   2

c. −2 + 6   Start at −2. ⟶ Move right 6 units.   −2 + 6 = 4

−4   −2   0   2   4   6

d. −2 + (−6)   Start at −2. Move left 6 units.   −2 + (−6) = −8

−10   −8   −6   −4   −2   0

✓**Quick Check** ❶ Use a number line to find each sum.

a. −6 + 4 **b.** 4 + (−6) **c.** −3 + (−8) **d.** 9 + (−3)

You can also find the sums in Example 1 using rules. Recall that numbers being added are called addends.

Key Concepts

Rule	Adding Numbers With the Same Sign

To add two numbers with the same sign, *add* their absolute values. The sum has the same sign as the addends.

Examples   2 + 6 = 8   −2 + (−6) = −8

Rule	Adding Numbers With Different Signs

To add two numbers with different signs, find the *difference* of their absolute values. The sum has the same sign as the addend with the greater absolute value.

Examples   −2 + 6 = 4   2 + (−6) = −4

2 EXAMPLE Adding Numbers

Simplify each expression.

a. −5 + (−6) = −11   Since both addends are negative, add their absolute values. The sum is negative.

b. 13 + (−34) = −21   The difference of the absolute values is 21. The negative addend has the greater absolute value, so the sum is negative.

c. 3.4 + 9.7 = 13.1   Since both addends are positive, add their absolute values. The sum is positive.

d. −1.5 + 3.4 = 1.9   The difference of the absolute values is 1.9. The positive addend has the greater absolute value, so the sum is positive.

✓**Quick Check** ❷ Find each sum.

a. −7 + (−4) **b.** −26.3 + 8.9 **c.** $-\frac{3}{4} + \left(-\frac{1}{2}\right)$ **d.** $\frac{8}{9} + \left(-\frac{5}{6}\right)$

You can use negative numbers to model real-world situations.

3 EXAMPLE <u>Real-World  Problem Solving</u>

Football A football team gains 2 yd and then loses 7 yd in two plays. You express a loss of 7 yd as −7. Use addition to find the result of the two plays.

$$2 + (−7) = −5$$

● The result of the two plays is a loss of 5 yd.

✓ Quick Check ③ **Temperature** The temperature falls 15 degrees and then rises 18 degrees. Use addition to find the change in temperature.

2 Applying Addition

You can evaluate expressions that involve addition. Substitute a value for the variable(s). Then simplify the expression. The expression $−n$ means the opposite of n. The expression $−n$ can represent a negative number, zero, or a positive number.

4 EXAMPLE **Evaluating Expressions**

Evaluate $−n + 8.9$ for $n = −2.3$.

$$
\begin{aligned}
−n + 8.9 &= −(−2.3) + 8.9 &&\textbf{Substitute −2.3 for } \textit{n.}\\
&= 2.3 + 8.9 &&\textbf{− (−2.3) means the opposite of −2.3, which is 2.3.}\\
&= 11.2 &&\textbf{Simplify.}
\end{aligned}
$$

✓ Quick Check ④ Evaluate each expression for $t = −7.1$.
    a. $t + (−4.3)$ **b.** $−2 + t$ **c.** $8.5 + (−t)$ **d.** $−t + 7.49$

You can write and evaluate expressions to model real-world situations.

5 EXAMPLE <u>Real-World  Problem Solving</u>

Climbing A rock climber climbs a mountain. The base of the mountain is 132 ft below sea level.
a. Write an expression to represent the climber's height below or above sea level.

    Relate   132 ft below sea level   plus   number of feet climbed

    Define   Let h = number of feet climbed.

    Write   −132   + h

    $−132 + h$

b. Find the climber's height above sea level when he is 485 ft above the base of the mountain.

$$
\begin{aligned}
−132 + h &= −132 + 485 &&\textbf{Substitute 485 for } \textit{h.}\\
&= 353 &&\textbf{Simplify.}
\end{aligned}
$$

● His height is 353 ft above sea level.

✓ Quick Check ⑤ **Temperature** The temperature one winter morning is −14°F. Define a variable and write an expression to find the temperature after it changes. Then evaluate your expression for a decrease of 11 degrees Fahrenheit.

	Public	Private
mentary	29.8	3.4
;h School	14.8	1.2	← row
.lege	12.4	3.5

↑ column

A1_3eSE0104ta07

You can use matrices to add rational numbers. A **matrix** is a rectangular arrangement of numbers in rows and columns. The plural of matrix is matrices (pronounced MAY-truh-seez). The matrix below shows the data in the table.

	Public	Private
Elementary	29.8	3.4
High School	14.8	1.2	← row
College	12.4	3.5

↑ column

You identify the size of a matrix by the number of rows and the number of columns. The matrix above has 3 rows and 2 columns, so it is a 3×2 matrix. Each item in a matrix is an **element.**

Matrices are equal if the elements in corresponding positions are equal.

$$\begin{bmatrix} -1 & 2 \\ 4 & 0 \end{bmatrix} = \begin{bmatrix} -1 & \frac{4}{2} \\ \frac{20}{5} & 0 \end{bmatrix}$$

You add matrices that are the same size by adding the corresponding elements.

6 EXAMPLE Adding Matrices

Add $\begin{bmatrix} -5 & 2.7 \\ 7 & -3 \end{bmatrix} + \begin{bmatrix} -3 & -3.9 \\ -4 & 2 \end{bmatrix}$.

$\begin{bmatrix} -5 & 2.7 \\ 7 & -3 \end{bmatrix} + \begin{bmatrix} -3 & -3.9 \\ -4 & 2 \end{bmatrix} = \begin{bmatrix} -5 + (-3) & 2.7 + (-3.9) \\ 7 + (-4) & -3 + 2 \end{bmatrix}$ **Add corresponding elements.**

$= \begin{bmatrix} -8 & -1.2 \\ 3 & -1 \end{bmatrix}$ **Simplify.**

✓ Quick Check 6 Find each sum.

a. $\begin{bmatrix} 5 \\ 3.2 \\ -4.9 \end{bmatrix} + \begin{bmatrix} -9 \\ -1.7 \\ -11.1 \end{bmatrix}$

b. $\begin{bmatrix} -4 & \frac{7}{8} \\ \frac{3}{4} & 0 \end{bmatrix} + \begin{bmatrix} -5 & -\frac{3}{4} \\ \frac{1}{2} & -1 \end{bmatrix}$

EXERCISES

For more exercises, see *Extra Skill and Word Problem Practice.*

Practice and Problem Solving

A Practice by Example

Example 1
(page 233)

GO for Help

Write the expression modeled by each number line. Then find the sum.

1.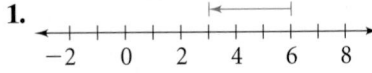

2.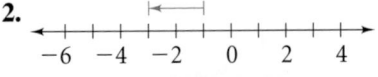

3.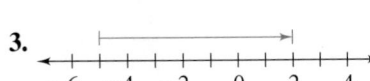

4.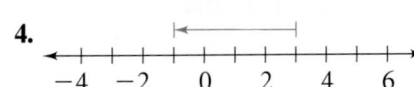

Example 2
(page 233)

Simplify.

5. 3 + 12   **6.** −7 + (−4)   **7.** −8.7 + (−10.3)   **8.** 5.04 + 7.1

9. 5 + (−9)   **10.** −8 + 13   **11.** −27 + 19   **12.** 45 + (−87)

13. −2.3 + 4.5   **14.** −8.05 + 7.4   **15.** 9.51 + (−17)   **16.** 3.42 + (−2.09)

17. $\frac{4}{5} + \frac{2}{15}$ **18.** $-\frac{5}{9} + \left(-\frac{1}{3}\right)$ **19.** $2\frac{1}{4} + 3\frac{15}{16}$ **20.** $-4\frac{3}{8} + \left(-1\frac{3}{4}\right)$

21. $-\frac{2}{3} + \frac{4}{6}$ **22.** $\frac{1}{9} + \left(-\frac{5}{6}\right)$ **23.** $-5\frac{7}{12} + 10\frac{3}{4}$ **24.** $\frac{9}{7} + \left(-2\frac{3}{14}\right)$

Example 3
(page 234)

25. A diver dives 47 ft below the surface of the water and then rises 12 ft. Use addition to find the diver's depth.

26. On two football plays, a team gains 8 yd, and then loses 5 yd. Use addition to find the result of the two plays.

27. One morning in Detroit, Michigan, the temperature at 6 A.M. was −6°F. The temperature rose 13 degrees Fahrenheit by noon. Use addition to find the temperature at noon.

Example 4
(page 234)

Evaluate each expression for $n = 3.5$.

28. $5.2 + n$ **29.** $-5.2 + n$ **30.** $-n + 5.2$ **31.** $-n + (-5.2)$

32. $9.1 + n$ **33.** $-9.1 + n$ **34.** $-n + 9.1$ **35.** $-9.1 + (-n)$

Example 5
(page 234)

36. Temperature The temperature one winter morning is −8°F. Define a variable and write an expression to find the temperature after each change below. Then evaluate your expression for each change.
  a. a rise of 7°F   **b.** a decrease of 3°F
  c. a rise of 19°F   **d.** a decrease of 12°F

37. Money You have $74 in a checking account. Define a variable and write an expression to find the balance in your account after each deposit or withdrawal below. Then evaluate your expression for each change.
  a. a deposit of $18   **b.** a withdrawal of $29
  c. a withdrawal of $47   **d.** a deposit of $120

Example 6
(page 235)

Simplify.

38. $\begin{bmatrix} 7 & -8 \\ -12 & 6.2 \end{bmatrix} + \begin{bmatrix} -8 & 9.4 \\ -9 & 17 \end{bmatrix}$ **39.** $\begin{bmatrix} -7.2 \\ 3.2 \\ -4.9 \end{bmatrix} + \begin{bmatrix} -11 \\ 8.4 \\ 24 \end{bmatrix}$

40. $\begin{bmatrix} \frac{1}{2} \\ 8 \\ -9 \end{bmatrix} + \begin{bmatrix} -\frac{1}{2} \\ 17 \\ -3 \end{bmatrix}$ **41.** $\begin{bmatrix} 1.3 & 26 \\ \frac{1}{8} & -2 \end{bmatrix} + \begin{bmatrix} 0.5 & -4 \\ -\frac{5}{8} & 9 \end{bmatrix}$

B Apply Your Skills

Copy and complete each table.

42.

a	a + 5
−7	■
−5	■
0	■
■	8

43.

x	−3 + x
−2	■
0	■
$1\frac{1}{2}$	■
■	6

44.

n	n + (−7)
−4	■
−1	■
3	■
■	−1

Real-World Connection

The art of photography is changing because of the development of digital cameras.

Art Use the table for Exercises 45–48.

Number of People Who Participate in Art Activities (millions)

Ages	Drawing	Pottery	Weaving	Photography	Creative Writing
18–24	9.2	5.0	5.2	6.6	7.6
25–34	7.2	6.8	10.0	7.2	5.2
35–44	6.8	8.2	13.1	8.2	5.4
45–54	4.4	6.1	9.8	6.1	3.4
55–64	1.9	2.1	6.1	2.1	1.0

SOURCE: *Statistical Abstract of the United States*

45. How many people aged 18 to 34 participate in photography?

46. How many people aged 45 to 64 draw?

47. Which of the activities is most popular? Explain how you found your answer.

48. a. Write a fraction to compare the number of people aged 25 to 34 who weave to the number of people aged 18 to 64 who weave.
   b. Write your answer from part (a) as a decimal to the nearest hundredth.
   c. What percent of the people who weave are aged 25 to 34?

Evaluate each expression for $a = -2, b = 3$, and $c = -4$.

49. $-a + 2 + c$ **50.** $-|a|$ **51.** $a + b$ **52.** $a + (-b)$

53. $a + 3b$ **54.** $c + 3b$ **55.** $c + a + 5$ **56.** $-(c + a + 5)$

 57. Writing Without calculating, which is greater, the sum of -227 and 319 or the sum of 227 and -319? Explain.

58. Reasoning Explain what is wrong with the reasoning in the statement: *Since 20 is the opposite of -20, then $20°F$ must be very hot, because $-20°F$ is very cold.*

Evaluate each expression for $b = -3.5$.

59. $b + 3.2$ **60.** $-9 + b + (-1.2)$ **61.** $b + |-2.9|$

62. $8.5 + b + 3.7$ **63.** $|b| + (-3.4)$ **64.** $-5.6 + b + 7.2$

65. Multiple Choice A charged atom of magnesium has 12 protons and 10 electrons. Each proton has a charge of $+1$, and each electron has a charge of -1. What is the total charge of the atom?
   Ⓐ -2 Ⓑ -1 Ⓒ $+1$ Ⓓ $+2$

66. Open-Ended Write a 2×3 matrix.

67. Error Analysis A student added two matrices as shown. What error did the student make?

$$\begin{bmatrix} 4 & -1 \\ -3 & 2 \\ 1.5 & 6 \end{bmatrix} + \begin{bmatrix} -2 & 2.3 & 0 \\ 7 & -4 & 5.1 \end{bmatrix} = \begin{bmatrix} 11 & -3 \\ -7 & 4.3 \\ 6.6 & 6 \end{bmatrix}$$

68. Math in the Media In the cartoon below, does the total "12 27" make sense? Explain.

Frank and Ernest

TIME	11:53
TEMP.	74°
TOTAL	12 27

© 1980 Thaves / Reprinted with permission. Newspaper dist. by NEA, Inc.

THAVES

Number of Employees

Saturday Schedule

| Shift | Hourly Wage | | | |
	$6.25	$6.50	$7.00	$7.50
Day	8	3	5	1
Evening	10	2	2	1
Night	4	1	0	1

Sunday Schedule

| Shift | Hourly Wage | | | |
	$6.25	$6.50	$7.00	$7.50
Day	5	2	1	1
Evening	8	2	0	1
Night	2	1	0	1

69. Jobs Use the data in the tables at the left.
  a. Write the data in each table as a matrix.
  b. Add the matrices to find the total number of workers in each pay category for each work shift.
  c. How many weekend employees on the evening shift earn $6.50 per hour?
  d. How many weekend employees work the night shift?
  e. Critical Thinking Suppose all employees work 8-hour shifts both Saturday and Sunday. How would you use the matrix to find the total wages of the weekend employees?
  f. Find the total wages of the weekend employees.

70. Suppose you overdrew your bank account. You have a balance of −$34. You then deposit checks for $17 and $49. At the same time the bank charges you a $25 fee for overdrawing your account. What is your balance?

71. a. What is the value of −n when $n = -4$?
  b. What is the value of −n when $n = 4$?
  c. Reasoning For what values of n will −n be positive? Negative?

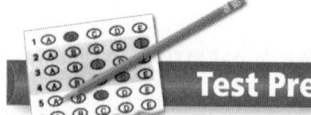 **Challenge**

Simplify each expression.

72. $\frac{w}{5} + \left(-\frac{w}{10}\right)$ **73.** $-\frac{c}{4} + \left(-\frac{c}{4}\right)$ **74.** $3\left(\frac{a}{7}\right) + 7\left(\frac{a}{3}\right)$

75. $-1\left(\frac{b}{9}\right) + \left(-\frac{b}{9}\right)$ **76.** $\frac{-x}{4} + \frac{x}{3}$ **77.** $\frac{x}{4} + \left(-\frac{x}{3}\right)$

Tell whether each sum is *positive, negative,* or *zero.* Explain.

78. n is positive and m is negative. $n + (-m)$ is ___?___ .

79. n is positive, and m is negative. $-n + m$ is ___?___ .

80. $|n| = |m|$, n is positive, and m is negative. $n + (-m)$ is ___?___ .

81. $|n| = |m|$, n is positive, and m is negative. $-n + (-m)$ is ___?___ .

Test Prep

Multiple Choice

82. Simplify $10 + |-3| + (-3)$.
  A. 16   **B.** 10   **C.** 7   **D.** 4

83. Evaluate $(3a + b) + (-20)$ for $a = 5$ and $b = -1$.
  F. −6   **G.** −2   **H.** 20   **J.** 22

84. Which expression has a value that is not the same as the value of the other expressions?

A. $-7 + 3$ **B.** $5 + (-9)$ **C.** $-8\frac{2}{3} + 4\frac{2}{3}$ **D.** $-9 + 13$

85. In a 12-hour period, the temperature rose from $-12°F$ to $18°F$. Find the increase in temperature in degrees.

F. 30   **G.** 6   **H.** -6 **J.** -30

86. The value of $-(-(-27))$ is NOT the same as which of the following expressions?

A. $-29 + 2$ **B.** $-12.8 + (-14.2)$
C. $-42 + 17$ **D.** $8 + (-35)$

87. Suppose you have $95 in your checking account. You pay for a $34 sweater using your debit card. Then you deposit a $32 check. The next day you withdraw $16 at the supermarket. What is the balance in your account?

F. $145   **G.** $81   **H.** $77   **J.** $13

Mixed Review

Lesson 4-3

Use <, =, or > to compare.

88. $-1.23 \ \blacksquare \ -1.18$

89. $1\frac{2}{4} \ \blacksquare \ 1\frac{5}{10}$

90. $|-5| \ \blacksquare \ |-6|$

91. $|-4.1| \ \blacksquare \ |-3.9|$

92. $\left|-\frac{3}{10}\right| \ \blacksquare \ \left|\frac{2}{9}\right|$

93. $|1.2| \ \blacksquare \ \left|-\frac{6}{5}\right|$

Lesson 4-2

Simplify each expression.

94. $(5 - 2)^2$ **95.** $-4 + 3.1(2)$ **96.** $9[5 + (-3)]$ **97.** $4^2 + 3^2 - 2^2$

A Point in Time

2000 B.C.   1000   0   1000   2000

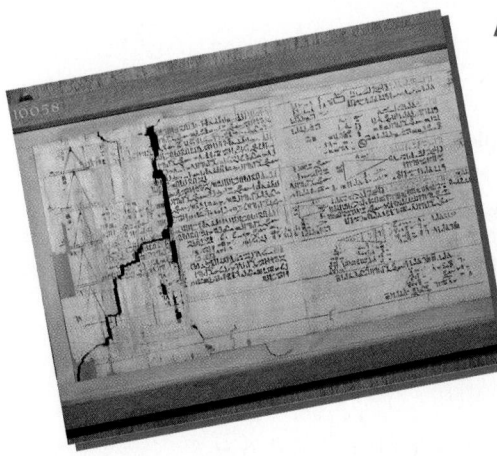

A papyrus scroll discovered in Egypt shows that Egyptians were using symbols for "plus," "minus," "equals," and "unknown quantity" more than 3500 years ago. Named for the scribe who copied it, the Ahmes Papyrus is 18 ft long and 1 ft wide. It is also known as the Rhind Papyrus, after the British Egyptologist who bought the papyrus. It is a practical handbook containing 85 problems that include work with rational numbers. In the Ahmes Papyrus, rational numbers are written as sums of unit fractions. A unit fraction has 1 as its numerator. Here are some examples.

$$\frac{3}{4} = \frac{1}{2} + \frac{1}{4} \qquad \frac{3}{8} = \frac{1}{4} + \frac{1}{8} \qquad \frac{21}{30} = \frac{1}{6} + \frac{1}{5} + \frac{1}{3}$$

Go Online
PHSchool.com   **For:** Information about the Ahmes Papyrus
Web Code: ate-2032

Subtracting Rational Numbers

What You'll Learn

- To subtract rational numbers
- To apply subtraction

. . . And Why

To find stock prices, as in Example 6

✅ **Check Skills You'll Need**

Find the opposite of each number.

1. 6   **2.** −7   **3.** 3.79   **4.** $-\frac{7}{19}$

Simplify.

5. $3 + (-2)$ **6.** $9.5 + (-3.5)$ **7.** $13 + (-8)$ **8.** $\frac{2}{3} + \left(-\frac{1}{6}\right)$

GO **for Help** Lessons 4-3 and 5-1

1 Subtracting Rational Numbers

You have learned to add rational numbers and to find the opposite of a number. You can use these two concepts to understand how to subtract rational numbers.

1 EXAMPLE   Using a Number Line Model

Find $4 - 7$.

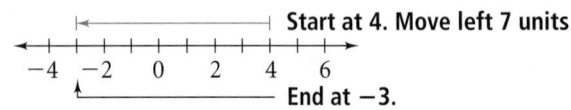

Start at 4. Move left 7 units.

End at −3.

• $4 - 7 = -3$

✅ **Quick Check** ❶ Use a number line to find each difference.
   a. $2 - 6$ **b.** $-1 - 4$ **c.** $-3 - 8$ **d.** $7 - 2$

You can use tiles to model subtraction. A ⬜ represents $+1$, and a ⬛ represents -1. A negative tile and a positive tile together (⬜⬛) represent zero. This is called a zero pair.

2 EXAMPLE   Using a Tile Model

Find $3 - (-5)$.

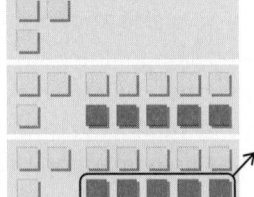

Start with 3 positive tiles.

Add zero pairs until there are 5 negative tiles.

Remove 5 negative tiles.
There are 8 positive tiles left.

• $3 - (-5) = 8$

✅ **Quick Check** ❷ Draw tiles to find each difference.
     a. $4 - 5$ **b.** $5 - (-9)$ **c.** $-6 - (-10)$ **d.** $6 - 3$

The number line below models the sum $2 + (-6)$ *and* the difference $2 - 6$.

Start at 2. Move left 6 units.

$-4 \quad -2 \quad 0 \quad 2$

Both $2 + (-6)$ and $2 - 6$ have the same value, -4. This illustrates the following rule for subtracting rational numbers.

 Key Concepts

Rule	Subtracting Numbers

To subtract a number, add its opposite.

Examples $\quad 3 - 5 = 3 + (-5) = -2 \qquad 3 - (-5) = 3 + 5 = 8$

3 EXAMPLE Subtracting Rational Numbers

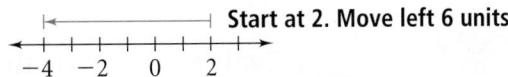

Simplify each expression.

a. $-4 - (-9)$

$\qquad -4 - (-9) = -4 + 9$ **The opposite of -9 is 9.**

$\qquad\qquad\qquad\quad = 5$ **Add.**

Video Tutor Help
Visit: PHSchool.com
Web Code: ate-0775

b. $\frac{3}{4} - \left(-\frac{11}{12}\right)$

$\qquad \frac{3}{4} - \left(-\frac{11}{12}\right) = \frac{3}{4} + \frac{11}{12}$ **The opposite of $-\frac{11}{12}$ is $\frac{11}{12}$.**

$\qquad\qquad\qquad\quad = \frac{9}{12} + \frac{11}{12}$ **Use common denominators.**

$\qquad\qquad\qquad\quad = \frac{20}{12}$ **Add.**

$\qquad\qquad\qquad\quad = \frac{5}{3}$ or $1\frac{2}{3}$ **Write $\frac{20}{12}$ in simplest form.**

✓ Quick Check ❸ Find each difference.

$\quad$ **a.** $-6 - 2$ $\qquad$ **b.** $8 - (-4)$ $\qquad$ **c.** $3.7 - (-4.3)$ $\qquad$ **d.** $-\frac{8}{9} - \left(-\frac{5}{6}\right)$

2 Applying Subtraction

Recall that when you simplify an expression, you work within grouping symbols first. Absolute value symbols are grouping symbols, so find the value of an expression within the absolute value symbols before finding the absolute value.

4 EXAMPLE Absolute Values

Simplify $|5 - 11|$.

$\quad |5 - 11| = |-6|$ **Subtract within absolute value symbols.**

$\qquad\qquad\quad = 6$ **Find the absolute value.**

✓ Quick Check ❹ Simplify each expression.

$\quad$ **a.** $|8 - 7|$ $\qquad$ **b.** $|7 - 8|$ $\qquad$ **c.** $|-10 - (-4)|$ $\qquad$ **d.** $|-4 - (-10)|$

You evaluate expressions that involve subtraction by substituting for the variable. Then simplify the expression.

5 EXAMPLE Evaluating Expressions

Evaluate $-a - b$ for $a = -3$ and $b = -5$.

$-a - b = -(-3) - (-5)$ **Substitute −3 for a and −5 for b.**

$= 3 - (-5)$ **The opposite of −3 is 3.**

$= 3 + 5$ **To subtract −5, add its opposite, 5.**

$= 8$ **Add.**

✅ **Quick Check** ⑤ Evaluate each expression for $t = -2$ and $r = -7$.

    a. $r - t$ **b.** $t - r$ **c.** $-t - r$ **d.** $-r - (-t)$

You can write expressions to model real-world situations.

6 EXAMPLE Real-World  Problem Solving

Stock Price Find the closing price of stock XYZ on Wednesday by subtracting the change in price from the closing price on Thursday.

$17.37 - (-0.87) = 17.37 + 0.87$ **Add the opposite.**

$= 18.24$ **Simplify.**

The closing share price on Wednesday was $18.24.

✅ **Quick Check** ⑥ **Stock Price** Find the closing price of stocks ABC and PQR on Wednesday.

STOCK PRICES

ge	Stock	Thurs Close	Change
5	ABC	32.79	0.32
2	PQR	14.23	-1.23
1	XYZ	17.37	-0.87

C3

EXERCISES

For more exercises, see *Extra Skill and Word Problem Practice.*

Practice and Problem Solving

A Practice by Example

Examples 1, 2
(page 240)

GO for Help

Draw a number line or tiles to model each difference. Then find each difference.

1. $1 - 2$ **2.** $7 - 9$ **3.** $-4 - 2$ **4.** $-2 - 3$

5. $-5 - (-6)$ **6.** $-3 - 8$ **7.** $5 - (-9)$ **8.** $-1 - (-4)$

Example 3
(page 241)

Simplify each expression.

9. $3 - 7$ **10.** $2 - (-9)$ **11.** $-4 - 6$ **12.** $-5 - (-1)$

13. $6.2 - 8.3$ **14.** $-7.4 - 1.8$ **15.** $5.3 - (-8.4)$ **16.** $-3.6 - (-7.1)$

17. $\frac{1}{3} - \frac{1}{2}$ **18.** $-\frac{2}{5} - \frac{7}{10}$ **19.** $\frac{2}{12} - \left(-\frac{3}{4}\right)$ **20.** $-\frac{5}{12} - \left(-\frac{1}{10}\right)$

Example 4
(page 241)

21. $|5 - 2|$ **22.** $|-7 - 1|$ **23.** $|4 - 10|$ **24.** $|-3 - (-5)|$

25. $|-6 - 7|$ **26.** $|8 - 6|$ **27.** $|3 - 9|$ **28.** $|-11 - (-8)|$

Example 5
(page 242)

Evaluate each expression for $x = 3$, $y = -4$, and $z = 6$.

29. $y - z$ **30.** $x - y$ **31.** $-y - x$ **32.** $-x - y$

33. $z - x$ **34.** $2x - z$ **35.** $x + y - z$ **36.** $-z + y - x$

Example 6
(page 242)

37. On Friday, the closing price of a KJL company share was $51.72. It had risen $1.08 from the previous day. Find the closing price of KJL on Thursday.

B **Apply Your Skills**

Evaluate each expression for $a = -2$, $b = 3.5$, **and** $c = -4$.

38. $a - b + c$ **39.** $-c - b + a$ **40.** $-|a|$ **41.** $|a| + |b|$

42. $|a + b|$ **43.** $-|3 + a|$ **44.** $4b - a$ **45.** $-4b - |a|$

46. $|c + a - 5|$ **47.** $|c + a + 5|$ **48.** $|a - c| - |c|$ **49.** $|a| + |3b|$

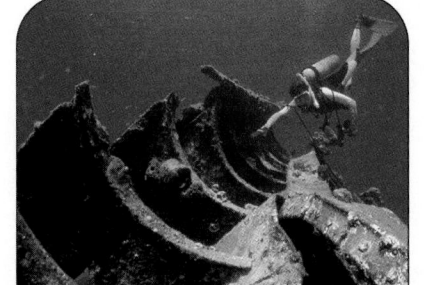

Real-World **Connection**

Careers Archaeologists uncover and study the remains of ancient cultures. Archaeologists may look for remains in remote locations, underground, in caves, or underwater.

50. Multiple Choice Archaeologists found a 1500-year-old ship at the bottom of the Black Sea. The ship is well preserved because oxygen could not make the ship decay. The ship is at a depth of 1000 ft below the surface. This is about 350 ft below the boundary between surface water, which has oxygen, and water below, which does not have oxygen. How deep is the boundary?
    Ⓐ 650 ft   Ⓑ 750 ft   Ⓒ 1150 ft   Ⓓ 1350 ft

51. Open-Ended Write two matrices with the same dimensions. Find the difference of the two matrices.

Decide if each statement is always true. If the statement is not always true, give a counterexample.

52. The difference of two numbers is less than the sum of those two numbers.

53. The difference of two numbers is less than each of those two numbers.

54. A number minus its opposite is twice the number.

55. a. Sports Write the data in each table below as a matrix.

City-Wide Participation in Sports Activities (thousands)

	Sport	Elementary	High School	College
2000	Basketball	5.5	8.2	4.9
	Tennis	1.4	3.2	3.9
	Soccer	4.2	3.8	1.3
	Volleyball	1.6	5.2	5.1

	Sport	Elementary	High School	College
2005	Basketball	6.8	7.9	4.9
	Tennis	1.0	1.8	1.7
	Soccer	5.6	4.1	1.3
	Volleyball	1.8	4.9	2.9

    b. Subtract the 2000 matrix from the 2005 matrix to find the changes in participation in sports activities.

     c. Writing Suppose you invest in sporting goods. In which sport would you invest? Use elements from your matrix to explain.

GO Online
Homework Video Tutor
Visit: PHSchool.com
Web Code: ate-0202

Subtract.

56. $\begin{bmatrix} -3 & 4 \\ 0 & -1 \end{bmatrix} - \begin{bmatrix} -5 & 6 \\ 9 & -4 \end{bmatrix}$ **57.** $\begin{bmatrix} \frac{3}{8} & \frac{1}{5} & 4 \end{bmatrix} - \begin{bmatrix} \frac{5}{8} & \frac{2}{10} & 7 \end{bmatrix}$ **58.** $\begin{bmatrix} \frac{1}{4} \\ -3 \end{bmatrix} - \begin{bmatrix} \frac{2}{3} \\ -2 \end{bmatrix}$

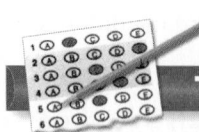

C Challenge

59. Critical Thinking Use examples to illustrate your answers.
   a. Is $|a - b|$ always equal to $|b - a|$?
   b. Is $|a + b|$ always equal to $|a| + |b|$?

Simplify each expression.

60. $1 - \frac{1}{2} - \frac{1}{3} - \frac{1}{4} - \frac{1}{5} - \frac{1}{6}$

61. $1 - \left(\frac{1}{2} - \left(\frac{1}{3} - \left(\frac{1}{4} - \left(\frac{1}{5} - \frac{1}{6}\right)\right)\right)\right)$

62. $-8t - 5m + 3m - 7t - (-3t) + m$

63. Order the expressions $|x + y|, |x - y|, |x| - |y|,$ and $x - y$ from least to greatest for $x = -8$ and $y = -10$.

Test Prep

Gridded Response

64. Evaluate $-|a - b| + |2c|$ for $a = -3$, $b = 4$, and $c = -4$.

65. Find the value of $12 + (-7)$.

66. Find the next number in the pattern 14, 11, 8, 5, . . .

67. Use the bar graph at the right. In dollars, estimate the average hourly earnings of U.S. nonfarm workers in 2010.

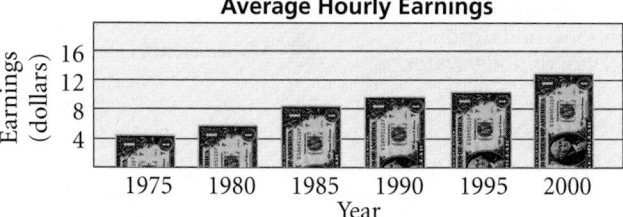

68. One January day, the temperature at dawn is –8°F. By noon, the temperature has risen 19 degrees. What is the noon temperature in degrees Fahrenheit?

Mixed Review

Lesson 5-1

Simplify each expression.

69. $6 + (-2)$

70. $-5 + (-4)$

71. $-3.4 + 2.7$

72. $5.9 + (-10)$

Simplify.

73. $\begin{bmatrix} 3 & -8 \\ 2 & 11 \end{bmatrix} + \begin{bmatrix} 1 & 8 \\ -2 & 5 \end{bmatrix}$ **74.** $\begin{bmatrix} 1.3 \\ -6.7 \\ 7.1 \end{bmatrix} + \begin{bmatrix} -0.1 \\ 4.2 \\ -1.9 \end{bmatrix}$ **75.** $\begin{bmatrix} \frac{1}{2} & -1 \\ 6 & \frac{2}{3} \end{bmatrix} + \begin{bmatrix} -4 & \frac{1}{3} \\ \frac{1}{3} & -5 \end{bmatrix}$

Lesson 4-1

Define variables and write an equation to model each situation.

76. The total cost equals the number of pounds of pears times $1.19/lb.

77. You have $20. Then you buy a bouquet. How much do you have left?

78. You go out to lunch with five friends and split the check equally. What is your share of the check?

Multiplying and Dividing Rational Numbers

What You'll Learn

- To multiply rational numbers
- To divide rational numbers

. . . And Why

To find the change in temperature with an increase in altitude, as in Example 3

GO for Help Lessons 5-1 and 5-2

Simplify each expression.

1. $-2 + (-2) + (-2) + (-2)$

2. $-5 + (-5) + (-5) + (-5) + (-5)$

3. $-6 - 6 - 6 - 6$

4. $-12 - 12 - 12 - 12 - 12 - 12$

Write the next three numbers in each pattern.

5. $2, 4, 6,$ ■, ■, ■

6. $6, 4, 2,$ ■, ■, ■

7. $12, 9, 6,$ ■, ■, ■

8. $-18, -12, -6,$ ■, ■, ■

◆)) **New Vocabulary**
- Identity Property of Multiplication
- Multiplication Property of Zero
- Multiplication Property of -1
- Inverse Property of Multiplication
- multiplicative inverse • reciprocal

1 Multiplying Rational Numbers

Activity: Multiplying Integers

1. **Patterns** Use patterns to complete each statement.

   a. $2 \cdot 3 =$ ■

   $2 \cdot 2 =$ ■

   $2 \cdot 1 =$ ■

   $2 \cdot 0 =$ ■

   $2(-1) =$ ■

   $2(-2) =$ ■

   $2(-3) =$ ■

   b. $3(-2) =$ ■

   $2(-2) =$ ■

   $1(-2) =$ ■

   $0(-2) =$ ■

   $-1(-2) =$ ■

   $-2(-2) =$ ■

   $-3(-2) =$ ■

2. **Make a Conjecture** From the patterns you found in Question 1, what seems to be the sign of the product of a positive number and a negative number?

3. **Make a Conjecture** From the patterns you found in Question 1, what seems to be the sign of the product of two negative numbers?

The product of a number and 1 is the original number. It does not matter whether the original number is positive or negative. The product of 0 and a number is 0. The product of -1 and a number is the opposite of the original number.

 **Key Concepts**

	Identity Property of Multiplication

Property   **Identity Property of Multiplication**

For every real number n, $1 \cdot n = n$ and $n \cdot 1 = n$.

Examples $1 \cdot (-5) = -5$ $-5 \cdot 1 = -5$

Property   **Multiplication Property of Zero**

For every real number n, $n \cdot 0 = 0$ and $0 \cdot n = 0$.

Examples $35 \cdot 0 = 0$ $0 \cdot 35 = 0$

Property   **Multiplication Property of −1**

For every real number n, $-1 \cdot n = -n$ and $n \cdot -1 = -n$.

Examples $-1 \cdot 5 = -5$ $5 \cdot (-1) = -5$

From the examples for the properties above, you can see a pattern for multiplying positive and negative numbers.

Multiplying Numbers With the Same Sign

$$1 \quad \cdot \quad 5 \quad = \quad 5$$
positive · positive = positive

$$-1 \quad \cdot \quad (-5) \quad = \quad 5$$
negative · negative = positive

Multiplying Numbers With Different Signs

$$1 \quad \cdot \quad (-5) \quad = \quad -5$$
positive · negative = negative

$$-1 \quad \cdot \quad 5 \quad = \quad -5$$
negative · positive = negative

This pattern also holds true when multiplying by numbers other than 1 and −1.

 Key Concepts

Rule   **Multiplying Numbers With the Same Sign**

The product of two positive numbers or two negative numbers is positive.

Examples $5 \cdot 2 = 10$ $-5(-2) = 10$

Rule   **Multiplying Numbers With Different Signs**

The product of a positive number and a negative number, or a negative number and a positive number, is negative.

Examples $3(-6) = -18$ $-3 \cdot 6 = -18$

1 EXAMPLE   **Multiplying Numbers**

Simplify each expression.

a. $-9(-4) = 36$ The product of two negative numbers is positive.

b. $5\left(-\frac{2}{3}\right) = -\frac{10}{3}$ The product of a positive number and a negative number is negative.

         $= -3\frac{1}{3}$ Write $-\frac{10}{3}$ as a mixed number.

 **Quick Check**   **1** Simplify each expression.

     a. $4(-6)$ **b.** $-10(-5)$ **c.** $-4.9(-8)$ **d.** $-\frac{2}{3}\left(\frac{3}{4}\right)$

When you simplify or evaluate expressions with three or more negative numbers, you must be careful to account for all of the negative signs as you multiply.

2 EXAMPLE Evaluating Expressions

Evaluate $-2xy$ for $x = -20$ and $y = -3$.

$-2xy = -2(-20)(-3)$ **Substitute −20 for x and −3 for y.**

$= -120$ **−2(−20) results in a positive number, 40. 40(−3) results in a negative number, −120.**

 **Quick Check** **2** Evaluate each expression for $c = -8$ and $d = -7$.
  a. $-(cd)$ **b.** $(-2)(-3)(cd)$ **c.** $c(-d)$

You can use expressions involving multiplication to model real-world situations.

8000 ft

3 EXAMPLE Real-World Problem Solving

Multiple Choice You can use the function $t = -5.5\left(\frac{a}{1000}\right)$ to calculate the change in temperature t in degrees Fahrenheit for an increase in altitude a, measured in feet. A hot-air balloon starts on the ground and then rises 8000 ft. What is the change in temperature at the altitude of the balloon?

  (A) $44°F$ (B) $40°F$ (C) $-40°F$ (D) $-44°F$

$-5.5\left(\frac{a}{1000}\right) = -5.5\left(\frac{8000}{1000}\right)$ **Substitute 8000 for a.**

$= -5.5(8)$ **Divide within parentheses.**

$= -44$ **Multiply.**

● The change in temperature is -44 degrees Fahrenheit. The answer is D.

 **Quick Check** **3** **a.** Find the change in temperature if a balloon rises 4500 ft from the ground.
  b. Suppose the temperature is 40°F at ground level. What is the approximate air temperature at the altitude of the balloon?

The expression -3^4 means the opposite of 3^4. The exponent 4 applies to the base 3. The negative sign is not part of the base. In the expression $(-3)^4$, the negative sign is part of the base -3. The exponent 4 applies to the base -3.

4 EXAMPLE Simplifying Exponential Expressions

Use the order of operations to simplify each expression.
  a. -3^4

$-3^4 = -(3 \cdot 3 \cdot 3 \cdot 3)$ **Write as repeated multiplication.**

$= -81$ **Simplify.**

  b. $(-3)^4$

$(-3)^4 = (-3)(-3)(-3)(-3)$ **Write as repeated multiplication.**

● $= 81$ **Simplify.**

 **Quick Check** **4** Simplify each expression.
  a. -4^3 **b.** $(-2)^4$ **c.** $(-0.3)^2$ **d.** $-\left(\frac{3}{4}\right)^2$

Test-Taking Tip

Remember that an exponent tells how many times a number is used as a factor.

The rules for finding the sign when dividing rational numbers are the same as the rules for finding the sign when multiplying rational numbers.

Key Concepts

Rule	Dividing Numbers With the Same Sign

The quotient of two positive numbers or two negative numbers is positive.

Examples $6 \div 3 = 2$ $\qquad -6 \div (-3) = 2$

Rule	Dividing Numbers With Different Signs

The quotient of a positive number and a negative number, or a negative number and a positive number, is negative.

Examples $-6 \div 3 = -2$ $\qquad 6 \div (-3) = -2$

You can use the rules for dividing numbers to simplify expressions.

5 EXAMPLE **Dividing Numbers**

Simplify each expression.

a. $12 \div (-4) = -3$ The quotient of a positive number and a negative number is negative.

b. $-12 \div (-4) = 3$ The quotient of a negative number and a negative number is positive.

 **Quick Check** ❺ Simplify each expression.

a. $-42 \div 7$ **b.** $-8 \div (-2)$ **c.** $8 \div (-8)$ **d.** $-39 \div (-3)$

You can evaluate expressions that involve division.

Vocabulary Tip

A fraction bar means divide: $\frac{15}{5} = 15 \div 5$.

6 EXAMPLE **Evaluating Expressions**

Evaluate $\frac{-x}{-4} + 2y \div z$ for $x = -20, y = 6,$ and $z = -1$.

$\frac{-x}{-4} + 2y \div z = \frac{-(-20)}{-4} + 2(6) \div (-1)$ Substitute -20 for x, 6 for y, and -1 for z.

$\qquad\qquad = -5 + (-12)$ Divide and multiply.

$\qquad\qquad = -17$ Add.

 **Quick Check** ❻ Evaluate each expression for $x = 8, y = -5,$ and $z = -3$.

a. $3x \div (2z) + y \div 10$ **b.** $\frac{2z + x}{2y}$ **c.** $3z^2 - 4y \div x$

A number and its multiplicative inverse have a special relationship.

 Key Concepts

Property	Inverse Property of Multiplication

For every nonzero real number a, there is a **multiplicative inverse** $\frac{1}{a}$ such that $a\left(\frac{1}{a}\right) = 1$.

Examples $5\left(\frac{1}{5}\right) = 1$ $\qquad -5\left(-\frac{1}{5}\right) = 1$

The **multiplicative inverse,** or **reciprocal,** of a nonzero rational number $\frac{a}{b}$ is $\frac{b}{a}$. Zero does not have a reciprocal. Division by zero is undefined.

GO for Help

For help with dividing fractions, see Skills Handbook p. 793.

7 EXAMPLE Division Using the Reciprocal

Evaluate $\frac{x}{y}$ for $x = -\frac{3}{4}$ and $y = -\frac{5}{2}$.

$\frac{x}{y} = x \div y$ **Rewrite the expression.**

$= -\frac{3}{4} \div \left(-\frac{5}{2}\right)$ **Substitute $-\frac{3}{4}$ for x and $-\frac{5}{2}$ for y.**

$= -\frac{3}{4}\left(-\frac{2}{5}\right)$ **Multiply by $-\frac{2}{5}$, the reciprocal of $-\frac{5}{2}$.**

$= \frac{3}{10}$ **Simplify.**

✓ Quick Check **7** Evaluate the expression in Example 7 for $x = 8$ and $y = -\frac{4}{5}$.

EXERCISES

For more exercises, see *Extra Skill and Word Problem Practice.*

Practice and Problem Solving

A Practice by Example

Example 1
(page 246)

Simplify each expression.

1. $3(-5)$
2. $5(-3)$
3. $3(5)$
4. $-3(-5)$
5. $8(-4.3)$
6. $9\left(-\frac{5}{18}\right)$
7. $10(-12)$
8. $7(-15)$
9. $-4(20)$
10. $-20(-4)$
11. $13(-6)$
12. $-9(-9)$

Example 2
(page 247)

Evaluate each expression for $m = -4$, $n = 3$, and $p = -1$.

13. mn
14. $-mn$
15. $3m - n$
16. $-5p$
17. $2m$
18. $7p - 2n$
19. $8p \cdot (-2n)$
20. $p \cdot (m + n)$
21. mnp
22. $m \cdot (3 + p)$
23. $4n^3 \cdot m$
24. $m \cdot p + (-n)$

Example 3
(page 247)

Evaluate each expression for $x = -12$ and $y = 4$.

25. $xy - 4y$
26. $2xy + 9$
27. $x + 4y$
28. $-x + 3y$
29. $3y - 2x$
30. $6y + x$

🌐 **31. Weather** The function $w = -39 + \frac{3}{2}t$, where t is the actual air temperature, gives the approximate wind chill temperature w when the wind speed is 20 mi/h. Find the approximate wind chill temperature for the given air temperatures with a 20 mi/h wind.
   a. 10°F   **b.** −24°F   **c.** −8°F   **d.** 5°F

Example 4
(page 247)

Simplify each expression.

32. $(-1)^5$
33. $-(-2)^3$
34. -5^2
35. $(-9)^2$
36. -9^2
37. $3(-4)^3$
38. $-5(-1)^4$
39. $-5^2(-3)^3$

Example 5
(page 248)

Simplify each expression.

40. $\frac{6}{-3}$ **41.** $\frac{-36}{9}$ **42.** $\frac{3-14}{-2}$ **43.** $-18 \div (-3)$

44. $-121 \div 11$ **45.** $-64 \div (-5)$ **46.** $2^3 \div (-4)$ **47.** $-56 \div (4 + 7)$

Example 6
(page 248)

Evaluate each expression for $x = -2$, $y = 3$, and $z = 3.5$.

48. $(y + 3x) \div y$ **49.** $4z \div x$

50. $4x^3 - \frac{2z}{x}$ **51.** $(3x + 2y) \div (2x + 3y)$

52. $(2z + 7) \div y$ **53.** $8 + 6x \div (4y) - \frac{3z}{y}$

Example 7
(page 249)

Evaluate each expression.

54. $\frac{x}{y}$, for $x = \frac{2}{5}$ and $y = \frac{3}{10}$ **55.** $\frac{-3m}{t}$, for $m = \frac{5}{6}$ and $t = \frac{1}{6}$

56. $\frac{r}{-3s}$, for $r = -\frac{1}{8}$ and $s = \frac{3}{4}$ **57.** $\frac{3x}{5y}$, for $x = \frac{1}{5}$ and $y = -\frac{1}{2}$

B   **Apply Your Skills**

Copy and complete each table.

58.

m	$-5m$
-4	▨
-1	▨
2	▨
▨	-25

59.

p	$\frac{3}{4}p - 5$
-4	▨
-3	▨
2	▨
▨	-2

60.

n	$\lvert 2n - 3 \rvert$
-5	▨
-1	▨
0	▨
4	▨

61. a. Find each product.
     i. $(-1)(-1)$ **ii.** $(-1)(-1)(-1)$
     iii. $(-1)(-2)$ **iv.** $(-1)(-2)(-3)$
     v. $(-1)(-2)(-3)(-4)$ **vi.** $(-1)(-2)(-3)(-4)(-5)$
   b. Patterns For an even number of negative factors, the product will be <u> ? </u>.
   c. For an odd number of negative factors, the product will be <u> ? </u>.
   d. Writing For a product that includes negative and positive factors, do the positive factors affect the sign of the product? Explain.

62. Suppose a and b are integers.
   a. When is the product ab positive?
   b. When is the product ab negative?

Evaluate each expression for the given value(s).

63. $\frac{3}{4}w - 7$, for $w = 1\frac{1}{3}$ **64.** $\frac{x}{2y}$, for $x = 3.6$ and $y = -0.4$

65. $\frac{n}{m}$, for $n = -\frac{4}{5}$ and $m = 8$ **66.** $\frac{3a}{b} + c$, for $a = -2$, $b = -5$, and $c = -1$

Open-Ended Use $a = -3$, $b = 2$, and $c = -5$ to write an algebraic expression that has each value.

67. 17 **68.** 0 **69.** -1 **70.** 1 **71.** 7

72. History A toll bridge in Maine in the early 1900s charged 2¢ per person and $6\frac{1}{4}$¢ for a dozen sheep.
   a. How much would the toll for 3 people and 4 dozen sheep have been?
   b. If the toll was 56¢ and there were 8 dozen sheep, how many people were there?

GO Online
Homework Video Tutor
Visit: PHSchool.com
Web Code: ate-0203

73. Reasoning Does $|ab|$ always equal $|a| \cdot |b|$? Explain.

74. a. Simplify each expression.
$$(-2)^2 \quad (-2)^3 \quad (-2)^4 \quad (-2)^5$$
$$(-3)^2 \quad (-3)^3 \quad (-3)^4 \quad (-3)^5$$

b. Make a Conjecture Do you think a negative number raised to an even power will be positive or negative? Explain.

c. What is the sign of a negative number raised to an odd power? Explain.

75. Is -10 or 0.1 the multiplicative inverse of 10? Explain.

76. Explain why the reciprocal of a nonzero number is *not* the same as the opposite of the number.

In *scalar multiplication*, you multiply the elements in a matrix by a number, called a *scalar*. **Find each product.**

Sample $3\begin{bmatrix} 4 & -1.5 \\ \frac{1}{2} & -6 \end{bmatrix} = \begin{bmatrix} 3 \cdot 4 & 3 \cdot (-1.5) \\ 3 \cdot \frac{1}{2} & 3 \cdot (-6) \end{bmatrix}$ **Multiply each entry by the scalar.**

$$= \begin{bmatrix} 12 & -4.5 \\ \frac{3}{2} & -18 \end{bmatrix}$$ **Simplify.**

77. $-2\begin{bmatrix} 11 & -5 \\ -9 & 6 \\ -4 & 3 \end{bmatrix}$ **78.** $\frac{3}{5}\begin{bmatrix} -25 & 35 \\ \frac{10}{9} & -15 \end{bmatrix}$ **79.** $-0.1\begin{bmatrix} -47 & 13 & -7.9 \\ 0.2 & -64 & 0 \end{bmatrix}$

80. $-4\begin{bmatrix} 3 & \frac{2}{3} \end{bmatrix}$ **81.** $2\begin{bmatrix} -4 & -5.3 & 2 \\ 3.1 & 0 & 6 \end{bmatrix}$ **82.** $\frac{1}{4}\begin{bmatrix} -1 & \frac{3}{4} \\ \frac{8}{9} & 0 \end{bmatrix}$

155 ft

83. Entertainment As riders plunge down the hill of a roller coaster, you can approximate the height h, in feet, above the ground of their roller-coaster car. Use the function $h = 155 - 16t^2$ where t is the number of seconds since the start of the descent.

a. How far is a rider from the bottom of the hill after 1 second? 2 seconds?

b. Critical Thinking Does it take more than or less than 4 seconds to reach the bottom? Explain.

84. Multiple Choice The formula $C = \frac{5}{9}(F - 32)$ changes a temperature reading from the Fahrenheit scale F to the Celsius scale C. What is the temperature measured in Celsius if the Fahrenheit temperature is $-13°$?

   Ⓐ 25°C   Ⓑ 15°C   Ⓒ $-15°C$ Ⓓ $-25°C$

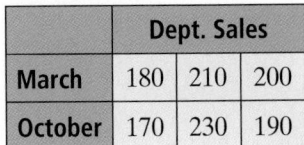

	Dept. Sales		
March	180	210	200
October	170	230	190

85. a. Sales The table at the left shows the monthly sales in March and October for three departments of a clothing store. Organize the data into a matrix.

b. Use a scalar to find the matrix for each month's average daily sales. Assume the store is open every day. Round to the nearest tenth.

c. Each department expects sales in March and October to increase by 10% next year. Find the matrix that shows the projected sales for these months.

Ⓒ Challenge

Evaluate each expression for $b = -\frac{1}{2}$.

86. b^3 **87.** b^4 **88.** b^5 **89.** b^6 **90.** $-b^6$

91. What is the greatest integer n for which $(-n)^3$ is positive and the value of the expression has a 2 in the ones place?

Rewrite each expression using the symbol ÷. Then find each quotient.

Sample $\dfrac{\frac{-7}{12}}{4} = \dfrac{-7}{12} \div 4$ Rewrite as $\dfrac{-7}{12} \div 4$.

$\qquad\qquad = \dfrac{-7}{12} \cdot \left(\dfrac{1}{4}\right)$ Multiply by $\dfrac{1}{4}$, the reciprocal of 4.

$\qquad\qquad = -\dfrac{7}{48}$

92. $\dfrac{\frac{5}{4}}{9}$

93. $\dfrac{\frac{3}{8}}{\frac{-2}{3}}$

94. $\dfrac{\frac{-5}{6}}{8}$

95. $\dfrac{\frac{-2}{5}}{\frac{-4}{5}}$

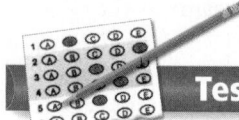

Test Prep

Multiple Choice

96. Simplify $(-3)(-3)(2)(2)(-1)$.
  A. -36 **B.** -6 **C.** 6   **D.** 36

97. Evaluate $-ac + bc$ for $a = -2$, $b = 6$, and $c = -3$.
  F. -24 **G.** -6 **H.** 6   **J.** 24

98. A Mach number M indicates the speed of a supersonic airplane. You can find an airplane's speed a in miles per hour using the formula $a = Ms$ where s is the speed of sound at the altitude of the airplane. Find an airplane's speed in miles per hour if the airplane travels at Mach 2.5 at an altitude where the speed of sound is 710 mi/h.
  A. 177.5 mi/h   **B.** 284 mi/h   **C.** 1775 mi/h   **D.** 2840 mi/h

99. Which expression does NOT have the same value as $-11 + (-11) + (-11) + (-11)$?
  F. -44 **G.** $4(-11)$ **H.** $(-11)^4$ **J.** $33 - 77$

100. Use the table below. What was the average temperature for the week?

Day	Mon.	Tues.	Wed.	Thur.	Fri.	Sat.	Sun.
Temperature	$-3°F$	$4°F$	$-2°F$	$-5°F$	$-3°F$	$1°F$	$1°F$

  A. $-7°F$ **B.** $-1°F$ **C.** $1°F$ **D.** $4°F$

Mixed Review

Lesson 5-2   **Subtract.**

101. $6 - 8$ **102.** $-3 - 17$ **103.** $-2.3 - (-3.1)$

104. $7 - (-2.8)$ **105.** $1\frac{3}{4} - \left(-\frac{1}{2}\right)$ **106.** $-\frac{7}{8} - \left(-\frac{8}{9}\right)$

Lesson 4-3   **Find each absolute value.**

107. $|4.95|$ **108.** $|-56|$ **109.** $|-4.59|$ **110.** $\left|-\frac{3}{4}\right|$

Lesson 4-2   **Evaluate each expression for $a = 4$ and $b = 7$.**

111. $a^2 + b$ **112.** $(a + b)^2$ **113.** ab^2

114. A sweater costs $32.95. The sales tax rate is 6%. Find the total cost.

You can use a graphing calculator to add and subtract matrices and to multiply a matrix by a number, or scalar.

Go Online
PHSchool.com
For: Graphing calculator procedures
Web Code: ate-2113

ACTIVITY   Matrix Operations

Let $A = \begin{bmatrix} 3 & 7 & 1 \\ 2 & -4 & 9 \end{bmatrix}$ and $B = \begin{bmatrix} 5 & 0 & -8 \\ 6 & 2 & 2 \end{bmatrix}$. Find $A + B$ and $5A$.

A calculator names the matrices using brackets [A] and [B] to remind you that you are working with matrices.

Step 1 To enter the first matrix, access the **MATRX** feature of your calculator. Use the arrow keys to highlight **EDIT** at the top of the screen. Press ENTER . Matrix A is a 2×3 matrix, so revise the numbers at the top of the screen, if necessary. Press ENTER to access the first entry of the matrix. Enter the values given for matrix A. Use (-) for negative.

Step 2 To enter the second matrix, access the matrix screen again. Use the arrow keys to highlight **EDIT**. Use the arrow keys to move down to [B]. Press ENTER . Change the dimensions and enter the values for matrix B.

Step 3 To find $A + B$, use the **NAMES** list on the matrix screen to select [A] or [B]. The calculator will display the matrix sum as shown at the right.

Step 4 To find $5A$, press 5, select [A] from the **NAMES** list, and ENTER . The result is also shown at the right.

```
[A] + [B]
          [[8  7  -7]
           [8 -2 11]]
5[A]
          [[15  35  5 ]
           [10 -20 45]]
```

EXERCISES

For $A = \begin{bmatrix} 4 & -2 \\ 8 & 6 \end{bmatrix}$, $B = \begin{bmatrix} -5 & 12 \\ 0 & 3 \end{bmatrix}$, and $C = \begin{bmatrix} 3 & 15 \\ 9 & -10 \end{bmatrix}$, find each of the following.

1. $A + B$ **2.** $B + C$ **3.** $C - A$

4. $A + C$ **5.** $B - C$ **6.** $3B$

7. $-4C$ **8.** $2A + B$ **9.** $-2B + C + A$

For $A = \begin{bmatrix} 4 & 7 & 3 \\ 8 & 2 & 1 \\ -7 & 5 & -2 \end{bmatrix}$, $B = \begin{bmatrix} -1 & 0 & 6 \\ 2 & -3 & 4 \\ 1 & 15 & 8 \end{bmatrix}$, and $C = \begin{bmatrix} 2 & 0 & 0 \\ 0 & -3 & 6 \\ 4 & 6 & 9 \end{bmatrix}$, find each of the following.

10. $A + 2B$ **11.** $C + B - A$ **12.** $2A + 5B - C$

13. $-4A + 5C$ **14.** $-4A - 5C$ **15.** $A + B - 2C$

From Lesson 5-2, you know that ▢ represents +1 and ■ represents −1. The tile ▮ represents a variable.

You can use tiles to represent an expression like $x + 5$.

$x \; + \; 5$

Write the expression represented by each group of tiles.

1.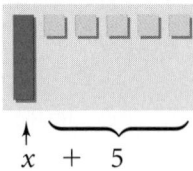

2.

3.

Represent each expression using tiles.

4. $x + 1$ 5. $2x + 4$ 6. $3x - 5$

The expression $2(x + 5)$ indicates two groups of tiles, as shown below on the left. You can add the variable tiles together and the unit tiles together to simplify the expression, as shown below on the right.

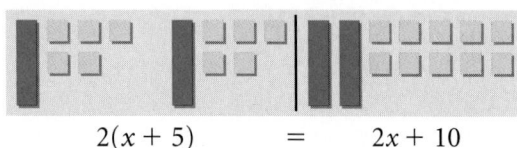

$2(x + 5) \qquad = \qquad 2x + 10$

The tiles show that the product $2(x + 5)$ equals $2x + 10$. This illustrates the Distributive Property.

Write an equation for each model.

7.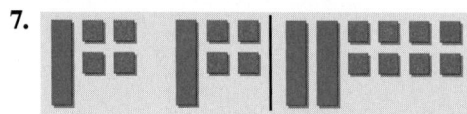

8.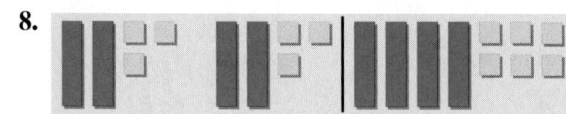

9.

Use tiles to rewrite each expression without grouping symbols.

10. $3(x + 1)$ 11. $2(x + 4)$ 12. $3(2x - 1)$

13. **Critical Thinking** Does $5(2x - 3)$ equal $10x - 3$ or $10x - 15$? Explain.

The Distributive Property

✓ Check Skills You'll Need

GO for Help Lessons 4-2 and 5-3

Use the order of operations to simplify each expression.

1. $3(4 + 7)$ **2.** $-2(5 + 6)$ **3.** $-1(-9 + 8)$

4. $-0.5(8 - 6)$ **5.** $\frac{1}{2}t(10 - 4)$ **6.** $m(-3 - 1)$

◀)) New Vocabulary • **Distributive Property** • **term** • **constant** • **coefficient** • **like terms**

---

1 Using the Distributive Property

You can use the Distributive Property to multiply a sum or difference by a number.

 Key Concepts

Property	**Distributive Property**

For every real number a, b, and c,

$a(b + c) = ab + ac$ $(b + c)a = ba + ca$

$a(b - c) = ab - ac$ $(b - c)a = ba - ca$

Examples $5(20 + 6) = 5(20) + 5(6)$ $(20 + 6)5 = 20(5) + 6(5)$

$9(30 - 2) = 9(30) - 9(2)$ $(30 - 2)9 = 30(9) - 2(9)$

You can use the Distributive Property to multiply some numbers using mental math. For instance, you can think of 102 as $100 + 2$ and 98 as $100 - 2$.

1 EXAMPLE Simplifying a Numerical Expression

Use the Distributive Property to simplify $34(102)$.

$34(102) = 34(100 + 2)$ **Rewrite 102 as 100 + 2.**

$= 34(100) + 34(2)$ **Use the Distributive Property.**

$= 3400 + 68$ **Simplify.**

$= 3468$

✓ Quick Check ❶ Simplify each expression.

a. $13(103)$ **b.** $21(101)$ **c.** $24(98)$ **d.** $15(99)$

You can also use the Distributive Property and mental math to calculate costs.

Test-Taking Tip

You can find some products faster by using the Distributive Property and mental math than by using a calculator.

2 EXAMPLE Using Mental Math

Gridded Response At Mars' Deli, you can find the cost c of n sandwiches using the function $c = 2.95n$. Find the cost of 8 sandwiches.

2	3	.	6

$$c = 2.95n$$
$$c = 2.95(8) \qquad \text{Substitute 8 for } n.$$
$$= (3 - 0.05)8 \qquad \text{Write 2.95 as } 3 - 0.05.$$
$$= (3)8 - (0.05)8 \qquad \text{Use the Distributive Property.}$$
$$= 24 - 0.40 \qquad \text{Simplify.}$$
$$= 23.60$$

The cost of 8 sandwiches is \$23.60. Grid 23.6.

 **2** Find the total cost of 6 pairs of socks that are \$2.95 per pair.

2 Simplifying Algebraic Expressions

You can use the Distributive Property to simplify an algebraic expression. An algebraic expression in simplest form has no grouping symbols.

3 EXAMPLE Simplifying an Expression

Simplify each expression.

a. $2(5x + 3)$

$$2(5x + 3) = 2(5x) + 2(3) \qquad \text{Use the Distributive Property.}$$
$$= 10x + 6 \qquad \text{Simplify.}$$

b. $(3b - 2)\left(\frac{1}{3}\right)$

$$(3b - 2)\left(\frac{1}{3}\right) = 3b\left(\frac{1}{3}\right) - 2\left(\frac{1}{3}\right) \qquad \text{Use the Distributive Property.}$$
$$= b - \frac{2}{3} \qquad \text{Simplify.}$$

 **3** Simplify each expression.   **a.** $2(3 - 7t)$ **b.** $(0.4 + 1.1c)(3)$

To simplify an expression like $-(6x + 4)$, rewrite the expression as $-1(6x + 4)$, using the Multiplication Property of -1.

4 EXAMPLE Using the Multiplication Property of -1

Simplify $-(6x + 4)$.

$$-(6x + 4) = -1(6x + 4) \qquad \text{Rewrite the expression using } -1.$$
$$= -1(6x) + (-1)(4) \qquad \text{Use the Distributive Property.}$$
$$= -6x - 4 \qquad \text{Simplify.}$$

 **4** Simplify each expression.   **a.** $-(2x + 1)$ **b.** $(3 - 8a)(-1)$

In an algebraic expression, a **term** is a number, a variable, or the product of a number and one or more variables.

$$6a^2 - 5ab + 3b - 12 \leftarrow \text{A } \textbf{constant} \text{ is a term that has no variable.}$$

A **coefficient** is a numerical factor of a term.

Think of $3b - 12$ as $3b + (-12)$ to determine that the constant is -12.

Like terms have exactly the same variable factors.

Like Terms	Not Like Terms
$3x$ and $-2x$	$8x$ and $7y$
$-5x^2$ and $9x^2$	$5y$ and $2y^2$
xy and $-xy$	$4y$ and $5xy$
$-7x^2y^3$ and $15x^2y^3$	x^2y and xy^2

An algebraic expression in simplest form has no like terms. You can use the Distributive Property to combine like terms when simplifying an expression. Think of the Distributive Property as $ba + ca = (b + c)a$.

5 EXAMPLE **Combining Like Terms**

Simplify each expression.

a. $3x^2 + 5x^2$

$\quad 3x^2 + 5x^2 = (3 + 5)x^2$ **Use the Distributive Property.**

$\quad\quad\quad\quad\quad = 8x^2$ **Simplify.**

b. $-5c + c$

$\quad -5c + c = -5c + 1c$ **Rewrite c as 1c.**

$\quad\quad\quad\quad = (-5 + 1)c$ **Use the Distributive Property.**

$\quad\quad\quad\quad = -4c$ **Simplify.**

Problem Solving Hint

Identity Property of multiplication:
$c = 1 \cdot c$ or $1c$

✓ **Quick Check** **5** Simplify each expression.

    a. $7y + 6y$ **b.** $3t - t$ **c.** $-9w^3 - 3w^3$ **d.** $8d + d$

You can write an expression from a verbal phrase. The word *quantity* indicates that two or more terms are within parentheses.

6 EXAMPLE **Writing an Expression**

Write an expression for "3 times the quantity x minus 5."

Relate   3   times   the quantity x minus 5

Write   3   · $(x - 5)$

$3(x - 5)$

✓ **Quick Check** **6** Write an expression for each phrase.
    a. -2 times the quantity t plus 7
    b. the product of 14 and the quantity 8 plus w

EXERCISES

For more exercises, see *Extra Skill and Word Problem Practice*.

Practice and Problem Solving

A Practice by Example

GO for Help

Example 1
(page 255)

Simplify each expression using the Distributive Property.

1. 12(201) **2.** 51(13) **3.** 11(499) **4.** 8(306)

5. 7(98) **6.** 3(999) **7.** 41(502) **8.** 24(1020)

Example 2
(page 256)

Mental Math Use the Distributive Property to find each price.

9. 4($.99) **10.** 6($1.97) **11.** 5($5.91) **12.** 7($29.93)

13. The school librarian got money to buy reference works on CDs. To find the cost c of n CDs, she used the function $c = 32.99n$. How much did she spend on 3 CDs?

14. You stopped on your way to basketball practice and bought four cans of fruit punch for $.69 each. How much did you spend in all?

Example 3
(page 256)

Simplify each expression.

15. $7(t - 4)$ **16.** $-2(n - 6)$ **17.** $3(m + 4)$

18. $(5b - 4)\frac{1}{5}$ **19.** $-2(x + 3)$ **20.** $\frac{2}{3}(6y + 9)$

21. $0.25(6q + 32)$ **22.** $(3n - 7)(6)$ **23.** $(8 - 3r)\frac{5}{16}$

24. $-4.5(b - 3)$ **25.** $\frac{2}{5}(5w + 10)$ **26.** $(9 - 4n)(-4)$

Example 4
(page 256)

27. $-(x + 3)$ **28.** $-(x - 3)$ **29.** $-(3 + x)$ **30.** $-(3 - x)$

31. $-(6k + 5)$ **32.** $-(7x - 2)$ **33.** $-(2 - 7x)$ **34.** $(4 - z)(-1)$

Example 5
(page 257)

35. $4t - 7t$ **36.** $12k^2 + 8k^2$ **37.** $9x - 2x$ **38.** $w + 23w$

39. $-18v^2 + 23v^2$ **40.** $7m - m$ **41.** $13q - 30q$ **42.** $x - 46x$

Example 6
(page 257)

Write an expression for each phrase.

43. 3 times the quantity m minus 7

44. -4 times the quantity 4 plus w

45. twice the quantity b plus 9

46. 2 times the quantity 3 times c plus 9

B Apply Your Skills

Simplify each expression.

47. 9(4998) **48.** 12(7.001) **49.** 7(2.003)

50. $144\left(\frac{15}{16}b + \frac{8}{9}\right)$ **51.** $3(6.2 + 5m)$ **52.** $\frac{7}{8}\left(\frac{10}{14}d - 48\right)$

Copy and complete each table.

53.

k	$2(k - 4)$
-10	▪
-5	▪
2.5	▪
▪	0

54.

n	$-(2n + 5)$
-3	▪
-1	▪
2	▪
▪	-15

55.

a	$-3(2 - a)$
-4	▪
0	▪
2	▪
▪	9

Write an expression for each phrase.

56. $2\frac{1}{4}$ times the quantity $5\frac{1}{2}$ minus k

57. $6\frac{7}{100}$ times the quantity 8 plus $\frac{4}{3}p$

58. the product of $\frac{11}{20}$ and the quantity b minus $\frac{13}{30}$

59. 17 divided by the quantity z minus 34

60. $4\frac{1}{3}$ times the quantity x minus $\frac{11}{12}$

61. Multiple Choice Which expression represents the perimeter of the figure?

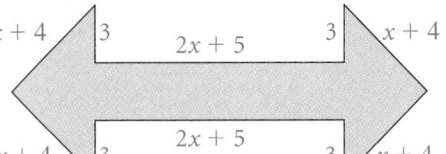

  (A) $8x + 38$

  (B) $46x$

  (C) $4x + 38$

  (D) $8x$

Problem Solving Hint

For Exercise 62, test positive and negative values of *a* and *b* as well as zero before writing your conclusion.

62. Writing Does $2ab = 2a \cdot 2b$? Explain.

63. Error Analysis A student rewrote $4(3x + 10)$ as $12x + 10$. Explain the student's error.

64. Open-Ended Write a variable expression that you could simplify using the Distributive Property. Then simplify your expression.

Simplify each expression.

65. $4.78d + 0d$

66. $-21p - 76p^2 - 9 + p$

67. $3.3t^2 + 8.7t - 9.4t^2 + 5t$

68. $1.5m - 4.2m - 12.5v + 4.2m$

69. $\frac{6}{7}n + n^3 - \left(-\frac{5}{6}n\right)$

70. $-\frac{16}{15}k + \frac{3}{20}h + \frac{7}{40}k$

71. $8m^2 - 5mz + 4mz - m^2 + 4$

72. $9 - 4t + 6y - 3t + 10$

73. $1.4b - 3b^2 + 4c - 2b^2 + c$

74. $8xyz + 4xy - 12yzx + 2xy$

75. Identify the terms, the coefficients, and the constant(s) in the expression $-7t + 6v + 7 - 19y$.

76. Sports A high school basketball court is 84 ft long by 50 ft wide. A college basketball court is 10 ft longer than a high school court but has the same width.

Real-World Connection

Basketball is one of the ten most popular sports activities in the United States, based on participation.

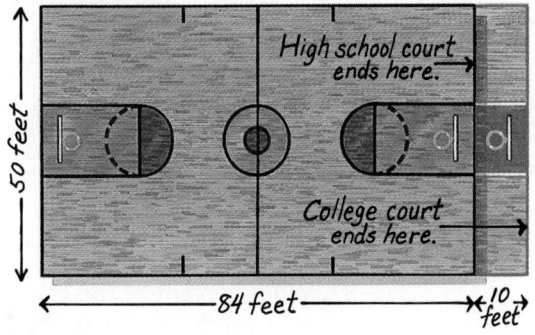

a. Write an expression using parentheses for the area of a college basketball court.

b. Simplify your expression.

77. A student searched the pockets of his jeans before doing laundry and found the following numbers of coins: 4 pennies, 2 nickels, and a quarter; 3 quarters and 6 pennies; 1 dime and 5 nickels. How many of each type of coin does the student have?

78. Shopping Suppose you buy 4 cans of tomatoes at $1.02 each, 3 cans of tuna for $.99 each, and 3 boxes of pasta at $.52 each. Write an expression to model this situation. Then use the Distributive Property to find the total cost.

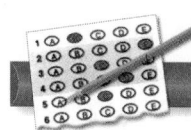 **Challenge**

Simplify each expression.

79. $9(5 + t) - 6(t + 3)$

80. $4(r + 8) - 5(2r - 1)$

81. $-(m + 3) - 2(m + 3)$

82. $a[2 + b(2 + c)]$

83. $7b[8 + 6(b - 1)]$

84. $-[-5(y + 2z) - 3z]$

85. Critical Thinking If $y = 3x - 10$, what is an expression for $\frac{y}{3}$?

86. a. Evaluate $(a + b) \div c$ and $a \div c + b \div c$ for $a = -10, b = 6$, and $c = -2$.
    b. Evaluate each expression for $a = -9, b = -3$, and $c = 6$.
    c. Reasoning Does it appear that $(a + b) \div c = a \div c + b \div c$? Explain.

87. a. Evaluate $a \div (b + c)$ and $a \div b + a \div c$ for $a = -60, b = 3$, and $c = -5$.
    b. Evaluate each expression for $a = -24, b = -4$, and $c = 2$.
    c. Reasoning Does it appear that $a \div (b + c) = a \div b + a \div c$? Explain.

Test Prep

Multiple Choice

88. Which expression is another form of $14x - 21x$?
    A. $-7x^2$ **B.** $7x^2(2 - 3x)$ **C.** $7x(2x - 3)$ **D.** $-7x$

89. Which expression is another form of $-6(k - 5)$?
    F. $-6k^2 - 30k$ **G.** $-6k + 30$ **H.** $-6k^2 - 5$ **J.** $-6k^2 + 5$

Use the table below for Exercises 90–92.

Competitors in the Ultra-Marathon 2000

Category	130-Mile Race		350-Mile Race	
	Number Started	Number Finished	Number Started	Number Finished
Bicycle	51	41	24	16
Foot	43	37	11	9
Ski	9	6	3	3

90. Which category had the most competitors in each race?
    A. bicycle   **B.** foot   **C.** ski   **D.** all of them

91. What percent of the competitors on bicycles completed the 350-mile race?
    F. 67%   **G.** 75%   **H.** 80%   **J.** 82%

92. What percent of the competitors completed the 130-mile race?
    A. 67%   **B.** 75%   **C.** 82%   **D.** 86%

93. Rocky Reifenstuhl won the 130-mile race on his bicycle. He finished in 11 hours and 45 minutes. What was his average speed?
   F. 11.8 mi/h   **G.** 11.4 mi/h   **H.** 11.1 mi/h   **J.** 10.8 mi/h

94. Simplify $7q + 8pq - 4pq - 9q$.
   A. $-2q + 12pq$ **B.** $16q + 4pq$
   C. $-2q + 4pq$ **D.** $16q + 12pq$

95. A notebook costs $1.89 at the school store. How much would notebooks for a class of 30 students cost?
   F. $59.70   **G.** $59.67   **H.** $57.30   **J.** $56.70

Mixed Review

Lessons 5-2, 5-3

for Help

Simplify each expression.

96. $8(-7) + 4(-3)$

97. $8 + (-4) \cdot 3$

98. $(-3)^2 + (-5)$

99. $(9^2 - 60) \div 3$

100. $\frac{-7 + 5}{-7 - 5}$

101. $\frac{7 - 2}{-12 + 8}$

102. $\frac{1 + (-4)}{21 - 6}$

103. $-3^4 \div 9 - 4 \cdot 2$

Lesson 5-1

Simplify each expression.

104. $6.034 + (-8.42)$

105. $9.73 + 2.397$

106. $-54.1 + 99.4$

107. $|-28.2| + 17.5$

108. $-6.45 + |-9.02|$

109. $3.02 + (-2.1)$

110. $-5.7 + (-3.9)$

111. $14.7 + |-8.3|$

Lesson 4-1

112. a. Write an expression for the phrase "4 more than the quotient of m and 3."
   b. Evaluate your expression for $m = 9$, $m = 3$, and $m = 12$.

✓ Checkpoint Quiz 1   Lessons 5-1 through 5-4

Simplify each expression.

1. $\left(-\frac{1}{3}\right) + \left(\frac{2}{9}\right)$

2. $-3 + (-17)$

3. $|-5| + (-5) + 5$

4. $\begin{bmatrix} 2 & -5 \\ 4.1 & 7 \\ -10 & 8 \end{bmatrix} + \begin{bmatrix} -2 & 0 \\ -6.2 & 1 \\ -13 & 3 \end{bmatrix}$

Evaluate each expression for $a = 4$ and $b = -5$.

5. $2a \cdot (-3b)$ **6.** $-b - a$ **7.** $(2a^2) \div (4b)$

8. Temperature The temperature one winter morning is $-5°$F. Define a variable and write an expression to find the temperature after it changes. Then evaluate your expression for an increase of 13 degrees Fahrenheit.

Use the Distributive Property to simplify each expression.

9. $\frac{1}{3}(24x - 36)$ **10.** $6t + 43t$

Properties of Numbers

What You'll Learn
- To identify properties
- To use deductive reasoning

...And Why
To use mental math when buying multiple items, as in Example 2

 Check Skills You'll Need

Simplify each expression.

1. $8 + (9 + 2)$
2. $3 \cdot (-2 \cdot 5)$
3. $7 + 16 + 3$
4. $-4(7)(-5)$
5. $-6 + 9 + (-4)$
6. $0.25 \cdot 3 \cdot 4$
7. $3 + x - 2$
8. $2t - 8 + 3t$
9. $-5m + 2m - 4m$

GO for Help Lessons 5-1 and 5-3

New Vocabulary • deductive reasoning

---

1 Identifying and Using Properties

The summary below reviews properties of real numbers. Recall that real numbers include rational numbers (the subject of this chapter), as well as irrational numbers (which you will study further in Chapter 6).

 Key Concepts

Property	Properties of Real Numbers
For every real number $a, b,$ and $c,$	
Commutative Property of Addition $a + b = b + a$	**Example** $3 + 7 = 7 + 3$
Commutative Property of Multiplication $a \cdot b = b \cdot a$	**Example** $3 \cdot 7 = 7 \cdot 3$
Associative Property of Addition $(a + b) + c = a + (b + c)$	**Example** $(6 + 4) + 5 = 6 + (4 + 5)$
Associative Property of Multiplication $(a \cdot b) \cdot c = a \cdot (b \cdot c)$	**Example** $(6 \cdot 4) \cdot 5 = 6 \cdot (4 \cdot 5)$
Identity Property of Addition $a + 0 = a$	**Example** $9 + 0 = 9$
Identity Property of Multiplication $a \cdot 1 = a$	**Example** $6 \cdot 1 = 6$
Inverse Property of Addition For every a, there is an additive inverse $-a$ such that $a + (-a) = 0$.	**Example** $5 + (-5) = 0$
Inverse Property of Multiplication For every a ($a \neq 0$), there is a multiplicative inverse $\frac{1}{a}$ such that $a\left(\frac{1}{a}\right) = 1$.	**Example** $5 \cdot \frac{1}{5} = 1$
Symmetric Property If $a = b$, then $b = a$.	**Example** $2 \cdot 3 = 6$, so $6 = 2 \cdot 3$

The following summary reviews some additional properties of real numbers.

 Key Concepts

Property	Properties of Real Numbers

For every real number a, b, and c,

Distributive Property	**Examples**
$a(b + c) = ab + ac$	$5(4 + 2) = 5 \cdot 4 + 5 \cdot 2$
$a(b - c) = ab - ac$	$5(4 - 2) = 5 \cdot 4 - 5 \cdot 2$

Multiplication Property of Zero

For every real number n, $n \cdot 0 = 0$. $-35 \cdot 0 = 0$

Multiplication Property of −1

For every real number n, $-1 \cdot n = -n$. $-1 \cdot (-5) = 5$

1 EXAMPLE   Identifying Properties

Name the property that each equation illustrates. Explain.

a. $9 + 7 = 7 + 9$ Commutative Property of Addition, because the order of the addends changes

b. $(d \cdot 4) \cdot 3 = d \cdot (4 \cdot 3)$ Associative Property of Multiplication, because the grouping of the factors changes

c. $t + 0 = t$ Identity Property of Addition, because the sum of a number and zero is the number

d. $-q = -1q$ Multiplication Property of −1, because the opposite of a value is the same as −1 times the value

✓ **Quick Check** **1** Name the property that each equation illustrates. Explain.
a. $1m = m$ **b.** $(-3 + 4) + 5 = -3 + (4 + 5)$ **c.** $(3 \cdot 8)0 = 3(8 \cdot 0)$
d. $2 + 0 = 2$ **e.** $np = pn$ **f.** $p + q = q + p$

You can also use the properties to reorganize the order of numbers in sums or products so that you can calculate more easily.

2 EXAMPLE   Real-World  Problem Solving

Shopping Suppose you buy the school supplies shown at the left. Find the total cost of the supplies.

$0.85 + 2.50 + 5.15 = 2.50 + 0.85 + 5.15$	**Commutative Property of Addition**
$= 2.50 + (0.85 + 5.15)$	**Associative Property of Addition**
$= 2.50 + 6$	**Add within parentheses first.**
$= 8.50$	**Simplify.**

● The total cost of the supplies is $8.50.

✓ **Quick Check** **2 Shopping** At the supermarket, you buy a package of cheese for $2.50, a loaf of bread for $2.15, a cucumber for $.65, and some tomatoes for $3.50. Find the total cost of the groceries.

Deductive reasoning is the process of reasoning logically from given facts to a conclusion. Using deductive reasoning, you justify each step in simplifying an expression with reasons such as properties, definitions, or rules.

3 EXAMPLE Justifying Steps

Simplify each expression. Justify each step.

a. $-4b + 9 + b$

Step	Reason
$-4b + 9 + b = -4b + 9 + 1b$	Identity Property of Multiplication
$= -4b + 1b + 9$	Commutative Property of Addition
$= (-4 + 1)b + 9$	Distributive Property
$= -3b + 9$	addition

b. $7z - 5(3 + z)$

Step	Reason
$7z - 5(3 + z) = 7z - 15 - 5z$	Distributive Property
$= 7z + (-15) + (-5z)$	definition of subtraction
$= 7z + (-5z) + (-15)$	Commutative Property of Addition
$= [7 + (-5)]z + (-15)$	Distributive Property
$= 2z + (-15)$	addition
$= 2z - 15$	definition of subtraction

> **Problem Solving Hint**
>
> To use the Commutative Property of Addition, write subtraction as addition of the opposite.

 Quick Check ❸ Simplify each expression. Justify each step.
a. $5a + 6 + a$ **b.** $2(3t - 1) + 2$

EXERCISES

For more exercises, see *Extra Skill and Word Problem Practice*.

Practice and Problem Solving

A Practice by Example

Example 1
(page 263)

 **for Help**

Name the property that each equation illustrates. Explain.

1. $-\frac{6}{7} + 0 = -\frac{6}{7}$ **2.** $8 + 43 = 43 + 8$ **3.** $1 \cdot \frac{21}{23} = \frac{21}{23}$

4. $(-7 + 4) + 1 = -7 + (4 + 1)$ **5.** $-0.3 + 0.3 = 0$

6. $9(7.3) = 7.3(9)$ **7.** $5(12 - 4) = 5(12) - 5(4)$

8. $8(9 \cdot 11) = (8 \cdot 9) \cdot 11$ **9.** $-0.5 \cdot (-2) = 1$

Example 2
(page 263)

Mental Math Simplify each expression.

10. $47 + 39 + 3 + 11$ **11.** $25 \cdot 74 \cdot 2 \cdot 2$ **12.** $4.75 + 2.95 + 1.25 + 6$

13. $10 \cdot 6 \cdot 7 \cdot 10$ **14.** $2(5 - 3.5) - 8$ **15.** $6\frac{1}{2} + 4\frac{1}{3} + 1\frac{1}{2} + \frac{2}{3}$

🌐 **16. Shopping** You buy 3 grapefruits for $1.50, a pound of apples for $.79, some grapes for $2.50, and some bananas for $1.21. Find the total cost of the fruit.

Example 3
(page 264)

Give a reason to justify each step.

17. a. $3y - 5y = 3y + (-5y)$ _____?_____

b. $\qquad = [3 + (-5)]y$ _____?_____

c. $\qquad = -2y$ _____?_____

18. a. $3 \cdot (12 \cdot 10) = 3 \cdot (10 \cdot 12)$ _____?_____

b. $\qquad = (3 \cdot 10) \cdot 12$ _____?_____

c. $\qquad = 30 \cdot 12$ _____?_____

d. $\qquad = 360$ _____?_____

Simplify each expression. Justify each step.

19. $25 \cdot 1.7 \cdot 4$

20. $-5(7y)$

21. $8 + 9m + 7$

22. $12x - 3 + 6x$

23. $29c + (-29c)$

24. $43\left(\frac{1}{43}\right) + 1$

B **Apply Your Skills**

Simplify each expression. Justify each step.

25. $2 + g\left(\frac{1}{g}\right)$

26. $36jkm - 36mjk$

27. $(3^2 - 2^3)(8759)$

28. $(7^6 - 6^5)(8 - 8)$

29. $4 + 6(8 - 3m)$

30. $5\left(w - \frac{1}{5}\right) - w(9)$

31. Shopping Suppose you are buying soccer equipment: a pair of cleats for $31.50, a soccer ball for $14.97, and shin guards for $6.50. Use mental math to find the total cost.

Tell whether the expressions in each pair are equivalent.

32. $6m + 1$ and $1 \cdot 6 + m$

33. $9y$ and $9 + y$

34. $mp + nq$ and $mq + np$

35. $-(5 - 9)$ and $9 - 5$

36. $8 - 4c$ and $4c - 8$

37. $3(5 + z)$ and $15 + z$

38. $6t - 4$ and $2[(2 + 1)t - 2]$

39. $vwx \cdot yz$ and $v \cdot w \cdot zxy$

GO for Help

For a guide to solving
Exercise 38, see p. 267.

Reasoning Explain your answer to each question.

40. Is subtraction commutative?

41. Is subtraction associative?

42. Is division commutative?

43. Is division associative?

44. Give a reason to justify each step.

a. $5t + 6 + 3(t + 2) = 5t + 6 + 3t + 6$ _____?_____

b. $\qquad = 5t + 3t + 6 + 6$ _____?_____

c. $\qquad = 5t + 3t + (6 + 6)$ _____?_____

d. $\qquad = 5t + 3t + 12$ _____?_____

e. $\qquad = (5 + 3)t + 12$ _____?_____

f. $\qquad = 8t + 12$ _____?_____

45. Reasoning The Distributive Property states that $a(b + c) = ab + ac$. Use this and the other properties to explain why $(b + c)a = ba + ca$ is also true.

46. Multiple Choice A member of the track team records the distance she runs each day. How many miles did she run?

Ⓐ 14.2 miles
Ⓑ 14.1 miles
Ⓒ 13.9 miles
Ⓓ 13.8 miles

Day	Distance (miles)
Sunday	4.2
Monday	0
Tuesday	1.5
Wednesday	1.8
Thursday	2.5
Friday	0
Saturday	3.9

47. Writing Suppose you make a peanut butter and jelly sandwich. Do you think it tastes the same regardless of whether the jelly is on top or the peanut butter is on top? Relate your answer to one of the properties of real numbers.

GO Online
Homework Video Tutor

Visit: PHSchool.com
Web Code: ate-0205

 **Challenge**

Critical Thinking The *closure properties* for a set of numbers assure that the sum and product of two numbers in a given set of numbers are also in the set of numbers. Determine whether each set of numbers is closed for addition, for multiplication, or for both. If not, give a counterexample.

48. rational numbers   **49.** integers   **50.** whole numbers

51. negative numbers   **52.** odd numbers   **53.** even numbers

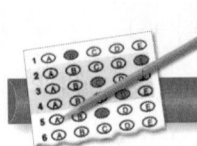

Test Prep

Multiple Choice

54. Simplify $-4 + 17 - 29 + 4 + 29 - 3$.
  A. 14   **B.** 20   **C.** 22   **D.** 72

55. Which of the following has the same result as dividing a number by $\frac{5}{2}$ and then multiplying by $\frac{1}{2}$?
  F. multiplying by 2   **G.** dividing by 2
  H. multiplying by 5   **J.** dividing by 5

56. In the formula $A = \pi r^2$, if the value of r is doubled, then what is the value of A multiplied by?
  A. $\frac{1}{4}$ **B.** $\frac{1}{2}$ **C.** 2   **D.** 4

57. The variable a is an integer. Which of the following could NOT equal a^3?
  F. -27 **G.** -16 **H.** 8   **J.** 64

58. What is the total cost if you buy 3 goldfish for $1.90 each, 3 angelfish for $6.10 each, and 12 neon tetras for $1.53 each?
  A. $39.36   **B.** $42.36   **C.** $60.36   **D.** $66.36

59. Simplify $-2h - (5 - 3h)$.
  F. $h - 5$ **G.** $-5h - 5$ **H.** h **J.** $-4h$

Mixed Review

Lesson 5-4

Simplify each expression.

60. $5(1.2 + k)$ **61.** $\frac{1}{3}(33 - b)$ **62.** $-2.5(4p + 14)$

63. $4(7 - n)$ **64.** $-(-7.4m + 0.05)$ **65.** $(3v - 5.2)(-6)$

Lesson 5-3

Write an expression for each phrase.

66. 7 plus the sum of m and -17

67. 8 minus the quantity 9 minus t

68. one half of the quotient of b and 4

69. one third of the sum of x and 5.1

Lesson 5-1

Simplify.

70. $12 + (-5)$ **71.** $9.2 + (-27.5)$ **72.** $\frac{5}{8} + \left(-\frac{7}{8}\right)$

73. $-4\frac{6}{10} + 3\frac{2}{5}$ **74.** $-11 + (-124)$ **75.** $|-2.4| + |6.8|$

Understanding Math Problems Read through the problem below. Let Franklin's thinking guide you through the solution. Check your understanding with the exercises at the bottom of the page.

Tell whether the expressions $6t - 4$ and $2[(2 + 1)t - 2]$ are equivalent.

What Franklin Thinks   ### What Franklin Writes

My first step is to make sure that I understand what the problem is about. Two expressions are equivalent if they simplify to the same expression.

$$6t - 4 \stackrel{?}{=} 2[(2 + 1)t - 2]$$

I'm going to look at the expression $2[(2 + 1)t - 2]$. If I can simplify this expression to $6t - 4$, then the expressions are equivalent.

$$2[(2 + 1)t - 2]$$

This expression looks complicated, but I know the Order of Operations. So I'll begin by working inside the innermost grouping symbols.

$$2[(3)t - 2]$$

I will write $(3)t$ without the parentheses.

$$2[3t - 2]$$

I will use the Distributive Property to simplify completely.

$$6t - 4$$

Now I need to write my answer.

Yes, $6t - 4$ and $2[(2 + 1)t - 2]$ are equivalent because $2[(2 + 1)t - 2]$ simplifies to $6t - 4$.

EXERCISES

Tell whether the expressions in each pair are equivalent.

1. $-(y - 4)$ and $4 - y$

2. $8 + 5m$ and $8 + 5 + m$

3. $2(t - 7)$ and $7(t - 2)$

4. $4(2b - 3)$ and $2[(2 - 1)b - 2]$

5. $3[2(a - 6)] - 4a$ and $2(a - 18)$

6. $-(b + 7) + 3(b - 7)$ and $2b$

7. $5(-8 + 3p) - 2[2(-4p + 3)]$ and $31p - 18$

8. $-2(m - 8) - 3[2(m + 5)]$ and $-2(4m + 7)$

Understanding Probability

Hands-On

FOR USE WITH LESSON 5-6

You can use number cubes to investigate probability concepts.

1 ACTIVITY

When you toss a number cube, there are a variety of possible results. You can find the probabilities of these results by first listing all the possible results.

1. List all the possible results of tossing one number cube.

2. How many possible results are there?

3. List all the possible results that are divisible by 3.

4. Use the ratio below to find the probability of tossing a number divisible by 3.

number of possible results that are divisible by 3
———————————————————————————————
total number of possible results

2 ACTIVITY

The table shows all the possible results of tossing two number cubes.

5. How many results are there?

6. a. List the results that have a sum of 1.
   b. What is the probability of a sum of 1?

7. a. List the results that have a sum of 4.
   b. What is the probability of a sum of 4?

8. a. List the results that have a sum of 11.
   b. What is the probability of a sum of 11?

9. Find another sum that has the same probability of occurring as 11.

10. Reasoning Are the sums 2–12 equally likely? Explain.

11. Are the probabilities of getting an even sum or an odd sum equal?

Results for Two Number Cubes

(1, 1)	(1, 2)	(1, 3)	(1, 4)	(1, 5)	(1, 6)
(2, 1)	(2, 2)	(2, 3)	(2, 4)	(2, 5)	(2, 6)
(3, 1)	(3, 2)	(3, 3)	(3, 4)	(3, 5)	(3, 6)
(4, 1)	(4, 2)	(4, 3)	(4, 4)	(4, 5)	(4, 6)
(5, 1)	(5, 2)	(5, 3)	(5, 4)	(5, 5)	(5, 6)
(6, 1)	(6, 2)	(6, 3)	(6, 4)	(6, 5)	(6, 6)

3 ACTIVITY

Assume you are tossing a pair of regular tetrahedrons with the numbers 1 through 4 printed on the faces, like those at the right. The same number appears at the bottom of each face, and this number is the result of the toss.

12. Construct a table that shows all the possible results.

13. How many results are there?

14. a. List the results that have a sum of 4.
   b. What is the probability of a sum of 4?

15. Critical Thinking Why is the probability of a sum of 4 with two regular tetrahedrons not the same as the probability of a sum of 4 with two cubes?

Activity Lab Understanding Probability

5-6 Theoretical and Experimental Probability

What You'll Learn

- To find theoretical probability
- To find experimental probability

. . . And Why

To analyze a manufacturing situation, as in Example 4

✓ **Check Skills You'll Need**

GO for Help Skills Handbook page 794

Rewrite each decimal or fraction as a percent.

1. 0.32   **2.** 0.09   **3.** $\frac{45}{200}$ **4.** $\frac{9}{50}$

 New Vocabulary
- probability
- outcome
- event
- sample space
- theoretical probability
- complement of an event
- odds
- experimental probability

---

1 Theoretical Probability

Vocabulary Tip

Read *P(event)* as "the probability of an event."

The **probability** of an event, or *P*(event), tells you how likely it is that something will occur. An **outcome** is the result of a single trial, like one roll of a number cube. The **sample space** is all of the possible outcomes. An **event** is any outcome or group of outcomes.

Here is how these terms apply to finding the probability of rolling an even number on a number cube.

event	sample space	favorable outcome
↓	↓	↓
rolling an even number	1, 2, 3, 4, 5, 6	2, 4, 6

The possible outcomes of rolling a fair number cube are *equally likely* to occur. When all possible outcomes are equally likely, you can find the theoretical probability of an event using the following formula.

theoretical probability $P(\text{event}) = \dfrac{\text{number of favorable outcomes}}{\text{number of possible outcomes}}$

$$P(\text{rolling an even number}) = \frac{3}{6} = \frac{1}{2}$$

You can write the probability of an event as a fraction, a decimal, or a percent. The probability of an event ranges from 0 to 1.

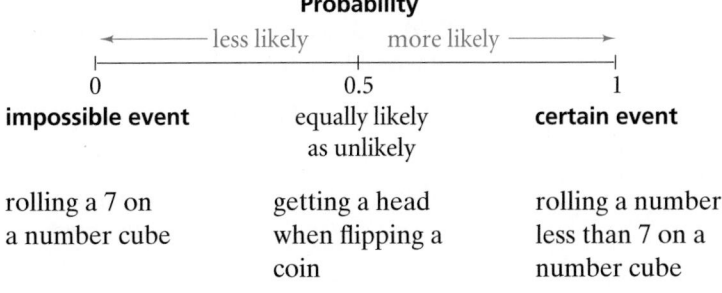

Probability

← less likely   more likely →

0	0.5	1
impossible event	**equally likely as unlikely**	**certain event**
rolling a 7 on a number cube	getting a head when flipping a coin	rolling a number less than 7 on a number cube

---

Test-Taking Tip

Ask yourself if your answer makes sense. If you find a probability greater than 1, then you have made an error.

1 EXAMPLE Finding Theoretical Probability

A bowl contains 12 slips of paper, each with a different name of a month. Find the theoretical probability that a slip selected at random from the bowl has a name of a month that starts with the letter J.

$P(\text{event}) = \dfrac{\text{number of favorable outcomes}}{\text{number of possible outcomes}}$

$\qquad = \dfrac{3}{12}$ **There are 3 months out of 12 that begin with the letter J: January, June, and July.**

$\qquad = \dfrac{1}{4}$ **Simplify.**

● The probability of picking a month that begins with the letter J is $\frac{1}{4}$.

 **1** Suppose you write the names of days of the week on identical pieces of paper. Find the theoretical probability of picking a piece of paper at random that has the name of a day that starts with the letter T.

The **complement of an event** consists of all the outcomes not in the event.

Vocabulary Tip

An event and its <u>complement</u> represent the *complete* set of possible outcomes.

possible outcomes for rolling a number cube	outcomes for rolling an even number	complement of rolling an even number
↓	↓	↓
$1, 2, 3, 4, 5, 6$	$2, 4, 6$	$1, 3, 5$

The sum of the probabilities of an event and its complement is 1.

$$P(\text{event}) + P(\text{not event}) = 1$$

or

$$P(\text{not event}) = 1 - P(\text{event})$$

2 EXAMPLE Finding the Complement of an Event

Games On a popular television game show, a contestant must choose one of five envelopes. One envelope contains the grand prize, a car. Find the probability of not choosing the car.

$P(\text{car}) = \dfrac{\text{number of favorable outcomes}}{\text{number of possible outcomes}} = \dfrac{1}{5}$

$P(\text{not choosing the car}) = 1 - P(\text{car})$ **Use the complement formula.**

$\qquad\qquad\qquad\qquad\quad = 1 - \dfrac{1}{5} = \dfrac{4}{5}$ **Simplify.**

● The probability of not choosing the car is $\frac{4}{5}$.

 **2 Critical Thinking** In Example 2, what happens to $P(\text{not choosing the car})$ as the number of envelopes increases?

Odds describes the likelihood of an event by comparing favorable and unfavorable outcomes.

odds in favor of an event → number of *favorable*   to   number of *unfavorable*
outcomes   outcomes

odds against an event → number of *unfavorable*   to   number of *favorable*
outcomes   outcomes

3 **EXAMPLE** Finding Odds

Find the odds in favor of the spinner landing on a number greater than or equal to 6.

Favorable outcomes: 6, 7, 8
Unfavorable outcomes: 1, 2, 3, 4, 5

● The odds are 3 : 5 in favor of the event.

✓ **Quick Check** ❸ Find the odds against the spinner landing on a number less than 3.

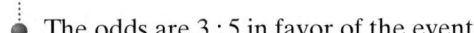

2 Experimental Probability

Probability based on data collected from repeated trials is experimental probability.

experimental probability $P(\text{event}) = \dfrac{\text{number of times an event occurs}}{\text{number of times the experiment is done}}$

4 **EXAMPLE** Finding Experimental Probability

Quality Control After receiving complaints, a skateboard manufacturer inspected 1000 skateboards at random. The manufacturer found no defects in 992 skateboards. What is the probability that a skateboard selected at random had no defects? Write the probability as a percent.

$P(\text{no defects}) = \dfrac{\text{number of times an event occurs}}{\text{number of times the experiment is done}}$

$= \dfrac{992}{1000}$ **Substitute.**

$= 0.992 \text{ or } 99.2\%$ **Simplify and write as a percent.**

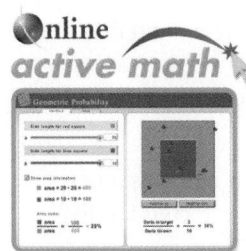

Real-World Connection

More than 100,000 skateboards are manufactured each month.

● The probability that a skateboard has no defects is 99.2%.

✓ **Quick Check** ❹ The manufacturer inspects 2500 skateboards. There are 2450 skateboards with no defects. Find the probability that a skateboard selected at random has no defects.

You can use experimental probability to make a prediction. Predictions are not exact, so round your results.

5 **EXAMPLE** Using Experimental Probability

Online active math

For: Probability Activity
Use: Interactive Textbook, 2-6

Quality Control The same manufacturer has 8976 skateboards in its warehouse. If the probability that a skateboard has no defect is 99.2%, predict how many skateboards are likely to have no defect.

number with no defects $= P(\text{no defects}) \cdot \text{number of skateboards}$

$= 0.992 \times 8976$ **Substitute. Use 0.992 for 99.2%.**

$= 8904.192$ **Simplify.**

● Approximately 8900 boards are likely to have no defect.

✓ **Quick Check** ❺ A manufacturer inspects 700 light bulbs. She finds that the probability that a light bulb works is 99.6%. There are 35,400 light bulbs in the warehouse. Predict how many light bulbs are likely to work.

EXERCISES

For more exercises, see *Extra Skill and Word Problem Practice.*

Practice and Problem Solving

A Practice by Example

Example 1
(page 270)

GO for Help

Example 2
(page 270)

For Exercises 1–13, use the spinner at the right. Find the theoretical probability of landing on the given section(s) of the spinner.

1. *P*(purple)   2. *P*(green)   3. *P*(5)

4. *P*(even)   5. *P*(purple or white)   6. *P*(8)

7. *P*(greater than 4) 8. *P*(even or odd)   9. *P*(1 or 6)

10. *P*(not white)   11. *P*(not 2)   12. *P*(not purple)   13. *P*(not 8)

14. Suppose the probability that you will be picked for a committee at school is 20%. What is the probability that you will not be picked?

Example 3
(page 271)

For Exercises 15–20, use the spinner at the right above. Find each odds.

15. odds in favor of green   16. odds against a factor of 6

17. odds against white   18. odds in favor of purple

19. odds in favor of a multiple of 5   20. odds against 2

Examples 4, 5
(page 271)

The results of a survey of 100 randomly selected students at a 2000-student high school are below. Find the experimental probability that a student selected at random makes the given response.

21. *P*(community college)

22. *P*(4-year college)

23. *P*(trade school)

24. *P*(not trade school)

25. *P*(trade school or community college)

26. *P*(community or 4-year college)

Plans for After Graduation

Response	Number of Respondents
Go to community college	24
Go to 4-year college	43
Take a year off before college	12
Go to trade school	15
Do not plan to go to college	6

27. A forest contains about 500 trees. You randomly pick 67 trees and find that 27 of them are oaks.
   a. What is the experimental probability that a tree in the forest is an oak?
   b. Predict how many oak trees there are in the forest.

28. Suppose 12 out of 30 families on your street have a cat or a dog as a pet.
   a. What is the experimental probability that a randomly selected family in your neighborhood will have a cat or a dog as a pet?
   b. Based on *P*(cat or dog) from part (a), predict how many cat- or dog-owning families you can expect among 57 families in your neighborhood.

B Apply Your Skills

Suppose you roll a number cube. Find each probability.

29. *P*(5)   30. *P*(7)   31. *P*(3 or 4)   32. *P*(not 5)

Suppose you select a 3-digit number at random from the set of all positive 3-digit numbers. Find each probability or odds. (*Hint:* First find how many positive 3-digit numbers there are.)

33. P(odd number)

34. P(number less than 900)

35. P(243 or 244)

36. P(number less than 100)

37. P(number is a multiple of 30)

38. P(number less than 500)

39. odds in favor of a multiple of 10

40. odds against 243 or 244

41. odds against a number greater than 400

42. Birthdays Each day in the United States, about 753,000 people have a birthday. Use the information at the left to find the probability that someone celebrating a birthday today will turn 16. Round to the nearest percent.

43. Multiple Choice The United States has a land area of about 3,536,278 mi². Illinois has a land area of about 57,918 mi². What is the probability that a location in the United States chosen at random is in Illinois?

Ⓐ 0.016%   Ⓑ 0.61%   Ⓒ 1.6%   Ⓓ 61%

44. Open-Ended Suppose your teacher chooses a student at random from your algebra class.
  a. What is the probability that you are selected?
  b. What is the probability that a boy is not selected?

45. Data Analysis The population of the United States is about 281,000,000. Use the circle graph at the right to answer the following questions. Round to the nearest percent.
  a. What is the probability of selecting at random a person whose age is between 10 and 19?
  b. What is the probability of selecting at random a person whose age is between 40 and 49?

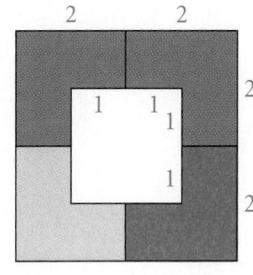

U.S. Population (millions)

7.7 ⌐1.4
16.2
39.7
20.3
31
40.7
42.5
38.3
43.2

Age
☐ 0–9
☐ 10–19
☐ 20–29
☐ 30–39
☐ 40–49
☐ 50–59
☐ 60–69
☐ 70–79
☐ 80–89
☐ 90+

Source: U.S. Census Bureau

46. Writing Explain the difference between theoretical probability and experimental probability.

Geometry Use the diagram at the right. Assume that the white square is centered in the large square. If you choose a point inside the figure, what is the probability that it will be in each shaded region?

47. P(red)

48. P(purple)

49. P(yellow or white)

50. P(not purple)

For Exercises 51–56, use the spinner at the left.

51. odds in favor of green

52. odds against white

53. odds against an even number

54. odds against a factor of 4

55. odds in favor of green or white

56. odds in favor of 6 or 7

57. Critical Thinking Explain how you can use odds to find probability. Include an example.

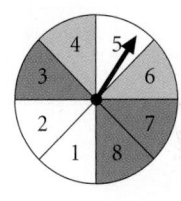

 **Challenge** 🌐 **Data Analysis** The stem-and-leaf plot at the right shows the difference between the points scored by the winning and losing teams in the Super Bowl from 1981 to 2000.

58. Find the probability that the winning team won by less than 10 points.

59. Find the odds that the winning team won by 10 to 15 points.

60. Find the probability that the winning team won by more than 20 points.

Difference Between Winning and Losing Super Bowl Scores

```
0 | 1  4  5  7  7
1 | 0  0  3  4  5  5  7  7  9
2 | 2  3  9
3 | 2  5  6
4 | 5
Key: 1|0 means 10 points
```

Real-World 🌐 Connection

The greatest total score of both teams in a Super Bowl was 75, in 1995.

61. Data Collection Roll a pair of number cubes and record the product of the results. Repeat 30 times.
  a. Use your data to find the following experimental probabilities: $P(5), P(6), P(12), P(36)$.
  b. Make a chart to find the sample space for the product of two cubes.
  c. Find the theoretical probabilities for $P(5), P(6), P(12), P(36)$.
  d. Are your experimental probabilities exactly the same as the theoretical probabilities?
  e. Suppose you roll the number cubes 1000 times. Would you expect the experimental probabilities and the theoretical probabilities to be about the same? Explain.

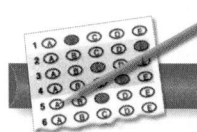 **Test Prep**

Multiple Choice

62. Suppose you roll a number cube with the numbers 1–6 on it. Which has the same probability as $P(\text{1 or prime})$?
  A. $P(\text{factor of 6})$ **B.** $P(\text{1 or 2})$
  C. $P(\text{less than 3})$ **D.** $P(\text{not odd})$

63. Of 150 widgets inspected, 142 passed inspection. Out of 2855 widgets, about how many would you predict would fail an inspection?
  F. 140   **G.** 150   **H.** 2700   **J.** 2850

64. There are 28 right-handed students in a class of 31. What is the probability that a student chosen at random will be left-handed?
  A. $\frac{31}{28}$ **B.** $\frac{28}{31}$ **C.** $\frac{3}{28}$ **D.** $\frac{3}{31}$

65. A "Bag-of-Beads" for crafts contains five different colors of beads. The company that makes them claims that each bag contains the same number of each color.

Rosheeda purchased a bag to test the company's claim. She recorded the number of each color. Based on the results in the table to the right, what is the experimental probability of picking a red bead out of the bag?

Color	Number
red	55
blue	53
green	64
yellow	47
purple	61

  F. $\frac{9}{56}$ **G.** $\frac{11}{56}$
  H. $\frac{11}{45}$ **J.** $\frac{9}{45}$

66. An inspector for an office-supply company checked a batch of 360 staplers. He found that 18 of them were defective. What is the experimental probability of getting a defective stapler in this batch?

    A. 18%   **B.** 5%   **C.** 0.5%   **D.** 0.05%

Mixed Review

Lessons 5-4 and 5-5

GO for Help

Name the property that each equation illustrates.

67. $-6g + 10 + g = -6g + 10 + 1g$

68. $-6g + 10 + 1g = -6g + 1g + 10$

69. $-6g + 1g + 10 = (-6 + 1)g + 10$

70. $-4s - 8 + 3(s + 5) = -4s - 8 + 3s + 15$

71. $-4s - 8 + 3s + 15 = -4s + 3s + (-8) + 15$

72. $-4s + 3s + (-8) + 15 = (-4 + 3)s + (-8) + 15$

Lesson 4-6

Find the mean, median, and mode of each set of numbers.

73. 3 4 5 5 8 11

74. 1 8 9 11 22 34 34

Make a stem-and-leaf plot for each set of data.

75. 34 37 39 41 49 65 71

76. 12 14 16 23 27 47 68 79

✓ Checkpoint Quiz 2   Lessons 5-5 through 5-6

Give a reason to justify each step.

1. $-7d + 3 + 5(d + 2) = -7d + 3 + 5d + 10$ $\underline{\quad ? \quad}$

2. $= -7d + 5d + 3 + 10$ $\underline{\quad ? \quad}$

3. $= -7d + 5d + (3 + 10)$ $\underline{\quad ? \quad}$

4. $= -7d + 5d + 13$ $\underline{\quad ? \quad}$

5. $= (-7 + 5)d + 13$ $\underline{\quad ? \quad}$

6. $= -2d + 13$ $\underline{\quad ? \quad}$

Use the spinner at the left.

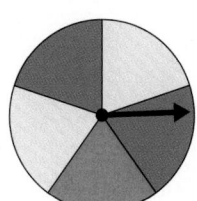

7. Find P(not yellow)   **8.** Find the odds against yellow.

9. Suppose you write the days of the week on identical pieces of paper. You mix them in a bowl and choose one at random. What is the probability that the day you select will have the letter E in it?

10. A manufacturer inspects 100 bicycles at random. She finds that 98 of them have no defects. There are 2400 bicycles in the warehouse. Predict how many bicycles are likely to be free of defects.

Conducting a Simulation

For: Graphing calculator procedures
Web Code: ate-2115

FOR USE WITH LESSON 5-7

A *simulation* is a model of a real-life situation. One way to do a simulation is to use random numbers generated by a graphing calculator or a computer program.

On a graphing calculator, the command randInt generates random integers. To create a list of random integers, press MATH ◄ 5. You will see randInt(. After the parenthesis, press 0 ❭ 99, and press ENTER repeatedly to create 1- and 2-digit random numbers.

ACTIVITY

About 40% of the people in the United States have type A blood. Find the experimental probability that the next two people who donate blood have type A blood.

To simulate this problem, use 2-digit numbers to represent groups of 2 people. Use your calculator to generate 40 random numbers.

Define how the simulation will be done.

Since about 40% of people have type A blood, let 40%, or 4 out of 10 digits, represent people in this group. Using numbers from the random number table, let 0, 1, 2, 3 represent people with type A blood. Let 4, 5, 6, 7, 8, 9 represent people who do not have type A blood.

Interpret the simulation.

The six numbers in red represent "the next two people have type A blood." Each of the other groups has at least one person with a different blood type.

25	71	47	46
66	13	63	36
01	59	27	07
83	25	72	24
73	52	59	81
14	09	40	64
81	72	02	38
21	09	92	10
93	34	36	45
53	18	23	75

P(next two people have type A blood) =

$$\frac{\text{number of times an event happens}}{\text{number of times the experiment is done}} = \frac{6}{40} = 0.15 = 15\%$$

The probability that the next two people will have type A blood is about 15%.

EXERCISES

1. **a.** **Blood Types** In the United States, about 50% of people have type O blood. Design an experiment using spinners, coins, or number cubes to find the experimental probability that the next two donors have type O blood. Describe your simulation.
   b. Conduct your simulation and interpret your results.

2. A basketball player has made 12 or her last 18 free throws. Design and describe a simulation to find the experimental probability that she will make her next five free throws. Conduct your simulation and interpret your results.

3. **a.** **Open-Ended** Write an experimental probability problem that you could solve using a simulation.
   b. Design and describe your simulation.
   c. Conduct your simulation and interpret your results.

5-7 Probability of Compound Events

What You'll Learn

- To find the probability of independent events
- To find the probability of dependent events

. . . And Why

To use probability in a game, as in Example 2

✓ **Check Skills You'll Need**

 **for Help** Lesson 5-6

Find each probability for one roll of a number cube.

1. $P(\text{multiple of } 3)$ **2.** $P(\text{greater than } 4)$

3. $P(\text{greater than } 5)$ **4.** $P(\text{greater than } 6)$

Simplify.

5. $\frac{2}{14} \cdot \frac{7}{6}$ **6.** $\frac{15}{24} \cdot \frac{12}{30}$ **7.** $\frac{6}{55} \cdot \frac{44}{3}$

🔊 **New Vocabulary** • independent events • dependent events

---

1   Finding the Probability of Independent Events

Activity: Compound Events

Suppose you draw cards at random from the following collection.

| R | R | A | N | N | N | D | O | M | M |

1. You draw an R card and replace it. What is the probability that the next card you draw will be an R card?

2. You draw an R card and do *not* replace it. What is the probability that the next card you draw will be an R card?

3. Copy and complete each table.

Probability With Replacement		Probability Without Replacement	
First Card	**Second Card Matches**	**First Card**	**Second Card Matches**
$P(\text{R}) = $ ▨	$P(\text{R}) = $ ▨	$P(\text{R}) = $ ▨	$P(\text{R}) = $ ▨
$P(\text{A}) = $ ▨	$P(\text{A}) = $ ▨	$P(\text{A}) = $ ▨	$P(\text{A}) = $ ▨
$P(\text{N}) = $ ▨	$P(\text{N}) = $ ▨	$P(\text{N}) = $ ▨	$P(\text{N}) = $ ▨
$P(\text{D}) = $ ▨	$P(\text{D}) = $ ▨	$P(\text{D}) = $ ▨	$P(\text{D}) = $ ▨
$P(\text{O}) = $ ▨	$P(\text{O}) = $ ▨	$P(\text{O}) = $ ▨	$P(\text{O}) = $ ▨
$P(\text{M}) = $ ▨	$P(\text{M}) = $ ▨	$P(\text{M}) = $ ▨	$P(\text{M}) = $ ▨

4. For each letter, the probability of drawing the first card is the same with replacement and without replacement. Explain why the probability of drawing the second card is not the same.

The diagram at the right shows the results of randomly choosing a checker, putting it back, and choosing again. The probability of getting a red on either pick is $\frac{1}{2}$. The first pick, or first event, does not affect the second event. The events are independent.

Independent events are events that do not influence one another.

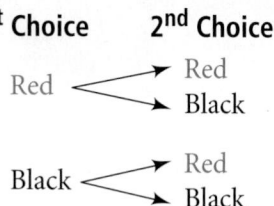

1st Choice   **2nd Choice**

Red $\longrightarrow$ Red
        Black

Black $\longrightarrow$ Red
          Black

Key Concepts

Rule	Probability of Two Independent Events

If A and B are independent events, $P(A \text{ and } B) = P(A) \cdot P(B)$.

---

1 EXAMPLE Independent Events

GO Online

Video Tutor Help
Visit: PHSchool.com
Web Code: ate-0775

Multiple Choice Suppose you roll a red number cube and a blue number cube. What is the probability that you will roll a 3 on the red cube and an even number on the blue cube?

Ⓐ $\frac{1}{12}$　　　Ⓑ $\frac{1}{6}$　　　Ⓒ $\frac{1}{2}$　　　Ⓓ $\frac{2}{3}$

$P(\text{red 3}) = \frac{1}{6}$　　There is one way to get a 3 out of six numbers.

$P(\text{blue even}) = \frac{3}{6} = \frac{1}{2}$　　There are three even numbers out of six numbers.

$P(\text{red 3 and blue even}) = P(\text{red 3}) \cdot P(\text{blue even})$

$= \frac{1}{6} \cdot \frac{1}{2}$　　**Substitute.**

$= \frac{1}{12}$　　**Simplify.**

The probability that you will roll a 3 on the red number cube and an even number on the blue cube is $\frac{1}{12}$. The answer is A.

✓ Quick Check　**①** Suppose you roll a red number cube and a blue number cube. What is the probability that you will roll a 5 on the red cube and a 1 or 2 on the blue cube?

2 EXAMPLE Selecting With Replacement

Games In a word game, you choose a tile at random from a bag containing the letter tiles shown. You *replace* the first tile in the bag and then choose again. What is the probability that you will choose an A and then an E?

Since you replace the first tile, the events are independent.

$P(\text{A}) = \frac{4}{15}$　　**There are 4 A's in the 15 tiles.**

$P(\text{E}) = \frac{3}{15}$　　**There are 3 E's in the 15 tiles.**

$P(\text{A and E}) = P(\text{A}) \cdot P(\text{E})$

$= \frac{4}{15} \cdot \frac{3}{15}$　　**Multiply.**

$= \frac{12}{225} = \frac{4}{75}$

The probability that you will choose an A and then an E is $\frac{4}{75}$.

✓ Quick Check　**②** Find the probability that you will choose at random a U and then an I after replacing the first tile.

Odds describe the likelihood of an event by comparing favorable and unfavorable outcomes.

$$\text{odds in favor of an event} = \frac{\text{number of } \textit{favorable} \text{ outcomes}}{\text{number of } \textit{unfavorable} \text{ outcomes}}$$

$$\text{odds against an event} = \frac{\text{number of } \textit{unfavorable} \text{ outcomes}}{\text{number of } \textit{favorable} \text{ outcomes}}$$

Find each probability for one roll of a number cube.

45. $P(\text{number} \geq 7)$ **46.** $P(\text{not } 5)$ **47.** $P(2 \text{ or } 6)$

48. $P(3)$ **49.** $P(\text{number} < 6)$ **50.** $P(\text{not odd})$

Use the spinner at the left. Find each odds.

51. odds in favor of 1   **52.** odds against even

53. odds in favor of green   **54.** odds against red

55. odds in favor of a multiple of 3   **56.** odds against a factor of 6

57. Suppose you toss a coin 4 times.
   a. What is the probability that you toss exactly 3 heads?
   b. Explain what $P(\text{not 3 heads})$ means.

58. **Science** An astronomer calculates that the probability that a visible meteor shower will occur in May is $\frac{3}{14}$. What is the probability that a visible meteor shower will not occur in May?

5-7 Objectives

▼ To find the probability of independent events (p. 277)

▼ To find the probability of dependent events (p. 279)

Independent events do not affect one another. When the outcome of one event affects the outcome of a second event, the events are **dependent events**.

For independent events A and B: For dependent events A and B:

$P(A \text{ and } B) = P(A) \cdot P(B)$. $P(A \text{ then } B) = P(A) \cdot P(B \text{ after } A)$.

For Exercises 59–63, suppose you choose two numbers from a box containing ten cards with the numbers 1–10. State whether the two events are independent or dependent. Then find each probability.

59. $P(6 \text{ then an even number})$ without replacing the card

60. $P(1 \text{ and an odd number})$ with replacing the card

61. $P(\text{an even number then an odd number})$ without replacing the card

62. $P(\text{an even number and an odd number})$ with replacing the card

63. $P(5 \text{ then an even number})$ without replacing the card

64. **Writing** Explain what the word *dependent* means in probability and what it means in everyday language.

Are the two events dependent or independent? Explain.

65. Roll a red and a blue number cube.

66. Randomly select a green sock and then another green sock from a drawer when you are getting ready for school.

Chapter Test

Go Online
PHSchool.com
For: Online chapter test
Web Code: ata-0252

Simplify each expression.

1. $-1.8 + 12.1 + (-7.6)$
2. $6.3 - 3.9 + 3.7$
3. $1\frac{7}{8} + 14\frac{1}{8}$
4. $-7\frac{7}{8} + \left(-2\frac{1}{2}\right)$
5. $-8\frac{5}{6} + 4\frac{1}{2}$
6. $3 + 5 - 4$

Find each sum or difference.

7. $\begin{bmatrix} 3 & 2 \\ -1 & 5 \end{bmatrix} + \begin{bmatrix} 8 & -5 \\ 3 & 0 \end{bmatrix}$

8. $\begin{bmatrix} \frac{1}{5} & -2 \\ 0 & \frac{4}{9} \end{bmatrix} + \begin{bmatrix} 4 & -\frac{1}{2} \\ -5 & \frac{4}{9} \end{bmatrix}$

9. $\begin{bmatrix} \frac{1}{2} & -\frac{3}{4} \\ -2 & 1 \end{bmatrix} - \begin{bmatrix} \frac{1}{4} & 1 \\ -\frac{1}{2} & 5 \end{bmatrix}$

10. $\begin{bmatrix} 1 & 9 & -4 \\ 5 & 2 & -1 \\ -6 & -2 & -1 \end{bmatrix} - \begin{bmatrix} 2 & -6 & 7 \\ -8 & 3 & -3 \\ 4 & -7 & 9 \end{bmatrix}$

11. On four plays, a football team gained 22 yd, lost 18 yd, gained 8 yd, and lost 14 yd. What is the total number of yards gained or lost on the four plays?

12. **Banking** Marcus had $163 in his checking account. On Monday, he wrote a check for $315. How much does Marcus need to deposit into his account to prevent the account balance from dipping below the minimum of $25?

Evaluate each expression for $x = 3$, $y = -1$, and $z = 2$.

13. $2x + 3y + z$
14. $-xyz$
15. $-3x - 2z - 7$
16. $-z^3 - 2z + z$
17. $\frac{xy - 3z}{-5}$
18. $|y - x| - z$
19. $x^2 + (-x)^2$
20. $y^2 - (-y)^2$

Simplify each expression.

21. $9(-5)$
22. $8 - 2^4 \div 2$
23. $-4\left(-\frac{2}{3}\right)$
24. $3\frac{1}{6} \div \left(-4\frac{2}{3}\right)$
25. $\frac{2 \cdot 3 - 1}{3^2}$
26. $36 - (4 + 5 \cdot 4)$
27. $3^3 \cdot 11 \div 9$
28. $-12 \div (-4) - 3$

29. **Writing** Tell if each of the subtraction sentences would *always*, *sometimes*, or *never* be true. Support your answer with two examples.
   a. $(+) - (+) = (+)$ **b.** $(+) - (-) = (-)$
   c. $(-) - (-) = (-)$ **d.** $(-) - (+) = (+)$

Simplify each expression.

30. $m(-3 + n)$
31. $6(2d - 5)$
32. $\frac{y}{5}(10 - x)$
33. $(7 - 42a)\left(-\frac{3}{7}\right)$

Simplify each expression. Justify each step.

34. $10x + 3\left(\frac{1}{3} - x\right)$
35. $2(25a - 5) - 100a$
36. $(3^3 - 3^3)(1 - 2^2)$
37. $-36 \div (-12)$
38. $27rst + 27tsr$
39. $6a - 5 + 3(3 - a)$
40. $5 + h\left(\frac{6}{h}\right) - h$
41. $4c - 6 - (-2c)$

42. **Survey** A random survey of 60 students showed that 36 students used calculators for computation. What is the probability that a student chosen at random used a calculator for computation?

43. A softball player made a hit 34 times in the last 170 times at bat. Find the probability that the softball player will get a hit the next time at bat.

Suppose you have a bag containing 3 red, 4 blue, 5 white, and 2 black marbles. You select one marble at random. Find each probability or odds.

44. $P(\text{not white})$
45. $P(\text{red or blue})$
46. $P(\text{orange})$
47. $P(\text{not black})$
48. odds in favor of red
49. odds against blue
50. odds against black or white
51. odds in favor of red, white, or blue

52. **Open-Ended** Write and solve a probability problem involving dependent events.

53. You have 8 red checkers and 8 black checkers in a bag. You choose two checkers. Find each probability.
   a. $P(\text{red and red})$ with replacing
   b. $P(\text{red then black})$ without replacing
   c. $P(\text{black and red})$ with replacing

288 Chapter 5 Chapter Test

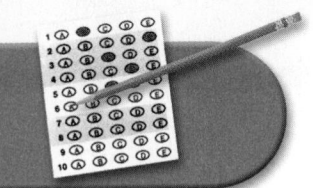

Standardized Test Prep

Multiple Choice

For Exercises 1–12, choose the correct letter.

1. Simplify $2(5 - 3)^2 + 4 \div 2$.

   Ⓐ 6 Ⓑ 8 Ⓒ 10 Ⓓ 18

2. Evaluate $\dfrac{3x - (-4)}{7}$ for $x = -6$.

   Ⓐ -3 Ⓑ -2 Ⓒ 2 Ⓓ 3

3. Name the property illustrated by the equation $(8 + 2) + 7 = (2 + 8) + 7$.

   Ⓐ Commutative Property of Addition

   Ⓑ Associative Property of Addition

   Ⓒ Distributive Property

   Ⓓ Identity Property of Addition

4. Find the difference.

   $\begin{bmatrix} 8 & -7 \\ 3 & -5 \end{bmatrix} - \begin{bmatrix} 4 & 0 \\ -2 & -4 \end{bmatrix}$

   Ⓐ $\begin{bmatrix} 4 & 7 \\ 5 & 1 \end{bmatrix}$ Ⓑ $\begin{bmatrix} 4 & -7 \\ 1 & -1 \end{bmatrix}$

   Ⓒ $\begin{bmatrix} 4 & -7 \\ 5 & -1 \end{bmatrix}$ Ⓓ $\begin{bmatrix} 4 & -7 \\ 1 & -9 \end{bmatrix}$

5. Evaluate $2y + 7$ for $y = 4$.

   Ⓐ 11 Ⓑ 15 Ⓒ 22 Ⓓ 31

6. Which product equals $9h - 36$?

   Ⓐ $4(h - 9)$ Ⓑ $(9 - h)4$

   Ⓒ $(4 - h)9$ Ⓓ $9(h - 4)$

7. Tamara's teacher allows students to decide whether to use the mean, median, or mode for their test averages. Tamara will receive the highest average if she uses the mean. Which set of test scores are Tamara's?

   Ⓐ 95, 82, 76, 95, 96 Ⓑ 79, 80, 91, 83, 80

   Ⓒ 65, 84, 75, 74, 65 Ⓓ 100, 87, 94, 94, 81

8. Evaluate $3n - 5$ for $n = -7$.

   Ⓐ -12 Ⓑ -16 Ⓒ -26 Ⓓ -35

9. A bag contains 10 red marbles and 20 white marbles. You draw a marble, keep it, and draw another. What is the probability of drawing two red marbles?

   Ⓐ $\dfrac{3}{29}$ Ⓑ $\dfrac{1}{10}$ Ⓒ $\dfrac{1}{9}$ Ⓓ $\dfrac{1}{3}$

10. Evaluate $\dfrac{4a^2}{2b - 3}$ for $a = 3$ and $b = 6$.

    Ⓐ 3 Ⓑ 4 Ⓒ 6 Ⓓ 16

11. Suppose you have five note cards, each with one letter either A, B, C, D, or E. What are the odds that you select a card containing a vowel?

    Ⓐ $2 : 5$ Ⓑ $3 : 5$

    Ⓒ $2 : 3$ Ⓓ $3 : 2$

12. Which ordered pair is graphed below?

    Ⓐ $(-2, 3)$

    Ⓑ $(-3, 2)$

    Ⓒ $(-2, -3)$

    Ⓓ $(-3, -2)$

    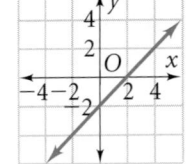

Gridded Response

Find each answer.

13. Simplify $\dfrac{3}{8} + \dfrac{3}{4}$. $\dfrac{9}{8}$

14. Simplify $\dfrac{3^2 + 3^2 + 3^2}{4^2 + 4^2 + 4^2}$ $\dfrac{9}{16}$

15. Simplify $\dfrac{3}{5}(28 - 3) - (-6)$.

16. Use the formula $A = \dfrac{1}{2}bh$ to find the area in square feet of a triangle with $b = 3.2$ ft and $h = 7.5$ ft.

17. Sean deposited $78.35 into his savings account. The next day he withdrew $29.59. What is the difference in dollars between the deposit and the withdrawal?

18. Jenna earns $7.95 per hour as a salesclerk. Find her total earnings in dollars for 6 hours.

19. Evaluate $ac^4 + (a - b)c$ for $a = 4$, $b = 5$, and $c = -2$.

Short Response

Show all of your work.

20. In 1996, an exhibit in Washington, D.C. showed 21 paintings by Johannes Vermeer. This is about $\dfrac{3}{5}$ of his known paintings. About how many of his paintings are known to exist?

Activity Lab

A Swing of the Bat

Applying Probability One of the most difficult athletic feats is also the one attempted most often in the United States—hitting a baseball with a baseball bat. A good batting average is .280 or better, which means that the batter gets a hit at least 28% of the time. The last major-league player with a season batting average above .400 was Ted Williams of the Boston Red Sox, who hit .406 in 1941. How do real batting averages compare with the probability of getting a hit?

Borders Cracks the Barrier

In 1997, Ila Borders, a left-handed pitcher with the St. Paul Saints, became the first woman to start and win a professional baseball game since the 1940s.

Activity 1

Materials: baseball bat, tape measure or ruler, pencil and paper

Suppose you are standing at the plate, ready to swing at a ball. Use the assumptions below.

- Every pitch will be in the strike zone.
- The timing of your swing will be correct so that the ball and bat are over the plate at the same time.

a. Use the given information to estimate the area of your strike zone.

b. Measure the bat and estimate the area that passes through the strike zone.

c. Use your answers to parts (a) and (b) to estimate the probability of making contact with the ball during a given swing.

Activity 2

a. Use your estimate from Activity 1 to calculate the probability of missing the ball during a given swing.

b. Use your answer to part (a) to estimate the probability of missing the ball three times in a row, or striking out.

c. Use your answer to part (b) to calculate the probability of not striking out.

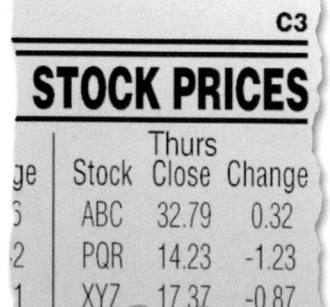

		C3
STOCK PRICES		
		Thurs	
ge	Stock	Close	Change
S	ABC	32.79	0.32
2	PQR	14.23	-1.23
1	XYZ	17.37	-0.87

The Strike Zone

Vertically, the strike zone extends from the hollow just below the batter's knee cap to a point midway between the top of the batter's belt and top of the batter's shoulders.

Horizontally, the strike zone is the width of home plate, which is 17 in., plus twice the diameter of the ball, or 5.8 in.

Power Hitter
The bat bends from the power of Mark McGwire's swing during the 1992 All-Star Game.

Activity 3

a. Having the bat make contact with the ball doesn't always mean that you get a hit. Estimate the percentage of contacts with the ball that result in a hit, either through interviewing baseball players in your school or by researching baseball statistics.

b. Use your answer to part (a) and your results from Activity 2 to estimate the batting average you could expect to have if you kept your eyes closed.

Anatomy of a Hit
Begin with your feet about shoulders-width apart. As you swing the bat, your hips turn and your hands follow your hips. As the bat makes contact with the ball, snap your wrists and watch the ball soar.

Heavy Hitter
Ted Williams of the Boston Red Sox watches the ball sail over the crowd.

Go Online
PHSchool.com

For: Information about baseball
Web Code: ate-0253

What You've Learned

● In previous courses, you learned to solve simple equations.

● In Chapter 4, you used variables to write expressions and equations that represent real-world situations.

● In Chapter 5, you extended your ability to do arithmetic operations to include rational numbers.

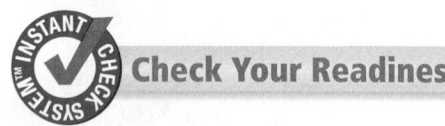 **Check Your Readiness**

 **for Help** to the Lesson in green.

Writing a Function Rule (Lesson 4-4)

The relationships in the tables below are functions. Write a function rule for each.

1.

Number of Lawns Mowed	Money Earned
1	$7.50
2	$15.00
3	$22.50
4	$30.00

2.

Number of Withdrawals	Money Remaining
1	$187
2	$174
3	$161
4	$148

Adding and Subtracting Rational Numbers (Lessons 5-1 and 5-2)

Simplify each expression.

3. $6 + (-3)$ **4.** $-4 - 6$ **5.** $-5 - (-13)$ **6.** $-7 + (-1)$

7. $-4.51 + 11.65$ **8.** $8.5 - (-7.9)$ **9.** $\frac{3}{10} - \frac{3}{4}$ **10.** $\frac{1}{5} + \left(-\frac{2}{3}\right)$

Multiplying and Dividing Rational Numbers (Lesson 5-3)

Simplify each expression.

11. $-85 \div (-5)$ **12.** $7\left(-\frac{6}{14}\right)$ **13.** $4^2(-6)^2$ **14.** $22 \div (-8)$

Combining Like Terms (Lesson 5-4)

Simplify each expression.

15. $14k^2 - (-2k^2)$ **16.** $4xy + 9xy$ **17.** $6t + 2 - 4t$ **18.** $9x - 4 + 3x$

Solving Equations

))) Key Vocabulary

- cross products (p. 320)
- equivalent equations (p. 294)
- identity (p. 312)
- inverse operations (p. 294)
- literal equation (p. 316)
- percent error (p. 346)
- percent of change (p. 344)
- principal square root (p. 352)
- proportion (p. 320)
- Pythagorean Theorem (p. 357)
- rate (p. 318)
- ratio (p. 318)
- similar figures (p. 326)
- solution of an equation (p. 294)

What You'll Learn Next

- In this chapter, you will solve equations, including equations with variables on both sides, using properties of equality.

- You will develop the ability to solve problems by defining variables, relating them to one another, and writing an equation.

- You will use proportions to measure objects indirectly.

Data Analysis **Activity Lab** You will apply what you learn about probability to investigate probability distributions, on pages 372–373.

293

Solving One-Step Equations

A **solution of an equation** is the value (or values) of the variable that makes the equation true. To find a solution, you can use properties of equality to form equivalent equations. **Equivalent equations** are equations that have the same solution (or solutions).

Addition Property of Equality

For all real numbers a, b, and c, if $a = b$, then $a + c = b + c$.

Example $8 = 5 + 3$, so $8 + 4 = 5 + 3 + 4$.

Subtraction Property of Equality

For all real numbers a, b, and c, if $a = b$ then $a - c = b - c$.

Example $8 = 5 + 3$, so $8 - 2 = 5 + 3 - 2$.

Multiplication Property of Equality

For all real numbers a, b, and c, if $a = b$, then $a \cdot c = b \cdot c$.

Example $\frac{6}{2} = 3$, so $\frac{6}{2} \cdot 2 = 3 \cdot 2$.

Division Property of Equality

For all real numbers a, b, and c, with $c \neq 0$, if $a = b$ then $\frac{a}{c} = \frac{b}{c}$.

Example $3 + 1 = 4$, so $\frac{3 + 1}{2} = \frac{4}{2}$.

One way to find the solution of an equation is to get the variable alone on one side of the equal sign. You can do this using **inverse operations,** which are operations that undo one another. Addition and subtraction are inverse operations. Multiplication and division are also inverse operations.

1 EXAMPLE Solving Using Addition or Subtraction

a. Solve $x - 3 = -8$.

$x - 3 + 3 = -8 + 3$ **Add 3 to each side of the equation.**

$x = -5$ **Simplify.**

b. Solve $g + 7 = 11$.

$g + 7 - 7 = 11 - 7$ **Subtract 7 from each side of the equation.**

$g = 4$ **Simplify.**

2 EXAMPLE Solving Using Multiplication or Division

a. Solve $\frac{3}{4}x = 9$.

$\frac{4}{3}\left(\frac{3}{4}x\right) = \frac{4}{3}(9)$ **Multiply each side by $\frac{4}{3}$, the reciprocal of $\frac{3}{4}$.**

$x = 12$ **Simplify.**

b. Solve $-96 = 4c$.

$\frac{-96}{4} = \frac{4c}{4}$ **Divide each side by 4.**

$-24 = c$ **Simplify.**

Solve each equation.

1. $x - 8 = 0$ **2.** $c - 4 = 9$ **3.** $-4 = \frac{2}{5}a$ **4.** $-8n = -64$

5. $b + 5 = -13$ **6.** $6 = x + 2$ **7.** $-7y = 28$ **8.** $-101 = -\frac{r}{3}$

9. $67 = w - 65$ **10.** $5b = 145$ **11.** $\frac{m}{7} = 12$ **12.** $-4 = k + 19$

Solving Two-Step Equations

What You'll Learn

- To solve two-step equations
- To use deductive reasoning

. . . And Why

To solve a problem involving ordering from a catalog, as in Example 3

✓ **Check Skills You'll Need**

GO for Help Review, page 294

Solve each equation and tell which property of equality you used.

1. $x - 5 = 14$ **2.** $x + 3.8 = 9$ **3.** $-7 + x = 7$

4. $x - 13 = 20$ **5.** $\frac{x}{4} = 8$ **6.** $9 = 3x$

Solve each equation.

7. $10x = 2$ **8.** $\frac{2}{3}x = -6$ **9.** $x + 2\frac{3}{4} = 6\frac{1}{2}$

---

1   Solving Two-Step Equations

A two-step equation involves two operations. Algebra tiles can help you understand how to solve equations. Since ■ represents -1 and ▢ represents 1, ■▢ is a zero pair representing zero. A green tile represents a variable.

The model below relates solving an equation algebraically and with algebra tiles.

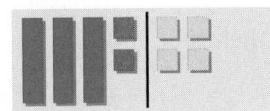

$3x - 2 = 4$

The tiles model the equation.

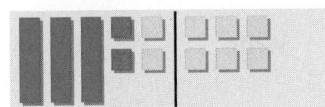

$3x - 2 + 2 = 4 + 2$

Add 2 to each side.

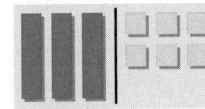

$3x = 6$

Simplify by removing zero pairs.

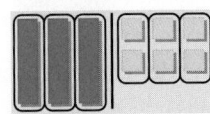

$\frac{3x}{3} = \frac{6}{3}$

Divide each side into three equal groups.

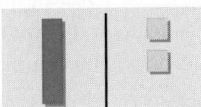

$x = 2$

Each green tile equals two yellow tiles, so $x = 2$.

Using the addition, subtraction, multiplication, and division properties of equality, you can form equivalent equations. The equations $3x - 2 = 4$, $3x = 6$, and $x = 2$ are all equivalent equations.

To solve equations, you use the properties of equality repeatedly to get the term with a variable alone on one side of the equation and with a coefficient of 1.

① EXAMPLE Solving a Two-Step Equation

Solve $10 = \frac{m}{4} + 2$.

$10 - 2 = \frac{m}{4} + 2 - 2$ **Subtract 2 from each side.**

$8 = \frac{m}{4}$ **Simplify.**

$4 \cdot 8 = 4 \cdot \frac{m}{4}$ **Multiply each side by 4.**

$32 = m$ **Simplify.**

Check $10 = \frac{m}{4} + 2$

$10 \stackrel{?}{=} \frac{32}{4} + 2$ **Substitute 32 for m.**

$10 \stackrel{?}{=} 8 + 2$

$10 = 10$ ✓

✓ Quick Check **①** Solve each equation. Check your answer.
a. $7 = 2y - 3$ b. $\frac{x}{9} - 15 = 12$ c. $-x + 15 = 12$

You can write two-step equations to model real-world situations.

② EXAMPLE <u>Real-World</u> 🌐 <u>Problem Solving</u>

A music store sells a copy of a deluxe electric guitar for $295. This is $30 more than $\frac{1}{3}$ the cost of the deluxe electric guitar it is modeled after. What is the cost of the deluxe electric guitar?

Relate | cost of the copy | is | $30 | more than | $\frac{1}{3}$ | the cost of the deluxe electric guitar |

Define   Let c = the cost of the deluxe electric guitar.

Write   295 = 30 + $\frac{1}{3}$ · c

$295 = 30 + \frac{1}{3}c$

$295 - 30 = 30 - 30 + \frac{1}{3}c$ **Subtract 30 from each side.**

$265 = \frac{1}{3}c$ **Simplify.**

$3 \cdot 265 = 3 \cdot \frac{1}{3}c$ **Multiply each side by 3.**

$795 = c$ **Simplify.**

The deluxe electric guitar costs $795.

✓ Quick Check **②** Suppose your high school's baseball team scored 5 runs in Saturday's game. This was four more than $\frac{1}{2}$ the runs scored by the opposing team. How many runs did the opposing team score?

Functions can model many real-world situations. If you have enough information, you can write a one-variable equation based on a function. Also, some real-world situations require whole numbers. Make sure your answer is reasonable for the given situation.

3 EXAMPLE Writing a Function

Retailing In a catalog, tulips cost $0.75 each and shipping costs are $3.00. Write a rule that describes the amount spent as a function of the number of bulbs ordered. Then determine the greatest number of bulbs that you can order for $14.

| **Relate** | amount spent | equals | cost per tulip bulb | times | number of tulip bulbs | plus | shipping |

Define Let a = amount spent.

Let b = number of bulbs you can order.

| **Write** | a | = | 0.75 | $\cdot$ | b | + | 3 |

$$14 = 0.75b + 3 \qquad \text{Substitute 14 for } a.$$
$$14 - 3 = 0.75b + 3 - 3 \qquad \text{Subtract 3 from each side.}$$
$$11 = 0.75b \qquad \text{Simplify.}$$
$$\frac{11}{0.75} = \frac{0.75b}{0.75} \qquad \text{Divide each side by 0.75.}$$
$$14.\overline{6} = b \qquad \text{Simplify.}$$

You can order 14 bulbs.

Check Is the solution reasonable? You can only order whole tulip bulbs. Since 15 bulbs would cost $15 \cdot \$0.75 = \$11.25$ plus $3 for handling, which is more than $14, you can only order 14 tulip bulbs.

✓ Quick Check ③ **a.** Suppose you have $25 to spend on tulips. What is the greatest number of bulbs that you can order?

b. Mrs. Simmons works at a furniture store. Her base salary is $125 a week plus $\frac{1}{12}$ of her sales. Write a rule that describes her total weekly salary as a function of her sales. Then find the amount of her sales if her total weekly salary is $255.

2 Using Deductive Reasoning

You can use deductive reasoning to justify steps as you solve an equation.

GO for Help

For help with deductive reasoning see p. 264.

4 EXAMPLE Using Deductive Reasoning

Solve $1 = \frac{k}{12} + 5$. Justify each step.

Steps	**Reasons**
$1 = \frac{k}{12} + 5$	original equation
$1 - 5 = \frac{k}{12} + 5 - 5$	Subtraction Property of Equality
$-4 = \frac{k}{12}$	Simplify.
$(12)(-4) = (12)\frac{k}{12}$	Multiplication Property of Equality
$-48 = k$	Simplify.

✓ Quick Check ④ Solve $-9 - 4m = 3$. Justify each step.

EXERCISES

For more exercises, see *Extra Skill and Word Problem Practice*.

Practice and Problem Solving

A Practice by Example

Example 1
(page 296)

GO for Help

Solve each equation. Check your answer.

1. $1 + \frac{a}{5} = -1$ **2.** $2n - 5 = 7$ **3.** $-1 = 3 + 4x$ **4.** $\frac{y}{2} + 5 = -12$

5. $3b + 7 = -2$ **6.** $\frac{x}{3} - 9 = 0$ **7.** $14 + \frac{h}{5} = 2$ **8.** $-10 = -6 + 2c$

9. $\frac{m}{8} + 4 = 16$ **10.** $\frac{a}{4} - 21 = 7$ **11.** $3x - 1 = 8$ **12.** $10 = 2n + 1$

13. $35 = 3 + 5x$ **14.** $41 = \frac{2}{5}x - 7$ **15.** $-3 + \frac{m}{3} = 12$ **16.** $9 + \frac{n}{5} = 19$

17. $-x - 4 = -20$ **18.** $-y + 10 = 25$ **19.** $5 = -z - 3$ **20.** $9 = -x + 8$

Example 2
(page 296)

Define a variable and write an equation for each situation. Then solve.

21. Donations A library receives a large cash donation and uses the funds to double the number of books it owns. Then a book collector gives the library 4028 books. After this, the library has 51,514 books. How many books did the library have before the cash donation and the gift of books?

22. Cooking Suppose you are helping to prepare a large meal. You can peel 2 carrots per minute. You need 60 peeled carrots. How long will it take you to finish if you have already peeled 18 carrots?

Example 3
(page 297)

23. Cell Phones One cell phone plan costs $39.95 per month. The first 500 minutes of usage are free. Each minute thereafter costs $.35. Write a rule that describes the total monthly cost as a function of the number of minutes of usage (over 500 minutes). Then find the number of minutes of usage over 500 minutes for a bill of $69.70.

Example 4
(page 297)

Justify each step.

24.
$$\frac{x}{5} + 9 = 11$$
$$\frac{x}{5} + 9 - 9 = 11 - 9$$
$$\frac{x}{5} = 2$$
$$5\left(\frac{x}{5}\right) = 5(2)$$
$$x = 10$$

25.
$$-y - 5 = 11$$
$$-y - 5 + 5 = 11 + 5$$
$$-y = 16$$
$$-1(-y) = -1(16)$$
$$y = -16$$

26.
$$18 - n = 21$$
$$18 - n - 18 = 21 - 18$$
$$-n = 3$$
$$-1(-n) = -1(3)$$
$$n = -3$$

27.
$$12 - 2h = 8$$
$$12 - 2h - 12 = 8 - 12$$
$$-2h = -4$$
$$\frac{-2h}{-2} = \frac{-4}{-2}$$
$$h = 2$$

B Apply Your Skills

Solve each equation.

28. $\frac{5}{7}x + \frac{1}{7} = 3$ **29.** $\frac{a}{5} + 15 = 30$ **30.** $-\frac{1}{5}t - 2 = 4$ **31.** $-6 + 6z = 0$

32. $3.5 + 10m = 7.32$ **33.** $7 = -2x + 7$ **34.** $\frac{1}{2} = \frac{2}{5}c - 3$ **35.** $10.7 = -d + 4.3$

36. $0.4x + 9.2 = 10$ **37.** $4x + 92 = 100$ **38.** $-t - 0.4 = -3$ **39.** $-10t - 4 = -30$

Solve each equation. Justify each step.

40. $8 + \frac{c}{-4} = -6$ **41.** $7 - 3k = -14$ **42.** $14 = 6 - 2p$ **43.** $\frac{-y}{2} + 14 = -1$

298 Chapter 6 Solving Equations

44. Multiple Choice Beneath Earth's surface, the temperature increases 10°C every kilometer. Suppose that the surface temperature is 22°C, and the temperature at the bottom of a coal mine is 45°C. Which equation could be used to find the depth d of the coal mine?

   (A) $10d + 22 = 45$ (B) $45d - 10 = 22$

   (C) $d = 22 + 10$ (D) $22 = 10d + 45$

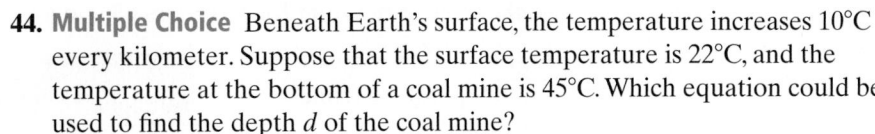 **45. Insurance** One health insurance policy pays people for claims by multiplying the claim amount by 0.8 and then subtracting $500. Write a rule that describes the insurance payment as a function of the claim amount. Then find the claim amount for an insurance payment of $4650.

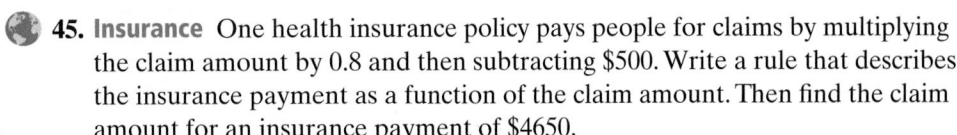 **46. Library** The Library of Congress in Washington, D.C., is the largest library in the world. It contains nearly 128 million items. The library adds about 10,000 items to its collection daily. Write a rule that describes the number of items in the Library of Congress as a function of the number of items added daily. Then find the number of days it will take the library to reach about 150 million items.

Real-World 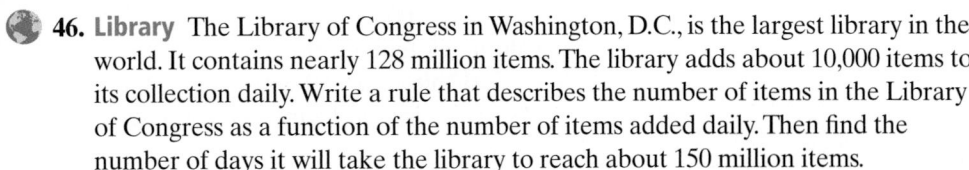 **Connection**

Since 1950, the size of the collections and the size of the staff of the Library of Congress have tripled.

Solve each equation. (*Hint:* As your first step, multiply each side by the denominator of the fraction.)

47. $\frac{x + 2}{9} = 5$ **48.** $\frac{y + 1}{3} = 2$ **49.** $\frac{a - 10}{-4} = 2$ **50.** $\frac{b - 7}{2} = 6$

51. $\frac{x - 5}{2} = 10$ **52.** $\frac{x - 3}{7} = 12$ **53.** $\frac{x + 4}{3} = -8$ **54.** $\frac{x + 6}{4} = -7$

Geometry In each triangle, the measure of $\angle A$ = the measure of $\angle B$. Find the value of x.

55. 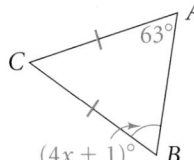   **56.** 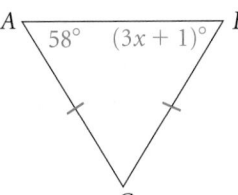   **57.**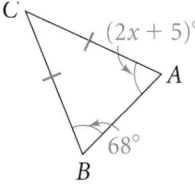

 58. Writing Miles has saved $40. He wants to buy a CD player for $129 in about four months. To find how much he should save each week, he wrote $40 + 16x = 129$. Explain his equation.

Error Analysis What is the error in the work? Solve each equation correctly.

59.

$12 - 3y = 15$
$3y = 3$
$y = 1$

60.

$\frac{m}{3} - 9 = -21$
$\frac{m}{3} - 9 + 9 = -21 + 9$
$\frac{m}{3} = -12$
$m = -4$

61. Open-Ended Write a problem that you can model with a two-step equation. Write an equation and solve the problem.

62. You can find the value of each variable in the matrices below by writing and solving equations. For example, to find the value of a, you solve the equation $2a + 1 = 11$. Find the values of a, x, y, and k.

$$\begin{bmatrix} 2a + 1 & -6 \\ -7 & -3k \end{bmatrix} = \begin{bmatrix} 11 & x - 5 \\ 5 - 2y & 27 \end{bmatrix}$$

GO Online

Homework Video Tutor

Visit: PHSchool.com
Web Code: ate-0301

Use the table at the right for Exercises 63 and 64.

 **63.** A formula for converting a temperature from Celsius C to Fahrenheit F is $F = 1.8C + 32$. Copy and complete the table. Round to the nearest degree.

Fahrenheit	Celsius	Description of Temperature
212°	■	boiling point of water
■	37°	human body temperature
68°	■	room temperature
■	0°	freezing point of water
■	−40°	

64. a. Estimation Use the formula $F = 2C + 30$ to estimate the Fahrenheit temperatures not shown in the table.

    b. Critical Thinking Compare your estimated values with the actual values. How good is your formula at estimating the actual temperatures? Explain.

 **Challenge**

65. Critical Thinking If you multiply each side of $0.24r + 5.25 = -7.23$ by 100, the result is an equivalent equation. Explain why it might be helpful to do this.

Solve the first equation for x. Then substitute your result into the second equation and solve for y.

66. $x + y = 8$
$2x + 3y = 21$

67. $x + 2y = 1$
$6x - y = -20$

68. $x + y = 12$
$2x + y = 17$

 **Test Prep**

Gridded Response

69. What is the value of the expression $-\frac{3}{5}x - 2$ when $x = -6$?

70. Dana has a photograph that is 4 in. wide and 5 in. long. She has the photo enlarged so that both dimensions are tripled. How many times larger than the original area will the area of the enlargement be?

71. What is the value of the following expression? $\dfrac{3^2 \times 4 - (-5)^2}{(-2)^3 + 3 \times 4}$

72. Last season, Everett scored 48 points. This is 6 less than twice the number of points Max scored. How many points did Max score?

73. A cable television company charges $24.95 a month for basic cable service and $6.95 a month for each additional premium channel. If Sami's monthly bill is $45.80, how many premium channels is he receiving?

Mixed Review

Lesson 5-3   **Simplify each expression.**

74. $-6(-4)$ **75.** $2(-5.5)$ **76.** $\frac{45}{-3}$

77. $\frac{-5 - 31}{-9}$ **78.** $-72 \div (4 - 12)$ **79.** $(18 - 10) \div (-2)$

Lessons 4-3, 5-1   **Simplify.**

80. $-2 + 6$ **81.** $9 + (-3)$ **82.** $-7 + (-4)$ **83.** $16 + (-4)$

You can solve some equations by using a table.

1 ACTIVITY

Solve $3x + 7 = 25$ using a table.

Make a table and evaluate the expression with a variable until you find the value that matches the constant side of the equation.

The value of x is the solution of the original equation. Since $3(6) + 7 = 25$, the solution of the equation is 6.

Variable side   Constant side

Equation: $3x + 7 = 25$

x	$3x + 7$
0	$3(0) + 7 = 7$
2	$3(2) + 7 = 13$
4	$3(4) + 7 = 19$
6	$3(6) + 7 = 25$ ✓

You can solve equations by using a graphing calculator to graph each side of the equation. The x-coordinate of the point where the graphs intersect is the solution of the equation.

2 ACTIVITY

Solve $9 = -\frac{3}{2}n + 4$ using a graphing calculator.

Step 1 Enter the equations using the $\boxed{Y=}$ feature. First clear any equations.
For $Y_1=$ enter 9. For $Y_2=$ enter $-\frac{3}{2}x + 4$ by pressing
$\boxed{(}$ $\boxed{(-)}$ 3 $\boxed{\div}$ 2 $\boxed{)}$ $\boxed{X,T,\theta,n}$ $\boxed{+}$ 4.

Step 2 Graph the equations. Use a standard graphing window, which you can find using the ZOOM feature.

Step 3 Use the CALC feature, select intersect to find the point where the lines intersect.

The calculator value for the x-coordinate of the point of intersection is -3.333333. The actual point of intersection is $-3\frac{1}{3}$.

The solution of the equation $9 = -\frac{3}{2}n + 4$ is $-3\frac{1}{3}$.

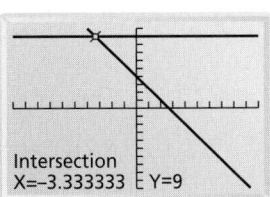

Intersection
X=-3.333333 Y=9

EXERCISES

Use a table to solve each equation.

1. $5c + 4 = 19$ **2.** $23 - 3x = 11$ **3.** $33 = 8t - 7$

4. $13 = -2x + 21$ **5.** $\frac{1}{2}n + 41 = 51$ **6.** $-9 = 3 + 6k$

Use a graphing calculator to solve each equation.

7. $8a - 12 = 6$ **8.** $-4 = -3t + 2$ **9.** $4 + \frac{3}{2}n = -7$

10. $-5 = -0.5g - 2$ **11.** $\frac{5}{4}d - \frac{1}{2} = 6$ **12.** $-3w - 1 = 3.5$

6-2

Solving Multi-Step Equations

What You'll Learn

- To use the Distributive Property when combining like terms
- To use the Distributive Property when solving equations

. . . And Why

To solve a problem involving building a fence, as in Example 2

✓ Check Skills You'll Need

GO for Help Lessons 4-2 and 5-4

Simplify each expression.

1. $2n - 3n$

2. $-4 + 3b + 2 + 5b$

3. $9(w - 5)$

4. $-10(b - 12)$

5. $3(-x + 4)$

6. $5(6 - w)$

Evaluate each expression.

7. $28 - a + 4a$ for $a = 5$

8. $8 + x - 7x$ for $x = -3$

9. $(8n + 1)3$ for $n = -2$

10. $-(17 + 3y)$ for $y = 6$

---

1 Using the Distributive Property to Combine Like Terms

You can solve equations that require more than two steps. If there are like terms on one side of an equation, first use the Distributive Property to combine them. Then use the properties of equality to solve the equation.

Problem Solving Hint

You use the Distributive Property whenever you add or subtract like terms.

$x + 4x = 1x + 4x$
$= (1 + 4)x$
$= 5x$

1 EXAMPLE Combining Like Terms

Solve each equation.

a. $2c + c + 12 = 78$

$2c + c + 12 = 78$

$3c + 12 = 78$ **Combine like terms.**

$3c + 12 - 12 = 78 - 12$ **Subtract 12 from each side.**

$3c = 66$ **Simplify.**

$\frac{3c}{3} = \frac{66}{3}$ **Divide each side by 3.**

$c = 22$ **Simplify.**

b. $4b + 16 + 2b = 46$

$4b + 16 + 2b = 46$

$4b + 2b + 16 = 46$ **Use the Commutative Property of Addition.**

$6b + 16 = 46$ **Combine like terms.**

$6b + 16 - 16 = 46 - 16$ **Subtract 16 from each side.**

$6b = 30$ **Simplify.**

$\frac{6b}{6} = \frac{30}{6}$ **Divide each side by 6.**

$b = 5$ **Simplify.**

✓ Quick Check ❶ Solve each equation. Check your answer.

a. $3x - 4x + 6 = -2$

b. $7 = 4m - 2m + 1$

c. $-2y + 5 + 5y = 14$

d. $-3z + 8 + (-2z) = -12$

You can model real-world situations using multi-step equations.

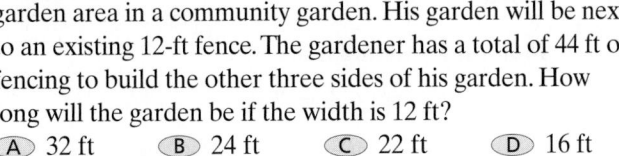

Multiple Choice A gardener is planning a rectangular garden area in a community garden. His garden will be next to an existing 12-ft fence. The gardener has a total of 44 ft of fencing to build the other three sides of his garden. How long will the garden be if the width is 12 ft?

Ⓐ 32 ft   Ⓑ 24 ft   Ⓒ 22 ft   Ⓓ 16 ft

Relate	length of side	plus	12 ft	plus	length of side	equals	amount of fencing

Define Let x = length of a side adjacent to the fence.

Write	x	+	12	+	x	=	44

$$x + 12 + x = 44$$

$$2x + 12 = 44 \qquad \text{Combine like terms on the left side of the equation.}$$

$$2x + 12 - 12 = 44 - 12 \qquad \text{Subtract 12 from each side.}$$

$$2x = 32 \qquad \text{Simplify.}$$

$$\frac{2x}{2} = \frac{32}{2} \qquad \text{Divide each side by 2.}$$

$$x = 16 \qquad \text{Simplify.}$$

● The garden will be 16 ft long. So D is the correct answer.

 **2** A carpenter is building a rectangular fence for a playground. One side of the playground is the wall of a building 70 ft wide. He plans to use 340 ft of fencing material. What is the length of the playground if the width is 70 ft?

Real-World Connection

In the United States, there are approximately 10,000 cities with community gardens.

---

2   Using the Distributive Property to Solve Equations

In the equation $-2(b - 4) = 12$, the parentheses indicate multiplication. Use the Distributive Property to multiply each term within the parentheses by -2. Then use the properties of equality to solve the equation.

3 EXAMPLE   Solving an Equation With Grouping Symbols

Solve $-2(b - 4) = 12$.

$$-2b + 8 = 12 \qquad \text{Use the Distributive Property.}$$

$$-2b + 8 - 8 = 12 - 8 \qquad \text{Subtract 8 from each side.}$$

$$-2b = 4 \qquad \text{Simplify.}$$

$$\frac{-2b}{-2} = \frac{4}{-2} \qquad \text{Divide each side by } -2.$$

$$b = -2 \qquad \text{Simplify.}$$

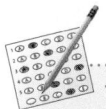

Test-Taking Tip

Remember to multiply the number outside the parentheses by both terms inside the parentheses.

 **3** Solve each equation.

a. $3(k + 8) = 21$

b. $15 = -3(x - 1) + 9$

Following are two ways you can solve an equation like $\frac{2x}{3} + \frac{x}{2} = 7$.

4 EXAMPLE Solving an Equation That Contains Fractions

Vocabulary Tip

$\frac{x}{2}$ and $\frac{1}{2}x$ both represent $x \div 2$.

$\frac{2x}{3}$ and $\frac{2}{3}x$ both represent $2x \div 3$.

Solve $\frac{2x}{3} + \frac{x}{2} = 7$.

Method 1 Adding fractions

$$\frac{2x}{3} + \frac{x}{2} = 7$$

$$\frac{2}{3}x + \frac{1}{2}x = 7 \qquad \text{Rewrite the equation with fractions as coefficients.}$$

$$\frac{4}{6}x + \frac{3}{6}x = 7 \qquad \text{Write the fractions with a denominator of 6.}$$

$$\frac{7}{6}x = 7 \qquad \text{Combine like terms.}$$

$$\frac{6}{7}\left(\frac{7}{6}x\right) = \frac{6}{7}(7) \qquad \text{Multiply each side by } \frac{6}{7}, \text{ the reciprocal of } \frac{7}{6}.$$

$$x = 6 \qquad \text{Simplify.}$$

Method 2 Multiplying to clear fractions

$$\frac{2x}{3} + \frac{x}{2} = 7$$

$$6\left(\frac{2x}{3} + \frac{x}{2}\right) = 6(7) \qquad \text{Multiply each side by 6, a common multiple of 3 and 2.}$$

$$6\left(\frac{2x}{3}\right) + 6\left(\frac{x}{2}\right) = 6(7) \qquad \text{Use the Distributive Property.}$$

$$4x + 3x = 42 \qquad \text{Multiply.}$$

$$7x = 42 \qquad \text{Combine like terms.}$$

$$\frac{7x}{7} = \frac{42}{7} \qquad \text{Divide each side by 7.}$$

$$x = 6 \qquad \text{Simplify.}$$

✓ Quick Check **4** Solve each equation. Explain why you chose the method you used.

a. $\frac{m}{4} + \frac{m}{2} = \frac{5}{8}$ **b.** $\frac{2}{3}x - \frac{5}{8}x = 26$

You can clear an equation of decimals by multiplying by a power of 10. In the equation $0.5a + 8.75 = 13.25$, the greatest number of digits to the right of a decimal point is 2. To clear the equation of decimals, multiply each side of the equation by 10^2, or 100.

Problem Solving Hint

Powers of 10:

$10^1 = 10$

$10^2 = 100$

$10^3 = 1000$

$10^4 = 10{,}000$

5 EXAMPLE Solving an Equation That Contains Decimals

Solve $0.5a + 8.75 = 13.25$.

$$100(0.5a + 8.75) = 100(13.25) \qquad \text{Multiply each side by } 10^2, \text{ or 100.}$$

$$100(0.5a) + 100(8.75) = 100(13.25) \qquad \text{Use the Distributive Property.}$$

$$50a + 875 = 1325 \qquad \text{Simplify.}$$

$$50a + 875 - 875 = 1325 - 875 \qquad \text{Subtract 875 from each side.}$$

$$50a = 450 \qquad \text{Simplify.}$$

$$\frac{50a}{50} = \frac{450}{50} \qquad \text{Divide each side by 50.}$$

$$a = 9 \qquad \text{Simplify.}$$

✓ Quick Check **5** Solve each equation.

a. $0.025x + 22.95 = 23.65$ **b.** $1.2x - 3.6 + 0.3x = 2.4$

Keep the steps in the summary below in mind as you solve equations that have variables on one side of the equation.

 Key Concepts

Summary	Steps for Solving a Multi-Step Equation
Step 1	Clear the equation of fractions and decimals.
Step 2	Use the Distributive Property to remove parentheses on each side.
Step 3	Combine like terms on each side.
Step 4	Undo addition or subtraction.
Step 5	Undo multiplication or division.

EXERCISES

For more exercises, see *Extra Skill and Word Problem Practice*.

Practice and Problem Solving

A Practice by Example

Example 1
(page 302)

 GO for Help

Solve each equation. Check your answer.

1. $4n - 2n = 18$

2. $y + y + 2 = 18$

3. $a + 6a - 9 = 30$

4. $5 - x - x = -1$

5. $72 + 4 - 14c = 36$

6. $13 = 5 - 13 + 3a$

7. $9 = -3 + n + 2n$

8. $7m - 3m - 6 = 6$

9. $-13 = 2b - b - 10$

Example 2
(page 303)

Write an equation to model each situation. Solve your equation.

10. Two friends are renting an apartment. They pay the landlord the first month's rent. The landlord also requires them to pay an additional half of a month's rent for a security deposit. The total amount they pay the landlord before moving in is $1725. What is the monthly rent?

11. You are fencing a rectangular puppy kennel with 25 ft of fence. The side of the kennel against your house does not need a fence. This side is 9 ft long. Find the dimensions of the kennel.

Example 3
(page 303)

Solve each equation. Check your answer.

12. $2(8 + p) = 22$

13. $5(a - 1) = 35$

14. $15 = -3(2q - 1)$

15. $26 = 6(5 - a)$

16. $m + 5(m - 1) = 7$

17. $-4(x + 6) = -40$

18. $48 = 8(x + 2)$

19. $5(y - 3) = 19$

20. $5(2 + y) = 77$

Example 4
(page 304)

21. $\frac{a}{7} - \frac{5}{7} = \frac{6}{7}$

22. $x - \frac{5}{8} = \frac{7}{8}$

23. $\frac{m}{6} - 7 = \frac{2}{3}$

24. $\frac{2}{3} + \frac{3k}{4} = \frac{71}{12}$

25. $4 + \frac{m}{8} = \frac{3}{4}$

26. $\frac{a}{2} + \frac{1}{5} = 17$

27. $\frac{1}{2} + \frac{7x}{10} = \frac{13}{20}$

28. $\frac{9y}{14} + \frac{3}{7} = \frac{9}{14}$

29. $\frac{1}{5} + \frac{3w}{15} = \frac{4}{5}$

Example 5
(page 304)

30. $3m + 4.5m = 15$

31. $7.8y + 2 = 165.8$

32. $3.5 = 12s - 5s$

33. $1.06y - 3 = 0.71$

34. $0.11p + 1.5 = 2.49$

35. $25.24 = 5y + 3.89$

36. $1.12 + 1.25y = 8.62$

37. $1.025x + 2.458 = 7.583$

38. $0.25m + 0.1m = 9.8$

Solve each equation.

39. $0.5t - 3t + 5 = 0$ **40.** $-(z + 5) = -14$ **41.** $\frac{a}{15} + \frac{4}{15} = \frac{9}{15}$

42. $0.5(x - 12) = 4$ **43.** $8y - (2y - 3) = 9$ **44.** $\frac{2}{3} + y = \frac{3}{4}$

45. $2 + \frac{a}{-4} = \frac{3}{5}$ **46.** $\frac{1}{4}(m - 16) = 7$ **47.** $x + 3x - 7 = 29$

48. $4x + 3.6 + x = 1.2$ **49.** $2(1.5c + 4) = -1$ **50.** $26.54 - p = 0.5(50 - p)$

51. Error Analysis Explain the error in the student's work at the right.

52. Critical Thinking Suppose you want to solve the equation $-3m + 4 + 5m = -6$. What would you do as your first step?

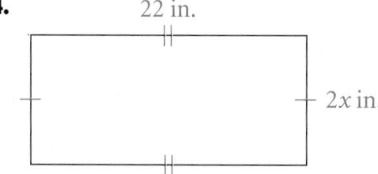

$$\frac{3}{8}x - 1 = 4$$
$$3x - 1 = 32$$
$$3x = 33$$
$$x = 11$$

 53. Writing To solve $-\frac{1}{2}(3x - 5) = 7$, you can use the Distributive Property, or you can multiply each side of the equation by -2. Which method do you prefer? Explain why.

Geometry **The perimeter of each rectangle is 64 in. Find the value of x.**

54.

22 in.

2x in.

55.

$(3x + 2)$ in.

CANOE RENTAL
$5.00 per hour
$2.00 life jacket

Use an equation to solve each problem.

56. John and two friends rent a canoe at a park. Each person must rent a life jacket. If the bill for the rental of the canoe and life jackets is $41, for how many hours did they rent the canoe?

57. Moving Costs The MacNeills rented a moving truck for $49.95 plus $.30 per mile. Before returning the truck, they filled the tank with gasoline, which cost $18.32. The total cost was $95.87. Find the number of miles the truck was driven.

58. Cell Phones Jane's cell phone plan is $40 per month plus $.15 per minute for each minute over 200 minutes of call time. If Jane's cell phone bill is $58.00, for how many extra calling minutes was she billed?

59. Open-Ended Write an expression with four terms that can be simplified to an expression with two terms.

Geometry **Find the value of x. (*Hint:* The sum of the measures of the angles of a triangle is 180°.)**

60.

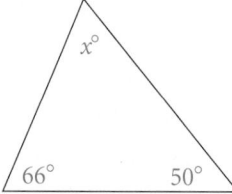

$x°$

66°   50°

61.

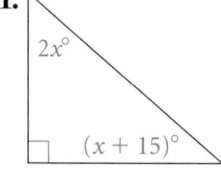

$2x°$

$(x + 15)°$

62.

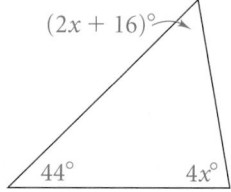

$(2x + 16)°$

44° $4x°$

Online
Homework Video Tutor

Visit: PHSchool.com
Web Code: ate-0302

63. Purchasing The function $c = p + 0.07p$ relates the price of an item p with its cost c after 7% tax is added. A student has $12.50. What is the cost of the most expensive item he can buy?

64. Finance Nadia has $70 in her bank account. Each week she deposits $3 from her allowance and $15 from babysitting. The function $b = 70 + (15 + 3)w$ relates her bank balance b to weeks w. When will she have $160 in her bank account?

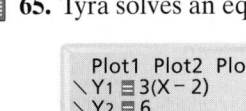

65. Tyra solves an equation using her graphing calculator. Use the screens below.

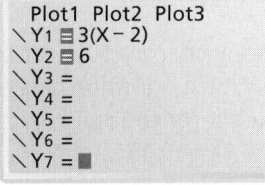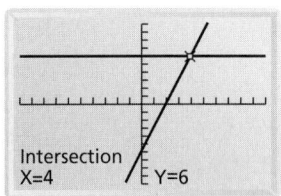

a. What was the original equation that Tyra was solving?
b. What is the point of intersection?
c. Show that the x-value of the intersection solves the original equation.

C  Challenge

For Exercises 66–68, use an equation to solve each problem.

 66. Cars You fill your car's gas tank when it is about $\frac{1}{2}$ empty. The next week, you fill the tank a second time when it is about $\frac{3}{4}$ empty. If you buy a total of $18\frac{1}{2}$ gal of gas on these two days, about how many gallons does the tank hold?

67. A work crew has two pumps, one new and one old. The new pump can fill a tank in 5 hours. The old pump can fill the same tank in 7 hours.
a. How much of a tank can be filled in 1 hour with the new pump? With the old pump?
b. Write an expression for the number of tanks the new pump can fill in t hours. (*Hint:* Write the rate at which the new pump fills tanks as a fraction and then multiply by t.)
c. Write an expression for the number of tanks the old pump can fill in t hours.
d. Write and solve an equation for the time it will take the pumps to fill one tank if the pumps are used together.

 68. Investing Mr. Fairbanks invested half his money in land, a tenth in stock, and a twentieth in bonds. He put the remaining $35,000 in a savings account. What is the total amount of money that Mr. Fairbanks saved or invested?

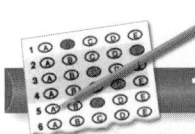

Test Prep

Multiple Choice

69. What is the value of the expression $-3r + 6 + r$ when $r = -2$?
A. -6 **B.** -2 **C.** 10   **D.** 14

70. Solve $8n + 5 - 2n = 41$.
F. $3\frac{1}{2}$ **G.** $4\frac{1}{2}$ **H.** 6   **J.** $7\frac{2}{3}$

71. If a number is increased by 3 and that number is doubled, the result is -8. What was the original number?
A. -7 **B.** -5.5 **C.** 1   **D.** 6

72. The gas tank in Royston's car holds 12 gal of gasoline. The car averages 29 mi/gal. Royston filled up the tank and then drove 140 mi. About how many gallons of gasoline are left in the tank?

    F. 6 gal   **G.** 7 gal   **H.** 8 gal   **J.** 9 gal

73. Josie's goal is to run 40 miles each week. This week she has already run distances of 5.3 miles, 6.5 miles, and 6.2 miles. If she wants to spread out the remaining miles evenly over the next 4 days, which equation can you use to find how many miles (m) per day she must run?

    A. $5.3 + 6.5 + 6.2 + 40 = m$ **B.** $40 - 5.2 - 6.5 - 6.2 = m$

    C. $5.3 + 6.5 + 6.2 + 4m = 40$ **D.** $5.3 + 6.5 + 6.2 + m = \frac{40}{4}$

74. A cell phone company charges \$.35 for the first minute but only \$.10 every minute after that. Which equation can you use to find how many minutes m Eric talked if the bill for the call was \$5.45?

    F. $0.35 + 0.10(m - 1) = 5.45$ **G.** $0.35 + 0.10m = 5.45$

    H. $0.10 + 0.35(m - 1) = 5.45$ **J.** $0.10 + 0.35m = 5.45$

Mixed Review

Lesson 6-1

Solve each equation.

75. $2y + 4 = -6$ **76.** $3x - 15 = 33$ **77.** $-4n + 20 = 36$ **78.** $-8 - c = 11$

79. $3x + 5 = 12$ **80.** $-4y - 3 = 15$ **81.** $8m - 4 = 8$ **82.** $-p + 3 = 10$

Lesson 5-5

Mental Math **Simplify each expression.**

83. $14 \cdot 4 \cdot 25$ **84.** $16 + 28 + 34 + 72$ **85.** $-8 + 15 + -9 + 2$

86. $3 \cdot 3 \cdot 10$ **87.** $2 \cdot 8 \cdot 5$ **88.** $27 + 46 - 17 - 16$

Lessons 5-1 through 5-3

Simplify each expression.

89. $2 - 6$ **90.** $-9 \cdot (-3)$ **91.** $-7 + (-4)$ **92.** $16 \div (-4)$

93. $-7 + (-3)$ **94.** $-5 - (-3)$ **95.** $-5 \cdot 6$ **96.** $-25 \div (-5)$

Algebra at Work

·········· Airline Pilot

Airline pilots make many calculations before, during, and after a flight. Pilots study weather conditions to determine the safest altitude, route, and speed for a flight. Pilots calculate lift, which must equal the airplane's weight in pounds. An airplane's lift capabilities are calculated using the formula $L = \frac{1}{2}dv^2sa$, where L is the lift, d is the density of the air, v is the velocity of the aircraft in feet per second, s is the wing area of the aircraft in square feet, and a is a value determined by the type of airfoil the airplane has and the pitch angle of the airplane.

Go Online

PHSchool.com **Web Code:** atb-2031

For: Information about a career as an airline pilot

Activity Lab
Hands-On

Modeling Equations

Models can help you understand how to solve equations that have variables on both sides.

EXAMPLE

Model and solve $3a - 2 = a + 4$.

$3a - 2 = a + 4$  The tiles model the equation.

$3a - 2 - a = a + 4 - a$
$2a - 2 = 4$ 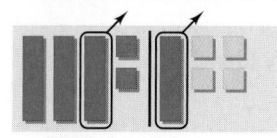 Use the Subtraction Property of Equality. Subtract a from each side to get the variable on one side of the equation.

$2a - 2 + 2 = 4 + 2$
$2a = 6$ 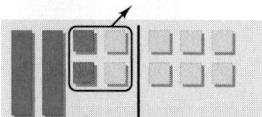 Use the Addition Property of Equality. Add 2 to each side. Remove zero pairs.

$\frac{2a}{2} = \frac{6}{2}$ 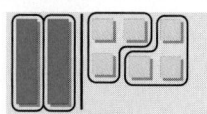 Use the Division Property of Equality. Divide each side into two identical groups.

$a = 3$ 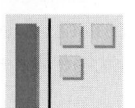 Each green tile equals three yellow tiles, so $a = 3$.

EXERCISES

Write an equation for each model. Use tiles to solve each equation.

1.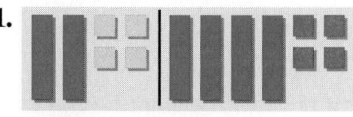

2.

3.

4.

Use tiles to model and solve each equation.

5. $4x + 2 = 2x + 6$

6. $2y - 2 = 4y + 2$

7. $2a + 2 = a + 8$

8. $5b - 4 = 2b + 5$

9. $z - 8 = 2z - 1$

10. $4(p + 1) = 2p - 2$

11. $5n - 3 = 2(n + 3)$

12. $2(k + 1) = 5(k - 2)$

Equations With Variables on Both Sides

What You'll Learn

- To solve equations with variables on both sides
- To identify equations that are identities or have no solution

...And Why

To solve a problem involving renting in-line skates, as in Example 2

✓ Check Skills You'll Need

Simplify.

1. $6x - 2x$ **2.** $2x - 6x$

Solve each equation.

5. $4x + 3 = -5$

7. $2t - 8t + 1 = 43$

 for Help Lessons 5-4 and 6-2

3. $5x - 5x$ **4.** $-5x + 5x$

6. $-x + 7 = 12$

8. $0 = -7n + 4 - 5n$

🔊 **New Vocabulary** • identity

---

1   Solving Equations With Variables on Both Sides

> **Activity:** Using a Table to Solve an Equation
>
> Costs for a key chain business are $540 to get started plus $3 per key chain. The cost of producing k key chains is $(540 + 3k)$ dollars.
>
> Key chains sell for $7 each. The revenue for selling k key chains is $7k$ dollars. To make a profit, revenue must be greater than costs.
>
> **1.** Copy and complete the following table.
>
> | Key Chains | Cost | Revenue |
> |:---:|:---:|:---:|
> | k | $540 + 3k$ | $7k$ |
> | 100 | 840 | 700 |
> | 110 | ▪ | ▪ |
> | 120 | ▪ | ▪ |
> | 130 | ▪ | ▪ |
> | 140 | ▪ | ▪ |
> | 150 | ▪ | ▪ |
>
> **2.** For 110 key chains, which is greater, the cost or the revenue?
>
> **3.** When will the revenue be greater than the cost?
>
> **4.** Use your table to estimate the solution of $540 + 3k = 7k$.
>
> **5.** Explain how solving an equation can help you decide whether a business can make a profit or not.

To solve an equation that has variables on both sides, use the Addition or Subtraction Properties of Equality to get the variables on one side of the equation.

1 EXAMPLE Variables on Both Sides

Geometry Find the value of x in the diagram below.

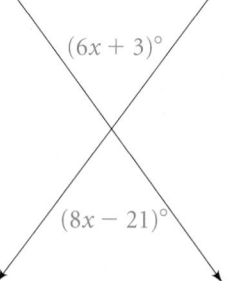

$(6x + 3)°$

$(8x - 21)°$

$6x + 3 = 8x - 21$	Vertical angles are congruent.
$6x + 3 - 6x = 8x - 21 - 6x$	Subtract 6x from each side.
$3 = 2x - 21$	Combine like terms.
$3 + 21 = 2x - 21 + 21$	Add 21 to each side.
$24 = 2x$	Simplify.
$\frac{24}{2} = \frac{2x}{2}$	Divide each side by 2.
$x = 12$	Simplify.

● The value of x is 12.

Vocabulary Tip

Vertical angles are congruent, so their measures are equal.

✓ **Quick Check** ❶ Solve each equation.
a. $-6d = d + 4$ **b.** $2(c - 6) = 9c + 2$
c. $m - 5 = 3m$ **d.** $7k - 4 = 5k + 16$

2 EXAMPLE Real-World 🌐 Problem Solving

Recreation You can buy used in-line skates from your friend for $40, or you can rent some. Either way, you must rent safety equipment. How many hours must you skate for the cost of renting and buying skates to be the same?

Relate	cost of friend's skates	plus	safety equipment rental	equals	skates plus equipment rental

Define Let h = the number of hours you must skate.

Write	40	+	$1.5h$	=	$3.5h$

$40 + 1.5h = 3.5h$	
$40 + 1.5h - 1.5h = 3.5h - 1.5h$	Subtract 1.5h from each side.
$40 = 2h$	Combine like terms.
$\frac{40}{2} = \frac{2h}{2}$	Divide each side by 2.
$20 = h$	Simplify.

You must skate for 20 hours for the cost to be the same.

Check Is the solution reasonable? Buying skates and renting safety equipment for 20 hours costs $40 + 1.5(20) = 70$, or $70. The cost of renting both skates and safety equipment for 20 hours is $3.5(20) = 70$, or $70. The answer is correct.

SKATE RENTALS
In-line skates and safety equipment
$3.50/hour

Safety equipment
$1.50/hour

✓ **Quick Check** ❷ **Business** A hairdresser is considering ordering a certain shampoo. Company A charges $4 per 8-oz bottle plus a $10 handling fee per order. Company B charges $3 per 8-oz bottle plus a $25 handling fee per order. How many bottles must the hairdresser buy to justify using Company B?

You can use a calculator to solve an equation. Using each side of the equation, you can graph two functions using the $\boxed{Y=}$ screen. The x-value of the point of intersection is the solution of the equation.

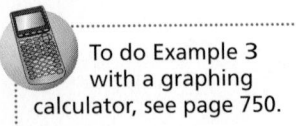
To do Example 3 with a graphing calculator, see page 750.

3 EXAMPLE Solving Using a Graphing Calculator

Solve $\frac{3}{4}m = 8 - \frac{1}{2}m$ using a graphing calculator.

Step 1 For $Y_1=$ enter $\frac{3}{4}x$. For $Y_2=$ enter $8 - \frac{1}{2}x$.

Step 2 Use the GRAPH feature to display the graph. You can adjust the window by using the ZOOM or WINDOW features.

Step 3 Use the CALC feature. Select intersect to find the point where the lines intersect.

Intersection
X=6.4   Y=4.8

● The lines intersect at $(6.4, 4.8)$. The x-value 6.4 is the solution of the equation.

For help entering functions in the Y= screen, see p. 301.

✔ **Quick Check** ③ Solve $4 + \frac{1}{2}x = x - 1$ using a graphing calculator.

2 Special Cases: Identities and No Solutions

An equation has **no solution** if no value of the variable makes the equation true. The equation $2x = 2x + 1$ has no solution. An equation that is true for every value of the variable is an **identity.** The equation $2x = 2x$ is an identity.

For: Solving Equations Activity
Use: Interactive Textbook, 3-3

4 EXAMPLE Identities and Equations with No Solutions

a. Solve $10 - 8a = 2(5 - 4a)$.

$$10 - 8a = 10 - 8a$$
$$10 - 8a + 8a = 10 - 8a + 8a$$
$$10 = 10 \quad \textbf{Always true!}$$

This equation is true for every value of a, so the equation is an identity.

b. Solve $6m - 5 = 7m + 7 - m$.

$$6m - 5 = 7m + 7 - m$$
$$6m - 5 = 6m + 7$$
$$6m - 5 - 6m = 6m + 7 - 6m$$
$$-5 = 7 \quad \textbf{Not true.}$$

This equation has no solution.

✔ **Quick Check** ④ Determine whether each equation is an *identity* or whether it has *no solution*.
a. $9 + 5n = 5n - 1$
b. $9 + 5x = 7x + 9 - 2x$

EXERCISES

For more exercises, see *Extra Skill and Word Problem Practice*.

Practice and Problem Solving

A Practice by Example

Example 1
(page 311)

Solve each equation. Check your answer.

1. $6x - 2 = x + 13$

2. $5y - 3 = 2y + 12$

3. $4k - 3 = 3k + 4$

4. $5m + 3 = 3m + 9$

5. $8 - x = 2x - 1$

6. $2n - 5 = 8n + 7$

7. $3a + 4 = a + 18$

8. $6b + 14 = -7 - b$

Geometry Find the value of x.

9.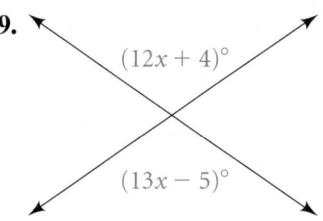

$(12x + 4)°$

$(13x - 5)°$

10.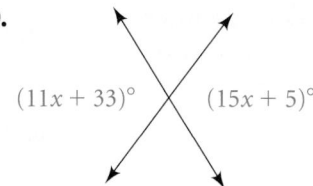

$(11x + 33)°$ $(15x + 5)°$

Example 2
(page 311)

Write and solve an equation for each situation. Check your solution.

11. Telephone Service One telephone company charges $16.95 per month and $.05 per minute for local calls. Another company charges $22.95 per month and $.02 per minute for local calls. For what number of minutes of local calls per month is the cost of the plans the same?

12. Fitness One health club charges a $44 sign-up fee and $30 per month. Another health club charges a $99 sign-up fee and $25 per month. For what number of months is the cost the same?

Example 3
(page 312)

Solve each equation using a graphing calculator.

13. $7(3 - k) = -3k + 4$

14. $a - 6 = 8 - (9 + a)$

15. $-\frac{1}{2}d + 2 = -4\left(d - \frac{1}{2}\right)$

16. $0.2n + 9 = 8(0.4n - 1)$

Example 4
(page 312)

17. a. Use the equation $9 - 6x = 3(3 - 2x)$. Substitute four different values for x and simplify.
   b. What kind of equation is $9 - 6x = 3(3 - 2x)$?

Determine whether each equation is an *identity* or whether it has *no solution*.

18. $14 - (2q + 5) = -2q + 9$

19. $6x + 1 = 6x - 8$

20. $-8x + 14 = -2(4x - 7)$

21. $y - 5 = -(5 - y)$

22. $a - 4a = 2a + 1 - 5a$

23. $9x + 3x - 10 = 3(3x + x)$

 Apply Your Skills

Solve each equation. If the equation is an identity, write *identity*. If it has no solution, write *no solution*.

24. $18x - 5 = 3(6x - 2)$

25. $9 + 5a = 2a + 9$

26. $3(x - 4) = 3x - 12$

27. $6x = 4(x + 5)$

28. $\frac{3}{5}k - \frac{1}{10}k = \frac{1}{2}k + 1$

29. $0 = 0.98b + 0.02b - b$

30. $5m - 2(m + 2) = -(2m + 15)$

31. $\frac{7}{8}w = \frac{4}{8}w + \frac{6}{8}w$

32. Multiple Choice A toy company spends $1500 per day for factory expenses plus $8 to make each teddy bear, like the one shown at the left. Which equation could be used to find the number of bears t the company has to sell in one day to equal its daily cost?

Ⓐ $1500 + 8t = 12$ Ⓑ $12 + 8t = 1500$
Ⓒ $1500 + 8t = 12t$ Ⓓ $8t = 12t + 1500$

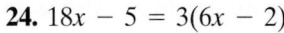

 33. Business A company manufactures tote bags. The company spends $1200 each day for overhead expenses plus $9 per tote bag for labor and materials. The tote bags sell for $25 each. How many tote bags must the company sell each day to equal its daily costs for overhead, labor, and materials? Write an equation and solve.

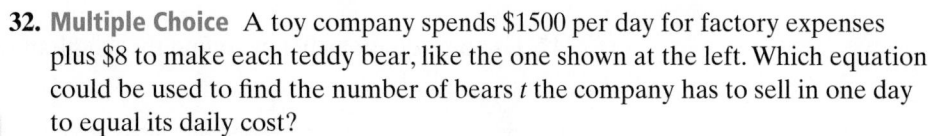

Find the value of each variable.

34. $\begin{bmatrix} 0.5x + 3 & w + 1.5 \\ 2.5y + 2.5 & a + 1 \end{bmatrix} = \begin{bmatrix} x + 0.5 & 2w - 1.5 \\ 5y - 2.5 & 19 - a \end{bmatrix}$

35. $\begin{bmatrix} \frac{1}{2} + a & \frac{1}{2}b + 2 \\ c - \frac{1}{3} & \frac{1}{3}d + \frac{2}{3} \end{bmatrix} = \begin{bmatrix} 6\frac{1}{2} - a & b - 1 \\ 4\frac{2}{3} & d + \frac{4}{9} \end{bmatrix}$

Error Analysis Find the mistake in the solution of each equation. Explain the mistake and solve the equation correctly.

36.

2x = 11x + 45
2x − 11x = 11x − 11x + 45
9x = 45
$\frac{9x}{9} = \frac{45}{9}$
x = 5

37.

4.5 − y = 2(y − 5.7)
4.5 − y = 2y − 11.4
4.5 − y − y = 2y − y − 11.4
4.5 = y − 11.4
4.5 + 11.4 = y − 11.4 + 11.4
15.9 = y

38. a. Solve $p + 2\left(p + \frac{1}{2}\right) = 9 - (4 - 3p)$ using a graphing calculator.
   b. Solve the same equation by hand.
   c. How do the answers in parts (a) and (b) relate to each other?

 39. Writing Is an equation that has 0 for a solution the same as an equation with no solution? Explain.

40. Spreadsheet Don set up a spreadsheet to solve $5(x - 3) = 4 - 3(x + 1)$.
   a. Does Don's spreadsheet show a solution to the equation?
   b. Between which two values of x is the solution to the equation? How do you know?
   c. For what values of x is $4 - 3(x + 1)$ less than $5(x - 3)$?

	A	B	C
1	x	5(x − 3)	4 − 3(x + 1)
2	−5	−40	16
3	−3	−30	10
4	−1	−20	4
5	1	−10	−2
6	3	0	−8

 **Challenge**

Open-Ended Write an equation with a variable on each side such that you get the solution described.

41. $x = 0$

42. x is a positive number.

43. x is a negative number.

44. All values of x are solutions.

45. No values of x are solutions.

46. $x = 1$

47. Use the equations below to find the length of the pipe.

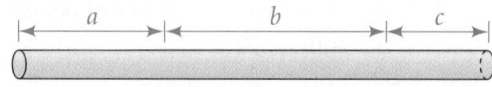

$a + b = 15 \quad b - a = 3 \quad a + b - 12 = c$

48. Geometry The perimeters of the rectangles at the right are equal. Find the length and width of each rectangle.

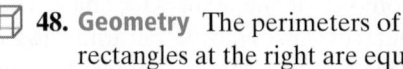
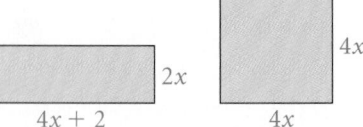

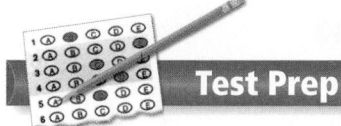
Multiple Choice

49. Solve $2y = 3y - 20$.
   A. -20 **B.** -4 **C.** 4   **D.** 20

50. Which of the following equations is NOT equivalent to the others?
   F. $-2(y - 3) = -6y$ **G.** $-2y - 6 = -6y$
   H. $y = -\frac{3}{2}$ **J.** $4y = -6$

51. Ace Truck Rental charges $54.00 a day plus 9¢ per mile. Roni's Truck Rental charges $38.00 a day plus 13¢ per mile. For how many miles will the cost of renting a truck for one day at Ace equal the cost at Roni's?
   A. 40 mi   **B.** 170 mi   **C.** 400 mi   **D.** 418 mi

52. Which equation is NOT equivalent to $3p - 2 = 6p + 4$?
   F. $3p = 6p + 6$ **G.** $-6 = 3p$
   H. $3p = 6$ **J.** $-3p - 2 = 4$

53. A record store sells CDs for $12.00 each. A music club offers 5 free CDs and charges $15.00 for each additional CD. Which equation can you use to find the number of CDs x that would cost the same under both plans?
   A. $15x - 5 = 12x$ **B.** $12x - 5 = 15x$
   C. $12x = 15(x - 5)$ **D.** $12(x - 5) = 15x$

54. Solve $2(y - 3) = 1.2 - y$.
   F. -1.6 **G.** 1.4   **H.** 1.6   **J.** 2.4

55. The perimeters of the rectangle and the triangle below are equal. Find the value of x.
   A. 6   **B.** 8   **C.** 10   **D.** 12

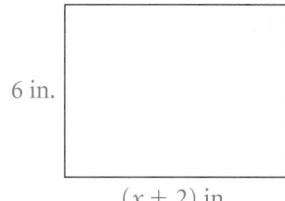
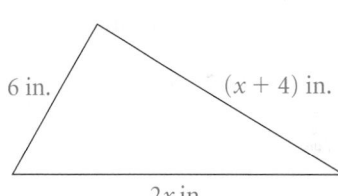

6 in. $(x + 2)$ in.   6 in. $(x + 4)$ in. $2x$ in.

Mixed Review

Lesson 6-2   **Solve each equation.**

56. $9 = -4y + 6y - 5$ **57.** $-2(a - 3) = 14$ **58.** $0.5m + 2.8 = 3.64$

59. $\frac{1}{2}x + 4 = \frac{2}{3}$ **60.** $4.8 = 1.25(y - 17)$ **61.** $4\left(\frac{1}{4} + x\right) = 5$

Lesson 6-1   **62. Art** An art gallery owner is framing a painting. The width of the painting to be displayed is 30 in. He wants the width of the framed painting to be $38\frac{1}{2}$ in. How wide should each section of the frame be?

Lesson 4-3   **Write the numbers in each group in order from least to greatest.**

63. $-\frac{3}{5}, -\frac{5}{8}, -\frac{4}{5}$ **64.** $5.04, 5.009, 5.043$ **65.** $8.1, 8.02, 8.3$

66. $-100, 93, -87, 500$ **67.** $0.45, -1.24, 2.24, 1.23$ **68.** $9.7, -9.8, 8.6, 0.9$

Transforming Formulas

A **literal equation** is an equation involving two or more variables. Formulas are special types of literal equations. To transform a literal equation, you solve for one variable in terms of the others. This is helpful when you need to use a formula numerous times.

1 EXAMPLE — Transforming Geometric Formulas

Geometry Solve the formula for the area of a triangle $A = \frac{1}{2}bh$ for height h. Then find the height of the triangle if the area is 48 in.^{2} and the base is 4 in.

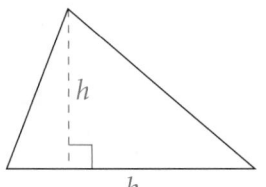

Step 1 Solve for h.

$$A = \frac{1}{2}bh$$

$2A = 2\left(\frac{1}{2}\right)bh$ **Multiply each side by 2.**

$2A = bh$ **Simplify.**

$\dfrac{2A}{} = \dfrac{bh}{}$ **Divide each side by *b* to get *h* alone on one side of the equation.**

$\dfrac{2A}{b} = h$ **Simplify.**

Step 2 Evaluate $\frac{2A}{b} = h$ for $A = 48$ and $b = 4$.

$\dfrac{2(48)}{4} = h$ **Substitute 48 for *A* and 4 for *b*.**

$\dfrac{96}{4} = h$ **Simplify.**

$24 = h$

● The height is 24 in.

Sometimes an equation will only have variables. Transforming this type of equation is no different from transforming equations with numbers. The goal is to get the variable you are solving for alone on one side of the equation.

2 EXAMPLE — Transforming Equations With Only Variables

Solve $ab - d = c$ for b in terms of a, d, and c.

$ab - d + d = c + d$ **Add *d* to each side.**

$ab = c + d$ **Combine like terms.**

$\dfrac{ab}{} = \dfrac{c + d}{}$ **Divide each side by *a*, *a* ≠ 0.**

$b = \dfrac{c + d}{a}$ **Simplify.**

3 EXAMPLE Transforming Formulas for Real-World Problems

The formula $C = \frac{5}{9}(F - 32)$ gives the Celsius temperature C in terms of the Fahrenheit temperature F. Transform the formula to find Fahrenheit temperature in terms of Celsius temperature. Then find the Fahrenheit temperature when the Celsius temperature is 30°.

Step 1 Solve for F.

$$C = \tfrac{5}{9}(F - 32)$$

$$\tfrac{9}{5} \cdot C = \tfrac{9}{5} \cdot \tfrac{5}{9}(F - 32) \qquad \textbf{Multiply each side by } \tfrac{9}{5}\textbf{, the reciprocal of } \tfrac{5}{9}\textbf{.}$$

$$\tfrac{9}{5}C = F - 32 \qquad \textbf{Simplify.}$$

$$\tfrac{9}{5}C + 32 = F - 32 + 32 \qquad \textbf{Add 32 to each side.}$$

$$\tfrac{9}{5}C + 32 = F \qquad \textbf{Simplify.}$$

Step 2 Find F when $C = 30$.

$$\tfrac{9}{5}(30) + 32 = F \qquad \textbf{Substitute 30 for C.}$$

$$54 + 32 = F \qquad \textbf{Find } \tfrac{9}{5}\textbf{(30).}$$

$$86 = F$$

30°C is equivalent to 86°F.

EXERCISES

1. a. Solve the formula $V = \ell wh$ for h.

   b. Copy and complete the table to find the height for rectangular prisms with the given volumes, lengths, and widths.

V	54 in.^{3}	64 in.^{3}	72 in.^{3}	90 in.^{3}
ℓ	3 in.	4 in.	3 in.	18 in.
w	2 in.	4 in.	8 in.	2 in.
h	■	■	■	■

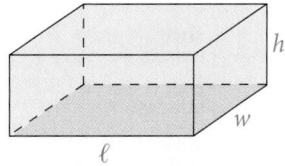

2. a. Construction Bricklayers use the formula $N = 7LH$ to estimate the number of bricks N needed to build a wall of height H given a length L in feet. Transform the formula to find the height of a wall in terms of the length and the number of bricks.

   b. What is the height of a wall that is 30 feet long and requires 2135 bricks to build?

3. You can use the number of chirps a cricket makes in one minute to estimate the outside temperature F in Fahrenheit. Transform the formula $F = \frac{n}{4} + 37$ to find the number of chirps a cricket makes in a minute in terms of a given temperature. How many chirps can you expect if the temperature is 60°F?

Ratio and Proportion

What You'll Learn

- To find ratios and rates
- To solve proportions

. . . And Why

To use proportions in application problems involving nutrition, as in Example 5.

 **Check Skills You'll Need**    **for Help** Skills Handbook pages 757

Write each fraction in simplest form.

1. $\frac{49}{84}$ **2.** $\frac{24}{42}$ **3.** $\frac{135}{180}$

Simplify each product.

4. $\frac{35}{25} \times \frac{40}{14}$ **5.** $\frac{99}{144} \times \frac{96}{88}$ **6.** $\frac{21}{81} \times \frac{108}{56}$

New Vocabulary • ratio • rate • unit rate • unit analysis • proportion
• extremes of a proportion • means of a proportion
• cross products

---

1 Ratios and Rates

A **ratio** is a comparison of two numbers by division. The ratio of a to b is $a:b$ or $\frac{a}{b}$, where $b \neq 0$. If a and b represent quantities measured in different units, then the ratio of a to b is a **rate.**

A **unit rate** is a rate with a denominator of 1. An example of a unit rate is $\frac{40 \text{ miles}}{1 \text{ hour}}$. You can write this rate as 40 miles per hour or 40 mi/h.

Price of Apple Juice

Price	Volume
$ .72	16 oz
$1.20	32 oz
$1.60	64 oz

1 EXAMPLE Using Unit Rates

Comparison Shopping The table at the left gives prices for different sizes of the same brand of apple juice. Find the unit rate (cost per ounce) for each. Which has the lowest cost per ounce?

cost → $\frac{\$.72}{16 \text{ oz}}$ = $.045/oz   **Divide the numerator and denominator by 16.**
ounces →

cost → $\frac{\$1.20}{32 \text{ oz}}$ = $.0375/oz   **Divide the numerator and denominator by 32.**
ounces →

cost → $\frac{\$1.60}{64 \text{ oz}}$ = $.025/oz   **Divide the numerator and denominator by 64.**
ounces →

The unit rate for the 16 oz bottle of apple juice is 4.5¢/oz, for the 32-oz bottle is 3.75¢/oz, and for the 64-oz bottle is 2.5¢/oz. The 64-oz bottle has the lowest cost per ounce.

 **Quick Check** ❶ Main Street Florist sells two dozen roses for $24.60. Flowers for You Florist sells six roses for $7.50. Find the unit rate for each. Which florist has the lower cost per rose?

You can use formulas like distance = rate × time ($d = rt$) to write a function to solve real-world problems. To write a function, you would use a unit rate for r.

2 **EXAMPLE** **Real-World** **Connection**

Cycling In 2004, Lance Armstrong won the Tour de France, completing the 3391 km course in about 83.6 hours. Find Lance's unit rate, which is his average speed. Write a rule to describe the distance he cycles d as a function of the time t he cycles. Cycling at his average speed, about how long it would take Lance to cycle 185 km?

Step 1 Find Lance's unit rate.

$$\text{distance} \rightarrow \frac{3391 \text{ km}}{83.6 \text{ h}} \approx 40.6 \text{ kilometers per hour}$$
$$\text{time} \rightarrow$$

Step 2 Write a function that includes the unit rate.

$d = rt$

$d = 40.6t$

Step 3 Use the function to find t when $d = 185$.

$$185 = 40.6t$$
$$\frac{185}{40.6} = \frac{40.6t}{40.6}$$
$$4.56 \approx t$$

Traveling at his average speed, it would take Lance a little over $4\frac{1}{2}$ hours to cycle 185 km.

 **2** Suppose you walk 2 miles in 35 minutes.

a. Find the average walking speed. Write a rule to describe the distance d you walk as a function of the time t you walk.

b. Use the function to find how far you would walk in an hour.

To change one unit of measure to another, you can use rates that equal 1. Since 60 min = 1 h, both $\frac{60 \text{ min}}{1 \text{ h}}$ and $\frac{1 \text{ h}}{60 \text{ min}}$ equal 1. You can use $\frac{60 \text{ min}}{1 \text{ h}}$ as a *conversion factor* to change hours into minutes and $\frac{1 \text{ h}}{60 \text{ min}}$ to change minutes into hours.

When converting from one unit to another, as in hours to minutes or minutes to hours, you must decide which conversion factor will produce the appropriate unit. This process is called **unit analysis,** or *dimensional analysis*.

3 **EXAMPLE** **Converting Rates**

Speed of Cheetah A cheetah ran 300 feet in 2.92 seconds. What was the cheetah's average speed in miles per hour?

You need to convert feet to miles and seconds to hours.

$$\frac{300 \text{ ft}}{2.92 \text{ s}} \cdot \frac{1 \text{ mi}}{5280 \text{ ft}} \cdot \frac{60 \text{ s}}{1 \text{ min}} \cdot \frac{60 \text{ min}}{1 \text{ h}}$$ **Use appropriate conversion factors.**

$$= \frac{300 \text{ ft}}{2.92 \text{ s}} \cdot \frac{1 \text{ mi}}{5280 \text{ ft}} \cdot \frac{60 \text{ s}}{1 \text{ min}} \cdot \frac{60 \text{ min}}{1 \text{ h}}$$ **Divide the common units.**

$$\approx 70 \text{ mi/h}$$ **Simplify.**

The cheetah's average speed was about 70 mi/h.

 **3** A sloth travels 0.15 miles per hour. Convert this speed to feet per minute.

A **proportion** is an equation that states that two ratios are equal.

$$\frac{a}{b} = \frac{c}{d} \text{ for } b \neq 0 \text{ and } d \neq 0$$

You read this proportion as "*a* is to *b* as *c* is to *d*." For this proportion *a* and *d* are the **extremes of the proportion,** and *b* and *c* are the **means of the proportion.** Another way you may see this proportion written is $a:b = c:d$.

Vocabulary Tip

<u>Multiplication Property of Equality</u>: For all numbers *a*, *b*, and *c*, if $a = b$, then $ac = bc$.

You can use the Multiplication Property of Equality to solve a proportion for a variable.

4 EXAMPLE   **Using the Multiplication Property of Equality**

Solve $\frac{t}{9} = \frac{5}{6}$.

$\frac{t}{9} \cdot 18 = \frac{5}{6} \cdot 18$ **Multiply each side by the least common multiple of 9 and 6, which is 18.**

$2t = 15$ **Simplify.**

$\frac{2t}{2} = \frac{15}{2}$ **Divide each side by 2.**

$t = 7.5$ **Simplify.**

 **Quick Check** **4** Solve each proportion.

a. $\frac{x}{8} = \frac{5}{6}$ **b.** $\frac{y}{12} = \frac{4}{7}$ **c.** $\frac{18}{50} = \frac{m}{15}$

You can use the Multiplication Property of Equality to prove an important property of proportions.

If $\frac{a}{b} = \frac{c}{d}$,

then $\frac{a}{b} \cdot bd = \frac{c}{d} \cdot bd$ **Multiplication Property of Equality**

$\frac{ab^1d}{1\cancel{b}} = \frac{cbd^1}{1\cancel{d}}$ **Divide the common factors.**

and $ad = cb$ **Simplify.**

or $ad = bc$ **Commutative Property of Multiplication**

The products ad and bc are the **cross products** of the proportion $\frac{a}{b} = \frac{c}{d}$.

 Key Concepts

Property	Cross Products of a Proportion

If $\frac{a}{b} = \frac{c}{d}$, then $ad = bc$.

Example $\frac{2}{3} = \frac{8}{12}$, so $2 \cdot 12 = 3 \cdot 8$.

Notice that for a proportion, the product of the extremes ad equals the product of the means bc. The Cross Products property is also called the means-extremes property of proportions.

5 EXAMPLE **Using Cross Products**

Nutrition A box of cereal weighing 354 grams contains 20 grams of fat. Find the number of grams of fat in the recommended serving size of 55 grams.

weight → $\dfrac{354}{20} = \dfrac{55}{x}$ ← fat
fat →

$354(x) = (55)(20)$ **Write cross products.**

$354x = 1100$ **Simplify.**

$\dfrac{354x}{354} = \dfrac{1100}{354}$ **Divide each side by 354.**

$x \approx 3.1$ **Simplify.**

● A 55-gram serving has about 3.1 grams of fat.

 **Quick Check** **5** Solve each proportion by using cross products.

a. $\dfrac{x}{4} = \dfrac{25}{12}$ **b.** $\dfrac{24}{5} = \dfrac{y}{7}$ **c.** $\dfrac{54}{d} = \dfrac{72}{64}$

In Example 6, the ratios that form the proportion have variable expressions with more than one term. To solve for the variable, you will use cross products and the Distributive Property.

6 EXAMPLE **Solving Multi-Step Proportions**

Solve the proportion $\dfrac{x+4}{5} = \dfrac{x-2}{7}$.

$\dfrac{x+4}{5} = \dfrac{x-2}{7}$

$(x+4)(7) = 5(x-2)$ **Write cross products.**

$7x + 28 = 5x - 10$ **Use the Distributive Property.**

$2x + 28 = -10$ **Subtract 5x from each side.**

$2x = -38$ **Subtract 28 from each side.**

$x = -19$ **Divide each side by 2.**

 **Quick Check** **6** Solve each proportion.

a. $\dfrac{x+2}{14} = \dfrac{x}{10}$ **b.** $\dfrac{y-15}{y+4} = \dfrac{35}{7}$ **c.** $\dfrac{3}{w+6} = \dfrac{5}{w-4}$

EXERCISES

For more exercises, see *Extra Skill and Word Problem Practice*.

Practice and Problem Solving

 **Practice by Example**

Example 1
(page 318)

 **for Help**

Find each unit rate.

1. $57 for 6 hours   **2.** $\dfrac{\$2}{5\,\text{lb}}$ **3.** $\dfrac{524\ \text{cars}}{4\ \text{weeks}}$ **4.** $\dfrac{600\ \text{calories}}{1.5\ \text{h}}$

5. A 10-oz bottle of shampoo costs $2.40 and a 12-oz bottle costs $2.64. Find the unit rate for each. Which bottle has the lower unit cost?

6. Two students are preparing for a marathon. Hector ran 8 miles in 85 minutes. Mario ran 6 miles in 55 minutes. Who has the faster average speed?

Example 2
(page 319)

7. Mrs. Magdalino kept records on how much she spent on gasoline and the maintenance of her car. She found that it cost $485 to drive 500 mi in a month.
  a. Find the cost per mile. Write a rule to describe the cost c for gasoline and maintenance of a car as a function the number of miles m the car is driven.
  b. Use the function to find the cost for driving 1,200 miles.
  c. About how many miles are driven for a cost of $820?

8. You are riding your bicycle. It takes you 20 minutes to go 5 miles.
  a. Find your average speed. Write a rule to describe the distance d you cycle as a function of the number of minutes m you cycle.
  b. How long would it take you to cycle 12 miles?

Example 3
(page 319)

Choose A or B for the correct conversion factor for each situation.

9. quarts to gallons
  A. $\frac{1 \text{ gal}}{4 \text{ qt}}$ **B.** $\frac{4 \text{ qt}}{1 \text{ gal}}$

10. ounces to pounds
  A. $\frac{1 \text{ lb}}{16 \text{ oz}}$ **B.** $\frac{16 \text{ oz}}{1 \text{ lb}}$

11. inches to yards
  A. $\frac{36 \text{ in.}}{1 \text{ yd}}$ **B.** $\frac{1 \text{ yd}}{36 \text{ in.}}$

12. miles to feet
  A. $\frac{5280 \text{ ft}}{1 \text{ mi}}$ **B.** $\frac{1 \text{ mi}}{5280 \text{ ft}}$

Complete each statement.

13. $8 \text{ h} = \blacksquare \text{ min}$ **14.** $120 \text{ cm} = \blacksquare \text{ m}$ **15.** $3 \text{ h} = \blacksquare \text{ s}$

Example 4
(page 320)

Solve each proportion.

16. $\frac{5}{6} = \frac{c}{9}$ **17.** $\frac{3}{8} = \frac{x}{30}$ **18.** $\frac{2}{8} = \frac{n}{20}$ **19.** $\frac{7}{5} = \frac{k}{18}$

20. $\frac{3}{4} = \frac{x}{10}$ **21.** $\frac{4}{6} = \frac{m}{9}$ **22.** $\frac{8}{d} = -\frac{12}{30}$ **23.** $\frac{5}{9} = \frac{8}{w}$

Example 5
(page 321)

24. A canary's heart beats 200 times in 12 seconds. Use a proportion to find how many times its heart beats in 42 seconds.

25. Suppose you traveled 66 kilometers in 1.25 hours. Moving at the same speed, how many kilometers would you cover in 2 hours?

Example 6
(page 321)

Solve each proportion.

26. $\frac{x+3}{4} = \frac{7}{8}$ **27.** $\frac{a-6}{5} = \frac{7}{12}$ **28.** $\frac{8}{9} = \frac{w-2}{6}$

29. $\frac{1}{c+5} = \frac{2}{3}$ **30.** $\frac{8}{b+10} = \frac{4}{2b-7}$ **31.** $\frac{k+5}{10} = \frac{k-12}{9}$

B **Apply Your Skills**

Complete each statement.

32. $\$2/\text{lb} = \blacksquare \text{ ¢/oz}$ **33.** $\$3/\text{lb} = \blacksquare \text{ ¢/oz}$

34. $4¢/\text{day} = \$ \blacksquare/\text{yr}$ **35.** $5¢/\text{day} = \$ \blacksquare/\text{yr}$

36. $5 \text{ cm/min} = \blacksquare \text{ m/week}$ **37.** $1 \text{ qt/min} = \blacksquare \text{ gal/week}$

Express each rate in miles per hour.

38. 1 mi in 3 min **39.** 1 mi in 4 min **40.** 1 mi in 300 s

41. 10,560 ft in 2 h **42.** 21,120 ft in 4 h **43.** 270 ft in 10.8 min

Solve each proportion.

44. $\frac{m+12}{9m} = \frac{5}{9}$ **45.** $\frac{p}{20} = \frac{p-4}{5}$ **46.** $\frac{n+12}{4} = \frac{n}{16}$

47. Hair Human hair grows at a rate of about 2.45 mm per week. Find the unit rate (millimeters per day). Write a rule that describes the amount of growth *g* as a function of *n* number of days. Use the function to find about how much hair grows in 30 days.

48. Record Speed According to the *Guinness Book of World Records*, the peregrine falcon has a record diving speed of 168 miles per hour. Write this speed in feet per second.

Data Analysis Below are the survey results of 60 students. These results are representative of the 1250 students in the school. Use the table for Exercises 49–51.

Question	Number Answering Yes
Do you work on weekends?	31
Do you spend 2 or more hours per night on homework?	36
Do you buy lunch in the school cafeteria?	48

49. Predict the number of students in the school who work on weekends.

50. Predict the number of students in the school who spend 2 or more hours per night on homework.

51. Predict the number of students in the school who buy lunch in the school cafeteria.

52. Writing Write an explanation telling an absent classmate how to use cross products to solve a proportion. Include an example.

53. Multiple Choice Your car averages 34 miles per gallon on the highway. If gas costs $2.10 per gallon, how much does it cost in dollars per mile, to drive your car on the highway?
- **A** $.06/mi
- **B** 16 mi/dollar
- **C** $16/mi
- **D** 0.06 mi/dollar

54 Demographics Population density is a unit rate describing the number of individuals per unit of area. An example of population density is 5 people per square mile. Use the diagram below. Find the population densities of Mongolia, Bangladesh, and the United States. Round your answers to the nearest integer.

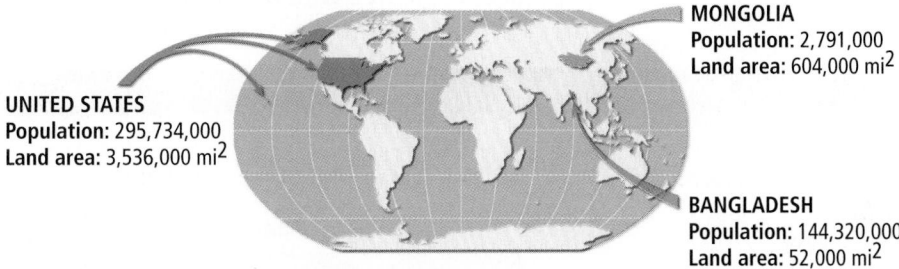

MONGOLIA
Population: 2,791,000
Land area: 604,000 mi^2

UNITED STATES
Population: 295,734,000
Land area: 3,536,000 mi^2

BANGLADESH
Population: 144,320,000
Land area: 52,000 mi^2

55. Open-Ended Estimate your walking rate in feet per second. Write this rate in miles per hour.

56. Bonnie and Tim do some yardwork for their neighbor. The ratio comparing the amount of time each one works is 7 : 4. The neighbor pays them $88. If Bonnie worked more, how much should each of them receive?

Real-World  **Connection**

Enrollment in grades 9 through 12 has risen over 19% since 1990.

Homework Video Tutor
Visit: PHSchool.com
Web Code: ate-0304

57. Engineering Transformers use coils of wire to increase or decrease voltage. The following proportion relates the number of turns of wire in the coils to the voltages. (*Note:* Each semi-circle in the diagram represents a turn of wire.)

primary coil   secondary coil

$$\frac{\text{primary turns}}{\text{secondary turns}} = \frac{\text{primary voltage}}{\text{secondary voltage}}$$

Suppose the primary-coil voltage is 120 volts. Use the proportion $\frac{5}{2} = \frac{120}{v}$ to find the secondary-coil voltage.

C Challenge   **Solve each proportion.**

58. $\frac{x^2 - 3}{5x + 2} = \frac{x}{5}$ **59.** $\frac{w^3 + 7}{w} = \frac{9w^2 + 7}{9}$ **60.** $\frac{m^2 - 8}{3m} = \frac{4m + 1}{12}$

61. Sports Long-distance runners usually refer to their speed in terms of pace, a rate measured in minutes per mile rounded to the nearest hundredth.
   a. Naoko Takahashi of Japan won the gold medal in the marathon at the 2000 Olympic games. She set an Olympic record, completing the 26.2-mile race in 2:23:14 (2 hours, 23 minutes, 14 seconds). Find her pace.
   b. Tegla Loroupe of Kenya set the women's world record at the 1999 Berlin marathon. Her time was 2:20:43. Find her pace.

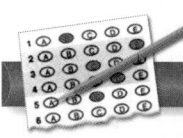

Test Prep

Multiple Choice

62. To the nearest tenth of a cent, what is the unit cost of a 28-ounce bottle of dish detergent that is on sale for $2.50?
   A. 8¢/ounce   **B.** 8.9¢/ounce   **C.** 11¢/ounce   **D.** 11.2¢/ounce

63. Most mammals breathe about once every 4 heartbeats. A large dog's heart beats about 180 times in one minute. Which unit rate represents the number of times this dog breathes in 1 minute?
   F. $\frac{40 \text{ breaths}}{\text{minute}}$ **G.** $\frac{45 \text{ breaths}}{\text{minute}}$ **H.** $\frac{180 \text{ breaths}}{4 \text{ minutes}}$ **J.** $\frac{720 \text{ breaths}}{\text{minute}}$

Short Response

64. Many trees have concentric rings that can be counted to determine the tree's age. Each ring represents one year's growth. If a maple tree with a diameter of 12 inches has 32 rings, write a proportion to find the number of rings in a maple tree that has a diameter of 20 inches. Estimate the age of a maple tree with a 20-inch diameter. Show your work.

Mixed Review

Lesson 4-5

65. Make a scatter plot of the data below.

Pond Depth

Annual Rainfall (inches)	50	48	64	55	68
Pond Depth (feet)	21	20	27	24	28

Lessons 6-1, 6-2   **Solve and check each equation.**

66. $15x + 30 = 90$ **67.** $34 = \frac{t}{4} + 5$ **68.** $-31 = 7h + 11$

69. $2b + 4.3 - b = 9.8$ **70.** $-\frac{3}{5}(c + 20) = 54$ **71.** $\frac{5v}{6} + \frac{7}{6} = \frac{1}{12}$

72. $6 = 7 - \frac{t}{2} + 8$ **73.** $9b + 8b - 13 = 106$ **74.** $2(p - 7.5) - 4 = 32$

Proportions and Similar Figures

What You'll Learn

- To find missing measures of similar figures
- To use similar figures when measuring indirectly

... And Why

To apply proportions when finding distances represented on maps, as in Example 4

✔ **Check Skills You'll Need**

GO for Help Skills Handbook and Lesson 6-4

Simplify each ratio.

1. $\frac{36}{42}$

2. $\frac{81}{108}$

3. $\frac{26}{52}$

Solve each proportion.

4. $\frac{x}{12} = \frac{7}{30}$

5. $\frac{y}{12} = \frac{8}{45}$

6. $\frac{w}{15} = \frac{12}{27}$

7. $\frac{9}{a} = \frac{81}{10}$

8. $\frac{25}{75} = \frac{z}{30}$

9. $\frac{n}{9} = \frac{n+1}{24}$

🔊 **New Vocabulary**
- similar figures
- dilation
- scale factor
- scale drawing
- scale

1 Similar Figures

Real-World Connection

The triangles in the quilt are the same shape, so they are *similar*.

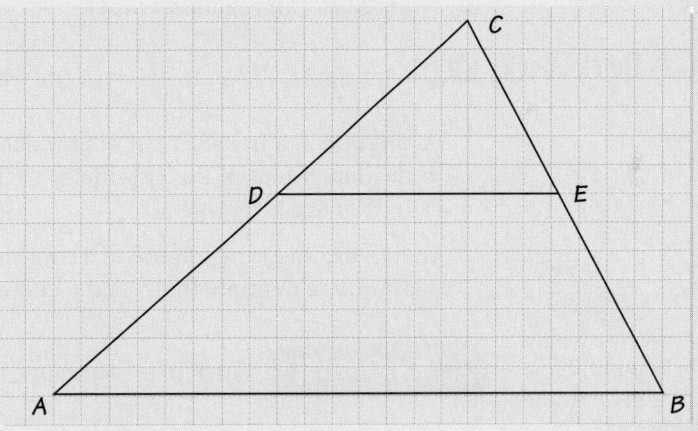

Activity: Proportions in Triangles

The figure below shows △ACB and △DCE.

1. Measure *AB*, *CA*, *CB*, *CD*, *CE*, and *DE* using a metric ruler.

2. Find each ratio. Round to the nearest hundredth.

   a. $\frac{DE}{AB}$

   b. $\frac{CE}{CB}$

   c. $\frac{CD}{CA}$

3. Tell whether each statement appears to be true.

   a. $\frac{DE}{AB} = \frac{CE}{CB}$

   b. $\frac{CD}{CA} = \frac{CE}{CB}$

   c. $\frac{DE}{AB} = \frac{CD}{CA}$

4. Using the lengths you have measured, write two ratios that equal $\frac{CB}{CE}$.

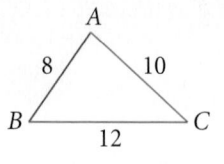

In the diagram, △ABC and △FGH are similar. **Similar figures** have the same shape but not necessarily the same size. The symbol ~ means *is similar to*.

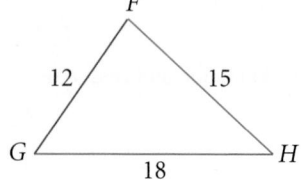

In similar triangles, corresponding angles are congruent and corresponding sides are in proportion. The order of the letters indicates the corresponding angles. If △ABC ~ △FGH, then the following is true.

$$\angle A \cong \angle F \qquad \angle B \cong \angle G \qquad \angle C \cong \angle H$$

$$\frac{AB}{FG} = \frac{AC}{FH} = \frac{BC}{GH}$$

1 EXAMPLE Finding the Length of a Side

Multiple Choice In the figure at the right, △ABC ~ △DEF. Find DE.

- (A) 36 cm
- (B) 28.45 cm
- (C) 20.25 cm
- (D) 18 cm

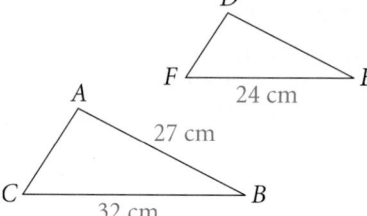

Test-Taking Tip

When setting up proportions, make sure that you are using corresponding sides. It may help to think:

$$\frac{\triangle ABC:\ \text{longest side}}{\triangle DEF:\ \text{longest side}} =$$

$$\frac{\triangle ABC:\ \text{middle-sized side}}{\triangle DEF:\ \text{middle-sized side}}$$

Relate $\dfrac{BC}{EF} = \dfrac{AB}{DE}$ Relate the lengths of corresponding sides.

Define Let $x = DE$.

Write $\dfrac{32}{24} = \dfrac{27}{x}$ Substitute lengths given in the diagram.

$32x = 24(27)$ Write cross products.

$\dfrac{32x}{32} = \dfrac{648}{32}$ Divide each side by 32.

$x = 20.25$ Simplify.

● *DE* is 20.25 cm. The answer is C.

 **Quick Check** ❶ Use the figure above. If *AC* = 14 cm, what is *DF* ?

A **dilation** is a transformation in which a figure and its image are similar. The ratio of the dimensions of the new image to the dimensions of the original figure is called the **scale factor.**

To find the image of a figure in a coordinate plane, with the origin as the center of dilation, you multiply the *x*- and *y*-coordinates by the scale factor.

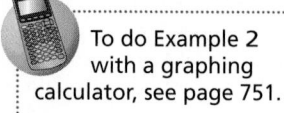

To do Example 2 with a graphing calculator, see page 751.

2 EXAMPLE Dilating Figures on the Coordinate Plane

Quadrilateral *PQRS* has vertices $P(-2, 4)$, $Q(4, 4)$, $R(4, -2)$, and $S(-4, -4)$. It is dilated by a scale factor of $\frac{1}{2}$, and the origin is the center of dilation. Graph the original figure and its dilation.

Multiply the *x*- and *y*-coordinates of each point by $\frac{1}{2}$. Then graph the figure.

$P(-2, 4) \rightarrow P'(-1, 2)$ $\qquad$ $Q(4, 4) \rightarrow Q'(2, 2)$
$R(4, -2) \rightarrow R'(2, -1)$ $\qquad$ $S(-4, -4) \rightarrow S'(-2, -2)$

● The coordinates of *S'* are $(-2, -2)$.

 **Quick Check** ❷ △*MNP* has vertices $M(3, -2)$, $N(3, 5)$, and $P(-4, -1)$. Graph the triangle and its image after a dilation with a scale factor of 2.

You can use proportions to find the dimensions of objects that are difficult to measure directly.

3 **EXAMPLE** **Applying Similarity**

Indirect Measurement A tree casts a shadow 7.5 ft long. A woman 5 ft tall casts a shadow 3 ft long. The triangle shown for the tree and its shadow is similar to the triangle shown for the woman and her shadow. How tall is the tree?

$\dfrac{3}{7.5} = \dfrac{5}{x}$ Corresponding sides of similar figures are in proportion.

$3x = 7.5 \cdot 5$ Write cross products.

$3x = 37.5$ Simplify.

$x = 12.5$ Divide each side by 3.

● The tree is 12.5 ft tall.

✓ Quick Check **3 a.** A tree casts a 26-ft shadow. A boy standing nearby casts a 12-ft shadow. His height is 4.5 ft. How tall is the tree?

b. A house casts a 56-ft shadow. A girl standing nearby casts a 7.2-ft shadow. Her height is 5.4 ft. What is the height of the house?

A **scale drawing** is an enlarged or reduced drawing that is similar to an actual object or place. Floor plans, blueprints, and maps are all examples of scale drawings. The ratio of a distance in the drawing to the corresponding actual distance is the **scale** of the drawing.

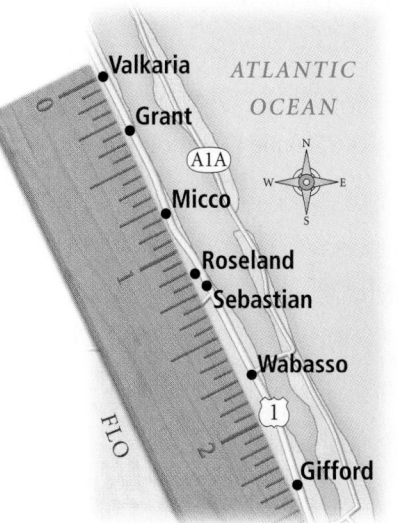

4 **EXAMPLE** **Finding Distances on Maps**

The scale of the map at the left is 1 inch : 10 miles. Approximately how far is it from Valkaria to Wabasso?

Map distance = 1.75 in.   **Measure the map distance.**

$\begin{array}{l} \text{map} \rightarrow \\ \text{actual} \rightarrow \end{array} \quad \dfrac{1}{10} = \dfrac{1.75}{d} \quad \begin{array}{l} \leftarrow \text{map} \\ \leftarrow \text{actual} \end{array}$ **Write a proportion.**

$1 \cdot d = 10 \cdot 1.75$ **Write cross products.**

$d = 17.5$ **Simplify.**

● Wabasso is about 17.5 mi from Valkaria.

✓ Quick Check **4 a.** On the map above, measure the map distance from Grant to Gifford. Find the actual distance.

b. **Critical Thinking** If another map showed the distance from Valkaria to Wabasso but had a scale of 1 inch : 5 miles, what would the map distance be between the two locations?

EXERCISES

For more exercises, see *Extra Skill and Word Problem Practice*.

Practice and Problem Solving

 Practice by Example

Example 1
(page 326)

The figures in each pair are similar. Identify the corresponding sides and angles.

1.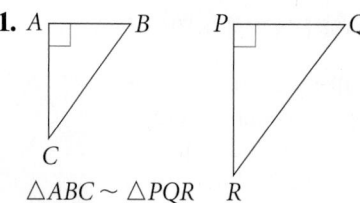
$\triangle ABC \sim \triangle PQR$

2.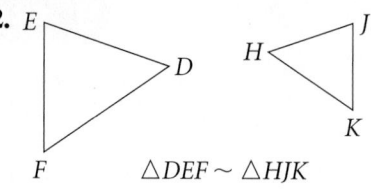
$\triangle DEF \sim \triangle HJK$

The figures in each pair are similar. Find the missing length.

3.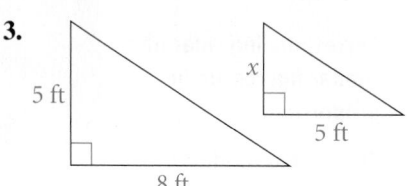

4.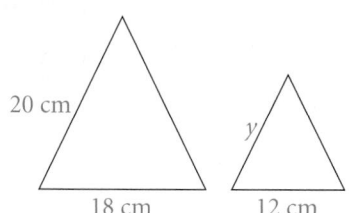

5.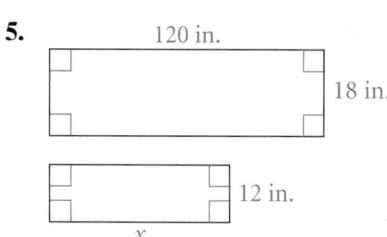

6.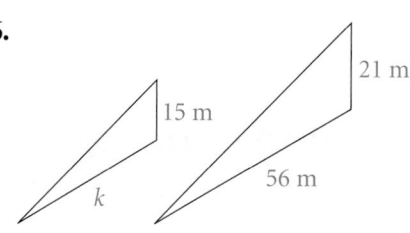

Example 2
(page 326)

Graph the coordinates of each figure. Find the coordinates of its image after a dilation centered at the origin with the given scale factor. Graph the image.

7. $\triangle ABC$; $A(3, 5)$, $B(1, -2)$, $C(-6, 3)$; scale factor of $\frac{1}{3}$

8. Rectangle $GHJK$; $G(-1, -2)$, $H(-1, 3)$, $J(4, 3)$, $K(4, -2)$; scale factor of 3

9. Quadrilateral $STUV$; $S(3, 5)$, $T(4, -3)$, $U(-2, -5)$, $V(-3, 2)$; scale factor of 0.5

Example 3
(page 327)

The child in the figure is 3 ft tall.

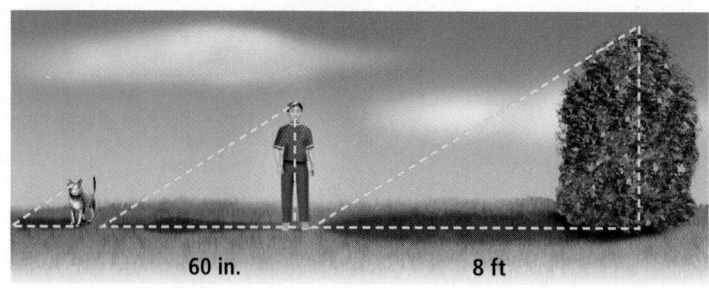

60 in.   8 ft

10. How tall is the tree?

11. The cat casts an 18-in. shadow. How tall is the cat?

Example 4
(page 327)

The scale of a map is 1 in. : 17.5 mi. Find the actual distance corresponding to each map distance.

12. 5 in.   **13.** 8.3 in.   **14.** 18.6 in.   **15.** 20 in.

SCALE
1 in. : 16 mi

16. a. Use a ruler and the map at the left. Find the distance from each town to the others.
   b. A student lives halfway between Lincoln and San Paulo and takes the shortest route to school in Duncanville. How far does the student travel each day to school?

17. The actual distance between two towns is 28 km. Suppose you measure the distance on your map and find that it is 3.5 cm. What is the scale of your map?

Using each of the following scales, find the dimensions in a blueprint of an 8 ft-by-12 ft room.

18. 1 in. : 2 ft   **19.** 1 in. : 3 ft   **20.** 1 in. : 4 ft   **21.** 1 in. : 2.5 ft

B **Apply Your Skills**

22. Two rectangles are similar. The first is 4 in. wide and 15 in. long. The second is 9 in. wide. Find the length of the second rectangle.

23. Architecture A blueprint scale is 1 in. : 9 ft. On the plan, the room measures 2.5 in. by 3 in. What are the actual dimensions of the room?

24. Error Analysis The two figures are similar. Robert uses the proportion $\frac{GH}{PQ} = \frac{GK}{RQ}$ to find RQ.
   a. What is Robert's error?
   b. What proportion should he have used?

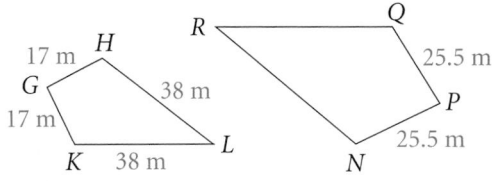

Architecture **A 2-in. length in the scale drawing represents an actual length of 24 ft.**

25. What is the scale of the drawing?

26. What are the actual dimensions of the kitchen?

27. Find the actual width of the doorways that lead into the kitchen and the dining room.

28. Find the actual area of the dining room.

29. Can a table 7 ft long and 4 ft wide fit into the narrower section of the dining room? Explain your answer.

30. Writing Are the trapezoids in the diagram similar figures? Explain your answer.

31. Open-Ended Give some examples of similar figures found in everyday life.

32. Two rectangles are similar. One is 5 cm by 12 cm. The longer side of the second rectangle is 8 cm greater than twice its shorter side. Find its length and width.

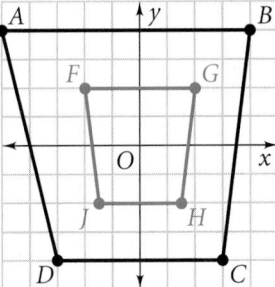

33. Multiple Choice $\triangle ABC$ and $\triangle TUV$ are similar figures. Which scale factor was used to transform $\triangle ABC$ to $\triangle TUV$?
   Ⓐ 20   Ⓑ $\frac{3}{7}$
   Ⓒ $\frac{7}{3}$ Ⓓ $\frac{7}{5}$

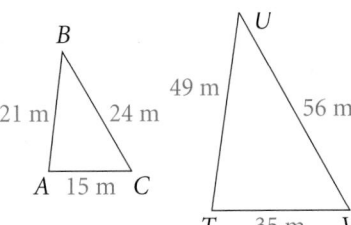

GO Online
Homework Video Tutor

Visit: PHSchool.com
Web Code: ate-0305

34. Geometry The perimeter of a triangle with sides a, b, and c is 24 cm. Side a is 2 cm longer than side b. The ratio of the lengths of sides b and c is 3 : 5. What are the lengths of the three sides of the triangle?

35. The state of Alabama is about 335 mi long and 210 mi wide. What scale would you use to draw a map of Alabama on an $8\frac{1}{2}$ in.-by-11 in. paper to make the map as large as possible?

C **Challenge** **36. Astronomy** You can block out the moon by holding a coin up at a distance from your eye that is 110 times the diameter of the coin. Using similar figures, $\frac{\text{coin diameter}}{\text{moon diameter}} = \frac{\text{coin distance}}{\text{moon distance}}$. The moon is roughly 3640 kilometers in diameter. How far away is it?

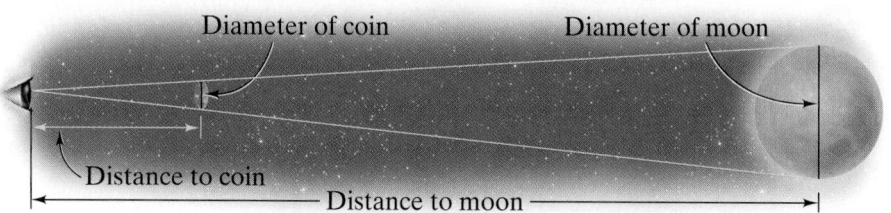

Diameter of coin   Diameter of moon

Distance to coin

Distance to moon

Not drawn to scale.

37. Geometry In the figure at the right, $\triangle ABC \sim \triangle ADE$.
  a. Substitute values from the diagram into the following proportion. $\frac{AD}{AB} = \frac{DE}{BC}$
  (*Hint:* $AB = AD + DB$.)
  b. Solve the proportion for x.
  c. Find the length of AB.
  d. What is the area of $\triangle ABC$?

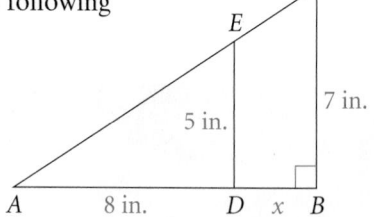

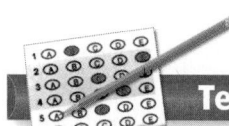

Test Prep

Multiple Choice

38. In the figure at the right, $\triangle ABC \sim \triangle XYZ$. Which proportion is incorrect?
  A. $\frac{AB}{AC} = \frac{XY}{XZ}$ **B.** $\frac{AB}{BC} = \frac{XY}{XZ}$
  C. $\frac{BC}{AC} = \frac{YZ}{XZ}$ **D.** $\frac{AC}{XZ} = \frac{BC}{YZ}$

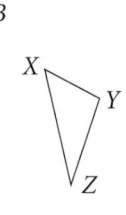

39. A map of Kentucky is drawn with a scale of 1 cm : 11 km. The map distance between Louisville and Bowling Green is 14.5 cm. Which is the best estimate of the actual distance?
  F. 1.3 km   **G.** 14 km   **H.** 100 km   **J.** 160 km

40. Which of the following would be most helpful as the first step in solving $45t + 9 = 23 - 7t$?
  A. Add $7t$ to each side of the equation.
  B. Divide each side of the equation by 9.
  C. Add 23 to each side of the equation.
  D. Multiply each side of the equation by negative 1.

330 Chapter 6 Solving Equations

41. You can paint a 6 ft-by-5 ft rectangular wall using 0.5 gallon of paint. How many gallons of paint will you need to cover a 10 ft-by-12 ft wall? Show your work.

Mixed Review

Lesson 6-4

Solve each proportion.

42. $\frac{x}{2} = \frac{9}{4}$

43. $\frac{5}{n} = \frac{3}{10}$

44. $\frac{-8}{m} = \frac{7}{20}$

45. $\frac{12}{30} = \frac{16}{v}$

46. $\frac{5}{2-x} = \frac{7}{10}$

47. $\frac{3+x}{8} = \frac{7}{12}$

Lesson 4-4

Write a function rule for each table.

48.

x	y
1	12
2	13
3	14
4	15

49.

x	y
1	18
2	14
3	10
4	6

50.

x	y
1	35
2	38
3	41
4	44

✓ Checkpoint Quiz 1

Lessons 6-1 through 6-5

Solve each equation.

1. $4n + 7 + 6n = 32$

2. $5(3 - d) = 2d + 1$

3. $8(h - 1) = 6h + 4 + 2h$

4. $43 = 8y - 11$

Solve each proportion.

5. $\frac{8}{k} = -\frac{12}{30}$

6. $\frac{3}{5} = \frac{y+1}{9}$

7. You are riding your bicycle to prepare for a race. It takes you 12 min to go 2.5 mi. If you continue traveling at the same rate, how long will it take you to go 7 mi?

The figures in each pair are similar. Find the missing length.

8.

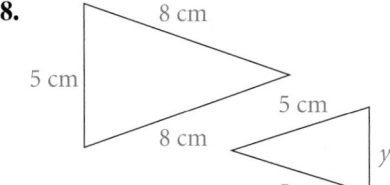

9.

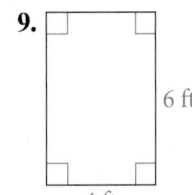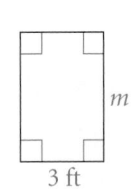

10. In the late afternoon, a 3.5-ft child casts a 60-in. shadow. She is standing next to a telephone pole that casts a 50-ft shadow. How tall is the telephone pole?

Scale Factor: Perimeter, Area, and Volume

FOR USE WITH LESSON 6-5

In this Activity Lab, you will investigate the perimeters and areas of similar figures and the surface areas and volumes of similar three-dimensional objects.

1 ACTIVITY

The graph shows four dilations of rectangle A.

1. Copy and complete the table below.

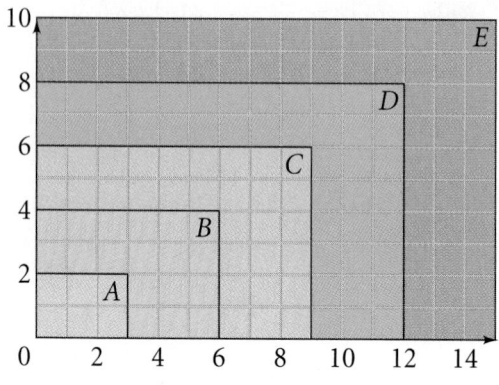

Rectangle	Width	Length	Perimeter	Area
A	2 units	3 units	10 units	6 units^2
B	■	■	■	■
C	■	■	■	■
D	■	■	■	■
E	■	■	■	■

2. Use the information in your table from Exercise 1. Copy and complete the table below.

Rectangles	Scale Factor	Ratio of Corresponding Sides	Ratio of Perimeters	Ratio of Areas
A : B	1 : 2	1 : 2	■	■
A : C	■	■	■	■
A : D	■	■	■	■
A : E	■	■	■	■
B : C	■	■	■	■

3. a. What can you conclude about the scale factor and the ratios of perimeters?
   b. Complete this statement: If the scale factor of two similar figures is $a : b$, then the ratio of the perimeters is __?__.

4. a. What can you conclude about the scale factor and the ratios of areas?
   b. Complete this statement: If the scale factor of two similar figures is $a : b$, then the ratio of the areas is __?__.

EXERCISES

5. The scale factor of two triangles is 3 : 5.
   a. What is the ratio of the perimeters of the triangles?
   b. What is the ratio of the areas of the triangles?

6. The ratio of the areas of two similar triangles is $\frac{25}{16}$. The measure of one side of the smaller triangle is 6 in. What is the measure of the corresponding side of the larger triangle?

2 ACTIVITY

Use the rectangular prisms at the right to answer the following questions.

7. Copy and complete the table.

Prism	Surface Area	Volume
A	22 units^2	6 units^3
B	■	■
C	■	■

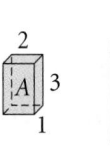
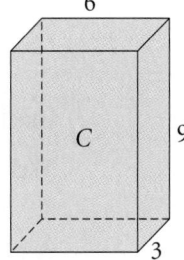

8. Use the information in your table from Exercise 7. Copy and complete the table below.

Prisms	Scale Factor	Ratio of Corresponding Sides	Ratio of Surface Areas	Ratio of Volumes
A : B	1 : 2	1 : 2	■	■
A : C	■	■	■	■
B : C	■	■	■	■

9. a. What can you conclude about the scale factor and the ratios of surface areas of similar three-dimensional objects?
   b. Complete this statement: If the scale factor of the lengths of corresponding sides of three-dimensional objects is $a : b$, then the ratio of the surface areas is _?_ .

10. a. What can you conclude about the scale factor and the ratios of volumes of similar three-dimensional objects?
   b. Complete this statement: If the scale factor of the lengths of corresponding sides of three-dimensional objects is $a : b$, then the ratio of the volumes is _?_ .

EXERCISES

11. The scale factor of two rectangular prisms is 5 : 8.
   a. What is the ratio of the surface areas of the rectangular prisms?
   b. What is the ratio of the volumes of the rectangular prisms?

12. The formula for the volume of a sphere is $V = \frac{4\pi r^3}{3}$. One sphere has a radius of 6 in. The second sphere has a radius of 10 in. Find the ratio of their volumes.

13. The ratio of the volumes of two similar pyramids is 27 : 125. What is the ratio of the heights of the two pyramids?

14. The ratio of the surface areas of two similar rectangular prisms is $\frac{36}{25}$. One side of the smaller prism is 4 cm long. What is the length of the corresponding side of the larger prism?

15. The ratio of the volumes of two similar cylinders is $\frac{27}{8}$. The radius of the larger cylinder is 12 cm. What is the length of the radius of the smaller cylinder?

Equations and Problem Solving

What You'll Learn

- To define a variable in terms of another variable

- To model distance-rate-time problems

. . . And Why

To solve real-world problems involving distance, rate, and time, as in Examples 3–5

Write a variable expression for each situation.

1. value in cents of q quarters   2. twice the length ℓ

3. number of miles traveled at 34 mi/h in h hours

4. weight of 5 crates if each crate weighs x kilograms

5. cost of n items at $3.99 per item

🔊 **New Vocabulary** • consecutive integers • uniform motion

---

1 Defining Variables

Some problems contain two or more unknown quantities. To solve such problems, first decide which unknown quantity the variable will represent. Then express the other unknown quantity or quantities in terms of that variable.

1 EXAMPLE Defining One Variable in Terms of Another

Geometry The length of a rectangle is 6 in. more than its width. The perimeter of the rectangle is 24 in. What is the length of the rectangle?

Relate The length is 6 in. more than the width.

Define Let w = the width.   The length is described in terms of the width.
                Then $w + 6$ = the length.   So define a variable for the width first.

Problem Solving Hint

For Example 1, drawing a diagram will help you understand the problem.

$w + 6$

w

Write $P = 2\ell + 2w$ Use the perimeter formula.

$24 = 2(w + 6) + 2w$ Substitute 24 for P and $w + 6$ for ℓ.

$24 = 2w + 12 + 2w$ Use the Distributive Property.

$24 = 4w + 12$ Combine like terms.

$24 - 12 = 4w + 12 - 12$ Subtract 12 from each side.

$12 = 4w$ Simplify.

$\dfrac{12}{4} = \dfrac{4w}{4}$ Divide each side by 4.

$3 = w$ Simplify.

The width of the rectangle is 3 in. The length of the rectangle is 6 in. more than the width. So the length of the rectangle is 9 in.

✓ **Quick Check** ❶ The width of a rectangle is 2 cm less than its length. The perimeter of the rectangle is 16 cm. What is the length of the rectangle?

Consecutive integers differ by 1. The integers 50 and 51 are consecutive integers, and so are -10, -9, and -8. For consecutive integer problems, it may help to define a variable before describing the problem in words. Let a variable represent one of the unknown integers. Then define the other unknown integers in terms of the first one.

2 EXAMPLE Consecutive Integer Problem

The sum of three consecutive integers is 147. Find the integers.

Define Let n = the first integer.
Then $n + 1$ = the second integer,
and $n + 2$ = the third integer.

Relate	first integer	plus	second integer	plus	third integer	is	147
Write	n	$+$	$n + 1$	$+$	$n + 2$	$=$	147

$$n + n + 1 + n + 2 = 147$$

$$3n + 3 = 147 \qquad \text{Combine like terms.}$$

$$3n + 3 - 3 = 147 - 3 \qquad \text{Subtract 3 from each side.}$$

$$3n = 144 \qquad \text{Simplify.}$$

$$\frac{3n}{3} = \frac{144}{3} \qquad \text{Divide each side by 3.}$$

$$n = 48 \qquad \text{Simplify.}$$

If $n = 48$, then $n + 1 = 49$, and $n + 2 = 50$. The three integers are 48, 49, and 50.

Check Is the solution correct? Yes; $48 + 49 + 50 = 147$.

 **Quick Check** ❷ The sum of three consecutive integers is 48.
  a. Define a variable for one of the integers.
  b. Write expressions for the other two integers.
  c. Write and solve an equation to find the three integers.

---

2 Distance-Rate-Time Problems

GO Online

Video Tutor Help
Visit: PHSchool.com
Web Code: ate-0775

An object that moves at a constant rate is said to be in **uniform motion.** The formula $d = rt$ gives the relationship between distance d, rate r, and time t. Uniform motion problems may involve objects going the same direction, opposite directions, or round trips.

In the diagram below, the two vehicles are traveling the same direction at different rates. The distances the vehicles travel are the same.

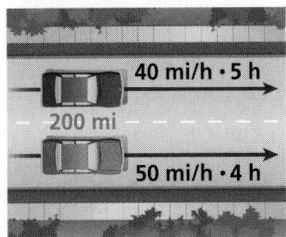

40 mi/h · 5 h
200 mi
50 mi/h · 4 h

Since the distances are equal, the products of rate and time for the two cars are equal. For the vehicles shown, $40 \cdot 5 = 50 \cdot 4$.

A table can also help you understand relationships in distance-rate-time problems.

3 EXAMPLE **Same-Direction Travel**

Engineering A train leaves a train station at 1 P.M. It travels at an average rate of 72 mi/h. A high-speed train leaves the same station an hour later. It travels at an average rate of 90 mi/h. The second train follows the same route as the first train on a track parallel to the first. In how many hours will the second train catch up with the first train?

Define Let t = the time the first train travels.

Then $t - 1$ = the time the second train travels.

Relate

Train	Rate	Time	Distance Traveled
1	72	t	$72t$
2	90	$t - 1$	$90(t - 1)$

Write $72t = 90(t - 1)$ **The distances traveled by the trains are equal.**

Method 1 **Solve by using a table.**

Use a table to evaluate each side of the equation. Look for matching values.

Time	$72t$	$90(t - 1)$
1	$72(1) = 72$	$90(1 - 1) = 0$
2	$72(2) = 144$	$90(2 - 1) = 90$
3	$72(3) = 216$	$90(3 - 1) = 180$
4	$72(4) = 288$	$90(4 - 1) = 270$
5	$72(5) = 360$	$90(5 - 1) = 360$ ✓

When the first train travels 5 hours, the second train travels 4 hours $(t - 1)$. The second train will catch up with the first train in 4 hours.

Method 2 **Solve the equation.**

$72t = 90t - 90$	**Use the Distributive Property to simplify $90(t - 1)$.**
$72t - 72t = 90t - 90 - 72t$	**Subtract 72t from each side.**
$0 = 18t - 90$	**Combine like terms.**
$0 + 90 = 18t - 90 + 90$	**Add 90 to each side.**
$90 = 18t$	**Simplify.**
$\dfrac{90}{18} = \dfrac{18t}{18}$	**Divide each side by 18.**
$t = 5$	**Simplify.**
$t - 1 = 4$	**Find the time the second train travels.**

The second train will catch up with the first train in 4 h.

Quick Check **3** A group of campers and one group leader left a campsite in a canoe. They traveled at an average rate of 10 km/h. Two hours later, the other group leader left the campsite in a motorboat. He traveled at an average rate of 22 km/h.
a. How long after the canoe left the campsite did the motorboat catch up with it?
b. How long did the motorboat travel?

Real-World **Connection**

High-speed trains that go from Boston to New York in less than 4 hours can reach a speed of 150 mi/h.

For uniform motion problems that involve a round trip, it is important to remember that the distance going is equal to the distance returning.

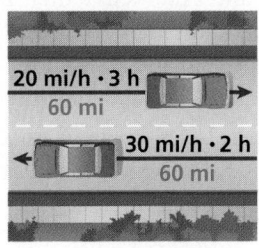

Since the distances are equal, the products of rate and time for traveling in both directions are equal. That is, $20 \cdot 3 = 30 \cdot 2$.

4 **EXAMPLE** **Round-Trip Travel**

Noya drives into the city to buy a software program at a computer store. Because of traffic conditions, she averages only 15 mi/h. On her drive home she averages 35 mi/h. If the total travel time is 2 hours, how long does it take her to drive to the computer store?

Define Let t = time of Noya's drive to the computer store.

$2 - t$ = the time of Noya's drive home.

Relate

Part of Noya's Travel	Rate	Time	Distance
To the computer store	15	t	$15t$
Return home	35	$2 - t$	$35(2 - t)$

Noya drives $15t$ miles to the computer store and $35(2 - t)$ miles back.

Write

$15t = 35(2 - t)$	**The distances traveled to and from the store are equal.**
$15t = 70 - 35t$	**Use the Distributive Property.**
$15t + 35t = 70 - 35t + 35t$	**Add 35t to each side.**
$50t = 70$	**Combine like terms.**
$\frac{50t}{50} = \frac{70}{50}$	**Divide each side by 50.**
$t = 1.4$	**Simplify.**

It took Noya 1.4 h to drive to the computer store.

 **4** On his way to work from home, your uncle averaged only 20 miles per hour. On his drive home, he averaged 40 miles per hour. If the total travel time was $1\frac{1}{2}$ hours, how long did it take him to drive to work?

For uniform motion problems involving two objects moving in opposite directions, you can write equations using the fact that the sum of their distances is the total distance.

Problem Solving Hint

The total travel time is for a round trip. If it takes t out of a 2-hour round trip to get to the store, then $2 - t$ is the time it will take for the drive home.

5 EXAMPLE Opposite-Direction Travel

Jane and Peter leave their home traveling in opposite directions on a straight road. Peter drives 15 mi/h faster than Jane. After 3 hours, they are 225 miles apart. Find Peter's rate and Jane's rate.

Define Let r = Jane's rate.
Then $r + 15$ = Peter's rate.

Relate

Person	Rate	Time	Distance
Jane	r	3	$3r$
Peter	$r + 15$	3	$3(r + 15)$

Jane's distance is $3r$. Peter's distance is $3(r + 15)$.

Write $3r + 3(r + 15) = 225$ — The sum of Jane's and Peter's distances is the total distance, 225 miles.

$$3r + 3(r + 15) = 225$$

$3r + 3r + 45 = 225$ **Use the Distributive Property.**

$6r + 45 = 225$ **Combine like terms.**

$6r + 45 - 45 = 225 - 45$ **Subtract 45 from each side.**

$6r = 180$ **Simplify.**

$\dfrac{6r}{6} = \dfrac{180}{6}$ **Divide each side by 6.**

$r = 30$ **Simplify.**

Jane's rate is 30 mi/h, and Peter's rate is 15 mi/h faster, which is 45 mi/h.

✓ Quick Check **5** Sarah and John leave Perryville traveling in opposite directions on a straight road. Sarah drives 12 miles per hour faster than John. After 2 hours, they are 176 miles apart. Find Sarah's speed and John's speed.

Test-Taking Tip

When you grid an integer, right-align your answer so the place-value is clear.

EXERCISES

For more exercises, see *Extra Skill and Word Problem Practice.*

Practice and Problem Solving

A **Practice by Example**

Example 1
(page 334)

GO for Help

1. The length of a rectangle is 3 in. more than its width. The perimeter of the rectangle is 30 in.
   a. Define a variable for the width.
   b. Write an expression for the length in terms of the width.
   c. Write an equation to find the width of the rectangle. Solve your equation.
   d. What is the length of the rectangle?

2. The length of a rectangle is 8 in. more than its width. The perimeter of the rectangle is 24 in. What are the width and length of the rectangle?

3. The width of a rectangle is one half its length. The perimeter of the rectangle is 54 cm. What are the width and length of the rectangle?

4. The length of a rectangular garden is 3 yd more than twice its width. The perimeter of the garden is 36 yd. What are the width and length of the garden?

Example 2
(page 335)

5. The sum of three consecutive integers is 915. What are the integers?

6. The sum of two consecutive *even* integers is 118.
  a. Define a variable for the smaller integer.
  b. What must you add to an even integer to get the next greater even integer?
  c. Write an expression for the second integer.
  d. Write and solve an equation to find the two even integers.

7. The sum of two consecutive *even* integers is −298. What are the integers?

8. The sum of two consecutive *odd* integers is 56.
  a. Define a variable for the smaller integer.
  b. What must you add to an odd integer to get the next greater odd integer?
  c. Write an expression for the second integer.
  d. Write and solve an equation to find the two odd integers.

Example 3
(page 336)

9. A moving van leaves a house traveling at an average rate of 40 mi/h. The family leaves the house $\frac{1}{2}$ hour later following the same route in a car. They travel at an average rate of 60 mi/h.
  a. Define a variable for the time traveled by the moving van.
  b. Write an expression for the time traveled by the car.
  c. Copy and complete the table.

Vehicle	Rate	Time	Distance Traveled
Moving van	▦	▦	▦
Car	▦	▦	▦

  d. Make a table comparing the distance traveled by the moving van and car for each hour. Use the table to find out how long it will take the car to catch up with the van.

10. Air Travel A jet leaves the Charlotte, North Carolina, airport traveling at an average rate of 564 km/h. Another jet leaves the airport one half hour later traveling at 744 km/h in the same direction. Use an equation to find how long the second jet will take to overtake the first.

Example 4
(page 337)

11. Juan drives to work. Because of traffic conditions, he averages 22 miles per hour. He returns home averaging 32 miles per hour. The total travel time is $2\frac{1}{4}$ hours.
  a. Define a variable for the time Juan takes to travel to work. Write an expression for the time Juan takes to return home.
  b. Write and solve an equation to find the time Juan spends driving to work.

12. Air Travel An airplane flies from New Orleans, Louisiana, to Atlanta, Georgia, at an average rate of 320 miles per hour. The airplane then returns at an average rate of 280 miles per hour. The total travel time is 3 hours.
  a. Define a variable for the flying time from New Orleans to Atlanta. Write an expression for the travel time from Atlanta to New Orleans.
  b. Write and solve an equation to find the flying time from New Orleans to Atlanta.

Example 5
(page 338)

13. John and William leave their home traveling in opposite directions on a straight road. John drives 20 miles per hour faster than William. After 4 hours they are 250 miles apart.
  a. Define a variable for John's rate. Write an expression for William's rate.
  b. Write and solve an equation to find John's rate. Then find William's rate.

14. Two bicyclists ride in opposite directions. The speed of the first bicyclist is 5 miles per hour faster than the second. After 2 hours they are 70 miles apart. Find their rates.

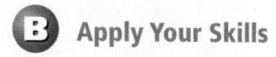
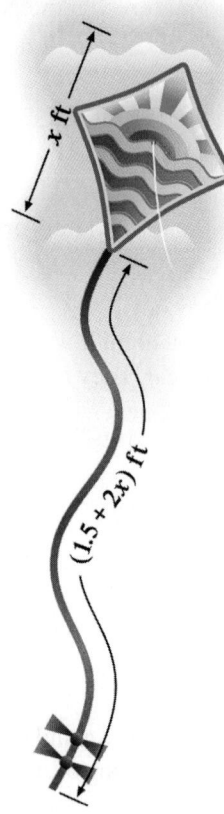

15. The sum of three consecutive *odd* integers is -87. What are the integers?

16. The tail of a kite is 1.5 ft plus twice the length of the kite. Together, the kite and tail are 15 ft 6 in. long.
   a. Write an expression for the length of the kite and tail together.
   b. Write 15 ft 6 in. in terms of feet.
   c. Write and solve an equation to find the length of the tail.

17. **Travel** A bus traveling at an average rate of 30 miles per hour left the city at 11:45 A.M. A car following the bus at 45 miles per hour left the city at noon. At what time did the car catch up with the bus?

18. Ellen and Kate raced on their bicycles to the library after school. They both left school at 3:00 P.M. and bicycled along the same path. Ellen rode at a speed of 12 miles per hour and Kate rode at 9 miles per hour. Ellen got to the library 15 minutes before Kate. At what time did Ellen get to the library?

19. a. Which of the following numbers is not the sum of three consecutive integers?
   I. 51   **II.** 61   **III.** 72   **IV.** 81
   b. **Critical Thinking** What common trait do the other numbers share?

20. At 1:30 P.M., Tom leaves in his boat from a dock and heads south. He travels at a rate of 25 miles per hour. Ten minutes later, Mary leaves the same dock in her speedboat and heads after Tom. If she travels at a rate of 30 miles per hour, when will she catch up with Tom?

21. **Air Travel** Two airplanes depart from an airport traveling in opposite directions. The second airplane is 200 miles per hour faster than the first. After 2 hours they are 1100 miles apart. Find the speeds of the airplanes.

22. At 1:00 P.M. a truck leaves Centerville traveling 45 mi/h. One hour later a train leaves Centerville traveling 60 mi/h. They arrive in Smithfield at the same time.
   a. Use the table to find when the train and truck arrive in Smithfield.
   b. **Critical Thinking** What piece of information can you get from the table that you would NOT get by solving the equation $45t = 60(t - 1)$?

Time	Truck 45t	Train 60(t − 1)
1 P.M.	45 mi	0 mi
2 P.M.	90 mi	60 mi
3 P.M.	135 mi	120 mi
4 P.M.	180 mi	180 mi
5 P.M.	225 mi	240 mi

23. Three friends were born in consecutive years. The sum of their birth years is 5982. Find the year in which each person was born.

 24. **Writing** Describe the steps you would use to solve consecutive integer problems.

25. **Open-Ended** Write a word problem that could be solved using the equation $35(t - 1) = 20t$.

26. a. Write and solve an equation to find three consecutive integers with a sum of 126. Let n = the first integer.
   b. **Critical Thinking** In part (a), could you solve the problem by letting n = the middle integer, $n - 1$ = the smallest integer, and $n + 1$ = the largest integer?

27. **Electricity** A group of ten 6- and 12-volt batteries are wired in series as shown at the right. The sum of their voltages is 84 volts. How many of each type of battery are used?

Batteries in Series

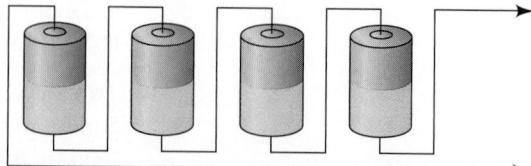

GO **Online**
Homework Video Tutor
Visit: PHSchool.com
Web Code: ate-0306

 **Challenge** 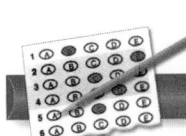 **28. Geometry** A triangle has a perimeter of 165 cm. The first side is 65 cm less than twice the second side. The third side is 10 cm less than the second side. Write and solve an equation to find the length of each side of the triangle.

29. At 9:00 A.M., your friends begin hiking at 2 mi/h. You begin from the same place at 9:25 A.M. You hike at 3 mi/h.
a. How long will you have hiked when you catch up with your friends?
b. At what time will you catch up with your friends?

30. Find five consecutive *odd* integers such that the sum of the first and the fifth is one less than three times the fourth.

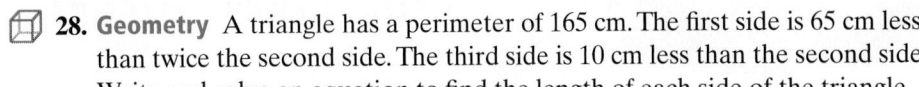

Test Prep

Multiple Choice

31. Solve $3n - 7 + 2n = 8n + 11$.
   A. -6 **B.** $1\frac{1}{3}$ **C.** $3\frac{3}{5}$ **D.** 9

32. Which expression represents the sum of 3 odd integers of which *n* is the least integer?
   F. $n + 3$ **G.** $3n + 3$
   H. $3n + 6$ **J.** $3n + 7$

33. Which equation does NOT have -2 as its solution?
   A. $2x + 5 = 5x + 11$ **B.** $7n + 9 = 3 - 9n$
   C. $3k + 6 - 4k = k + 10$ **D.** $4 + 3q = 7q + 12$

34. A truck traveling at an average rate of 45 miles per hour leaves a rest stop. Fifteen minutes later a car traveling at an average rate of 60 miles per hour leaves the same rest stop traveling the same route. How long will it take for the car to catch up with the truck?
   F. 15 minutes   **G.** 45 minutes
   H. 1 hour 15 minutes   **J.** 3 hours

35. The perimeter of the triangle at the right is 22.6 in. What is the value of *n*?
   A. 3.5   **B.** 4.6
   C. 7.8   **D.** 9.4

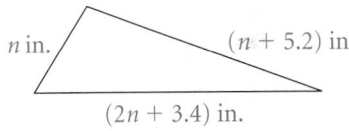
n in. $(n + 5.2)$ in. $(2n + 3.4)$ in.

Mixed Review

Lesson 6-3

GO for Help

Solve each equation. If the equation is an identity, write *identity*. If it has no solution, write *no solution*.

36. $2x = 7x + 10$ **37.** $2q + 4 = 4 - 2q$

38. $0.5t + 3.6 = 4.2 - 1.5t$ **39.** $2x + 5 + x = 2(3x + 3)$

40. $4 + x + 3x = 2(2x + 5)$ **41.** $8z + 2 = 2(z - 5) - z$

Lesson 6-2

42. Brendan earns $8.25 per hour at his job. He also makes $12.38 per hour for any number of hours over 40 that he works in one week. He worked 40 hours last week, plus some overtime, and made $385.71. How many overtime hours did he work?

Proportions and Percents

To solve a percent problem such as "Find 38% of 320," you change the percent to a decimal and multiply.

$$38\% \text{ of } 320 \rightarrow 0.38 \cdot 320 = 121.6$$

For more involved percent problems, you can think of a percent as a ratio that compares a number to 100. You can solve problems involving percents using this proportion. Diagrams will help you visualize relationships.

$$\text{percent} \left\{ \frac{n}{100} = \frac{\text{part}}{\text{whole}} \right.$$

1 EXAMPLE

At Summerville High School there are 553 freshmen, which is 35% of the total number of students. How many students attend the high school?

Relate 35% of the total number of students is 553 students.

Define Let n = the total number of students.

Write $\frac{35}{100} = \frac{553}{n}$ $\leftarrow$ **part**
$\leftarrow$ **whole**

$35n = 55,300$ **Find the cross products.**

$n = 1580$ **Divide each side by 35.**

There are a total of 1580 students at Summerville High School.

When you use proportions to solve real-world problems involving percents, first establish what is the part and what is the whole. In the next example, notice that the part is actually greater than the whole.

2 EXAMPLE

Band members had a fundraising goal of $2500 as they earned money to go to the state competition. The fundraiser was more successful than they expected, and they raised $3275. What percent of their goal did they raise?

Relate What percent of $2500 is $3275?

Define Let n = the percent.

Write $\frac{n}{100} = \frac{3275}{2500}$ $\leftarrow$ **part**
$\leftarrow$ **whole**

$2500n = 327,500$ **Find the cross products.**

$n = 131$ **Divide each side by 2500.**

The band members raised 131% of their goal.

You can estimate some percents using fractions. These are some of the percent-fraction equivalents that you should remember.

$20\% = \frac{1}{5}$ $25\% = \frac{1}{4}$ $33.\overline{3}\% = \frac{1}{3}$ $50\% = \frac{1}{2}$ $66.\overline{6}\% = \frac{2}{3}$ $75\% = \frac{3}{4}$

You can also solve a percent problem by translating from words to an equation.

3 EXAMPLE

Water Supply According to the United States Geological Survey, surface water accounts for 77.6% of our country's total daily water supply. The daily surface water supply is about 264 billion gallons. Estimate the total daily water supply.

Relate   77.6%   of   total daily water supply   is   264 billion gallons

Define   Let w = the total water supply.

Write   77.6%   · w =   264

$\frac{3}{4}w = 264$ **75% is close to 77.6%. Use $\frac{3}{4}$ to estimate.**

$\left(\frac{4}{3}\right)\frac{3}{4}w = \left(\frac{4}{3}\right)264$ **Multiply by $\frac{4}{3}$, the reciprocal of $\frac{3}{4}$.**

$w = 352$ **Simplify.**

The total daily water supply is about 352 billion gallons.

EXERCISES

Solve each problem.

1. What percent of 40 is 20?

2. What percent of 20 is 40?

3. 20% of what number is 40?

4. 40% of what number is 20?

5. 8% of 125 is what number?

6. What percent of 125 is 8?

7. 15% of what number is 24?

8. 120% of what number is 48?

9. Carlos worked 31.5 hours at a hospital as a volunteer. This represents 87.5% of his school's requirement for community service. How many hours does his school require for community service?

10. **Sales** Suppose you work in an electronics store. You earn a 6% commission on every item that you sell. How much commission do you earn if you sell a $545 sound system?

11. **Sales** Juan earns a 5.5% commission on his bicycle sales. In September, he earned $214.28 in commissions. What were his sales for the month?

12. **Sales Tax** Jane paid $1185 in sales tax on her new car. The car cost $15,800 before the tax was added. What percent was the sales tax rate?

13. **Finance** The formula for simple interest is $I = prt$, where I is the interest, p is the principal, r is the interest rate per year, and t is the time in years.
   a. You invest $550 for three years. Find the amount of simple interest you earn with an annual interest rate of 4.5%.
   b. Suppose you invested $900 for two years. You earned $67.50 in simple interest. What was the annual rate of interest?
   c. You invest $812 with an annual interest rate of 6.5%. You earned $316.68 in simple interest. For how many years was the money invested?

14. **Sales** A store advertises sneakers on sale for 33% off. The original price of sneakers is $56.
   a. Estimate the amount the sneakers have been marked down.
   b. Estimate the sale price of the sneakers.

Percent of Change

What You'll Learn

- To find percent of change
- To find percent error

...And Why

To use percent of change in a real-world situation involving farming, as in Example 2

☑ **Check Skills You'll Need**

GO for Help Review page 342

Write an equation for each problem and solve.

1. What is 20% of 20?   **2.** 8 is what percent of 20?

3. 18 is 90% of what number?   **4.** 27 is 90% of what number?

Estimate each answer.

5. 67.3% of 24   **6.** 65% of 48

◀)) **New Vocabulary**
- percent of change
- percent of decrease
- percent error
- percent of increase
- greatest possible error

---

1 Percent of Change

Suppose the price of a $20 sweatshirt increases by $2. You can express the increase as a percent.

increase in price ⟶ $\frac{2}{20} = \frac{1}{10} = 10\%$
original price ⟶

There was 10% increase in the price. This is an example of percent of change. **Percent of change** is the ratio $\frac{\text{amount of change}}{\text{original amount}}$ expressed as a percent. When a value increases from its original amount, it is the **percent of increase.** When a value decreases from its original amount, it is the **percent of decrease.**

1 EXAMPLE Finding Percent of Change

The price of a sweater decreased from $29.99 to $24.49. Find the percent of decrease.

percent of decrease $= \dfrac{\text{amount of change}}{\text{original amount}}$

$= \dfrac{29.99 - 24.49}{29.99}$ **Subtract to find the amount of change. Substitute the original amount.**

$= \dfrac{5.50}{29.99}$ **Simplify the numerator.**

≈ 0.18 or 18%   **Write as a decimal and then as a percent.**

● The price of the sweater decreased by about 18%.

☑ **Quick Check** ❶ **a.** Find the percent of change if the price of a CD increases from $12.99 to $13.99. Round to the nearest percent.

b. Find the percent of change if the CD is on sale, and its price decreases from $13.99 to $12.99. Round to the nearest percent.

2 EXAMPLE Real-World Problem Solving

Farming In 1990, there were 1330 registered alpacas in the United States. By the summer of 2000, there were 29,856. What was the percent of increase in registered alpacas?

$$\text{percent of increase} = \frac{\text{amount of change}}{\text{original amount}}$$

$$= \frac{29{,}856 - 1330}{1330} \qquad \textbf{Substitute.}$$

$$= \frac{28{,}526}{1330} \qquad \textbf{Simplify the numerator.}$$

$$\approx 21.448 \text{ or } 2145\% \qquad \textbf{Write as a decimal and then as a percent.}$$

● The number of registered alpacas increased by nearly 2145%.

Real-World Connection

Alpacas produce 5 to 8 pounds of fleece per year, which sells for $32 to $128 per pound.

✓ Quick Check ② The number of alpaca owners increased from 146 in 1991 to 2919 in 2000. Find the percent of increase. Round to the nearest percent.

---

2 Percent Error

Think about the last time you used a ruler. You probably measured to the nearest inch, half-inch, centimeter, or millimeter. Because no measurement is exact, you always measure to the nearest "something." The **greatest possible error** in a measurement is one half of that measuring unit.

3 EXAMPLE Finding the Greatest Possible Error

You use a beam balance to find the mass of a rock sample for a science lab. You read the scale as 3.8 g. What is your greatest possible error?

The rock's mass was measured to the nearest 0.1 g, so the greatest possible error is one half of 0.1 g, or 0.05 g.

✓ Quick Check ③ You measure a picture for the yearbook and record its height as 9 cm. What is your greatest possible error?

4 EXAMPLE Finding Maximum and Minimum Areas

You measure a room and make the diagram shown at the left. Use the greatest possible error to find the maximum and minimum possible areas.

Both measurements were made to the nearest whole foot, so the greatest possible error is 0.5 ft. The length could be as little as 12.5 ft or as great as 13.5 ft. The width could be as little as 6.5 ft or as great as 7.5 ft. Find the minimum and maximum areas.

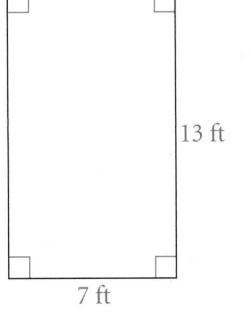

13 ft

7 ft

Minimum Area	**Maximum Area**
12.5 ft × 6.5 ft = 81.25 ft²	13.5 ft × 7.5 ft = 101.25 ft²

● The minimum area is 81.25 ft², and the maximum area is 101.25 ft².

✓ Quick Check ④ You measure a wall of your room as 8 ft high and 12 ft wide. Find the minimum and maximum possible areas of the wall.

Percent error is another useful way to think of the error in a measurement. It is the ratio of the greater possible error and the measurement.

$$\textbf{percent error} = \frac{\text{greatest possible error}}{\text{measurement}}$$

5 EXAMPLE **Finding Percent Error**

Suppose you measure a CD and record its diameter as 12.1 cm. Find the percent error in your measurement.

Since the measurement is to the nearest 0.1 cm, the greatest possible error is 0.05 cm.

percent error $= \dfrac{\text{greatest possible error}}{\text{measurement}}$	**Use the percent error formula.**
$= \dfrac{0.05}{12.1}$	**Substitute.**
≈ 0.0041322314	**Divide.**
$\approx 0.4\%$	**Round and write as a percent.**

● The percent error is about 0.4%.

✓ Quick Check ⑤ **a.** You measure the length of a table as 168 inches. Find the percent error in this measurement.

  b. You measure the length of a table as 168.0 inches. Find the percent error in this measurement.

6 EXAMPLE **Finding Percent Error in Calculating Volume**

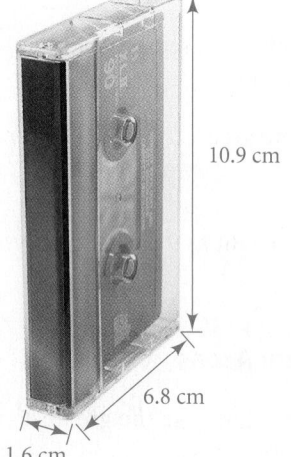

10.9 cm

6.8 cm

1.6 cm

The diagram at the left shows the dimensions of a cassette case. Find the percent error in calculating its volume.

The measurements are to the nearest 0.1 cm. The greatest possible error is 0.05 cm.

as measured	**maximum value**	**minimum value**
$V = \ell \cdot w \cdot h$	$V = \ell \cdot w \cdot h$	$V = \ell \cdot w \cdot h$
$= 6.8 \cdot 1.6 \cdot 10.9$	$= 6.85 \cdot 1.65 \cdot 10.95$	$= 6.75 \cdot 1.55 \cdot 10.85$
$\approx 118.59 \text{ cm}^3$	$\approx 123.76 \text{ cm}^3$	$\approx 113.52 \text{ cm}^3$
Difference	**maximum − measured** $123.76 - 118.59 = 5.17$	**measured − minimum** $118.59 - 113.52 = 5.07$

Use the greater of the differences to find the percent error.

percent error $= \dfrac{\text{greater difference}}{\text{measurement}}$	**Use the percent error formula.**
$= \dfrac{123.76 - 118.59}{118.59}$	**Substitute.**
$= \dfrac{5.17}{118.59}$	**Simplify the numerator.**
≈ 0.0435955814	**Write as a decimal.**
$\approx 4\%$	**Round and write as a percent.**

● The percent error is about 4%.

✓ Quick Check ⑥ Suppose you measured your math book and recorded the dimensions as 1 in. × 9 in. × 10 in. Find the percent error in calculating its volume.

EXERCISES

For more exercises, see *Extra Skill and Word Problem Practice*.

Practice and Problem Solving

A Practice by Example

GO for Help

Example 1
(page 344)

Find each percent of change. Describe the percent of change as an increase or decrease. If necessary, round to the nearest tenth.

1. $2 to $3
2. $3 to $2
3. 4 ft to 5 ft
4. 5 ft to 4 ft

5. 9 m to 12 m
6. 12 cm to 9 cm
7. 12 in. to 15 in.
8. 15 lb to 18 lb

9. 4.5 cm to 8.3 cm
10. $38 to $65
11. $12.20 to $4.80
12. 125 lb to 143 lb

Example 2
(page 345)

13. Physical Therapy Physical therapists measure strength on a dynamometer, which uses a unit called a foot-pound. Suppose you increase the strength in your elbow joint from 90 foot-pounds to 125 foot-pounds. Find the percent of increase to the nearest percent.

14. Environment From 1999 to 2000, the number of days of unhealthy air quality in Charlotte, North Carolina, dropped from 5 to 2. Find the percent of decrease in the number of days of unhealthy air.

Example 3
(page 345)

Find the greatest possible error for each measurement.

15. 14 ft
16. 3.5 cm
17. 56.38 g
18. 17 in.

Example 4
(page 345)

Find the minimum and maximum possible areas for rectangles with the following measured areas.

19. 4 cm × 6 cm
20. 7 mi × 8 mi
21. 6 in. × 9 in.

22. 12 km × 5 km
23. 18 in. × 15 in.
24. 23 km × 14 km

Example 5
(page 346)

Find the percent error of each measurement.

25. 2 cm
26. 0.2 cm
27. 4 cm
28. 0.4 cm

Example 6
(page 346)

29. The table below shows the measured dimensions of the prism and the maximum and minimum possible values based on the greatest possible error.

Dimensions	ℓ	w	h
Measured	8	3	2
Maximum	8.5	3.5	2.5
Minimum	7.5	2.5	1.5

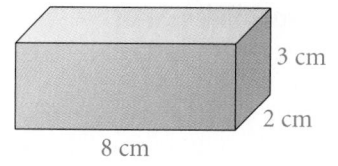

3 cm
2 cm
8 cm

a. Find the measured volume.
b. Find the maximum volume.
c. Find the minimum volume.
d. Find the greater difference.
e. What is the percent error? Round to the nearest percent.

B Apply Your Skills

Find each percent of change. Describe the percent of change as an increase or decrease. Round to the nearest percent.

30. 26 to 20
31. $4.95 to $3.87
32. 21 in. to 54 in.

33. 2 ft to $5\frac{1}{2}$ ft
34. $24,000 to $25,000
35. 18 to $17\frac{1}{2}$

36. 8.99 to 3.99
37. 132 lb to 120 lb
38. $42.69 to $49.95

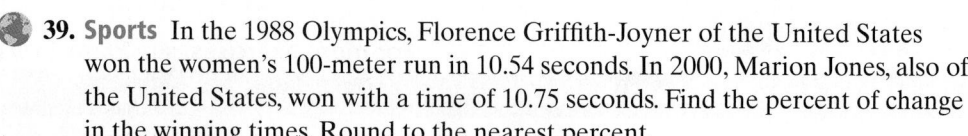

39. Sports In the 1988 Olympics, Florence Griffith-Joyner of the United States won the women's 100-meter run in 10.54 seconds. In 2000, Marion Jones, also of the United States, won with a time of 10.75 seconds. Find the percent of change in the winning times. Round to the nearest percent.

40. Meteorology In 1999, the National Oceanographic and Atmospheric Administration reported a total of 16 Atlantic cyclones. In 2000, there were 19 Atlantic cyclones. Find the percent of change in the number of cyclones from 1999 to 2000. Round to the nearest percent.

41. If you want accuracy of 0.5 mm, what measuring unit should you use?

42. Critical Thinking An item costs $64. The price is increased by $10, then reduced by $10. Is the percent of increase equal to the percent of decrease? Explain your answer.

43. Critical Thinking An item costs $64. The price is increased by 10%, then reduced by 10%. Is the final price equal to the original price? Explain.

Real-World Connection

Atlantic cyclones can be tropical depressions, tropical storms, or hurricanes.

44. Open-Ended Write a word problem involving percent of change. Include your solution.

Find the minimum and maximum possible areas for rectangles with the following measured dimensions. Round to the nearest tenth.

45. 4.1 cm × 6.1 cm   **46.** 7.0 mi × 8.4 mi   **47.** 6.01 in. × 9.02 in.

48. Writing Explain how to find the percent error when calculating the area of a rectangle.

49. Error Analysis Jorge found the percent of change from $15 to $10 to be 50%. What error did he make?

Online
Homework Video Tutor
Visit: PHSchool.com
Web Code: ate-0307

50. Sales Suppose that you are selling sweatshirts for a class fund-raiser. The wholesaler charges you $8 for each sweatshirt.
 a. You charge $16 for each sweatshirt. Find the percent of increase.
 b. Generalize your answer to part (a). Doubling a price is the same as a __?__ percent of increase.
 c. After the fund-raiser is over, you reduce the price on the remaining sweatshirts to $8. Find the percent of decrease.
 d. Generalize your answer to part (c). Cutting a price in half is the same as a __?__ percent of decrease.

Find the percent error in calculating the volume of each rectangular prism. Round to the nearest percent.

GO for Help

For a guide to solving Exercise 51, see p. 350.

51.
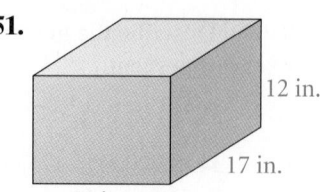
12 in.
17 in.
15 in.

52.
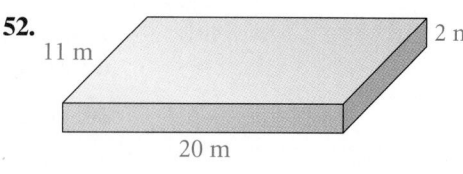
11 m
2 m
20 m

Challenge

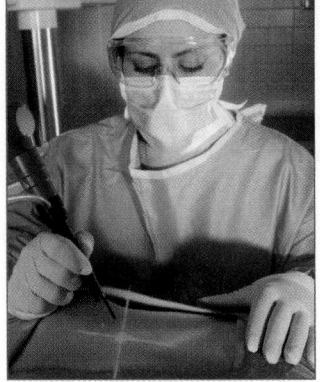

Real-World Connection

Careers Students who want to become physicians must take calculus, physics, biology, and chemistry before going to medical school.

53. Suppose you measure two cubes. The smaller one measures 18 cm on each side. The larger one measures 45 cm on each side.
  a. Find the percent error of the volume of each cube. Round to the nearest percent.
  b. Critical Thinking Explain why using the same measuring unit did not yield the same percent error for the two cubes.

54. Data Analysis A reporter states, "From 1980 to 1996, the number of female physicians more than tripled." A second reporter states, "From 1980 to 1996, the number of female physicians increased about 205%." Can both reports be correct? Explain.

Year	U.S. Female Physicians
1980	48,700
1990	96,100
1996	148,300

55. a. The sides of a 12 cm × 12 cm square are all increased in length by 10%. Find the percent of increase in the area.
  b. The sides of a 14 cm × 14 cm square are all increased in length by 10%. Find the percent of increase in the area.
  c. Predict the percent of increase in the area if the sides of a 16 cm × 16 cm square are all increased by 10%. Explain your prediction and check.

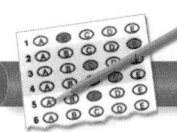

Test Prep

Multiple Choice

56. Which percent of change best reflects a price increase from $32 to $36?
  A. 4%   **B.** 8%   **C.** 12%   **D.** 89%

57. A carpenter measured a rectangle as 5 in. by 8 in. Which number is the maximum possible area?
  F. 40 in.^{2} **G.** 42.5 in.^{2} **H.** 44 in.^{2} **J.** 46.75 in.^{2}

58. A student records the measured length of an object as 24.7 cm. What is the greatest possible error in this measurement?
  A. 0.05 cm   **B.** 0.2 cm   **C.** 0.5 cm   **D.** 1.0 cm

Short Response

59. A softball diamond is a 60 ft-by-60 ft square. The base lines of a baseball diamond are 50% longer than those of a softball diamond. What is the percent of increase from a softball diamond to a baseball diamond of the trip around all four bases? What is the percent of increase in the area from a softball diamond to a baseball diamond?

Mixed Review

Lesson 6-6

Write an equation and solve.

60. The sum of two consecutive *odd* integers is 56. Find the two odd integers.

61. The sum of four consecutive *even* integers is 308. Find the four integers.

62. The length of a rectangle is 8 cm more than twice the width. The perimeter of the rectangle is 34 cm. What is the length of the rectangle?

Lesson 6-1

Solve each equation.

63. $5t - 2 = 14$ **64.** $4 = 3 - 8h$ **65.** $3w + 11 = -10$

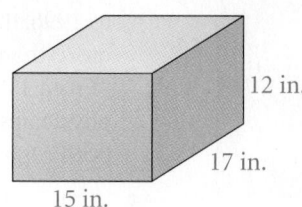

Understanding Math Problems   Read through the problem below. Then follow along with what Rasia thinks as she solves the problem. Check your understanding with the exercise at the bottom of the page.

Find the percent error in calculating the volume of the rectangular prism. Round to the nearest percent.

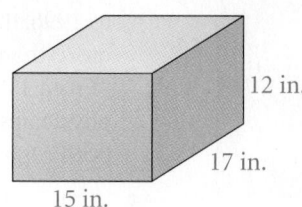

12 in.

17 in.

15 in.

What Rasia Thinks

I need to write down the important information.

I need to find the greatest possible error. Since all the measurements are to the nearest inch, the greatest possible error is 0.5 inch.

I should find the volume as measured and then find the volume using the maximum and minimum values.

I need to find which is the greater difference, maximum−measured or measured−minimum.

Maximum−measured gives the greater difference. I'll use it in the percent error formula.

My calculator shows the answer as 0.1080473856. I need to round my answer to the nearest hundredth and then write it as a percent.

What Rasia Writes

Volume of prism: V = LWH

Dimensions: L = 17 in., W = 15 in., H = 12 in.

measured: 17 · 15 · 12 = 3060
maximum: 17.5 · 15.5 · 12.5 = 3390.625
minimum: 16.5 · 14.5 · 11.5 = 2751.375

3390.625 - 3060 = 330.625

3060 - 2751.375 = 308.625

percent error = $\frac{330.625}{3060}$

≈ 11%

EXERCISE

A rectangular prism has dimensions of 8 cm, 12 cm, and 20 cm. Find the percent error in calculating its volume. Round to the nearest percent.

Learning Vocabulary

FOR USE WITH LESSON 6-7

As you study mathematics this year, make your own mathematics dictionary of new vocabulary terms. Use the following guide for each new term.

- Write the vocabulary term and its definition. Include any symbols for the term.
- If possible, draw a diagram. Include details using other related terms you know.
- Give one or more examples of the term.
- Give one or more "nonexamples" and explain how they are different.

EXAMPLE

Percent of change: $\dfrac{\text{amount of change}}{\text{original amount}}$

Percent of decrease: $\dfrac{\text{amount of decrease}}{\text{original amount}}$

Example: The price of an item goes from $20 to $18.

$$\text{Percent of decrease} = \frac{20 - 18}{20}$$
$$= \frac{2}{20}$$
$$= 0.10$$
$$= 10\%$$

Percent of increase: $\dfrac{\text{amount of increase}}{\text{original amount}}$

Example: The price of an item goes from $18 to $20.

$$\text{Percent of increase} = \frac{20 - 18}{18}$$
$$= \frac{2}{18}$$
$$= 0.\overline{11}$$
$$\approx 11\%$$

Non-example: "45% of students passed the test" is a percent but not a percent of change because there are no changing values.

EXERCISES

Write an entry for your dictionary for each term.

1. greatest possible error
2. percent error
3. similar figures
4. scale factor
5. dilation
6. proportion

Write an entry for the first term. Your entry should include the second term.

7. ratio, division
8. rate, ratio
9. unit rate, rate
10. cross products, proportion
11. identity, equation
12. literal equation, variables

6-8

Finding and Estimating Square Roots

What You'll Learn

- To find square roots
- To estimate and use square roots

...And Why

To apply square roots in a real-world situation involving construction, as in Example 5

✓ **Check Skills You'll Need**

GO for Help Lesson 4-2

Simplify each expression.

1. 11^2 **2.** $(-12)^2$ **3.** $-(12)^2$ **4.** 1.5^2

5. 0.6^2 **6.** $\left(\frac{1}{2}\right)^2$ **7.** $\left(-\frac{2}{3}\right)^2$ **8.** $\left(\frac{4}{5}\right)^2$

🔊 **New Vocabulary**
- square root
- principal square root
- negative square root
- radicand
- perfect squares

---

1   Finding Square Roots

The diagram at the right shows the relationship between squares and square roots. Every positive number has *two* square roots.

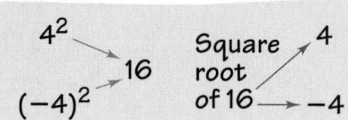

🔑 **Key Concepts**

Definition	**Square Root**

The number a is a **square root** of b if $a^2 = b$.

Example $4^2 = 16$ and $(-4)^2 = 16$, so 4 and -4 are square roots of 16.

Vocabulary Tip

Read $\sqrt{16}$ as "the square root of 16." Read $\pm$ as "plus or minus."

A radical symbol $\sqrt{}$ indicates a square root. The expression $\sqrt{16}$ means the positive, or **principal square root** of 16. The expression $-\sqrt{16}$ means the **negative square root** of 16. The expression under the radical sign is a **radicand.** You can use the symbol $\pm$ to indicate both square roots.

1 EXAMPLE   **Simplifying Square Root Expressions**

Simplify each expression.

a. $\sqrt{64} = 8$ positive square root

b. $-\sqrt{100} = -10$ negative square root

c. $\pm\sqrt{\frac{9}{16}} = \pm\frac{3}{4}$ The square roots are $\frac{3}{4}$ and $-\frac{3}{4}$.

d. $\pm\sqrt{0} = 0$ There is only one square root of 0.

e. $\sqrt{-16}$ is undefined.   For real numbers, the square root of a negative number is undefined.

✓ **Quick Check** **①** Simplify each expression.

a. $\sqrt{49}$ **b.** $\pm\sqrt{36}$ **c.** $-\sqrt{121}$ **d.** $\sqrt{\frac{1}{25}}$

Vocabulary Tip

In decimal form, a <u>rational</u> number terminates or repeats. In decimal form, an <u>irrational</u> number continues without repeating.

Some square roots are rational numbers and some are irrational numbers.

Rational: $\sqrt{100} = 10$ $\qquad \pm\sqrt{0.36} = \pm 0.6$ $\qquad \sqrt{\frac{16}{121}} = \frac{4}{11}$

Irrational: $\sqrt{10} \approx 3.16227766$ $\qquad \sqrt{\frac{1}{7}} \approx 0.377964473$

2 EXAMPLE **Rational and Irrational Square Roots**

Tell whether each expression is *rational* or *irrational*.

a. $\pm\sqrt{81} = \pm 9$ $\qquad$ rational

b. $-\sqrt{1.44} = -1.2$ $\qquad$ rational

c. $-\sqrt{5} \approx -2.23606798$ $\qquad$ irrational

d. $\sqrt{\frac{4}{9}} = \frac{2}{3}$ $\qquad$ rational

e. $\sqrt{\frac{1}{3}} \approx 0.57735026$ $\qquad$ irrational

Quick Check **2** Tell whether each expression is *rational* or *irrational*.

a. $\sqrt{8}$ $\qquad$ **b.** $\pm\sqrt{225}$ $\qquad$ **c.** $-\sqrt{75}$ $\qquad$ **d.** $\sqrt{\frac{1}{4}}$

---

2 **Estimating and Using Square Roots**

The squares of integers are called **perfect squares.**

consecutive integers:	1	2	3	4	5	6
	↓	↓	↓	↓	↓	↓
consecutive perfect squares:	1	4	9	16	25	36

You can estimate square roots by using perfect squares.

Online
active math

For: Square Root Activity
Use: Interactive Textbook, 3-8

3 EXAMPLE **Estimating Square Roots**

Estimation Between what two consecutive integers is $\sqrt{14.52}$?

$\sqrt{9} \ < \ \sqrt{14.52} \ < \ \sqrt{16}$ $\qquad$ 14.52 is between the two consecutive perfect squares 9 and 16.

$\downarrow \qquad\qquad \downarrow \qquad\qquad \downarrow$

$3 \ < \ \sqrt{14.52} \ < \ 4$ $\qquad$ The square roots of 9 and 16 are 3 and 4, respectively.

$\sqrt{14.52}$ is between 3 and 4.

Quick Check **3** Between what two consecutive integers is $-\sqrt{105}$?

You can find the approximate value of a square root using a calculator.

4 EXAMPLE **Approximating Square Roots With a Calculator**

Calculator Find $\sqrt{14.52}$ to the nearest hundredth.

$\sqrt{14.52} \approx 3.810511777$ $\qquad$ Use the calculator sequence $\boxed{\sqrt{}}$ 14.52 $\boxed{\text{ENTER}}$.

≈ 3.81 $\qquad$ Round to the nearest hundredth.

Quick Check **4** Find $\sqrt{17.81}$ to the nearest hundredth.

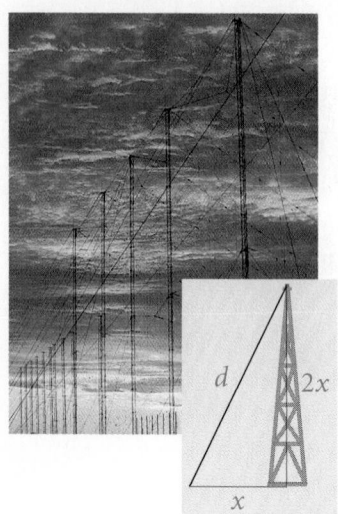

Many real-world formulas involve square roots.

5 EXAMPLE Real-World Problem Solving

Construction The formula $d = \sqrt{x^2 + (2x)^2}$ gives the length d of each wire for the tower at the left. Find the length of the wire if $x = 12$ ft.

$d = \sqrt{x^2 + (2x)^2}$

$d = \sqrt{12^2 + (2 \cdot 12)^2}$ **Substitute 12 for x.**

$d = \sqrt{144 + 576}$ **Simplify.**

$d = \sqrt{720}$

$d \approx 26.8$ **Use a calculator. Round to the nearest tenth.**

The wire is about 26.8 ft long.

Quick Check **5** Suppose the tower is 140 ft tall. How long is the supporting wire? Round to the nearest tenth of a foot.

EXERCISES

For more exercises, see *Extra Skill and Word Problem Practice.*

Practice and Problem Solving

A Practice by Example

Example 1
(page 352)

 for Help

Simplify each expression.

1. $\sqrt{169}$ 2. $\sqrt{400}$ 3. $\sqrt{\frac{1}{9}}$ 4. $\sqrt{900}$

5. $\sqrt{0.25}$ 6. $\sqrt{\frac{36}{49}}$ 7. $-\sqrt{1.21}$ 8. $\sqrt{1.96}$

9. $\sqrt{0.36}$ 10. $-\sqrt{144}$ 11. $\sqrt{\frac{25}{16}}$ 12. $\pm\sqrt{0.01}$

Example 2
(page 353)

Tell whether each expression is *rational* or *irrational*.

13. $\sqrt{37}$ 14. $-\sqrt{0.04}$ 15. $\pm\sqrt{\frac{1}{5}}$ 16. $-\sqrt{\frac{16}{121}}$

Example 3
(page 353)

Between what two consecutive integers is each square root?

17. $\sqrt{35}$ 18. $\sqrt{27}$ 19. $-\sqrt{130}$ 20. $\sqrt{170}$

Example 4
(page 353)

Use a calculator to find each square root to the nearest hundredth.

21. $\sqrt{12}$ 22. $-\sqrt{203}$ 23. $\sqrt{11,550}$ 24. $-\sqrt{150}$

Example 5
(page 354)

25. **Sports** The elasticity coefficient e of a ball relates the height r of its rebound to the height h from which it is dropped. You can use the function $e = \sqrt{\frac{r}{h}}$ to find the elasticity coefficient. What is the elasticity coefficient of a tennis ball that rebounds 3 ft after it is dropped from a height of 3.5 ft? Round to the nearest hundredth.

B Apply Your Skills

Find the square root(s) of each number.

26. 400   27. 0   28. 625   29. $\frac{9}{49}$

30. 1.69   31. $\frac{1}{81}$ 32. 729   33. 2.25

34. 256   35. 0.01   36. $\frac{64}{121}$ 37. 40,804

38. **Critical Thinking** What number other than 0 is its own square root?

39. Multiple Choice The formula $d = \sqrt{12{,}800h + h^2}$ gives the distance d in kilometers to the horizon from a satellite h kilometers above Earth. Find the distance to the horizon from a satellite 4200 km above Earth. Round to the nearest kilometer.

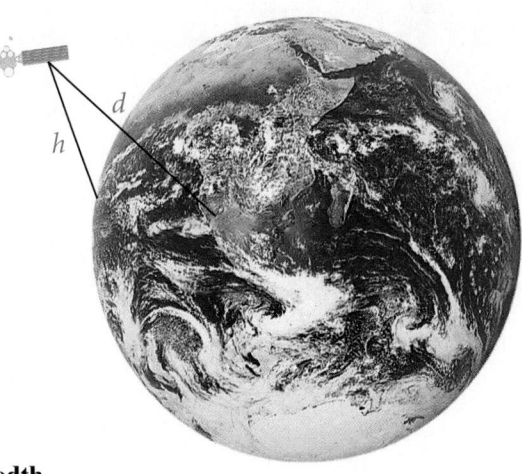

     Ⓐ 130 km   Ⓑ 7333 km

     Ⓒ 8450 km   Ⓓ 11,532 km

Find the value of each expression. If necessary, round to the nearest hundredth.

GO Online
Homework Video Tutor
Visit: PHSchool.com
Web Code: ate-0308

40. $\sqrt{441}$ **41.** $-\sqrt{\dfrac{4}{25}}$ **42.** $\sqrt{2}$

43. $\sqrt{1.6}$ **44.** $-\sqrt{30}$ **45.** $-\sqrt{1089}$

46. $-\sqrt{0.64}$ **47.** $\sqrt{41}$ **48.** $\sqrt{75}$

 **49. Writing** Explain the difference between $-\sqrt{1}$ and $\sqrt{1}$.

50. Open-Ended Find two integers a and b between 1 and 20 such that $a^2 + b^2$ is a perfect square.

51. Math in the Media In the cartoon, to what number is the golfer referring?

 52. Physics If you drop an object, the time t in seconds that it takes to fall d feet is given by the formula $t = \sqrt{\dfrac{d}{16}}$.
    a. Find the time it takes an object to fall 400 ft.
    b. Find the time it takes an object to fall 1600 ft.
    c. Critical Thinking In part (b), the object falls four times as far as in part (a). Does it take four times as long to fall? Explain.

 Challenge

Critical Thinking For Exercises 53–56, tell whether each statement is *true* or *false*. If the statement is false, give a counterexample.

53. Every nonnegative number has two square roots.

54. The square root of a positive number is always less than the number.

55. The square root of an even perfect square is always an even number.

56. $\sqrt{p} + \sqrt{q} = \sqrt{p + q}$

57. a. What is the total area of the large square shown at the right?
    b. What is the area of each shaded triangle?
    c. What is the area of the shaded square?
    d. What is the length of the diagonal of each 1×1 square?

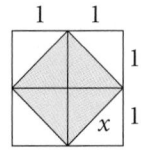

Gridded Response

58. Find the area of the shaded region.

59. Find the value of $\sqrt{1.69}$.

60. Find the value of $\sqrt{\frac{4}{81}}$.

61. Round $\sqrt{80}$ to the nearest whole number.

62. Simplify $\sqrt{4^2 + 3^2 + 11}$.

63. The formula $\ell = \sqrt{\frac{A}{6}}$ relates the surface area A of a cube to the length of its edge ℓ. A cube has a surface area of 726 cm². How many centimeters is the length of the edge?

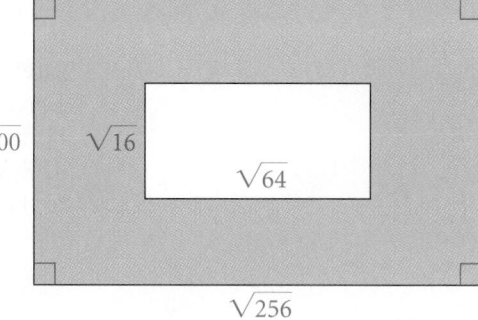

$\sqrt{100}$ $\sqrt{16}$ $\sqrt{64}$ $\sqrt{256}$

Mixed Review

Lesson 6-7

Find each percent of change. Describe the percent of change as an increase or decrease. If necessary, round to the nearest tenth.

64. $5 to $6

65. 40 in. to 36 in.

66. 10 m to 11 m

67. 18° to 24°

Lesson 6-5

Simplify each expression. Justify each step.

68. $8 \cdot 7 \cdot 5$

69. $14 + 23 + 56$

70. $16\left(\frac{1}{16}\right) + 5$

71. $(6^8 - 6^9)(11 - 11)$

72. $-7(3w)$

73. $8m + 145 + 4m$

Checkpoint Quiz 2   **Lessons 6-6 to 6-8**

1. The length of a rectangle is 5 cm more than its width. The perimeter of the rectangle is 46 cm. What is the length of the rectangle?

2. The sum of three consecutive odd integers is 465. Find the integers.

3. Marcus and Beth leave college traveling in opposite directions on a straight road. Beth drives 13 mi/h faster than Marcus. After 4 hours, they are 452 miles apart. Find their rates.

Find the percent error for each measurement.

4. 210 cm

5. 25 cm

6. A student measures a rectangle as 14 in. × 23 in. Find the minimum and maximum possible areas for the rectangle.

Simplify each expression.

7. $-\sqrt{256}$

8. $\sqrt{\frac{64}{121}}$

9. $\pm\sqrt{0.0025}$

10. Between what two consecutive integers is $\sqrt{52}$?

The Pythagorean Theorem

What You'll Learn

- To solve problems using the Pythagorean Theorem
- To identify right triangles

... And Why

To calculate heights indirectly, as in Example 2

✓ Check Skills You'll Need

GO ▸ for Help Lessons 4-2 and 6-8

Simplify each expression.

1. $5^2 + 6^2$

2. $9^2 - 4^2$

3. $(3t)^2 + (4t)^2$

4. $\sqrt{196}$

5. $\sqrt{\dfrac{25}{49}}$

6. $\sqrt{1.44}$

 **New Vocabulary**
- hypotenuse • leg • Pythagorean Theorem
- conditional • hypothesis • conclusion • converse

---

1 | **Solving Problems Using the Pythagorean Theorem**

Activity: The Pythagorean Theorem

1. The values in the chart represent the lengths of the sides of a right triangle. Copy and complete the chart.

a	b	c	a^2	b^2	$a^2 + b^2$	c^2
3	4	5	■	■	■	■
5	12	13	■	■	■	■
$\frac{3}{5}$	$\frac{4}{5}$	1	■	■	■	■
0.9	1.2	1.5	■	■	■	■

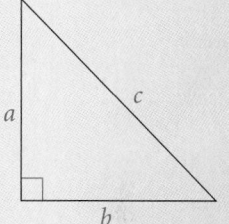

2. Compare the values of $a^2 + b^2$ for each row to the values of c^2.

3. Complete the following statement: For a right triangle, the square of the longest side ? the sum of the squares of the other two sides.

Vocabulary Tip

The <u>Pythagorean Theorem</u> is named after Pythagoras, a Greek philosopher and mathematician who taught about 530 B.C.

In a right triangle, the side opposite the right angle is the **hypotenuse.** It is the longest side. Each of the sides forming the right angle is a **leg.**

The **Pythagorean Theorem** describes the relationship of the lengths of the sides of a right triangle.

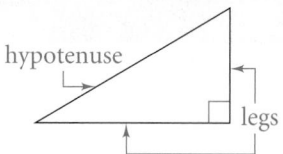

🔑 Key Concepts

Theorem	**The Pythagorean Theorem**

In any right triangle, the sum of the squares of the lengths of the legs is equal to the square of the length of the hypotenuse.

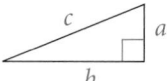

$$a^2 + b^2 = c^2$$

Sometimes you will need to find square roots to determine the length of a side or of a hypotenuse of a triangle. In real-world situations, $x^2 = a^2$, you find the principal square root of each side. So $\sqrt{x^2} = \sqrt{a^2}$, and $x = a$.

1 EXAMPLE Using the Pythagorean Theorem

What is the length of the hypotenuse of the triangle at the right?

$$a^2 + b^2 = c^2 \qquad \text{Use the Pythagorean Theorem.}$$
$$9^2 + 12^2 = c^2 \qquad \text{Substitute 9 for } a \text{ and 12 for } b.$$
$$81 + 144 = c^2 \qquad \text{Simplify.}$$
$$\sqrt{225} = \sqrt{c^2} \qquad \text{Find the principal square root of each side.}$$
$$15 = c \qquad \text{Simplify.}$$

9 cm

c

12 cm

● The length of the hypotenuse is 15 cm.

Quick Check ❶ What is the length of the hypotenuse of a right triangle with legs of lengths 7 cm and 24 cm?

You can also use the Pythagorean Theorem to find the length of a leg of a right triangle when you know the lengths of the hypotenuse and the other leg.

2 EXAMPLE Real-World 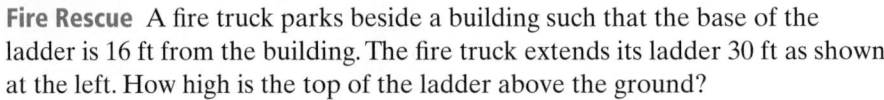 Problem Solving

Fire Rescue A fire truck parks beside a building such that the base of the ladder is 16 ft from the building. The fire truck extends its ladder 30 ft as shown at the left. How high is the top of the ladder above the ground?

Define Let b = height (in feet) of the ladder from a point 10 ft above the ground.

Relate The triangle formed is a right triangle. Use the Pythagorean Theorem.

Write
$$a^2 + b^2 = c^2$$
$$16^2 + b^2 = 30^2 \qquad \text{Substitute.}$$
$$256 + b^2 = 900 \qquad \text{Simplify.}$$
$$b^2 = 644 \qquad \text{Subtract 256 from each side.}$$
$$\sqrt{b^2} = \sqrt{644} \qquad \text{Find the principal square root of each side.}$$
$$b \approx 25.4 \qquad \text{Use a calculator and round to the nearest tenth.}$$

The height to the top of the ladder is 10 feet higher than 25.4 ft, so it is about ● 35.4 ft from the ground.

Quick Check ❷ Use the figure at the right. About how many miles is it from downtown to the harbor? Round to the nearest tenth of a mile.

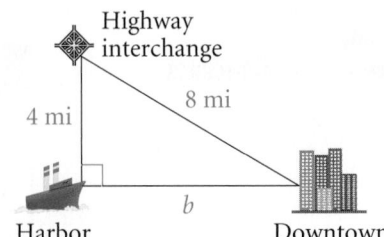

An *if-then* statement like "If an animal is a horse, then it has four legs" is called a **conditional.** Every conditional has two parts. The part following *if* is the **hypothesis,** and the part following *then* is the **conclusion.**

The **converse** of a conditional switches the hypothesis and the conclusion. Somtimes converses of conditionals are not true. For example, "If an animal has four legs, then the animal is a horse" is not a true statement.

You can rewrite the Pythagorean Theorem as an *if-then* statement, "If a triangle is a right triangle with legs of lengths a and b and hypotenuse of length c, then $a^2 + b^2 = c^2$." The Pythagorean Theorem has a converse that is always true.

 Key Concepts

Property	The Converse of the Pythagorean Theorem

If a triangle has sides of lengths a, b, and c, and $a^2 + b^2 = c^2$, then the triangle is a right triangle with hypotenuse of length c.

You can use the converse of the Pythagorean Theorem to determine whether a triangle is a right triangle. Since the Pythagorean Theorem and its converse are always true, you can also determine whether a triangle is *not* a right triangle.

3 EXAMPLE Using the Converse of the Pythagorean Theorem

Determine whether the given lengths can be sides of a right triangle.

a. 5 in., 12 in., and 13 in.
$$5^2 + 12^2 \overset{?}{=} 13^2$$
$$25 + 144 \overset{?}{=} 169$$
$$169 = 169 \checkmark$$
The triangle is a right triangle.

Determine whether $a^2 + b^2 = c^2$, where c is the longest side.

b. 7 m, 9 m, and 12 m
$$7^2 + 9^2 \overset{?}{=} 12^2$$
$$49 + 81 \overset{?}{=} 144$$
$$130 \neq 144$$
The triangle is not a right triangle.

✓**Quick Check** ❸ A triangle has sides of lengths 10 m, 24 m, and 26 m. Is the triangle a right triangle?

You can use the converse of the Pythagorean Theorem to solve a physics problem involving force.

4 EXAMPLE Real-World  Problem Solving

Physics If two forces pull at right angles to each other, the resultant force is represented as the diagonal of a rectangle, as shown at the left. The diagonal forms a right triangle with two of the perpendicular sides of the rectangle. For a 30-lb force and a 40-lb force, the resultant force is 50 lb. Are the forces pulling at right angles to each other?

$$30^2 + 40^2 \overset{?}{=} 50^2$$ **Determine whether $a^2 + b^2 = c^2$, where c is the greatest force.**
$$900 + 1600 \overset{?}{=} 2500$$
$$2500 = 2500 \checkmark$$

Yes, the 30-lb and 40-lb forces are pulling at right angles to each other.

Force A

Resultant Force C

Force B

 **Quick Check** 4 For a 70-lb force and a 60-lb force, the resultant force is 100 lb. Are the forces pulling at right angles to each other?

EXERCISES

For more exercises, see *Extra Skill and Word Problem Practice.*

Practice and Problem Solving

A Practice by Example

Example 1
(page 358)

 **GO** for Help

Example 2
(page 358)

Use the triangle at the right. Find the length of the missing side. If necessary, round to the nearest tenth.

1. $a = 6, b = 8$ **2.** $a = 15, b = 20$

3. $a = 8, b = 15$ **4.** $a = 10, b = 24$

5. $a = 1.5, b = 2$ **6.** $a = \frac{3}{5}, b = \frac{4}{5}$

7. $a = 3, c = 5$ **8.** $b = 12, c = 13$

9. $a = 9, c = 15$ **10.** $b = 7, c = 10$

11. $a = 5, c = 9$ **12.** $a = 0.8, c = 1$

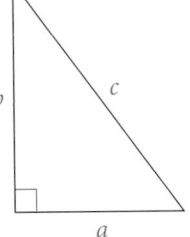

13. Packaging Use the diagram at the right. Find the width w that the box needs to be for the fishing rod to fit flat inside of it.

14. A 16-ft ladder is placed 4 ft from the base of a building. How high on the building will the ladder reach?

15. A pigeon leaves its nest in New York City and flies 5 km due east. The pigeon then flies 3 km due north. How far is the pigeon from its nest?

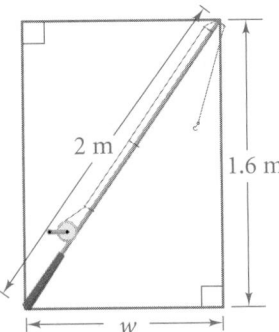

Example 3
(page 359)

Determine whether the given lengths can be sides of a right triangle.

16. 9 ft, 12 ft, 15 ft   **17.** 1 in., 2 in., 3 in.   **18.** 2 m, 4 m, 5 m

19. 16 cm, 30 cm, 34 cm   **20.** 4 m, 4 m, 8 m   **21.** 10 in., 24 in., 26 in.

Example 4
(page 359)

Physics Determine whether the forces in each pair are pulling at right angles to each other.

22. 45 lb, 24 lb, resultant force 51 lb   **23.** 3.5 lb, 6.2 lb, resultant force 9.1 lb

24. 20 lb, 10 lb, resultant force 30 lb   **25.** 1.25 lb, 3 lb, resultant force 3.25 lb

B Apply Your Skills

For the values given, a and b are legs of a right triangle, and c is the hypotenuse. Find the length of the missing side of each right triangle. If necessary, round to the nearest tenth.

26. $a = 1.2, b = 0.9$ **27.** $a = \frac{1}{5}, c = \frac{1}{3}$ **28.** $a = 1, c = 2$

29. $a = \frac{3}{4}, b = 1$ **30.** $a = 2.4, b = 1.0$ **31.** $a = 2\frac{1}{2}, b = 6\frac{1}{2}$

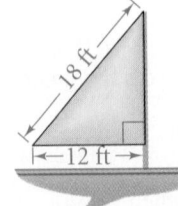

🌐 **32. Sailing** The diagram at the left shows a sailboat.
   a. Use the Pythagorean Theorem to find the height of the sail. Round to the nearest tenth.
   b. Use the result of part (a) and the formula for the area of a triangle to find the area of the sail. Round to the nearest tenth.

33. Multiple Choice What is the diameter of the smallest circular opening through which the rectangular rod shown at the right will fit? Round to the nearest tenth.

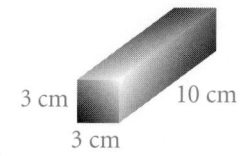
3 cm   3 cm   10 cm

Ⓐ 2.12 cm   Ⓑ 3 cm   Ⓒ 4.3 cm   Ⓓ 9 cm

34. Physics Two utility vehicles at a 90° angle to each other try to pull a third vehicle out of the snow. If one utility vehicle exerts a force of 600 lb, and the other exerts a force of 800 lb, what is the resulting force on the vehicle stuck in the snow?

Find the missing length to the nearest tenth.

35.
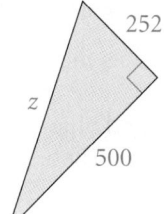
252
z
500

36.
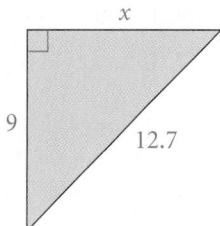
x
9
12.7

37.
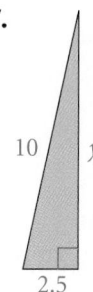
10
y
2.5

38. You know that two sides of a right triangle measure 10 in. and 8 in.

   a. Writing Explain why this is not enough information to be sure of finding the length of the third side.

   b. Give two possible values for the length of the third side.

39. Any set of three positive integers that satisfies the relationship $a^2 + b^2 = c^2$ is called a *Pythagorean triple*.

   a. Verify that the numbers 6, 8, and 10 form a Pythagorean triple.

   b. Copy the table at the right. Complete the table so that the values in each row form a Pythagorean triple.

   c. Open-Ended Find a Pythagorean triple that does not appear in the table.

a	b	c
3	4	▪
5	▪	13
▪	24	25
9	40	▪

40. Solar Power Solar cars use panels built out of photovoltaic cells, which convert sunlight into electricity. Consider a car like the one shown. Not counting the driver's "bubble," the panels form a rectangle.

   a. The length of the rectangle is 13 ft and the diagonal is 14.7 ft. Find the width. Round to the nearest tenth of a foot.

   b. Find the area of the rectangle.

   c. The panels produce a maximum power of about 11 watts/ft^2. Find the maximum power produced by the panels on the car. Round to the nearest watt.

41. Construction A carpenter braces an 8 ft × 10 ft wall by nailing a board diagonally across the wall. How long is the bracing board?

42. a. Open-Ended Find a right triangle that has legs with irrational lengths and a hypotenuse with a rational length.

   b. Use a calculator to find the area of your triangle. Round to the nearest tenth.

Real-World Connection

This solar-powered car only weighs 110 lb. It can reach a top speed of 80 mi/h.

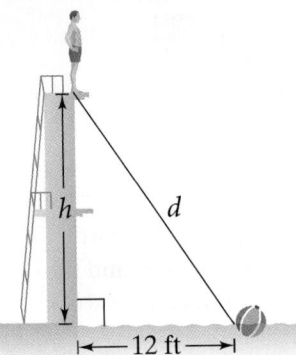

$\longmapsto$ 12 ft $\longmapsto$

43. Diving Suppose you are standing at the top of a diving platform h feet tall. Looking down, you see a ball on the water 12 feet from the bottom of the diving platform as in the diagram at the left.
  a. Find the distance d to the ball if $h = 6$ feet; if $h = 12$ feet.
  b. Suppose you know the distance d to the ball is 16 feet. About how tall is the diving platform?
  c. Critical Thinking Could the distance d to the ball be 7 feet? Explain.

State the hypothesis and the conclusion of each conditional. Then write the converse. Tell whether the converse is true or false.

44. If an integer has 2 as a factor, then the integer is even.

45. If a figure is a square, then the figure is a rectangle.

46. If you are in Brazil, then you are south of the equator.

47. If an angle is a right angle, then its measure is 90°.

GO ●nline
Homework Video Tutor
Visit: PHSchool.com
Web Code: ate-0309

48. Geometry The yellow, green, and blue figures at the right are squares. Use the Pythagorean Theorem to find the area of the blue square.

49. Geometry The diagonal of a square measures $6\sqrt{2}$ in. Find the length of the side of the square.

For any two points $P(x_1, y_1)$ and $Q(x_2, y_2)$ not on the same horizontal or vertical line, you can graph the points and form a right triangle as shown at the right. You can then use the Pythagorean Theorem to find the distance between the points. The result is called the Distance Formula.

$$PQ = \sqrt{(x_2 - x_1)^2 + (y_2 - y_1)^2}$$

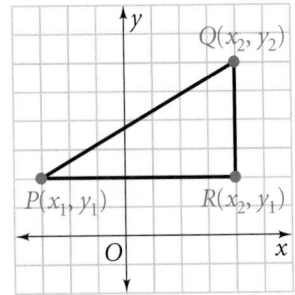

Use the Distance Formula to find the distance between each pair of points. Where necessary, round to the nearest tenth.

50. $(7, -3), (-8, -3)$ **51.** $(-2, 7), (-3, -7)$ **52.** $(0, 0), (6, -8)$

53. $(-4, -4), (4, 4)$ **54.** $(9, 10), (11, 12)$ **55.** $(3, -2), (-1, 5)$

ⓒ Challenge   **Use the Pythagorean Theorem to find s.**

56.

57.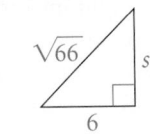

58.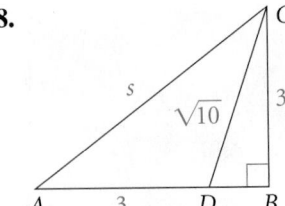

59. Geometry The lengths of the sides of a right triangle are three consecutive integers. Write and solve an equation to find the three integers.

60. a. Critical Thinking The vertex of the right angle of a right triangle is at the origin of coordinate axes. The length of the horizontal side is 5 units. The length of the vertical side is 7 units. The triangle is located in Quadrant II. Sketch the graph.
  b. Find the length of the hypotenuse. Round to the nearest tenth.

61. On graph paper, draw a right triangle like the one at the right. Then draw the square by drawing four right triangles as shown.

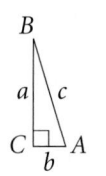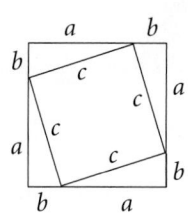

a. Find the area of the larger square. Write your answer as a trinomial.

b. Find the area for the smaller square. Write your answer as a monomial.

c. Find the area of each triangle in terms of a and b.

d. The area of the larger square equals the sum of the area of the smaller square and the areas of the four triangles. Write this equation and simplify.

e. What do you notice about the equation you wrote for part (d)?

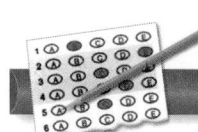

Test Prep

Multiple Choice

62. Find the approximate length of the hypotenuse of a right triangle with leg lengths 8.4 cm and 7.6 cm.

  A. 4.00 cm   **B.** 5.66 cm   **C.** 7.99 cm   **D.** 11.33 cm

63. Find the approximate length of the leg of a right triangle with one leg length 8 and hypotenuse length 19.

  F. 20.3   **G.** 20.6   **H.** 17.7   **J.** 17.2

64. Find the approximate perimeter of the right triangle.

  A. 29 cm   **B.** 25 cm

  C. 32 cm   **D.** 70 cm

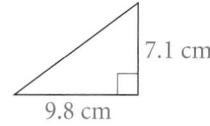

65. Find the approximate area of the right triangle.

  F. 32 in.^{2} **G.** 24 in.^{2}

  H. 36 in.^{2} **J.** 18 in.^{2}

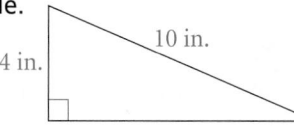

Short Response

66. The sides of a triangular garden are 8 ft, 17 ft, and 15 ft. Is the garden in the shape of a right triangle? Justify your answer.

Mixed Review

GO for Help

Lesson 6-8

Between which two consecutive integers is each square root?

67. $\sqrt{11}$ **68.** $\sqrt{80}$ **69.** $-\sqrt{51}$ **70.** $\sqrt{125}$

Tell whether each expression is rational or irrational.

71. $-\sqrt{1.44}$ **72.** $\sqrt{130}$ **73.** $\sqrt{\frac{2}{3}}$ **74.** $\sqrt{\frac{1}{36}}$

Lesson 5-7

Suppose you choose a tile from a bag containing 4 A's, 5 B's, and 3 C's. You replace the first tile in the bag and then choose again. Find each probability.

75. P(B and B)   **76.** P(A and C)   **77.** P(C and C)

78. P(A and B)   **79.** P(C and A)   **80.** P(B and C)

Special Right Triangles

You can use the Pythagorean Theorem to explore properties of some special right triangles. You will also need the *Multiplication Property of Square Roots* to work with square roots efficiently. The property allows you to combine or separate products in square roots as follows.

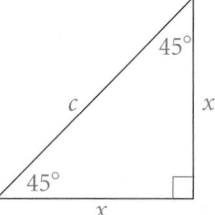

If $a \geq 0$ and $b \geq 0$ then $\sqrt{a} \cdot \sqrt{b} = \sqrt{a \cdot b}$.

Consider the isosceles right triangle. It is called a 45°-45°-90° triangle.

$c^2 = a^2 + b^2$	Use the Pythagorean Theorem.
$c^2 = x^2 + x^2$	Substitute *x* for *b* and for *a*.
$c^2 = 2x^2$	Simplify.
$\sqrt{c^2} = \sqrt{2x^2}$	Find the principal square root of each side.
$c = \sqrt{2} \cdot \sqrt{x^2}$	Use the Multiplication Property of Square Roots.
$c = \sqrt{2} \cdot x$, or $x\sqrt{2}$	Simplify.

Theorem   **45°-45°-90° Triangle Theorem**

In a 45°-45°-90° triangle, the length of the hypotenuse is the length of the leg times $\sqrt{2}$.

$$\text{hypotenuse} = \text{leg} \cdot \sqrt{2}$$

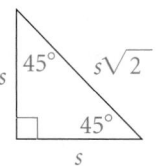

---

1   **EXAMPLE**   **Finding Lengths in a 45°-45°-90° Triangle**

Find the length of the hypotenuse in the triangle at the right.

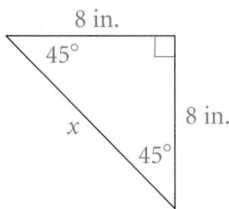

$$\text{hypotenuse} = \text{leg} \cdot \sqrt{2}$$

$x = 8 \cdot \sqrt{2}$	The length of either leg is 8 in.
≈ 11.3	Round to the nearest tenth.

● The length of the hypotenuse is about 11.3 in.

EXERCISES

Find the hypotenuse of each 45°-45°-90° triangle. Round to the nearest tenth.

1.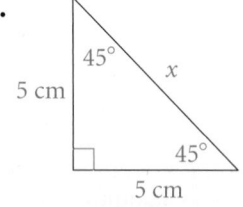

2.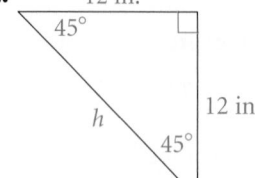

3.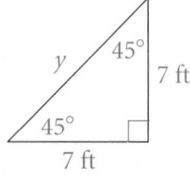

4. A baseball diamond is a square. The distance from any base to the next base is 90 ft. How far is it from home plate to second base? (*Hint:* Draw a diagram.)

5. The hypotenuse of a 45°-45°-90° triangle is 40.2 ft long. How long is each leg? Round to the nearest tenth.

Another special right triangle is the 30°-60°-90° triangle. You can form two congruent 30°-60°-90° triangles by bisecting an angle of an equilateral triangle. As the diagram at the right shows, the length of the hypotenuse is twice the length of the shorter leg. You can use the Pythagorean Theorem to find the length of the longer leg b shown in the diagram at the right below.

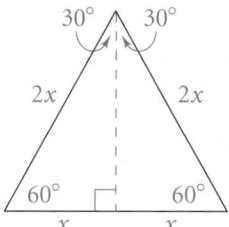

$$(2x)^2 = x^2 + b^2 \quad \text{Use the Pythagorean Theorem.}$$
$$4x^2 = x^2 + b^2 \quad \text{Simplify.}$$
$$3x^2 = b^2 \quad \text{Subtract } x^2 \text{ from each side.}$$
$$\sqrt{3x^2} = \sqrt{b^2} \quad \text{Find the principal square root of each side.}$$
$$\sqrt{3} \cdot \sqrt{x^2} = b \quad \text{Use the Multiplication Property of Square Roots.}$$
$$b = \sqrt{3} \cdot x \quad \text{Simplify.}$$

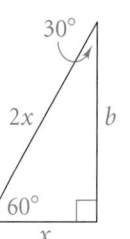

The length of the longer leg is $\sqrt{3} \cdot x$, or $x\sqrt{3}$.

Theorem	30°-60°-90° Triangle Theorem

In a 30°-60°-90° triangle, the length of the hypotenuse is twice the length of the shorter leg. The length of the longer leg is $\sqrt{3}$ times the length of the shorter leg.

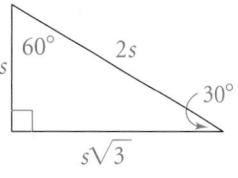

$$\text{hypotenuse} = 2 \cdot \text{shorter leg}$$

$$\text{longer leg} = \sqrt{3} \cdot \text{shorter leg}$$

2 EXAMPLE Finding Lengths in a 30°-60°-90° Triangle

Find the missing lengths in the triangle at the right.

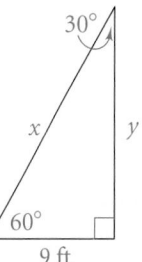

$$\text{hypotenuse} = 2 \cdot \text{shorter leg}$$
$$x = 2 \cdot 9 \quad \text{The length of the shorter leg is 9.}$$
$$x = 18 \quad \text{Simplify.}$$
$$\text{longer leg} = \sqrt{3} \cdot \text{shorter leg}$$
$$y = 9 \cdot \sqrt{3} \quad \text{The length of the shorter leg is 9.}$$
$$y \approx 15.6 \quad \text{Simplify. Round to the nearest tenth.}$$

The length of the hypotenuse is 18 ft, and the length of the longer leg is about 15.6 ft.

EXERCISES

Find the missing lengths in each triangle. Round to the nearest tenth.

6.
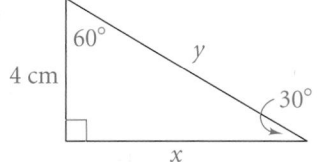

7.
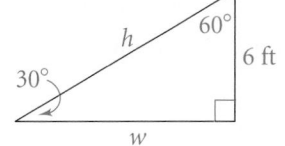

8.
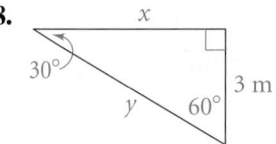

Writing Extended Responses

An extended-response question is usually worth a maximum of 4 points in this textbook. It sometimes has multiple parts. To get full credit, you need to answer each part and show all your work or justify your reasoning.

EXAMPLE

The Theatre Club needs to raise $440 to cover the cost of its children's play. The ticket prices are $14 for an adult and $2 for a child. The club expects that three times as many children as adults will attend the play. Write and solve an equation to find how many adults and children have to buy tickets in order for the club to cover its costs.

Three responses are below with the points each received.

4 points	3 points	1 point
x = number of adults $3x$ = number of children $14(x) + 2(3x) = 440$ $\quad 14x + 6x = 440$ $\quad\quad\quad 20x = 440$ $\quad\quad\quad\quad x = 22$ $\quad\quad\quad 3x = 66$ 22 adults and 66 children must attend the play.	x = number of adults $14(x) + 2(3x) = 440$ $\quad 14x + 5x = 440$ $\quad\quad\quad 19x = 440$ $\quad\quad\quad\quad x = 23.2$ 24 adults and $3(24) = 72$ children must attend the play.	x = number of adults $x + 3x = 440$ $\quad 4x = 440$ $\quad\quad x = 110$

The 4-point response shows the work and gives a written answer to the problem. Note that it begins by identifying the variable before writing the equation.

The 3-point response contains a computational error, but the student completed both parts.

The 1-point response shows an incorrect equation, and it does not give the number of children who must attend to cover costs.

EXERCISES

Use the Example above to answer each question.

1. Read the 3-point response. What error did the student make?

2. Write a 2-point response that begins by defining variables.

3. Error Analysis Why is the equation in the 1-point response incorrect?

Chapter Review

Vocabulary Review

Addition Property of Equality (p. 294)
conclusion (p. 359)
conditional (p. 359)
consecutive integers (p. 335)
converse (p. 359)
cross products (p. 320)
dilation (p. 326)
Division Property of Equality (p. 294)
equivalent equations (p. 294)
extremes of a proportion (p. 320)
greatest possible error (p. 345)
hypotenuse (p. 357)
hypothesis (p. 359)
identity (p. 312)

inverse operations (p. 294)
leg (p. 357)
literal equation (p. 316)
means of a proportion (p. 320)
Multiplication Property of Equality (p. 294)
negative square root (p. 352)
percent error (p. 346)
percent of change (p. 344)
percent of decrease (p. 344)
percent of increase (p. 344)
perfect squares (p. 353)
principal square root (p. 352)
proportion (p. 320)

Pythagorean Theorem (p. 357)
radicand (p. 352)
rate (p. 318)
ratio (p. 318)
scale (p. 327)
scale drawing (p. 327)
scale factor (p. 326)
similar figures (p. 326)
solution of an equation (p. 294)
square root (p. 352)
Subtraction Property of Equality (p. 294)
uniform motion (p. 335)
unit analysis (p. 319)
unit rate (p. 318)

Choose the correct item to complete each sentence.

1. Addition and subtraction are examples of (*inverse operations, extremes of a proportion*).

2. (*Consecutive integers, Solutions of equivalent equations*) have the same value.

3. To change one unit of measure to another you can use a (*proportion, rate*) that is equal to 1.

4. You can use (*cross products, unit analysis*) to solve a proportion that involves one variable.

5. The (*greatest possible error, percent error*) in a measurement is one half of the measuring unit.

For: Vocabulary quiz
Web Code: atj-0351

Skills and Concepts

6-1 Objectives

▼ To solve two-step equations (p. 295)

▼ To use deductive reasoning (p. 297)

A two-step equation is an equation that has two operations. You can use tiles to model and solve a two-step equation. To solve a two-step equation, first add or subtract. Then multiply or divide.

Solve each equation. Then check your solution.

6. $5x - 8 = 12$ **7.** $7t - 3 = 18$ **8.** $\frac{c}{5} - 4 = -3$

9. $-2q - 5 = -11$ **10.** $-3m + 8 = 2$ **11.** $11y + 9 = 130$

12. A state park charges admission of $6 per person plus $3 for parking. Jo paid $27 when her car entered the park. Write and solve an equation to find the number of people in Jo's car. Be sure to explain what your variable represents.

Solve each equation. Justify each step.

13. $314 = -n + 576$ **14.** $-\frac{1}{4}w - 1 = 6$ **15.** $3h - 4 = 5$

6-2 and 6-3 Objectives

- To use the Distributive Property when combining like terms (p. 302)
- To use the Distributive Property when solving equations (p. 303)
- To solve equations with variables on both sides (p. 310)
- To identify equations that are identities or have no solution (p. 312)

You can combine like terms and use the Distributive Property to simplify expressions and solve equations. You can also use the properties of equality to solve an equation.

An equation has no solution if no value of the variable makes the equation true. An equation is an **identity** if every value of the variable makes the equation true.

Solve each equation. If the equation is an identity or if it has no solution, write *identity* or *no solution.*

16. $b + 4b = -90$ **17.** $-x + 7x = 24$ **18.** $2(t + 5) = 9$

19. $-(3 - 10y) = 12$ **20.** $x - (4 - x) = 0$ **21.** $4n - 6n = 2n$

22. $3(5x - 2) - 6x = 3(3x + 2)$ **23.** $3(2t - 6) = 2(3t - 9)$

24. $\frac{3y}{4} - \frac{y}{2} = 5$ **25.** $0.36p + 0.26 = 3.86$

26. Geometry The width of a rectangle is 6 cm less than the length. The perimeter is 72 cm. Write and solve an equation to find the dimensions of the rectangle.

6-4 Objectives

- To find ratios and rates (p. 318)
- To solve proportions (p. 320)

A **ratio** is a comparison of two numbers by division. A **rate** is a ratio that compares quantities measured in different units. A **proportion** is a statement that two ratios are equal. You can solve a proportion involving a single variable by finding the **cross products.**

Write in miles per hour. Round to the nearest tenth where necessary.

27. 2.5 mi/min **28.** 300 ft/min **29.** 4 in./s

Solve each proportion.

30. $\frac{4}{12} = \frac{c}{6}$ **31.** $\frac{t}{5} = \frac{23}{50}$ **32.** $\frac{-9}{m} = \frac{3}{2}$

33. $\frac{x}{8} = \frac{x - 5}{6}$ **34.** $\frac{12}{r} = \frac{4}{0.5r - 1}$ **35.** $\frac{d - 2}{d + 9} = \frac{3}{14}$

6-5 Objectives

- To find missing measures of similar figures (p. 325)
- To use similar figures when measuring indirectly (p. 327)

Similar figures have the same shape but not necessarily the same size. If two figures are **similar,** then corresponding angles are congruent and corresponding sides are in proportion.

A scale drawing is an enlarged or reduced drawing of an object. The ratio of the length of drawing to the actual length is the **scale** of the drawing. You can use proportions to solve problems involving scale drawings. A map is an example of a scale drawing.

In the figure at the right $\triangle DEF \sim \triangle QRS$.

36. Find RS. **37.** Find QR.

38. Hobbies A certain model airplane is $\frac{1}{48}$ of the airplane's actual size. The length of the model airplane's wing is $\frac{3}{4}$ ft. How long is the airplane's wing?

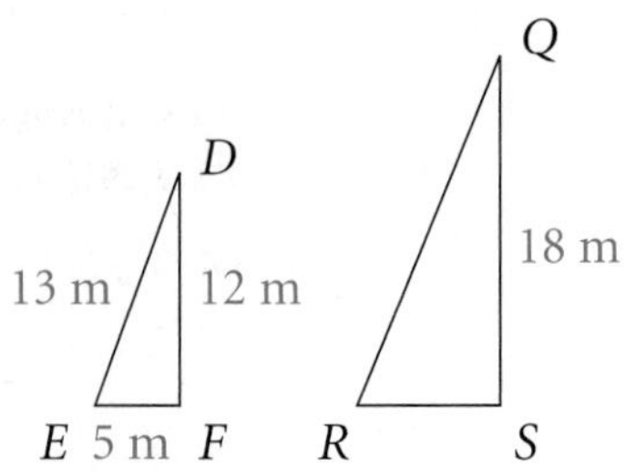

▼ To define a variable in terms of another variable (p. 334)

▼ To model distance-rate-time problems (p. 335)

Many types of real-world problems can be solved using equations. You can also use tables and diagrams to help organize information or solve the problem.

Write and solve an equation for each situation.

39. **Travel Time** The Great Seto Bridge in Japan is about 7.6 mi long. How long would it take you to cross the bridge if you were walking at 4 mi/h?

40. The sum of three consecutive integers is 582. Find the three integers.

41. **Ocean Travel** A supertanker left port traveling north at an average speed of 10 knots. Two hours later a cruise ship leaves the same port, heading south at an average speed of 18 knots. How many hours after the cruise ship sails will the two ships be 209 nautical miles apart? (1 knot = 1 nautical mile per hour)

6-7 Objectives

▼ To find percent of change (p. 344)

▼ To find percent error (p. 345)

The **percent of change** $= \dfrac{\text{amount of change}}{\text{original amount}}$. If a value increases, the percent of change is the **percent of increase.** If a value decreases, the change is the **percent of decrease.** The greatest possible error in a measurement is one half of the measuring unit. The percent error is $\dfrac{\text{greater difference}}{\text{measurement}}$.

For Exercises 42–44, find each percent of change. Where necessary, round to the nearest percent. Describe the percent of change as a percent of increase or decrease.

42. $75,000 to $85,000   43. 20 ft to 15 ft   44. 60 h to 40 h

45. Suppose you measure a box. Its dimensions are 32 in. $\times$ 28 in. $\times$ 25 in. Find the percent of error in calculating its volume to the nearest tenth of a percent.

6-8 Objectives

▼ To find square roots (p. 352)

▼ To estimate and use square roots (p. 353)

If $a^2 = b$, then a is a **square root** of b. The positive or **principal square root** of b is indicated by $\sqrt{b}$. The **negative square root** is indicated by $-\sqrt{b}$. The squares of integers are called **perfect squares.**

Tell whether each expression is rational or irrational. Then find the value of each expression. If necessary, round to the nearest hundredth.

46. $\sqrt{86}$ 47. $-\sqrt{121}$ 48. $\pm\sqrt{\tfrac{1}{2}}$ 49. $\sqrt{2.55}$ 50. $-\sqrt{\tfrac{4}{25}}$

6-9 Objectives

▼ To solve problems using the Pythagorean Theorem (p. 357)

▼ To identify right triangles (p. 359)

For a right triangle with **legs** a and b and **hypotenuse** c, the **Pythagorean Theorem** states that $a^2 + b^2 = c^2$. The converse of the Pythagorean Theorem states that if a triangle has sides of lengths a, b, and c, and if $a^2 + b^2 = c^2$, then it is a right triangle with hypotenuse c.

Find the length of the hypotenuse with the given leg lengths. Round to the nearest tenth.

51. $a = 3, b = 5$ 52. $a = 11, b = 14$ 53. $a = 7, b = 13$ 54. $a = 4, b = 9$

Determine whether the given lengths can be sides of a right triangle.

55. $XY = 16, YZ = 34, XZ = 30$ 56. $XY = 2.5, YZ = 2.4, XZ = 0.7$

Chapter Test

Go Online
PHSchool.com
For: Chapter Test
Web Code: ata-0352

Solve each equation. Then check.

1. $3w + 2 - w = -4$

2. $\frac{1}{4}(k - 1) = 10$

3. $6(y + 3) = 24$

4. $\frac{5n + 1}{8} = \frac{1}{2}$

5. If $2t + 3 = -9$ what is the value of $-3t - 7$?

6. Solve $2x - 4 = -7$. Justify each step.

Define a variable and write an equation to model each situation. Then solve.

7. Your chorus holds a car wash. They have $25.00 for making change. At the end of the car wash, they have $453.50. How much money did they make?

8. **Truck Rental** The rate to rent a certain truck is $55 per day and $0.20 per mile. Your family pays $80 to rent this truck for one day. How many miles did your family drive?

9. **Entertainment** Movie tickets for an adult and three children cost $20. An adult's ticket costs $2 more than a child's ticket. Find the cost of an adult's ticket.

Solve each proportion.

10. $\frac{3}{4} = \frac{c}{20}$

11. $\frac{8}{15} = \frac{4}{w}$

12. $\frac{w}{6} = \frac{6}{15}$

13. $\frac{5}{t} = \frac{25}{100}$

Solve. If the equation is an identity, write *identity*. If it has no solution, write *no solution*.

14. $9j + 3 = 3(3j + 1)$

15. $4v - 9 = 6v + 7$

16. $2(1 - 2y) = 4y + 18$

17. $4p - 5 + p = 7 + 5p + 2$

Calculate the percent of change. Describe each as a percent of increase or a percent of decrease.

18. $4.50/h to $5/h

19. 60 km/h to 45 km/h

20. 150 lb to 135 lb

21. $18 to $24

Complete each statement.

22. 14¢/oz = $■/lb

23. 7 gal/wk = ■ qt/h

24. 35 mi/h = ■ ft/min

25. 120 ft/day = ■ in./min

26. A scale on a map is 1 in. : 25 mi. You measure 6.5 inches. How many miles is the actual distance?

27. A taxicab company charges a flat fee of $1.85, plus an additional $.40 per quarter-mile.
  a. Write a formula to find the total cost for each fare.
  b. Use this formula to find the cost for 1 person to travel 8 mi.

Find the principal and negative square root of each number. If necessary, round to the nearest hundredth.

28. 1.44

29. 1600

30. $\frac{4}{9}$

31. 0.4

Define a variable and write an equation to model each situation. Then solve.

32. Jan is one year younger than her brother Bill and one year older than her sister Sue. The sum of the three children's ages is 57. How old is each child?

33. **Travel** At noon, your family starts out from Louisville to go to Memphis driving at 40 mi/h. Your uncle leaves Memphis to come to Louisville two hours later. He is taking the same route and driving at 60 mi/h. The two cities are 380 miles apart. At what time do the cars meet?

Between what two consecutive integers is each square root?

34. $\sqrt{28}$

35. $\sqrt{136}$

36. $\sqrt{332}$

37. $-\sqrt{8.99}$

Determine whether the given lengths can be sides of a right triangle.

38. 6, 8, 10

39. 6, 7, 9

40. 4, 8, 11

41. 10, 24, 26

42. The length of each leg of an isosceles right triangle is 40.9 cm. Find the length of the hypotenuse to the nearest tenth.

43. One house is 12 mi east of a school. Another house is 9 mi north of the school. How far apart are the houses?

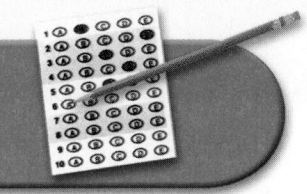

Standardized Test Prep

Reading Comprehension **Read the passage below. Then answer the questions on the basis of what is *stated* or *implied* in the passage.**

> **Geometry of Earth** Long before Columbus, a Greek scholar named Eratosthenes (274–194 B.C.) calculated the circumference of Earth by making some simple observations about shadows at noon and applying some insights from geometry.
>
> The size of Earth has been estimated and measured many times since then. The French Academy of Sciences tried to make an accurate measurement in the late 1700s in order to create a new unit of measure, the meter. They proposed to define the meter as one ten-millionth of the distance from the North Pole to the equator.
>
> Today we can measure Earth's circumference very accurately using data from satellites and making calculations on computers. The circumference at the equator is 24,901.55 miles. Earth is not a perfect sphere, however, because its rotation causes it to bulge a little at the equator. So the circumference from pole to pole is a bit smaller, about 24,859.82 miles.

1. How many centuries before the French Academy of Sciences measured the circumference of Earth did Eratosthenes live?

    Ⓐ 22 centuries   Ⓑ 20 centuries

    Ⓒ 18 centuries   Ⓓ 16 centuries

2. How much greater is the circumference of Earth at the equator than the circumference at the poles?

    Ⓕ about 20 miles

    Ⓖ about 40 miles

    Ⓗ about 80 miles

    Ⓙ about 200 miles

3. Earth is divided into 24 time zones. About how wide is each time zone at the equator?

    Ⓐ 1031 miles

    Ⓑ 1036 miles

    Ⓒ 1038 miles

    Ⓓ 1042 miles

4. Which is the best estimate of the diameter of Earth measured from pole to pole?

    Ⓕ 3960 miles

    Ⓖ 4530 miles

    Ⓗ 6300 miles

    Ⓙ 7920 miles

5. A geostationary satellite moves in an orbit 22,300 miles above the equator. The satellite moves at a rate such that it stays at the same point above Earth as Earth rotates on its axis. What is the approximate speed of the satellite?

    Ⓐ 700 miles per hour

    Ⓑ 7000 miles per hour

    Ⓒ 10,000 miles per hour

    Ⓓ 14,000 miles per hour

6. a. One mile is equal to about 1610 meters. Write an equation expressing this relationship. Use the equation to calculate the approximate circumference of Earth from pole to pole in meters.

    b. Is the meter unit of measure you found close to the Academy of Sciences' original definition? Explain.

7. a. As Earth rotates, the line separating night from day moves west across Earth's surface. How fast is this line moving in miles per minute at the equator? Show your work.

    b. Does the day-night dividing line move more quickly or more slowly across your state than it does at the equator? Explain.

Data Analysis

Activity Lab

Probability Distributions

A probability distribution is a function that gives the probability for each outcome in a sample space. You can show a probability distribution using a table or a graph.

Forty people are surveyed about the number of siblings they have. The results are below, including the probability of a person making each response. The graph below shows the probability distribution.

Number of Siblings	Response	Probability of Response
0	ⅧⅡ |||	$\frac{1}{5}$ = 20%
1	ⅧⅡ ⅧⅡ ||	$\frac{3}{10}$ = 30%
2	ⅧⅡ ⅧⅡ	$\frac{1}{4}$ = 25%
3	ⅧⅡ		$\frac{3}{20}$ = 15%
4 or more	||||	$\frac{1}{10}$ = 10%

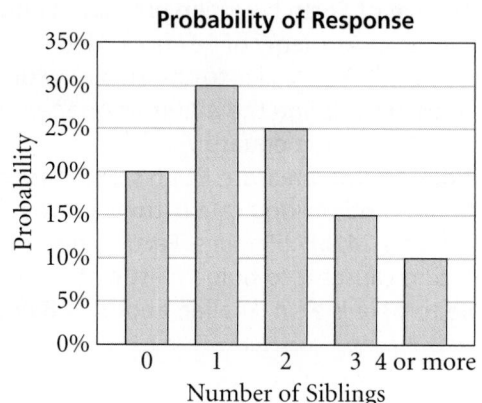

One kind of probability distribution is called a **discrete probability distribution**. In this case, the sample space contains a countable number of values. For example, there are only three possible outcomes when two coins are tossed, heads-heads, heads-tails, and tails-tails.

1 ACTIVITY

1. **Data Collection** Roll a pair of number cubes 20 times. Record the sum of each roll. Write the frequency of each sum in a table like the one at the right.

2. Find the experimental probability for each outcome and enter it in the table.

3. Make a graph of the probability distribution.

4. **Critical Thinking** Find the sum of the experimental probabilities. Does your answer make sense? Explain.

Sum of Cubes	Frequency	Experimental Probability
1	■	■
2	■	■
3	■	■
4	■	■
5	■	■
:	■	■

2 ACTIVITY

For this activity you will need 4 coins.

5. Data Collection Toss all of the coins at once. Record the number of tails. Record the results of 30 tosses in a table like the one at the right.

6. Find the experimental probability for each outcome (0 tails, 1 tail, 2 tails, and so on.) Round the probabilities to the nearest hundredth.

7. Make a graph of the probability distribution.

8. Critical Thinking Do the probabilities add to 1? If they don't, explain why.

Number of Tails	Frequency
0	■
1	■
2	■
3	■
4	■

9. Critical Thinking If you were to repeat this activity would you expect to see the same probability distribution? Explain.

EXERCISES

10. A bag contains tiles with letters A, B, C, D, E, and F. The probability distribution shows the probabilities of selecting each letter.
 a. If there are 80 tiles in bag, how many are B's?
 b. How many more E's than D's are in the bag?
 c. Suppose you pick a tile at random, replace it and pick a second tile. Find P(C then A).

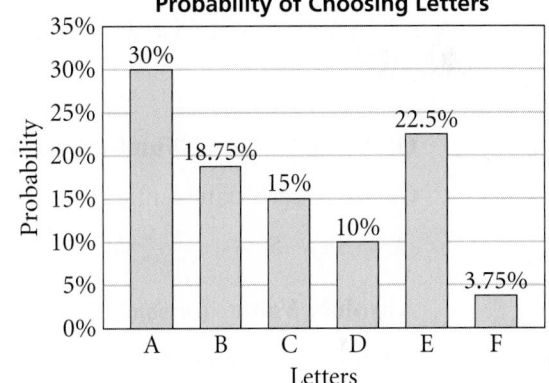

Probability of Choosing Letters

11. Odds Recall that the odds in favor of an event equal the ratio of the number of times the event occurs to the number of times the event does not occur.

The odds in favor of event M are 1 : 3.

The odds in favor of event N are also 1 : 3.

The odds in favor of event P are 1 : 5.

The odds in favor of event Q are 1 : 2.

Assume the events above are independent and complete a sample space. Graph the probability distribution of events M, N, P, and Q.

12. Data Collection Use the color palette. Ask 20 people which of the colors shown is their favorite. Make a table and graph of the probability distribution.

What You've Learned

- In Chapter 4 you learned about the real number system.

- In Chapter 5 you learned how to add, subtract, multiply, and divide using rational numbers.

- In Chapters 4 and 6 you used this knowledge to evaluate variable expressions and solve equations.

 **Check Your Readiness**   **for Help** to the Lesson in green.

Ordering Rational Numbers (Lesson 4-3)

Complete each statement with $<$, $=$, or $>$.

1. $-3 \ \blacksquare \ -5$ **2.** $7 \ \blacksquare \ \frac{14}{2}$ **3.** $-8 \ \blacksquare \ -8.4$ **4.** $-\frac{3}{2} \ \blacksquare \ -1$

Absolute Value (Lesson 4-3)

Simplify each expression.

5. $5 + |4 - 6|$ **6.** $|30 - 28| - 6$ **7.** $|-7 + 2| - 4$

Solving One-Step Equations (Review page 294)

Solve each equation. Check your solution.

8. $x - 4 = -2$ **9.** $b + 4 = 7$ **10.** $-\frac{3}{4}y = 9$ **11.** $\frac{m}{12} = 2.7$

12. $-8 + x = 15$ **13.** $n - 7 = 22.5$ **14.** $-\frac{12}{7}z = 48$ **15.** $\frac{5y}{4} = -15$

Solving Two-Step Equations (Lesson 6-1)

Solve each equation. Check your solution.

16. $-5 + \frac{b}{4} = 7$ **17.** $4.2m + 4 = 25$ **18.** $-12 = 6 + \frac{3}{4}x$ **19.** $6 = -z - 4$

20. $4m + 2.3 = 9.7$ **21.** $\frac{5}{8}t - 7 = -22$ **22.** $-4.7 = 3y + 1.3$ **23.** $12.2 = 5.3x - 3.7$

Solving Multi-Step Equations (Lesson 6-2)

Solve each equation. Check your solution.

24. $4t + 7 + 6t = -33$ **25.** $2a + 5 = 9a - 16$ **26.** $\frac{1}{3} + \frac{4y}{6} = \frac{2}{3}$

27. $6(y - 2) = 8 - 2y$ **28.** $n + 3(n - 2) = 10.4$ **29.** $\frac{1}{2}w + 3 = \frac{2}{3}w - 5$

An inequality has an infinite number of solutions, so it is not possible to check all the solutions. You can check your computations and the direction of the inequality symbol. The steps below show how to check that $x < 8$ describes the solutions to Example 1.

Step 1 Check the computation. See if 8 is the solution to the equation $x - 3 = 5$.

$x - 3 = 5$

$8 - 3 \stackrel{?}{=} 5$ **Substitute 8 for x.**

$5 = 5$ ✓

Step 2 Check the inequality symbol. Choose any number less than 8 and substitute it into $x - 3 < 5$. In this case, use 7.

$x - 3 < 5$

$7 - 3 < 5$ **Substitute 7 for x.**

$4 < 5$ ✓

Since the computation and the direction of the inequality symbol are correct, $x - 3 < 5$ and $x < 8$ are equivalent inequalities. So the solution of $x - 3 < 5$ is $x < 8$.

Online
active math

For: Linear Inequalities Activity
Use: Interactive Textbook, 4-2

2 EXAMPLE   Solving and Checking Solutions

Solve $12 \leq x - 5$. Graph and check your solution.

$12 + 5 \leq x - 5 + 5$ **Add 5 to each side.**

$\quad\quad 17 \leq x$ **Simplify.**

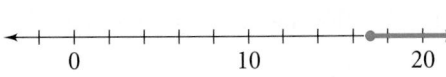

Check $12 = x - 5$ **Check the computation.**

$12 \stackrel{?}{=} 17 - 5$ **Substitute 17 for x.**

$12 = 12$ ✓

$12 \leq x - 5$ **Check the direction of the inequality.**

$12 \leq 18 - 5$ **Substitute 18 for x.**

$12 \leq 13$ ✓

 **Quick Check**   ② Solve $n - 7 \leq -2$. Graph and check your solution.

2   Using Subtraction to Solve Inequalities

You can subtract the same number from each side of an inequality to create an equivalent inequality.

🔑 **Key Concepts**

Property	Subtraction Property of Inequality
For every real number a, b, and c, if $a > b$, then $a - c > b - c$; if $a < b$, then $a - c < b - c$.	
Examples $3 > -1$, so $3 - 2 > -1 - 2$ $-5 < 4$, so $-5 - 2 < 4 - 2$	
This property is also true for $\geq$ and $\leq$.	

3 EXAMPLE Using the Subtraction Property of Inequality

Solve $y + 5 < -7$. Graph the solution.

$$y + 5 - 5 < -7 - 5 \quad \textbf{Subtract 5 from each side.}$$
$$y < -12 \quad \textbf{Simplify.}$$

✔ **Quick Check** ❸ Solve $t + 3 \geq 8$. Graph and check your solution.

You can use inequalities to model real-world situations.

4 EXAMPLE Real-World 🌐 Problem Solving

Multiple Choice The maximum safe load of a chairlift is 680 lb. In the spring, a cyclist and bicycle go to the top of the slope using the chairlift. The weight of the person is 124 lb, and the weight of the bicycle is 32 lb. Which inequality best describes how much additional weight w the chairlift could safely carry?

Ⓐ $124 + w \leq 680 + 32$ Ⓑ $124 + 32 + w \leq 680$

Ⓒ $32 + w \geq 680 + 124$ Ⓓ $124 + 32 + w \geq 680$

Test-Taking Tip

You can test inequality choices by substituting a reasonable value for the variable. If the value is NOT a solution of the inequality you can eliminate that choice as the correct answer.

Relate | weight of a person and a bicycle | plus | additional weight | is at most | safe load |

Define Let w = the amount of weight that can be added to the chairlift.

Write | $124 + 32$ | + | w | $\leq$ | 680 |

The inequality $124 + 32 + w \leq 680$ models the situation. So B is the correct answer.

✔ **Quick Check** ❹ Your baseball team has a goal to collect at least 160 blankets for a shelter. Team members brought 42 blankets on Monday and 65 blankets on Wednesday. Write an inequality to describe how many blankets the team must donate on Friday to make or exceed their goal.

EXERCISES

For more exercises, see *Extra Skill and Word Problem Practice*.

Practice and Problem Solving

Ⓐ **Practice by Example**

Examples 1, 2
(pages 382, 383)

State what number you would add to each side of the inequality to solve the inequality.

1. $d - 5 \geq -4$ **2.** $0 < c - 8$ **3.** $z - 4.3 \geq 1.6$

Solve each inequality. Graph and check your solution.

4. $x - 1 > 10$ **5.** $t - 3 < -2$ **6.** $-5 > b - 1$ **7.** $7 \leq d - 3$

8. $s - 2 \geq -6$ **9.** $r - 9 \leq 0$ **10.** $8 < n - 2$ **11.** $-4 \geq w - 2$

12. $-1 < -4 + d$ **13.** $y - \frac{1}{2} \leq -5$ **14.** $-\frac{2}{3} > q - 4$ **15.** $x - 2 \geq 0.5$

16. $3.2 > -1.3 + r$ **17.** $-3.4 > m - 1.8$ **18.** $b - \frac{3}{8} < \frac{1}{8}$ **19.** $n - 2\frac{1}{2} > \frac{1}{2}$

Example 3
(page 384)

State what number you would subtract from each side of the inequality to solve the inequality.

20. $w + 2 > -1$ **21.** $8 < \frac{5}{3} + r$ **22.** $5.7 \geq k + 3.1$

Solve each inequality. Graph and check your solution.

23. $w + 4 \leq 9$ **24.** $m + 5 > -3$ **25.** $1 < 8 + b$ **26.** $-2 \geq 4 + a$

27. $r + 1 \geq -5$ **28.** $k + 3 \leq 4$ **29.** $3 > 4 + x$ **30.** $-5 < 1 + p$

31. $\frac{3}{5} + z \geq -\frac{2}{5}$ **32.** $7.5 + y < 13$ **33.** $\frac{1}{2} < m + 2$ **34.** $2.7 \geq a + 3$

35. $-2.9 < 4.1 + p$ **36.** $\frac{1}{4} \geq h + \frac{3}{4}$ **37.** $5.3 + d > 3.8$ **38.** $t + \frac{3}{8} < -\frac{1}{8}$

Example 4
(page 384)

39. Vacation Budget Your brother has $2000 saved for a vacation. His airplane ticket is $637. Write and solve an inequality to find how much he can spend for everything else.

40. Weekly Budget You have an allowance of $15.00 per week. You are in a bowling league that costs $6.50 each week, and you save at least $5.00 each week. Write and solve an inequality to show how much you have left to spend each week.

41. Fund-Raising A school club is selling reflectors for Bicycle Safety Day. Each member is encouraged to sell at least 50 reflectors. You sell 17 on Monday and 12 on Tuesday. How many reflectors do you need to sell on Wednesday to meet your goal?

 **Apply Your Skills**

State what you must do to the first inequality in order to get the second.

42. $36 \leq -4 + y;\ 40 \leq y$ **43.** $9 + b > 24;\ b > 15$ **44.** $m - \frac{1}{2} < \frac{3}{8};\ m < \frac{7}{8}$

Solve each inequality.

45. $w - 3 + 1 \geq 9$ **46.** $\frac{1}{2} + c \leq 3\frac{1}{2}$ **47.** $y - 0.3 < 2.8$

48. $-6 > n - \frac{1}{5}$ **49.** $z + 4.1 < -5.6$ **50.** $-4.1 > y - 0.9$

51. $\frac{2}{3} + t - \frac{5}{6} > 0$ **52.** $5 \leq v - 4 - 7$ **53.** $3.6 + k \geq -4.5$

54. $6 + b - 7 < 5$ **55.** $m + 2.3 \leq -1.2$ **56.** $4 \geq k - \frac{3}{4}$

57. $h - \frac{1}{2} \geq -1$ **58.** $-7.7 \geq x - 2$ **59.** $-2 > 9 + 3 + w$

60. Banking Your local bank offers free checking for accounts with a balance of at least $500. Suppose you have a balance of $516.46 and you write a check for $31.96. How much must you deposit to avoid being charged a service fee?

61. a. If $45 + 47 = t$, does $t = 45 + 47$?
     b. If $45 + 47 < r$, is $r < 45 + 47$?
     c. Discuss the differences between these two examples.

62. Gymnastics Suppose your sister wants to qualify for a regional gymnastics competition. At today's competition she must score at least 34.0 points. She scored 8.8 on the vault, 7.9 on the balance beam, and 8.2 on the uneven parallel bars. The event that remains is the floor exercise.
     a. Write and solve an inequality that models the information.
     b. Explain what the solution means in terms of the original situation.
     c. Open-Ended Write three scores your sister could make that would allow her to qualify for the regional gymnastics competition.

Real-World Connection

More than 71,000 athletes compete in gymnastic programs in the United States.

Real-World  **Connection**

In 1971, a computer chip could hold 2300 transistors. In 2004, a chip could hold 410,000,000 transistors.

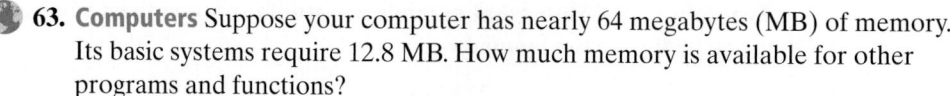

63. Computers Suppose your computer has nearly 64 megabytes (MB) of memory. Its basic systems require 12.8 MB. How much memory is available for other programs and functions?

64. To earn an A in Ms. Orlando's math class, students must score a total of at least 135 points on the three tests. On the first two tests, Amy's scores were 47 and 48. What is the minimum score she must get on the third test to earn an A?

65. a. Open-Ended Use each of the inequality symbols $<$, $\leq$, $>$, and $\geq$ to write four addition or subtraction inequalities.
   b. Solve each of the inequalities in part (a) and graph your solution.

66. a. Sam says that he can solve $z - 8.6 \geq 5.2$ by replacing z with 13, 14, and 15. When $z = 13$, the inequality is false. When $z = 14$ and $z = 15$, the inequality is true. So Sam says that the solution is $z \geq 14$. Is his reasoning correct? Justify your answer.
   b. Critical Thinking Explain why substituting values into the inequality does not guarantee that your solution is correct.

Solve each inequality.

67. $4x + 4 - 3x \geq 5$ **68.** $-5n - 3 + 6n < 2$

69. $7t - (6t - 2) \leq -1$ **70.** $5k - 2(2k + 1) > 8$

71. $-6(a + 2) + 7a \leq 12$ **72.** $-2(a - 3) + 3(a + 2) < 4$

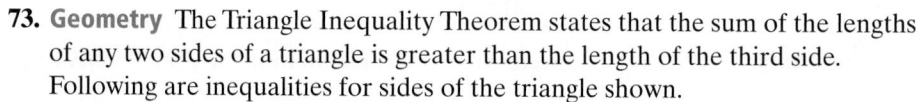

73. Geometry The Triangle Inequality Theorem states that the sum of the lengths of any two sides of a triangle is greater than the length of the third side. Following are inequalities for sides of the triangle shown.

$$a + b > c \qquad b + c > a \qquad a + c > b$$

a. Write an inequality using $c - b$ and a.
b. Write an inequality using $a - c$ and b.
c. Write an inequality using $b - a$ and c.
d. Writing Write a generalization about the length of the third side and the difference of the lengths of the other two sides.

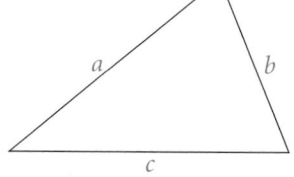

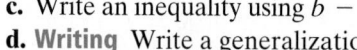

GO **Online**

Homework Video Tutor

Visit: PHSchool.com
Web Code: ate-0402

 **Challenge**

Reasoning **Decide if each inequality is true for all real numbers. If the inequality is _not_ true, give a counterexample.**

74. $a - b < a + b$ **75.** If $a \geq b$, then $a + c \geq b + c$.

76. If $c > d$, then $a - c < a - d$.   **77.** If $a < b$, then $a < b + c$.

78. Reasoning Find real numbers x, y, z, and w for which it is true that $x > y$ and $z > w$, but it is not true that $x - z > y - w$.

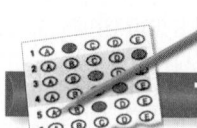

Test Prep

Multiple Choice

79. Solve $x + 5 < 13$.
     A. $x > 8$ **B.** $x < 8$ **C.** $x > 18$ **D.** $x < 18$

80. Solve $-12 + n > 20$.
     F. $n < 32$ **G.** $n > 32$ **H.** $n < 8$ **J.** $n > 8$

81. Which graph represents all real number solutions of $x + 4 \geq 8$?

A. ![number line from -1 to 5 with closed dot at 4 shaded right]

B. ![number line from -5 to 1 with open dot]

C. ![number line from -1 to 5]

D. ![number line from -3 to 3 with open dot]

82. Which of the following is a solution for $5 < n - 0.1$?

F. 4.99　　　　G. 5.01　　　　H. 5.10　　　　J. 5.11

83. Hector is flying his plane. To avoid a storm, he climbs 5500 ft without going above his plane's maximum safe altitude of 35,000 ft. The inequality $a + 5500 \leq 35,000$ represents his original altitude a in feet. Which of the following could have been the original altitude?

A. 40,500 ft　　　B. 30,000 ft　　　C. 29,750 ft　　　D. 27,750 ft

Short Response

84. The leading scorer in your high school's basketball division finished the season with a game average of 20 points for 25 games. As the division's second leading scorer, you have a 19.5 point per game average for 24 games. You have your last game yet to play.

How many points must you score in the final game of the season to overtake the division's leading scorer? Show your work.

Mixed Review

Lesson 6-1

Define a variable and write an inequality to model each situation.

85. An octopus can be up to 10 ft long.

86. A hummingbird migrates more than 1850 mi.

87. Your average in algebra class must be 90 or greater for you to receive an A for the term.

88. You must read at least 25 pages this weekend.

Lesson 4-2

Simplify.

89. $9^2 + 17$ 　　　　**90.** $4(5 - 3)^2 - 3^2$ 　　　　**91.** $0.2(4.2 - 3.4) + 0.4$

92. $3 \cdot 2 + 5^2$ 　　　　**93.** $3 + 7^2 - 4$ 　　　　**94.** $4^3 + 3^2$

95. $6(5 - 2)^2 + 4$ 　　　　**96.** $2 + 8(6 + 2^2)$ 　　　　**97.** $3^3 - 2^3 + 7$

Algebra at Work

·Marketing Director

Marketing directors rely on equations and inequalities to predict the actions their companies must take to stay competitive. For example, the marketing director of a manufacturing company determines how much the cost of raw materials can increase before the company must raise the price of its finished goods or services. The director also predicts the effect of price changes on the quantity of goods and services sold by his company.

Go Online
PHSchool.com　**For:** Information about a career in marketing
Web Code: atb-2031

7-3 Solving Inequalities Using Multiplication and Division

What You'll Learn

- To use multiplication to solve inequalities
- To use division to solve inequalities

. . . And Why

To find how much food can be purchased for a food bank, as in Example 4

Solve each equation.

1. $8 = \frac{1}{2}t$

2. $14 = -21x$

3. $\frac{x}{6} = -1$

4. $5d = 32$

5. $\frac{2}{3}x = -12$

6. $0.5n = 9$

Write an inequality for each graph.

7.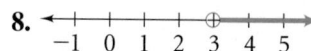
$$-3\ -2\ -1\ \ 0\ \ 1\ \ 2\ \ 3$$

8.
$$-1\ \ 0\ \ 1\ \ 2\ \ 3\ \ 4\ \ 5$$

---

1 Using Multiplication to Solve Inequalities

Activity: Multiplying Each Side of an Inequality

Consider the inequality $4 > 1$.

1. Copy and complete each statement at the right by replacing each ■ with $<$, $>$, or $=$.

2. What happens to the inequality symbol when you multiply each side by a positive number?

3. What happens to the inequality symbol when you multiply each side by zero?

4. What happens to the inequality symbol when you multiply each side by a negative number?

$4 \cdot 3$ ■ $1 \cdot 3$	
$4 \cdot 2$ ■ $1 \cdot 2$	
$4 \cdot 1$ ■ $1 \cdot 1$	
$4 \cdot 0$ ■ $1 \cdot 0$	
$4 \cdot -1$ ■ $1 \cdot -1$	
$4 \cdot -2$ ■ $1 \cdot -2$	
$4 \cdot -3$ ■ $1 \cdot -3$	

You can multiply each side of an inequality by the same number, just as you did with equations. When you multiply each side of an inequality by a positive number, the direction of the inequality symbol stays the same. When you multiply each side by a negative number, the direction of the inequality symbol reverses.

 Key Concepts

Property	**Multiplication Property of Inequality for $c > 0$**

For every real number a and b, and for $c > 0$,

$$\text{if } a > b, \text{then } ac > bc; \qquad\qquad \text{if } a < b, \text{then } ac < bc.$$

Examples $4 > -1$, so $4(5) > -1(5)$. $\qquad -6 < 3$, so $-6(5) < 3(5)$.

This property is also true for $\geq$ and $\leq$.

You can use the Multiplication Property of Inequality to solve inequalities that involve division.

1 EXAMPLE Multiplying by a Positive Number

Solve $\frac{x}{2} < -1$. Graph and check the solution.

$2\left(\frac{x}{2}\right) < 2(-1)$ **Multiply each side by 2. Do not reverse the inequality symbol.**

$x < -2$ **Simplify each side.**

$$\xleftarrow{\hspace{0.3cm}}\underset{-5\ -4\ -3\ -2\ -1\ \ 0\ \ 1\ \ 2\ \ 3\ \ 4\ \ 5}{\overset{\oplus}{\vdash\!\!\!+\!\!\!+\!\!\!+\!\!\!+\!\!\!+\!\!\!+\!\!\!+\!\!\!+\!\!\!+\!\!\!+}}\xrightarrow{\hspace{0.3cm}}$$

Check $\frac{x}{2} = -1$ **Check the computation.**

$\frac{-2}{2} \overset{?}{=} -1$ **Substitute −2 for x.**

$-1 = -1$ ✓   **Simplify.**

$\frac{x}{2} < -1$ **Check the direction of the inequality.**

$\frac{-3}{2} < -1$ ✓   **Substitute −3 for x.**

Quick Check ❶ Solve each inequality. Graph and check your solution.

a. $\frac{b}{4} > \frac{1}{2}$ **b.** $\frac{d}{3} \geq \frac{5}{6}$ **c.** $\frac{y}{0.5} \leq -3$

Key Concepts

Property	Multiplication Property of Inequality for $c < 0$

For every real number a and b, and for $c < 0$,

if $a > b$, then $ac < bc$;   if $a < b$, then $ac > bc$.

Examples $4 > -1$, so $4(-2) < -1(-2)$. $-6 < 3$, so $-6(-2) > 3(-2)$.

This property is also true for $\geq$ and $\leq$.

2 EXAMPLE Multiplying by a Negative Number

Multiple Choice Which graph shows the solution of $-\frac{2}{3}n \leq 2$?

Ⓐ $\xleftarrow{\hspace{0.2cm}}\underset{-6\ -5\ -4\ -3\ -2\ -1\ \ 0\ \ 1\ \ 2\ \ 3\ \ 4}{\overset{\oplus}{\vdash\!\!\!+\!\!\!+\!\!\!+\!\!\!+\!\!\!+\!\!\!+\!\!\!+\!\!\!+\!\!\!+\!\!\!+}}\xrightarrow{\hspace{0.2cm}}$

Ⓑ $\xleftarrow{\hspace{0.2cm}}\underset{-6\ -5\ -4\ -3\ -2\ -1\ \ 0\ \ 1\ \ 2\ \ 3\ \ 4}{\overset{\bullet}{\vdash\!\!\!+\!\!\!+\!\!\!+\!\!\!+\!\!\!+\!\!\!+\!\!\!+\!\!\!+\!\!\!+\!\!\!+}}\xrightarrow{\hspace{0.2cm}}$

Ⓒ $\xleftarrow{\hspace{0.2cm}}\underset{-6\ -5\ -4\ -3\ -2\ -1\ \ 0\ \ 1\ \ 2\ \ 3\ \ 4}{\overset{\bullet}{\vdash\!\!\!+\!\!\!+\!\!\!+\!\!\!+\!\!\!+\!\!\!+\!\!\!+\!\!\!+\!\!\!+\!\!\!+}}\xrightarrow{\hspace{0.2cm}}$

Ⓓ $\xleftarrow{\hspace{0.2cm}}\underset{-4\ -3\ -2\ -1\ \ 0\ \ 1\ \ 2\ \ 3\ \ 4\ \ 5\ \ 6}{\overset{\bullet}{\vdash\!\!\!+\!\!\!+\!\!\!+\!\!\!+\!\!\!+\!\!\!+\!\!\!+\!\!\!+\!\!\!+\!\!\!+}}\xrightarrow{\hspace{0.2cm}}$

$\left(-\frac{3}{2}\right)\left(-\frac{2}{3}n\right) \geq \left(-\frac{3}{2}\right)2$ **Multiply each side by $-\frac{3}{2}$, the reciprocal of $-\frac{2}{3}$. Reverse the inequality symbol.**

$n \geq -3$ **Simplify.**

$$\xleftarrow{\hspace{0.3cm}}\underset{-6\ -5\ -4\ -3\ -2\ -1\ \ 0\ \ 1\ \ 2\ \ 3\ \ 4}{\overset{\bullet}{\vdash\!\!\!+\!\!\!+\!\!\!+\!\!\!+\!\!\!+\!\!\!+\!\!\!+\!\!\!+\!\!\!+\!\!\!+}}\xrightarrow{\hspace{0.3cm}}$$

B is the correct answer.

Test-Taking Tip

You can use the endpoint and another point on a graph to determine if the graph shows the solution of an inequality. Use the endpoint to check for equality. For the answer B, −3 is the endpoint and 0 is another point.

$-\frac{2}{3}(-3) = 2$ ✓

$-\frac{2}{3}(0) \leq 2$ ✓

This confirms that B is the graph of the solution of $-\frac{2}{3}(n) \leq 2$.

Quick Check ❷ Solve each inequality. Graph and check the solution.

a. $-\frac{k}{4} > -1$ **b.** $-t < \frac{1}{2}$ **c.** $6 \leq -\frac{3}{5}w$

Solving inequalities using division is similar to solving inequalities using multiplication. Remember that division by zero is undefined.

Key Concepts

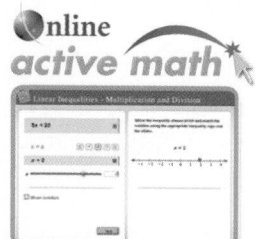

For: Solving Inequalities Activity
Use: Interactive Textbook, 4-3

Property	Division Property of Inequality

For every real number a and b, and for $c > 0$,

if $a > b$, then $\dfrac{a}{c} > \dfrac{b}{c}$;   if $a < b$, then $\dfrac{a}{c} < \dfrac{b}{c}$.

Examples $6 > 4$, so $\dfrac{6}{2} > \dfrac{4}{2}$. $2 < 8$, so $\dfrac{2}{2} < \dfrac{8}{2}$.

For every real number a and b, and for $c < 0$,

if $a > b$, then $\dfrac{a}{c} < \dfrac{b}{c}$;   if $a < b$, then $\dfrac{a}{c} > \dfrac{b}{c}$.

Examples $6 > 4$, so $\dfrac{6}{-2} < \dfrac{4}{-2}$. $2 < 8$, so $\dfrac{2}{-2} > \dfrac{8}{-2}$.

This property also applies to $\geq$ and $\leq$.

3 **EXAMPLE** **Dividing to Solve an Inequality**

Solve $-5z \geq 25$. Graph the solution.

$\dfrac{-5}{-5}z \leq \dfrac{25}{-5}$ **Divide each side by −5. Reverse the inequality symbol.**

$z \leq -5$ **Simplify.**

$-9\ -8\ -7\ -6\ -5\ -4\ -3\ -2\ -1\ \ 0\ \ 1$

✓ **Quick Check** **3** Solve the inequality. Graph and check your solution.
   a. $-2t < -8$ **b.** $-3w \geq 12$ **c.** $0.6 > -0.2n$

There are times when you must think about which types of numbers are acceptable as solutions of inequalities that represent real-world situations.

4 **EXAMPLE** **Real-World 🌐 Problem Solving**

Community Service The student council votes to buy food for a local food bank. A case of 12 jars of spaghetti sauce costs $13.75. What is the greatest number of cases of sauce the student council can buy if they use at most $216 for this project?

Relate cost per case times the number of cases is at most total cost

Define Let c = the number of cases of spaghetti sauce.

Write   13.75   · c ≤   216

$13.75c \leq 216$

$\dfrac{13.75c}{13.75} \leq \dfrac{216}{13.75}$ **Divide each side by 13.75.**

$c \leq 15.71$ **Simplify and round to the nearest hundredth.**

The student council does not have enough money to buy 16 cases, so they can buy at most 15 cases of sauce for the food bank.

Real-World 🌐 Connection

Careers The duties of a manager of a nonprofit organization, such as a food bank, include organizing and supervising volunteers.

✓ Quick Check ④ Students in the school band are selling calendars. They earn $.40 on each calendar they sell. Their goal is to earn more than $327. Write and solve an inequality to find the fewest number of calendars they can sell and still reach their goal.

EXERCISES

For more exercises, see *Extra Skill and Word Problem Practice*.

Practice and Problem Solving

A Practice by Example

Examples 1, 2
(page 389)

GO for Help

Solve each inequality. Graph and check your solution.

1. $\frac{t}{4} \geq -1$ **2.** $\frac{s}{6} < 1$ **3.** $1 \leq -\frac{w}{2}$ **4.** $2 < -\frac{p}{4}$

5. $-2 < \frac{y}{2}$ **6.** $-\frac{v}{3} \geq 0.5$ **7.** $4 > \frac{2}{3}x$ **8.** $-5 \leq \frac{5}{2}k$

9. $0 < -\frac{7}{8}x$ **10.** $\frac{4}{3}y \geq 0$ **11.** $-\frac{5}{7}x > -5$ **12.** $6 \geq -\frac{3}{2}d$

13. $-\frac{4}{9} < \frac{2}{3}c$ **14.** $\frac{3}{4}b \geq -\frac{9}{8}$ **15.** $-\frac{5}{3}u > \frac{5}{6}$ **16.** $-\frac{5}{8} > -\frac{5}{6}n$

Example 3
(page 390)

17. $3t < -9$ **18.** $4m \geq 8$ **19.** $10 \leq -2w$ **20.** $-20 > -5c$

21. $-27 \geq 3z$ **22.** $-7b > 42$ **23.** $18d < -12$ **24.** $-3x \leq 16$

25. $-7 < 2q$ **26.** $16 > 3.2h$ **27.** $-1.5d < -6$ **28.** $3.6 \leq -0.8m$

Example 4
(page 390)

29. Fund-Raising The science club charges $4.50 per car at their car wash. Write and solve an inequality to find how many cars they have to wash to earn at least $300.

30. Earnings Suppose you earn $6.15 per hour working part time at a dry cleaner. Write and solve an inequality to find how many full hours you must work to earn at least $100.

B Apply Your Skills

Write four solutions to each inequality.

31. $\frac{x}{2} \leq -1$ **32.** $\frac{r}{3} \geq -4$ **33.** $-1 \geq \frac{t}{3}$ **34.** $0.5 > \frac{1}{2}c$

35. $-\frac{3}{4}q > 4$ **36.** $1 < -\frac{5}{7}s$ **37.** $-4.5 \leq -0.9p$ **38.** $-2.7w \geq 28$

Tell what you must do to the first inequality in order to get the second.

39. $-\frac{c}{4} > 3;\ c < -12$ **40.** $\frac{n}{5} \leq -2;\ n \leq -10$

41. $5z > -25;\ z > -5$ **42.** $\frac{3}{4}b \leq 3;\ b \leq 4$

43. $-12 < 4a;\ -3 < a$ **44.** $-b \geq 3.4;\ b \leq -3.4$

Replace each ■ with the number that makes the inequalities equivalent.

45. $■s > 14;\ s < -7$ **46.** $■x \geq 25;\ x \leq -5$

47. $-8u \leq ■;\ u \geq -0.5$ **48.** $-2a > ■;\ a < -9$

49. $36 < ■r;\ r < -3.6$ **50.** $-k \leq ■;\ k \geq -7.5$

51. Critical Thinking If $x \geq y$ and $-x \geq -y$, what can you conclude about x and y?

GO Online
Homework Video Tutor
Visit: PHSchool.com
Web Code: ate-0403

Estimation Estimate the solution of each inequality.

52. $-2.099r < 4$ **53.** $3.87j > -24$ **54.** $20.95 \geq \frac{1}{2}p$ **55.** $-\frac{20}{39}s \leq -14$

56. Safe Load An elevator like the one at the left can safely lift at most 4400 lb. A concrete block has an average weight of 42 lb. What is the maximum number of concrete blocks that the elevator can lift?

57. Writing Explain how solving the equation $-\frac{x}{3} = 4$ is similar to and different from solving the inequality $-\frac{x}{3} > 4$.

58. Open-Ended Write four different inequalities with $x > 3$ as their solution that you can solve using multiplication or division.

Real-World Connection

Depending on its size, an elevator at a construction site can have a maximum load from 900 lb to 20,000 lb.

Solve each inequality.

59. $4d \le -28$ **60.** $\frac{u}{7} > 5$ **61.** $2 < -8s$ **62.** $\frac{3}{2}k \ge -45$

63. $0.3y < 2.7$ **64.** $9.4 \le -4t$ **65.** $-h \ge 4$ **66.** $\frac{5}{2}x > 5$

67. $24 < -\frac{8}{3}x$ **68.** $0 < -\frac{1}{6}b$ **69.** $\frac{5}{6} > -\frac{1}{3}p$ **70.** $-0.2m \ge 9.4$

71. $6 < -9g$ **72.** $4n \ge 9$ **73.** $-3.5 < -m$ **74.** $\frac{2}{5}z \ge -1$

75. Michael solved the inequality $-2 > \frac{y}{-3}$ and got $6 < y$. Erica solved the same inequality and got $y > 6$. Are they both correct? Explain.

76. A friend calls you and asks you to meet at a location 3 miles from your home in 20 minutes. You set off on your bicycle after the telephone call. Write and solve an inequality to find the average rate in miles per minute you could ride to be at your meeting place within 20 minutes.

77. a. Error Analysis Kia solved $-15q \le 135$ by adding 15 to each side of the inequality. What mistake did she make?
   b. Kia's solution was $q \le 150$. She checked her work by substituting 150 for q in the original inequality. Why didn't her check let her know that she had made a mistake?
   c. Open-Ended Find a number that satisfies Kia's solution but does not satisfy the original inequality.

Challenge

Reasoning If a, b, and c are real numbers, for which values of a is each statement true?

78. If $c < 0$, then $ac < a$.   **79.** If $b > c$, then $ab > ac$.

80. If $b > c$, then $a^2b > a^2c$.   **81.** If $b > c$, then $\frac{b}{a} < \frac{c}{a}$.

82. Packaging Suppose you have a plastic globe that you wish to put into a gift box. The circumference of the globe is 15 in. The edges of cube-shaped boxes are either 3 in., 4 in., 5 in., or 6 in. Write and solve an inequality to find the boxes that will hold the globe. (*Hint:* circumference = $\pi \cdot$ diameter)

83. Tiling a Floor The Sumaris' den floor measures 18 ft by 15 ft. They want to cover the floor with square tiles that are $\frac{9}{16}$ ft². Write and solve an inequality to find the least number of tiles they need to cover the floor.

Test Prep

Gridded Response   **84.** Solve $\frac{2}{5}x = 16$.

85. Paul expects to pay $1680 in income taxes. This is no more than $\frac{1}{5}$ of his salary. What is his least possible earned income?

3 EXAMPLE Using the Distributive Property

Solve $2(t + 2) - 3t \geq -1$.

$2t + 4 - 3t \geq -1$	**Use the Distributive Property.**
$-t + 4 \geq -1$	**Combine like terms.**
$-t + 4 - 4 \geq -1 - 4$	**Subtract 4 from each side.**
$-t \geq -5$	**Simplify.**
$\dfrac{-t}{-1} \leq \dfrac{-5}{-1}$	**Divide each side by -1. Reverse the inequality symbol.**
$t \leq 5$	**Simplify.**

✓ Quick Check **3** Solve each inequality. Check your solution.

    a. $4p + 2(p + 7) < 8$ **b.** $15 \leq 5 - 2(4m + 7)$ **c.** $8 > 3(5 - b) + 2$

---

2 Solving Inequalities With Variables on Both Sides

Many inequalities have variables on both sides of the inequality symbol. You need to gather the variable terms on one side of the inequality and the constant terms on the other side.

Video Tutor Help
Visit: PHSchool.com
Web Code: ate-0775

4 EXAMPLE Gathering Variables on One Side of an Inequality

Solve $6z - 15 < 4z + 11$.

$6z - 15 - 4z < 4z + 11 - 4z$	**To gather variables on the left, subtract 4z from each side.**
$2z - 15 < 11$	**Combine like terms.**
$2z - 15 + 15 < 11 + 15$	**To gather the constants on the right, add 15 to each side.**
$2z < 26$	**Simplify.**
$\dfrac{2z}{2} < \dfrac{26}{2}$	**Divide each side by 2.**
$z < 13$	**Simplify.**

✓ Quick Check **4** Solve $3b + 12 > 27 - 2b$. Check your solution.

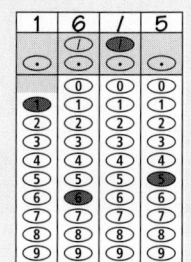

Test-Taking Tip

To grid a mixed number, write it as an improper fraction:
$3\frac{1}{5} = \frac{16}{5}$.

5 EXAMPLE Multi-Step Inequalities

Gridded Response Solve $-3(4 - m) \geq 2(4m - 14)$.

$-12 + 3m \geq 8m - 28$	**Use the Distributive Property.**
$-12 + 3m - 8m \geq 8m - 28 - 8m$	**Subtract 8m from each side.**
$-12 - 5m \geq -28$	**Combine like terms.**
$-12 - 5m + 12 \geq -28 + 12$	**Add 12 to each side.**
$-5m \geq -16$	**Simplify.**
$\dfrac{-5m}{-5} \leq \dfrac{-16}{-5}$	**Divide each side by -5. Reverse the inequality symbol.**
$m \leq 3\frac{1}{5}$	**Simplify.**

✓ Quick Check **5** Solve $-6(x - 4) \geq 7(2x - 3)$. Check your solution.

EXERCISES

For more exercises, see *Extra Skill and Word Problem Practice.*

Practice and Problem Solving

**Practice by Example**

Example 1
(page 396)

for Help

Solve each inequality. Check your solution.

1. $4d + 7 \le 23$

2. $5m - 3 > -18$

3. $-4x - 2 < 8$

4. $5 - 3n \ge -4$

5. $8 \le -12 + 5q$

6. $5 \le 11 + 3h$

7. $-7 \le 5 - 4a$

8. $10 > 29 - 3b$

9. $5 - 9c > -13$

Example 2
(page 396)

Write and solve an inequality.

10. On a trip from Virginia to Florida, the Sampson family wants to travel at least 420 miles in 8 hours of driving. What must be their average rate of speed?

11. Geometry The perimeter of an isosceles triangle is at most 27 cm. The base is 8 cm long. Find the possible lengths of the two congruent sides.

Example 3
(page 397)

12. You want to solve an inequality containing the expression $-3(2x - 3)$. The next line in your solution would rewrite this expression as ___?___.

Solve each inequality.

13. $2(j - 4) \ge -6$

14. $-(6b - 2) > 0$

15. $-2(h + 2) < -14$

16. $-3 \le 3(5x - 16)$

17. $25 > -(4y + 7)$

18. $4(w - 2) \le 10$

19. $-3(c + 4) - 2 > 7$

20. $-2(r - 3) + 7 \ge 8$

21. $16 \le 4 - 3(n - 13)$

Example 4
(page 397)

22. $3w + 2 < 2w + 5$

23. $3t + 7 \ge 5t + 9$

24. $4d + 7 \ge 1 + 5d$

25. $5 - 2n \le 3 - n$

26. $2k - 3 \le 5k + 9$

27. $3s + 16 > 6 + 4s$

28. $6p - 1 > 3p + 8$

29. $3x + 2 > -4x + 16$

30. $2 - 3m < 4 + 5m$

Example 5
(page 397)

31. $-3(v - 3) \ge 5 - 4v$

32. $3q + 6 \le -5(q + 2)$

33. $3(2 + r) \ge 15 - 2r$

34. $9 + x < 7 - 2(x - 3)$

35. $2(m - 8) < -8 + 3m$

36. $2v - 4 \le 2(3v - 6)$

**Apply Your Skills**

Tell what you must do to the first inequality in order to get the second.

37. $8 - 4s > 16;\ -4s > 8$

38. $\frac{2}{3}g + 7 \ge 9;\ \frac{2}{3}g \ge 2$

39. $2y - 5 > 9 + y;\ y > 14$

40. $-8 > \frac{z}{-5} - 2;\ 30 < z$

41. Writing Suppose a friend is having difficulty solving $2.5(p - 4) > 3(p + 2)$. Explain how to solve the inequality, showing all necessary steps and identifying the properties you would use.

 42. Multiple Choice Mandela is starting a part-time word-processing business out of his home. He plans to charge $15 per hour. The table at the right shows his expected monthly business expenses. Which inequality describes the number of hours h he must work in a month to make a profit of at least $600?

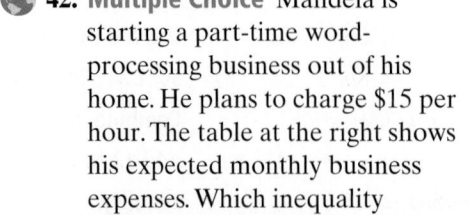

Expense	Cost
Equipment rental	$490
Materials	$45
Business phone	$65

Ⓐ $15h \ge 600$

Ⓑ $15h + 600 \ge 490 + 45 + 65$

Ⓒ $15h \ge 490 + 45 + 65 + 600$

Ⓓ $15h + 600 \le 490 + 45 + 65$

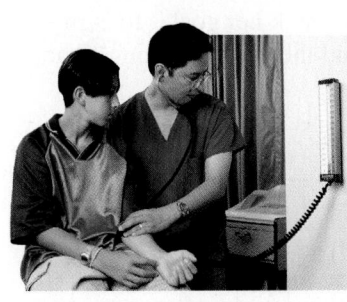

43. Expenses The sophomore class is planning a picnic. The cost of a permit to use a city park is $250. To pay for the permit, there is a fee of $.75 for each sophomore and $1.25 for each guest who is not a sophomore. Two hundred sophomores plan to attend. Write and solve an inequality to find how many guests must attend for the sophomores to pay for the permit.

44. Health Care Systolic blood pressure is the higher number in a blood pressure reading. It is measured as your heart muscle contracts. The formula $P \le \frac{1}{2}a + 110$ gives the normal systolic blood pressure P based on age a.
   a. At age 20, does 120 represent a maximum or a minimum normal systolic pressure?
   b. Find the normal systolic blood pressure for a 50-year-old person.

Match each inequality with its graph below.

45. $-2x - 2 > 4$ **46.** $2 - 2x > 4$ **47.** $2x + 2 > 4$

48. $2x + 2 > 4x$ **49.** $2x - 2 > 4$ **50.** $-2(x - 2) > 4$

A. ![number line from -5 to 3, open circle at 1]

B. ![number line from -5 to 3, open circle at -4]

C. ![number line from -5 to 3, open circle at 1]

D. ![number line from -3 to 5, open circle at 3]

E. ![number line from -5 to 3, open circle at -1]

F. ![number line from -3 to 5, open circle at 1]

51. Open-Ended Write two different inequalities that you can solve by adding 5 and multiplying by -3. Solve each inequality.

Solve each inequality.

52. $\frac{4}{3}r - 3 < r + \frac{2}{3} - \frac{1}{3}r$ **53.** $4 - 2m \le 5 - m + 1$

54. $-2(0.5 - 4s) \ge -3(4 - 3.5s)$ **55.** $\frac{1}{2}n - \frac{1}{8} \ge \frac{3}{4} + \frac{5}{6}n$

56. $-(8 - s) < 0$ **57.** $3.8 - k \le 5.2 - 2k$

58. $10 > 3(2n - 1) - 5(4n + 3)$ **59.** $3(3r + 1) - (r + 4) \le 13$

60. $2(3x + 7) > 4(7 - 2x)$ **61.** $4(a - 2) - 6a \le -9$

62. $4(3m - 1) \ge 2(m + 3)$ **63.** $17 - (4k - 2) \ge 2(k + 3)$

64. $2n - 3(n + 3) \le 14$ **65.** $5x - \frac{1}{2}(3x + 8) \le -4 + 3x$

66. $5a - 2(a - 15) < 10$ **67.** $5c + 4(c - 1) \ge 2 + 5(2 + c)$

68. a. Solve $5t + 4 \le 8t - 5$ by gathering the variable terms on the left side and the constant terms on the right side of the inequality.
   b. Solve $5t + 4 \le 8t - 5$ by gathering the constant terms on the left side and the variable terms on the right side of the inequality.
   c. Compare the results of parts (a) and (b).

69. a. Mental Math Like equations, some inequalities are true for all values of the variable, and some inequalities are not true for any values of the variable. Determine whether each inequality is *always* true or *never* true.
   i. $4s + 6 \ge 6 + 4s$ **ii.** $3r + 5 > 3r - 2$ **iii.** $4(n + 1) < 4n - 3$
   b. Critical Thinking How can you tell whether an inequality is always true or never true without solving?

70. Commission Joleen is a sales associate in a clothing store. Each week she earns $250 plus a commission equal to 3% of her sales. This week her goal is to earn no less than $460. Write and solve an inequality to find the dollar amount of the sales she must have to reach her goal.

71. A student uses the table below to help solve $6x + 1 < 5(3 - x)$.

x	6x + 1	<	5(3 - x)
0	6(0) + 1 = 1	true	5(3 - 0) = 15
0.5	6(0.5) + 1 = 4	true	5(3 - 0.5) = 12.5
1	6(1) + 1 = 7	true	5(3 - 1) = 10
1.5	6(1.5) + 1 = 10	false	5(3 - 1.5) = 7.5

    a. Critical Thinking Based on the table, would you expect the solution of $6x + 1 < 5(3 - x)$ to be of the form $x < n$ or $x > n$? Explain.

    b. Estimate Based on the table, estimate the value of n.

    c. Solve the inequality. Compare the actual solution to your estimated solution.

Error Analysis **Find and correct the mistake in each student's work.**

For a guide to solving
Exercise 72, see p. 402.

72.
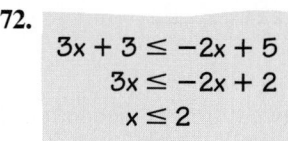
$$3x + 3 \le -2x + 5$$
$$3x \le -2x + 2$$
$$x \le 2$$

73.
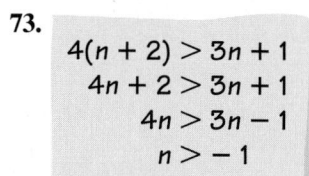
$$4(n + 2) > 3n + 1$$
$$4n + 2 > 3n + 1$$
$$4n > 3n - 1$$
$$n > -1$$

 **Challenge**

74. a. Solve $ax + b > c$ for x, where a is positive.

    b. Reasoning Solve $ax + b > c$ for x, where a is negative.

75. Geometry The base of a triangle is 10 in. Its height is $(x + 4)$ in. Its area is no more than 56 in.^{2}. What are the possible integer values of x?

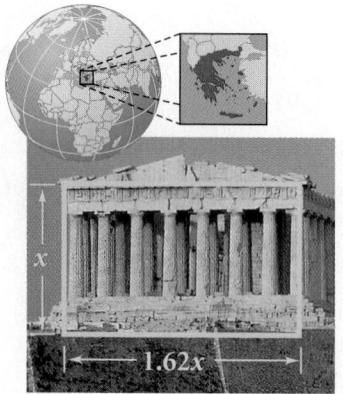

Real-World **Connection**

The Parthenon, an ancient
Greek temple, has dimensions
that form a golden rectangle.

76. Architecture The rectangle shown on the building at the left is a golden rectangle. Artists often use the golden rectangle because they consider it to be pleasing to the eye. The ratio of two sides of a golden rectangle is approximately 1 : 1.62. Suppose you are making a picture frame in the shape of a golden rectangle. You have a 46-in. length of wood to use for a frame. What are the dimensions of the largest frame you can make? Round to the nearest tenth of an inch.

77. Critical Thinking Find a value of a such that the number line below shows all the solutions of $ax + 4 \le -12$.

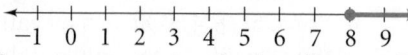

78. Earning You can earn money by handing out flyers in the afternoon for $6.50 an hour and by typing a newsletter in the evening for $8 an hour. You have 20 hours available to work. What are the greatest number of hours you can spend handing out flyers and still make at least $145?

 79. Freight Handling The freight elevator of a building can safely carry a load of at most 4000 lb. A worker needs to move supplies in 50-lb boxes from the loading dock to the fourth floor of the building. The worker weighs 160 lb. The cart she uses weighs 95 lb.

    a. What is the greatest number of boxes she can move in one trip?

    b. The worker must deliver 310 boxes to the fourth floor. How many trips must she make?

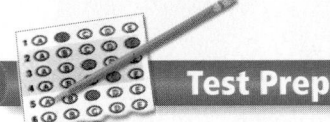

Multiple Choice

80. The Science Club hopes to collect at least 200 kg of aluminum cans for recycling this semester (21 weeks). The graph at the right shows the first week's results.

Let x represent the average mass of cans required per week for the remainder of the semester. Which inequality would you use to find x?

A. $x \geq \frac{200}{21}$ **B.** $x \geq \frac{(200 - 8)}{21}$

C. $x \geq \frac{(200-8)}{20}$ **D.** $x > \left(\frac{200}{20}\right) - 8$

Aluminum Cans Collected in Week 1

(Bar graph: Mass (kg) on vertical axis from 0 to 5; Day on horizontal axis. Mon. = 4, Wed. = 1, Fri. = 3.)

81. Solve $2x - 8 > 4x + 2$.
  F. $x < -5$ **G.** $x > -5$ **H.** $x < 5$ **J.** $x > 5$

82. Solve $-5n + 16 \leq -7n$.
  A. $n \leq -8$ **B.** $n \geq -8$ **C.** $n \leq 8$ **D.** $n \geq 8$

83. Great Gifts pays its supplier $65 for each box of 12 bells. The owner wants to determine the least amount x he can charge his customers per bell in order to make at least a 50% profit per box. Which inequality should he use?
  F. $12x \geq 1.50(65)$ **G.** $65x \leq 1.50(12)$
  H. $0.50(12x) \geq 65$ **J.** $0.50(12x) \leq 65$

Short Response

84. Maxwell orders at least 30 bottles of flea shampoo per month for his pet-grooming business. His supplier charges $3 per quart bottle plus a $25 handling fee per order. A competing supplier offers a similar product for $4 per quart bottle plus a $5 handling fee per order. The salesman for the competitor shows Maxwell that 10 bottles from his company would cost only $45 compared to $55 from Maxwell's current supplier.

Which supplier would you advise Maxwell to use? Explain or show work to support your advice to Maxwell.

Mixed Review

Lesson 7-3

Solve each inequality.

85. $-9m \geq 36$ **86.** $-24 \leq 3y$ **87.** $\frac{x}{3} > -4$

88. $-\frac{t}{3} \leq 1$ **89.** $\frac{2}{3}b < 18$ **90.** $42 > -\frac{3}{7}w$

91. $56 < 42p$ **92.** $0.5d \geq 3.5$ **93.** $\frac{x}{5} > 10$

Lesson 6-6

94. Your family leaves your town traveling at an average rate of 45 mi/h. Two hours later, your neighbor leaves your town along the same road at an average rate of 60 mi/h. How many hours will it take your neighbor to overtake you?

Lesson 5-3

Simplify each expression.

95. -4^2 **96.** $(-4)^2$ **97.** $(-2)^3(-3)$ **98.** -2^4

Analyzing Errors Read the exercise below and then follow along with what Gina thinks and writes. Check your understanding with the exercise at the bottom of the page.

Error Analysis Find and correct the mistake in the student's work at the right.

$$3x + 3 \leq -2x + 5$$
$$3x \leq -2x + 2$$
$$x \leq 2$$

What Gina Thinks

I am going to solve the inequality and see where my work is different from the student's work.

I'll subtract 3 from each side, and then simplify.

Our work agrees. There is no mistake so far.

I'll add 2x to each side so I can get the x's on the left. Then I'll divide each side by 5 to get x alone. My solution is different from the student's work!

I think the student *subtracted* 2x from each side. That's the mistake, because $-2x - 2x$ equals $-4x$, not zero! If the student thought it was zero, the equation would have x on the left side and 2 on the right side. That's what they wrote: $x \leq 2$.

I'll write my answer in a sentence.

What Gina Writes

$$3x + 3 \leq -2x + 5$$

$$3x + 3 - 3 \leq -2x + 5 - 3$$
$$3x \leq -2x + 2$$

$$3x + 2x \leq -2x + 2x + 2$$
$$5x \leq 2$$
$$\frac{5x}{5} \leq \frac{2}{5}$$
$$x \leq \frac{2}{5}$$

The student tried to subtract 2x from each side instead of adding it to each side.

EXERCISE

Find and correct the mistake in the work at the right.

$$1 - 3x < 7$$
$$1 - 3x - 1 < 7 - 1$$
$$-3x < 6$$
$$\frac{-3x}{-3} < \frac{6}{-3}$$
$$x < -2$$

Compound Inequalities

What You'll Learn

- To solve and graph inequalities containing *and*
- To solve and graph inequalities containing *or*

. . . And Why

To solve a problem involving the chemistry of a swimming pool, as in Example 3

✓ **Check Skills You'll Need**

GO for Help Lessons 4-2 and 7-1

Graph each pair of inequalities on one number line.

1. $c < 8; c \geq 10$ **2.** $t \geq -2; t \leq -5$ **3.** $m \leq 7; m > 12$

Use the given value of the variable to evaluate each expression.

4. $3n - 6; 4$ **5.** $7 - 2b; 5$

6. $\dfrac{12 + 13 + y}{3}; 17$ **7.** $\dfrac{2d - 3}{5}; 9$

◀))) **New Vocabulary** • compound inequality

---

1 Solving Compound Inequalities Containing *And*

Two inequalities that are joined by the word *and* or the word *or* form a **compound inequality.**

You can write the compound inequality $x \geq -5$ and $x \leq 7$ as $-5 \leq x \leq 7$.

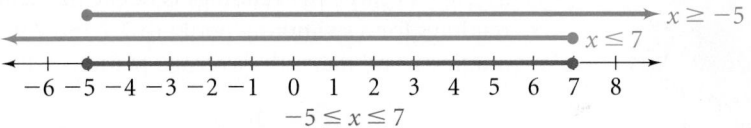

$$-5 \leq x \leq 7$$

Vocabulary Tip

The word <u>inclusive</u> is related to the word <u>included</u>.

The graph above shows that a solution of $-5 \leq x \leq 7$ is in the overlap of the solutions of the inequality $x \geq -5$ and the inequality $x \leq 7$.

You can read $-5 \leq x \leq 7$ as "x is greater than or equal to -5 and less than or equal to 7." Another way to read it is "x is between -5 and 7, inclusive."

1 EXAMPLE Writing a Compound Inequality

Write a compound inequality that represents each situation. Graph the solutions.

a. all real numbers that are at least -2 and at most 4
$n \geq -2$ and $n \leq 4$
$-2 \leq n \leq 4$

b. Today's temperatures will be above 32°F, but not as high as 40°F.
$32 < t$ and $t < 40$
$32 < t < 40$

✓ **Quick Check**  Write a compound inequality that represents each situation. Graph your solution.

a. all real numbers greater than -2 but less than 9

b. The books were priced between $3.50 and $6.00, inclusive.

A solution of a compound inequality joined by *and* is any number that makes both inequalities true. One way you can solve a compound inequality is by writing two inequalities.

2 EXAMPLE Solving a Compound Inequality Containing *And*

Solve $-4 < r - 5 \leq -1$. Graph your solution.

Write the compound inequality as two inequalities joined by *and*.

$-4 < r - 5$	and	$r - 5 \leq -1$
$-4 + 5 < r - 5 + 5$		$r - 5 + 5 \leq -1 + 5$ **Solve each inequality.**
$1 < r$	and	$r \leq 4$ **Simplify.**

$$1 < r \leq 4$$

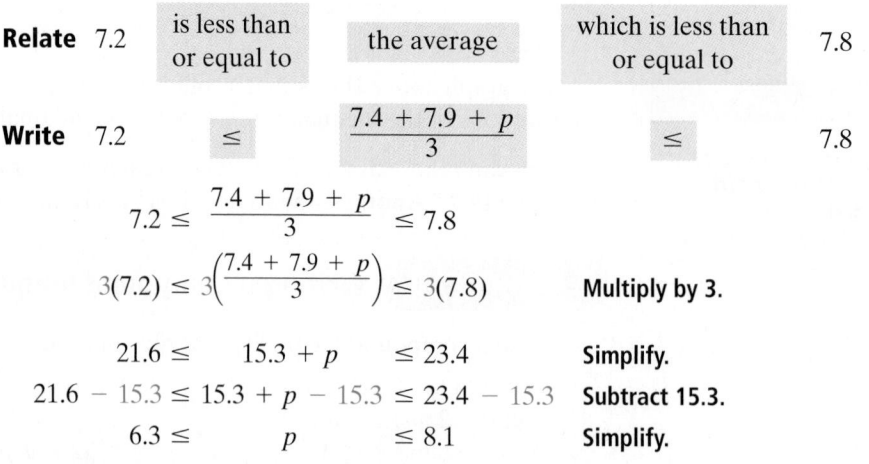

✔ Quick Check **2** Solve each inequality. Graph your solution.
a. $-6 \leq 3x < 15$ **b.** $-3 < 2x - 1 < 7$ **c.** $7 < -3n + 1 \leq 13$

You could also solve an inequality like $-4 < r - 5 \leq -1$ by working on all three parts of the inequality at the same time. You work to get the variable alone between the inequality symbols.

3 EXAMPLE Real-World  Problem Solving

Chemistry The acidity of the water in a swimming pool is considered normal if the average of three pH readings is between 7.2 and 7.8, inclusive. The first two readings for a swimming pool are 7.4 and 7.9. What possible values for the third reading p will make the average pH normal?

Relate	7.2	is less than or equal to	the average	which is less than or equal to	7.8
Write	7.2	$\leq$	$\dfrac{7.4 + 7.9 + p}{3}$	$\leq$	7.8

$$7.2 \leq \frac{7.4 + 7.9 + p}{3} \leq 7.8$$

$$3(7.2) \leq 3\left(\frac{7.4 + 7.9 + p}{3}\right) \leq 3(7.8) \qquad \textbf{Multiply by 3.}$$

$$21.6 \leq 15.3 + p \leq 23.4 \qquad \textbf{Simplify.}$$

$$21.6 - 15.3 \leq 15.3 + p - 15.3 \leq 23.4 - 15.3 \qquad \textbf{Subtract 15.3.}$$

$$6.3 \leq p \leq 8.1 \qquad \textbf{Simplify.}$$

● The value for the third reading must be between 6.3 and 8.1, inclusive.

Real-World  Connection

The lifeguard is checking the pH of swimming pool water. The pH of a substance is a measure of how acidic or basic it is. pH is measured on a scale from 0 to 14. Pure water is neutral, with a pH of 7.

✔ Quick Check **3 a.** Suppose the first two readings for the acidity of water in a swimming pool are 7.0 and 7.9. What possible values for the third reading will make the average pH normal?

b. Critical Thinking If two readings are 8.0 and 8.4, what possible values for the third reading will make the average pH normal? Are these third readings likely? Explain.

A solution of a compound inequality joined by *or* is any number that makes either inequality true.

4 **EXAMPLE** **Writing Compound Inequalities**

Write a compound inequality that represents each situation. Graph the solution.

a. all real numbers that are less than -3 or greater than 7
$x < -3$ or $x > 7$

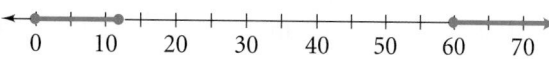

b. Discounted fares are available to children 12 and under or to adults at least 60 years of age.
$n \leq 12$ or $n \geq 60$; $n \geq 0$ because age cannot be negative.

✓ Quick Check **4** Write an inequality that represents all real numbers that are at most -5 or at least 3. Graph your solution.

For a compound inequality joined by *or*, you must solve each of the two inequalities separately.

Online
active math

For: Compound Inequality Activity
Use: Interactive Textbook, 4-5

5 **EXAMPLE** **Solving a Compound Inequality Containing *Or***

Solve the compound inequality $4v + 3 < -5$ or $-2v + 7 < 1$. Graph the solution.

$$4v + 3 < -5 \qquad \text{or} \qquad -2v + 7 < 1$$
$$4v + 3 - 3 < -5 - 3 \qquad \qquad -2v + 7 - 7 < 1 - 7$$
$$4v < -8 \qquad \qquad -2v < -6$$
$$\frac{4v}{4} < \frac{-8}{4} \qquad \qquad \frac{-2v}{-2} > \frac{-6}{-2}$$
$$v < -2 \qquad \text{or} \qquad v > 3$$

✓ Quick Check **5** Solve the compound inequality $-2x + 7 > 3$ or $3x - 4 \geq 5$. Graph your solution.

EXERCISES

For more exercises, see *Extra Skill and Word Problem Practice.*

Practice and Problem Solving

A **Practice by Example**

Example 1
(page 403)

GO for Help

Write a compound inequality that represents each situation. Graph your solution.

1. all real numbers that are between -4 and 6

2. all real numbers that are at least 2 and at most 9

3. The circumference of a baseball is between 23 cm and 23.5 cm.

4. Tropical Storm The wind speeds of a tropical storm are at least 40 mi/h but no more than 74 mi/h.

Examples 2, 3
(page 404)

Solve each compound inequality. Graph your solution.

5. $-3 < j + 2 < 7$ **6.** $3 \le w + 2 \le 7$ **7.** $2 < 3n - 4 \le 14$

8. $7 \le 3 - 2p < 11$ **9.** $-2 < -3x + 7 < 4$ **10.** $1.5 < w + 3 \le 6.5$

11. $-16 < -3x + 8 < -7$ **12.** $-1 < 4m + 7 \le 11$ **13.** $-9 < -2s - 1 \le -7$

14. $12 \le \dfrac{14 + 17 + a}{3} \le 16$ **15.** $\dfrac{1}{2} < \dfrac{3x - 1}{4} < 5$ **16.** $-2 \le \dfrac{5 - x}{3} \le 2$

Example 4
(page 405)

For each situation write and graph an inequality.

17. all real numbers n that are at most -3 or at least 5

18. all real numbers x that are less than 3 or greater than 7

19. all real numbers h less than 1 or greater than 3

20. all real numbers b less than 100 or greater than 300

Example 5
(page 405)

Solve each compound inequality. Graph your solution.

21. $3b - 1 < -7$ or $4b + 1 > 9$ **22.** $4 + k > 3$ or $6k < -30$

23. $3c + 4 \ge 13$ or $6c - 1 < 11$ **24.** $6 - a < 1$ or $3a \le 12$

25. $7 - 3c \ge 1$ or $5c + 2 \ge 17$ **26.** $5y + 7 \le -3$ or $3y - 2 \ge 13$

27. $2d + 5 \le -1$ or $-2d + 5 \le 5$ **28.** $5z - 3 > 7$ or $4z - 6 < -10$

B **Apply Your Skills**

Write a compound inequality that each graph could represent.

29.

30.

31.

32.

Solve each compound inequality.

33. $3q - 2 > 10$ or $3q - 2 \le -10$ **34.** $3 - 2h > 17$ or $5h - 3 > 17$

35. $1 \le 0.25t \le 3.5$ **36.** $25r < 400$ or $100 < 4r$

37. $-20 \le 3t - 2 < 1$ **38.** $\dfrac{3x + 1}{4} - 4 > 3$ or $\dfrac{3 - 2x}{5} > 3$

39. Multiple Choice The force exerted on a spring is proportional to the distance the spring stretches from its relaxed position. Suppose you stretch a spring distance d in inches by applying force F in pounds. For a certain spring, $\frac{d}{F} = 0.8$. You apply forces between 25 and 40 pounds, inclusive. Which inequality describes the stretch of the spring?

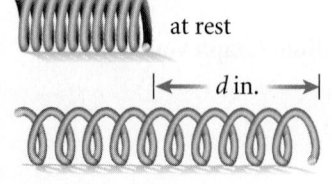
at rest

$\longleftarrow$ d in. $\longrightarrow$

Ⓐ $25 \le d \le 40$ Ⓑ $20 < d < 32$

Ⓒ $31.25 \le d \le 40$ Ⓓ $20 \le d \le 32$

40. Reasoning Describe the solutions of $3x - 8 < 7$ or $2x - 9 > 1$.

41. Writing Explain the difference between the words *and* and *or* in a compound inequality.

Geometry The sum of the lengths of any two sides of a triangle is greater than the length of the third side. The lengths of two sides of a triangle are given. Find the range of values for the possible lengths of the third side.

Sample 3 cm, 7 cm

Write inequalities for x as the longest side and for 7 cm as the longest side. The length 3 cm cannot be the longest side.

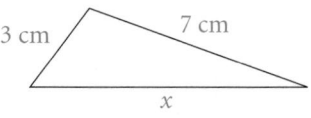

$x + 3 > 7$ and $3 + 7 > x$

$x > 4$ and $10 > x$ **Solve each inequality.**

$4 < x < 10$

The length of the third side is greater than 4 cm and less than 10 cm.

42. 2.5 in., 5 in.   **43.** 12 ft, 18 ft   **44.** 28 mm, 21 mm   **45.** 5 m, 16 m

Meteorology The graph below shows the average monthly high and low temperatures for Detroit, Michigan, and Charlotte, North Carolina.

46. Write a compound inequality for Charlotte's average temperature in June.

47. Write a compound inequality for Detroit's average temperature in January.

48. Write a compound inequality for the yearly temperature range for each city.

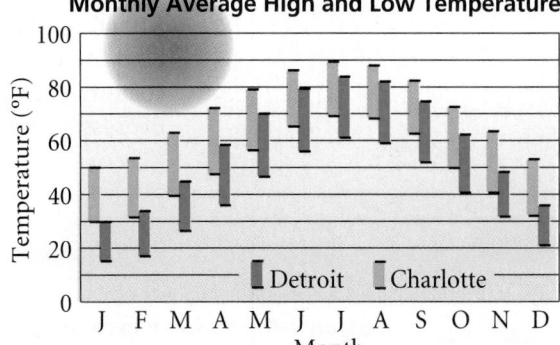

SOURCE: Statistical Abstract of the United States

49. Open-Ended Describe a real-life situation that you could represent with the inequality $-2 < x < 8$.

Challenge

50. Nursing In nursing school, students learn temperature ranges for bath water. Tepid water is approximately 80°F to 93°F, warm water is approximately 94°F to 98°F, and hot water is approximately 110°F to 115°F. Model these ranges on one number line. Label each interval.

Write a compound inequality that each graph could represent.

51.
```
<--+--⊖--⊖--+--⊖--+-->
  -4  -2   0   2   4
```

52.
```
<--+--+--●--+--●--+-->
     -2   0   2   4
```

Real-World Connection

To estimate your pulse rate, count the number of beats you feel in 15 seconds at a pressure point. Multiply this number by 4.

53. Pulse Rates When you exercise, your pulse rate rises. Recommended pulse rates vary with age and physical condition. For vigorous exercise, such as jogging, the inequality $0.7(220 - a) \le R \le 0.85(220 - a)$ gives a target range for pulse rate R (in beats per minute), based on age a (in years).

    a. What is the target range for pulse rates for a person 35 years old? Round to the nearest whole number.

    b. Your cousin's target pulse rate is in the range between 140 and 170 beats per minute. What is your cousin's age?

54. Find three consecutive even integers whose sum is between 48 and 60.

55. Find three consecutive even integers such that one half of their sum is between 15 and 21.

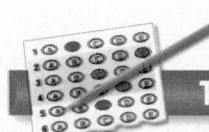
Multiple Choice

56. An emergency vehicle responding to a 911 call for a heart attack victim traveled 5 miles to the patient's home and then delivered him to the hospital 10 miles away. Which graph below represents the possible distances the emergency vehicle was from the hospital when the call was received?

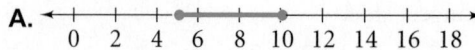

57. Which value below is a solution of neither $-3x - 7 \geq 8$ nor $-2x - 11 \leq -31$?
    F. -6 **G.** 0   **H.** 10   **J.** 16

Short Response

58. The County Water Department charges a monthly administration fee of $10.40 plus $.0059 for each gallon g of water used, up to 7,500 gallons. Find the minimum and maximum water consumption (in gallons) for customers whose monthly charge is at least $35 but no more than $50. Express amounts to the nearest gallon. Show your work.

Mixed Review

GO for Help

Lesson 7-4

Solve each inequality.

59. $5 < 6b + 3$ **60.** $12n \leq 3n + 27$ **61.** $2 + 4r \geq 5(r - 1)$

Lesson 6-3

Solve. If the equation is an identity or if it has no solution, write *identity* or *no solution.*

62. $x - 3 = 5x + 1$ **63.** $4(w + 3) = 10w$ **64.** $8p - 4 = 4(2p - 1)$

✓ Checkpoint Quiz 2   Lessons 7-4 through 7-5

Solve each inequality. Graph the solution.

1. $8d + 2 < 5d - 7$ **2.** $2n + 1 \geq -3$ **3.** $-1 \leq 4m + 7 \leq 11$

4. $5s - 3 + 1 < 8$ **5.** $5(3p - 2) > 50$ **6.** $3 - x \geq 7$ or $2x - 3 > 5$

Write an inequality that represents each situation.

7. A cat weighs less than 8 pounds.

8. We expect today's temperature to be between 65°F and 75°F, inclusive.

9. Geometry The length of each side of a rectangular picture frame needs to be 15 in. You have only one 48 in. piece of wood to use for this frame. Write and solve an inequality that describes the possible widths for this frame.

10. Solve $-2x + 7 \leq 45$.

Union and Intersection of Sets

The word *set* often indicates a group of things, like a set of dishes or set of luggage. In mathematics, the word **set** indicates a well-defined collection of **elements,** usually numbers. Below are two ways to indicate the set of integers.

$$Z = \{\ldots -3, -2, -1, 0, 1, 2, 3, \ldots\} \qquad Z = \{x \mid x \text{ is an integer}\}$$

In set notation, the content within braces lists the elements of a set or tells how a set is built. You read $Z = \{x \mid x \text{ is an integer}\}$ as "The set Z equals all the values of x such that x is an integer." The notation $3 \in Z$ means 3 is an element of the set Z.

The **intersection** of two sets is the set of all elements that are common to both sets. $A \cap B$ means "A intersection B."

1 EXAMPLE

Use a Venn diagram to find $C \cap D$, where $C = \{6, 9, 12, 15, 18, 21\}$ and $D = \{x \mid x \text{ is a positive odd integer}\}$.

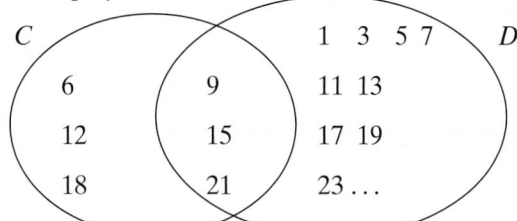

$C \cap D = \{9, 15, 21\}$

The empty set, or **null set,** has no elements, and is indicated by $\{\ \}$ or $\varnothing$. So for $A = \{x \mid x \text{ is an even integer}\}$ and $B = \{x \mid x \text{ is an odd integer}\}$, $A \cap B = \{\ \}$ or $A \cap B = \varnothing$.

The **union** of two sets is the set of all elements that are in either of the sets. $A \cup B$ means "A union B."

2 EXAMPLE

Find $P \cup Q$, where $P = \{5, 10, 15, 20\}$ and $Q = \{8, 10, 18, 20\}$.

$P \cup Q = \{5, 8, 10, 15, 18, 20\}$

EXERCISES

Let $A = \{2, 5, 8\}$, $B = \{5, 7, 9\}$, $C = \{2, 7, 8\}$ and $D = \{x \mid x \text{ is a positive even integer less than 9}\}$. Find the union and intersection of each of the following sets.

1. A and B **2.** B and C **3.** C and D **4.** A and C **5.** B and D **6.** A and D

7. a. Find $P \cap Q$, where $P = \{x \mid x \text{ is a multiple of 3}\}$ and $Q = \{x \mid x \text{ is a multiple of 4}\}$.
    b. Is $40 \in P \cup Q$? Explain.

8. Find two sets whose intersection is $\{2\}$ and whose union is $\{1, 2, 3, 4, 5\}$.

High-Use Academic Words

High-use academic words are words that you see often in textbooks and on tests. These words are not math vocabulary terms, but they are important for you to know to be successful in mathematics.

Words to Learn: Direction Words

Some words tell you what to do in a problem. You need to understand what these words are asking so that you give the correct answer.

Word(s)	Meaning
Describe	To write about a topic so the reader can understand or visualize it
Explain	To give the reasoning for an answer
Define	To give the meaning of a word or expressions or to tell what a variable stands for in order to model a real-world situation

EXERCISES

1. Describe how you walk from your classroom to the cafeteria.

2. Explain why you participate in your favorite school activity.

3. Define the term *extracurricular*.

Describe each of the following.

4. data that can show a negative correlation

5. a real-world situation that can be modeled by the equation $3x - 2 = 5$

Explain why each statement is *true* or *false*.

6. All integers are positive.

7. The median of a set of data may better represent the data than the mean.

Define a variable and write an inequality to model each situation.

8. The elevator can hold no more than 14 people.

9. Miguel needs to earn at least 86 on his test to maintain his A average.

10. Word Knowledge Think about the word *identify*.
    a. Choose the letter for how well you know the word.
        A. I know its meaning.
        B. I have seen it, but I do not know its meaning.
        C. I don't know it.
    b. Research Look up *identify* in a dictionary or online. Write any definition that might apply to its use in mathematics.
    c. Write a sentence involving mathematics that uses the word *identify*.

Absolute Value Equations and Inequalities

What You'll Learn

- To solve equations that involve absolute value
- To solve inequalities that involve absolute value

. . . And Why

To find a range of acceptable measurements for parts of an engine, as in Example 4

✓ Check Skills You'll Need

GO for Help Lessons 4-3 and 5-1

Simplify.

1. $|15|$ **2.** $|-3|$ **3.** $|18 - 12|$

4. $-|-7|$ **5.** $|12 - (-12)|$ **6.** $|-10 + 8|$

Complete each statement with <, =, or >.

7. $|3 - 7|$ ▩ 4 **8.** $|-5| + 2$ ▩ 6 **9.** $|7| - 1$ ▩ 8

10. $\left|6 - 2\frac{1}{4}\right|$ ▩ $3\frac{5}{8}$ **11.** $\left|-4\frac{2}{3}\right| + 2\frac{1}{3}$ ▩ $2\frac{1}{2}$ **12.** $\left|-3\frac{1}{8} - 4\frac{1}{2}\right|$ ▩ $7\frac{5}{8}$

---

1 Solving Absolute Value Equations

Recall that the absolute value of a number is its distance from zero on a number line. Since absolute value represents distance, it can never be negative.

The graph of $|x| = 3$ is below.

Problem Solving Hint

$|3| = 3$

$|-3| = 3$

3 units 3 units

−5 −4 −3 −2 −1 0 1 2 3 4 5

Find the numbers that are 3 units from 0.

The two solutions of the equation $|x| = 3$ are −3 and 3.

You can use the properties of equality to solve an absolute value equation.

1 EXAMPLE **Solving an Absolute Value Equation**

Solve $|x| + 5 = 11$.

$|x| + 5 - 5 = 11 - 5$ **Subtract 5 from each side.**

$\qquad |x| = 6$ **Simplify.**

$\quad x = 6 \quad$ or $\quad x = -6$ **Definition of absolute value.**

Check $|x| + 5 = 11$

$\qquad |6| + 5 \stackrel{?}{=} 11$ ← **Substitute 6 and −6 for x.** → $|-6| + 5 \stackrel{?}{=} 11$

$\qquad\quad 6 + 5 = 11$ ✓ $\qquad\qquad\qquad\qquad\qquad 6 + 5 = 11$ ✓

✓ Quick Check  Solve each equation. Check your solution.

a. $|t| - 2 = -1$ **b.** $3|n| = 15$ **c.** $4 = 3|w| - 2$

d. Critical Thinking Is there a solution of $2|n| = -15$? Explain.

Some absolute value equations such as $|2p + 5| = 11$ have variable expressions within the absolute value symbols. The expression inside the absolute value symbols can be either positive or negative.

 Key Concepts

Rule	**Solving Absolute Value Equations**

To solve an equation in the form $|A| = b$, where A represents a variable expression and $b > 0$, solve $A = b$ and $A = -b$.

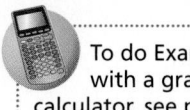 To do Example 2 with a graphing calculator, see page 753.

2 EXAMPLE Solving an Absolute Value Equation

Solve $|2p + 5| = 11$.

$$2p + 5 = 11 \qquad \leftarrow \text{Write two equations.} \rightarrow \qquad 2p + 5 = -11$$

$$2p + 5 - 5 = 11 - 5 \quad \leftarrow \text{Subtract 5 from each side.} \rightarrow \quad 2p + 5 - 5 = -11 - 5$$

$$2p = 6 \qquad\qquad\qquad\qquad\qquad\qquad\qquad 2p = -16$$

$$\frac{2p}{2} = \frac{6}{2} \qquad\qquad \leftarrow \text{Divide each side by 2.} \rightarrow \qquad \frac{2p}{2} = \frac{-16}{2}$$

$$p = 3 \qquad\qquad\qquad\qquad\qquad\qquad\qquad\qquad p = -8$$

● The value of p is 3 or -8.

✓ **Quick Check** ② Solve each equation. Check your solution.

a. $|c - 2| = 6$ **b.** $-5.5 = |t + 2|$ **c.** $|7d| = 14$

2 Solving Absolute Value Inequalities

You can write absolute value inequalities as compound inequalities.

The graphs below show two absolute value inequalities.

$|n - 1| < 3$

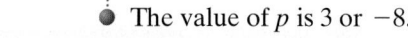

$|n - 1| > 3$

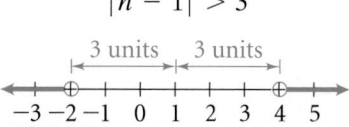

$|n - 1| < 3$ represents all numbers whose distance from 1 is less than 3 units. So $-3 < n - 1 < 3$.

$|n - 1| > 3$ represents all numbers whose distance from 1 is greater than 3 units. So $n - 1 < -3$ or $n - 1 > 3$.

 Key Concepts

Rule	**Solving Absolute Value Inequalities**

To solve an inequality in the form $|A| < b$, where A is a variable expression and $b > 0$, solve $-b < A < b$.

To solve an inequality in the form $|A| > b$, where A is a variable expression and $b > 0$, solve $A < -b$ or $A > b$.

Similar rules are true for $|A| \leq b$ or $|A| \geq b$.

3 EXAMPLE Solving an Absolute Value Inequality

Solve $|v - 3| \geq 4$. Graph the solutions.

$$v - 3 \leq -4 \quad\quad \text{or} \quad\quad v - 3 \geq 4 \quad\quad \text{Write a compound inequality.}$$
$$v - 3 + 3 \leq -4 + 3 \quad\quad\quad v - 3 + 3 \geq 4 + 3 \quad\quad \text{Add 3.}$$
$$v \leq -1 \quad\quad \text{or} \quad\quad v \geq 7 \quad\quad \text{Simplify.}$$

$$\begin{array}{ccccccccccc} -2 & -1 & 0 & 1 & 2 & 3 & 4 & 5 & 6 & 7 & 8 \end{array}$$

✓ **Quick Check** **3** **a.** Solve and graph $|w + 2| > 5$.
b. Critical Thinking What are the solutions of $|w + 2| > -5$?

To maintain quality, a manufacturer sets limits for how much an item can vary from its specifications. You can use an absolute value equation to model a quality-control situation.

4 EXAMPLE Real-World  Problem Solving

Manufacturing The ideal diameter of a piston for one type of car engine is 90.000 mm. The actual diameter can vary from the ideal by at most 0.008 mm. Find the range of acceptable diameters for the piston.

Relate | difference between actual and ideal | is at most | 0.008 mm |

Define Let d = actual diameter in millimeters of the cylindrical part.

Write | $|d - 90.000|$ | $\leq$ | 0.008 mm |

$$|d - 90.000| \leq 0.008$$
$$-0.008 \leq \quad d - 90.000 \quad \leq 0.008 \quad\quad \text{Write a compound inequality.}$$
$$-0.008 + 90.000 \leq d - 90.000 + 90.000 \leq 0.008 + 90.000 \quad\quad \text{Add 90.000.}$$
$$89.992 \leq \quad\quad d \quad\quad \leq 90.008 \quad\quad \text{Simplify.}$$

● The actual diameter must be between 89.992 mm and 90.008 mm, inclusive.

Real-World **Connection**

Careers A quality-control inspector inspects products to maintain quality. For engines produced on an assembly line, an inspector selects engines at random to check quality of materials and manufacturing.

✓ **Quick Check** **4** The ideal weight of one type of model airplane engine is 33.86 ounces. The actual weight may vary from the ideal by at most 0.05 ounce. Find the range of acceptable weights for this engine.

EXERCISES

For more exercises, see *Extra Skill and Word Problem Practice.*

Practice and Problem Solving

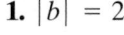 **Practice by Example**

Example 1
(page 411)

GO for Help

Solve each equation. If there is no solution, write *no solution.*

1. $|b| = 2$ **2.** $4 = |y|$ **3.** $|w| = \frac{1}{2}$

4. $|n| + 2 = 8$ **5.** $7 = |s| + 4$ **6.** $|x| - 10 = -3$

7. $4|d| = 20$ **8.** $-3|m| = -6$ **9.** $|y| + 3 = 3$

10. $12 = -4|k|$ **11.** $2|z| - 5 = 1$ **12.** $16 = 5|p| - 4$

Example 2
(page 412)

Solve each equation. If there is no solution, write *no solution.*

13. $|r - 8| = 5$ **14.** $|c + 2| = 6$ **15.** $2 = |g + 1|$

16. $3 = |m + 2|$ **17.** $|v - 2| = 7$ **18.** $-3|y - 3| = 9$

19. $2|d + 3| = 8$ **20.** $-2|7d| = -14$ **21.** $1.2|5p| = 3.6$

Example 3
(page 413)

22. Complete each statement with *less than* or *greater than.*
   a. For $|x| < 5$, the graph includes all points whose distance is __?__ 5 units from 0.
   b. For $|x| > 5$, the graph includes all points whose distance is __?__ 5 units from 0.

Solve each inequality. Graph your solution.

23. $|k| > 2.5$ **24.** $|w| < 2$ **25.** $|x + 3| < 5$

26. $|n + 8| \geq 3$ **27.** $|y - 2| \leq 1$ **28.** $|p - 4| \leq 3$

29. $|2c - 5| < 9$ **30.** $|2y - 3| \geq 7$ **31.** $|3t + 1| > 8$

32. $|4x + 1| > 11$ **33.** $|5t - 4| \geq 16$ **34.** $|3 - r| < 5$

Example 4
(page 413)

35. Manufacturing The ideal diameter of a gear for a certain type of clock is 12.24 mm. An actual diameter can vary by 0.06 mm. Find the range of acceptable diameters.

36. Manufacturing The ideal width of a certain conveyor belt for a manufacturing plant is 50 in. An actual conveyor belt can vary from the ideal by at most $\frac{7}{32}$ in. Find the acceptable widths for this conveyor belt.

B **Apply Your Skills**

Solve each equation or inequality.

37. $|2d| + 3 = 21$ **38.** $|-3n| - 2 = 7$ **39.** $|p| - \frac{2}{3} = \frac{5}{6}$

40. $|t| + 2.7 = 4.5$ **41.** $4|k + 1| = 16$ **42.** $-2|c - 4| = -8$

43. $|3d| \geq 6$ **44.** $|n| - 3 > 7$ **45.** $9 < |c + 7|$

46. $\frac{|v|}{-3} = -4.2$ **47.** $|6.5x| < 39$ **48.** $4|n| = 32$

49. $\left|\frac{1}{2}a\right| + 1 = 5$ **50.** $|a| + \frac{1}{2} = 3\frac{1}{2}$ **51.** $4 - 3|m + 2| > -14$

Write an absolute value inequality that represents each situation.

52. all numbers less than 3 units from 0

53. all numbers more than 7.5 units from 0

54. all numbers more than 2 units from 6

55. all numbers at least 3 units from –1

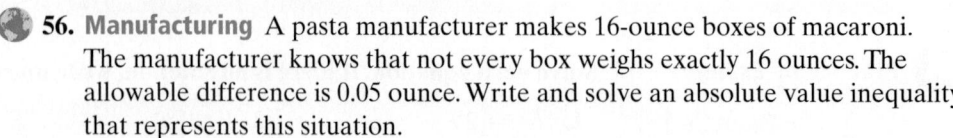 **56. Manufacturing** A pasta manufacturer makes 16-ounce boxes of macaroni. The manufacturer knows that not every box weighs exactly 16 ounces. The allowable difference is 0.05 ounce. Write and solve an absolute value inequality that represents this situation.

57. Elections In a poll for the upcoming mayoral election, 42% of likely voters said they planned to vote for Lucy Jones. This poll has a margin of error of ± 3 percentage points. Use the inequality $|v - 42| \leq 3$ to find the least and greatest percent of voters v likely to vote for Lucy Jones according to this poll.

58. Quality Control A box of one brand of crackers should weigh 454 g. The quality-control inspector randomly selects boxes to weigh. The inspector sends back any box that is not within 5 g of the ideal weight.
  a. Write an absolute value inequality for this situation.
  b. What is the range of allowable weights for a box of crackers?

59. Gears Acceptable diameters for one type of gear are from 6.25 mm to 6.29 mm. Write an absolute value inequality for the acceptable diameters for the gear.

60. Writing Explain why the absolute value inequality $|2c - 5| + 9 < 4$ has no solution.

61. Open-Ended Write an absolute value equation using the numbers $5, 3, -12$. Then solve your equation.

Write an absolute value equation that has the given values as solutions.

Sample $8, 2$

$|x - 5| = 3$ Since 8 and 2 are both 3 units from 5, write $|x - 5| = 3$.

62. $2, 6$ **63.** $-2, 6$ **64.** $-3, 9$ **65.** $9, 16$

66. $-1, 7$ **67.** $3, 8$ **68.** $-15, -3$ **69.** $2, 10$

70. Banking The ideal weight of a nickel is 0.176 ounce. To check that there are 40 nickels in a roll, a bank weighs the roll and allows for an error of 0.015 ounce in the total weight.
  a. What is the range of acceptable weights if the wrapper weighs 0.05 ounce?
  b. Critical Thinking For any given roll of nickels, can you be certain that all the coins are acceptable? Explain.

71. a. Meteorology A meteorologist reported that the previous day's temperatures varied 14 degrees from the normal temperature of 25°F. What were the maximum and minimum temperatures possible on the previous day?
  b. Write an absolute value equation for the temperature.

Challenge   **Solve each equation. Check your solution.**

72. $|x + 4| = 3x$ **73.** $|4x - 5| = 2x + 1$ **74.** $\frac{4}{3}|2x + 3| = 4x$

Replace the ■ with ≤, ≥, or =.

75. $|a + b|$ ■ $|a| + |b|$ **76.** $|a - b|$ ■ $|a| - |b|$

77. $|ab|$ ■ $|a| \cdot |b|$ **78.** $\left|\frac{a}{b}\right|$ ■ $\frac{|a|}{|b|}, b \neq 0$

Write an absolute value inequality that each graph could represent.

79.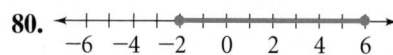

80. ◄─┼─┼─┼─┼─◆─┼─┼─┼─┼─◆─┼─┼─►
       -6 -4 -2 0 2 4 6

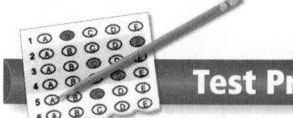

Test Prep

Multiple Choice

81. Which compound inequality has the same meaning as $|x + 4| < 8$?
     A. $-12 < x < 4$ **B.** $-12 > x > 4$
     C. $x < -12$ or $x > 4$ **D.** $x > -12$ or $x < 4$

82. Which of the following values is a solution of $|2 - x| < 4$?
     F. -2 **G.** -1 **H.** 6 **J.** 7

83. The ideal diameter of a metal rod for a lamp is 1.25 inches with an allowable error of at most 0.005 inch. Which rod below would not be suitable?
  A. a rod with diameter 1.249 inches
  B. a rod with diameter 1.251 inches
  C. a rod with diameter 1.253 inches
  D. a rod with diameter 1.355 inches

84. A delivery driver receives a bonus if he delivers pizza to a customer in 30 minutes plus or minus 5 minutes. Which inequality or equation represents the driver's allotted time to receive a bonus?

  F. $|x - 30| < 5$ **G.** $|x - 30| > 5$

  H. $|x - 30| = 5$ **J.** $|x - 30| \leq 5$

85. Water is in a liquid state if its temperature t, in degrees Fahrenheit, satisfies the inequality $|t - 122| < 90$. Which graph represents the temperatures described by this inequality?

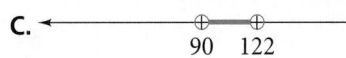
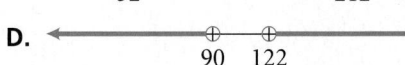

Short Response

86. A bicycling club is planning a trip. The graphs below show the number of miles three people want to cycle per day.

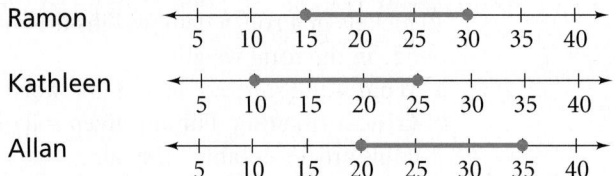

  a. Draw a graph showing a trip length that would be acceptable to all three bikers.
  b. Explain how your graph relates to the graphs above.

Mixed Review

Lesson 7-5

Write a compound inequality to model each situation.

87. Elevation in North America is between the highest elevation of 20,320 ft above sea level at Mount McKinley, Alaska, and the lowest elevation of 282 ft below sea level at Death Valley, California.

88. Normal body temperature t is within 0.6 degrees of 36.6°C.

Lesson 6-2

Solve each equation.

89. $3t + 4t = -21$ **90.** $9(-2n + 3) = -27$ **91.** $k + 5 - 4k = -10$

92. $5x + 3 - 2x = -21$ **93.** $5.4m - 2.3 = -0.5$ **94.** $3(y - 4) = 9$

Lesson 4-3

Write each group of numbers from least to greatest.

95. $3, -2, 0, -2.5, \pi$ **96.** $\frac{15}{2}, -1.5, -\frac{4}{3}, 7, -2$

97. $0.001, 0.01, 0.009, 0.011$ **98.** $-\pi, 2\pi, -2.5, -3, 3$

You can use the properties you have studied along with the four properties below to prove algebraic relationships.

Reflexive, Symmetric, and Transitive Properties of Equality

For every real number a, b, and c:

Reflexive Property: $a = a$ **Example:** $5x = 5x$

Symmetric Property: If $a = b$, then $b = a$.   **Example:** If $15 = 3t$, then $3t = 15$.

Transitive Property: If $a = b$ and $b = c$,   **Example:** If $d = 3y$ and $3y = 6$,
then $a = c$.   then $d = 6$.

Transitive Property of Inequality

For all real numbers a, b, and c,   **Example:** If $8x < 7$ and $7 < y^2$, then
if $a < b$ and $b < c$, then $a < c$. $8x < y^2$.

EXAMPLE

Prove each statement for all real numbers a, b, and c.

a. If $a = b$, then $ac = bc$.

$a = b$	Given
$ac = ac$	Reflexive Property
$ac = bc$	Substitute b for a.

b. If $c < 0$ and $a < b$, then $c < b - a$.

$c < 0$	Given
$a < b$	Given
$a - a < b - a$	Subtraction Property of Inequality
$a + (-a) < b - a$	Definition of subtraction
$0 < b - a$	Inverse Property of Addition
$c < b - a$	Transitive Property of Inequality

EXERCISES

Name the property that each exercise illustrates.

1. If $3.8 = z$, then $z = 3.8$.   **2.** If $x = \frac{1}{2}y$ and $\frac{1}{2}y = -2$, then $x = -2$.   **3.** $-r = -r$

4. If $k < m^2$ and $m^2 < 4$, then $k < 4$.   **5.** If $x = w^2$, then $w^2 = x$.

Supply the missing reasons to prove each statement.

6. $(a + b) + (-a) = b$

$(a + b) + (-a) = (b + a) + (-a)$	?
$= b + [a + (-a)]$	?
$= b + 0$	?
$= b$	?
$(a + b) + (-a) = b$	?

7. If $a < b$ and $c < d$, then $a + c < b + d$.

$a < b$	Given
$a + c < b + c$	?
$c < d$	Given
$b + c < b + d$	?
$a + c < b + d$	?

Some test items may ask you to interpret a situation displayed in a graph. To answer the questions correctly, you must read the data shown in the graph carefully.

EXAMPLE

The graph shows the number of hours Gloria worked over a seven-day period.

Based on the graph, which statement is NOT true?
- (A) Gloria worked more than 21.5 hours over the course of the week.
- (B) Gloria worked fewer hours on Wednesday than she did on Monday.
- (C) Gloria worked more hours on Friday than she did on Monday, Tuesday, and Wednesday combined.
- (D) Gloria never worked more than 8 hours on any single day.
- (E) Gloria averaged more than 3 hours per day over the seven days.

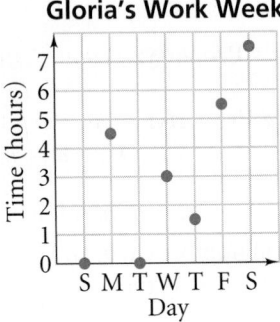

Gloria's Work Week

Read the values off the graph to test the statements.

A. Find the total number of hours Gloria worked.
   Total hours = $0 + 4.5 + 0 + 3 + 1.5 + 5.5 + 7.5 = 22$ ✓   Statement A is true.

B. Compare the number of hours Gloria worked on Monday and Wednesday.
   $3 < 4.5$ ✓   Statement B is true.

C. Find the total hours Gloria worked on Monday, Tuesday, and Wednesday. Then compare with the hours she worked on Friday.
   $4.5 + 0 + 3 = 7.5$, $5.5 > 7.5$ ✗   Statement C is false.

D. The greatest number of hours Gloria worked on a single day was 7.5 hours on Saturday. $7.5 \leq 8$ ✓   Statement D is true.

E. Divide the total hours by the number of days.
   $\frac{22}{7} = 3\frac{1}{7} > 3$ ✓   Statement E is true.

● Statement C is NOT true so C is the correct answer.

EXERCISE

1. Based on the graph shown above, which statement is true?
- (A) Gloria worked 3 hours more on Monday than she did on Wednesday.
- (B) If Gloria earns $7 per hour, she would have earned $140.50 over the course of the week.
- (C) Gloria worked all 7 days that week.
- (D) Gloria worked a total of 13 hours on her two longest workdays.
- (E) Gloria did not work on Saturday.

Chapter Review

Vocabulary Review

🔊 compound inequalities (p. 403)   equivalent inequalities (p. 382)   solution of an inequality (p. 376)

Write the letter of the choice that correctly completes each sentence.

1. A solution of an inequality is any number that makes the inequality __?__.
   A. complete
   C. true
   B. reverse direction
   D. false

2. An inequality is equivalent to another inequality if the two inequalities have __?__.
   A. the same number of terms
   C. real-number solutions
   B. the same graphs
   D. no solutions

Go Online
PHSchool.com

For: Vocabulary quiz
Web Code: atj-0451

3. Compound inequalities are joined by __?__.
   A. either the word *and* or the word *or*
   C. the word *and*
   B. the word *or*
   D. equations

4. Write the expression "absolute value of *x*" as __?__.
   A. [*x*]   **B.** −*x*   **C.** |*x*| **D.** *a* = *x*

5. A number's distance from 0 on a number line is the number's __?__.
   A. solution of an inequality
   C. equivalent form
   B. compound form
   D. absolute value

Skills and Concepts

7-1 Objectives

▼ To identify solutions of inequalities (p. 376)

▼ To graph and write inequalities (p. 377)

A **solution of an inequality** is any number that makes the inequality true. A graph can indicate all the solutions of an inequality. On the graph, a closed dot indicates that the number is a solution. An open dot indicates that the number is *not* a solution.

Graph each inequality.

   6. $x > 3$ **7.** $m \le -5$ **8.** $10 \ge p$ **9.** $r < 2.5$

Write an inequality for each graph.

10.
−4 −3 −2 −1 0 1

11.
−5 −4 −3 −2 −1 0 1

12.
−10 −8 −6 −4 −2 0 2

13.
−2 −1 0 1 2 3 4

Define a variable and write an inequality to model each situation.

14. At least 600 people attended a school play.

15. An elevator can carry at most 15 people.

16. The temperature was less than 32°F.

7-2 and 7-3 Objectives

▼ To use addition to solve inequalities (p. 382)

▼ To use subtraction to solve inequalities (p. 383)

▼ To use multiplication to solve inequalities (p. 388)

▼ To use division to solve inequalities (p. 390)

To solve inequalities, you may need to find a simpler, equivalent inequality. **Equivalent inequalities** have the same solution. You can add, subtract, multiply, or divide both sides of an inequality by the same number to find a simpler equivalent inequality. Multiplying or dividing by a negative number causes the direction of the inequality symbol to be *reversed*.

Properties of Inequality

For all real numbers a, b, and c:

- If $a > b$, then $a + c > b + c$ and $a - c > b - c$.
- If $a < b$, then $a + c < b + c$ and $a - c < b - c$.
- If $a > b$ and $c > 0$, then $ac > bc$ and $\frac{a}{c} > \frac{b}{c}$.
- If $a < b$ and $c > 0$, then $ac < bc$ and $\frac{a}{c} < \frac{b}{c}$.
- If $a > b$ and $c < 0$, then $ac < bc$ and $\frac{a}{c} < \frac{b}{c}$.
- If $a < b$ and $c < 0$, then $ac > bc$ and $\frac{a}{c} > \frac{b}{c}$.

These properties are also true for inequalities involving $\leq$ and $\geq$.

Solve each inequality. Graph and check the solution.

17. $h + 3 > 2$ **18.** $t - 4 < -9$ **19.** $8m \geq -24$ **20.** $-6w \leq 12$

21. $q + 0.5 > -2$ **22.** $y - 8 > -22$ **23.** $-\frac{3}{5}n \geq -9$ **24.** $\frac{5}{8}d \geq \frac{5}{2}$

25. $0 \leq 2 + t$ **26.** $0 < 4c$ **27.** $-0.3 \geq u - 2.8$ **28.** $3 > -\frac{1}{3}p$

29. Weekly Budget You have an allowance of $12.00. You buy a discount movie ticket that costs at least $3.50 and popcorn that costs $2.75. Write and solve an inequality to find how much you have for other spending.

30. Jobs Suppose you earn $7.25 per hour working part-time as a florist. Write and solve an inequality to find how many full hours you must work to earn at least $200.

7-4 Objectives

▼ To solve multi-step inequalities with variables on one side (p. 395)

▼ To solve multi-step inequalities with variables on both sides (p. 397)

When you solve equations, sometimes you need to use more than one step. The same is true for inequalities. Many inequalities have variables on both sides of the inequality symbol. You need to gather the variable terms on one side of the inequality and the constant terms on the other side.

Solve each inequality. Check your solution.

31. $3n + 5 > -1$ **32.** $4k - 1 \leq -3$ **33.** $\frac{5}{8}b < 25$

34. $6(c - 1) \leq -18$ **35.** $3m > 5m + 12$ **36.** $t - 4t < -9$

37. $0.5x - 2 \geq -4x + 7$ **38.** $-\frac{6}{7}y - 6 \geq 42$ **39.** $4 + \frac{x}{2} > 2x$

40. Commission Trenton sells electronic supplies. Each week he earns $190 plus a commission equal to 4% of his sales. This week his goal is to earn no less than $500. Write and solve an inequality to find the amount of sales he must have to reach his goal.

Two inequalities that are joined by the word *and* or the word *or* are called **compound inequalities.** A solution of a compound inequality joined by *and* makes both inequalities true. A solution of a compound inequality joined by *or* makes either inequality true. A number sentence with two inequality symbols, such as $a < x < b$ represents the compound inequality $a < x$ and $x < b$.

Graph each compound inequality.

41. $x > -3$ and $x < 2$　　**42.** $m < -2$ or $m \geq 1$　　**43.** $-3 \leq k < 4$

Solve each compound inequality and graph the solutions.

44. $-3 \leq z - 1 < 3$　　**45.** $-2 \leq d + \frac{1}{2} < 4\frac{1}{2}$　　**46.** $0 < -8b \leq 12$

47. $2t \leq -4$ or $7t \geq 49$　　**48.** $-1 \leq a - 3 < 2$　　**49.** $-2 \leq 3a - 8 < 4$

50. Climate In Miami, Florida, July's average high temperature is 89°F. July's average low temperature is 75°F. Write a compound inequality to represent Miami's average temperature in July.

Recall that the absolute value of a number is its distance from 0 on a number line. Since absolute value represents distance, it can never be negative.

Solving Absolute Value Equations and Inequalities

- To solve an equation in the form $|A| = b$, where A represents a variable expression and $b > 0$, solve the equations $A = b$ or $A = -b$.
- To solve an inequality in the form $|A| < b$, where A represents a variable expression and $b > 0$, solve $-b < A < b$.
- To solve an inequality in the form $|A| > b$, where A represents a variable expression and $b > 0$, solve $A < -b$ or $A > b$.

Similar rules are true for $|A| \leq b$ and $|A| \geq b$.

Write an absolute value inequality that represents each set of numbers.

51. all numbers n that are more than 3 units from -2

52. all numbers n that are within 5 units of 12

Solve each equation or inequality.

53. $|y| = 5$　　　　**54.** $|n + 2| \geq 4$　　　**55.** $|-5x| \leq 15$

56. $\left|\frac{1}{2}m\right| < 4.8$　　**57.** $|2x - 7| - 1 > 0$　　**58.** $|p + 3| = 9.5$

59. $|k - 8| = 0$　　**60.** $|3x + 5| > -2$　　**61.** $|6 - b| = -1$

62. $4|k + 5| > 8$　　**63.** $4 + |r + 2| = 7$　　**64.** $-2 + |3.6z| \geq -1.1$

65. Manufacturing The ideal diameter of a steel reinforcement rod is 2.8 cm. The actual diameter may vary from the ideal by at most 0.06 cm. Find the range of acceptable diameters for this steel rod.

66. Manufacturing The ideal length of a certain nail is 20 mm. The actual length can vary from the ideal by at most 0.4 mm. Find the range of acceptable lengths of the nail.

Chapter Test

Go Online
PHSchool.com
For: Chapter Test
Web Code: ata-0452

Determine whether each number is a solution of the given inequality.

1. $4z + 7 \geq 15$ **a.** -2 **b.** 2 **c.** 5

2. $-2g + 3 > 5$ **a.** -3 **b.** -1 **c.** 4

Define a variable and write an inequality to model each situation.

3. A student can take at most 7 classes.

4. The school track team needs at least 5 runners to compete at Saturday's meet.

5. Elephants can drink up to 40 gallons of water at a time.

6. Your cousin's early-morning paper route has more than 32 homes.

Write an inequality for each graph.

7. [number line: $-12 \, -10 \, -8 \, -6 \, -4 \, -2 \, 0 \, 2 \, 4$; open circle at -7, shaded left]

8. [number line: $-1 \, 0 \, 1 \, 2 \, 3 \, 4 \, 5 \, 6$; closed circle at 4, shaded left]

9. [number line: $-6 \, -5 \, -4 \, -3 \, -2 \, -1 \, 0 \, 1$; closed circle at -5, shaded right]

10. [number line: $-2 \, -1 \, 0 \, 1 \, 2 \, 3 \, 4 \, 5$; open circle at 3, shaded right]

Solve each inequality. Graph the solution.

11. $z + 7 \leq 9$

12. $-16 \geq 4y$

13. $-\frac{1}{3}x < 2$

14. $8 - u > 4$

15. $-5 + 4t \leq 3$

16. $5w \geq -6w + 11$

17. $-\frac{7}{2}m < 14$

18. $6y - 7 < -2y + 13$

19. $|x - 5| \geq 3$

20. $|2h + 1| < 5$

21. $9 \leq 6 - b < 12$

22. $-10 < 4q < 12$

23. $4 + 3n \geq 1$ or $-5n > 25$

24. $10k < 75$ and $4 - k \leq 0$

Solve each inequality. Check your solution.

25. $3(d - 1) > -4$

26. $5(-2 + b) < 3b + 2$

27. $3(m + 3) + 4 \leq 15$

28. $0.5(x + 3) - 2.1 \geq -1$

Write a compound inequality that each graph could represent.

29. [number line: $-10 \, -8 \, -6 \, -4 \, -2 \, 0 \, 2 \, 4 \, 6$; closed circle at -7, open circle at 3]

30. [number line: $-4 \, -3 \, -2 \, -1 \, 0 \, 1 \, 2 \, 3 \, 4$; open circle at -3, open circle at 2]

Solve each equation. Check your solution.

31. $|4k - 2| = 11$

32. $23 = |n + 10|$

33. $|3c + 1| - 4 = 13$

34. $4|5 - t| = 20$

35. **Writing** Explain why the solution to $ax - 1 < 3$ is not $x < \frac{4}{a}$. Use solutions of the inequality with different values of a to support your explanation.

36. **Open-Ended** Write an absolute value inequality that has 3 and -5 as two of its solutions.

37. **Community Service** The chart below shows the number of cans of food collected by a club during the first four weeks of a food drive.

Food Drive

Week	Number of Cans
1	702
2	470
3	492
4	547

The goal is to collect at least 3000 cans in 5 weeks. Write and solve an inequality to find how many cans should be collected during Week 5 to meet or exceed the goal.

38. **Safe Load** A freight elevator can safely hold no more than 2000 pounds. An elevator operator must take 55-pound boxes to a storage area. If he weighs 165 pounds, how many boxes can he safely move at one time?

39. **Manufacturing** A manufacturer is cutting plastic sheets to make rectangles that are 11.125 in. by 7.625 in. Each rectangle's length and width must be within 0.005 in. of the desired size. Write and solve inequalities to find the acceptable range for the length ℓ and for the width w.

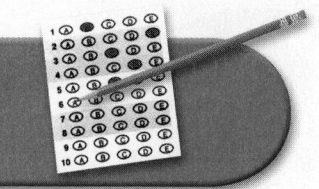

Standardized Test Prep

Multiple Choice

For Exercises 1–14, choose the correct letter.

1. A store owner has a bicycle priced at $100. She raises the price 10%. During a sale, she then lowers the price 10%. What is the new price of the bicycle?

   Ⓐ $101   Ⓑ $100   Ⓒ $99   Ⓓ $98

2. A bag contains 8 green marbles and 12 blue marbles. You draw a marble, return it to the bag, and draw another. What is the probability of drawing two green marbles?

   Ⓔ $\frac{4}{25}$ Ⓕ $\frac{4}{9}$ Ⓖ $\frac{7}{50}$ Ⓗ $\frac{4}{5}$

3. Which equation does *not* have the same solution as $\frac{7}{y} = \frac{31}{36}$?

   Ⓐ $\frac{7}{31} = \frac{y}{36}$ Ⓑ $7 \cdot 36 = 31y$

   Ⓒ $\frac{y}{36} = \frac{7}{31}$ Ⓓ $\frac{36}{31} = \frac{7}{y}$

4. The number of subscribers to a magazine fell from 210,000 to 190,000. Find the approximate percent of decrease.

   Ⓔ 5%   Ⓕ 10%   Ⓖ 20%   Ⓗ 90%

5. Which are solutions of $3(x - 4) \le 18$ and $2(x - 1) \ge 6$?

   I. 9   II. 12   III. 15

   Ⓐ I only   Ⓑ II only
   Ⓒ I and III   Ⓓ II and III

6. In February, rent increased from $875 per month to $915 per month. What was the percent of increase to the nearest percent?

   Ⓔ 4%   Ⓕ 5%   Ⓖ 40%   Ⓗ 50%

7. The solutions of which inequality are $x > 9$ or $x < -1$?

   Ⓐ $|x + 4| < 5$ Ⓑ $|x - 4| < 5$
   Ⓒ $|x + 4| > 5$ Ⓓ $|x - 4| > 5$

8. Which equation has no solution?

   Ⓔ $4\left(\frac{1}{2}x - 1\right) = \frac{1}{2}$ Ⓕ $5 - 6x = 2(1 - 3x)$

   Ⓖ $6(2x - 3) = 2(6x - 9)$

   Ⓗ $7(x + 8) - x = 0$

9. Simplify $15 - 5 \times 2 + 4^2$.

   Ⓐ 13   Ⓑ 21   Ⓒ 28   Ⓓ 36

10. Solve $8x - 2y = 3$ for y.

    Ⓔ $y = \frac{-5x}{2}$ Ⓕ $y = \frac{3 - 8x}{2}$

    Ⓖ $y = \frac{8x - 3}{2}$ Ⓗ $y = \frac{8x + 3}{2}$

11. What percent of 280 is 350?

    Ⓐ 125%   Ⓑ 80%   Ⓒ 25%   Ⓓ 20%

12. Between which two integers is $\sqrt{45}$?

    Ⓔ 22 and 23   Ⓕ 45 and 46
    Ⓖ 7 and 8   Ⓗ 6 and 7

13. Simplify $-6(2t - 8)$.

    Ⓐ $-12t + 48$ Ⓑ $-6t + 48$
    Ⓒ $-4t - 8$ Ⓓ $-12t - 48$

14. If you roll a number cube, what are the odds in favor of getting a multiple of 3?

    Ⓔ 1 : 1   Ⓕ 1 : 2
    Ⓖ 1 : 3   Ⓗ 3 : 1

Gridded Response

Find each answer.

15. A CD player that normally costs $225 would cost an employee $180. What is the percent of the employee's discount?

16. The two rectangles are similar. Find the perimeter of the smaller rectangle in centimeters.

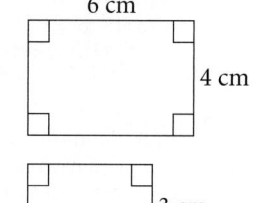

17. A right triangle has legs which are 7 in. and 9 in. Find the length of the hypotenuse to the nearest tenth of an inch.

Short Response

Show your work.

18. Suppose you earn $80 a week at your summer job. Your employer offers you a $20 raise or a 20% raise. Which should you take? Explain.

19. Two boats leave a ramp traveling in opposite directions. The second boat is 10 miles per hour faster than the first. After 3 hours they are 150 miles apart. Find the speeds of the boats.

Activity Lab

Shifting Gears

Applying Variation Gears and levers can make a job easier, but there is a trade-off for efficiency. For instance, the higher gears on a bicycle allow you to go farther with each rotation of the pedals, but the price you pay is pushing harder. Conversely, in first gear you don't have to push hard, but you also don't go very fast.

Activity 1

Materials: paper and pencil

Bicycle data: tire diameter = 26 in., chainwheel diameter = 6 in., sprocket diameter in first gear = 5 in., sprocket diameter in second gear = 4.5 in., sprocket diameter in third gear = 4 in.

a. Use the transmission equation and the bike travel equation below to find out how far the bicycle will travel in first gear when the chainwheel is turned once by the rider. Repeat the calculation for second gear and for third gear.

b. Your calculations indicate the relative speeds at which the bicycle moves in different gears. How many times faster is third gear than first gear?

Transmission Equation

$$\frac{d_1}{d_2} = \frac{N_2}{N_1}$$

N_1 and N_2 are the number of rotations of the chainwheel and the sprocket.

Bike Travel Equation

$$L = \pi d_3 N_3$$

N_3 is the number of rotations of the back tire.
(*Hint:* How does N_3 relate to N_2?)

d_1 = diameter of chainwheel
d_2 = diameter of sprocket
d_3 = diameter of back tire
L = distance bicycle travels

Shifting Gears
Some mountain bikes have gears you can shift with your thumb, allowing your other fingers to remain curled around the handlebars to maintain control.

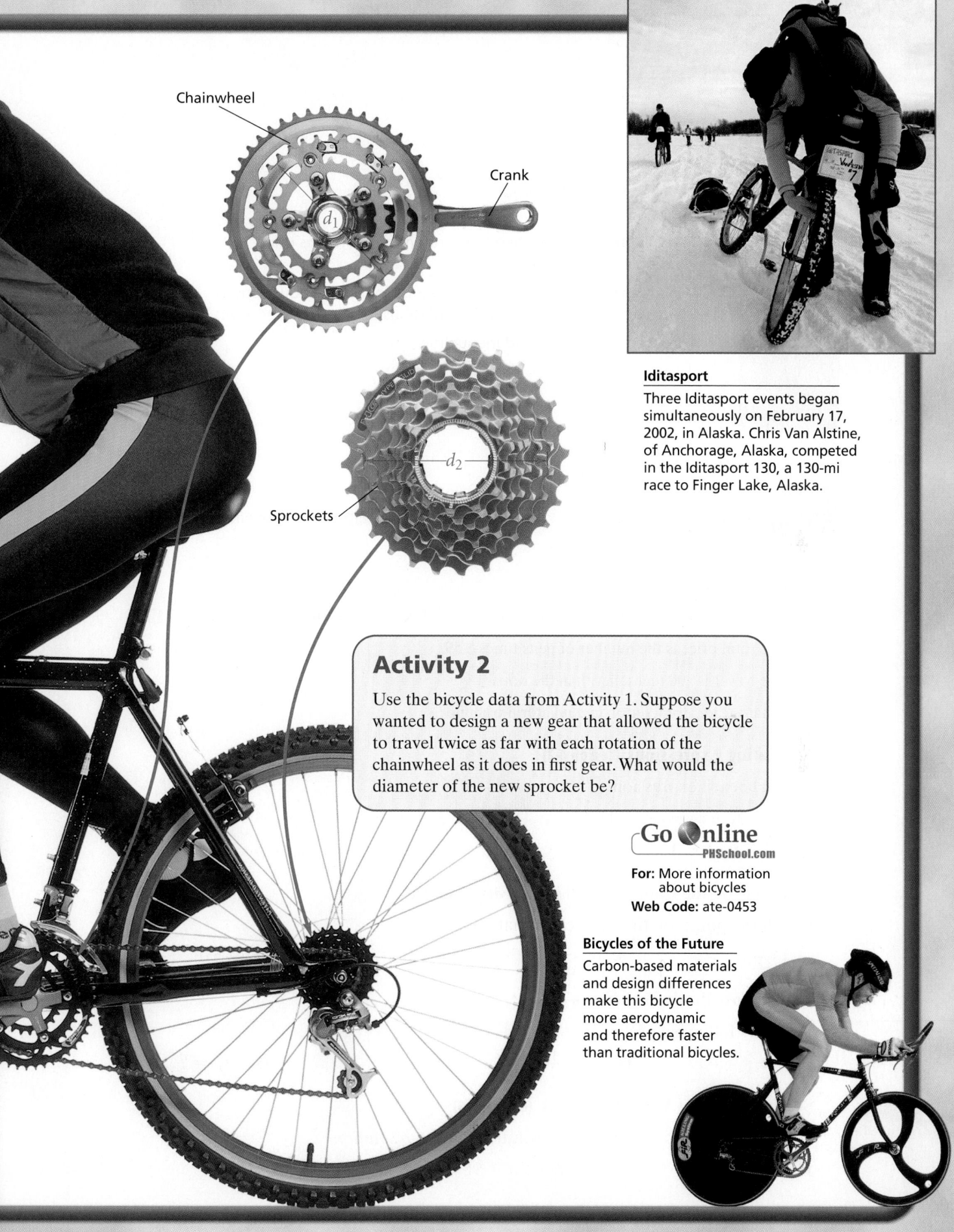

Chainwheel

Crank

d_1

Sprockets

d_2

Iditasport

Three Iditasport events began simultaneously on February 17, 2002, in Alaska. Chris Van Alstine, of Anchorage, Alaska, competed in the Iditasport 130, a 130-mi race to Finger Lake, Alaska.

Activity 2

Use the bicycle data from Activity 1. Suppose you wanted to design a new gear that allowed the bicycle to travel twice as far with each rotation of the chainwheel as it does in first gear. What would the diameter of the new sprocket be?

Go Online
PHSchool.com

For: More information about bicycles
Web Code: ate-0453

Bicycles of the Future

Carbon-based materials and design differences make this bicycle more aerodynamic and therefore faster than traditional bicycles.

What You've Learned

- In Chapter 4, you learned to represent relationships using variables, and explored function patterns.

- In Chapter 6, you learned the methods for solving equations in one variable and applied those methods to solving proportions.

- In Chapter 7, you solved inequalities.

 **Check Your Readiness** **for Help** to the Lesson in green.

Writing Equations (Lesson 4-1)

Define a variable and write an equation to model each situation.

1. The total price is the number of pens times $.59.

2. The tower is 200 feet taller than the house.

3. What is the perimeter of an equilateral triangle?

Evaluating Expressions (Lesson 4-2)

Evaluate each expression.

4. $3x - 2y$, for $x = -1$ and $y = 2$

5. $-w^2 + 3w$, for $w = -3$

6. $\frac{3 + k}{k}$, for $k = 3$

7. $h - (h^2 - 1) \div 2$, for $h = -1$

Graphing on the Coordinate Plane (Review page 200)

Graph the points on the same coordinate plane.

8. $(3, -3)$ **9.** $(0, -5)$ **10.** $(-2, 2)$ **11.** $(-2, 0)$

Using Cross Products (Lesson 6-4)

Solve the following proportions.

12. $\frac{4}{w} = \frac{5}{8}$ **13.** $\frac{c}{2.2} = \frac{3}{11}$ **14.** $\frac{4}{0.5} = \frac{36}{p}$ **15.** $-\frac{29}{2} = \frac{d}{4}$

Solving Absolute Value Equations (Lesson 7-6)

Solve each equation. If there is no solution, write *no solution*.

16. $|r + 2| = 2$ **17.** $-3|d - 5| = -6$ **18.** $-3.2 = |8p|$

Graphs and Functions

◀)) **Key Vocabulary**

- arithmetic sequence (p. 469)
- common difference (p. 469)
- conjecture (p. 468)
- constant of variation for direct variation (p. 454)
- constant of variation for inverse variation (p. 461)
- continuous data (p. 440)
- direct variation (p. 454)
- discrete data (p. 440)
- function notation (p. 434)
- inductive reasoning (p. 468)
- inverse variation (p. 461)
- relation (p. 433)
- sequence (p. 469)
- term (p. 469)
- vertical-line test (p. 434)

What You'll Learn Next

- In this chapter, you will move from the specific case of equations in one variable to the study of functions in two variables.

- You will learn about function rules, and model data using equations, tables, and graphs.

- You will learn how to use inductive reasoning for recognizing number patterns called sequences.

Data Analysis

Activity Lab Extending your knowledge and understanding of data analysis, you will interpret and construct histograms, on pages 480–481.

Relating Graphs to Events

What You'll Learn

- To interpret, sketch, and analyze graphs from situations

...And Why

To use a sketch in showing a plane's altitude during a flight, as in Example 2

Check Skills You'll Need

Use the graph at the right.

Name the point with the given coordinates.

1. $(4, -2)$ **2.** $(4, 3)$

3. $(2, -4)$ **4.** $(-2, 1)$

Name the coordinates of each given point.

5. B **6.** F **7.** G

GO for Help Review page 200

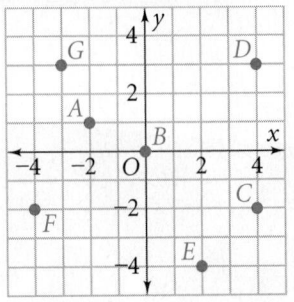

---

1   Interpreting, Sketching, and Analyzing Graphs

You can use an equation, an inequality, or a proportion to make a statement about a variable. You can use a graph to show the relationship between two variables. For example, you can use a graph to show how a quantity changes over time.

1 EXAMPLE   Interpreting Graphs

Commute One student walks and takes a bus to get from school to home each day. The graph at the right shows the student's commute by relating the time the student spends commuting and the distance he travels.

Describe what the graph shows by labeling each part.

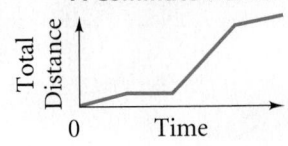

A Commute Home

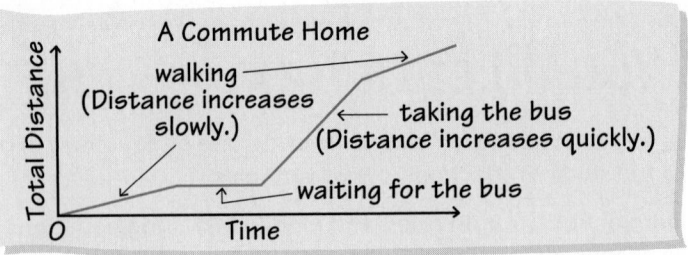

Quick Check

1 The graph at the right shows a trip from home to school and back. The trip involves walking and getting a ride from a neighbor. Copy the graph and label each section.

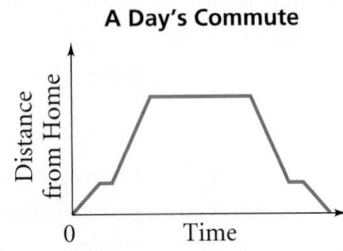

A Day's Commute

Real-World Connection

The Statue of Liberty, in New York harbor, is 151 ft from base to torch. The clock tower, which is part of the Houses of Parliament in London, is 320 ft tall.

In Example 1, distance, which is on the vertical axis, depends on time, which is on the horizontal axis. When one quantity depends on another, show the dependent quantity on the vertical axis.

2 EXAMPLE Sketching a Graph

Travel A plane is flying from New York to London. Sketch a graph of the plane's altitude during the flight. Label each section.

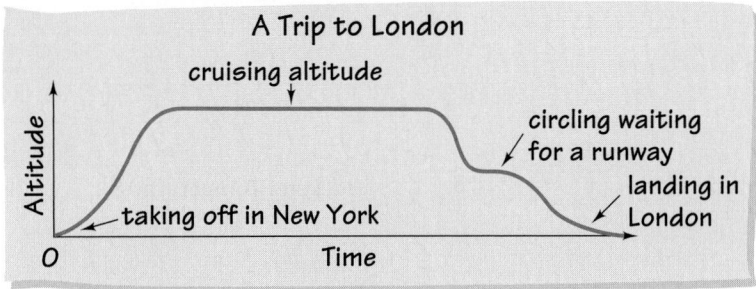

✓ Quick Check ② Sketch a graph of the distance from a child's feet to the ground as the child jumps rope. Label each section.

Most of the graphs in this lesson do not have numbers along the axes. You can analyze a graph based on the shape of the graph alone.

3 EXAMPLE Relating Graphs to Situations

Multiple Choice Suppose you pour water into the container at a steady rate. Which graph shows the change in the height of the liquid in the container over time?

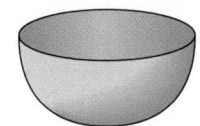

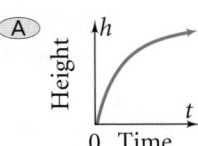 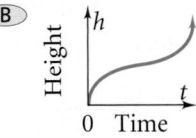

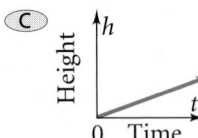 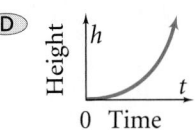

The rate that water rises will decrease steadily because the container gets wider from the bottom to the top. So, A is the correct answer.

✓ Quick Check ③ The graph at the right shows the time and distance of a moving object. Which of the following situations could be described by the graph?
- Ⓕ A car travels at a steady speed.
- Ⓖ A cyclist slows down as she rides up a hill and speeds up as she peddles over the top.
- Ⓗ A train slows down as it arrives at the station.
- Ⓙ A plane accelerates steadily down the runway until it takes off.

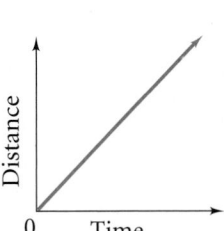

EXERCISES

For more exercises, see *Extra Skill and Word Problem Practice*.

Practice and Problem Solving

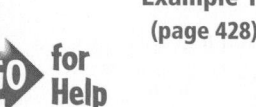 **Practice by Example**

Example 1
(page 428)

for Help

Copy each graph. Label each section of the graph.

1.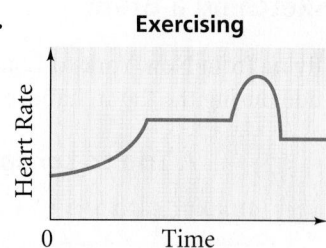
Exercising

2.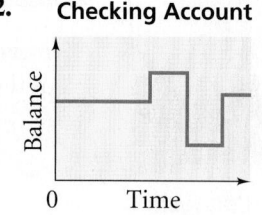
Checking Account

3.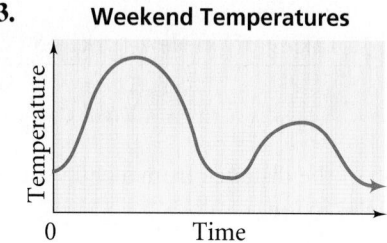
Weekend Temperatures

4.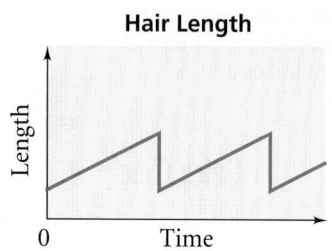
Hair Length

Example 2
(page 429)

Sketch a graph of each situation. Label each section.

5. hours of daylight over the course of one year

6. your distance from the ground as you ride a Ferris wheel for five minutes

7. your pulse rate as you watch a scary movie

8. your walking speed during five minutes between classes

Example 3
(page 429)

9. Cooking You turn on your oven to bake a casserole. Which graph best represents the oven temperature over time? Explain your choice.

A. 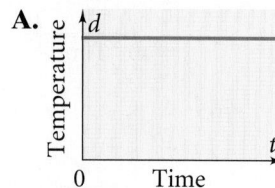   **B.** 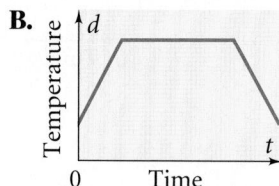   **C.**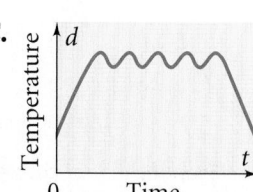

 Apply Your Skills

10. Weather The graph shows the barometric pressure in Pittsburgh, Pennsylvania, during a blizzard. Describe what happened to the pressure during the storm.

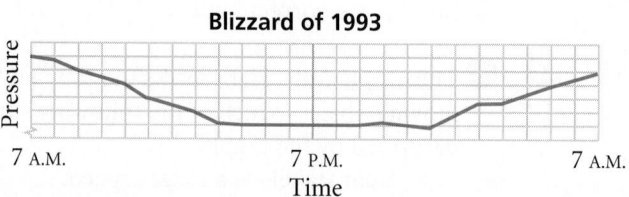

Blizzard of 1993

SOURCE: Purdue Weather Processor

11. Sketch graphs of each situation. Are the graphs the same? Explain.
  a. Your speed as you travel from the bottom of a ski slope to the top.
  b. Your speed as you travel from the top of a ski slope to the bottom.

Weight Gains

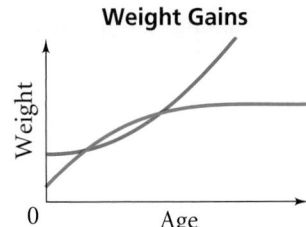

12. The graph at the left shows the weight of a baby and the weight of a puppy for their first two years.
  a. Which curve represents the puppy's weight? The baby's weight?
  b. Writing Describe the growth patterns of the baby and the puppy.

13. You pour juice into a pitcher like the one shown in the photographs below. You pour the juice at a constant rate. Make a sketch to show the height of juice in the pitcher as you fill it.

14. Error Analysis The graph at the right shows a person's speed over the course of a bike ride. Your friend said that this graph describes a person bicycling up and then down a hill. Explain your friend's error.

Speed on a Bike Ride

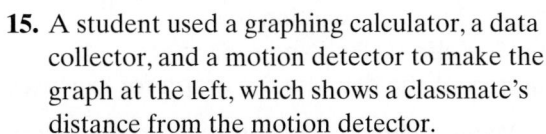

15. A student used a graphing calculator, a data collector, and a motion detector to make the graph at the left, which shows a classmate's distance from the motion detector.
  a. Copy the graph and label each section.
  b. During which section was the student walking toward the motion detector?
  c. During which section(s) was the student walking at a constant speed?

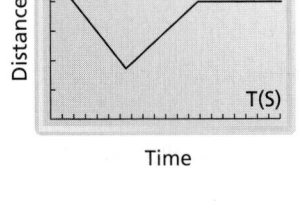

16. Multiple Choice Which graph best represents a person's height from birth to age 80?

17. a. Data Collection Sketch a graph of the daily high temperatures over the course of one year for your town.
  b. Critical Thinking How would your graph be different if you lived at the equator?

18. a. In-Line Skating Describe what the graph at the right shows about a student's in-line skating experience.
  b. Label each section.

In-Line Skating After School

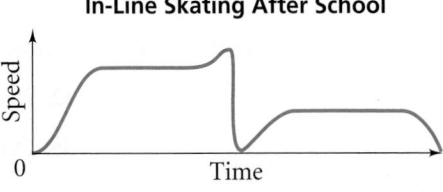

C Challenge

Use the graph at the right for Exercises 19–22.

19. How much does it cost to park for 2 hours?

20. How much does it cost to park for 121 minutes?

21. Suppose your mother pays $6 for parking. About how long was her car parked in the garage?

22. **Vocabulary** This graph is a *step graph*. Does this name make sense? Explain.

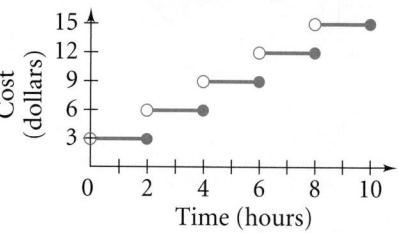

Parking Garage Costs

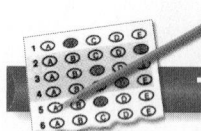

Test Prep

Multiple Choice

The graph at the right shows the distance Molly was from home throughout Tuesday. She spent about six hours at school, one hour at a friend's house, and about 30 minutes waiting for a bus. She also walked and rode the bus part of the day. Use the graph for Exercises 23–24.

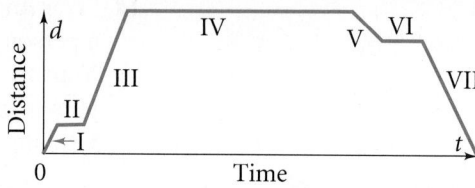

23. What section most likely represents walking to her friend's house?
    A. I   B. II   C. IV   D. V

24. What section most likely represents spending time at a friend's house?
    F. II   G. IV   H. VI   J. VII

Short Response

25. An hourglass has two compartments that hold sand. The graph at the right shows the height of the sand in the bottom container as it fills. Which hourglass does the graph represent? Explain your choice.

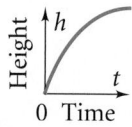

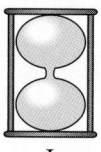
I

II

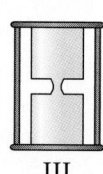
III

IV

Mixed Review

Lesson 7-4

Solve each inequality.

26. $5x + 2 < 37$ 27. $x + 4 > 2x - 4$ 28. $8x + 4 - 3x \geq 3x$

29. $7 > -4x - 9$ 30. $7(x + 1) \leq 6(x - 1)$ 31. $-2 + 5x < 8 - 10x$

Lesson 5-7

You roll a red number cube and a blue number cube. Find each probability.

32. P(red 1 and blue 6)   33. P(red 3 and blue 5)   34. P(red > 4 and blue 5)

35. P(red odd and blue 3)   36. P(red and blue even)   37. P(red and blue equal)

Relations and Functions

What You'll Learn

- To identify relations and functions
- To evaluate functions

. . . And Why

To determine whether a relation is a function, as in Examples 1 and 2

✓ **Check Skills You'll Need**

GO for Help Review page 24 and Lesson 1-2

Graph each point on a coordinate plane.

1. $(2, -4)$ **2.** $(0, 3)$ **3.** $(-1, -2)$ **4.** $(-3, 0)$

Evaluate each expression.

5. $3a - 2$ for $a = -5$ **6.** $9(x - 9)$ for $x = 3$ **7.** $3x^2$ for $x = 6$

◀)) **New Vocabulary** • relation • vertical-line test • function notation

---

1   Identifying Relations and Functions

A **relation** is a set of ordered pairs. The (age, height) ordered pairs below form a relation.

Giraffes

Age (years)	18	20	21	14	18
Height (meters)	4.25	4.40	5.25	5.00	4.85

You can list the set of ordered pairs in a relation using braces.

$$\{(18, 4.25), (20, 4.40), (21, 5.25), (14, 5.00), (18, 4.85)\}$$

Recall from Lesson 1-4 that a function is a relation that assigns exactly one output (range) value for each input (domain) value.

One way you can tell if a relation is a function is by making a *mapping diagram*. List the domain values and the range values in order. Draw arrows from the domain values to their range values.

①nline
active math

For: Function Activity
Use: Interactive Textbook, 8-2

1 EXAMPLE   Using a Mapping Diagram

Determine whether each relation is a function.

a. $\{(11, -2), (12, -1), (13, -2), (20, 7)\}$

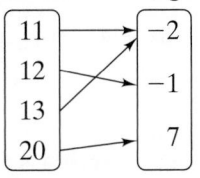

There is no value in the domain that corresponds to more than one value of the range.

The relation is a function.

b. $\{(-2, -1), (-1, 0), (6, 3), (-2, 1)\}$

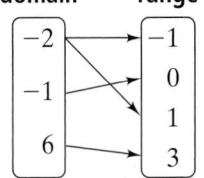

The domain value -2 corresponds to two range values, -1 and 1.

The relation is not a function.

✓ **Quick Check** ❶ Use a mapping diagram to determine whether each relation is a function.
     a. $\{(3, -2), (8, 1), (9, 2), (3, 3), (-4, 0)\}$ **b.** $\{(6.5, 0), (7, -1), (6, 2), (2, 6), (5, -1)\}$

Another way you can tell whether a relation is a function is to analyze the graph of the relation using the **vertical-line test.** If any vertical line passes through more than one point of the graph then for some value of x there is more than one value of y. Therefore, the relation is not a function.

2 EXAMPLE Using the Vertical-Line Test

Determine whether the relation $\{(3, 0), (-2, 1), (0, -1), (-3, 2), (3, 2)\}$ is a function.

Step 1 Graph the ordered pairs on a coordinate plane.

Step 2 Pass a pencil across the graph as shown.

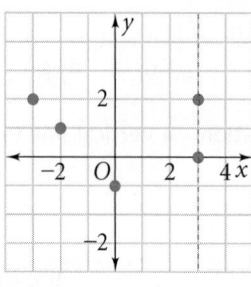

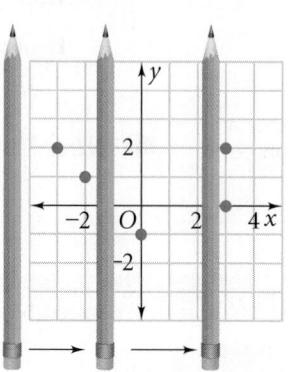

● A vertical line would pass through $(3, 0)$ and $(3, 2)$. The relation is not a function.

✓ **Quick Check** ❷ Use the vertical-line test to determine whether each relation is a function.
a. $\{(4, -2), (1, 2), (0, 1), (-2, 2)\}$ **b.** $\{(0, 2), (1, -1), (-1, 4), (0, -3), (2, 1)\}$

2 Evaluating Functions

Recall from Lesson 1-4 that a function rule is an equation that describes a function. You can think of a function rule as an input-output machine.

Words and Notations Used With a Function

Domain	Range
input	output
x	$f(x)$
x	y

The domain is the set of input values.

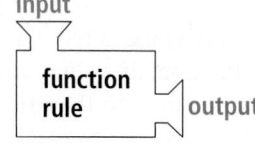

The range is the set of output values.

If you know the input values, you can use a function rule to find the output values. The output values depend on the input values.

$$y = 3x + 4$$
↑   ↑
output input

input values for x

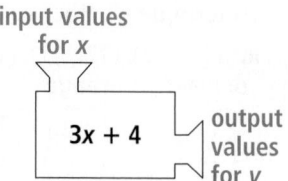

Input	Output
x	y
1	7
2	10
3	13

Another way to write the function $y = 3x + 4$ is $f(x) = 3x + 4$. A function is in **function notation** when you use $f(x)$ to indicate the outputs. You read $f(x)$ as "f of x" or "f is a function of x." The notations $g(x)$ and $h(x)$ also indicate functions of x.

In Lesson 1-4 you wrote function rules from tables. You can also make a table using values from a function rule.

3 EXAMPLE Making a Table From a Function Rule

Make a table for $f(n) = -2n^2 + 7$. Use 1, 2, 3, and 4 as domain values.

n	$-2n^2 + 7$	$f(n)$
1	$-2(1)^2 + 7$	5
2	$-2(2)^2 + 7$	-1
3	$-2(3)^2 + 7$	-11
4	$-2(4)^2 + 7$	-25

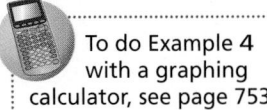 **3** Make a table for $y = 8 - 3x$. Use 1, 2, 3, and 4 as domain values.

You can use a function rule and a given domain to find the range of the function. After computing the range values, write the values in order from least to greatest.

 To do Example 4 with a graphing calculator, see page 753.

4 EXAMPLE Finding the Range

Evaluate the function rule $f(a) = -3a + 5$ to find the range of the function for the domain $\{-3, 1, 4\}$.

$f(a) = -3a + 5$ $f(a) = -3a + 5$ $f(a) = -3a + 5$

$f(-3) = -3(-3) + 5$ $f(1) = -3(1) + 5$ $f(4) = -3(4) + 5$

$f(-3) = 14$ $f(1) = 2$ $f(4) = -7$

The range is $\{-7, 2, 14\}$.

 **4** Find the range of each function for the domain $\{-2, 0, 5\}$.
   a. $f(x) = x - 6$ **b.** $y = -4x$ **c.** $g(t) = t^2 + 1$

EXERCISES

For more exercises, see *Extra Skill and Word Problem Practice.*

Practice and Problem Solving

A Practice by Example

Example 1
(page 433)

Example 2
(page 434)

Example 3
(page 435)

Example 4
(page 435)

Use a mapping diagram to determine whether each relation is a function.

1. $\{(3, 7), (3, 8), (3, -2), (3, 4), (3, 1)\}$ **2.** $\{(6, -7), (5, -8), (1, 4), (5, 5)\}$

3. $\{(0.04, 0.2), (0.2, 1), (1, 5), (5, 25)\}$ **4.** $\{(4, 2), (1, 1), (0, 0), (1, -1), (4, -2)\}$

Use the vertical-line test to determine whether each relation is a function.

5. $\{(2, 5), (3, -5), (4, 5), (5, -5)\}$ **6.** $\{(5, 0), (0, 5), (5, 1), (1, 5)\}$

7. $\{(3, -1), (-2, 3), (-1, -5), (3, 2)\}$ **8.** $\{(-2, 9), (3, 9), (-0.5, 9), (4, 9)\}$

Make a table for each function. Use 1, 2, 3, and 4 for the domain.

9. $f(x) = x + 7$ **10.** $y = 11x - 1$ **11.** $f(x) = x^2$ **12.** $f(x) = -4x$

13. $f(x) = 15 - x$ **14.** $y = 3x + 2$ **15.** $y = \frac{1}{4}x$ **16.** $f(x) = -x + 2$

Find the range of the function rule $y = 5x - 2$ for each domain.

17. $\{0.5, 11\}$ **18.** $\{-1.2, 0, 4\}$ **19.** $\{-5, -1, 0, 2, 10\}$ **20.** $\left\{-\frac{1}{2}, \frac{1}{4}, \frac{2}{5}\right\}$

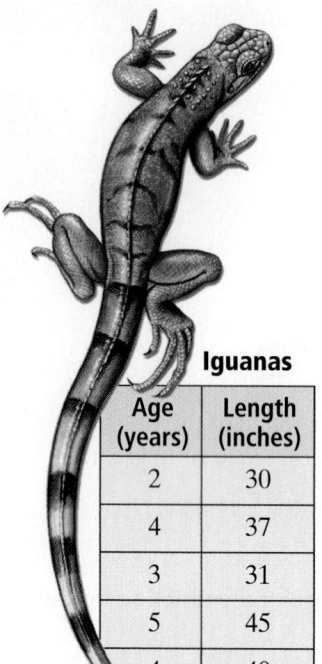

Iguanas

Age (years)	Length (inches)
2	30
4	37
3	31
5	45
4	40

Determine whether each relation is a function. If the relation is a function, state the domain and range.

21.

x	y
1	−3
6	−2
9	−1
1	3

22.

x	y
0	2
3	1
3	−1
5	3

23.

x	y
−4	−4
−1	−4
0	−4
3	−4

24. Error Analysis A student thinks that the relation $\{(2, 1), (3, -2), (4, 5), (5, -2)\}$ is not a function because two values in the domain have the same range value. What is the student's error?

25. Iguanas Use the data in the table at the left. Is an iguana's length a function of its age? Explain.

26. Open-Ended Create a data table for a relation that is *not* a function. Describe what your data might represent.

Find the range of each function for the domain $\{-1, 0.5, 3.7\}$.

27. $f(x) = 4x + 1$ **28.** $g(x) = -4x + 1$ **29.** $y = |x| - 1$ **30.** $s(t) = t^2 - 1$

31. a. Profit A store bought a case of disposable cameras for $300. The store's profit p on the cameras is a function of the number c of cameras sold. Find the range of the function $p = 6c - 300$ when the domain is $\{0, 15, 50, 62\}$.
   b. Critical Thinking In this situation, what do the domain and range represent?

Determine whether each graph is the graph of a function.

32.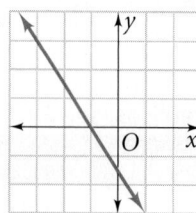

33.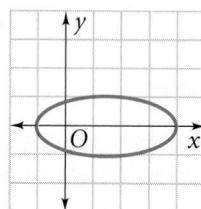

34.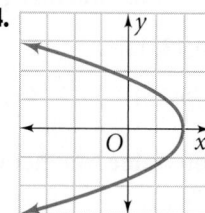

35.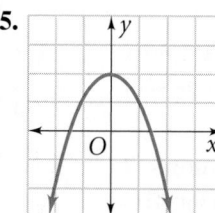

36. Physics Light travels about 186,000 miles per second. The rule $d = 186{,}000t$ describes the relationship between distance d in miles and time t in seconds.
   a. How far does light travel in 20 seconds?
   b. How far does light travel in 1 minute?

GO **Online**
Homework Video Tutor
Visit: PHSchool.com
Web Code: ate-0502

For Exercises 37–40 assume that each variable has a different value. Determine whether each relation is a function.

37. $\{(a, b), (b, a), (c, c), (e, d)\}$ **38.** $\{(b, b), (c, d), (d, c), (c, a)\}$
39. $\{(c, e), (c, d), (c, b)\}$ **40.** $\{(a, b), (b, c), (c, d), (d, e)\}$

Real-World 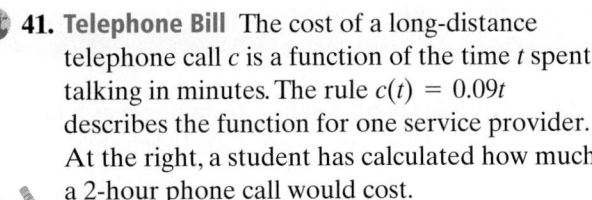 **Connection**

A telecommunications device for the deaf (TDD) includes a keyboard and a visual display of the conversation. This lets a hearing-impaired person use a telephone.

41. **Telephone Bill** The cost of a long-distance telephone call c is a function of the time t spent talking in minutes. The rule $c(t) = 0.09t$ describes the function for one service provider. At the right, a student has calculated how much a 2-hour phone call would cost.

> $c = 0.09 \times 2$
> $= 0.18$
> $\$.18$ for 2 hours

    a. Writing Why does the student's answer seem unreasonable?

    b. Error Analysis What mistake(s) did the student make?

    c. How much would it cost to make a 2-hour phone call?

    d. Critical Thinking What set of numbers is reasonable for the domain values? For the range values?

42. **Travel** Suppose your family is driving home from vacation. The car averages 25 miles per gallon, and you are 180 miles from home. The function $d = 180 - 25g$ relates the number of gallons of gas g the car will use to your distance from home d.

    a. Make a table for $d = 180 - 25g$. Use 2, 4, 6, and 8 as domain values.

    b. Estimation Based on the table, how many gallons of gasoline are needed to get home?

    c. The gas tank holds 15 gallons when it is full. Describe a reasonable domain and range for this situation. Explain your answer.

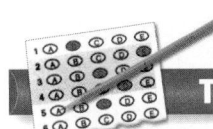 **Challenge**

Use the functions $f(x) = 2x$ and $g(x) = x^2 + 1$ to find the value of each expression.

43. $f(3) + g(4)$ 44. $g(3) + f(4)$ 45. $f(5) - 2g(1)$ 46. $f(g(3))$

47. **Critical Thinking** Can the graph of a function be a horizontal line? A vertical line? Explain why or why not.

48. The function $y = [x]$ is called the *greatest-integer function*. $[x]$ is the greatest integer less than or equal to x. For example, $[2.99] = 2$ and $[-2.3] = -3$.

    a. Evaluate the function for 0.5, -0.1, -1.99, and -5.2.

    b. The domain of $y = [x]$ is all real numbers. What is the range of $y = [x]$?

Test Prep

Gridded Response

49. Evaluate the function rule $f(x) = 7x$ for $x = 0.75$.

50. Evaluate the function rule $f(x) = 9 - 0.2x$ for $x = 1.5$.

51. What is the greatest value in the range of $y = x^2 - 7$ for the domain $\{-2, 0, 1\}$?

Short Response

52. Determine whether the data below are a function. Show your work.

Mount Rushmore Temperatures (°F)

At Base of Mountain	At Top of Mountain
80	72
65	58
93	84
98	91
74	69

GO for Help

Lesson 8-1

53. The graph shows distance from home as a family drives to the mountains for a vacation. Copy the graph. Label each section of the graph.

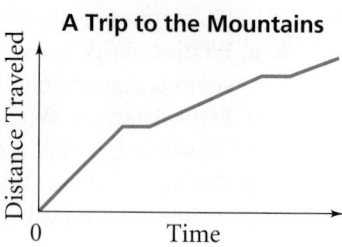

A Trip to the Mountains

Distance Traveled

0   Time

Lesson 6-5

The scale of a map is 1 in. : 15 mi. Find the actual distance corresponding to each map distance.

54. 2 in.   **55.** 1.5 in.   **56.** 0.5 in.

57. 3.25 in.   **58.** 5.5 in.   **59.** 7.25 in.

Lesson 4-6

Find the mean, median, mode, and range.

60. 34 33 35 33 32 35 34 32

61. 1 −2 0 −1 1 −2 2 0 1 −2

62. 4 5 3 7 1 12 6 9 5

63. 15 13 19 20 9 13 15 13

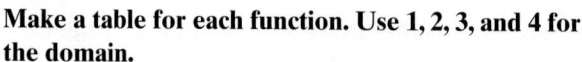

Checkpoint Quiz 1   **Lessons 8-1 through 8-2**

Sketch a graph of each situation. Label each section.

1. the height of a plant that grows at a steady rate

2. the temperature in a classroom after the heater is turned on

3. a child's height above the ground while on a swing

4. Is the graph at the right the graph of a function? Explain.

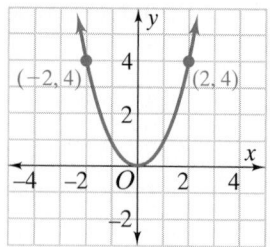

$(-2, 4)$ $(2, 4)$

Make a table for each function. Use 1, 2, 3, and 4 for the domain.

5. $f(x) = -5x$ **6.** $g(x) = x + 1.4$

7. $f(n) = 3n^2$ **8.** $y = 2 - 0.5x$

Determine whether each relation is a function.

9.

x	y
0	6
1	7
5	8
8	9

10.

x	y
5	1
−6	8
5	3
6	7

Function Rules, Tables, and Graphs

What You'll Learn

• To model functions using rules, tables, and graphs

. . . And Why

To find the cost of making CDs, as in Example 2

✓ Check Skills You'll Need

 **for Help** Lesson 4-4

Identify the independent and dependent quantities in each situation.

1. A runner averages 7 miles per hour.

2. A customer can buy a dozen apples for $2.40 or two dozen apples for $4.50.

🔊 **New Vocabulary** • discrete data • continuous data

---

1 Modeling Functions

9P1. Define function with ordered pairs.

9P2. Generalize and represent patterns using functions or relationships.

10P2. Describe and compare characteristics of the families of functions.

You can model functions using rules, tables, and graphs. A function rule shows how the variables are related. A table identifies specific input and output values of the function. A graph gives a visual picture of the function.

Recall from Lesson 1-4 that the inputs are values of the independent variable. The outputs are the corresponding values of the dependent variable.

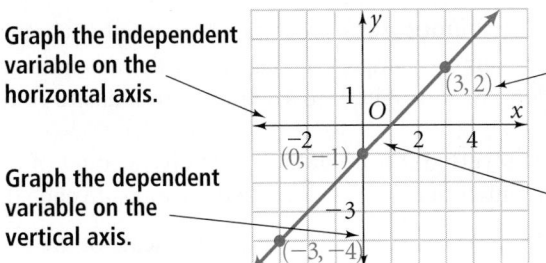

Graph the independent variable on the horizontal axis.

Graph the dependent variable on the vertical axis.

Use the input and output values as ordered pairs to plot points.

Join the points with a line or smooth curve to give a general picture of the function.

---

1 EXAMPLE Three Views of a Function

GO Online

Video Tutor Help
Visit: PHSchool.com
Web Code: ate-0775

Model the function rule $y = -\frac{1}{2}x + 1$ using a table of values and a graph.

Step 1 Choose input values for x. Evaluate to find y.

Step 2 Plot points for the ordered pairs.
Step 3 Join the points to form a line.

x	$y = -\frac{1}{2}x + 1$	(x, y)
-4	$y = -\frac{1}{2}(-4) + 1 = 3$	$(-4, 3)$
0	$y = -\frac{1}{2}(0) + 1 = 1$	$(0, 1)$
2	$y = -\frac{1}{2}(2) + 1 = 0$	$(2, 0)$

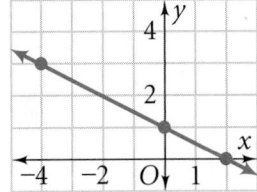

✓ Quick Check

1 **a.** How would the table and graph of $f(x) = -\frac{1}{2}x + 1$ compare to the table and graph in Example 1?

b. Model the rule $f(x) = 3x + 4$ with a table of values and a graph.

When you draw a graph for a real-world situation, choose appropriate intervals for the units on the axes. Be sure the intervals are equal. Also, if the data are positive numbers, use only the first quadrant.

2 EXAMPLE <u>Real-World 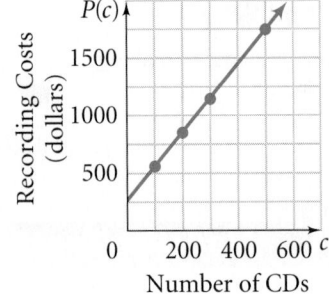 Problem Solving</u>

Recording Costs Suppose your group recorded a CD. Now you want to copy and sell it. One company charges $250 for making a master CD and designing the art for the cover. There is also a cost of $3 to burn each CD. The total cost $P(c)$ depends on the number of CDs c burned. Use the function rule $P(c) = 250 + 3c$ to make a table of values and a graph.

c	P(c) = 250 + 3c	(c, P(c))
100	250 + 3(100) = 550	(100, 550)
200	250 + 3(200) = 850	(200, 850)
300	250 + 3(300) = 1150	(300, 1150)
500	250 + 3(500) = 1750	(500, 1750)

✓ Quick Check **2** **a.** Another company charges $300 for making a master and designing the art. It charges $2.50 for burning each CD. Use the function rule $P(c) = 300 + 2.5c$. Make a table of values and a graph.
  b. Your band decides to use the second company. You plan on making between 100 and 300 CDs. Find a reasonable range for this situation.

Continuous data are data where numbers between any two data values have meaning. Examples of continuous data include measurement of temperature, length, or weight. Use a solid line to indicate continuous data.

Discrete data are data that involve a count of items, such as number of people or number of cars. For discrete data, indicate each data item with a point.

In some cases, like Example 2, the scale of the graph makes it impractical to use a dot for each value in the domain. So a solid line is used. Be aware of the real-world situation to determine if data graphed is continuous or discrete.

3 EXAMPLE **Discrete and Continuous Data**

Determine whether the function rule models discrete or continuous data. Then make a table and graph each function.
a. Photography An automatic photo booth charges $3 for a sheet of photos. The function $C(p) = 3p$ describes the cost of p sheets of photos.

You cannot buy part of a sheet in a photo booth, so the data are discrete. Use points for each input value.

p	C(p) = 3p	(p, C(p))
1	3(1) = 3	(1, 3)
2	3(2) = 6	(2, 6)
3	3(3) = 9	(3, 9)
4	3(4) = 12	(4, 12)

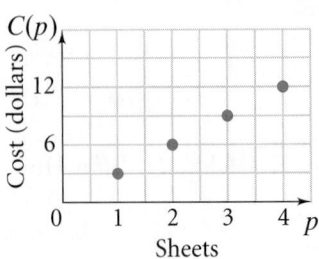

 26. a. Geometry The function $A(\ell) = \frac{1}{2}\ell^2$ describes the area of an isosceles right triangle with leg ℓ. Make a table of values for $\ell = 1, 2, 3,$ and 4.
  b. Does the function describe discrete or continuous data? Explain.
  c. Graph the function.

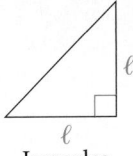

Isosceles
right triangle

Graph each function.

27. $f(x) = \frac{3}{4}x + 7$

28. $y = x^2 - 4x + 4$

29. $y = |2x|$

30. $y = x + \frac{1}{2}$

31. $f(x) = 7 - 5x$

32. $f(x) = \left|\frac{1}{2}x\right|$

33. $f(x) = \left|\frac{1}{2}x\right| + 1$

34. $y = 1 - x^2$

35. $f(x) = -5x^2$

36. Multiple Choice Which function rule best models the data in the table?
  Ⓐ $y = x + 3$
  Ⓑ $y = 4x$
  Ⓒ $y = 3x + 1$
  Ⓓ $y = x^2 + 3$

x	y
0	3
1	4
2	7
3	12

37. a. Graph $y = |x|$ and $y = -|x|$ on the same coordinate plane.
  b. The graph of $y = -|x|$ is the reflection of the graph of $y = |x|$. Over which axis is the graph of $y = |x|$ reflected?
  c. Write an equation of the reflection of the graph of $y = |x| + 1$ over the same axis.

To review reflections, see
Skills Handbook p. 799.

38. a. Make a table for the perimeters of the rectangles formed by each set of blue tiles.
  b. The perimeter $P(t)$ is a function of the number of tiles t. Write a rule for the data in your table and graph the function.

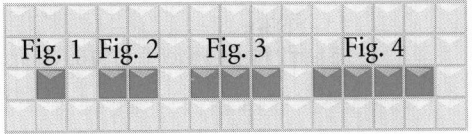

Fig. 1 Fig. 2 Fig. 3 Fig. 4

39. a. Graph each function on the same coordinate plane.
    i. $f(x) = |x| + 2$
    ii. $f(x) = |x| + 4$
    iii. $f(x) = |x| - 3$
  b. Critical Thinking In the function $y = |x| + b$, how does changing the value of b change the graph of the function?

40. a. Graph each function on the same coordinate plane.
    i. $f(x) = |2x|$
    ii. $f(x) = |0.5x|$
    iii. $f(x) = |3x|$
  b. Critical Thinking In the function $y = |ax|$, how does changing the value of a change the graph of the function?

Ⓒ Challenge

41. The function $s(x)$, sometimes called the signum function, is defined as
$$s(x) = \begin{cases} 1 \text{ if } x > 0 \\ 0 \text{ if } x = 0 \\ -1 \text{ if } x < 0 \end{cases}$$
For example, $s(17) = 1, s(0) = 0,$ and $s(-32) = -1$.
  a. Evaluate $s(3.77), s(0.003), s(-1.5),$ and $s(-2300)$.
  b. The domain of the function is all real numbers. What is the range?
  c. Make a table of values and graph the function.
  d. Make a Conjecture Do you think $s(a + b) = s(a) + s(b)$? First, test some values of a and b. If your answer is *yes*, justify your answer. If your answer is *no*, give a counterexample.

Multiple Choice

42. Suppose you hire an electrician to install several electrical outlets in your home. The electrician charges $68 for materials plus $40 per hour (or fraction of an hour). How much will the electrician charge you if the job takes $2\frac{1}{4}$ hours?

A. $148   **B.** $158   **C.** $188   **D.** $208

43. Which is the graph of the function rule $f(x) = \frac{1}{2}x - 2$?

F.   **G.** 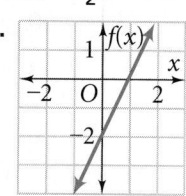   **H.**   **J.**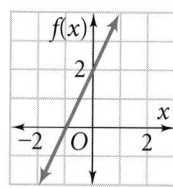

44. Which function is modeled by the table at the right?

x	$f(x)$
-3	-5
0	1
2	5
3	7

   A. $f(x) = x - 2$ **B.** $f(x) = 2x + 1$

   C. $f(x) = -x + 1$ **D.** $f(x) = \frac{1}{2}x - 1$

45. Which points are on the graph of the function rule $f(x) = 10 - 4x$?

   F. (18, −2), (10, 0), (2, 2)

   G. (−18, 2), (−10, 0), (−2, −2)

   H. (2, −18), (0, −10), (−2, −2)

   J. (−2, 18), (0, 10), (2, 2)

Short Response

46. Graph the equations $y = x + 3$, $y = x^2 + 3$, and $y = |x| + 3$ on the same coordinate plane. Describe the similarities and differences in the graphs.

Extended Response

47. a. Make a table of values for the function rule $f(x) = |x + 1| - 2$.

   b. Graph $f(x) = |x + 1| - 2$.

Mixed Review

Lesson 8-2

GO for Help

Find the range of each function for the domain {−2, 0, 3.5}.

48. $f(x) = 3x + 1$ **49.** $g(x) = 3x - 5$ **50.** $f(s) = -3s + 4$

51. $g(v) = |v| - 5$ **52.** $h(n) = 12 - n$ **53.** $g(w) = 5(w - 2)$

54. $p(n) = 6n + 1$ **55.** $f(x) = 0.5x - 8$ **56.** $k(n) = -11n + 9$

Lesson 6-5

The scale of a map is 1 cm : 16 km. Find the actual distance corresponding to each map distance.

57. 3 cm   **58.** 2.5 cm   **59.** 6.3 cm   **60.** 8.5 cm   **61.** 10.2 cm

62. Architecture The Lyndon Johnson Presidential Library has a model of the Oval Office in the White House. The model in the Johnson Library is $\frac{7}{8}$ the size of the original. Write and solve a proportion to find each dimension in the Johnson Library given the following actual Oval Office dimensions. Round to the nearest tenth of a foot.

   a. greatest width: 29 ft

   b. greatest length: 35 ft 10 in.

   c. height: 18 ft 6 in.

Go Online
PHSchool.com

For: Graphing calculator procedures
Web Code: ate-2104

You can use a graphing calculator to explore the relationship among a function rule, a table, and a graph. When you use the table feature, the calculator computes the values for y based on the values of x that you enter.

1 EXAMPLE

For the function $y = -2x + 5$, find the range when the domain is $\{-12, 2, 0, 3, 8\}$.

Access the **TBLSET** feature. Use the arrow key to shade the **Ask** to the right of **Indpnt**.

Press **ENTER**.

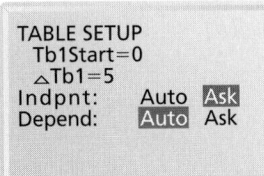

Press **Y=**. Enter the function. Access the **TABLE** feature. Enter values for x.

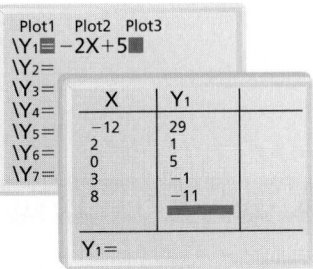

● The range is $\{29, 1, 5, -1, -11\}$.

To graph an equation, use the **GRAPH** feature. You can use the **TRACE** feature to find x- and y-values. If you graph and trace the equation in Example 1, you will see that the x- and y-values are generally given as 8-digit numbers. To see values for x that are given in tenths, press **ZOOM** 4 and then **TRACE**.

2 EXAMPLE

Graph $y = -0.5x - 2$. Where does the graph cross each axis?

Press **Y=**. Enter the function rule. Then press **GRAPH**.

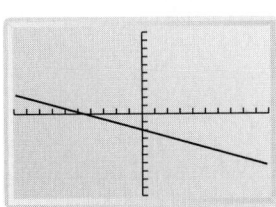

Press **ZOOM** 4 and then **TRACE** to find where the graph crosses the axes.

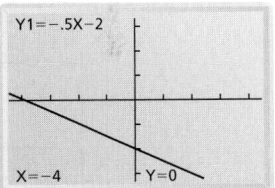

● The graph crosses the y-axis at -2 and the x-axis at -4.

EXERCISES

Find the range of each function for the given domain.

1. $y = 3x + 6; \{-5, 0, 3, 7\}$

2. $y = 0.4x - 5.1; \{-2.1, 1.35, 5.7\}$

Determine where each graph crosses the y-axis and the x-axis.

3. $y = -2x + 3$

4. $y = -0.25x - 1$

5. $y = 1.2x + 2.16$

6. Open-Ended Graph $y = -0.2x + 6$. Using the **WINDOW** screen, experiment with values for Xmin, Xmax, Ymin, and Ymax until you can see the graph crossing both axes. What values did you use for Xmin, Xmax, Ymin, and Ymax?

Writing a Function Rule

What You'll Learn

- To write a function rule given a table or a real-world situation

...And Why

To write a function rule for finding profit, as in Example 3

Check Skills You'll Need

 **for Help** Lesson 8-3

Model each rule with a table of values.

1. $f(x) = 5x - 1$ **2.** $y = -3x + 4$ **3.** $g(t) = 0.2t - 7$

4. $y = 4x + 1$ **5.** $f(x) = 6 - x$ **6.** $c(d) = d + 0.9$

Evaluate each function rule for $n = 2$.

7. $A(n) = 2n - 1$ **8.** $f(n) = -3 + n - 1$ **9.** $g(n) = 6 - n$

1 Writing Function Rules

You can write a rule for a function by analyzing a table of values. Look for a pattern relating the independent and dependent variables.

1 EXAMPLE   Writing a Rule From a Table

Write a function rule for each table.

a.

x	f(x)
1	5
2	6
3	7
4	8

Ask yourself, "What can I do to 1 to get 5, to 2 to get 6, . . . ?"

You add 4 to each x-value to get the $f(x)$ value.

Relate	$f(x)$	equals	x	plus	4
Write	$f(x)$	=	x	+	4

A rule for the function is $f(x) = x + 4$.

b.

x	y
1	1
3	9
6	36
9	81

Ask yourself, "What can I do to 3 to get 9, to 6 to get 36, . . . ?"

You multiply each x-value times itself to get the $f(x)$ value.

Relate	y	equals	x times itself
Write	y	=	x^2

A rule for the function is $y = x^2$.

Quick Check ❶ Write a function rule for each table.

a.

x	f(x)
1	−1
2	0
3	1
4	2

b.

x	y
1	2
2	4
3	6
4	8

c.

x	y
1	3
2	4
3	5
4	6

2 EXAMPLE <u>Real-World Problem Solving</u>

Scale Model The exhibit at the left is a scale model of a desktop computer. It is about 20 times the size of a normal-sized desktop computer.

a. Write a function rule to describe this relationship.

Relate larger is 20 times normal

Define Let n = length of normal-sized computer.

Let $L(n)$ = length of larger size shown in museum exhibit.

Write $L(n)$ = 20 · n

The function rule $L(n) = 20n$ describes the relationship between the size of the computer in the exhibit and a normal-sized computer.

b. A space bar on a normal-sized computer is $4\frac{3}{8}$ in long. About how long is the space bar in the exhibit?

$L(n) = 20 \cdot n$

$L(n) = 20 \cdot 4\frac{3}{8}$ **Substitute $4\frac{3}{8}$ for n.**

$L(n) = 87\frac{1}{2}$ **Simplify.**

The space bar in the exhibit is about $87\frac{1}{2}$ in. long.

 **2** **a. Carpentry** A carpenter buys finishing nails by the pound. Each pound of nails costs $1.19. Write a function rule to describe this relationship.

b. How much do 12 lb of finishing nails cost?

When you write a function, the dependent variable is defined in terms of the independent variable. In Example 3 below, profit depends on the number of lawns mowed, so profit is a function of the number of lawns mowed.

3 EXAMPLE <u>Real-World Problem Solving</u>

Multiple Choice Suppose you borrow money from a relative to buy a lawn mower that costs $245. You charge $18 to mow a lawn. Write a rule to describe your profit $P(n)$ as a function of the number of lawns mowed n. Which equation best describes the situation?

Ⓐ $P(n) = 18n$ Ⓑ $P(n) = 18 + 245$

Ⓒ $P(n) = 18n - 245$ Ⓓ $P(n) = 245 + 18n$

Relate	total profit	is	$18	times	lawns mowed	minus	cost of mower
Write	$P(n)$	=	18	·	n	−	245

The function rule $P(n) = 18n - 245$ describes your profit as a function of the number of lawns mowed. So C is the correct answer.

 **3 Earnings** Suppose you buy a word-processing software package for $199. You charge $15 per hour for word processing. Write a rule to describe your profit as a function of the number of hours you work.

EXERCISES

For more exercises, see *Extra Skill and Word Problem Practice*.

Practice and Problem Solving

 **Practice by Example**

Example 1
(page 446)

GO for Help

Match each table with its rule.

1. $y = 4x$

2. $y = x - 4$

3. $y = -4 - x$

A.

x	y
−2	−6
−1	−5
0	−4
1	−3

B.

x	y
−1	−4
−2	−8
−3	−12
−4	−16

C.

x	y
−1	−3
0	−4
1	−5
2	−6

Write a function rule for each table.

4.

x	f(x)
1	3
2	6
3	9
4	12

5.

x	f(x)
1	0.5
2	1.5
3	2.5
4	3.5

6.

x	f(x)
1	0.5
2	1
3	1.5
4	2

7.

x	f(x)
1	−3
2	−6
3	−9
4	−12

8.

x	y
−2	−8
−1	−4
0	0
1	4

9.

x	y
−8	64
−4	16
0	0
4	16
8	64

Example 2
(page 447)

Write a function rule for each situation.

10. the total cost $t(c)$ of c ounces of cinnamon if each ounce costs $.79

11. the total distance $d(n)$ traveled after n hours at a constant speed of 45 miles per hour

12. the height $f(h)$ of an object in feet when you know the height h in inches

13. a worker's earnings $e(n)$ for n hours when the worker's hourly wage is $6.37

14. the area $A(n)$ of a square when you know the length n of a side

15. the volume $V(n)$ of a cube when you know the length n of a side

16. the area $A(r)$ of a circle with radius r

Example 3
(page 447)

17. Food Costs At a supermarket salad bar, the price of a salad depends on its weight. Salad costs $.19 per ounce.
   a. Write a rule to describe the function.
   b. How much would an 8-ounce salad cost?

18. Postage In 2002, the price of mailing a letter was $.34 for the first ounce or part of an ounce and $.21 for each ounce or part of an ounce after the first ounce.
   a. Write a rule to describe the function.
   b. How much did it cost to mail a 4-ounce letter?

448 Chapter 8 Graphs and Functions

Write a function rule for each table.

19.

Distance (km)	Distance (m)
0.5	500
1.0	1000
1.5	1500
2.0	2000

20.

Inches	Centimeters
1	2.54
2	5.08
3	7.62
4	10.16

Math in the Media Use the advertisement at the left for Exercises 21–22.

BOOK EXPRESS!

Get your first **6** books for $1.00

Buy additional books at our regular low Club price of $10.00 per book. To become a Book Express member, just buy 2 additional books within the first year. You may resign your membership at any time.

21. a. Write a rule to find the total cost $C(a)$ for all the books a person buys through Book Express. Let a represent the number of additional books bought (after the first 6 books).
   b. Suppose a person buys 9 books in all. Find the total cost.
   c. Evaluate the function for $a = 6$. What does the output represent?
   d. Does the function rule model discrete or continuous data? Explain.

22. A bookstore sells the same books for an average price of $6 each.
   a. Write a function rule to model the total cost $C(b)$ of books bought at the bookstore. Let b represent the number of books bought.
   b. Evaluate your function for $b = 12$. What does the output represent?
   c. You plan to buy 12 books. What is your average cost per book as a member of Book Express?
   d. Is it less expensive to buy 12 books through the club or at the bookstore? Explain.

23. Writing What advantage(s) can you see of having a function rule instead of a table of values for a function?

24. Water Usage Use the function in the table at the right.
   a. Identify the dependent and independent variables.
   b. Write a rule to describe the function.
   c. How many gallons of water would you use for 7 loads of laundry?
   d. Critical Thinking In one month, you used 442 gallons of water for laundry. How many loads did you wash?

Water Used for Laundry	
1 load	34 gallons
2 loads	68 gallons
3 loads	102 gallons
4 loads	136 gallons

25. Open-Ended Write a function rule that models a real-world situation. Evaluate your function for an input value and explain what the output represents.

26. Multiple Choice The graph of $f(x) = \frac{1}{2}x$ is shown at the right. Which statement about the function is always true?
   Ⓐ The value of y is always less than the value of x.
   Ⓑ When the value of x is positive, the value of y is negative.
   Ⓒ As the value of x increases, the value of y increases.
   Ⓓ The value of y is always different from the value of x.

Make a table of values for each graph. Use the table to write a function rule.

27.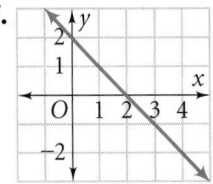

28.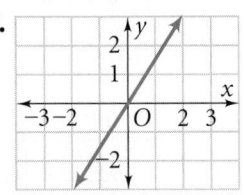

29.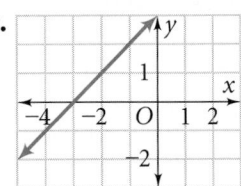

For a guide to solving
Exercise 30, see p. 452.

30. Tipping You go to dinner and decide to leave a 15% tip for the server. You had $45 when you came to the restaurant.
  a. Make a table that shows how much money you would have left after buying a $12, $18, $24, or $28 meal.
  b. Write a function that relates the cost of the meal c to the amount of money you have left $A(c)$.
  c. Graph the function.

31. a. Geometry Make a table for the area of the largest shaded triangle in each figure.
  b. Write a function rule that relates the height of each figure h to the area of the triangle $A(h)$.
  c. Critical Thinking Does the function model discrete or continuous data? Explain.
  d. Graph the function.

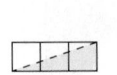

Fig. 1   Fig. 2   Fig. 3

C **Challenge**

Write a function rule for each table.

32.

x	f(x)
1	1
2	8
3	27
4	64

33.

x	f(x)
−1	1
−2	8
−3	27
−4	64

34.

x	f(x)
−1	0
−2	7
−3	26
−4	63

35. Truck Rental A truck rental company charges $44 per day for renting a medium-sized truck. There is also a charge of $.38 per mile.
  a. Write a function rule $c(m)$ to model the cost of renting a truck for a day and driving m miles.
  b. Evaluate your function rule for $m = 70$ and $m = 120$.
  c. You return the truck to the rental company and pay $58.44 (excluding tax). How far did you drive?
  d. Suppose you need to rent a truck for two days. You plan to drive 150 miles each day. How much will this cost?

Real-World Connection

Pickling preserves vegetables by inhibiting the growth of bacteria. Pickling requires salt and acids, such as vinegar.

36. Making Pickles The table at the right shows the relationship between the amount of pickling salt added to a gallon of water and the brine concentration, which is the percent of salt by weight.
  a. Write a function rule to describe the relationship between salt volume and brine concentration.
  b. Write a function rule to describe the relationship between salt weight and brine concentration.

Brine Strength

Salt Volume (cup)	Salt Weight (oz)	Brine Concentration (percent salt)
$\frac{1}{3}$	3.3	2.31
$\frac{1}{2}$	4.95	3.465
$\frac{2}{3}$	6.6	4.62
$\frac{3}{4}$	7.425	5.1975
1	9.9	6.93

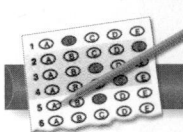

Multiple Choice

37. What is the function rule for the total cost $T(b)$ of b books, if each book costs $11.95?

A. $T(b) = 11.95b$ **B.** $T(b) = b + 11.95$

C. $T(b) = 11.95 - b$ **D.** $T(b) = b - 11.95$

38. What is the function rule for the amount of change $C(x)$ you receive from a $50 bill if you buy x pounds of dog food at $1.60 a pound?

F. $C(x) = 1.6x - 50$ **G.** $C(x) = 50x - 1.6$

H. $C(x) = 50 - 1.6x$ **J.** $C(x) = 160 - 50x$

39. What is the function rule for the table at the right?

A. $f(x) = x - 5$

B. $f(x) = -5x - 4$

C. $f(x) = 5x - 1$

D. $f(x) = -5x + 1$

x	$f(x)$
0	1
1	-4
2	-9
3	-14
4	-19

Short Response

40. The recommended dosage D in milligrams of a certain medicine depends on a person's body mass w in kilograms. The function rule $D = 0.1w^2 + 5w$ describes the relationship of the dosage to body mass. Evaluate the function for a person who has a mass of 60 kilograms. Show your work.

Lesson 8-3

Model each rule with a table of values and a graph.

41. $f(x) = x - 3$ **42.** $y = 5 - x$ **43.** $g(x) = -x + 3$

44. $f(x) = 2x - 3$ **45.** $y = |2x| - 3$ **46.** $y = 2x^2 - 3$

Lesson 6-7

Find each percent of change. Describe the percent of change as an increase or decrease. Round to the nearest percent.

47. 12 cm to 14 cm   **48.** 98 oz to 100 oz   **49.** 65 ml to 60 ml

50. 6 ft to 1 ft   **51.** 1.4 m to 1.8 m   **52.** $1\frac{1}{2}$ in. to $\frac{7}{8}$ in.

Lesson 6-4

53. Measurement The figure at the right shows how much juice you can get from some fruits.

a. What is the minimum number of oranges needed to make a cup of orange juice? What is the maximum number of oranges needed? (*Hint:* 16 tablespoons = 1 cup)

b. Suppose you buy a bag of 6 lemons and a bag of 5 limes. What is the most juice you can expect to get from these bags of fruit?

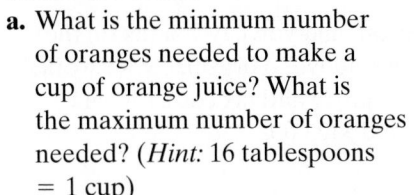

How Much Juice in an Average Fruit?

Orange 6–8 tbsp

Lemon 2.5–3 tbsp

Lime 1.5–2 tbsp

Understanding Math Problems Read the exercise below and then follow along with Raymond as he uses the four-corner method to solve the problem. Check your understanding with the exercise at the bottom of the page.

Tipping You go to dinner and decide to leave a 15% tip for the server. You had $45 when you came to the restaurant.
a. Make a table that shows how much money you would have left after buying a $12, $18, $24, or $28 meal.
b. Graph the function.
c. Write a function to describe the situation.

---

1. I'll use the four-corner method to solve the problem. First, I'll write the original word problem.

You go to dinner and decide to leave a 15% tip for the server. You had $45 when you came to the restaurant.

4. To write a function, I need to define the variables.

Let d = cost of meal.

Let A(d) = amount of money remaining after paying the bill and the tip.

A(d) = 45 - (d + 0.15d)

---

2. Now I'll make a table of values.

Cost of Meal	Process	Amount Left
$12	45 – [12 + 0.15(12)]	$31.20
$18	45 – [18 + 0.15(18)]	$24.30
$24	45 – [24 + 0.15(24)]	$17.40
$28	45 – [28 + 0.15(28)]	$12.80

3. Next, I graph the function.

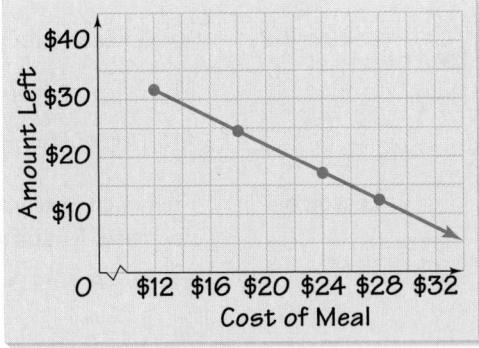

EXERCISE

Suppose it costs $50 to register your car, and you pay 7% tax on the purchase price. Use the method shown above to organize your work.
a. Make a table that shows the total registry and tax costs for cars which cost $6000, $8000, $10,000, and $12,000.
b. Graph the function.
c. Write a function to describe the situation.

Direct Variation

What You'll Learn

- To write an equation of a direct variation
- To use ratios and proportions with direct variations

. . . And Why

To write a direct variation relating to weather, as in Example 3

 Check Skills You'll Need

GO for Help   Lesson 6-4

Solve each proportion.

1. $\frac{5}{8} = \frac{x}{12}$

2. $\frac{4}{9} = \frac{n}{45}$

3. $\frac{25}{15} = \frac{y}{3}$

4. $\frac{7}{n} = \frac{35}{50}$

5. $\frac{8}{d} = \frac{20}{36}$

6. $\frac{14}{18} = \frac{63}{n}$

◀)) **New Vocabulary**   • direct variation   • constant of variation for direct variation

---

1 ▶ **Writing the Equation of a Direct Variation**

Activity: Direct Variation

As you watch a movie, 24 individual pictures, or frames, flash on the screen each second. Here are three ways you can model the relationship between the number of frames $f(s)$ and the number of seconds s.

Table

s number of seconds	$f(s)$ number of frames
1	24
2	48
3	72
4	96
5	120

Graph

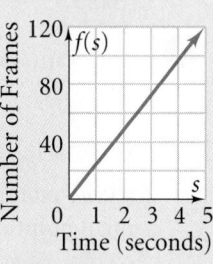

Function Rule

$f(s) = 24s$

1. As the number of seconds doubles, what happens to the number of frames?

2. Find the ratio $\frac{\text{number of frames}}{\text{number of seconds}}$ for each pair of data in the table.

3. For every increase of 1 second on the horizontal axis of the graph, what is the increase on the vertical axis?

4. What do you notice about your answers to Questions 2 and 3 and the coefficient of s in the function rule?

5. **a.** What number of frames corresponds to $s = 0$?
   b. What is the ordered pair on the graph for the seconds and number of frames when $s = 0$?

The table in the activity on page 277 shows the number of frames of a movie that are projected over various lengths of time. The ratio $\frac{\text{number of frames}}{\text{time}} = 24$, which is constant. The number of frames is proportional to the time and 24 is the constant of variation.

 Key Concepts

Definition	**Direct Variation**

A function in the form $y = kx$, where $k \neq 0$, is a **direct variation.** The **constant of variation for direct variation** k is the coefficient of x. The variables y and x are said to vary directly with each other.

Vocabulary Tip

Constant means *remaining the same.* <u>Constant of variation</u> means changing at the *same* rate.

For $y = kx$, y is a function of x. If $x = 0$, then $y = 0$, so the graph of a direct variation is a line that passes through $(0, 0)$. To tell whether an equation represents a direct variation, solve for y. If the equation can be written in the form $y = kx$, where $k \neq 0$, it represents a direct variation.

1 EXAMPLE **Is an Equation a Direct Variation?**

Is each equation a direct variation? If it is, find the constant of variation.

a. $5x + 2y = 0$

$\qquad 2y = -5x$ **Subtract 5x from each side.**

$\qquad y = -\frac{5}{2}x$ **Divide each side by 2.**

The equation has the form $y = kx$, so the equation is a direct variation. The constant of variation is $-\frac{5}{2}$.

b. $5x + 2y = 9$

$\qquad 2y = 9 - 5x$ **Subtract 5x from each side.**

$\qquad y = \frac{9}{2} - \frac{5}{2}x$ **Divide each side by 2.**

The equation cannot be written in the form $y = kx$. It is not a direct variation.

✓ Quick Check **1** Is each equation a direct variation? If it is, find the constant of variation.
   a. $7y = 2x$ **b.** $3y + 4x = 8$ **c.** $y - 7.5x = 0$

To write an equation for a direct variation, you first find the constant of variation k using a point other than the origin that lies on the graph of the equation. Then use the value of k to write an equation.

 **GO** **Online**

Video Tutor Help
Visit: PHSchool.com
Web Code: ate-0775

2 EXAMPLE **Writing an Equation Given a Point**

Write an equation of the direct variation that includes the point $(4, -3)$.

$\quad y = kx$ **Start with the function form of a direct variation.**

$-3 = k(4)$ **Substitute 4 for x and −3 for y.**

$-\frac{3}{4} = k$ **Divide each side by 4 to solve for k.**

$\quad y = -\frac{3}{4}x$ **Write an equation. Substitute $-\frac{3}{4}$ for k in y = kx.**

An equation of the direct variation is $y = -\frac{3}{4}x$.

✓ Quick Check **2** Write an equation of the direct variation that includes the point $(-3, -6)$.

You can use a direct variation to describe a real-world situation in which the dependent variable varies directly with the independent variable.

3 EXAMPLE Real-World Problem Solving

Weather Your distance from lightning varies directly with the time it takes you to hear thunder. If you hear thunder 10 seconds after you see lightning, you are about 2 miles from the lightning. Write an equation for the relationship between time and distance.

Relate   The distance varies directly with the time. When $x = 10, y = 2$.

Define   Let x = the number of seconds between your seeing lightning and your hearing thunder.

Let y = your distance in miles from the lightning.

Write

$y = kx$	Use the general form of a direct variation.
$2 = k(10)$	Substitute 10 for x and 2 for y.
$\frac{1}{5} = k$	Divide each side by 10 to solve for k.
$y = \frac{1}{5}x$	Write an equation. Substitute $\frac{1}{5}$ for k in $y = kx$.

The equation $y = \frac{1}{5}x$ relates the time x in seconds it takes you to hear the thunder to the distance y in miles you are from the lightning.

Real-World Connection

The total energy released by a single flash of lightning could power an ordinary light bulb for a few months.

 **Quick Check** **3** A recipe for a dozen corn muffins calls for 1 cup of flour. The number of muffins varies directly with the amount of flour you use. Write a direct variation for the relationship between the number of cups of flour and the number of muffins.

---

2 Proportions and Equations of Direct Variations

You can rewrite a direct variation $y = kx$ as $\frac{y}{x} = k$. When two sets of data vary directly, the ratio $\frac{y}{x}$ is the constant of variation. It is the same for each data pair.

4 EXAMPLE Direct Variations and Tables

For each table, use the ratio $\frac{y}{x}$ to tell whether y varies directly with x. If it does, write an equation for the direct variation.

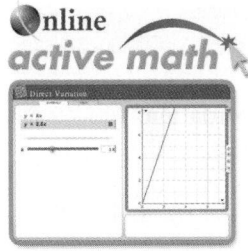

Online active math

For: Direct Variation Activity
Use: Interactive Textbook, 8-5

a.

x	y	$\frac{y}{x}$
-3	2.25	$\frac{2.25}{-3} = -0.75$
1	-0.75	$\frac{-0.75}{1} = -0.75$
4	-3	$\frac{-3}{4} = -0.75$
6	-4.5	$\frac{-4.5}{6} = -0.75$

Yes, the constant of variation is -0.75. The equation is $y = -0.75x$.

b.

x	y	$\frac{y}{x}$
2	-1	$\frac{-1}{2} = -0.5$
4	1	$\frac{1}{4} = 0.25$
6	3	$\frac{3}{6} = 0.5$
9	4.5	$\frac{4.5}{9} = 0.5$

No, the ratio $\frac{y}{x}$ is not the same for all pairs of data.

④ For the data in each table, tell whether y varies directly with x. If it does, write an equation for the direct variation.

a.

x	y
−2	3.2
1	2.4
4	1.6

b.

x	y
4	6
8	12
10	15

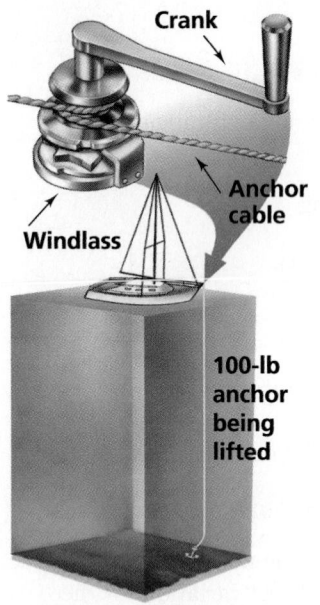

Crank

Anchor cable

Windlass

100-lb anchor being lifted

A windlass is a winch turned by a crank. It is used in a water well and to raise an anchor on a boat.

In a direct variation, the ratio $\frac{y}{x}$ is the same for all pairs of data where $x \neq 0$. So the proportion $\frac{y_1}{x_1} = \frac{y_2}{x_2}$ is true for the ordered pairs (x_1, y_1) and (x_2, y_2), where neither x_1 nor x_2 are zero. You can rewrite a proportion as an equation of direct variation.

5 **EXAMPLE** **Real-World** 🌐 **Problem Solving**

Physics The force you must apply to lift an object is proportional to the object's weight. You would need to apply 0.625 lb of force to a windlass to lift a 28-lb weight. How much force would you need to lift 100 lb?

Relate $\frac{\text{force}}{\text{weight}} = \frac{0.625}{28}$, which is about 0.0223.

Define Let $n =$ the force you need to lift 100 lb.

Write Let $w =$ the weight and $f =$ the force.

$f = 0.0223w$ **Write an equation.**

$f = 0.0223(100)$ **Substitute 100 for *w*.**

$f = 2.23$ **Simplify.**

● You need about 2.2 lb of force to lift 100 lb.

☑ **Quick Check** ⑤ **Physics** Suppose a second windlass requires 0.5 lb of force to lift an object that weighs 32 lb. How much force would you need to lift 160 lb?

EXERCISES

For more exercises, see *Extra Skill and Word Problem Practice*.

Practice and Problem Solving

Ⓐ **Practice by Example**

Example 1
(page 454)

GO for **Help**

Is each equation a direct variation? If it is, find the constant of variation.

1. $2y = 5x + 1$ **2.** $8x + 9y = 10$ **3.** $-12x = 6y$

4. $y + 8 = -x$ **5.** $5x - 6y = 0$ **6.** $-4 + 7x + 4 = 3y$

7. $-x = 10y$ **8.** $0.7x - 1.4y = 0$ **9.** $\frac{1}{2}x + \frac{1}{3}y = 0$

Example 2
(page 454)

Write an equation of the direct variation that includes the given point.

10. $(1, 5)$ **11.** $(5, 1)$ **12.** $(-8, 10)$ **13.** $(-5, -9)$

14. $(-2, 3)$ **15.** $(-6, 1)$ **16.** $(3, -4)$ **17.** $(6, -8)$

18. $(-6, 8)$ **19.** $(-5, -10)$ **20.** $(12, -8)$ **21.** $(35, 7)$

Example 3
(page 455)

Define the variables. Then write a direct variation to model each relationship.

 22. Geometry The perimeter p of a regular octagon varies directly with the length ℓ of one side of the octagon.

23. Earnings When you have a job that pays an hourly wage, the amount you earn varies directly with the number of hours you work. Suppose you earn $7.10/hour working at the library.

Example 4
(page 455)

For the data in each table, tell whether y varies directly with x. If it does, write an equation for the direct variation.

24.
x	y
3	5.4
7	12.6
12	21.6

25.
x	y
−2	1
3	6
8	11

26.
x	y
−6	9
1	−1.5
8	−12

Example 5
(page 456)

27. Physics The force you apply to a lever is proportional to the weight you can lift. Suppose you can lift a 50-lb weight by applying 20 lb of force to a certain lever.
a. What is the ratio of force to weight for the lever?
b. Write an equation and find the force you need to lift a friend weighing 130 lb.

28. Bicycling A bicyclist traveled at a constant speed during a timed practice period. Write an equation and find the distance the cyclist traveled in 30 min.

A Bicyclist's Practices

Elapsed Time	Distance
10 min	3 mi
25 min	7.5 mi

B **Apply Your Skills**

Write an equation of the direct variation that includes the given point.

29. $\left(3, \frac{1}{2}\right)$　　**30.** $\left(\frac{1}{4}, -5\right)$　　**31.** $\left(\frac{-5}{6}, \frac{6}{5}\right)$　　**32.** $(1.2, 7.2)$

33. $(0.5, 4.5)$　　**34.** $\left(-2, \frac{1}{16}\right)$　　**35.** $(5.2, -1.5)$　　**36.** $\left(-\frac{8}{3}, -\frac{9}{8}\right)$

37. a. Writing How can you tell whether two sets of data vary directly?
b. How can you tell if a line is the graph of a direct variation?

Critical Thinking **Is each statement true or false? Explain.**

38. The graph of a direct variation may pass through $(-2, 4)$.

39. The graph of a direct variation may pass through $(0, 3)$.

40. If you triple an x-value of a direct variation, the y-value also triples.

Graph the direct variation that includes the given point. Write an equation of the line.

41. $(2, 5)$　　**42.** $(-2, 5)$　　**43.** $(2, -5)$　　**44.** $(-2, -5)$

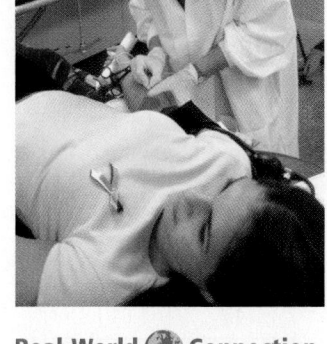

Real-World **Connection**

You must be at least 17 years old and weigh at least 110 pounds to give blood.

45. Biology The amount of blood in a person's body varies directly with body weight. A person who weighs 160 lb has about 5 qt of blood.
a. Find the constant of variation.
b. Write an equation relating quarts of blood to weight.
c. Open-Ended Estimate the number of quarts of blood in your body.

46. Electricity Ohm's Law $V = I \times R$ relates the voltage, current, and resistance of a circuit. V is the voltage measured in volts. I is the current measured in amperes. R is the resistance measured in ohms.
  a. Find the voltage of a circuit that has a current of 24 amperes and resistance of 2 ohms.
  b. Find the resistance of a circuit that has a current of 24 amperes and a voltage of 18 volts.

47. Graph each direct variation on the same coordinate plane.
  i. $y = x$ **ii.** $y = 2x$ **iii.** $y = 3x$ **iv.** $y = 4x$
  a. Describe how the graphs change as the constant of variation increases.
  b. Predict how the graph of $y = \frac{1}{2}x$ would appear.

 **Challenge**

The ordered pairs in each exercise are for the same direct variation. Find each missing value.

48. $(3, 4)$ and $(9, y)$ **49.** $(-1, 2)$ and $(4, y)$ **50.** $(-5, 3)$ and $(x, -4.8)$

51. $(1, y)$ and $\left(\frac{3}{2}, -9\right)$ **52.** $(2, 5)$ and $(x, 12.5)$ **53.** $(-2, 5)$ and $(x, -5)$

Problem Solving Hint

For Exercise 54, start with the relationship of miles and gallons:
$\frac{m}{g} = 24$.

 54. Gas Mileage A car gets 24 miles per gallon. The number of gallons g of gas used varies directly with the number of miles m traveled.
  a. Suppose the price of gas is \$1.83 per gallon. Write a function relating the cost c for g gallons of gas. Is this a direct variation?
  b. Write a direct variation relating the cost of gas to the miles traveled.

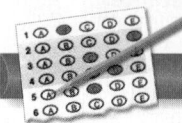
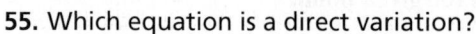
Test Prep

Multiple Choice   **55.** Which equation is a direct variation?
  A. $y = -0.7x$ **B.** $y = \frac{21}{x}$ **C.** $y - x = 4$ **D.** $y = 3x + 2$

56. A direct variation includes the point $(-8, 2)$. Which is an equation of the direct variation?
  F. $-8y = x + 2$ **G.** $2y = -8x$ **H.** $y = \frac{x}{-4}$ **J.** $y = -4x$

57. Each point is included in a different direct variation. In which variation is the constant of variation $\frac{3}{5}$?
  A. $(-3, -5)$ **B.** $(-3, 5)$ **C.** $(-2, -3)$ **D.** $(15, 9)$

58. Each point is included in a different direct variation. Which has the greatest constant of variation?
  F. $(-1, 4)$ **G.** $(10, -5)$ **H.** $(6, 2)$ **J.** $(-3, -3)$

Short Response   **59.** The table at the right shows the number of hours a clerk works per week and the amount of money she earns before taxes. Write an equation for the direct variation. Then use it to find how much money the clerk would earn if she works for 34 hours per week.

60. Write an equation of the direct variation that includes the point $(-1, -4)$. Show your work.

Hours Worked	Dollars Earned
12	\$99.00
17	\$140.25
21	\$173.25
32	\$264.00

Lesson 8-4

Write a function rule for each table.

61.

Number of People	Total Bill
1	$3.00
2	$6.00
3	$9.00
4	$12.00

62.

Amount Earned	Amount Spent
$15	$5
$30	$10
$45	$15
$60	$20

63.

Number of Days	Supplies Remaining
0	12 lb
2	10 lb
4	8 lb
6	6 lb

64.

Weight on Earth (lb)	Weight on Moon (lb)
96	16
123	20.5
144	24
171	28.5

Lessons 7-2, 7-3

Solve each inequality.

65. $r + 6 > -12$ **66.** $5 + c \leq 3.2$ **67.** $7m < -21$ **68.** $a - 4.5 \geq 12.1$

69. $\frac{n}{4} < -20$ **70.** $3t \geq 9.12$ **71.** $\frac{v}{-5} \leq \frac{1}{2}$ **72.** $b + 4\frac{2}{3} > 5\frac{1}{6}$

Lesson 5-3

 73.

Shipping For the ships that pass through the Panama Canal, the average toll is $45,000 per ship. The canal authority earned about $700 million in the year 2000. About how many ships passed through the canal that year? Round to the nearest hundred.

✓ Checkpoint Quiz 2
Lessons 8-3 through 8-5

Model each rule with a table of values and a graph. If the rule describes a direct variation, state the constant of variation.

1. $y = 4x + 1$ **2.** $y = \frac{1}{2}x$ **3.** $f(x) = -3x$ **4.** $y = -3x + 2$

Write a function rule for each situation.

5. the total cost $t(p)$ of p pounds of potatoes at $.79 per pound

6. the total distance $d(n)$ traveled in n hours at a constant speed of 60 mi/h

Write an equation for the direct variation that includes the given point.

7. $(7, -2)$ **8.** $(-3, -6)$ **9.** $(-4, -5)$

10. a. Bicycling The distance a wheel moves forward varies directly with the number of rotations. Suppose the distance d the wheel moves is 56 ft when the number of rotations n is 8. Find the constant of variation and write a direct variation equation to model this situation.

b. Use the direct variation you wrote for part (a) to find the distance the wheel moves in 20 rotations.

Inverse Variation

What You'll Learn

- To solve inverse variations
- To compare direct and inverse variation

. . . And Why

To balance weights on a fulcrum, as in Example 3

✓ **Check Skills You'll Need**   **GO** for Help   Lesson 8-5

Suppose y varies directly with x. Find each constant of variation.

1. $y = 5x$ **2.** $y = -7x$ **3.** $3y = x$ **4.** $0.25y = x$

Write an equation of the direct variation that includes the given point.

5. $(2, 4)$ **6.** $(3, 1.5)$ **7.** $(-4, 1)$ **8.** $(-5, -2)$

🔊 **New Vocabulary**
- inverse variation
- constant of variation for inverse variation

---

1   Solving Inverse Variations

Real-World Connection

With volunteer labor, Habitat for Humanity helped build over 115,000 homes for families around the world in its first 25 years.

SOURCE: *Habitat for Humanity*

Activity: Inverse Variation

Suppose you are part of a volunteer crew constructing affordable housing. Building a house requires a total of 160 workdays. For example, a crew of 20 people can complete a house in 8 days.

1. How long should it take a crew of 40 people?

2. Copy and complete the table.

Crew size (x)	Construction Days (y)	Total Workdays
2	80	160
5	■	160
8	■	■
■	16	■
20	8	160
40	■	■

3. Graph the (x, y) data in the table above.

4. Describe what happens to construction time as the crew size increases.

In the table, the total number of workdays remains the same. The number of construction days decreases as the number of people on the crew increases. The relationship of construction days and crew size is an inverse variation.

 **Key Concepts**

Definition	Inverse Variation

An equation in the form $xy = k$ or $y = \frac{k}{x}$, where $k \neq 0$, is an **inverse variation**.

The **constant of variation for inverse variation** is k, the product $x \cdot y$ for an ordered pair (x, y).

Inverse variations have graphs with the same general shape. You can see from the graph at the right how the constant of variation k affects the graph of $xy = k$.

If you know the values of x and y for one point on the graph of an inverse variation, you can use the point to find the constant of variation k and the equation of the inverse variation.

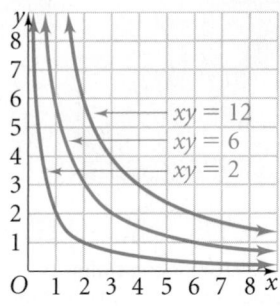

1 EXAMPLE **Writing an Equation Given a Point**

Suppose y varies inversely with x and $y = 7$ when $x = 5$. Write an equation for the inverse variation.

$xy = k$	Use the general form of an inverse variation.
$5(7) = k$	Substitute 5 for x and 7 for y.
$35 = k$	Multiply to solve for k.
$xy = 35$	Write an equation. Substitute 35 for k in $xy = k$.

● The equation of the inverse variation is $xy = 35$, or $y = \frac{35}{x}$.

 **❶** Suppose y varies inversely with x and $y = 9$ when $x = 2$. Write an equation for the inverse variation.

Suppose (x_1, y_1) and (x_2, y_2) are two ordered pairs of an inverse variation. Each ordered pair of an inverse variation has the same product k, that is $x_1 \cdot y_1 = k$ and $x_2 \cdot y_2 = k$. So $x_1 \cdot y_1 = x_2 \cdot y_2$.

2 EXAMPLE **Finding the Missing Coordinate**

The points $(3, 8)$ and $(2, y)$ are two points on the graph of an inverse variation. Find the missing value.

$x_1 \cdot y_1 = x_2 \cdot y_2$	Use the equation $x_1 \cdot y_1 = x_2 \cdot y_2$ since you know coordinates but not the constant of variation.
$3(8) = 2(y_2)$	Substitute 3 for x_1, 8 for y_1, and 2 for x_2.
$24 = 2(y_2)$	Simplify.
$12 = y_2$	Solve for y_2.

The missing value is 12. The point $(2, 12)$ is on the graph of the inverse variation that includes the point $(3, 8)$.

 **❷** Each pair of points is on the graph of an inverse variation. Find the missing value.
a. $(3, y)$ and $(5, 9)$ **b.** $(75, 0.2)$ and $(x, 3)$

3 EXAMPLE **Real-World** **Problem Solving**

Physics The weight needed to balance a lever varies inversely with the distance from the fulcrum to the weight. Where should Julio, who weighs 150 lb, sit to balance the lever?

Relate A weight of 120 lb is 6 ft from the fulcrum. A weight of 150 lb is x ft from the fulcrum.

Weight and distance vary inversely.

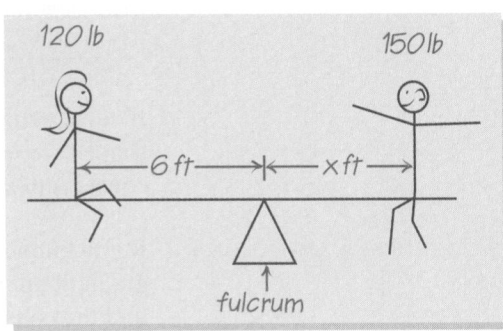

Define Let $weight_1 = 120$ lb.
Let $weight_2 = 150$ lb.
Let $distance_1 = 6$ ft.
Let $distance_2 = x$ ft.

Real-World **Connection**

A fulcrum is the point at which a lever pivots. Students can use levers in science labs to investigate physical properties.

Write $weight_1 \cdot distance_1 = weight_2 \cdot distance_2$

$120 \cdot 6 = 150 \cdot x$ **Substitute.**

$720 = 150x$ **Simplify.**

$\frac{720}{150} = x$ **Solve for x.**

$4.8 = x$ **Simplify.**

Julio should sit 4.8 feet from the fulcrum to balance the lever.

 Quick Check **3 a. Physics** A 100-lb weight is placed 4 ft from a fulcrum. How far from the fulcrum should a 75-lb weight be placed to balance the lever?

b. An 80-lb weight is placed 9 ft from a fulcrum. What weight should you put 6 ft from the fulcrum to balance the lever?

---

2 Comparing Direct and Inverse Variation

Recall that a direct variation is an equation in the form $y = kx$. This summary will help you recognize and use direct and inverse variations.

Key Concepts

Summary	**Direct and Inverse Variation**

Direct Variation

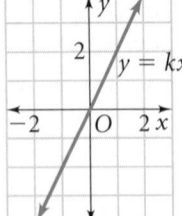 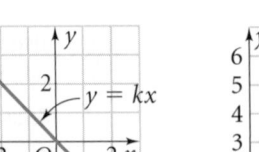

Inverse Variation

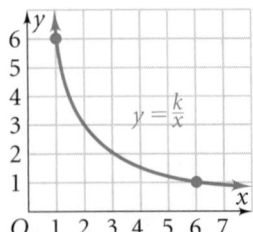

y varies directly with x.

y is directly proportional to x.

The ratio $\frac{y}{x}$ is constant.

y varies inversely with x.

y is inversely proportional to x.

The product xy is constant.

4 EXAMPLE Determining Direct or Inverse Variation

Do the data in each table represent a *direct variation* or an *inverse variation*? For each table, write an equation to model the data.

a.

x	y
2	5
4	10
10	25

The values of y seem to vary directly with the values of x. Check each ratio $\frac{y}{x}$.

$\begin{array}{c}y \to \\ x \to\end{array} \frac{5}{2} = 2.5 \qquad \frac{10}{4} = 2.5 \qquad \frac{25}{10} = 2.5$

The ratio $\frac{y}{x}$ is the same for all pairs of data. So this is a direct variation, and $k = 2.5$.

The equation is $y = 2.5x$.

b.

x	y
5	20
10	10
25	4

The values of y seem to vary inversely with the values of x. Check each product xy.

xy: $5(20) = 100 \qquad 10(10) = 100 \qquad 25(4) = 100$

The product xy is the same for all pairs of data. So this is an inverse variation, and $k = 100$.

The equation is $xy = 100$.

Quick Check  **4** Determine whether the data in each table represent a direct variation or an inverse variation. Write an equation to model the data in each table.

a.

x	y
3	12
6	6
9	4

b.

x	y
3	12
5	20
8	32

Many real-world situations involve variation. You can look for a constant ratio or a constant product to determine whether the relationship is a direct variation or an inverse variation.

5 EXAMPLE Real-World Problem Solving

Explain whether each situation represents a direct variation or an inverse variation.

a. Carpooling The cost of $20 worth of gasoline is split among several people.

The cost per person times the number of people equals the total cost of the gasoline. Since the total cost is a constant product of $20, this is an inverse variation.

b. School Supplies You buy several markers for 70¢ each.

The cost per marker times the number of markers equals the total cost of the markers. Since the ratio $\frac{\text{cost}}{\text{marker}}$ is constant at 70¢ each, this is a direct variation.

Quick Check  **5** Explain whether each situation represents a direct variation or an inverse variation.
a. You are in a discount store. All sweaters are on sale for $15 each.
b. You walk 5 miles each day. Your speed and time vary from day to day.

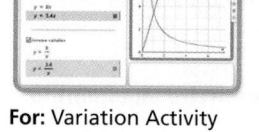

Online
active math

For: Variation Activity
Use: Interactive Textbook, 8-6

EXERCISES

For more exercises, see *Extra Skill and Word Problem Practice*.

Practice and Problem Solving

 Practice by Example

Example 1
(page 461)

Suppose y varies inversely with x. Write an equation for the inverse variation.

1. $y = 6$ when $x = 3$ **2.** $y = 1$ when $x = 2$ **3.** $y = 7$ when $x = 8$

4. $y = 3$ when $x = 0.5$ **5.** $y = 10$ when $x = 2.4$ **6.** $y = 3.5$ when $x = 2.2$

7. $y = 6$ when $x = \frac{1}{3}$ **8.** $y = \frac{1}{16}$ when $x = 8$ **9.** $y = \frac{1}{10}$ when $x = \frac{3}{5}$

Example 2
(page 461)

Each pair of points is on the graph of an inverse variation. Find the missing value.

10. $(6, 12)$ and $(9, y)$ **11.** $(3, 5)$ and $(1, n)$ **12.** $(x, 11)$ and $(1, 66)$

13. $(x, 55)$ and $(5, 77)$ **14.** $(9.4, b)$ and $(6, 4.7)$ **15.** $(50, 13)$ and $(t, 5)$

16. $(4, 3.6)$ and $(1.2, g)$ **17.** $(24, 1.6)$ and $(c, 0.4)$ **18.** $(500, 25)$ and $(4, n)$

19. $\left(\frac{1}{2}, 24\right)$ and $(6, y)$ **20.** $\left(x, \frac{1}{2}\right)$ and $\left(\frac{1}{3}, \frac{1}{4}\right)$ **21.** $\left(\frac{1}{2}, 5\right)$ and $\left(b, \frac{1}{8}\right)$

Example 3
(page 462)

22. Travel Suppose you take $2\frac{1}{2}$ h to drive from your house to the lake at 48 mi/h. How long will your return trip take at 40 mi/h?

23. Bicycling Suppose a camper took 2 h to ride around a reservoir at 10 mi/h at the beginning of the summer. By the end of the summer, she can ride around the reservoir in $1\frac{1}{2}$ h. What is her rate at the end of the summer?

Example 4
(page 463)

Do the data in each table represent a direct variation or an inverse variation? Write an equation to model the data in each table.

24.

x	y
2	1
5	2.5
8	4

25.

x	y
4	15
6	10
10	6

26.

x	y
3	24
9	8
12	6

Example 5
(page 463)

Explain whether each situation represents a direct variation or an inverse variation.

27. You buy some chicken for \$1.79/lb.

28. An 8-slice pizza is shared equally by a group of friends.

29. You find the length and width of several rectangles. Each has an area of 24 square units.

 Apply Your Skills

Find the constant of variation k for each inverse variation. Then write an equation for the inverse variation.

30. $y = 8$ when $x = 4$ **31.** $r = 3.3$ when $t = \frac{1}{3}$ **32.** $x = \frac{1}{2}$ when $y = 5$

33. $a = 25$ when $b = 0.04$ **34.** $p = 10.4$ when $q = 1.5$ **35.** $x = 5$ when $y = 75$

Geometry **Does each formula represent a direct or an inverse variation? Explain.**

36. the perimeter of an equilateral triangle: $P = 3s$

37. the time t to travel 150 mi at r mi/h: $t = \frac{150}{r}$

38. the circumference of a circle with radius r: $C = 2\pi r$

Real-World  **Connection**

Careers Surveyors determine boundaries and elevations of geographical features.

🌐 **39. Surveying** Each of two rectangular building lots is one quarter acre in size. One lot measures 99 ft by 110 ft. The other lot is 90 ft wide. What is the second lot's length?

🌐 **40. Construction** Suppose 4 people can paint a house if they work 3 days each. How long would it take a crew of 5 people to paint the house?

Do the data in each table represent a direct or an inverse variation? Write an equation to model the data. Then complete the table.

41.

x	y
10	4
20	■
8	3.2

42.

x	y
0.4	28
1.2	84
■	63

43.

x	y
1.6	30
4.8	10
■	96

🌐 **44. Math in the Media** According to the First Law of Air Travel, for each situation below, will the distance to your gate be *greater* or *less* for this trip than for your last trip?
 a. You have more luggage.
 b. You have less time to make your flight.
 c. You have less luggage.

🌐 **45. a. Earnings** Suppose you want to earn $80. How long will it take you if you are paid $5/h; $8/h; $10/h; $20/h?
 b. What are the two variable quantities in part (a)?
 c. Write an equation to represent this situation.

46. Open-Ended Write and graph a direct variation and an inverse variation that have the same constant of variation.

CLOSE TO HOME by John McPherson

GATE 31-Y
3.4 MILES

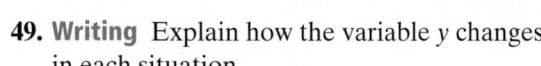

The First Law of Air Travel
The distance to your connecting gate is directly proportional to the amount of luggage you are carrying and inversely proportional to the amount of time you have.

47. Multiple Choice Boyle's Law states that volume V varies inversely with pressure P for any gas at a constant temperature in an enclosed space. Suppose a gas at constant temperature occupies 15.3 liters at a pressure of 40 millimeters of mercury. Which equation models this situation?
 (A) $612 = PV$ (B) $P = 15.3V$ (C) $V = 40P$ (D) $P + V = 40$

48. Critical Thinking The graphs p and q represent a direct variation and an inverse variation. Write an equation for each graph.

49. Writing Explain how the variable y changes in each situation.
 a. y varies directly with x. The value of x is doubled.
 b. y varies inversely with x. The value of x is doubled.

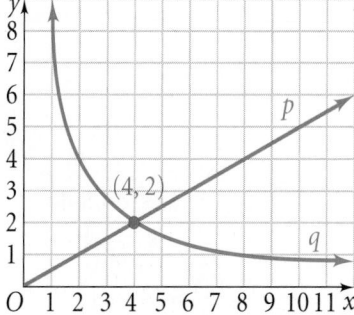

Challenge  **50. Physics** The intensity of a sound s varies inversely with the square of the distance d from the sound. This can be modeled by the equation $sd^2 = k$. If you move half the distance closer to the source of a sound, by what factor will the intensity of the sound increase? Explain your reasoning.

51. Write an equation to model each situation.
  a. y varies inversely with the fourth power of x.
  b. y varies inversely with the fourth power of x and directly with z.

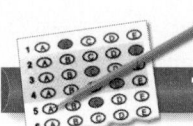

Test Prep

Multiple Choice

52. Suppose y varies inversely with x and $x = 12$ when $y = 3$. What is the equation of the inverse variation?

  A. $\frac{y}{x} = 36$ **B.** $y = \frac{12}{3}$ **C.** $y = \frac{36}{x}$ **D.** $12 = \frac{3}{y}$

53. The volume V of a gas varies inversely with the pressure P. When the volume is 75 in.^{3}, the pressure is 30 lb/in.^{2}. What is the volume when the pressure is 25 lb/in.^{2}?

  F. 90 in.^{3} **G.** $58\frac{1}{3}$ in.^{3} **H.** 60 in.^{3} **J.** 30 in.^{3}

Short Response

54. Use the table at the right. Find a value such that the y-values vary directly with the x-values. Then find a value such that the y-values vary inversely with the x-values. Show your work.

x	y
5	10
8	■

Extended Response

55. You are traveling to visit your best friend who moved 100 miles away.
  a. Copy and complete the table below to find the time the trip takes at different speeds.
  b. Describe the relationship of the variables.
  c. How long would the round trip take if you could travel at 80 mi/h?

Distance (d)	100	100	100	100
Speed (r)	30	40	50	60
Time (t)	■	■	■	■

Mixed Review

Lesson 8-5

Write an equation of the direct variation that includes the given point.

56. $(1, 6)$ **57.** $(-2, 8)$ **58.** $(10, -1)$

59. $(-5, -4)$ **60.** $(7, 11)$ **61.** $(-28, 4)$

Lesson 6-9

Use the Pythagorean Theorem to find the hypotenuse or the missing leg. Round to the nearest hundredth if necessary.

62. $FH = 25$ in., $HG = 10$ in.

63. $FH = 8$ cm, $FG = 15$ cm

64. $GH = 17$ ft, $FG = 20$ ft

65. $GH = 1.4$ in., $FH = 3.2$ in.

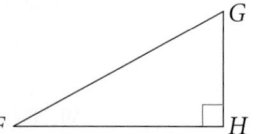

Lesson 5-4

Simplify each expression.

66. $-(x + 1)$ **67.** $6(8 - p)$ **68.** $(4n + 7)(1.5)$

69. $5k + 11k$ **70.** $0.25(24 - 16t)$ **71.** $99m - 36m$

Activity Lab

Hands-On

Inverse Variation

FOR USE WITH LESSON 8-6

In this activity you will use a paper "telescope." You will need two meter sticks, tape, two sheets of 8.5 × 11 in. paper (approximately 21.6 × 27.9 cm). Follow the steps below.

Step 1 Take each sheet of paper and draw dashed lines on them, as shown below.

Step 2 Take one sheet and add marks and labels at 4 cm, 8 cm, 12 cm, 16 cm, 20 cm, and 24 cm.

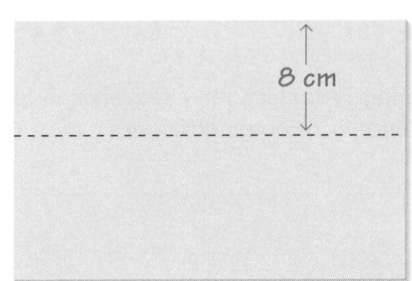

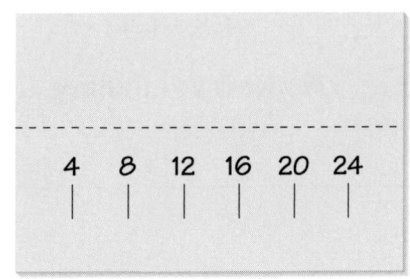

Step 3 Roll each sheet into a tube so that the bottom edge meets the dashed line. Tape it in place.

Step 4 Slide the measured tube inside the other tube.

ACTIVITY

Tape a meter stick to a wall at eye level. Stand between 1 m and 3 m from the target meter stick and mark your spot on the floor. You will take all measurements from the same distance.

Collapse the telescope so the measured tube is completely hidden. Draw a mark on the top of the telescope. Hold the telescope so the mark remains on the top. Also, do not bend the telescope.

1. **Data Collection** Copy the table at the right. When the telescope is completely collapsed, it will be nearly 28-cm long. Look through the telescope at the target and record the width of your view.

2. Extend the telescope so the 4-cm mark is just visible. Now the telescope is 32-cm long. Record the width of your view from the same spot on the floor. Repeat and complete the table. Graph your data.

3. **Predict** Use your graph to predict your width of view if the telescope was 24-cm long.

4. Based on the data, do you think this is a direct or inverse variation?

5. **a.** Find (length of telescope) × (width of view) for each pair of points.

   b. Find the mean of the products and use this for your value of k.

   c. Predict Use $w = \frac{k}{\ell}$ to predict the width of view w when the length of telescope ℓ is 40 cm.

   d. How does your prediction compare with the measured value?

Length of Telescope	Width of View
28 cm	■
32 cm	■
36 cm	■
40 cm	■
44 cm	■
48 cm	■
52 cm	■

Describing Number Patterns

What You'll Learn

- To use inductive reasoning in continuing number patterns
- To write rules for arithmetic sequences

...And Why

To predict the next numbers in a pattern, as in Example 1

✓ **Check Skills You'll Need**

GO **for Help** Lesson 4-2 and 5-2

Evaluate each expression for $x = 2, 3, 4$.

1. $9 + 3(x - 1)$ **2.** $8 + 7(x - 1)$ **3.** $0.4 - 3(x - 1)$

Subtract.

4. $8 - (-6)$ **5.** $-7 - 10$ **6.** $1.5 - 3.4$

◀)) **New Vocabulary**   • inductive reasoning   • conjecture   • sequence   • term
   • arithmetic sequence   • common difference

---

1   Inductive Reasoning and Number Patterns

Suppose you are in a city and notice that the first three streets you pass are 10th Street, 11th Street, and 12th Street. You would probably conclude that the next street would be 13th Street. You would be basing your conclusion on inductive reasoning.

Inductive reasoning is making conclusions based on patterns you observe. A conclusion you reach by inductive reasoning is a **conjecture.**

1 EXAMPLE   Extending Number Patterns

Use inductive reasoning to describe each pattern. Then find the next two numbers in each pattern.

a. 2,   5,   8,   11
   $+3$ $+3$ $+3$

The pattern is "add 3 to the previous term." To find the next two numbers, you add 3 to each previous term: $11 + 3 = 14$ and $14 + 3 = 17$.

b. 2,   4,   8,   16
   $\times 2$ $\times 2$ $\times 2$

The pattern is "multiply the previous term by 2." To find the next two numbers, you multiply each previous term by 2: $16 \times 2 = 32$ and $32 \times 2 = 64$.

c. $1, 4, 9, 16, \ldots$

The pattern is "square consecutive integers": $1^2, 2^2, 3^2, 4^2$. To find the next two numbers, square the next two consecutive integers: $5^2 = 25$ and $6^2 = 36$.

Vocabulary Tip

You read "..." at the end of a sequence as "and so on."

✓ **Quick Check** ❶ Use inductive reasoning to describe each pattern. Then find the next two numbers in each pattern.
   a. $3, 9, 27, 81, \ldots$ **b.** $9, 15, 21, 27, \ldots$ **c.** $2, -4, 8, -16, \ldots$

A number pattern is also called a **sequence.** Each number in a sequence is a **term** of the sequence.

One kind of number sequence is an arithmetic sequence. You form an **arithmetic sequence** by adding a fixed number to each previous term. This fixed number is the **common difference.**

$$-4, \quad 5, \quad 14, \quad 23$$
$$+9 \quad +9 \quad +9$$

2 **EXAMPLE** **Finding the Common Difference**

Find the common difference of each arithmetic sequence.

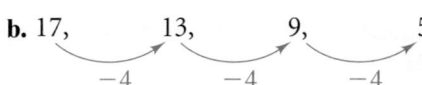

a. $-7, \quad -3, \quad 1, \quad 5$ 　　　**b.** $17, \quad 13, \quad 9, \quad 5$
$\quad +4 \quad +4 \quad +4$ 　　　　　　 $\quad -4 \quad -4 \quad -4$

The common difference is 4.　　　The common difference is -4.

 Quick Check **2** Find the common difference of each sequence.
a. $11, 23, 35, 47, \ldots$ 　　　　　　　**b.** $8, 3, -2, -7, \ldots$

Consider the sequence $7, 11, 15, 19, \ldots$ Think of each term as the output of a function. Think of the term number as the input.

term number	1	2	3	4	← input
term	7	11	15	19	← output

You can use the common difference of the terms of an arithmetic sequence to write a function rule for the sequence. For the sequence $7, 11, 15, 19, \ldots$, the common difference is 4.

Let n = the term number in the sequence.

Let $A(n)$ = the value of the nth term of the sequence.

$A(1) = 7$

$A(2) = 7 + 4 = 7 + 1 \cdot 4$ 　　　　**4 is the common difference.**

$A(3) = 7 + 4 + 4 = 7 + 2 \cdot 4$ 　　　**Note that the number in red is one less**

$A(4) = 7 + 4 + 4 + 4 = 7 + 3 \cdot 4$ 　**than the term number, which is in blue.**

$A(n) = 7 + 4 + 4 + 4 + \ldots + 4 = 7 + (n - 1) 4$

For an arithmetic sequence, you can use the first term, the term number, and the common difference to find the value of any given term.

Key Concepts

Rule	Arithmetic Sequence
$A(n) = a + (n - 1)d$	
nth　 first　 term　 common	
term　 term　 number　 difference	

Test-Taking Tip

When you simplify products with negative numbers, keeping the parentheses in place can help you avoid computational errors.

3 EXAMPLE **Finding Terms of a Sequence**

Gridded Response Find the tenth term of the sequence that has the rule $A(n) = 32 + (n - 1)(-2)$.

$$A(10) = 32 + (10 - 1)(-2)$$
$$= 32 + 9(-2)$$
$$= 14$$

● Fill in the grid with 14.

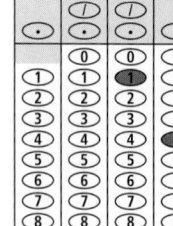

 Quick Check ③ Find the first, sixth, and twelfth terms of each sequence.
  a. $A(n) = -5 + (n - 1)(3)$ **b.** $A(n) = 6.3 + (n - 1)(5)$

EXERCISES

For more exercises, see *Extra Skill and Word Problem Practice.*

Practice and Problem Solving

A Practice by Example

Example 1
(page 468)

Use inductive reasoning to describe each pattern. Then find the next two numbers in each pattern.

1. $4, 6, 8, 10, \ldots$ **2.** $4, 6, 9, 13\frac{1}{2}, \ldots$ **3.** $4, 6, 9, 13, \ldots$

4. $3, 3.04, 3.08, 3.12, \ldots$ **5.** $3, 3.3, 3.63, 3.993, \ldots$ **6.** $3, 1, -1, -3, \ldots$

7. $1.1, 2.2, 3.3, 4.4, \ldots$ **8.** $0.001, 0.01, 0.1, 1, \ldots$ **9.** $2, 8, 32, 128, \ldots$

10. $1, \frac{1}{4}, \frac{1}{9}, \frac{1}{16}, \ldots$ **11.** $9, -5, -19, -33, \ldots$ **12.** $1.5, 7.5, 37.5, 187.5, \ldots$

Example 2
(page 469)

Find the common difference of each arithmetic sequence.

13. $-5, -2, 1, 4, \ldots$ **14.** $-6, -10, -14, -18, \ldots$ **15.** $18, 7, -4, -15, \ldots$

16. $8, 21, 34, 47, \ldots$ **17.** $\frac{1}{2}, \frac{1}{3}, \frac{1}{6}, 0, \ldots$ **18.** $0.7, 1.5, 2.3, 3.1, \ldots$

19. $8, 6, 4, 2, \ldots$ **20.** $10, 22, 34, 46, \ldots$ **21.** $-9, -4, 1, 6, \ldots$

Example 3
(page 470)

Find the second, fifth, and ninth terms of each sequence.

22. $A(n) = 2 + (n - 1)(3)$ **23.** $A(n) = -9 + (n - 1)(6)$

24. $A(n) = -7 + (n - 1)(4)$ **25.** $A(n) = 8 + (n - 1)(9)$

26. $A(n) = 0.5 + (n - 1)(3)$ **27.** $A(n) = -5 + (n - 1)(7)$

28. $A(n) = 9 + (n - 1)(-6)$ **29.** $A(n) = -2.1 + (n - 1)(-5)$

30. $A(n) = 65 + (n - 1)(-7)$ **31.** $A(n) = 21 + (n - 1)(-4)$

32. $A(n) = -5 + (n - 1)(-3)$ **33.** $A(n) = 0.2 + (n - 1)(-1)$

B Apply Your Skills

Find the next two terms in each sequence.

34. $20, 14, 8, 2, \ldots$ **35.** $2, 2\frac{1}{4}, 2\frac{1}{2}, 2\frac{3}{4}, 3, \ldots$ **36.** $2, 5, 10, 17, \ldots$

37. $12, 4, 1\frac{1}{3}, \frac{4}{9}, \ldots$ **38.** $0, 3, 8, 15, 24, \ldots$ **39.** $-5, 4, 13, 22, \ldots$

40. $40, 20, 10, 5, \ldots$ **41.** $7, 7\frac{1}{4}, 7\frac{1}{2}, 7\frac{3}{4}, \ldots$ **42.** $12, -4, \frac{4}{3}, -\frac{4}{9}, \ldots$

43. a. Writing Explain the difference between inductive and deductive reasoning.
  b. Open-Ended Give an example of inductive reasoning and of deductive reasoning.

Real-World **Connection**

About 15% of all trips on mass transit are students going to or from school or college.

44. Transportation Buses on your route run every 7 minutes from 6:30 A.M. to 10:00 A.M. You get to the bus stop at 7:56 A.M. How long will you have to wait for a bus?

45. Open-Ended Write a function rule for a sequence that has -30 as the eighth term.

For Exercises 46 and 47, write the first five terms in each sequence. Explain what the fifth term means in the context of the situation.

46. A baby's birth weight is 7 lb 4 oz. The baby gains 5 oz each week.

47. The balance of a car loan starts at $4,500 and decreases $150 each month.

48. Use the sequence $1, 2, 4, \ldots$
  a. Find the difference between consecutive terms in the sequence. Use inductive reasoning to make a conjecture about the next term in the sequence.
  b. Find the quotient of consecutive terms in the sequence. Use inductive reasoning to make a conjecture about the next term in the sequence.
  c. Critical Thinking Explain why having more than three terms in a sequence can help you make a conjecture that is more likely to be correct.

Is each given sequence arithmetic? Justify your answer.

49. $0.3, 3, 30, 300, \ldots$ **50.** $-3, -7, -11, -15, \ldots$ **51.** $1, 8, 27, 64, \ldots$

52. $2, 4, 8, 16, 32, \ldots$ **53.** $46, 31, 16, 1, \ldots$ **54.** $0.2, -0.6, -1.4, -2.2, \ldots$

55. The first five rows of Pascal's Triangle are at the right.
  a. Predict the numbers in the sixth row.
  b. Find the sum of the numbers in each of the first five rows. Predict the sum of the numbers in the sixth row.

```
            1
          1   1
        1   2   1
      1   3   3   1
    1   4   6   4   1
```

Find the second, fourth, and eighth terms of each sequence.

56. $A(n) = 11 + (n - 1)\left(\frac{1}{3}\right)$ **57.** $A(n) = 9 + (n - 1)(-4.5)$

58. $A(n) = -2 + (n - 2)(-1.6)$ **59.** $A(n) = \frac{1}{5} + (n - 1)\left(\frac{4}{5}\right)$

60. a. Complete the table at the right for an arithmetic sequence.
  b. Graph the ordered pairs (term number, term) on a coordinate plane.
  c. What do you notice about the points on your graph?

x	y
1	5
2	8
3	■
4	■

61. Music There are 52 white keys on a piano. The frequency produced when a key is struck is the number of vibrations per second the key's string makes.
  a. Reasoning Is this relation a function? Explain.
  b. Writing Describe the pattern in the relation.

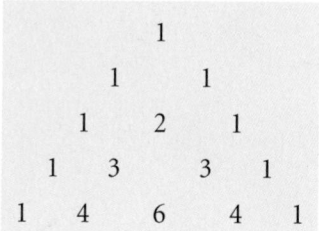

Frequency   27.5   55   110   220   440   880   1760

62. Number Theory The Fibonacci sequence is $1, 1, 2, 3, 5, 8, 13, \ldots$ After the first two numbers, each number is the sum of the two previous numbers.
  a. What is the next term of the sequence?
  b. What is the eleventh term of the sequence?
  c. Open-Ended Choose two other numbers to start a Fibonacci-like sequence. Write the first seven terms of your sequence.

A *recursive formula* relates a new term of a sequence to the previous term of the sequence. **Describe each of the sequences using a recursive formula.**

Sample $3, 7, 11, 15, \ldots$

value of new term = value of previous term + 4

63. $12, 18, 24, 30, \ldots$ **64.** $12, 18, 27, 40.5, \ldots$ **65.** $54, 51.5, 49, 46.5, \ldots$

66. $1.1, 5.1, 9.1, 13.1, \ldots$ **67.** $98, 14, 2, \frac{2}{7}, \ldots$ **68.** $-8, 20, -50, 125, \ldots$

 Challenge

Find the common difference of each sequence. Then find the next term.

69. $4, x + 4, 2x + 4, 3x + 4, \ldots$

70. $a + b + c, 4a + 3b + c, 7a + 5b + c, \ldots$

71. Use the sequence $10, 4, -2, -8, \ldots$
  a. What is the first term of the sequence?
  b. What is the common difference of the sequence?
  c. Write a function rule $A(n)$ for the sequence.

72. a. Draw the next figure in the pattern.

  b. Reasoning What is the color of the 20th figure? Explain.
  c. How many sides does the 28th figure have? Explain.

73. Use the arithmetic sequence $-5, 1, 7, 13, \ldots$
  a. What is the first term?
  b. What is the common difference?
  c. Use your answers from parts (a) and (b) to write a rule for the sequence.

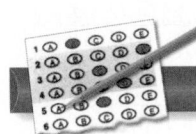

Test Prep

Multiple Choice

74. What is the seventh term of the sequence 24, 12, 6, 3, . . . ?
  A. 0   **B.** 0.25   **C.** 0.375   **D.** 1.5

75. What is the common difference of the arithmetic sequence $9, -1, -11, -21, \ldots$?
  F. -10 **G.** -9 **H.** 9   **J.** 10

76. What is the common difference of the arithmetic sequence $\frac{1}{5}, \frac{6}{5}, \frac{11}{5}, \frac{16}{5}, \ldots$?
  A. 1   **B.** $1\frac{1}{5}$ **C.** $\frac{21}{5}$ **D.** 5

77. What is the seventh term of the sequence $A(n) = -9 + (n - 1)0.5$?
  F. -7 **G.** -6.5 **H.** -6 **J.** -5.5

78. What is the first term of the sequence $A(n) = (n - 1)(-3)$?

    A. -3 **B.** -2 **C.** 0 **D.** 1

79. What is the next term in the sequence $x - 4, x - 2, x, x + 2, \ldots$?

    F. $2x$ **G.** $x + 3$ **H.** $x + 4$ **J.** $2x + 2$

Short Response

80. Explain how to find the seventh term of the sequence 24, 21, 18, 15, . . .

Extended Response

81. Marta started to work at a company in the year 2001. Her yearly salary was $26,500. At the beginning of the next year she received a $2,880 raise. Assume that she receives the same raise each year.

    a. Write a function $f(n)$ to find Marta's salary n years after 2001.

    b. Find Marta's salary in 2008. Show your work.

Mixed Review

for Help

Lesson 8-6

Suppose y varies inversely with x. Write an equation for the inverse variation.

82. $y = 4$ when $x = 5$ **83.** $y = 1.2$ when $x = 8$

84. $y = \frac{1}{2}$ when $x = 24$ **85.** $y = 7$ when $x = 6.1$

Each pair of points is on the graph of an inverse variation. Find the missing value.

86. $(8, 9)$ and $(p, 6)$ **87.** $(x, 12)$ and $\left(\frac{1}{3}, 18\right)$

88. $(2.5, 16)$ and $(5, m)$ **89.** $(30, 2)$ and $(t, 6)$

Lesson 8-5

Write an equation of the direct variation that includes the given point.

90. $(4, -5)$ **91.** $(0.5, 12)$ **92.** $(-1, 14)$ **93.** $(10, 1.4)$

94. $(1.1, -3.1)$ **95.** $(11, -3.1)$ **96.** $(2, -3)$ **97.** $\left(\frac{1}{2}, \frac{1}{3}\right)$

Lesson 8-2

Find the range of each function for the domain $\{-2, 1, 5\}$.

98. $f(x) = -4x$ **99.** $g(x) = 1 - 4x$ **100.** $y = 3x + 4$

101. $y = 2|x|$ **102.** $h(x) = |2x|$ **103.** $f(x) = \frac{3}{4}x - 5$

A Point in Time

1500   1600   1700   1800   1900   2000

In 1971, Romana Acosta Bañuelos became the first Mexican American woman to hold the office of United States Treasurer. Before her appointment to this post by President Nixon, she founded and managed her own multimillion-dollar food enterprise and established the Pan American National Bank of East Los Angeles. As a highly successful businesswoman, she had to work on a daily basis with interest rates, balance sheets, investments, and other activities required in the corporate world.

Go Online
PHSchool.com

For: Information about the office of United States Treasurer

Web Code: ate-2032

Using a Variable

You can solve many problems by using a variable to represent an unknown quantity. Try to let the variable be the quantity that you are looking for. Then use the variable to write an equation or inequality.

1 EXAMPLE

A brand of cereal comes in two sizes. The 12-oz size costs $4.35. At that rate, how much should the 20-oz box cost?

The problem is asking for the cost of a 20-oz box. Let the variable x be the cost of the 20-oz box. Write and solve a proportion to answer the question.

$\frac{12}{20} = \frac{4.35}{x}$ **Write a proportion.**

$12x = 20(4.35)$ **Find the cross products.**

$12x = 87.00$ **Simplify.**

$x = 7.25$ **Divide each side by 12.**

● The 20-oz box should cost about $7.25.

2 EXAMPLE

One house painter charges an initial fee of $25, plus $15 per hour. A second painter charges $25 per hour. Find out how many hours a job takes for the charge of the second painter to be the same as the charge of the first painter.

Let h = number of hours each painter must work for the charges to be the same. Then write an equation that expresses the charges for each painter.

First painter   Second painter

$25 + 15h$ $=$ $25h$

$25 = 10h$ **Subtract 15h from each side.**

$2.5 = h$ **Divide each side by 10.**

● The charges are the same when both painters have worked 2.5 hours.

EXERCISES

1. Another way to solve the problem in Example 2 is to try values and test them until you find the correct answer. What is the advantage of using a variable?

2. The pressure of water varies directly with the depth. At 98 meters, the pressure is 10.21 atmospheres. Round to the nearest tenth.
   a. Let x be the depth where the pressure is 5 atmospheres. Use this variable to write and solve an equation to find that depth.
   b. Let x be the pressure at a depth of 150 meters. Use this variable to write and solve an equation to find the pressure.

Chapter Review

Vocabulary Review

 arithmetic sequence (p. 469)
common difference (p. 469)
conjecture (p. 468)
constant of variation for direct
    variation (p. 454)

constant of variation for inverse
    variation (p. 461)
continuous data (p. 440)
direct variation (p. 454)
discrete data (p. 440)
function notation (p. 434)

inductive reasoning (p. 468)
inverse variation (p. 461)
relation (p. 433)
sequence (p. 469)
term (p. 469)
vertical-line test (p. 434)

Match the vocabulary term in the column on the left with the most specific description in the column on the right.

1. direct variation

2. inductive reasoning

3. independent variable

4. function

5. range

6. sequence

7. conjecture

A. x-coordinate

B. y-coordinate

C. a function that can be expressed in the form $y = kx$, where $k \neq 0$

D. drawing conclusions based on observed patterns

E. a relation with exactly one value of the dependent variable for each value of the independent variable

F. a conclusion based on inductive reasoning

G. a number pattern

Go Online
PHSchool.com
For: Vocabulary quiz
Web Code: atj-0551

Skills and Concepts

8-1 Objective

▼ To interpret, sketch, and analyze graphs from situations (p. 428)

A graph shows a visual representation of the relationship between two sets of data.

Describe a situation for each graph.

8.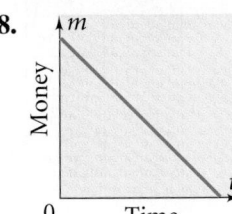

9.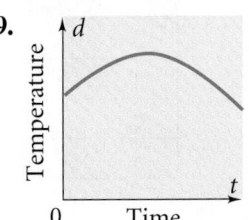

10.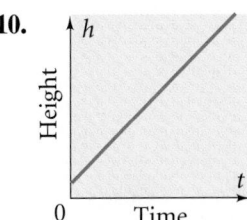

Sketch a graph of each situation. Label each section.

11. the height of a sunflower over a summer

12. the number of customers in a restaurant each hour of one day

13. the number of vehicles that enter a school parking lot during one day

14. the number of bags of peanuts sold during a 2-hour baseball game

A **relation** is a set of ordered pairs. A function is a relation that assigns exactly one value in the range to each value in the domain. A function rule is an equation that describes a function. A function is in **function notation** when it uses $f(x)$ for the outputs.

Find the range of each function when the domain is $\{-4, 0, 1, 5\}$.

15. $y = 4x - 7$ **16.** $m = 0.5n + 3$ **17.** $p = q^2 + 1$ **18.** $w = 5 - 3z$

Determine whether each relation is a function.

19.

x	y
0	1
1	2
2	3
1	4

20.

x	y
0	-2
2	0
-2	-4
4	2

21.

x	y
2	-3
-1	-3
0	-3
5	-3

22. Use the vertical-line test to determine if the graph at the right is a function.

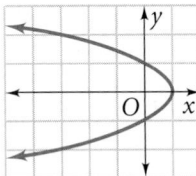

23. Writing When is a relation also a function?

When you graph data, put the independent variable on the horizontal axis and the dependent variable on the vertical axis.

Discrete data are data that involve a count of items. For discrete data, indicate each data item with a point and connect the points with a dashed line. **Continuous data** are data where numbers between any two data values have meaning. Use a solid line to indicate continuous data.

Model each rule with a table of values and a graph.

24. $f(x) = x^2 - 3$ **25.** $f(x) = -\frac{1}{2}x - 3$ **26.** $y = |x| - 7$ **27.** $y = 2x + 1$

Write a function rule for each table of values.

28.

x	f(x)
2	3
4	5
6	7
8	9

29.

x	f(x)
-3	3
0	0
3	-3
6	-6

30.

x	f(x)
3.0	6.5
3.5	7.0
4.0	7.5
4.5	8.0

 31. Weather The table at the right compares inches of snow to the corresponding amounts of rain.

   a. Write a function rule that models the data.

   b. Does the function represent discrete or continuous data? Explain.

Precipitation

Snow (in.)	Rain (in.)
3	0.3
5	0.5
10	1.0
7.5	0.75

8-5 and 8-6 Objectives

▼ To write an equation of a direct variation (p. 453)
▼ To use ratios and proportions with direct variations (p. 455)
▼ To solve inverse variations (p. 460)
▼ To compare direct and inverse variation (p. 462)

A function is a **direct variation** if it has the form $y = kx$, where $k \neq 0$. The coefficient k is the **constant of variation**.

Is each equation a direct variation? If it is, find the constant of variation.

32. $f(x) = -3x$ **33.** $y = x - 3$

34. $y = 2x + 5$ **35.** $y = \frac{2}{5}x$

Write an equation of the direct variation that includes the given point.

36. $(5, 1)$ **37.** $(-2, -2)$

38. $(1, 2)$ **39.** $(-2, 6)$

When two quantities are related so that their product is a nonzero constant, they form an **inverse variation**. An inverse variation can be written $xy = k$, where k is the **constant of variation**.

Suppose y varies inversely with x. Write an equation for each inverse variation.

40. $x = 6$ when $y = 1$ **41.** $x = 90$ when $y = 0.1$ **42.** $x = 88$ when $y = 0.05$

Each pair of points is on the graph of an inverse variation. Find the missing value.

43. $(9, x)$ and $(3, 12)$ **44.** $(4, 2.65)$ and $(y, 4.24)$ **45.** $(r, 100)$ and $(75, 25)$

Do the data in each table represent a direct variation or an inverse variation? Write an equation to model the data in each table.

46.

x	y
2	35
5	14
10	7

47.

x	y
3	24.6
5	41
10	82

48.

x	y
1	3
4	$\frac{3}{4}$
9	$\frac{1}{3}$

Inductive reasoning is the process of making conclusions or **conjectures** based on patterns you observe. A number pattern is called a **sequence**, and each number in the sequence is a **term**.

An **arithmetic sequence** is formed by adding a fixed number, the **common difference**, to each previous term.

Use inductive reasoning to describe each pattern. Then find the next three numbers in each pattern.

49. $99, 90, 81, 72, \ldots$ **50.** $5, 8, 11, 14, \ldots$ **51.** $12, 23, 34, 45, \ldots$

Find the third, eighth, and tenth terms of each sequence.

52. $A(n) = -1 + (n - 1)2$ **53.** $A(n) = 4 + (n - 1)3$

54. $A(n) = 1.5 + (n - 1)1.5$ **55.** $A(n) = 4 + (n - 1)(-3)$

Determine whether each sequence is arithmetic. If it is, find the next three terms.

56. $14, 21, 28, 35, \ldots$ **57.** $16, -8, 4, -2, \ldots$

Chapter Test

Go Online
PHSchool.com
For: Chapter Test
Web Code: ata-0552

Sketch a graph of each situation. Label each section.

1. the speed of a bicycle during an afternoon ride

2. the amount of milk in your container over one lunch period

Determine whether each relation is a function. If the relation is a function, state the domain and range.

3.

x	y
−2	5
8	6
3	12
5	6

4.

x	y
9	6
3	8
4	9.5
9	2

5. **Writing** Explain how to use the vertical-line test to determine whether a graph is a graph of a function.

Find the range of each function when the domain is {−3, −1.5, 0, 1, 4}.

6. $r = 4t^2 + 5$

7. $m = -3n - 2$

Model each rule with a table of values and a graph.

8. $f(x) = 1.5x - 3$

9. $f(x) = -x^2 + 4$

Write a function rule to describe each statement.

10. the cost in dollars of printing dollar bills when it costs 3.8¢ to print a dollar bill

11. the amount of money you earn mowing lawns at $15 per lawn

12. the profit you make selling flowers at $1.50 each when each flower costs you $.80

Write a function rule for each table of values.

13.

x	y
0	1
1	3
2	5
−3	−5

14.

x	f(x)
0	0
1	−4.5
−1	4.5
2	−9

15. **Open-Ended** Describe a situation that could be modeled by the equation $y = 5x$.

16. **Purchasing** The price of turkey depends on its weight. Suppose turkeys sell for $.59 per lb.
   a. Write a rule to describe the function.
   b. What is the price of a 14-lb turkey?
   c. If you had $10 to buy a turkey, how big a turkey could you buy?

Write an equation of the direct variation that includes the given point.

17. $(2, 2)$ 18. $(-8, -4)$ 19. $(3, -1)$ 20. $(-5, 3)$

Determine whether each of the following graphs shows a direct variation. Write an equation for each direct variation.

21.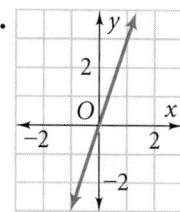

22.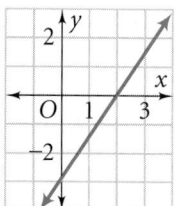

23. **Plumbing** The total amount of water dripping from a leaky faucet varies directly with time. If water drips at the rate of 5 mL/min, how much water drips in 30 min?

Find the common difference for each arithmetic sequence. Then find the next three terms.

24. $-55, -50, -45, -40, \ldots$ 25. $1.7, 2.7, 3.7, 4.7, \ldots$

Find the fifth term of each arithmetic sequence.

26. $A(n) = 2 + (n - 1)(-2.5)$
27. $A(n) = -9 + (n - 1)\,3$

Find the constant of variation k for each inverse variation.

28. $y = 5$ when $x = 6$ 29. $y = 78$ when $x = 0.1$

30. Write a function rule for the cost of catfish shown in the table below.

Weight (lb)	1	2	3	4	5
Cost (dollars)	3	6	9	12	15

Is each sequence arithmetic? Justify your answer.

31. $128, 64, 32, 16, \ldots$ 32. $3, 3.25, 3.5, 3.75, \ldots$

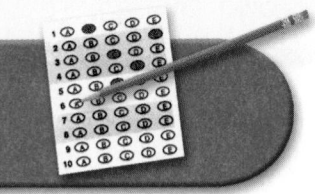

Standardized Test Prep

Reading Comprehension Read the passage below. Then answer the questions on the basis of what is *stated* or *implied* in the passage.

> **Train Math** Amtrak's Acela regional train has taken more than an hour off the old five-hour train trip from Boston to New York City. The faster Acela Express makes the 231-mile run in about 3.5 hours. The Express goes from New York to Washington, D.C., in about 2.75 hours.
>
> A train's speed depends on how secure the track is and how well banked the curves are. On the best stretches, the Express can go as fast as 150 miles an hour.
>
> For the New York–Washington, D.C., run, Amtrak carries 70% of the passengers traveling by either train or air. For the Boston–New York run, Amtrak carries only 30% of the passengers. The average number of riders that Amtrak carries in one month on the Boston–New York run is 100,404. The average number of riders in a month on the New York–Washington, D.C., run is 771,900. Amtrak hopes the new, faster train will increase ridership between Boston and New York.

1. Which is closest to the average speed for the old five-hour Boston–New York run?

   Ⓐ 30 miles per hour
   Ⓑ 40 miles per hour
   Ⓒ 80 miles per hour
   Ⓓ 1000 miles per hour

2. How much longer was the old five-hour Boston–New York run than the same trip on the Acela Express?

   Ⓕ 0.75 hour
   Ⓖ 1.5 hours
   Ⓗ 2.25 hours
   Ⓙ 2.5 hours

3. Which is closest to the average speed of the Boston–New York run for the Acela Express?

   Ⓐ 57 miles per hour
   Ⓑ 70 miles per hour
   Ⓒ 85 miles per hour
   Ⓓ 114 miles per hour

4. What is the percent of change between the Acela and Acela Express Boston–New York trip times?

   Ⓕ 12.5%   Ⓖ 20%
   Ⓗ 30%   Ⓙ 70%

5. If the Acela Express could make the entire trip from Boston to New York at 150 miles an hour, about how long would it take?

   Ⓐ 1 hour
   Ⓑ $1\frac{1}{2}$ hours
   Ⓒ $2\frac{1}{5}$ hours
   Ⓓ 3 hours

6. If you took the Acela Express train from Boston to Washington, D.C., what portion of your travel time would be spent on the part of the trip between Boston and New York?

   Ⓕ $\frac{11}{14}$ Ⓖ $\frac{14}{25}$
   Ⓗ $\frac{14}{11}$ Ⓙ $\frac{25}{14}$

7. Providence, Rhode Island, is on the Boston–New York run. It is about 180 miles from New York City. If the Acela travels at a constant speed, what portion of its Boston–New York run is spent on the Boston–Providence section?

8. If the number of passengers on the Boston–New York run doubled, would the percent of passengers on the Boston–New York run also double? Justify your answer.

Data Analysis

Histograms

A histogram is a special type of bar graph that shows the frequency a data item occurs. Histograms often combine data into intervals of equal size. The intervals do not overlap.

1 ACTIVITY

The histogram shows the amount of money that 50 customers spent in a supermarket.

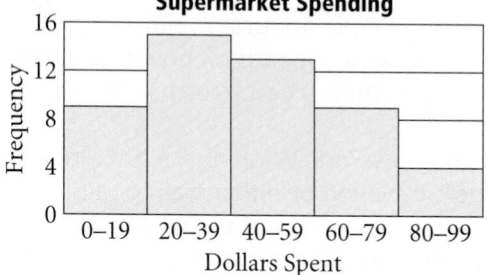

1. Based on the intervals, what is the greatest amount of money that any customer spent?

2. Which interval represents the greatest number of customers?

3. How many customers spent less than $20?

4. **Writing** Summarize the spending of the 50 customers represented in the histogram.

2 ACTIVITY

The data below shows the number of winning points scored at 15 NCAA Division I Women's Basketball Championship games from 1991 to 2005.

Winning Points Scored

84	70	73	82	68
71	62	93	68	83
70	60	84	78	70

Number of Winning Points

Winning	Tally	Frequency
59–64	■	■
65–70	■	■
71–76	■	■
77–82	■	■
83–88	■	■
89–94	■	■

5. a. Copy the frequency table at the right.
   b. Make a tally mark for each score in the appropriate interval.
   c. After you have tallied all the scores, record the frequency in the third column.

6. Use the intervals and the frequencies to construct a histogram.

7. What interval do most of the scores fall into?

8. Critical Thinking How would a histogram with 5-point intervals differ from the one you made with 6-point intervals?

You can describe histograms by their shape. Three types are shown below.

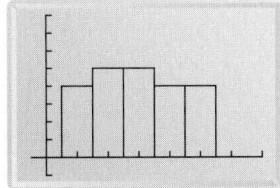

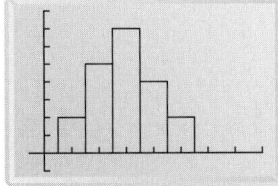

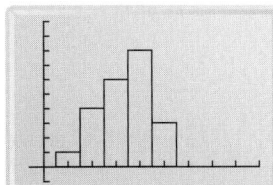

If the bars are roughly the same height, the histogram has a uniform shape.

A histogram with a central peak has a symmetric shape.

If the peak is not in the center of the distribution, the histogram has a skewed shape.

3 ACTIVITY

9. a. Make a histogram using the data at the right.
 b. Which shape best describes your histogram: *uniform, symmetric,* or *skewed*? Explain.

You can also construct a cumulative frequency histogram. This displays the *total* frequency of all data up to and including each interval.

10. Copy and complete the table below.

Interval (pounds)	0–3	0–7	0–11	0–15	0–19
Cumulative Frequency	3	13	■	■	■

Weight of Cats

Interval (pounds)	Frequency
0–3	3
4–7	10
8–11	7
12–15	4
16–19	1

11. a. Draw vertical and horizontal axes.
 b. Use the interval labels from the table to mark the horizontal axis. Label it: "Weights."
 c. Mark the vertical axis up to 25. Label it: "Cumulative Frequency."
 d. Use the cumulative frequencies you found to construct a cumulative frequency histogram.

12. Writing The bars that represent the last three intervals are all about the same height. Explain what this means.

EXERCISES

13. a. Data Collection Roll three number cubes at least 40 times. Record the sum of each roll.
 b. Make a frequency table of the sums using an interval of 3. The first interval will be 3–5. Then construct a histogram.
 c. Which shape best describes your histogram: *uniform, symmetric,* or *skewed*? Explain.

14. a. Data Collection Gather 30 or more pennies. Record their dates. Make a frequency table of the dates and construct a histogram.
 b. Which shape best describes your histogram: *uniform, symmetric* or *skewed*? Explain.

What You've Learned

- In Chapter 4, you explored patterns and functions.
- In Chapters 6 and 7, you solved multi-step problems, including equations, inequalities, and proportions.
- In Chapter 8, you graphed functions by making a table of values.

 Check Your Readiness

 **for Help** to the Lesson in green.

Adding and Subtracting Real Numbers (Lessons 5-1 and 5-2)

Simplify each expression.

1. $-5 + 7$ **2.** $2 - (-3)$ **3.** $-\frac{3}{4} + \frac{5}{6}$ **4.** $11 + (-4)$ **5.** $|1 - 8|$

Analyzing Data Using Scatter Plots (Lesson 4-5)

Make a scatter plot of the data below.

6.

Average Life Span of American Currency

Value of Currency ($)	1	5	10	20	50	100
Time (years)	1.5	1.25	1.5	2	5	8.5

Solving Equations (Lesson 6-3)

Solve each equation. Check your solution.

7. $3x + 4x = 8 - x$ **8.** $12 - 3d = d$ **9.** $6x - 8 = 7 + x$

Transforming Equations (Review page 316)

Solve each equation for y.

10. $2y - x = 4$ **11.** $3x = y + 2$ **12.** $-2y - 2x = 4$

Graphing Functions (Lesson 8-3)

Make a table of values and graph each function.

13. $y = -\frac{2}{3}x$ **14.** $y = 2x + 1$ **15.** $y = x - 5$

Linear Equations and Their Graphs

Chapter 9

Key Vocabulary

- absolute value equation (p. 535)
- correlation coefficient (p. 527)
- line of best fit (p. 527)
- linear equation (p. 493)
- linear function (p. 493)
- linear parent function (p. 493)
- negative reciprocal (p. 520)
- parallel lines (p. 519)
- parent function (p. 493)
- perpendicular lines (p. 520)
- point-slope form (p. 512)
- rate of change (p. 484)
- slope (p. 486)
- slope-intercept form (p. 494)
- standard form (p. 506)
- translation (p. 535)
- x-intercept (p. 506)
- y-intercept (p. 493)

What You'll Learn Next

- You will write linear equations and recognize their different forms.

- By working with the rate of change, you will understand how the slope of a line can be interpreted in real-world situations.

- You will determine whether the graphs of two linear equations are parallel or perpendicular.

Activity Lab Applying what you learn, you will do activities involving pyramids, on pages 546–547.

483

Rate of Change and Slope

What You'll Learn

- To find rates of change from tables and graphs
- To find slope

. . . And Why

To find the rate of change of an airplane's altitude, as in Example 2

✓ Check Skills You'll Need

GO for Help Lessons 8-2 and 5-2

Evaluate each function rule for $x = -5$.

1. $y = x - 7$
2. $y = 7 - x$
3. $y = 2x + 5$
4. $y = -\frac{2}{5}x + 3$

Write in simplest form.

5. $\frac{7 - 3}{3 - 1}$
6. $\frac{3 - 5}{6 - 0}$
7. $\frac{8 - (-4)}{3 - 7}$
8. $\frac{-1 - 2}{0 - 5}$
9. $\frac{-6 - (-4)}{-2 - 6}$
10. $\frac{0 - 1}{1 - 0}$

◀)) **New Vocabulary** • rate of change • slope

---

1 Finding Rates of Change

Activity: Exploring Rate of Change

The diagram at the right shows the side view of a ski lift.

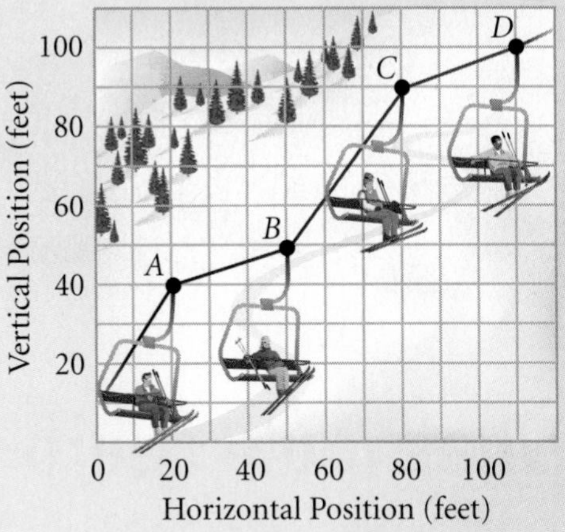

1. What is the vertical change from A to B? From B to C? From C to D?

2. What is the horizontal change from A to B? From B to C? From C to D?

3. Find the ratio of the vertical change to the horizontal change for each section of the ski lift.

4. Which section is the steepest? How does the ratio for that section compare to the ratios of the other sections?

In the graph above, $\overline{AB}$ and $\overline{BC}$ have different rates of change.

Rate of change allows you to see the relationship between two quantities that are changing. If one quantity depends on the other, then the following is true.

$$\text{rate of change} = \frac{\text{change in the dependent variable}}{\text{change in the independent variable}}$$

Vocabulary Tip

A <u>rate</u> is a comparison of two quantities measured in different units.

Cost of Renting a Computer	
Number of Days	Rental Charge
1	$60
2	$75
3	$90
4	$105
5	$120

1 EXAMPLE Finding Rate of Change Using a Table

Business For the data at the left, is the rate of change for each pair of consecutive days the same? What does the rate of change represent?

rate of change = $\dfrac{\text{change in cost}}{\text{change in number of days}}$ **Cost depends on the number of days.**

$\dfrac{75 - 60}{2 - 1} = \dfrac{15}{1}$ $\dfrac{90 - 75}{3 - 2} = \dfrac{15}{1}$

$\dfrac{105 - 90}{4 - 3} = \dfrac{15}{1}$ $\dfrac{120 - 105}{5 - 4} = \dfrac{15}{1}$

The rate of change for each consecutive pair of days is $\dfrac{15}{1}$. The rate of change is the same for all the data. It costs $15 for each day a computer is rented after the first day.

✓ Quick Check **1** **a.** Find the rate of change using Days 5 and 2.
b. Critical Thinking Does finding the rate of change for just one pair of days mean that the rate of change is the same for all the data? Explain.

The graphs of all the ordered pairs (number of days, cost) in Example 1 lie on a line as shown at the right. So, the data are linear.

You can use a graph to find a rate of change. Recall that the independent variable is plotted on the horizontal axis and the dependent variable is plotted on the vertical axis.

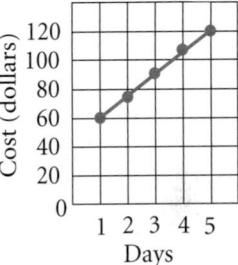

rate of change = $\dfrac{\text{vertical change}}{\text{horizontal change}}$ = $\dfrac{\text{change in the dependent variable}}{\text{change in the independent variable}}$

2 EXAMPLE Finding Rate of Change Using a Graph

Airplane Altitude The graph shows the altitude of an airplane as it comes in for a landing. Find the rate of change. Explain what this rate of change means.

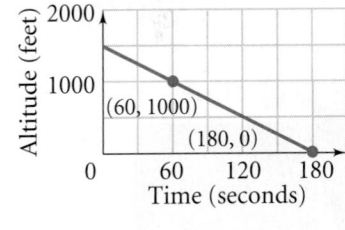

rate of change = $\dfrac{\text{vertical change}}{\text{horizontal change}}$ ← change in altitude
  ← change in time

$= \dfrac{1000 - 0}{60 - 180}$ **Use two points.**

$= \dfrac{1000}{-120}$ **Divide the vertical change by the horizontal change.**

$= -8\dfrac{1}{3}$ **Simplify.**

The rate of change is $-8\dfrac{1}{3}$. The airplane descends $8\dfrac{1}{3}$ feet each second.

✓ Quick Check **2** Find the rate of change of the data in the graph.

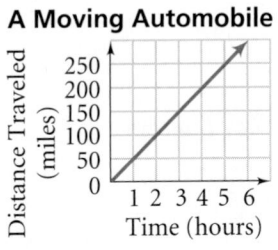

Some roads are steeper than others. A steeper road has a greater rate of change.

Real-World **Connection**

The grade of a road is the ratio of rise to run expressed as a percent. For example, a road with 100% grade is at a 45° angle with level ground.

The slope of a line is its rate of change.

$$\textbf{slope} = \frac{\text{vertical change}}{\text{horizontal change}} = \frac{\text{rise}}{\text{run}}$$

3 EXAMPLE **Finding Slope Using a Graph**

Find the slope of each line.

a.

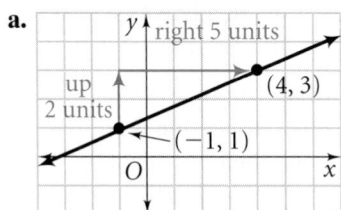

$$\text{slope} = \frac{\text{rise}}{\text{run}}$$
$$= \frac{3 - 1}{4 - (-1)}$$
$$= \frac{2}{5}$$

The slope of the line is $\frac{2}{5}$.

b.

$$\text{slope} = \frac{\text{rise}}{\text{run}}$$
$$= \frac{2 - 5}{4 - (-1)}$$
$$= \frac{-3}{5} = -\frac{3}{5}$$

The slope of the line is $-\frac{3}{5}$.

Quick Check **3** Find the slope of each line.

a.

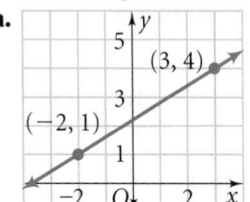

b.

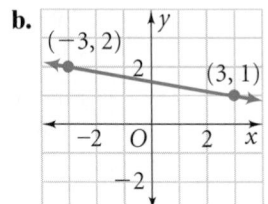

Video Tutor Help

Visit: PHSchool.com
Web Code: ate-0775

You can use any two points on a line to find its slope. You use subscripts to distinguish between two points. In the diagram, (x_1, y_1) are the coordinates of P, and (x_2, y_2) are the coordinates of Q. To find the slope of $\overleftrightarrow{PQ}$, you can use the following formula.

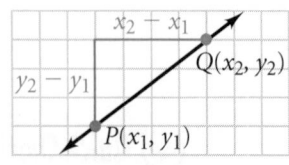

Key Concepts

Formula	Slope

$$\text{slope} = \frac{\text{rise}}{\text{run}} = \frac{y_2 - y_1}{x_2 - x_1}, \text{ where } x_2 - x_1 \neq 0$$

Keep in mind that when calculating slope, the *x*-coordinate you use first in the denominator must belong to the same ordered pair as the *y*-coordinate you use first in the numerator.

Test-Taking Tip

To set up the subtraction in the slope formula, think of moving from the coordinates of *B* to the coordinates of *A*.

4 EXAMPLE **Finding Slope Using Points**

Gridded Response Find the slope of the line through $A(-2, 1)$ and $B(6, 7)$.

slope $= \dfrac{y_2 - y_1}{x_2 - x_1}$

$= \dfrac{7 - 1}{6 - (-2)}$ **Substitute (6, 7) for (x_2, y_2) and (−2, 1) for (x_1, y_1).**

$= \dfrac{6}{8}$ **Simplify.**

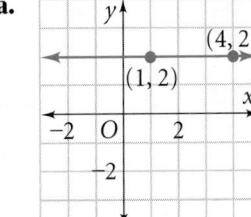

• The slope of $\overleftrightarrow{AB}$ is $\dfrac{6}{8}$ or $\dfrac{3}{4}$. Fill in the grid with 3/4.

✓ **Quick Check** ❹ Find the slope of the line through each pair of points.
   a. $C(2, 5)$ and $D(4, 7)$ **b.** $P(-1, 4)$ and $Q(3, -2)$ **c.** $M(a, b)$ and $N(c, d)$

You can also analyze the graphs of horizontal and vertical lines. The next example shows why the slope of a horizontal line is 0, and the slope of a vertical line is undefined.

5 EXAMPLE **Horizontal and Vertical Lines**

Find the slope of each line.

a.
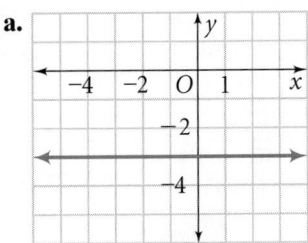

slope $= \dfrac{y_2 - y_1}{x_2 - x_1}$

$= \dfrac{2 - 2}{4 - 1}$ **Substitute (4, 2) for (x_2, y_2) and (1, 2) for (x_1, y_1).**

$= \dfrac{0}{3}$ **Simplify.**

$= 0$

The slope of the horizontal line is 0.

b.
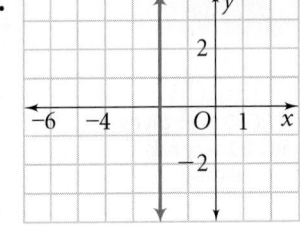

slope $= \dfrac{y_2 - y_1}{x_2 - x_1}$

$= \dfrac{2 - (-1)}{4 - 4}$ **Substitute (4, 2) for (x_2, y_2) and (4, −1) for (x_1, y_1).**

$= \dfrac{3}{0}$ **Simplify.**

Division by zero is undefined. So, the slope of the vertical line is undefined.

✓ **Quick Check** ❺ Find the slope of each line.

a.

b.

The following summarizes what you have learned about slope.

Key Concepts

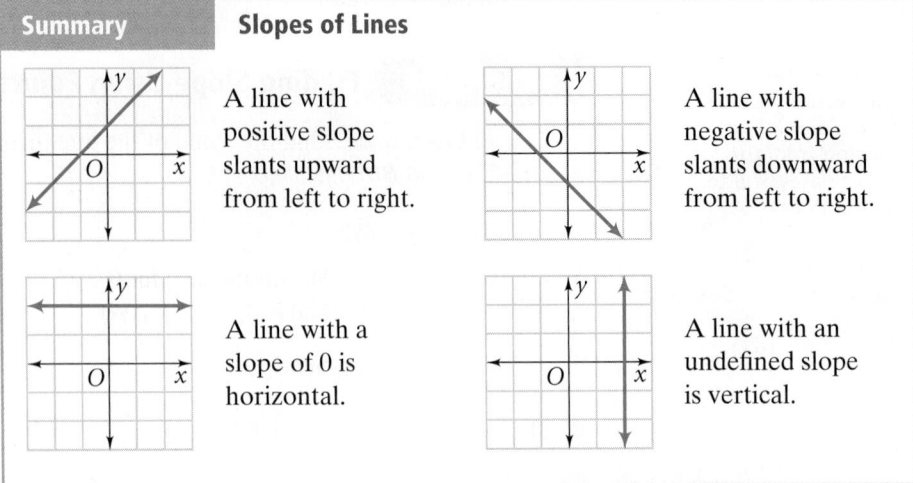

Summary	Slopes of Lines

A line with positive slope slants upward from left to right.

A line with negative slope slants downward from left to right.

A line with a slope of 0 is horizontal.

A line with an undefined slope is vertical.

EXERCISES

For more exercises, see *Extra Skill and Word Problem Practice.*

Practice and Problem Solving

Practice by Example

Examples 1, 2
(page 485)

for Help

The rate of change is constant in each table and graph. Find the rate of change. Explain what the rate of change means for each situation.

1.

Time (hours)	Temperature (°F)
1	−2
4	7
7	16
10	25
13	34

2.

People	Cost (dollars)
2	7.90
3	11.85
4	15.80
5	19.75
6	23.70

3.

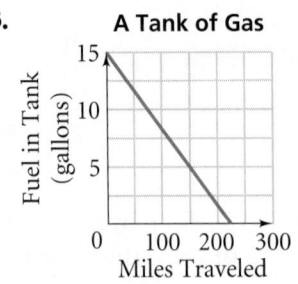

A Tank of Gas

4.

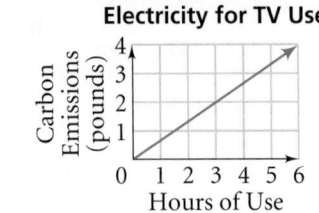

Emissions: Generating Electricity for TV Use

5.

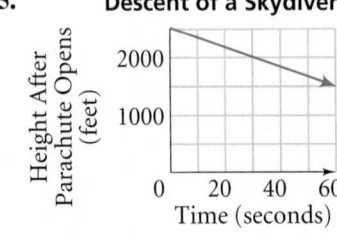

Descent of a Skydiver

6.

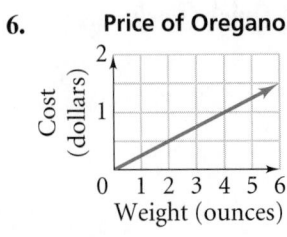

Price of Oregano

Real-World Connection

A jump from 11,000 feet gives a skydiver about 60 seconds of free fall at more than 100 mi/h.

Slope-Intercept Form

What You'll Learn

- To write linear equations in slope-intercept form
- To graph linear equations

...And Why

To use a graph to relate total earnings to sales, as in Example 5

☑ **Check Skills You'll Need**

Evaluate each expression.

1. $6a + 3$ for $a = 2$

2. $-2x - 5$ for $x = 3$

3. $\frac{1}{4}x + 2$ for $x = 16$

4. $0.2x + 2$ for $x = 15$

5. $8 - 5n$ for $n = 3$

6. $-4p + 9$ for $p = 2$

GO **for Help** Lessons 4-2 and 5-3

🔊 **New Vocabulary** • linear function • parent function • linear parent function • linear equation • *y*-intercept • slope-intercept form

---

▼ 1 Writing Linear Equations

Vocabulary Tip

The word <u>linear</u> contains the word "line."

In lesson 5-5, you studied direct variations such as $y = 3x$. The graph of a direct variation is a straight line. All direct variations are linear functions. A **linear function** is a function that graphs a line. Direct variations are only part of the family of linear functions. For example, $y = -\frac{1}{2}x + 1$ is a linear function but not a direct variation because it does not go through $(0, 0)$.

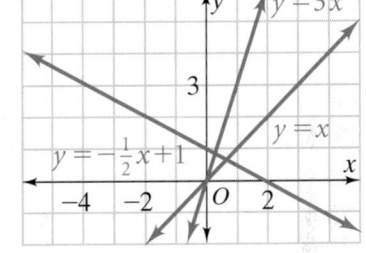

A **parent function** is the simplest equation of a function. The equation $y = x$ or $f(x) = x$ is the **linear parent function**.

A **linear equation** is an equation that models a linear function. In a linear equation, the variable cannot be raised to a power other than 1. So $y = 2x$ is the equation of a linear function, but $y = x^2$ or $y = 2^x$ are not.

The equation of a line gives important information about its graph. Consider the table and graph of the equation $y = -2x + 1$.

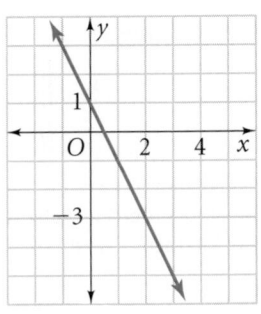

x	−2x + 1	y
0	−2(0) + 1	1
1	−2(1) + 1	−1
2	−2(2) + 1	−3

Two points on the line are $(0, 1)$ and $(2, -3)$. The slope is $\frac{1 - (-3)}{0 - 2} = -\frac{4}{2}$ or -2. The **y-intercept** is the *y*-coordinate of the point where a line crosses the *y*-axis. Since $y = -2x + 1$ crosses the *y*-axis at $(0, 1)$, the *y*-intercept is 1.

If you know the slope of a line and its *y*-intercept, you can write the equation of the line. The letter *m* refers to the *slope*.

 **Key Concepts**

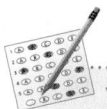
Definition	Slope-Intercept Form of a Linear Equation

The **slope-intercept form** of a linear equation is $y = mx + b$.

slope y-intercept

1 EXAMPLE Identifying Slope and y-Intercept

What are the slope and y-intercept of $y = 3x - 5$?

$y = mx + b$ **Use the slope-intercept form.**

$y = 3x + (-5)$ **Think of $y = 3x - 5$ as $y = 3x + (-5)$.**

● The slope is 3; the y-intercept is -5.

✓ **Quick Check** ❶ **a.** Find the slope and y-intercept of $y = \frac{7}{6}x - \frac{3}{4}$.

b. Critical Thinking For the equation in Example 1, what happens to the graph of the line and to the equation if the y-intercept is moved down 3 units?

2 EXAMPLE Writing an Equation

Write an equation of the line with slope $\frac{3}{8}$ and y-intercept 6.

$y = mx + b$ **Use the slope-intercept form.**

$y = \frac{3}{8}x + 6$ **Substitute $\frac{3}{8}$ for m and 6 for b.**

✓ **Quick Check** ❷ Write an equation of a line with slope $m = \frac{2}{5}$ and y-intercept $b = -1$.

3 EXAMPLE Writing an Equation From a Graph

Multiple Choice Which equation models the linear function shown in the graph?

Ⓐ $y = -\frac{3}{4}x + 2$ Ⓑ $y = -\frac{4}{3}x + 2$

Ⓒ $y = 2x - \frac{4}{3}x$ Ⓓ $y = 2x - \frac{3}{4}$

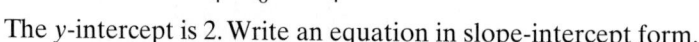

Find the slope. Two points on the line are $(0, 2)$ and $(4, -1)$.

$\text{slope} = \frac{-1 - 2}{4 - 0} = -\frac{3}{4}$

The y-intercept is 2. Write an equation in slope-intercept form.

$y = mx + b$

$y = -\frac{3}{4}x + 2$ **Substitute $-\frac{3}{4}$ for m and 2 for b.**

● The equation is $y = -\frac{3}{4}x + 2$. So the answer is A.

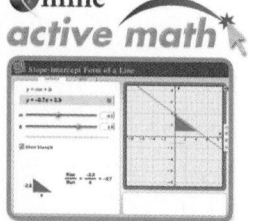

For: Slope-Intercept Activity
Use: Interactive Textbook, 6-2

✓ **Quick Check** ❸ **a.** Write the equation of the line using the points $(0, 1)$ and $(2, 2)$.

b. Critical Thinking Does the equation of the line change if you use $(-2, 0)$ instead of $(2, 2)$? Explain.

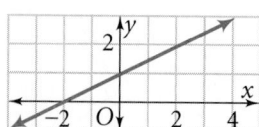

Each point on the graph of an equation is an ordered pair that makes the equation true. The graph of a linear equation is a line that indicates all the solutions of the equation. You can use the slope and y-intercept to graph a line.

4 **EXAMPLE** **Graphing Equations**

Graph $y = 3x - 1$.

Step 1
The y-intercept is -1. So plot a point at $(0, -1)$.

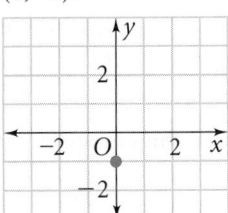

Step 2
The slope is 3, or $\frac{3}{1}$. Use the slope to plot a second point.

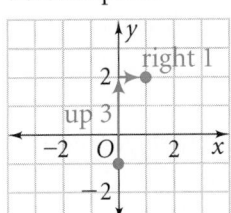

Step 3
Draw a line through the two points.

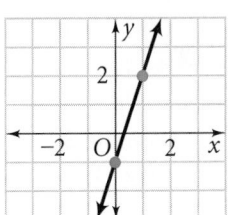

✓ Quick Check **4** Graph $y = \frac{3}{2}x - 2$.

When you graph equations for real-world situations, use scales on the x- and y-axes that are reasonable for the situation. Recall that you can avoid having a large blank space in a graph by using a zigzag line to show a break in a scale.

5 **EXAMPLE** **Real-World 🌐 Problem Solving**

Commission The base pay of a water-delivery person is $210 per week. He also earns 20% commission on any sale he makes. The equation $t = 210 + 0.2s$ relates total earnings t to sales s. Graph the equation.

Step 1 Identify the slope and y-intercept.

$t = 210 + 0.2s$

$t = 0.2s + 210$ **Rewrite the equation in slope-intercept form.**

↑   ↑
slope y-intercept

Step 2 Plot two points. First plot $(0, 210)$, the y-intercept. Then use the slope to plot a second point.

The slope is 0.2, which equals $\frac{2}{10}$, or $\frac{20}{100}$. Plot a second point 20 units above and 100 units to the right of the y-intercept.

Step 3 Draw a line through the points.

Weekly Earnings for a Water-Delivery Person

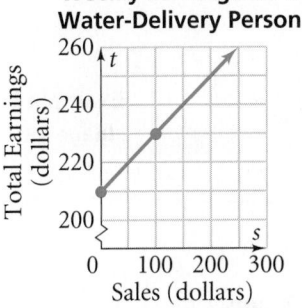

✓ Quick Check **5** Suppose the base pay of the delivery person is $150, and his commission on each sale is 30%. The equation relating his total earnings t to sales s is $t = 150 + 0.3s$. Graph the equation.

Real-World 🌐 Connection

Between 1990 and 1999, the sales of bottled water in the United States increased 107.6%, which means that sales more than doubled.

EXERCISES

For more exercises, see *Extra Skill and Word Problem Practice*.

Practice and Problem Solving

A Practice by Example

Example 1
(page 494)

Find the slope and *y*-intercept of each equation.

1. $y = -2x + 1$ **2.** $y = -\frac{1}{2}x + 2$ **3.** $y = x - \frac{5}{4}$

4. $y = 5x + 8$ **5.** $y = \frac{2}{3}x + 1$ **6.** $y = -4x$

7. $y = -x - 7$ **8.** $y = -0.7x - 9$ **9.** $y = -\frac{3}{4}x - 5$

Example 2
(page 494)

Write an equation of a line with the given slope and *y*-intercept.

10. $m = \frac{2}{9}, b = 3$ **11.** $m = 3, b = \frac{2}{9}$ **12.** $m = \frac{9}{2}, b = 3$

13. $m = 0, b = 1$ **14.** $m = -1, b = -6$ **15.** $m = -\frac{2}{3}, b = 5$

16. $m = 0.3, b = 4$ **17.** $m = 0.4, b = 0.6$ **18.** $m = -7, b = \frac{1}{3}$

19. $m = -\frac{1}{5}, b = -\frac{2}{5}$ **20.** $m = -\frac{1}{4}, b = \frac{5}{4}$ **21.** $m = \frac{8}{3}, b = \frac{2}{3}$

Example 3
(page 494)

Write the slope-intercept form of the equation for each line.

22. 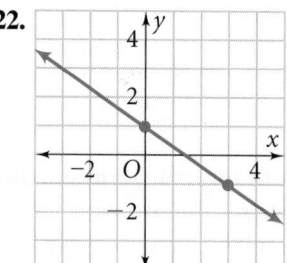   **23.** 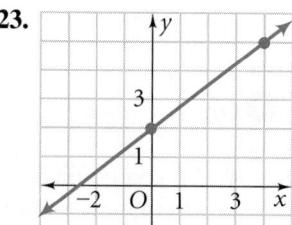   **24.**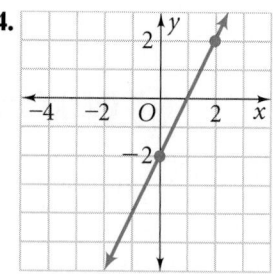

25. 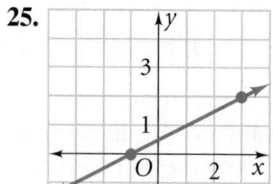   **26.** 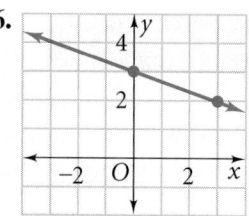   **27.**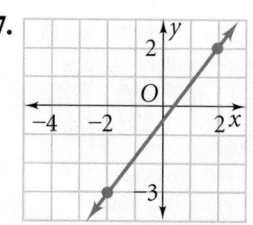

Example 4
(page 495)

Use the slope and *y*-intercept to graph each equation.

28. $y = \frac{1}{2}x + 4$ **29.** $y = \frac{2}{3}x - 1$ **30.** $y = -5x + 2$ **31.** $y = 2x + 5$

32. $y = x + 4$ **33.** $y = -x + 2$ **34.** $y = 4x - 3$ **35.** $y = -\frac{3}{2}x$

36. $y = \frac{2}{5}x - 3$ **37.** $y = -\frac{2}{3}x + 2$ **38.** $y = -\frac{4}{5}x + 4$ **39.** $y = -0.5x + 2$

Example 5
(page 495)

40. Retail Sales A music store is offering a coupon promotion on its CDs. The regular price for CDs is $14. With the coupon, customers are given $4 off the total purchase. The equation $t = 14c - 4$, where c is the number of CDs and t is the total cost of the purchase, models this situation.
a. Graph the equation.
b. Find the total cost for a sale of 6 CDs.

B Apply Your Skills

Find the slope and *y*-intercept of each equation.

41. $y - 2 = -3x$ **42.** $y + \frac{1}{2}x = 0$ **43.** $y - 9x = \frac{1}{2}$

44. $y = 3x - 9$ **45.** $2y - 6 = 3x$ **46.** $-2y = 6(5 - 3x)$

47. $y - d = cx$ **48.** $y = (2 - a)x + a$ **49.** $2y + 4n = -6x$

Use the slope and *y*-intercept to graph each equation.

50. $y = 7 - 3x$ **51.** $2y + 4x = 0$ **52.** $3y + 6 = -2x$

53. $y + 2 = 5x - 4$ **54.** $4x + 3y = 2x - 1$ **55.** $-2(3x - 4) + y = 0$

56. Error Analysis Fred drew the graph at the right for the equation $y = -2x + 1$. What error did he make?

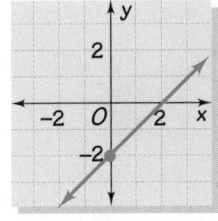

57. a. A candle begins burning at time $t = 0$. Its original height is 12 in. After 30 min the height of the candle is 8 in. Draw a graph showing the change in the height of the candle.

b. Write an equation that relates the height of the candle to the time it has been burning.

c. How many minutes after the candle is lit will it burn out?

58. Airplane Fuel The graph shows the relationship between the number of gallons of fuel in the tank of an airplane and the weight of the airplane. The equation $y = 6x + 2512$, where x is the number of gallons of fuel and y is the weight of the airplane, models this situation.

a. What does the slope represent?

b. Use the equation to predict the weight of the plane when the tank contains 25 gallons of fuel.

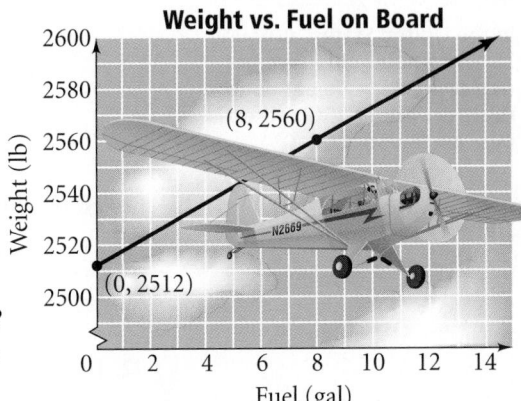

Weight vs. Fuel on Board

(8, 2560)

(0, 2512)

Is the ordered pair on the graph of the given equation?

59. $(-3, 4); y = -2x + 1$ **60.** $(-6, 5); y = -\frac{1}{2}x + 2$ **61.** $(0, -1); y = x - \frac{5}{4}$

62. Multiple Choice At the right is the graph of $y = \frac{1}{4}x - 2$. Which of the graphs below represents the linear function if the slope is doubled and the *y*-intercept stays the same?

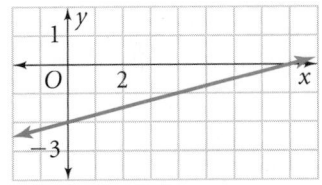

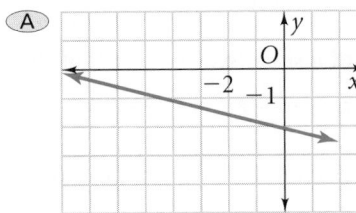
A

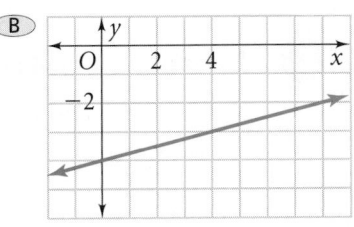
B

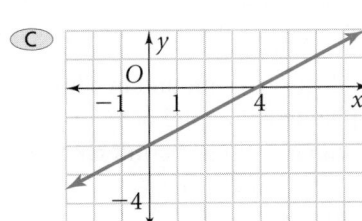
C

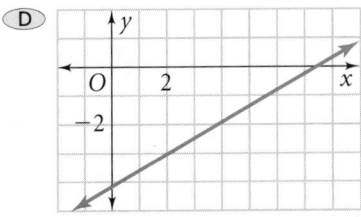
D

63. **Pet Care** When the Bryants leave town for a vacation, they put their dog Tyco in a kennel. The kennel charges $15 for a first-day flea bath and $5 per day. The equation $t = 15 + 5d$ relates the total charge t to the number of days d.
   a. Rewrite the equation in slope-intercept form.
   b. Graph the equation.
   c. Explain why the line you graph should lie only in Quadrant I.

64. **Writing** Explain the steps you would use to graph $y = \frac{3}{4}x + 5$.

65. **Critical Thinking** Which graphed line has the greater slope? Explain.

   A. 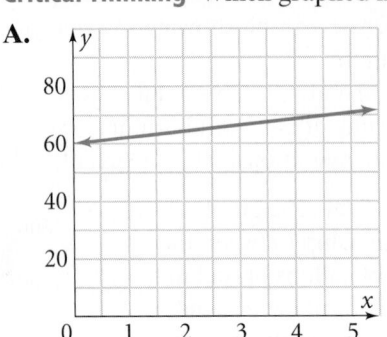 B.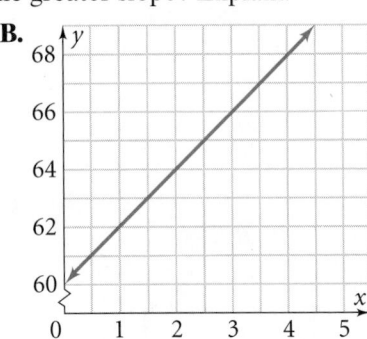

Real-World Connection

In the United States, although 35% of households have pet cats and 37% have pet dogs, there are about 25% more pet cats than pet dogs.

Given two points on a line, write the equation of the line in slope-intercept form.

66. $(3, 5), (5, 9)$ 67. $(5, -13), (2, -1)$ 68. $(-4, 10), (6, 5)$

69. $(8, 7), (-12, 2)$ 70. $(-7, 4), (11, -14)$ 71. $(-1, -9), (2, 0)$

72. **Graphing Calculator** Suppose you want to graph the equation $y = \frac{5}{4}x - 3$. Enter each key sequence and display the graph.
   a.
   b. [Y=] [(] 5 [÷] 4 [)] [X,T,θ,n] [−] 3
   c. Which equation gives you the graph of $y = \frac{5}{4}x - 3$? Explain.

73. a. What is the slope of each line?
   b. What is the y-intercept of each line?
   c. **Geometry** The lines in the graph are parallel. What appears to be true about the slopes of parallel lines?

   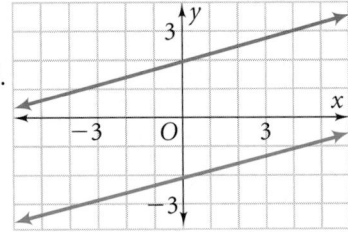

74. **Open-Ended** Write a linear equation. Identify the slope and y-intercept. Then graph your equation.

C Challenge

Find the value of a such that the graph of the equation has the given slope.

75. $y = 2ax + 4; m = -1$ 76. $y = -\frac{1}{2}ax - 5; m = \frac{5}{2}$ 77. $y = \frac{3}{4}ax + 3; m = \frac{9}{16}$

78. a. **Geometry** Graph these equations on the same grid.
   $y = 3$ $y = -3$ $x = 2$ $x = -2$
   b. What geometric figure did you draw? Justify your answer.
   c. Draw a diagonal of the figure. What is the equation of this line? Explain.

79. **Recreation** A group of mountain climbers begin an expedition with 265 lb of food. They plan to eat a total of 15 lb of food per day.
   a. Write an equation in slope-intercept form relating the remaining food supply r to the number of days d.
   b. Graph your equation.
   c. The group plans to eat the last of their food the day their expedition ends. Use your graph to find how many days they expect the expedition to last.

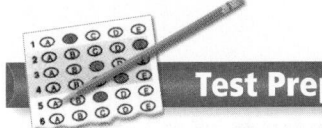

Multiple Choice

80. Which equation has the same *y*-intercept as $y = 4x - 3$?

   A. $y - 3 = x$ **B.** $y = 8x + 3$ **C.** $3 - y = 4x$ **D.** $y = -3 + 8x$

81. Which of the following is the equation of the line that has the same slope as $y = -\frac{3}{2}x + 2$ and the same *y*-intercept as $y = 3x - 2$?

   F. $y - 2 = -\frac{3}{2}x$ **G.** $-\frac{3}{2}x = y + 2$

   H. $y + 2 = -\frac{3}{2}$ **J.** $-\frac{3}{2}x = y + 3$

82. A software company started with 2 employees. In 6 months, the company had 7 employees. The number of employees increased at a steady rate. Which equation models the relationship between the number of employees *n* and the number of months *m* since the company started?

   A. $n = \frac{5}{6}m + 2$ **B.** $m = 2n + \frac{5}{6}$

   C. $n = \frac{6}{5}m + 2$ **D.** $m = \frac{5}{6}n + 2$

Short Response

83. A line passes through the points (0, 3) and (1, 5). Graph this line and find an equation for the line in slope-intercept form. Show your work.

Mixed Review

Lesson 9-1

for Help

Review page 342

Find the slope of the line that passes through each pair of points.

84. $(-2, 8), (5, -1)$ **85.** $(0, 0), (-6, 5)$ **86.** $(4, 6), (2, -3)$ **87.** $(1, 2), (2, 1)$

88. The greeting card industry sells over 6 billion cards annually. Women purchase 80% of all greeting cards sold. How many cards do women purchase annually?

A P•int in Time

1500   1600   1700   1800   1900   2000

On August 30, 1984, Astronaut Judith A. Resnik became the second American woman in space, on the shuttle *Discovery*'s first voyage. Resnik was an electrical engineer with a Ph.D. from the University of Maryland. Prior to her mission, she helped to design and develop a remote manipulator system. This required skill in writing linear equations. Her job during *Discovery*'s six-day voyage was to manipulate a robotic arm and to extend and retract the shuttle's solar power array. Resnik died tragically in the *Challenger* disaster in 1986.

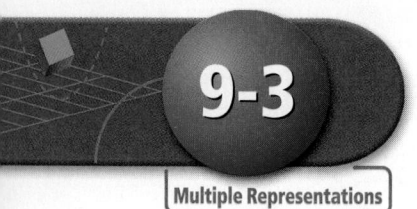

Applying Linear Functions

What You'll Learn

• To interpret linear graphs

. . . And Why

To analyze real-world situations involving fund raisers, as in Example 2

 Check Skills You'll Need

GO for Help Lesson 9-2

Find the slope and y-intercept of each equation.

1. $y = 4x - 3$

2. $y = \frac{4}{5}x + 7$

3. $y = -\frac{1}{3}x - 8$

4. $y = 6x$

Write an equation of a line with the given slope and y-intercept.

5. $m = 5, b = -1$

6. $m = \frac{2}{5}, b = 4$

7. $m = 6, b = \frac{1}{4}$

1 Interpreting Linear Graphs

9P2. Generalize patterns using functions or relationships, and freely translate among tabular, graphical and symbolic representations.

10P10. Solve real-world problems that can be modeled using functions.

You can model many real world situations with linear equations. Recall that the graph of an equation shows the solutions of the equation. However, for a discrete real-world situation not every point may represent a reasonable value.

1 EXAMPLE Real-World Connection

Automobiles A car dealership has 40 cars in stock. The auto manufacturer will deliver new cars to the dealership by car carrier. Each carrier holds 6 cars. Write a linear function that relates the number of carriers used to the total number of cars at the dealership. Graph the function that models the situation.

Relate | total number of cars at dealership | equals | 40 | plus | 6 | times | number of car carriers |

Define The total number of cars depends on the number of car carriers. So total number of cars is the dependent variable and number of car carriers is the independent variable.

Let x = the number of car carriers.

Let y = the total number of cars at the dealership.

Write y = 40 + 6 · x

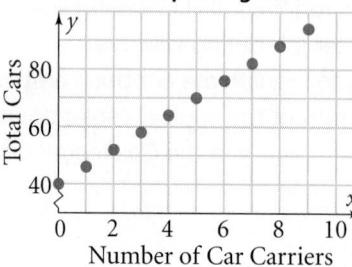

Transporting Cars

Total Cars vs Number of Car Carriers

The number of car carriers is the domain. A reasonable domain is whole numbers.

✓ Quick Check ❶ A sporting goods store sells cans of tennis balls. There are 3 tennis balls in each can. The coach of the tennis team is buying supplies. Write a linear function that relates the number of cans to the total number of tennis balls. Graph the function that models the situation.

2 EXAMPLE **Analyzing Linear Graphs**

Students in a ninth-grade class drew the following graph to represent how much money would be in the class fund after washing cars at a fundraiser.

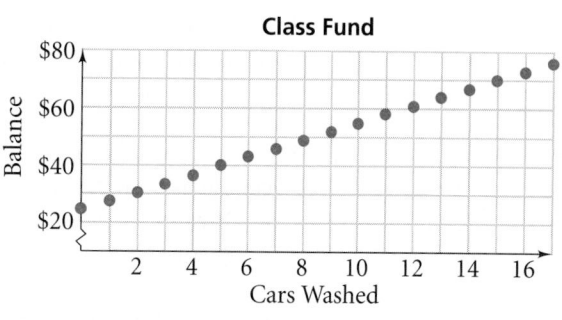

Class Fund

a. What does the slope and *y*-intercept of the graph mean for the given situation?

The slope is 3, which indicates the class charged $3 per car. The *y*-intercept is 25, which means they had $25 in the class fund before the fundraiser.

b. If the graph had the same slope but a *y*-intercept of 15, what could you conclude about the fundraiser?

You could conclude that there were $15 in the class fund instead of $25.

c. If the graph had a slope of 5, what could you conclude about the fundraiser?

You could conclude that the students decided to charge $5 per car.

✓ Quick Check ❷ **a.** Suppose you drew the following graph to represent how far you ride your bike at a steady rate. What is your rate?
b. If the graph had a slope of 10, what could you conclude about your bike ride?

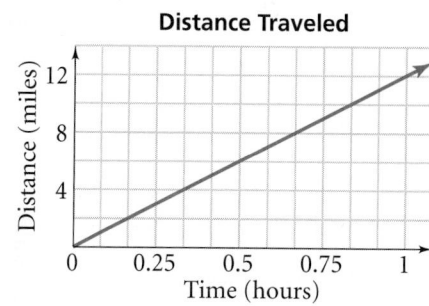

Distance Traveled

EXERCISES

For more exercises, see *Extra Skill and Word Problem Practice*.

Practice and Problem Solving

A Practice by Example

Example 1
(page 500)

GO for Help

Model each situation with a linear function and graph.

1. A lumber yard sells pre-cut 6-, 8-, 10-, and 12-foot beams for $1.20 per foot.

2. A market sells chicken for $2.99 a pound.

3. Suppose your family buys a "movie card" from a DVD store that entitles you to rent 25 movies. You rent 3 movies per week.

Example 2
(page 501)

4. A helicopter takes off from the roof of a building. The graph shows the altitude of the helicopter as it rises steadily for several minutes.

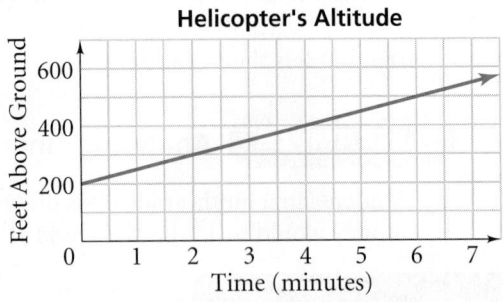

Helicopter's Altitude

a. What does the slope and *y*-intercept reveal about the original situation?
b. For a similar situation, the slope is 85 and *y*-intercept is 250. What can you conclude?

B **Apply Your Skills**

5. The graph models the height in inches of a burning candle as a function of time in hours.
  a. Does every point on the line represent a reasonable value? Explain.
  b. Write a linear function for the graph.
  c. A second 8-in. candle burns at a rate of 3 in./hr. How would the graph for that candle compare with the one shown here?

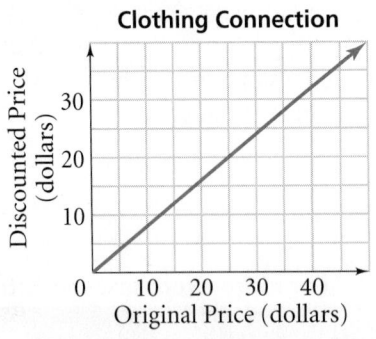

Burning Candle

6. Suppose an elevator is 400 feet above the ground. It descends at a steady rate. After 15 seconds it is 250 feet above the ground.
  a. Write a linear function for the height of the elevator as a function of time.
  b. Graph the function.
  c. **Critical Thinking** Is it reasonable to include negative numbers in the range?

7. **Shopping** Clothing Connection and Teen World are having sales. The graphs show the discounted price as a function of the original price for merchandise from each shop.

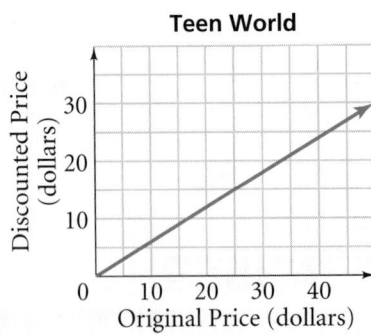

Clothing Connection

Teen World

a. Which store has a greater discount? Explain.
b. Write a linear function to model the situation in each store.
c. A customer buys merchandise originally priced at $16 from each store. What is the discounted price at each store?

8. a. **Open-Ended** Describe a real-world situation that you could model with a linear function.
  b. Describe a reasonable domain and range for the situation.

GO **nline**
Homework Video Tutor
Visit: PHSchool.com
Web Code: ate-0603

For a guide to solving
Exercise 9, see p. 505.

9. Two friends are paddling a kayak
downstream (with the current). The
graph shows their distance from camp
as a function of time.
   a. Is every point on the line a reasonable
   value? Explain.
   b. Critical Thinking Suppose they were
   paddling back toward the camp,
   upstream (against the current) rather
   than downstream. How would the
   graph compare with the downstream
   graph? Explain.

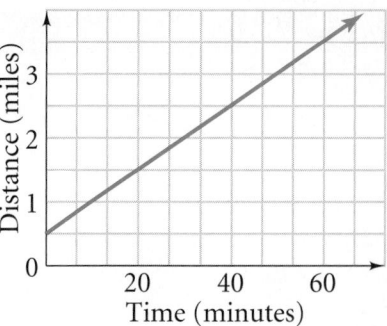

10. **a.** Direct variations model some linear relationships. How is the equation of a
   direct variation similar to the linear equation $y = mx + b$? How are they
   different?
   b. Writing Describe a situation that could be modeled by a linear function but
   NOT by a direct variation.

11. **Multiple Choice** Which situation could best be
   modeled by the graph at the right?
   Ⓐ the cost of buying muffins
   Ⓑ the distance between a train and the station
   as the train travels towards the station
   Ⓒ the amount of money left in a roll of quarters
   after paying a toll each day
   Ⓓ the distance a runner covers, traveling at a
   steady pace

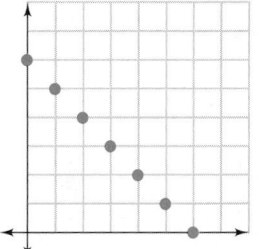

12. **a. Math in the Media** Write an equation relating the data in the cartoon.
   b. How many dog years are 12 human years?

Mother Goose and Grimm

C Challenge

13. **Sports** Four friends go bowling. For each person, it costs $2.50 to rent shoes
   and $2.00 per game of bowling. They all bowl the same number of games.
   a. Model the total cost with a linear function. Graph the function.
   b. Describe a reasonable domain and range.

14. **Biology** The table shows the average height of
   female infants.
   a. Write a linear function using the data for 3- and
   9-month-old girls.
   b. Use your model to find the height of a
   15-year-old girl, to the nearest foot.
   c. Critical Thinking Based on your answer, what can
   you conclude about the linear model?

Age (months)	Height (inches)
3	23.5
6	25.6
9	27.5

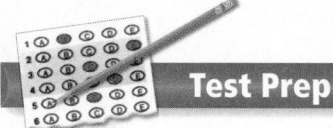

Multiple Choice

15. Which graph best models the amount of money in a bank account after the same amount is withdrawn each week?

A.

Balance / Week
0 1 2 3 4

B.

Balance / Week
0 1 2 3 4

C.

Balance / Week
0 1 2 3 4

D.

Balance / Week
0 1 2 3 4

16. Find the slope of the line through the points $(-3, 1)$ and $(6, -7)$.

F. 2   **G.** $\frac{1}{2}$ **H.** $-\frac{8}{9}$ **J.** $-\frac{9}{8}$

17. Which equation models a line with the same y-intercept but half the slope of the line $y = 4 - 10x$?

A. $y = -5x + 4$ **B.** $y = 2 - 10x$ **C.** $y = 2 - 5x$ **D.** $y = -5x - 2$

Short Answer

18. The drama club plans to attend a professional production. From 10 to 35 students will go. There is a one-time handling fee of $3. Each ticket costs $25 plus a $2 surcharge. Write a linear function that models this situation. Describe a reasonable domain and range.

Mixed Review

Lesson 9-2

GO for Help

Write the slope-intercept form of the equation for each line.

19.

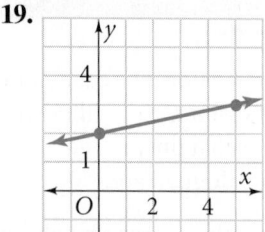

20.

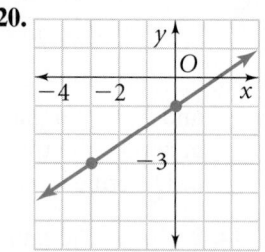

21.

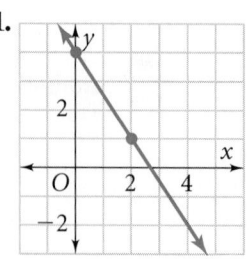

Lesson 6-8

Tell whether each number is *rational* or *irrational*.

22. $\sqrt{\frac{1}{4}}$ **23.** $\sqrt{\frac{8}{5}}$ **24.** $\sqrt{11}$ **25.** $\sqrt{\frac{121}{100}}$ **26.** $-\sqrt{0.81}$

Lesson 6-2

Solve each equation.

27. $5(x + 1) = 8$ **28.** $-33 = 6h + 7 + 2h$ **29.** $-2(3 - k) = 15$

30. $17 = 4t - 2t + 1$ **31.** $4(n + 1) - 3 = 16$ **32.** $40 = 8p + 5 - p$

Understanding Word Problems Read the exercise below and then follow along with what Vera thinks and writes. Check your understanding with the exercise at the bottom of the page.

Two friends are paddling a kayak downstream (with the current). The graph shows their distance from camp as a function of time.

a. Is every point on the line a reasonable value for this situation? Explain.

b. Critical Thinking Suppose they were paddling back toward the camp, upstream (against the current) rather than downstream. How would the graph compare with the downstream graph? Explain.

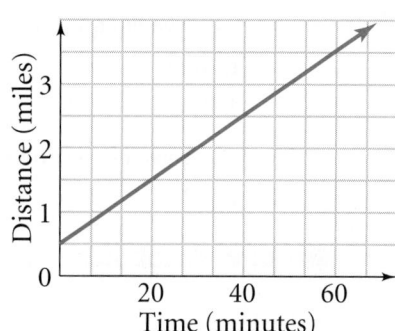

What Vera Thinks

The graph of the line is rising, so the kayakers' distance from camp is steadily increasing. After 20 minutes they are 1.5 miles from camp. After 40 minutes they are 2.5 miles away.

I can look at any point on the line between (20, 1.5) and (40, 2.5) and see a meaningful time and distance.

When you paddle upstream, the current slows you down. The slope of the line is the kayakers' rate, so the new line would be less steep than the downstream line.

Since the kayakers are traveling toward camp, their distance from the camp would decrease over time. The new line would have a negative slope.

What Vera Writes

a. Yes. Both time and distance are continuous, so every point on the line is a reasonable value.

b. The upstream graph would be less steep than the downstream graph because the kayakers would move more slowly against the current.

The graph for paddling upstream would have a negative slope because they are getting closer to camp.

EXERCISE

The graph shows the cost of buying bagels.

a. What is the cost per bagel?

b. Is every point on the graph a reasonable value? Explain.

c. How would the graph be different if the bagels sold for $.75 each?

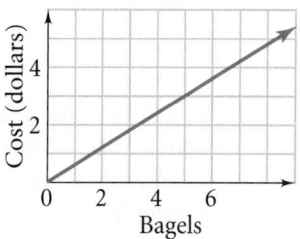

Standard Form

What You'll Learn

- To graph equations using intercepts
- To write equations in standard form

. . . And Why

To use an equation to model a real-world situation that involves exercise, as in Example 5

✓ **Check Skills You'll Need**

 **for Help** Review page 416 and Lesson 6-2

Solve each equation for y.

1. $3x + y = 5$ **2.** $y - 2x = 10$ **3.** $x - y = 6$

4. $20x + 4y = 8$ **5.** $9y + 3x = 1$ **6.** $5y - 2x = 4$

Clear each equation of decimals.

7. $6.25x + 8.5 = 7.75$ **8.** $0.4 = 0.2x - 5$ **9.** $0.9 - 0.222x = 1$

🔊 **New Vocabulary** • standard form of a linear equation • *x*-intercept

---

1   Graphing Equations Using Intercepts

Activity: Intercepts

1. Make a table of values for the equation $3y - 2x = 12$.

2. Use the table of values to graph $3y - 2x = 12$.

3. What is the y-intercept?

4. What is the value of x when the line crosses the x-axis?

5. In the equation $3y - 2x = 12$, what is the value of y when $x = 0$? What is the value of x when $y = 0$?

6. Using your answers to 3, 4, and 5, explain how you can make a graph of $3y - 2x = 12$ without making a table.

The slope-intercept form is just one form of a linear equation. Another form is standard form, which is useful in making quick graphs.

 Key Concepts

Definition	Standard Form of a Linear Equation

The **standard form of a linear equation** is $Ax + By = C$, where A, B, and C are real numbers, and A and B are not both zero.

You can use the x- and y-intercepts to make a graph. The **x-intercept** is the x-coordinate of the point where a line crosses the x-axis. To graph a linear equation in standard form, you can find the x-intercept by substituting 0 for y and solving for x. Similarly, to find the y-intercept, substitute 0 for x and solve for y.

1 EXAMPLE Finding *x*- and *y*-Intercepts

Find the *x*- and *y*-intercepts of $3x + 4y = 8$.

Step 1 To find the *x*-intercept, substitute 0 for *y* and solve for *x*.

$$3x + 4y = 8$$
$$3x + 4(0) = 8$$
$$3x = 8$$
$$x = \frac{8}{3}$$

The *x*-intercept is $\frac{8}{3}$.

Step 2 To find the *y*-intercept, substitute 0 for *x* and solve for *y*.

$$3x + 4y = 8$$
$$3(0) + 4y = 8$$
$$4y = 8$$
$$y = 2$$

The *y*-intercept is 2.

✓ **Quick Check** ❶ Find the *x*- and *y*-intercepts of $4x - 9y = -12$.

If the *x*- and *y*-intercepts are integers, you can use them to make a quick graph.

2 EXAMPLE Graphing Lines Using Intercepts

Graph $2x + 3y = 12$ using intercepts.

Step 1 Find the intercepts.

$$2x + 3y = 12$$
$$2x + 3(0) = 12 \quad \textbf{Substitute 0 for } y.$$
$$2x = 12 \quad \textbf{Solve for } x.$$
$$x = 6$$

$$2(0) + 3y = 12 \quad \textbf{Substitute 0 for } x.$$
$$3y = 12 \quad \textbf{Solve for } y.$$
$$y = 4$$

Step 2 Plot $(0, 4)$ and $(6, 0)$. Draw a line through the points.

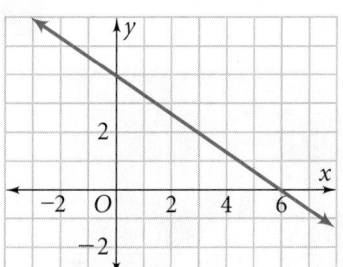

✓ **Quick Check** ❷ Graph $5x + 2y = -10$ using the *x*- and *y*-intercepts.

In the standard form of an equation $Ax + By = C$, either *A* or *B*, but not both, may be zero. If *A* or *B* is zero, the line is either horizontal or vertical.

3 EXAMPLE Graphing Horizontal and Vertical Lines

a. Graph $y = -3$.

$0x + 1y = -3$ ← **Write in standard form.** →
For all values of *x*, $y = -3$.

b. Graph $x = 2$.

$1x + 0y = 2$
For all values of *y*, $x = 2$.

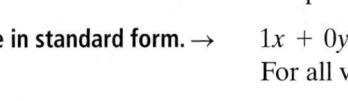

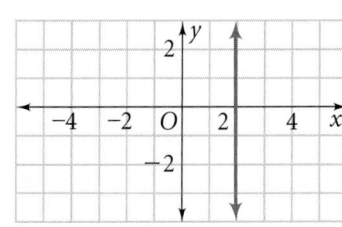

✓ **Quick Check** ❸ Graph each equation.

    a. $y = 5$ **b.** $y = 0$ **c.** $x = -4$ **d.** $x = 0$

You can change an equation from slope-intercept form to standard form. If the equation contains fractions or decimals, multiply to write the equation using integers.

4 **EXAMPLE** **Transforming to Standard Form**

Write $y = \frac{3}{4}x + 2$ in standard form using integers.

$$y = \frac{3}{4}x + 2$$

$4y = 4\left(\frac{3}{4}x + 2\right)$ **Multiply each side by 4.**

$4y = 3x + 8$ **Use the Distributive Property.**

$-3x + 4y = 8$ **Subtract 3x from each side.**

● The standard form of $y = \frac{3}{4}x + 2$ is $-3x + 4y = 8$.

 **Quick Check** **4** Write $y = -\frac{2}{5}x + 1$ in standard form using integers.

You can write equations for real-world situations using standard form.

5 **EXAMPLE** **Real-World 🌐 Problem Solving**

Data Analysis Write an equation in standard form to find the minutes someone who weighs 150 lb would need to bicycle and swim laps in order to burn 300 calories. Use the data below.

Activity by a 150-lb Person	Calories Burned per Minute
Bicycling	10
Bowling	4
Hiking	7
Running 5.2 mi/h	11
Swimming, laps	12
Walking 3.5 mi/h	5

Define   Let x = the minutes spent bicycling.

           Let y = the minutes spent swimming laps.

Relate   10 · minutes bicycling   plus   12 · minutes swimming laps   equals   300 calories

Write $10x$ + $12y$ =   300

● The equation in standard form is $10x + 12y = 300$.

Real-World 🌐 Connection

Doctors recommend 30 minutes of exercise each day.

 **Quick Check** **5** **Data Analysis** Write an equation in standard form to find the minutes someone who weighs 150 lb would need to bowl and walk to burn 250 calories.

EXERCISES

For more exercises, see *Extra Skill and Word Problem Practice.*

Practice and Problem Solving

 Practice by Example

Example 1
(page 507)

 GO for Help

Find the *x*- and *y*-intercepts of each equation.

1. $x + 2y = 18$ **2.** $3x - y = 9$ **3.** $-5x + y = 30$

4. $-6x + 3y = -9$ **5.** $4x + 12y = -18$ **6.** $9x - 6y = -72$

7. $-2x - 3y = -12$ **8.** $7x - 2y = 4$ **9.** $-8x + 10y = 40$

Example 2
(page 507)

Match each equation with its graph.

10. $2x - 5y = 10$ **11.** $-2x + 5y = 10$ **12.** $2x + 5y = 10$

A. 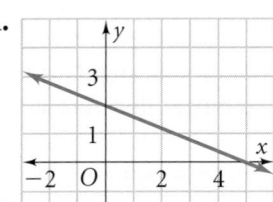   **B.** 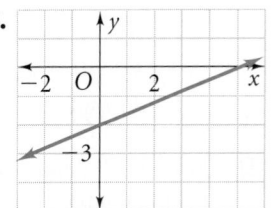   **C.**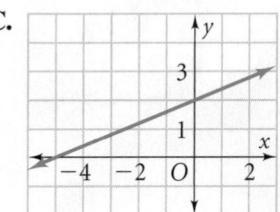

Graph each equation using *x*- and *y*-intercepts.

13. $x + y = 2$ **14.** $x + y = -5$ **15.** $x - y = -7$

16. $-3x + y = 6$ **17.** $-2x + y = -6$ **18.** $5x - 3y = 15$

Example 3
(page 507)

For each equation, tell whether its graph is a horizontal or a vertical line.

19. $y = -1$ **20.** $x = 4$ **21.** $y = 2\frac{1}{2}$ **22.** $x = -3.75$

Graph each equation.

23. $y = 3$ **24.** $x = -7$ **25.** $y = -1.5$ **26.** $x = 4.5$

Example 4
(page 508)

Write each equation in standard form using integers.

27. $y = 3x + 1$ **28.** $y = 4x - 7$ **29.** $y = \frac{1}{2}x - 3$

30. $y = \frac{2}{3}x + 5$ **31.** $y = -\frac{3}{4}x - 4$ **32.** $y = -\frac{4}{5}x - 7$

33. $y = \frac{7}{2}x + \frac{1}{4}$ **34.** $y = -\frac{2}{5}x + \frac{1}{10}$ **35.** $y = -3x$

Example 5
(page 508)

36. Fund-Raising The sophomore class holds a car wash to raise money. A local merchant donates all of the supplies. A wash costs \$5 per car and \$6.50 per van or truck.
  a. Define a variable for the number of cars. Define a different variable for the number of vans or trucks.
  b. Write an equation in standard form to relate the number of cars and vans or trucks the students must wash to raise \$800.

37. Fitness Larry runs at an average rate of 8 mi/h. He walks at an average rate of 3 mi/h.
  a. Define a variable for time spent walking. Define a different variable for time spent running.
  b. Write an equation in standard form to relate the times he could spend running and walking if he travels a distance of 15 mi.

B **Apply Your Skills**

Graph each equation.

38. $-3x + 2y = -6$ **39.** $x + y = 1$ **40.** $2x - 3y = 18$

41. $y - x = -4$ **42.** $y = 2x + 5$ **43.** $y = -3x - 1$

44. $2 - y = x - 6$ **45.** $9 + y = 8 - x$ **46.** $6x = y$

47. Nutrition Suppose you are preparing a snack mix. You want the total protein from peanuts and granola to equal 28 grams. Peanuts have 7 grams of protein per ounce, and granola has 3 grams of protein per ounce.
   a. Write an equation for the protein content of your mix.
   b. Graph your equation. Use your graph to find how many ounces of granola you should use if you use 1 ounce of peanuts.

48. You are sent to the store to buy sliced meat for a party. You are told to get roast beef and turkey, and you are given $30. Roast beef is $4.29/lb and turkey is $3.99/lb. Write an equation in standard form to relate the pounds of each kind of meat you could buy at the store with $30.

Real-World Connection

A peanut contains about 0.24 gram of protein.

Graphing Calculator **Write each equation in slope-intercept form. Then use a graphing calculator to graph each equation. Make a sketch of the graph. Include the x- and y-intercepts.**

49. $8x - 10y = -100$ **50.** $-6x + 7y = 21$ **51.** $12x + 15y = -45$

52. $-5x + 9y = -15$ **53.** $16x + 11y = -88$ **54.** $3x - 27y = 18$

55. Writing Two of the forms of a linear equation are slope-intercept form and standard form. Explain when each is the more useful.

56. Critical Thinking The definition of standard form states that A and B can't both be zero. Explain why.

57. Error Analysis A student says that the equation $3x + 2y = 6$ is a standard form of the equation $y = \frac{3}{2}x + 3$. What is the student's error?

Write an equation for each line on the graph.

58. a **59.** b **60.** c **61.** d

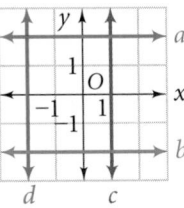

62. a. Fund-Raising Suppose your school is having a talent show to raise money for new music supplies. You estimate that 200 students and 150 adults will attend. You estimate $200 in expenses. Write an equation to find what ticket prices you should set to raise $1000.
   b. Open-Ended Graph your equation. Choose three possible prices you could set for students' and adults' tickets. Which is the best choice? Explain.

C **Challenge**

63. Write an equation of a line that has the same slope as the line $3x - 5y = 7$ and the same y-intercept as the line $2y - 9x = 8$.

64. Geometry Graph each of the four lines below on the same graph. What figure do the four lines appear to form?
   $-2x + 3y = 10$ $3x + 2y = -2$ $-2x + 3y = -3$ $3x + 2y = 11$

65. a. Graph $2x + 3y = 6$ and $2x + 3y = 18$.
   b. What is the slope of each line?
   c. Compare the x-intercepts of the two lines. How are they related? How are the y-intercepts related?

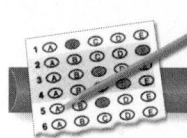

Multiple Choice

66. Which of the following is the standard form of $y = -\frac{2}{3}x + 6$ written using integers?

    A. $\frac{2}{3}x + y = 6$ **B.** $-6 = -\frac{2}{3}x - y$ **C.** $2x + 3y = 18$ **D.** $-2x - 3y = 18$

67. If $A \neq 0$ and $B \neq 0$, which is the slope of $Ax + By = C$?

    F. $-\frac{B}{A}$ **G.** $\frac{C}{A}$ **H.** $-\frac{A}{B}$ **J.** $\frac{C}{B}$

Short Response

68. A basket with 4 apples weighs 2 pounds. The same basket with 12 apples weighs 4 pounds. Write an equation in slope-intercept form for the weight y in terms of the number of apples x. Write an equation in standard form with integer coefficients that shows the relationship of the weight y and the number of apples x.

Extended Response

69. A tire dealer sells Supreme tires for $48 each and Prestige tires for $56 each. During one week, the sales for both tires totaled $2008.
    a. Write an equation that you can use to determine the possible combinations of Supreme tires x and Prestige tires y sold.
    b. Graph your equation on a coordinate plane.
    c. Use your graph to list 3 possible combinations of Supreme and Prestige tires sold.

Mixed Review

Lesson 9-2

Determine whether the ordered pair is a solution of the equation.

70. $(2, -3); y = -x - 1$ **71.** $(6, -1); y = 2x - 15$ **72.** $(-5, -7); y = -3x - 8$

Lesson 6-4

Solve each proportion.

73. $\frac{a}{5} = \frac{12}{15}$ **74.** $\frac{2}{8} = \frac{w}{9}$ **75.** $\frac{x+2}{4} = \frac{3}{8}$ **76.** $\frac{14}{4m} = \frac{16}{5m+9}$

Lesson 5-7

Find each probability for rolling a number cube.

77. P(rolling a 2, then a 4)   **78.** P(rolling a 5, then an even number)

✓ Checkpoint Quiz 1   Lessons 9-1 through 9-4

Find the slope of the line passing through each pair of points.

    1. $(-1, 3), (6, -2)$ **2.** $(4, 5), (0, 2)$ **3.** $(-2, -3), (-1, -7)$ **4.** $(4, -4), (-5, 5)$

    5. Credit Cards In 1990, people charged $534 billion on the two most-used types of credit cards. In 1994, people charged $1.021 trillion on these same two types of credit cards. What was the rate of change?

Graph each equation.

    6. $y = 4x - 1$ **7.** $y = -\frac{2}{5}x + 6$ **8.** $5x + 3y = -30$ **9.** $2x - 7y = 15$

    10. Writing How are the graphs of $y = 3x + 5$, $y = \frac{2}{3}x + 5$, and $y = \frac{3}{5}x + 5$ alike? How are they different?

Point-Slope Form and Writing Linear Equations

What You'll Learn

- To graph and write linear equations using point-slope form
- To write a linear equation using data

. . . And Why

To write an equation relating altitude and the boiling point of water, as in Example 5

✓ **Check Skills You'll Need**   **GO for Help** Lessons 9-1 and 5-4

Find the rate of change of the data in each table.

1.

x	y
2	4
5	−2
8	−8
11	−14

2.

x	y
−3	−5
−1	−4
1	−3
3	−2

3.

x	y
10	4
7.5	−1
5	−6
2.5	−11

Simplify each expression.

4. $-3(x - 5)$ **5.** $5(x + 2)$ **6.** $-\frac{4}{9}(x - 6)$

🔊 **New Vocabulary** • point-slope form

---

1 Using Point-Slope Form

You can use the definition of slope to find another form of a linear equation called the point-slope form.

$$\frac{y_2 - y_1}{x_2 - x_1} = m \qquad \text{Use the definition of slope.}$$

Suppose you know that a line passes through the point $(3, 4)$ and has slope 2.

$$\frac{y - 4}{x - 3} = 2 \qquad \text{Substitute (3, 4) for } (x_1, y_1) \text{ and substitute } (x, y) \text{ for } (x_2, y_2).$$
$$\text{Substitute 2 for } m.$$

$$\frac{y - 4}{x - 3}(x - 3) = 2(x - 3) \qquad \text{Multiply each side by } x - 3.$$

$$y - 4 = 2(x - 3) \qquad \text{Simplify the left side of the equation.}$$

The equation $y - 4 = 2(x - 3)$ is in point-slope form.

$$y - 4 = 2(x - 3)$$

y-coordinate   slope   x-coordinate

 Key Concepts

Definition	Point-Slope Form of a Linear Equation

The **point-slope form** of the equation of a nonvertical line that passes through the point (x_1, y_1) and has slope m is

$$y - y_1 = m(x - x_1)$$

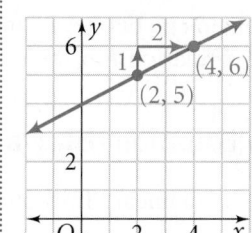

1 EXAMPLE **Graphing Using Point-Slope Form**

Graph the equation $y - 5 = \frac{1}{2}(x - 2)$.

The equation shows that the line passes through (2, 5) and has a slope $\frac{1}{2}$.

Start at (2, 5). Using the slope, go up 1 unit and right 2 units to (4, 6). Draw a line through the two points.

 **1** Graph the equation $y - 5 = -\frac{2}{3}(x + 2)$.

2 EXAMPLE **Writing an Equation in Point-Slope Form**

Vocabulary Tip

Square brackets, [ ], are grouping symbols commonly used when parentheses, ( ), are inside.

Write the equation of the line that has slope -3 that passes through the point $(-1, 7)$.

$y - y_1 = m(x - x_1)$ Use the point-slope form.

$y - 7 = -3[x - (-1)]$ Substitute $(-1, 7)$ for (x_1, y_1) and -3 for m.

$y - 7 = -3(x + 1)$ Simplify inside the grouping symbols.

 **2** Write the equation of the line that has slope $\frac{2}{5}$ that passes through the point $(10, -8)$.

If you know two points on a line, first use them to find the slope. Then you can write an equation using either point.

3 EXAMPLE **Using Two Points to Write an Equation**

Write equations for the line in point-slope form and in slope-intercept form.

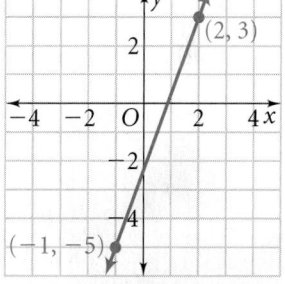

Online active math

For: Point-Slope Activity
Use: Interactive Textbook, 6-5

Step 1 Find the slope.

$$\frac{y_2 - y_1}{x_2 - x_1} = m$$

$$\frac{-5 - 3}{-1 - 2} = \frac{8}{3}$$

The slope is $\frac{8}{3}$.

Step 2 Use either point to write the equation in point-slope form. Use (2, 3).

$y - y_1 = m(x - x_1)$

$y - 3 = \frac{8}{3}(x - 2)$

Step 3 Rewrite the equation from Step 2 in slope-intercept form.

$y - 3 = \frac{8}{3}(x - 2)$

$y - 3 = \frac{8}{3}x - 5\frac{1}{3}$

$y = \frac{8}{3}x - 2\frac{1}{3}$

 **3 a.** Write an equation for the line in Example 3 in point-slope form using the point $(-1, -5)$.
   b. Write the equation you found in part (a) in slope-intercept form.
   c. What is true about the equation you wrote in part (b) and the equation in Step 3 of Example 3?

You can write a linear equation to model data in tables. Two sets of data have a linear relationship if the rate of change between consecutive pairs of data is the same. For data that have a linear relationship, the rate of change is the slope.

4 EXAMPLE Writing an Equation Using a Table

Is the relationship shown by the data linear? If so, model the data with an equation.

Step 1 Find the rate of change for consecutive ordered pairs.

x	y
−1	4
3	6
5	7
11	10

$4 \big) \quad 2 \quad \frac{2}{4} = \frac{1}{2}$

$2 \big) \quad 1 \quad \frac{1}{2} = \frac{1}{2}$

$6 \big) \quad 3 \quad \frac{3}{6} = \frac{1}{2}$

Step 2 Use the slope and a point to write an equation.

$$y - y_1 = m (x - x_1)$$

Substitute (5, 7) for (x_1, y_1) and $\frac{1}{2}$ for m.

$$y - 7 = \frac{1}{2}(x - 5)$$

 **Quick Check** **4** Is the relationship shown by the data at the right linear? If so, model the data with an equation.

x	y
−11	−7
−1	−3
4	−1
19	5

5 EXAMPLE Real-World  Problem Solving

Is the relationship shown by the data linear? If so, model the data with an equation.

Boiling Point of Water

Altitude (1000 ft)	Temperature (°F)
8	197.6
4.5	203.9
3	206.6
2.5	207.5

$−3.5 \big) \quad 6.3$

$−1.5 \big) \quad 2.7$

$−0.5 \big) \quad 0.9$

Step 1 Find the rates of change for consecutive ordered pairs.

$$\frac{6.3}{-3.5} = -1.8 \qquad \frac{2.7}{-1.5} = -1.8 \qquad \frac{0.9}{-0.5} = -1.8$$

The relationship is linear. The rate of change is $−1.8$ degrees Fahrenheit per 1000 ft of altitude.

Step 2 Use the slope and a point to write an equation.

$$y - y_1 = m (x - x_1) \qquad \text{Use the point-slope form.}$$
$$y - 206.6 = -1.8(x - 3) \qquad \text{Substitute (3, 206.6) for (x_1, y_1) and −1.8 for m.}$$

The equation $y - 206.6 = -1.8(x - 3)$ relates altitude in thousands of feet x to the boiling point temperature in degrees Fahrenheit.

Real-World  **Connection**

At 5280 feet above sea level it takes 17 minutes to hard-boil an egg. This is more than 40% longer than it takes the same egg to cook at sea level.

 **Quick Check** 5 Is the relationship shown by the data in the table linear? If it is, model the data with an equation.

Working Outdoors

Temperature	Calories Burned per Day
68°F	3030
62°F	3130
56°F	3230
50°F	3330

In Example 5 you could rewrite $y - 206.6 = -1.8(x - 3)$ as $y = -1.8x + 212$. This form gives you useful information about the y-intercept. For instance, 212°F is the boiling point of water at sea level.

Here are the three forms of linear equations you have studied.

 Key Concepts

 **GO for Help**

For more help with the three forms of a linear equation, see page 518.

Summary	**Linear Equations**	
Slope-Intercept Form	**Standard Form**	**Point-Slope Form**
$y = mx + b$	$Ax + By = C$	$(y - y_1) = m(x - x_1)$
m is the slope and b is the y-intercept.	A and B are not both 0.	(x_1, y_1) lies on the graph of the equation, and m is the slope.
Examples		
$y = -\frac{2}{3}x + \frac{5}{3}$	$2x + 3y = 5$	$y - 1 = -\frac{2}{3}(x - 1)$

EXERCISES

For more exercises, see *Extra Skill and Word Problem Practice.*

Practice and Problem Solving

 A Practice by Example

Example 1
(page 513)

 **GO for Help**

Graph each equation.

1. $y - 2 = (x - 3)$ **2.** $y - 2 = 2(x - 3)$ **3.** $y - 2 = -\frac{3}{2}(x - 3)$

4. $y + 5 = -(x - 2)$ **5.** $y + 1 = \frac{2}{3}(x + 4)$ **6.** $y - 1 = -3(x + 2)$

7. $y + 3 = -2(x - 1)$ **8.** $y - 4 = (x - 5)$ **9.** $y - 2 = 3(x + 2)$

Example 2
(page 513)

Write an equation in point-slope form for the line through the given point that has the given slope.

10. $(3, -4); m = 6$ **11.** $(4, 2); m = -\frac{5}{3}$ **12.** $(0, 2); m = \frac{4}{5}$

13. $(-2, -7); m = -\frac{3}{2}$ **14.** $(4, 0); m = 1$ **15.** $(5, -8); m = -3$

16. $(-5, 2); m = 0$ **17.** $(1, -8); m = -\frac{1}{5}$ **18.** $(-6, 1); m = \frac{2}{3}$

Example 3
(page 513)

A line passes through the given points. Write an equation for the line in point-slope form. Then rewrite the equation in slope-intercept form.

19. $(-1, 0), (1, 2)$ **20.** $(3, 5), (0, 0)$ **21.** $(4, -2), (9, -8)$

22. $(6, -4), (-3, 5)$ **23.** $(-1, -5), (-7, -6)$ **24.** $(-3, -4), (3, -2)$

25. $(2, 7), (1, -4)$ **26.** $(-2, 6), (5, 1)$ **27.** $(3, -8), (-2, 5)$

28. $\left(1, \frac{1}{2}\right), (3, 2)$ **29.** $\left(\frac{1}{2}, 2\right), \left(-\frac{3}{2}, 4\right)$ **30.** $(0.2, 1.1), (7, 3)$

Example 4
(page 514)

Is the relationship shown by the data linear? If so, model the data with an equation.

31.

x	y
−4	9
2	−3
5	−9
9	−17

32.

x	y
−10	−5
−2	19
5	40
11	58

33.

x	y
3	1
6	4
9	13
15	49

Example 5
(page 514)

34.

Speed Over Posted Speed Limit (mi/h)	Fine ($)
10	75
12	95
15	125
19	165

35.

Volume (gal)	Weight (lb)
0	0
2	16
4	33
6	50

B **Apply Your Skills**

Write an equation of each line in point-slope form.

36.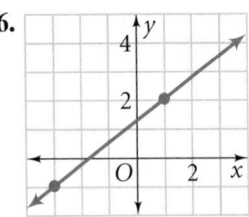

37.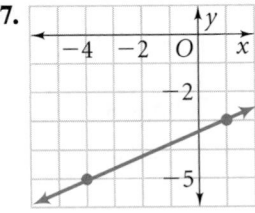

38.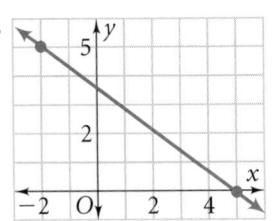

Write one equation of the line through the given points in point-slope form and one in standard form using integers.

39. $(1, 4), (−1, 1)$

40. $(6, −3), (−2, −3)$

41. $(0, 0), (−1, −2)$

42. $(0, 2), (−4, 2)$

43. $(−6, 6), (3, 3)$

44. $(2, 3), (−1, 5)$

45. $(5, −3), (3, 4)$

46. $(2, 2), (−1, 7)$

47. $(−7, 1), (5, −1)$

48. $(−8, 4), (−4, −2)$

49. $(2, 4), (−3, −6)$

50. $(5, 3), (4, 5)$

51. $(0, 1), (−3, 0)$

52. $(−2, 4), (0, −5)$

53. $(6, 2), (1, −1)$

54. **Science** At the surface of the ocean, pressure is 1 atmosphere. At 66 ft below sea level, the pressure is 3 atmospheres. The relationship of pressure and depth is linear.
   a. Write an equation for the data.
   b. Predict the pressure at 100 ft below sea level.

55. **Environment** Worldwide carbon monoxide emissions are decreasing about 2.6 million metric tons each year. In 1991, carbon monoxide emissions were 79 million metric tons. Use a linear equation to model the relationship between carbon monoxide emissions and time. Let $x = 91$ correspond to 1991.

56. a. **Open-Ended** Write an equation in point-slope form that contains the point $(−4, −6)$. Explain your steps.
   b. How many equations could you write in part(a)? Explain.

57. **Critical Thinking** How would the graph of $y − 12 = 8(x − 2)$ change if all of the subtraction signs were changed to addition signs?

58. **Reasoning** Is $y − 5 = 2(x − 1)$ an equation of a line through $(4, 11)$? Explain.

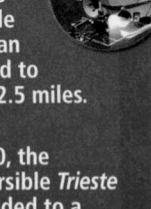

P
R
E
S
S
U
R
E

I
N
C
R
E
A
S
E
S

A scuba diver can descend to about 131 feet.

The submersible *Alvin* can descend to about 2.5 miles.

In 1960, the submersible *Trieste* descended to a record depth of 6.8 miles.

59. Open-Ended Write an equation in each of the following forms.
  a. slope-intercept form
  b. standard form
  c. point-slope form

 60. Science Use the scatter plot.
  a. Write an equation to model the data.
  b. What is the speed of sound at 15°C?
  c. Predict the speed of sound at 60°C.

Effect of Air Temperature on Speed of Sound

 **Challenge**

Write an equation in slope-intercept form of each line described below.

61. The line contains the point $(-3, -5)$ and has the same slope as $y + 2 = 7(x + 3)$.

62. The line contains the point $(1, 3)$ and has the same y-intercept as $y - 5 = 2(x - 1)$.

63. The line contains the point $(2, -2)$ and has the same x-intercept as $y + 9 = 3(x - 4)$.

64. The table shows data that you can model using a linear function.
  a. Find the value of y when $x = 6$.
  b. Find the value of y when $x = 120$.
  c. Find the value of x when $y = 11$.
  d. Find the value of x when $y = 50$.

x	y
4	14
8	15.5
12	17
16	18.5

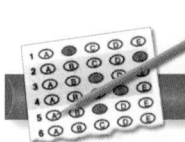
Test Prep

Gridded Response

65. What is the slope of the graph of $y - 8 = \frac{1}{2}(x + 2)$?

66. Find the y-intercept of the line $y + 3 = 4(x + 3)$.

67. What is the x-intercept of the line $y = 3x - 7$?

68. When $y - 1 = -\frac{4}{5}(x - 3)$ is written in standard form using positive integers, what is the smallest possible coefficient of x?

69. When $y = -\frac{5}{2}x + \frac{2}{3}$ is written in standard form using positive integers, what is the smallest possible coefficient of y?

Mixed Review

Lesson 9-4

Graph each line.

70. $6x + 7y = 14$ **71.** $-2x + 9y = -9$ **72.** $5x - 4y = 24$

73. $3x - 8y = 4$ **74.** $5x + 18y = 6$ **75.** $-7x + 4y = -21$

Lesson 8-7

Find the common difference of each sequence. Then write the next two terms.

76. $-12, -7, -2, \ldots$ **77.** $\frac{1}{2}, \frac{5}{6}, \frac{7}{6}, \ldots$ **78.** $2.45, 2.52, 2.59, \ldots$

79. $-3.2, -3.25, -3.3, \ldots$ **80.** $18, 35, 52, \ldots$ **81.** $-7, -3, 1, \ldots$

There are three forms of a linear equation that you have studied in this chapter:

- slope-intercept form
- standard form
- point-slope form

To understand and remember these forms, it may help you to connect the common meaning of the words with their specialized meanings in mathematics.

Word	Common Meaning	Mathematical Meaning
Slope	An inclined surface (for example, the slope of a hill)	The rate of change that gives the steepness of a line: $\text{slope} = \dfrac{\text{vertical change}}{\text{horizontal change}} = \dfrac{\text{rise}}{\text{run}}$
Intercept	To cut off from a path (for example, to intercept a football)	The values of the points at which a line intersects (or cuts) the x-axis or y-axis
Standard	Generally accepted	A general form of an equation
Point	A dot or speck (noun)	A fixed location on a coordinate plane; every point has a unique x-value and y-value.

Slope-intercept form, standard form, and point-slope form all give clues about the lines they will graph.

- Slope-intercept form tells the slope of the line and its y-intercept.

  Example $y = 3x - 1$ The graph of this equation has a slope of 3 and a y-intercept of -1.

- Standard form is the general form for linear equations. You can model many real-world situations using the standard form. Also, it is easy to find the x- and y-intercepts of the graph of an equation in this form.

  Example $5x - 2y = 100$ The graph of this equation intersects the y-axis at $\frac{100}{-2} = -50$ and intersects the x-axis at $\frac{100}{5} = 20$.

- Point-slope form tells a point on the line and the slope of the line.

  Example $y - 2 = 3(x - 5)$ The graph of this equation passes through the point (5, 2), and its slope is 3.

EXERCISES

For each situation, which form of a linear equation is easiest to write?

1. A submarine started at sea level and submerged at a steady rate of 8 feet per minute.

2. A plant growing at a steady rate measured 2 in. on day 5 and 13 in. on day 21.

Find the common meaning and the mathematical meaning of each word.

3. function   **4.** relation   **5.** range   **6.** domain

7. variable   **8.** base   **9.** element   **10.** term

Parallel and Perpendicular Lines

What You'll Learn

• To determine whether lines are parallel

• To determine whether lines are perpendicular

. . . And Why

To use parallel and perpendicular lines to plan a bike path, as in Example 4

☑ **Check Skills You'll Need**

GO **for Help** Lessons 5-3 and 9-2

What is the reciprocal of each fraction?

1. $\frac{1}{2}$ **2.** $\frac{4}{3}$ **3.** $-\frac{2}{5}$ **4.** $-\frac{7}{5}$

What are the slope and y-intercept of each equation?

5. $y = \frac{5}{3}x + 4$ **6.** $y = \frac{5}{3}x - 8$ **7.** $y = 6x$ **8.** $y = 6x + 2$

◀)) **New Vocabulary**   • **parallel lines**   • **perpendicular lines**
                              • **negative reciprocal**

▬ 1   Parallel Lines

In the graph at the right, the red and blue lines are parallel. **Parallel lines** are lines in the same plane that never intersect. The equation of the red line is $y = \frac{1}{2}x + \frac{3}{2}$. The equation of the blue line is $y = \frac{1}{2}x - 1$.

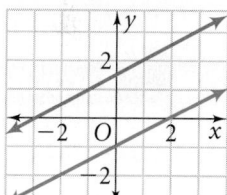

Key Concepts

Property	**Slopes of Parallel Lines**

Nonvertical lines are parallel if they have the same slope and different y-intercepts. *Any* two vertical lines are parallel.

Example   The equations $y = \frac{2}{3}x + 1$ and $y = \frac{2}{3}x - 3$ have the same slope, $\frac{2}{3}$, and different y-intercepts. The graphs of the two equations are parallel.

You can use slope-intercept form to determine whether the lines are parallel.

1 **EXAMPLE**   **Determining Whether Lines Are Parallel**

Are the graphs of $y = -\frac{1}{3}x + 5$ and $2x + 6y = 12$ parallel? Explain.

Write $2x + 6y = 12$ in slope-intercept form. Then compare with $y = -\frac{1}{3}x + 5$.

$6y = -2x + 12$ **Subtract 2x from each side.**

$\dfrac{6y}{6} = \dfrac{-2x + 12}{6}$ **Divide each side by 6.**

$y = -\frac{1}{3}x + 2$ **Simplify.**

The lines are parallel. The equations have the same slope, $-\frac{1}{3}$, and different y-intercepts.

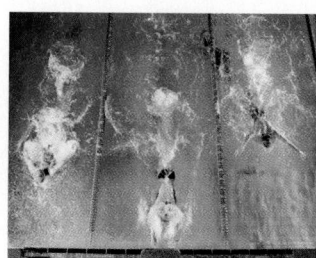

Real-World 🌐 **Connection**

The lanes for competitive swimming are parallel.

☑ **Quick Check**   **1** Are the graphs of $-6x + 8y = -24$ and $y = \frac{3}{4}x - 7$ parallel? Explain.

You can use the fact that the slopes of parallel lines are the same to write the equation of a line parallel to a given line. To write the equation, you use the slope of the given line and the point-slope form of a linear equation.

To do Example 2 with a graphing calculator, see page 754.

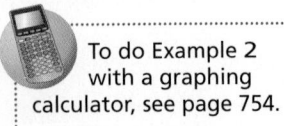

Video Tutor Help

Visit: PHSchool.com
Web Code: ate-0775

2 EXAMPLE Writing Equations of Parallel Lines

Write an equation for the line that contains $(5, 1)$ and is parallel to $y = \frac{3}{5}x - 4$.

Step 1 Identify the slope of the given line.

$$y = \frac{3}{5}x - 4$$

slope

Step 2 Write the equation of the line through $(5, 1)$ using slope-intercept form.

$y - y_1 = m(x - x_1)$	point-slope form
$y - 1 = \frac{3}{5}(x - 5)$	Substitute $(5, 1)$ for (x_1, y_1) and $\frac{3}{5}$ for m.
$y - 1 = \frac{3}{5}x - \frac{3}{5}(5)$	Use the Distributive Property.
$y - 1 = \frac{3}{5}x - 3$	Simplify.
$y = \frac{3}{5}x - 2$	Add 1 to each side.

✓ Quick Check ② Write an equation for the line that contains $(2, -6)$ and is parallel to $y = 3x + 9$.

2 Perpendicular Lines

The lines at the right are perpendicular. **Perpendicular lines** are lines that intersect to form right angles. The equation of the red line is $y = -\frac{1}{4}x - 1$. The equation of the blue line is $y = 4x + 2$.

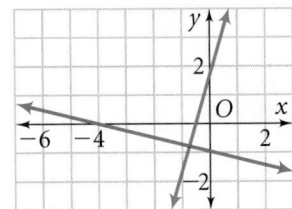

Key Concepts

Property	**Slopes of Perpendicular Lines**

Two lines are perpendicular if the product of their slopes is -1. A vertical and a horizontal line are also perpendicular.

Example The slope of $y = -\frac{1}{4}x - 1$ is $-\frac{1}{4}$. The slope of $y = 4x + 2$ is 4. Since $-\frac{1}{4} \cdot 4 = -1$, the graphs of the two equations are perpendicular.

The product of two numbers is -1 if one number is the **negative reciprocal** of the other. Here is how to find the negative reciprocal of a number.

Start with a fraction: $-\frac{3}{5}$. → Find its reciprocal: $-\frac{5}{3}$. → Write the negative reciprocal: $\frac{5}{3}$.

Since $-\frac{3}{5} \cdot \frac{5}{3} = -1$, $\frac{5}{3}$ is the negative reciprocal of $-\frac{3}{5}$.

Start with an integer: 4. → Find its reciprocal: $\frac{1}{4}$. → Write its negative reciprocal: $-\frac{1}{4}$.

Since $4\left(-\frac{1}{4}\right) = -1$, $-\frac{1}{4}$ is the negative reciprocal of 4.

You can use the negative reciprocal of the slope of a given line to write an equation of a line perpendicular to that line.

3 EXAMPLE Writing Equations for Perpendicular Lines

Multiple Choice Which equation describes a line that contains $(0, -2)$ and is perpendicular to $y = 5x + 3$?

Ⓐ $y = 5x - 2$ Ⓑ $y = \frac{1}{5}x - 2$ Ⓒ $y = \frac{1}{5}x + 2$ Ⓓ $y = -\frac{1}{5}x - 2$

Step 1 Identify the slope of the given line.

$$y = 5\underset{\uparrow}{x} + 3$$
slope

Step 2 Find the negative reciprocal of the slope.

The negative reciprocal of 5 is $-\frac{1}{5}$.

Step 3 Use the slope-intercept form to write an equation.

$y = mx + b$

$y = -\frac{1}{5}x + (-2)$ **Substitute $-\frac{1}{5}$ for m, and -2 for b.**

$y = -\frac{1}{5}x - 2$ **Simplify.**

● The equation is $y = -\frac{1}{5}x - 2$. So D is the correct answer.

 **Quick Check** ❸ Write an equation of the line that contains $(1, 8)$ and is perpendicular to $y = \frac{3}{4}x + 1$.

Test-Taking Tip

After finding the slopes of the perpendicular lines, multiply the two slopes as a check.

$5\left(-\frac{1}{5}\right) = -1$

You can use equations of parallel and perpendicular lines to solve some real-world problems.

4 EXAMPLE Real-World 🌐 Problem Solving

Urban Planning A bike path for a new city park will connect the park entrance to Park Road. The path will be perpendicular to Park Road. Write an equation for the line representing the bike path.

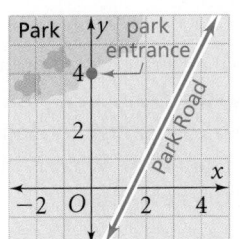
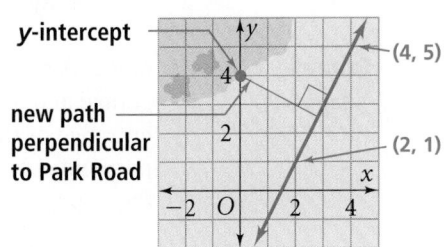

Step 1 Find the slope m of Park Road.

$m = \dfrac{y_2 - y_1}{x_2 - x_1} = \dfrac{5 - 1}{4 - 2} = \dfrac{4}{2} = 2$ **Points (2, 1) and (4, 5) are on Park Road.**

Step 2 Find the negative reciprocal of the slope.

The negative reciprocal of 2 is $-\frac{1}{2}$. So the slope of the bike path is $-\frac{1}{2}$. The y-intercept is 4.

● The equation for the bike path is $y = -\frac{1}{2}x + 4$.

Quick Check ❹ A second bike path is planned. It will be parallel to Park Road and will also contain the park entrance. Write an equation for the line representing this bike path.

Real-World 🌐 Connection

Careers Urban planners use mathematics to make decisions on community problems such as traffic congestion and air pollution.

EXERCISES

For more exercises, see *Extra Skill and Word Problem Practice.*

Practice and Problem Solving

 Practice by Example

Example 1
(page 519)

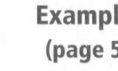 for Help

Find the slope of a line parallel to the graph of each equation.

1. $y = \frac{1}{2}x + 2.3$ **2.** $y = -\frac{2}{3}x - 1$ **3.** $y = x$

4. $y = 6$ **5.** $3x + 4y = 12$ **6.** $7x - y = 5$

Are the graphs of the lines in each pair parallel? Explain.

7. $y = 4x + 12$ **8.** $y = -\frac{3}{2}x + 2$ **9.** $y = \frac{1}{3}x + 3$
    $-4x + 3y = 21$ $3x + 2y = 8$ $x - 3y = 6$

10. $y = -\frac{1}{2}x + \frac{3}{2}$ **11.** $y = -3x$ **12.** $y = \frac{3}{4}x - 2$
     $5x - 10y = 15$ $21x + 7y = 14$ $-3x + 4y = 8$

Example 2
(page 520)

Write an equation for the line that is parallel to the given line and that passes through the given point.

13. $y = 6x - 2; (0, 0)$ **14.** $y = -3x; (3, 0)$ **15.** $y = -2x + 3; (-3, 5)$

16. $y = -\frac{7}{2}x + 6; (-4, -6)$ **17.** $y = 0.5x - 8; (8, -5)$ **18.** $y = -\frac{2}{3}x + 12; (5, -3)$

Example 3
(page 521)

Find the slope of a line perpendicular to the graph of each equation.

19. $y = 2x$ **20.** $y = -3x$ **21.** $y = \frac{7}{5}x - 2$

22. $y = -\frac{x}{5} - 7$ **23.** $2x + 3y = 5$ **24.** $y = -8$

Write an equation for the line that is perpendicular to the given line and that passes through the given point.

25. $y = 2x + 7; (0, 0)$ **26.** $y = x - 3; (4, 6)$

27. $y = -\frac{1}{3}x + 2; (4, 2)$ **28.** $3x + 5y = 7; (-1, 2)$

29. $-10x + 8y = 3; (15, 12)$ **30.** $4x - 2y = 9; (8, -2)$

Example 4
(page 521)

31. Maps A city's civil engineer is planning a new parking garage and a new street. The new street will go from the entrance of the parking garage to Handel St. It will be perpendicular to Handel St. What is the equation of the line representing the new street?

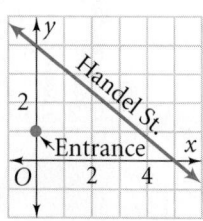

 Apply Your Skills

Tell whether the lines for each pair of equations are *parallel,* *perpendicular,* **or** *neither.*

32. $y = 4x + \frac{3}{4}, y = -\frac{1}{4}x + 4$ **33.** $y = \frac{2}{3}x - 6, y = \frac{2}{3}x + 6$

34. $y = -x + 5, y = x + 5$ **35.** $y = 5x, y = -5x + 7$

36. $y = \frac{x}{3} - 4, y = \frac{1}{3}x + 2$ **37.** $x = 2, y = 9$

38. $2x + y = 2, 2x + y = 5$ **39.** $3x - 5y = 3, -5x + 3y = 8$

40. Multiple Choice Which pair of equations graph as perpendicular lines?

Ⓐ $y = 4x + \frac{1}{2}$ Ⓑ $y = \frac{2}{3}x + 1$ Ⓒ $y = -\frac{3}{5}x - 9$ Ⓓ $y = -\frac{3}{5}x - 9$

      $y = -4x + 3$ $y = 3x - 1$ $y = \frac{5}{3}x + 8$ $y = \frac{3}{5}x + 4$

Find the equation for each line.

41.
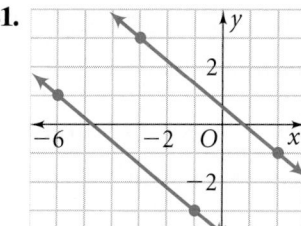

42.
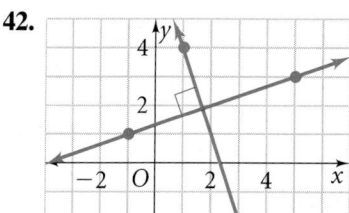

43.
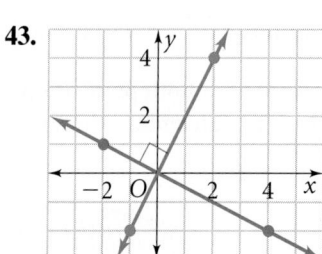

44.
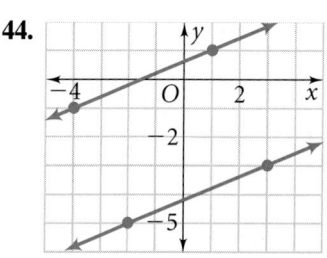

45.
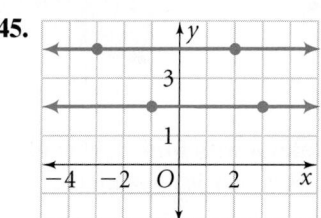

46.
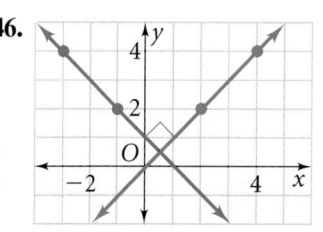

🌐 **Maps** Use the map below for Exercises 47–49.

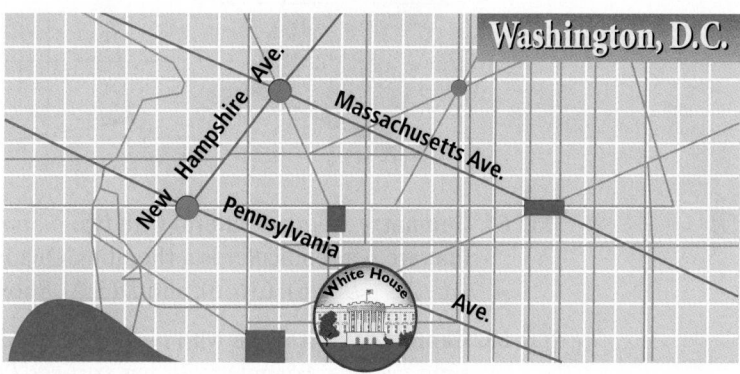

47. What is the slope of New Hampshire Avenue?

48. Show that the parts of Pennsylvania Avenue and Massachusetts Avenue near New Hampshire Avenue are parallel.

49. Show that New Hampshire Avenue is not perpendicular to Pennsylvania Avenue.

50. a. The graphs of $y = x$ and $y = -x$ are shown on the standard screen at the right. The product of the slopes is -1. Explain why the lines do not appear to be perpendicular.

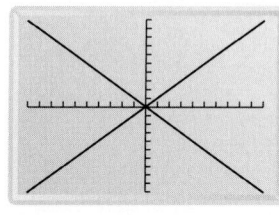

  b. Graphing Calculator Graph $y = x$ and $y = -x$ on a graphing calculator. In the ZOOM feature, choose the square screen. What do you notice?

51. Open-Ended Write an equation for a line parallel to the graph of $4x - y = 1$.

52. Are the graphs of $2x + 7y = 6$ and $7y = 2x + 6$ parallel? Explain.

53. Are the graphs of $8x + 3y = 6$ and $8x - 3y = 6$ perpendicular? Explain.

54. Writing Are all horizontal lines parallel? Explain.

Tell whether each statement is *true* or *false*. Explain your choice.

55. Two lines with positive slopes can be perpendicular.

56. Two lines with positive slopes can be parallel.

57. The graphs of two different direct variations can be parallel.

Problem Solving Hint

For Exercises 55–57, sketch a graph to help you understand the statement in each exercise.

Geometry A quadrilateral with both pairs of opposite sides parallel is a parallelogram. Use slopes to determine whether each figure is a parallelogram.

58. 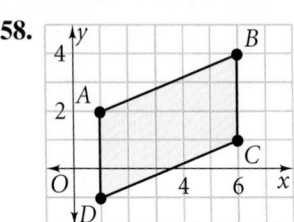 **59.** 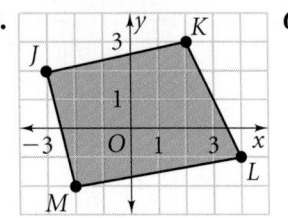 **60.**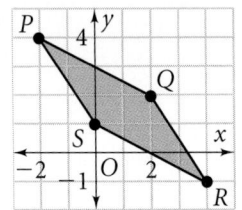

Geometry A quadrilateral with four right angles is a rectangle. Use slopes to determine whether each figure is a rectangle.

61. 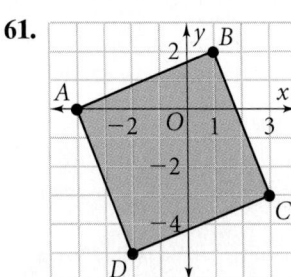 **62.** 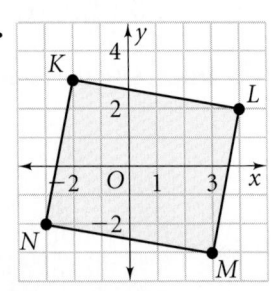 **63.**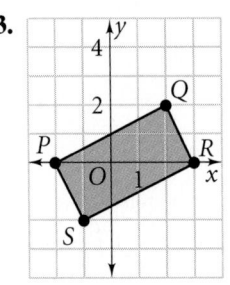

Challenge

64. Geometry A quadrilateral with two pairs of parallel sides and with diagonals that are perpendicular is a rhombus. Quadrilateral $ABCD$ has vertices $A(-2, 2)$, $B(1, 6)$, $C(6, 6)$, and $D(3, 2)$. Show that $ABCD$ is a rhombus.

65. Geometry A triangle with two sides that are perpendicular to each other is a right triangle. Triangle PQR has vertices $P(3, 3)$, $Q(2, -2)$, and $R(0, 1)$. Determine whether PQR is a right triangle. Explain.

Tell whether the lines in each pair are *parallel*, *perpendicular*, or *neither*.

66. $ax - by = 5$; $-ax + by = 2$ **67.** $ax + by = 8$; $bx - ay = 1$

Assume the two lines are perpendicular. Find an equation for each line.

68. 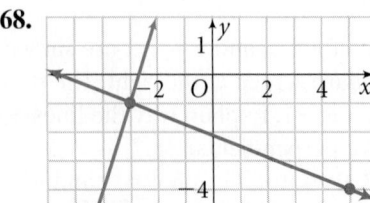 **69.**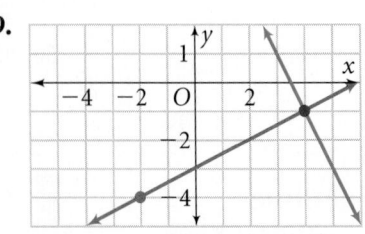

70. For what value of k are the graphs of $3x + 12y = 8$ and $6y = kx - 5$ parallel? Perpendicular?

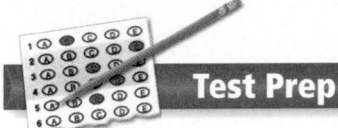

Multiple Choice

71. Which equation has as its graph a line perpendicular to a line that has a slope of $\frac{2}{3}$?

A. $y = \frac{2}{3}x + 5$ **B.** $y = \frac{3}{2}x - 1$ **C.** $y = 3x - 2$ **D.** $3x + 2y = 8$

72. Which equation has as its graph a line parallel to the graph of $-2x - 4y = 3$?

F. $y = -\frac{1}{2}x + 5$ **G.** $y = 2x - 6$ **H.** $y = -2x + 4$ **J.** $y = \frac{1}{2}x - 2$

73. A parallelogram has vertices $A(0, 2)$, $B(2, -1)$, $C(6, 3)$, and $D(p, q)$. Which of the following ordered pairs has possible values for (p, q)?

A. (0, 6) **B.** (6, 1) **C.** (4, 6) **D.** (6, 4)

74. Which equation has as its graph a line perpendicular to the graph of the line that passes through the points $(0, -1)$ and $(8, 9)$?

F. $(y - 2) = -\frac{4}{5}(x + 1)$ **G.** $y = \frac{4}{5}x + 10$

H. $4x - 5y = 0$ **J.** $y = -x + 7$

75. Which equation has as its graph a line parallel to the graph of the line that passes through the points $(-8, 2)$ and $(-3, 3)$?

A. $(y - 2) = -(x + 8)$ **B.** $y = -5x + 10$

C. $x \quad 5y \quad 6$ **D.** $-y = -\frac{1}{5}x + 7$

Short Response

76. Suppose the line through points $(x, 6)$ and $(1, 2)$ is parallel to the graph of $2x + y = 3$. Find the value of x. Show your work.

Lesson 9-4

Write an equation for the line through the given point with the given slope.

77. $(0, 4); m = 3$ **78.** $(-2, 0); m = -4$

79. $(5, -3); m = \frac{3}{4}$ **80.** $(-1, -9); m = -\frac{2}{3}$

81. $(-6, 4); m = -\frac{3}{5}$ **82.** $(7, 11); m = \frac{1}{2}$

Lesson 9-1

Find the slope of each line.

83. 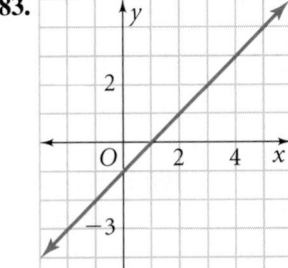 **84.** **85.**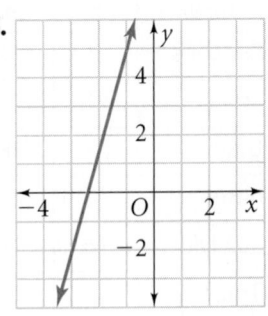

Lesson 8-2

Determine whether each relation is a function.

86. $\{(1, 1), (2, 2), (3, 3)\}$ **87.** $\{(1, 3), (2, 5), (3, 5)\}$

88. $\{(5, 1), (5, 2), (4, 3)\}$ **89.** $\{(1, 3), (2, 2), (3, 1)\}$

Scatter Plots and Equations of Lines

What You'll Learn

• To write an equation for a trend line and use it to make predictions

• To write the equation for a line of best fit and use it to make predictions

. . . And Why

To use a trend line to make a prediction, as in Example 1

✓ Check Skills You'll Need

GO for Help Lesson 4-5

Use the data in each table to draw a scatter plot.

1.

x	y
1	2
2	−3
3	8
4	9
5	−25

2.

x	y
1	21
2	15
3	12
4	9
5	7

🔊 **New Vocabulary** • line of best fit • correlation coefficient

---

1 Writing an Equation for a Trend Line

In Chapter 4 you used scatter plots to determine how two sets of data are related. You can now write an equation for a trend line.

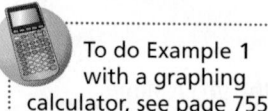

To do Example 1 with a graphing calculator, see page 755.

Length and Wingspan of Hawks

Type of Hawk	Length (in.)	Wing-span (in.)
Cooper's	21	36
Crane	21	41
Gray	18	38
Harris's	24	46
Roadside	16	31
Broad-winged	19	39
Short-tailed	17	35
Swanson's	19	46

SOURCE: *Birds of North America*

1 EXAMPLE Trend Line

Birds Make a scatter plot of the data at the left. Draw a trend line and write its equation. Use the equation to predict the wingspan of a hawk that is 28 in. long.

Step 1 Make a scatter plot and draw a trend line. Estimate two points on the line.

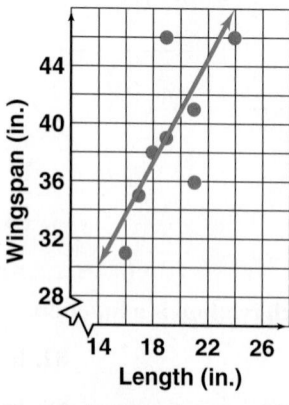

Length and Wingspan of Hawks

Two points on the trend line are (14, 30) and (19, 39).

Step 2 Write an equation of the trend line.

$$m = \frac{y_2 - y_1}{x_2 - x_1} = \frac{39 - 30}{19 - 14} = \frac{9}{5}$$

$y - y_1 = m(x - x_1)$ Use point-slope form.

$y - 30 = \frac{9}{5}(x - 14)$ Substitute $\frac{9}{5}$ for m and (14, 30) for (x_1, y_1).

Step 3 Predict the wingspan of a hawk that is 28 in. long.

$y - 30 = \frac{9}{5}(28 - 14)$ Substitute 28 for x.

$y - 30 = \frac{9}{5}(14)$ Simplify within the parentheses.

$y - 30 = 25.2$ Multiply.

$y = 55.2$ Add 30 to each side.

The wingspan of a hawk 28 in. long is about 55 in.

1 Graph the data below and draw a trend line. Find an equation for the trend line. Estimate the number of Calories in a fast-food that has 14g of fat.

Calories and Fat in Selected Fast-Food Meals

Fat (g)	6	7	10	19	20	27	36
Calories	276	260	220	388	430	550	633

2 Writing an Equation for a Line of Best Fit

The trend line that shows the relationship between two sets of data most accurately is called the **line of best fit.** A graphing calculator computes the equation of a line of best fit using a method called linear regression.

The graphing calculator also gives you the **correlation coefficient** r, which tells you how closely the equation models the data.

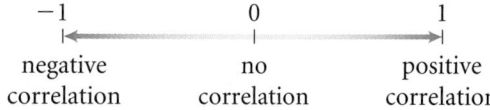

-1 0 1

negative   no   positive
correlation   correlation   correlation

When the data points cluster around a line, there is a strong correlation between the line and the data. So the nearer r is to 1 or -1, the more closely the data cluster around the line of best fit. In later chapters, you will learn how to find non-linear models which may better describe some data.

nline
active math

For: Correlation Activity
Use: Interactive Textbook, 6-7

2 EXAMPLE Line of Best Fit

Recreation Use a graphing calculator to find the equation of the line of best fit for the data at the right. What is the correlation coefficient to three decimal places?

Step 1 Use the **EDIT** feature of the
STAT screen on your graphing calculator. Let 93 correspond to 1993 and 100 correspond to 2000. Enter the data for years and then the data for expenditures.

Step 2 Use the **CALC** feature in the
STAT screen. Find the equation for the line of best fit.

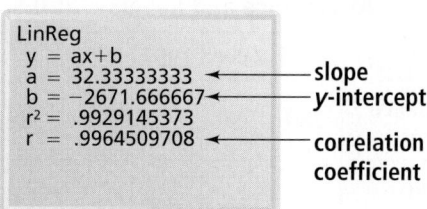

LinReg
y = ax+b
a = 32.33333333 ◄——— slope
b = −2671.666667 ◄——— *y*-intercept
r² = .9929145373
r = .9964509708 ◄——— correlation
                       coefficient

Recreation Expenditures

Year	Dollars (billions)
1993	340
1994	369
1995	402
1996	430
1997	457
1998	489
1999	527
2000	574

SOURCE: *Statistical Abstract of the United States.* Go to **www.PHSchool.com** for a data update.
Web Code: atg-9041

Go nline
PHSchool.com

For: Graphing calculator procedures
Web Code: ate-2122

The equation for the line of best fit is $y = 32.33x - 2671.67$ for values of a and b rounded to the nearest hundredth. The correlation coefficient is about 0.996.

✓ **Quick Check** ❷ Find the equation of the line of best fit. Let 95 correspond to 1995 and 103 correspond to 2003. What is the correlation coefficient to three decimal places?

Yearly Box Office Gross for Movies (billions)

1995	1996	1997	1998	1999	2000	2001	2002	2003
$5.5	$6.0	$6.4	$7.0	$7.4	$7.7	$8.4	$9.5	$9.5

EXERCISES

For more exercises, see *Extra Skill and Word Problem Practice*.

Practice and Problem Solving

A Practice by Example

Example 1
(page 526)

 **for Help**

Find an equation of a reasonable trend line for each scatter plot.

1.

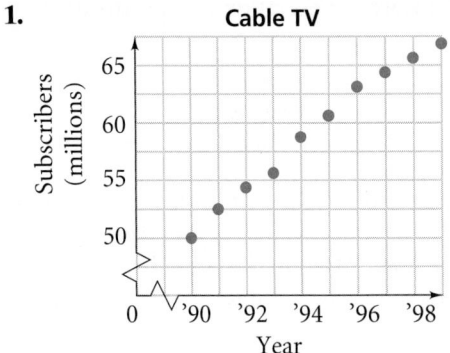

2.

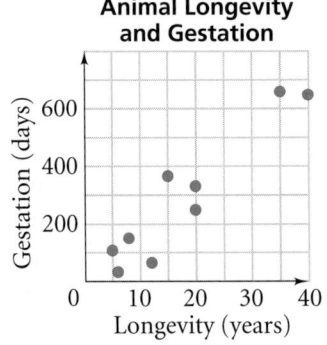

3.

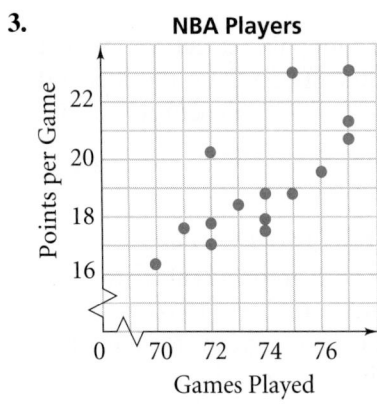

4.

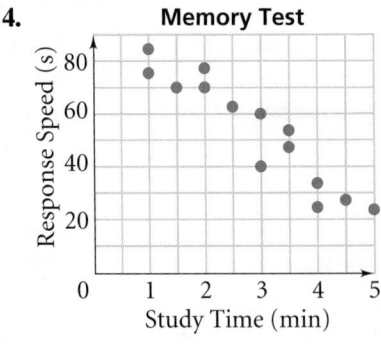

5. Graph the data in the table below for the attendance and revenue at theme parks. Find an equation for a trend line of the data.

Attendance and Revenue at U.S. Theme Parks

Year	1995	1996	1997	1998	1999	2000	2001	2002	2003
Attendance (millions)	280	290	300	300	309	317	319	324	322
Revenue (billions of dollars)	7.4	7.9	8.4	8.7	9.1	9.6	9.6	9.9	10.3

SOURCE: International Association of Amusement Parks and Attractions.
Go to **www.PHSchool.com** for a data update. Web Code: atg-9041

6. Graph the data for the average July temperature and the annual precipitation of the cities in the table below. Find an equation for the line of best fit of the data. Estimate the average rainfall for a city with average July temperature of 75° F.

Precipitation and Temperature in Selected Eastern Cities

City	Average July Temperature (°F)	Average Annual Precipitation (in.)
New York	76.4	42.82
Baltimore	76.8	41.84
Atlanta	78.6	48.61
Jacksonville	81.3	52.76
Washington, D.C.	78.9	39.00
Boston	73.5	43.81
Miami	82.5	57.55

SOURCE: Time *Almanac*

Example 2
(page 527)

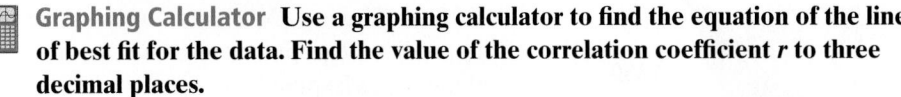 **Graphing Calculator** Use a graphing calculator to find the equation of the line of best fit for the data. Find the value of the correlation coefficient *r* to three decimal places.

7.
Average Temperatures in Northern Latitudes

Latitude (° N)	0	10	20	30	40	50	60	70	80
Temp. (°F)	79.2	80.1	77.5	68.7	57.4	42.4	30.0	12.7	1.0

8.
Retail Department Store Sales (billions of dollars)

Year	1980	1985	1990	1994	1995	1996	1997	1998
Sales	86	126	166	217	231	245	261	279

SOURCE: *Statistical Abstract of the United States.*
Go to **www.PHSchool.com** for an update. Web Code: atg-9041

9. Olympic 5000-Meter Men's Gold Medal Speed Skating Times

Year	1980	1984	1988	1992	1994	1998	2002
Time (seconds)	422	432	404	420	395	382	402

SOURCE: International Skating Union

10.
Average Male Lung Power

Respiration (breaths/min)	50	30	25	20	18	16	14
Heart Rate (beats/min)	200	150	140	130	120	110	100

SOURCE: *Encyclopeadia Britannica*

Real-World Connection

The 500-meter men's speed skating race has been an Olympic event since 1924.

11.
Wind Chill Temperature for 15 mi/h Wind

Air Temp. (°F)	35	30	25	20	15	10	5	0
Wind-Chill Temp. (°F)	16	9	2	−5	−11	−18	−25	−31

12. **Geometry** Students measured the diameters and circumferences of the tops of a variety of cylinders. Below is the data that they collected.

Cylinder Tops

Diameter (cm)	3	3	5	6	8	8	9.5	10	10	12
Circumference (cm)	9.3	9.5	16	18.8	25	25.6	29.5	31.5	30.9	39.5

a. Graph the data. **b.** Find the equation of a trend line.
c. What does the slope of the equation mean?
d. Find the diameter of a cylinder with a circumference of 45 cm.

Population Growth

1790

1860

Today

■ More than 2 persons
per square mile

13. **Population** Use the data at the right.
   a. Graph the data for the male and female populations of the United States.
   b. Find the equation of a trend line.
   c. Use your equation to predict the number of females if the number of males were to increase to 150,000,000.
   d. **Critical Thinking** Would it be reasonable to predict the population in 2025 from these data? Explain.

14. **a.** **Open-Ended** Make a table of data for a linear function. Use a graphing calculator to find the equation of the line of best fit.
   b. What is the correlation coefficient for your linear data?

15. **Writing** What kind of trend line do you think data for the following comparison would be likely to show? Explain.
   temperature and the number of students absent from school

Estimated Population of the United States (thousands)

Year	Male	Female
1991	122,956	129,197
1992	124,424	130,606
1993	125,788	131,995
1994	127,049	133,278
1995	128,294	134,510
1996	129,504	135,724
1997	130,783	137,001
1998	132,030	138,218
1999	133,277	139,414
2000	138,054	143,368

SOURCE: U.S. Census Bureau. Go to
www.PHSchool.com for a data update.
Web Code: atg-9041

16. **Graphing Calculator** A school collected data on math and science grades of nine randomly selected students.

Student	1	2	3	4	5	6	7	8	9
Math	76	89	84	79	94	71	79	91	84
Science	82	94	89	89	94	84	68	89	84

a. Use a graphing calculator to find the equation of the line of best fit for the data.
b. **Critical Thinking** Should the equation for the line of best fit be used to predict grades? Explain.

17. **Graphing Calculator** Use a graphing calculator to find the equation of the line of best fit for the data below. Predict sales of greeting cards in the year 2010.

Greeting Card Sales

Year	1989	1990	1991	1992	1993	1994	1995	1996	1997	1998
Sales (billions)	$4.2	$4.6	$5.0	$5.3	$5.6	$5.9	$6.3	$6.8	$7.3	$7.5

SOURCE: Greeting Card Association

18. a. Data Collection Find two sets of data that you could display in a scatter plot, such as the number of boys and girls in each class in your school, or the population and the number of airports in some states. Then graph the data.
   b. Find the equation of a trend line.
   c. Use the equation to predict another value that could be on your scatter plot.
   d. What is the correlation coefficient?

19. Another way you can find a line of best fit is the *median-median method*. The graph below shows how this method works. The points in red indicate the original data.

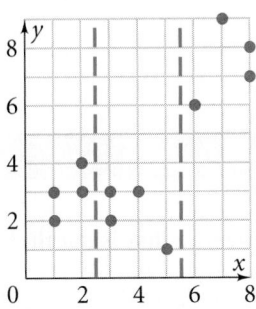

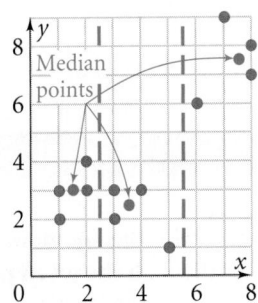

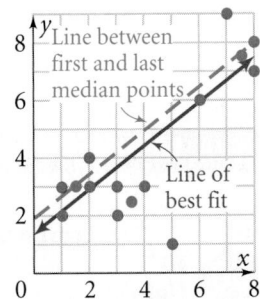

Divide the data into three groups of equal size.

Find and plot the median points, (*x*-median, *y*-median).

Find the line parallel to the line between the first and last median points and $\frac{1}{3}$ of the way to the middle median point.

   a. Estimate two coordinates on the purple line in the graph at the right above. Find the equation of the line of best fit.
    b. Graphing Calculator You can use a graphing calculator to find the line of best fit with the median-median method. Below are the coordinates of the points graphed in red. Use the **EDIT** feature of the **STAT** screen on your graphing calculator. Use the **Med-Med** feature to find a line of best fit.
   $(1, 2), (1, 3), (2, 3), (2, 4), (3, 2), (3, 3), (4, 3), (5, 1), (6, 6), (7, 9), (8, 8), (8, 7)$

Challenge

20. a. Make a scatter plot of the data below. Then find the equation of the line of best fit.

Car Stopping Distances

Speed (mi/h)	10	15	20	25	30	35	40	45
Stopping Distances (ft)	27	44	63	85	109	136	164	196

   b. Use your equation to predict the stopping distance at 90 mi/h.
   c. Critical Thinking The actual stopping distance at 90 mi/h is close to 584 ft. Why do you think this is not close to your prediction?

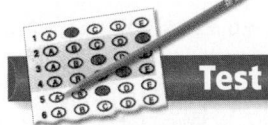
Test Prep

Multiple Choice

21. A horizontal line passes through $(5, -2)$. Which other point does it also pass through?
   A. $(5, 2)$ **B.** $(-5, -2)$ **C.** $(-5, 2)$ **D.** $(5, 0)$

22. Which of the following equations has a graph that contains the ordered pairs $(-3, 4)$ and $(1, -4)$?
   F. $x + 2y = 8$ **G.** $2x - y = 4$ **H.** $2x + y = -2$ **J.** $x - 2y = -6$

Extended Response

23. The table at the right shows the number of elderly in the United States from 1960 through 2000.
   a. Graph the data and draw a trend line.
   b. Write an equation for the trend line you drew.
   c. Predict the elderly population in the United States in 2005. Show your work.

U.S. Elderly Population

Year	Elderly (millions)
1960	16.560
1970	19.980
1980	25.550
1990	31.235
2000	34.709

SOURCE: *Statistical Abstract of the United States.*
Go to **www.PHSchool.com** for a data update.
Web Code: atg-9041

Mixed Review

GO for Help

Lesson 9-6

Write the equation for the line that is parallel to the given line and that passes through the given point.

24. $y = 5x + 1; (2, -3)$ **25.** $y = -x - 9; (0, 5)$ **26.** $2x + 3y = 9; (-1, 4)$

27. $y = -\frac{1}{2}x; (3, -4)$ **28.** $y = -2x + 3; (-2, -1)$ **29.** $y = \frac{2}{3}x + 7; (-1, 2)$

Lesson 7-4

Solve each inequality.

30. $1 + 5x + 1 > x + 9$ **31.** $7x + 3 < 2x + 28$ **32.** $4x + 4 > 2 + 2x$

33. $4x + 3 \le 2x - 7$ **34.** $-x + 5 < 3x - 1$ **35.** $2x > 7x - 3 - 4x$

✓ Checkpoint Quiz 2   Lessons 9-5 through 9-7

Write an equation for the line through the given point that has the given slope.

1. $(3, 4); m = -\frac{1}{4}$ **2.** $(0, -3); m = 18$ **3.** $(-7, -5); m = 0$

4. Write an equation for the line through the points $(2, -6)$ and $(-1, -4)$.

Write an equation of the line that is parallel to the given line and that passes through the given point.

5. $x + y = 3; (5, 4)$ **6.** $3x + 2y = 1; (-2, 6)$

Write an equation of the line that is perpendicular to the given line and that passes through the given point.

7. $y = -4x + 2; (0, 2)$ **8.** $y = \frac{2}{3}x + 6; (-6, 2)$

9. Find the equation for a trend line for the data at the right.

x	1	2	3	4	5	6	7
y	7	12	19	20	28	33	40

 10. Graphing Calculator Use a graphing calculator to find the equation for the line of best fit for the data at the right.

x	1	2	3	4	5	6	7
y	54	52	45	40	33	27	18

Activity Lab

Collecting Linear Data

Hands-On

FOR USE WITH LESSON 9-7

In this activity, you will release a ball from various heights and record the maximum height after its first bounce. Complete this activity over a hard surface. Measure all heights from the bottom of the ball.

ACTIVITY

Place one end of a meter stick on the floor and tape it to the wall. Tape a second meter stick to the wall starting with the top of the first meter stick.

1. **Data Collection** Drop the ball from 50 cm. Carefully record its maximum height after the first bounce. Repeat.

2. Copy and complete the table shown below. You may make additional measurements using different starting heights.

Initial Height	Maximum Height After First Bounce	
	Trial 1	Trial 2
50 cm	■	■
100 cm	■	■
150 cm	■	■
200 cm	■	■

3. Graph the data from both trials on the same coordinate plane.

4. **Critical Thinking** Why is it reasonable to use $(0, 0)$ as a data point?

5. Draw a trend line which includes $(0, 0)$.

6. **a. Predict** Use your line to predict the maximum height of the first bounce after the ball was dropped from 175 cm.
   b. From what height would you have to drop the ball for it to reach 2 meters after the first bounce?

7. Write an equation for your trend line.

EXERCISES

8. **Multiple Choice** The graph at the right shows the bounce data for a ball. Which equation best models the data?

   Ⓐ $y = 0.4x$ Ⓑ $y = 0.5x$
   Ⓒ $y = 0.6x$ Ⓓ $y = 0.7x$

9. Suppose students used several different types of balls and found that the slopes of the trend lines were not the same. What is the significance of the slope?

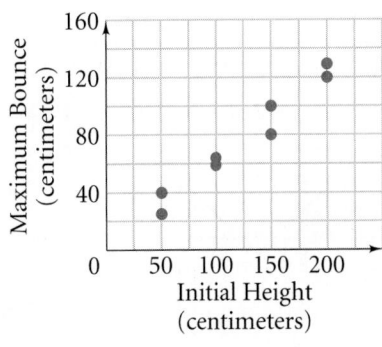

Activity Lab   Collecting Linear Data   **533**

Exploring Absolute Value Functions

FOR USE WITH LESSON 9-8

In Chapter 5, you solved absolute value equations. Here you will explore graphs of absolute value functions.

ACTIVITY

Graph the absolute value *parent function* $y = |x|$.

Press Y= . Select **abs(** by pressing
MATH ▶ 1. Complete the equation
by pressing X,T,θ,n and) .

To graph, press ZOOM 5
and then GRAPH .

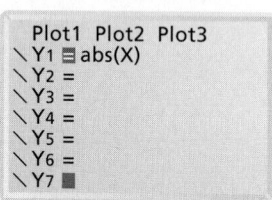

```
Plot1 Plot2 Plot3
\Y1 ▤abs(X)
\Y2 =
\Y3 =
\Y4 =
\Y5 =
\Y6 =
\Y7 ■
```

1. Graph the equations $y = |x| - 3$ and $y = |x| + 3$.
   a. The equation __?__ translates the parent graph $y = |x|$ __?__ units up.
   b. The equation __?__ translates the parent graph $y = |x|$ __?__ units down.

2. **Critical Thinking** Explain how the translations of $y = |x| + k$ as k changes are similar to translations of $y = mx + b$ as b changes.

3. Graph the equations $y = |x + 2|$ and $y = |x - 2|$. The first equation should appear as follows in the **Y=** screen.

```
Plot1 Plot2 Plot3
\Y1 ▤abs(X+2)
\Y2 =
\Y3 =
\Y4 =
\Y5 =
\Y6 =
\Y7 =
```

   a. The equation __?__ translates the parent graph __?__ units to the left.
   b. The equation __?__ translates the parent graph __?__ units to the right.

4. **Predict** Based on your results from questions 1 and 3, predict how the equation $y = |x - 2| + 3$ would translate the graph of $y = |x|$.

EXERCISES

5. Match each equation with the best choice for its graph.

   A. $y = |x + 6| - 2$ **B.** $y = |x - 6| - 2$ **C.** $y = |x + 6| + 2$

   I.   **II.**   **III.**

Graphing Absolute Value Equations

What You'll Learn

• To translate the graph of an absolute value equation

. . . And Why

To graph an absolute value equation quickly, as in Examples 2 and 4

✓ **Check Skills You'll Need**

Simplify each expression.

1. $|2 - 7|$ **2.** $|7 - 12|$ **3.** $|38 - 56|$ **4.** $|-24 + 12|$

Model each rule using a table of values.

5. $y = 6 - x$ **6.** $y = |x| + 1$ **7.** $y = |x + 1|$

GO for Help Lessons 5-1 and 9-3

🔊 **New Vocabulary** • absolute value equation • translation

---

1 Translating Graphs of Absolute Value Equations

Vocabulary Tip

The <u>absolute value</u> of a number is its distance from 0 on a number line.

A V-shaped graph that points upward or downward is the graph of an **absolute value equation.** In Lesson 5-3, you graphed absolute value equations by making tables of values.

In this lesson you will graph by translating the graph of $y = |x|$. A **translation** is a shift of a graph horizontally, vertically, or both. The result is a graph of the same shape and size, but in a different position.

1 EXAMPLE   Vertical Translations

Below are the graphs of $y = |x|$ and $y = |x| + 2$. Describe how the graphs are the same and how they are different.

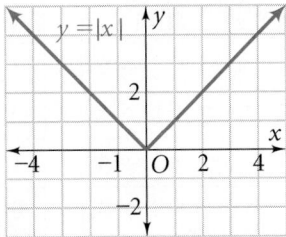 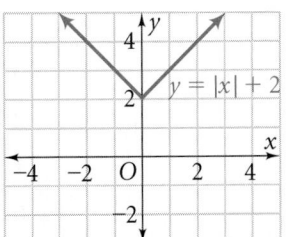

The graphs are the same shape. The y-intercept of the first graph is 0. The y-intercept of the second graph is 2.

✓ **Quick Check** ❶ Describe how each graph below is like $y = |x|$ and how it is different.

a. 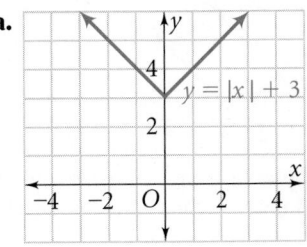   **b.**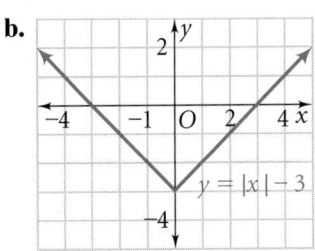

The graph of $y = |x| + k$ is a translation of $y = |x|$. Let k be a positive number. Then $y = |x| + k$ translates the graph of $y = |x|$ up k units, while $y = |x| - k$ translates the graph of $y = |x|$ down k units.

2 EXAMPLE Graphing a Vertical Translation

Graph $y = |x| - 1$.

Start with the graph of $y = |x|$. Translate the graph *down* 1 unit.

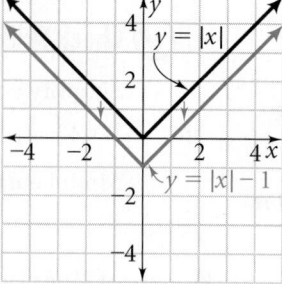

Moving this chess piece is a horizontal and vertical translation.

 **Quick Check** **2** Graph each function by translating $y = |x|$.
  a. $y = |x| + 4$ **b.** $y = |x| - 5$

You can write an equation to describe a vertical translation.

3 EXAMPLE Writing an Absolute Value Equation

Write an equation for each translation of $y = |x|$.
  a. 8 units down
    The equation is $y = |x| - 8$.
  b. 6 units up
    The equation is $y = |x| + 6$.

Quick Check **3** For each translation of $y = |x|$, write an equation.
  a. 2 units up   **b.** 5 units down

The following tables of values and graphs show what happens when you graph $y = |x - 3|$ and $y = |x + 3|$.

x	$y = |x|$	$y = |x - 3|$
-3	$|-3| = 3$	$|-3 - 3| = 6$
-2	$|-2| = 2$	$|-2 - 3| = 5$
-1	$|-1| = 1$	$|-1 - 3| = 4$
0	$|0| = 0$	$|0 - 3| = 3$
1	$|1| = 1$	$|1 - 3| = 2$
2	$|2| = 2$	$|2 - 3| = 1$
3	$|3| = 3$	$|3 - 3| = 0$

x	$y = |x|$	$y = |x + 3|$
-3	$|-3| = 3$	$|-3 + 3| = 0$
-2	$|-2| = 2$	$|-2 + 3| = 1$
-1	$|-1| = 1$	$|-1 + 3| = 2$
0	$|0| = 0$	$|0 + 3| = 3$
1	$|1| = 1$	$|1 + 3| = 4$
2	$|2| = 2$	$|2 + 3| = 5$
3	$|3| = 3$	$|3 + 3| = 6$

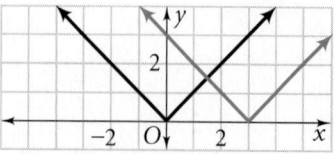

For the graph of $y = |x - 3|$, $y = |x|$ is translated 3 units to the right.

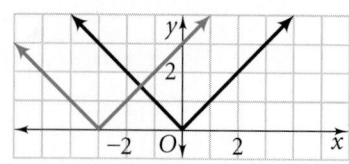

For the graph of $y = |x + 3|$, $y = |x|$ is translated 3 units to the left.

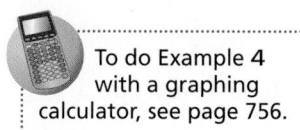

To do Example 4 with a graphing calculator, see page 756.

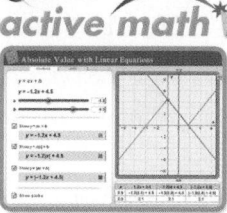

For: Absolute Value Activity
Use: Interactive Textbook, 6-8

So for a positive number h, $y = |x + h|$ translates the graph of $y = |x|$ by h units to the left, and $y = |x - h|$ translates the graph of $y = |x|$ by h units to the right.

4 EXAMPLE Graphing a Horizontal Translation

Graph each equation by translating $y = |x|$.
a. $y = |x + 2|$
b. $y = |x - 2|$

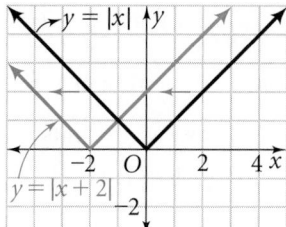
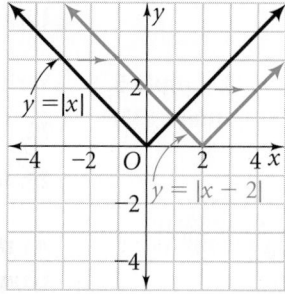

✓ **Quick Check** **4** Graph each equation by translating $y = |x|$.
a. $y = |x - 4|$
b. $y = |x + 1|$

If you know the number of units that a function is to be translated and the direction of the translation, you can write an equation to describe the horizontal translation.

5 EXAMPLE Writing an Absolute Value Equation

Write an equation for each translation.
a. $y = |x|$, 8 units left
The equation is $y = |x + 8|$.
b. $y = |x|$, 6 units right
The equation is $y = |x - 6|$.

✓ **Quick Check** **5** Write an equation for each translation of $y = |x|$.
a. 5 units right
b. 7 units left

EXERCISES

For more exercises, see *Extra Skill and Word Problem Practice*.

Practice and Problem Solving

A Practice by Example

Example 1
(page 535)

Describe how each graph is like the graph of $y = |x|$ and how it is different.

1.

2.

3.

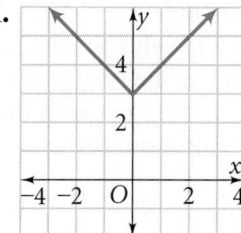

Example 2
(page 536)

Graph each function by translating $y = |x|$.

4. $y = |x| + 2$
5. $y = |x| - 4$
6. $y = |x| + 8$

7. $y = |x| + 1$
8. $y = |x| - 6$
9. $y = |x| - 2.5$

Example 3
(page 536)

Write an equation for each translation of $y = |x|$.

10. 9 units up   **11.** 6 units down   **12.** 0.25 units up

13. $\frac{5}{2}$ units up   **14.** 5.90 units up   **15.** 1 unit down

Example 4
(page 537)

Graph each function by translating $y = |x|$.

16. $y = |x - 3|$ **17.** $y = |x + 3|$ **18.** $y = |x - 1|$

19. $y = |x + 5|$ **20.** $y = |x - 7|$ **21.** $y = |x + 2.5|$

Example 5
(page 537)

Write an equation for each translation of $y = |x|$.

22. left 9 units   **23.** right 9 units   **24.** right $\frac{5}{2}$ units

25. left $\frac{3}{2}$ units   **26.** left 0.5 unit   **27.** right 8.2 units

 Apply Your Skills

At the right is the graph of $y = -|x|$.
Graph each function by translating $y = -|x|$.

28. $y = -|x| + 3$ **29.** $y = -|x| - 3$

30. $y = -|x + 3|$ **31.** $y = -|x - 3|$

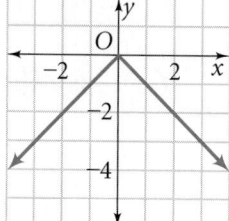

Write an equation for each translation of $y = -|x|$.

32. 2 units up   **33.** 2.25 units left

34. $\frac{3}{2}$ units down   **35.** 4 units right

Problem Solving Hint

For Exercises 28–31, you can check your work by substituting ordered pairs from the graph into the corresponding equation.

36. The graph at the right shows a translation of $y = |x|$ where there is both a vertical and a horizontal change. Which equation below is an equation for this graph?

    A. $y = |x + 2| - 1$ **B.** $y = |x - 2| + 1$

    C. $y = |x - 2| - 1$ **D.** $y = |x + 2| + 1$

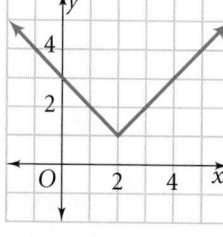

Graph each translation of $y = |x|$.

Sample For $y = |x + 3| - 2$, add 3 indicates the translation of the graph 3 units left. Subtract 2 indicates the translation of the graph 2 units down.

37. $y = |x - 1| + 2$ **38.** $y = |x + 2| - 1$

39. $y = |x - 3| - 4$ **40.** $y = |x + 3| + 4$

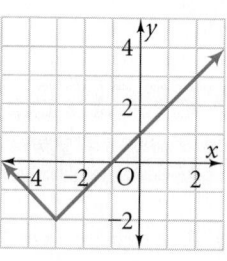

Homework Video Tutor
Visit: PHSchool.com
Web Code: ate-0608

41. a. Graph $y = |x - 2| + 3$. (*Hint:* Read the sample above for Exercises 37–40.)

    b. The vertex of an absolute value function is the point at which the function changes direction. What is the vertex of $y = |x - 2| + 3$?

    c. What relationship do you see between the vertex and the equation?

    d. Writing Explain how you would graph any equation of the form $y = |x - a| + b$.

 Challenge

42. a. Graph $y = |2x|$ by making a table of values.

    b. Translate $y = |2x|$ to graph $y = |2x| + 3$.

    c. Translate $y = |2x|$ to graph $y = |2(x - 1)|$.

    d. Translate $y = |2x|$ to graph $y = |2(x - 1)| + 3$.

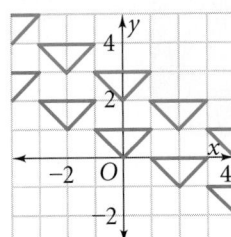

43. Programming A computer programmer is plotting the triangles at the left. The pattern extends infinitely in both directions. She will use two equations for each triangle: some translation of $y = |x|$ and $y = c$ (c is a constant).

a. What equations will the programmer use to plot the red triangle with vertices at $(0, 0), (-1, 1)$, and $(1, 1)$?

b. What are the least and greatest values in the domain for the equations the programmer would use to plot the triangle with vertices $(0, 0), (-1, 1)$ and $(1, 1)$?

c. What linear equation can the programmer use to find the lowest vertex on each red triangle? Each blue triangle?

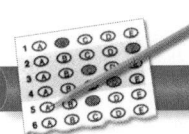

Test Prep

Multiple Choice

44. Which equation translates $y = |x|$ by 8 units to the left?

　A. $y = |x| + 8$ 　　**B.** $y = |x + 8|$ 　　**C.** $y = |x| - 8$ 　　**D.** $y = |x - 8|$

45. What is the lowest point of the graph of $y = |x - 9|$?

　F. $(0, -9)$ 　　**G.** $(-9, 0)$ 　　**H.** $(9, 0)$ 　　**J.** $(0, 9)$

46. What point do the graphs of $y = |x - 3|$ and $y = |x + 5|$ have in common?

　A. $(-1, 4)$ 　　**B.** $(1, 4)$ 　　**C.** $(4, 1)$ 　　**D.** $(4, -1)$

47. The graph of which equation contains the point $(3, 5)$?

　F. $y = |x + 3| + 5$ 　　　　　　**G.** $y = |x - 3| + 5$
　H. $y = |x + 3| - 5$ 　　　　　　**J.** $y = |x - 3| - 5$

Extended Response

48. a. Graph the equation $y = |x| - 4$ on a coordinate plane.

b. Graph the equation $y = |x| + 4$ on the same coordinate plane.

c. Describe the relationship of the ordered pairs in the graphs of $y = |x| - 4$ to the graph of $y = |x| + 4$.

Mixed Review

Lesson 9-7 **Graphing Calculator** **The data below follow a linear pattern. Write an equation for a trend line or use a graphing calculator to find the equation of the line of best fit.**

49.

Year	Sales
1988	$27,000
1989	$32,000
1990	$37,000
1991	$42,000
1992	$47,000
1993	$52,000
1994	$57,000

50.

Year	Sales
1990	$47,000
1991	$51,000
1992	$55,000
1993	$59,000
1994	$63,000
1995	$67,000
1996	$71,000

Lesson 5-1 **Add the matrices.**

51. $\begin{bmatrix} 5 & 3 \\ 1 & 2 \end{bmatrix} + \begin{bmatrix} 7 & 2 \\ 1 & 4 \end{bmatrix}$ 　**52.** $\begin{bmatrix} -3 & 2 \\ -7 & 4 \end{bmatrix} + \begin{bmatrix} 7 & -1 \\ 8 & 0 \end{bmatrix}$ 　**53.** $\begin{bmatrix} -5.6 & 9.8 \\ -4.2 & 3.2 \end{bmatrix} + \begin{bmatrix} 8.1 & 4.2 \\ 2.2 & 7.5 \end{bmatrix}$

For some problems, it may help to draw a diagram of the given information if one is not provided.

1 EXAMPLE

The points R, S, and T lie on a line in order such that the length of $\overline{ST}$ is twice the length of $\overline{RS}$. The length of $\overline{RT}$ is 5 cm more than the length of $\overline{ST}$. Find the length of $\overline{RS}$ and $\overline{ST}$.

Draw $\overline{RT}$. Since $\overline{ST}$ is twice as long as $\overline{RS}$, let $RS = x$ and $ST = 2x$. Since the length of $\overline{RT}$ is 5 cm more than the length of $\overline{ST}$, let $RT = 5 + 2x$.

You can see from your diagram that $2x + x = 5 + 2x$. Solve this equation, and you find that $x = 5$. The length of $\overline{RS}$ is 5 cm and the length of $\overline{ST}$ is 10 cm.

2 EXAMPLE

The points $A(-8, 1)$, $B(-2, 7)$ and $C(4, -11)$ are the vertices of a triangle. Is Triangle ABC a right triangle?

Two lines form a right angle if the product of their slopes is -1.

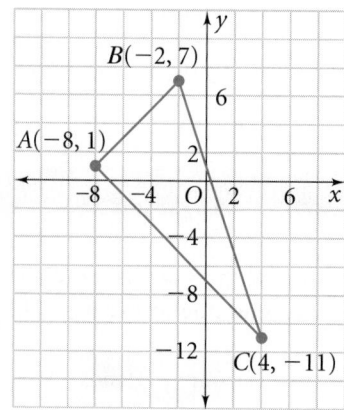

When you draw a diagram, you can see that the right angle cannot be at point C. You need to see if the product of the slopes of $\overline{AC}$ and $\overline{AB}$ or of $\overline{BC}$ and $\overline{AB}$ is -1. The slope of $\overline{AB}$ is 1, and the slope of $\overline{AC}$ is -1. The product of 1 and -1 is -1. So Triangle ABC is a right triangle.

EXERCISES

Draw a diagram to solve each exercise.

1. The points $L(4, 0)$, $M(10, 0)$, and $N(7, 5)$ form $\triangle LMN$. What is the sum of the slopes of the three sides of the triangle?

2. Three towns A, B, and C lie on a straight road in that order. The distance from B to C is 6 miles more than twice the distance from A to B. The distance from A to C is 2 miles more than four times the distance from A to B. What is the distance from A to B?

3. $P(1, 3)$ and $R(5, 5)$ are the endpoints of a diagonal of the rectangle $PQRS$. Point Q has the same x-coordinate as point P. Which sides of the rectangle are parallel to the x-axis? To the y-axis? What is the perimeter of the rectangle?

Chapter Review

Vocabulary Review

🔊 **absolute value equation** (p. 535)
correlation coefficient (p. 527)
line of best fit (p. 527)
linear equation (p. 493)
linear function (p. 493)
linear parent function (p. 493)
negative reciprocal (p. 520)

parallel lines (p. 519)
parent function (p. 493)
perpendicular lines (p. 520)
point-slope form (p. 512)
rate of change (p. 484)
slope (p. 486)

slope-intercept form (p. 494)
standard form of a
   linear equation (p. 506)
translation (p. 535)
x-intercept (p. 506)
y-intercept (p. 493)

Go Online
PHSchool.com

For: Vocabulary quiz
Web Code: atj-0651

Choose the vocabulary term that correctly completes the sentence.

1. Two lines are __?__ if the product of their slopes is -1.

2. Two lines in the same plane that never intersect are __?__.

3. A(n) __?__ shifts a graph horizontally, vertically, or both.

4. The ratio of the vertical change to the horizontal change is called the __?__.

5. The y-coordinate of the point at which the graph of a line crosses the vertical axis is called the __?__.

Skills and Concepts

9-1 Objectives

▼ To find rates of change from tables and graphs (p. 484)

▼ To find slope (p. 486)

Rate of change allows you to look at how two quantities change relative to each other.

$$\text{rate of change} = \frac{\text{change in the dependent variable}}{\text{change in the independent variable}}$$

Slope is the ratio of the vertical change to the horizontal change.

$$\text{slope} = \frac{\text{vertical change}}{\text{horizontal change}} = \frac{\text{rise}}{\text{run}}$$

Find the rate of change for each situation.

6. A kitten grows from 5 oz at birth to 3 lb 5 oz at 6 months. (*Hint:* 1 lb $=$ 16 oz)

7. A plant measures 0.5 in. at the end of Week 1 and 14 in. at the end of Week 5.

Find each rate of change. Explain what *rate of change* means in each situation.

8.
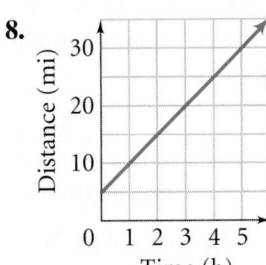

9.
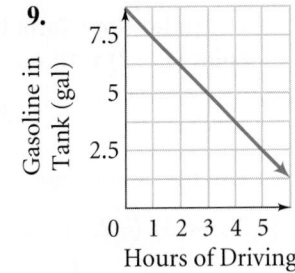

10.
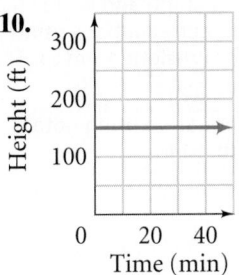

Find the slope of the line that passes through each pair of points.

11. $(3, -2)$ and $(-5, -4)$ **12.** $(4.5, -1)$ and $(4.5, 2.6)$ **13.** $(2, 5)$ and $(-5, -2)$

9-2 and 9-3 Objectives

▼ To write linear equations in slope-intercept form (p. 493)

▼ To graph linear equations (p. 495)

▼ To interpret linear graphs (p. 500)

The graph of a **linear equation** is a line. The **x-intercept** of a line is the x-coordinate of the point where the line crosses the x-axis, and the **y-intercept** is the y-coordinate of the point where the line crosses the y-axis.

The **slope-intercept form of a linear equation** is $y = mx + b$, where m is the slope and b is the y-intercept.

Write an equation of a line with the given slope and y-intercept. Then graph the equation.

14. $m = 0, b = -3$ **15.** $m = -7, b = \frac{1}{2}$ **16.** $m = \frac{2}{5}, b = 0$

Write the slope-intercept form of the equation for each line.

17. 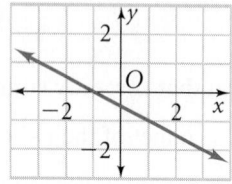   **18.**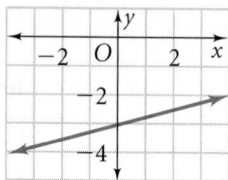

 19. Earnings A job at a retail store pays $75 each week plus 25% commission on total weekly sales.
   a. Write an equation for the total weekly pay p for total weekly sales s.
   b. Use p as the vertical axis and s as the horizontal axis. Graph your equation.
   c. What is the total weekly pay if total weekly sales are $800?
   d. What is the p intercept? What does it mean in this situation?

9-4 Objectives

▼ To graph equations using intercepts (p. 506)

▼ To write equations in standard form (p. 508)

The **standard form of a linear equation** is $Ax + By = C$, where $A, B,$ and C are real numbers, and A and B are not both zero.

Find the x- and y-intercepts. Then graph each equation.

20. $5x + 2y = 10$ **21.** $6.5x - 4y = 52$ **22.** $x + 3y = -1$

Write each equation in standard form.

23. $y = \frac{3}{5}x + 7$ **24.** $y = -\frac{1}{3}x + 2$ **25.** $y = \frac{4}{3}x - 5$

9-5 Objectives

▼ To graph and write linear equations using point-slope form (p. 512)

▼ To write a linear equation using data (p. 514)

The **point-slope form of a linear equation** is $y - y_1 = m(x - x_1)$, which passes through the point (x_1, y_1) and has slope m.

Use point-slope form to write an equation of a line that passes through the point $(1, -2)$ with slope m.

26. $m = 2$ **27.** $m = \frac{3}{4}$ **28.** $m = -3$ **29.** $m = 0$

Use the point-slope form to write an equation of a line through the given points.

30. $(4, 3), (-2, 1)$ **31.** $(5, -4), (0, 2)$ **32.** $(-1, 0), (-3, -1)$

542 Chapter 9 Chapter Review

▼ To determine whether lines are parallel (p. 519)

▼ To determine whether lines are perpendicular (p. 520)

Parallel lines are lines in the same plane that never intersect. Nonvertical lines are parallel if they have the same slope. Two lines are **perpendicular lines** if they intersect to form right angles. For perpendicular lines that are not horizontal and vertical, the product of their slopes is -1.

Write an equation for each of the following conditions.

33. parallel to $y = 5x - 2$, through $(2, -1)$

34. perpendicular to $y = -3x + 7$, through $(3, 5)$

35. parallel to $y = 9x$, through $(0, -5)$

36. perpendicular to $y = 8x - 1$, through $(4, 10)$

9-7 Objectives

▼ To write an equation for a trend line and use it to make predictions (p. 526)

▼ To write the equation for a line of best fit and use it to make predictions (p. 527)

You can find an equation to model the relationship between two sets of data in a scatter plot by sketching a trend line and using two points on the line to write an equation.

The **line of best fit** of a scatter plot is the most accurate trend line for the data. You can find the equation of a line of best fit using a graphing calculator. The **correlation coefficient** tells how well the equation of the line of best fit models the data.

37. Write an equation of a reasonable trend line for the scatter plot.

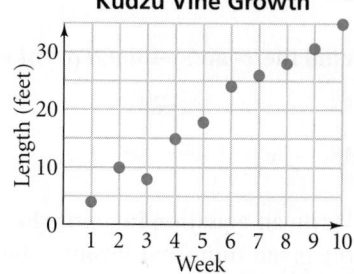

Kudzu Vine Growth

 38. Graphing Calculator The table shows the average consumption of poultry in the United States in pounds per person from 1970 to 2000.
  a. Find the equation of a trend line or use a graphing calculator to find the equation of the line of best fit.
  b. Use your equation to **predict** how much poultry the average person will eat in 2010.

Years	1970	1975	1980	1985	1990	1995	2000
Pounds	33.8	32.9	40.8	45.5	56.3	62.9	68.4

9-8 Objective

▼ To translate the graph of an absolute value equation (p. 535)

The graph of an **absolute value equation** is a V-shaped graph that points upward or downward.

A **translation** shifts a graph either vertically, horizontally, or both. It results in a graph of the same shape and size in a different position.

Graph each equation by translating $y = |x|$.

39. $y = |x - 2|$ **40.** $y = |x| - 3$

Go Online
PHSchool.com
For: Chapter Test
Web Code: ata-0652

Tell whether each statement is *true* or *false*. Explain.

1. A rate of change must be positive.

2. The rate of change for a vertical line is 0.

Find the slope of the line that passes through each pair of points.

3. $(4, 3), (3, 8)$

4. $(-2, 1), (6, -1)$

Graph each equation.

5. $x - 4y = 8$

6. $2x + 4y = -4$

7. $y = \frac{1}{3}x + 2$

8. $y - 1 = -3(x - 3)$

Write each equation in slope-intercept form.

9. $-7y = 8x - 3$

10. $x - 3y = -18$

11. $5x + 4y = 100$

12. $9x = 2y + 13$

Find the *x*- and *y*-intercepts of each line.

13. $3x + 4y = -24$

14. $-6x + 2y = -8$

15. $-5x + 10y = 60$

16. $x + y = 1$

Write an equation in point-slope form for the line with the given slope and through the given point.

17. slope $= \frac{8}{3}, (-2, -7)$

18. slope $= 3, (4, -8)$

19. slope $= \frac{-1}{2}, (0, 3)$

20. slope $= -5, (9, 0)$

Write an equation in point-slope form for the line through the given points.

21. $(4, 9), (-2, -6)$

22. $(-1, 0), (3, 10)$

23. $(5, -8), (-9, -8)$

24. $(0, 7), (1, 5)$

25. Which of the following lines is *not* perpendicular to $y = -2.5x + 13$?
   A. $y = 0.4x - 7$
   B. $-2x + 5y = 8$
   C. $y = \frac{2}{5}x + 4$
   D. $2y = 5x + 1.5$

Write an equation in slope-intercept form for a line that passes through the given point and is parallel to the given line.

26. $y = 5x; (2, -1)$

27. $y = 5; (-3, 6)$

Write an equation in slope-intercept form for a line that passes through the given point and that is perpendicular to the given line.

28. $y = -2x; (4, 0)$

29. $x = -7; (0, 2)$

30. Open-Ended Write the equation of a line parallel to $y = 0.5x - 10$.

31. You start a pet-washing service. You spend $30 on supplies. You plan to charge $5 to wash each pet.
   a. Write an equation to relate your profit y to the number of pets x you wash.
   b. Graph the equation. What are the x- and y-intercepts?

Write an equation for each translation of $y = |x|$.

32. 2 units down

33. right $\frac{3}{4}$ unit

Graph each function by translating $y = |x|$.

34. $y = |x - 4|$

35. $y = |x| + 2$

Use the data below for Exercises 36 and 37.

Local Governments in the United States (thousands)

Year	Municipalities	School Districts
1967	18.0	21.8
1972	18.5	15.8
1977	18.9	15.2
1982	19.1	14.9
1987	19.2	14.7
1992	19.3	14.4
1997	19.4	13.7

SOURCE: *Statistical Abstract of the United States.*
Go to **www.PHSchool.com** for a data update.
Web Code: atg-2041

36. a. Graphing Calculator Find an equation of a trend line or the line of best fit for the number of municipalities and the year.
   b. Predict the number of municipalities in 2010.

37. a. Graphing Calculator Find the equation of a trend line or the line of best fit for the number of school districts and the year.
   b. Predict the number of school districts in the year 2010.

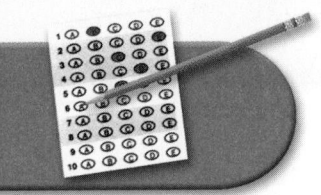
Standardized Test Prep

Multiple Choice

For Exercises 1–11, choose the correct letter.

1. Suppose you earn $74.25 for working 9 hours. How much will you earn for working 15 hours?
   - Ⓐ $120
   - Ⓑ $123.75
   - Ⓒ $124.50
   - Ⓓ $127.25

2. Which is *not* a solution of $5x - 4 < 12$?
   - Ⓕ -2
   - Ⓖ 0
   - Ⓗ 3
   - Ⓙ 4

3. A line perpendicular to $y = 3x - 2$ passes through the point (0, 6). Which other point lies on the line?
   - Ⓐ (9, 3)
   - Ⓑ (−9, 3)
   - Ⓒ (9, −3)
   - Ⓓ (−9, −3)

4. If *a*, *b*, and *c* are three consecutive positive integers, which of the following is true?
   - **I.** $a + c < 2b$
   - **II.** $a + b < c$
   - **III.** $a + c > 2b$
   - **IV.** $b + c > a$
   - Ⓕ I only
   - Ⓖ IV only
   - Ⓗ I and II
   - Ⓙ III and IV

5. A scatter plot shows a positive correlation. Which of the following could be an equation of the line of best fit?
   - Ⓐ $y = -5x + 1$
   - Ⓑ $2x + 3y = 6$
   - Ⓒ $x = 16$
   - Ⓓ $y = 2x - 1$

6. Which of the following is the solution of $6(4x - 3) = -54$?
   - Ⓕ -3
   - Ⓖ -1.5
   - Ⓗ 1.5
   - Ⓙ 3

7. Find $f(-2)$ when $f(x) = -3x + 4$.
   - Ⓐ -10
   - Ⓑ -2
   - Ⓒ 2
   - Ⓓ 10

8. Mariko runs 800 ft in one minute. What is her approximate speed in miles per hour? (*Hint:* 5280 ft = 1 mi)
   - Ⓕ 6
   - Ⓖ 8
   - Ⓗ 9
   - Ⓙ 12

9. Which of the following formulas correctly represent(s) the perimeter of the rectangle?
   - **I.** $p = c + c + d + d$
   - **II.** $p = cd$
   - **III.** $p = 2c + 2d$

   (rectangle with height labeled c and width labeled d)

   - Ⓐ I and III
   - Ⓑ II and III
   - Ⓒ I only
   - Ⓓ II only

10. A local club has 15 girls and 21 boys who are members. A representative from the club is randomly selected to meet with the town mayor. To the nearest percent, what is the probability that the representative is a girl?
    - Ⓕ 40%
    - Ⓖ 42%
    - Ⓗ 58%
    - Ⓙ 71%

11. Which situation is best modeled by the graph shown below?
    - Ⓐ the amount of fuel remaining in a plane as it flies
    - Ⓑ the cost of buying blank DVDs
    - Ⓒ the amount of money remaining in a bank account after monthly withdrawals
    - Ⓓ the cost of buying hamburger meat in the supermarket

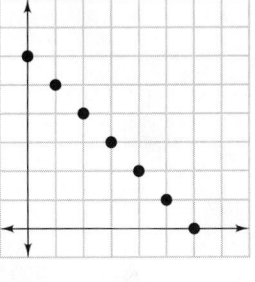

Gridded Response

Find each answer.

12. A car rental company charges $19.95 per day plus $.15 per mile. Calculate the cost in dollars to travel 250 miles over a 2-day period.

13. The ratio of crocus bulbs to tulip bulbs at a nursery is 5 to 2. The nursery has 175 crocus bulbs. How many crocus and tulip bulbs does the nursery have altogether?

14. A train moving at a constant speed travels 260 miles in 5 hours. At this rate, how many miles does the train travel in 9 hours?

Short Response

Show all of your work.

15. Write an equation in slope-intercept form of the line through (2, −1) and (3, 4).

16. Write an equation in slope-intercept form of the line through (2, −3) that is perpendicular to the line $y = \frac{2}{5}x - \frac{7}{8}$.

17. Solve $-3 \le 2x + 1 < 7$. Graph the solutions.

Activity Lab

Mathematically Inclined

Measuring Force Although there are more than 80 pyramids in Egypt, the most famous are the three at Giza, near Cairo. Archaeologists think that the ancient Egyptians used ramps, either similar to the one below, or in a spiral around the perimeter of the pyramid, to lift the stone blocks into place. Moving heavy objects up a ramp requires a certain amount of effort, or force. The heavier the object, the more force is required.

Made of mud bricks, the ramp grew in height as layers were added to the pyramid.

Stone blocks were dragged on sleds with wooden rollers underneath.

Solidly Built

The Great Pyramid, around the Pharaoh's Chamber, is almost entirely solid. It contains more than 2,300,000 blocks, or 90 million ft^3 of stone. The same volume of brick and stone would build 40 Empire State Buildings.

Activity

Materials: paper and pencil, yardstick, wooden board at least 30 in. long, toy truck with a rubber band attached to the front axle

a. Raise one end of the plank to a height of 10 in. Hold the rubber band and pull the truck up the ramp. When your hand reaches the top, stop pulling, keeping the rubber band stretched. Hold the truck still while your partner records the height of the ramp (x) and the length of the rubber band (y).

b. **Data Collection** Raise the end of the ramp in 2-in. increments. Repeat part (a) until you have at least 10 (x, y) pairs of data. Record your data.

c. Graph your data and draw a line of best fit. Determine the equation of the line.

d. **Writing** The variable y represents the force required to move the toy truck. How does the height of the plank affect the force required?

rubber band

y

toy truck

x

wooden board

The Pharaoh's Chamber lies almost in the center of the pyramid.

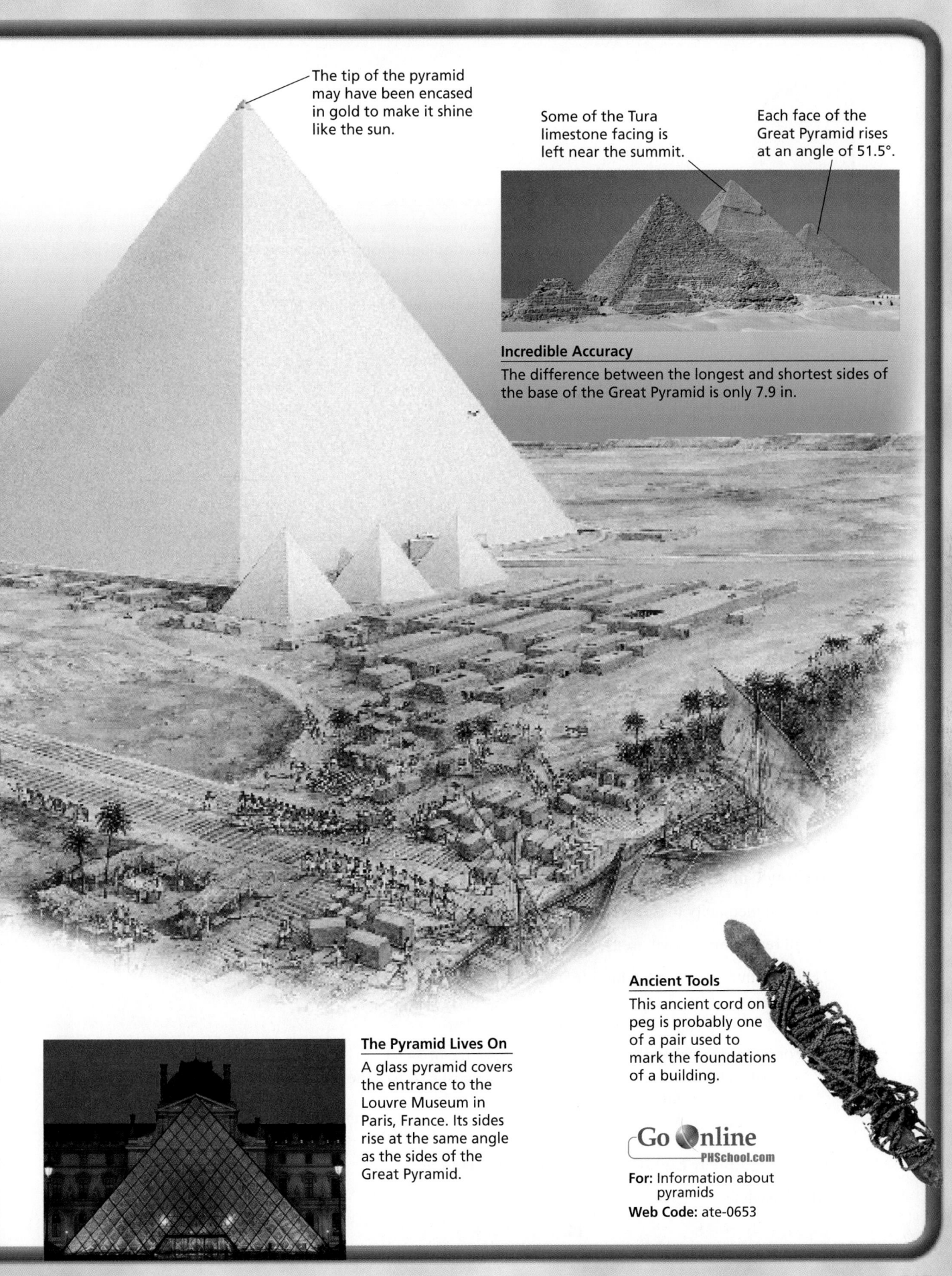

The tip of the pyramid may have been encased in gold to make it shine like the sun.

Some of the Tura limestone facing is left near the summit.

Each face of the Great Pyramid rises at an angle of 51.5°.

Incredible Accuracy

The difference between the longest and shortest sides of the base of the Great Pyramid is only 7.9 in.

Ancient Tools

This ancient cord on a peg is probably one of a pair used to mark the foundations of a building.

The Pyramid Lives On

A glass pyramid covers the entrance to the Louvre Museum in Paris, France. Its sides rise at the same angle as the sides of the Great Pyramid.

Go Online
PHSchool.com

For: Information about pyramids
Web Code: ate-0653

547

What You've Learned

- In Chapter 4, you solved multi-step equations, employing the Distributive Property and the properties of equality.

- In Chapter 7, you graphed one-variable inequalities and interpreted their solutions.

- In Chapters 8 and 9, you graphed linear equations and used them to model real-world situations.

 **Check Your Readiness** **for Help** to the Lesson in green.

Solving Equations (Lesson 6-3)

Solve each equation. If the equation is an identity, write *identity*. If it has no solution, write *no solution*.

1. $3(2 - 2x) = -6(x - 1)$ **2.** $3m + 1 = -m + 5$ **3.** $4x - 1 = 3(x + 1) + x$

4. $\frac{1}{2}(6x - 4) = 4 + x$ **5.** $5x = 2 - (x - 7)$ **6.** $x + 5 = x - 5$

Solving for a Variable (Review page 316)

Solve for y in terms of x.

7. $3x - 2y = -2$ **8.** $10 = x + 5y$ **9.** $2y = -2x - 8$

Writing Compound Inequalities (Lesson 7-5)

Write an inequality that represents each situation. Graph the solutions.

10. all real numbers that are between -10 and 3

11. Discounts are given to children under 12 and seniors over 60.

Writing a Function Rule (Lesson 8-4)

12. For every $35 ticket, the box office charges a fee of $4.50.
   a. Write a function rule that relates the total cost $C(t)$ to t, the number of tickets.
   b. What is the total cost for 3 tickets?
   c. How many tickets were purchased if the total cost was $237?

Graphing Linear Equations (Lessons 9-2, 9-4, and 9-5)

Graph each line.

13. $2x + 4y = -8$ **14.** $y = -\frac{2}{3}x + 3$ **15.** $2x = y - 4$

Systems of Equations and Inequalities

🔊 **Key Vocabulary**

- elimination method (p. 563)
- infinitely many solutions (p. 552)
- linear inequality (p. 581)
- no solution (p. 552)
- solution of a system of linear equations (p. 550)
- solution of a system of linear inequalities (p. 587)
- solutions of an inequality (p. 581)
- substitution method (p. 558)
- system of linear equations (p. 550)
- system of linear inequalities (p. 587)

What You'll Learn Next

- In this chapter, you will extend your ability to solve equations to include solving a system of two equations with two variables.

- You will learn methods of solving a linear system, including graphing, substitution, and elimination, and how to determine which method is best for a given situation.

Data Analysis

Activity Lab You will design and conduct a survey, on pages 602–603.

549

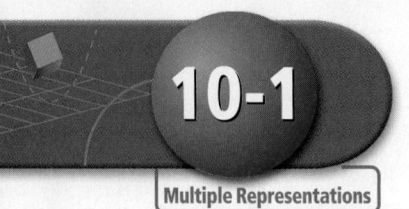

Solving Systems by Graphing

What You'll Learn

- To solve systems by graphing
- To analyze special types of systems

. . . And Why

To use graphs to compare growth of plants, as in Example 2

✓ **Check Skills You'll Need**

GO for Help   Lessons 6-3 and 9-2

Solve each equation.

1. $2n + 3 = 5n - 2$ **2.** $8 - 4z = 2z - 13$ **3.** $8q - 12 = 3q + 23$

Graph each pair of equations on the same coordinate plane.

4. $y = 3x - 6$
    $y = -x + 2$

5. $y = 6x + 1$
    $y = 6x - 4$

6. $y = 2x - 5$
    $6x - 3y = 15$

7. $y = x + 5$
    $y = -3x + 5$

🔊 **New Vocabulary**   • system of linear equations   • solution of a system of linear equations   • no solution   • infinitely many solutions

---

1   Solving Systems by Graphing

Two or more linear equations together form a **system of linear equations.** One way to solve a system of linear equations is by graphing each equation. Look for any point common to all the lines. Any ordered pair in a system that makes *all* the equations true is a **solution of the system of linear equations.**

1 EXAMPLE   Solving a System of Equations

Solve by graphing. $y = 2x - 3$
                $y = x - 1$

Graph both equations on the same coordinate plane.

$y = 2x - 3$ The slope is 2. The y-intercept is -3.
$y = x - 1$ The slope is 1. The y-intercept is -1.

Find the point of intersection.

The lines intersect at $(2, 1)$, so $(2, 1)$ is the solution of the system.

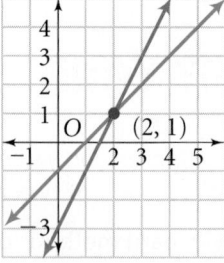

Check   See if $(2, 1)$ makes both equations true.

$y = 2x - 3$ $y = x - 1$
$1 \overset{?}{=} 2(2) - 3$ ←**Substitute (2, 1)**→ $1 \overset{?}{=} 2 - 1$
               for (x, y). $1 = 1$ ✓
$1 \overset{?}{=} 4 - 3$
$1 = 1$ ✓

✓ **Quick Check**   **1** Solve by graphing. Check your solution.

   a. $y = x + 5$
      $y = -4x$

   b. $y = -\frac{1}{2}x + 2$
      $y = -3x - 3$

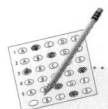

2 EXAMPLE Real-World Connection

Multiple Choice Suppose you are testing two fertilizers on bamboo plants A and B, which are growing under identical conditions. Plant A is 6 cm tall and growing at a rate of 4 cm/day. Plant B is 10 cm tall and growing at a rate of 2 cm/day. Which system of equations models the height of each plant $H(d)$ as a function of days d?

Ⓐ $H(d) = 6d + 4$
     $H(d) = 10d + 2$

Ⓑ $H(d) = 4d + 6$
     $H(d) = 10d + 2$

Ⓒ $H(d) = 6d + 4$
     $H(d) = 2d + 10$

Ⓓ $H(d) = 4d + 6$
     $H(d) = 2d + 10$

Relate   plant height   is   initial height   plus   daily growth

Write   Plant A: $H(d)$ =   6   + $4d$

          Plant B: $H(d)$ =   10   + $2d$

The system is $H(d) = 4d + 6$
               $H(d) = 2d + 10$.

● So, D is the correct answer.

✓ Quick Check   ❷ You are testing two fertilizers on bamboo plants C and D. Plant C is 5 cm tall and growing at a rate of 3 cm/day. Plant D is 1 cm tall and growing at a rate of 4 cm/day. Write a system of equations that models the height $H(d)$ of each plant as a function of days d.

3 EXAMPLE Interpreting Solutions

The system below models the heights of the bamboo plants in Example 2. Find the solution of the system by graphing. What does the solution mean in terms of the original situation?

Part 1 Find the solution by graphing.

$H(d) = 4d + 6$ **The slope is 4. The *y*-intercept is 6.**
$H(d) = 2d + 10$ **The slope is 2. The *y*-intercept is 10.**

Graph the equations.

$H(d) = 4d + 6$
$H(d) = 2d + 10$

The lines intersect at (2, 14).

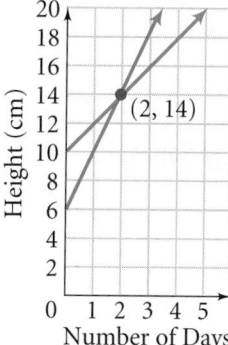

Part 2 Interpret the solution.

After 2 days, both plants will be the same height, 14 cm tall.

✓ Quick Check   ❸ Two friends are walking around a quarter-mile track. One person has completed six laps before the second one starts. The system below models the distance $d(t)$ in miles each walker covers as a function of time t in hours.

$$d(t) = 3t + 1.5 \qquad d(t) = 4t$$

a. Find the solution of the system by graphing. Use units of 0.5 on your graph.

b. What does the solution mean in terms of the original situation?

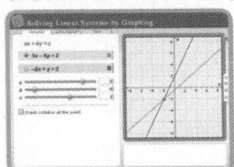

For: Linear System Activity
Use: Interactive Textbook, 10-1

When two lines are parallel, there are no points of intersection. So a system of linear equations has **no solution** when the graphs of the equations are parallel.

4 EXAMPLE Systems With No Solution

Solve by graphing. $y = -2x + 1$
                      $y = -2x - 1$

Graph both equations on the same coordinate plane.

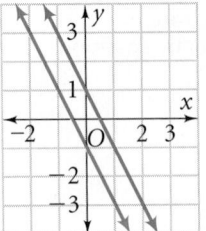

$y = -2x + 1$ **The slope is −2. The y-intercept is 1.**
$y = -2x - 1$ **The slope is −2. The y-intercept is −1.**

● The lines are parallel. There is no solution.

 **Quick Check** **4** **Critical Thinking** Without graphing, how can you tell if a system has no solution? Give an example.

A system of linear equations has **infinitely many solutions** when the graphs of the equations are the same line. The coordinates of the points on the common line are all solutions of the system.

5 EXAMPLE Systems With Infinitely Many Solutions

Vocabulary Tip

Infinitely many solutions is another way of saying that there is an infinite number of solutions of a system.

Solve by graphing. $2x + 4y = 8$
                      $y = -\frac{1}{2}x + 2$

Graph both equations on the same coordinate plane.

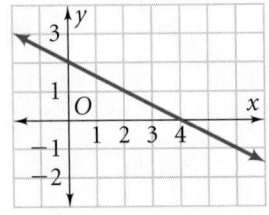

$2x + 4y = 8$ **The y-intercept is 2. The x-intercept is 4.**
$y = -\frac{1}{2}x + 2$ **The slope is $-\frac{1}{2}$. The y-intercept is 2.**

The graphs are the same line. The solutions are an infinite number of ordered pairs (x, y) such that $y = -\frac{1}{2}x + 2$.

 **Quick Check** **5** Solve by graphing. $y = \frac{1}{5}x + 9$
                                                    $5y = x + 45$

 Key Concepts

Summary	Numbers of Solutions of Systems of Linear Equations	
different slopes	same slope different y-intercepts	same slope same y-intercept
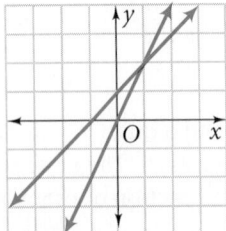	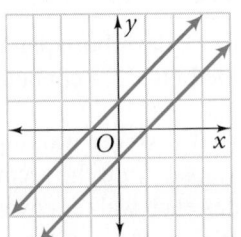	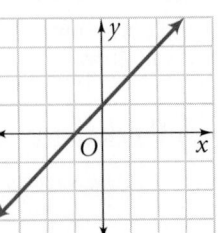
The lines intersect so there is one solution.	The lines are parallel so there are no solutions.	The lines are the same so there are infinitely many solutions.

EXERCISES

For more exercises, see *Extra Skill and Word Problem Practice*.

Practice and Problem Solving

 Practice by Example

Example 1
(page 550)

Is $(-1, 5)$ a solution of each system? Explain.

1. $x + y = 4$
$x = -1$

2. $y = -x + 4$
$y = -\frac{1}{5}x$

3. $y = 5$
$x = y - 6$

4. $y = 2x + 7$
$y = x + 6$

Solve by graphing. Check your solution.

5. $y = x + 2$
$y = -2x + 2$

6. $y = x$
$y = 5x$

7. $y = 1$
$y = x$

8. $y = x + 4$
$y = 4x + 1$

9. $y = -\frac{1}{3}x + 1$
$y = \frac{1}{3}x - 3$

10. $y = \frac{1}{2}x + 1$
$y = -3x + 8$

11. $3x + 4y = 12$
$2x + 4y = 8$

12. $y = \frac{1}{2}x + 2$
$y = -x + 5$

Examples 2, 3
(page 551)

13. Suppose you have $20 in your bank account. You start saving $5 each week. Your friend has $5 in his account and is saving $10 each week. Assume that neither you nor your friend makes any withdrawals.
   a. After how many weeks will you and your friend have the same amount of money in your accounts?
   b. How much money will each of you have?

14. Suppose you have $55 in your bank account. You start saving $10 each week. Your friend has $20 in her account and is saving $15 each week. When will you and your friend have the same amount of money in your accounts?

Examples 4, 5
(page 552)

Graph each system. Tell whether the system has *no solution* or *infinitely many solutions*.

15. $y = -2x + 1$
$y = -2x - 3$

16. $x + 2y = 10$
$2x + 4y = 10$

17. $y = 3x + 4$
$-12x + 4y = 16$

18. $y = 2x + 6$
$4x - 2y = 8$

 Apply Your Skills

Without graphing, decide whether each system has *one solution, no solution,* or *infinitely many solutions*. Explain.

19. $y = 2x$
$y = 2x - 5$

20. $x + y = 4$
$2x + 2y = 8$

21. $y = -3x + 1$
$y = 3x + 7$

22. $3x - 5y = 0$
$y = \frac{3}{5}x$

23. Which graphing calculator screen shows the solution of the system below?
$y = -5x + 4$
$y = \frac{3}{4}x - 3$

A.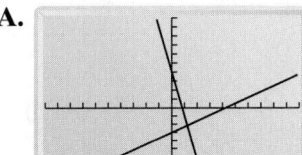

B.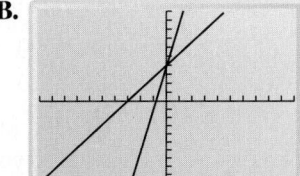

 24. Communications A communications company offers a variety of calling card options. Card A has a 30¢ connection fee and then costs 2¢ per minute. Card B has a 10¢ connection fee and then costs 6¢ per minute. Find the length of the call that would cost the same with both cards.

100 m

0 m   73 m

25. Soccer Jim and Tony are on opposing teams in a soccer match. They are running after the same ball. Jim's path is the line $y = 3x$. Tony's path is the line $y = -2x + 100$. Solve by graphing to find the coordinates of the ball.

Open-Ended **Write a system of two linear equations with the given characteristics.**

26. One solution; perpendicular lines

27. No solution; one equation is $y = 2x + 5$.

28. Infinitely many solutions; the graph of one equation has a y-intercept of 3.

Solve by graphing. Check your solution.

29. $y = 4x + 12$
$y = -2x + 24$

30. $y = 3x - 5$
$y = 2x + 10$

31. $y = x + 18$
$y = -\frac{1}{2}x + 36$

32. $y = 4x + 80$
$y = \frac{1}{2}x + 10$

33. Below is a retelling of one of Aesop's fables. Read it and use the story to answer the questions below.

One day, the tortoise challenged the hare to a race. The hare laughed while bragging about how fast a runner he was. On the day of the race, the hare was so confident that he took a nap during the race. When he awoke, he ran as hard as he could, but he could not beat the slow-but-sure tortoise across the finish line.

a. The graph at the right shows the race of the tortoise and the hare. Which label should be on each axis?
b. Writing Which color indicates the tortoise? Which indicates the hare? Explain your answers.
c. What does the point of intersection mean?

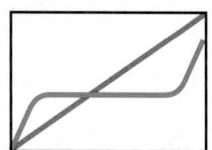

Graphing Calculator **Find the solution of each system. If necessary, round answers to the nearest tenth.**

34. $y = 1.5x + 2$
$y = 2.5x + 14$

35. $y = -\frac{7}{3}x + \frac{16}{3}$
$y = \frac{4}{3}x + \frac{38}{3}$

36. $y = 0.2x + 3.5$
$y = 0.4x + 9.5$

37. $y = 3.2x + 4.5$
$y = -8.7x - 6.1$

38. Use the spreadsheet to find the solution of the following system.
$y = -4x + 11$
$y = 3x - 3$

	A	B	C
1	x	$y = -4x + 11$	$y = 3x - 3$
2	−1	15	−6
3	0	11	−3
4	1	7	0
5	2	3	3
6	3	−1	6

39. Recording Music Suppose you and your friends form a band. You want to record a demo. Studio A rents for $100 plus $50/hour. Studio B rents for $50 plus $75/hour.

a. Write a system that models the situation and solve by graphing.
b. Explain what the solution of the system means in terms of renting a studio.

Homework Video Tutor
Visit: PHSchool.com
Web Code: ate-0701

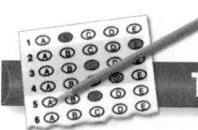

C Challenge

40. a. Critical Thinking For what values of w and v does the system have exactly one solution?
$$y = -5x + w$$
$$y = -5x + v$$
b. For what values of w and v does the system have no solution?
c. For what values of w and v does the system have infinitely many solutions?

41. a. If $g \geq h$, the system at the right has no solution *always, sometimes,* or *never?*
$$y = gx + 3$$
$$y = hx + 7$$
b. If $g \leq h$, the system has infinitely many solutions *always, sometimes,* or *never?*

42. The slope of the line joining point P to the origin is $\frac{2}{9}$. The slope of the line joining point P to $(-4, 3)$ is 1. Find the coordinates of point P.

Test Prep

Multiple Choice

43. Which ordered pair is the solution of the system?
$$6x - 6y = 2$$
$$3x + 9y = -7$$
A. $\left(\frac{2}{3}, -\frac{1}{3}\right)$
B. $\left(\frac{1}{3}, \frac{2}{3}\right)$
C. $\left(-\frac{2}{3}, \frac{1}{3}\right)$
D. $\left(-\frac{1}{3}, -\frac{2}{3}\right)$

44. Which value of b will make the graphs of $y = 2x + 3$ and $y = 2.5x + b$ intersect at (2, 7)?
F. 2   **G.** 3   **H.** 5   **J.** 7

Short Response

45. The first equation in a system of two equations is $x - 2y = 10$. The graph of the second equation does not intersect the first.
a. Write a possible second equation for the system.
b. Explain your answer to part (a).

Extended Response

46. The advertisements at the right are for two jobs you are considering.
a. Write a system of equations that relates the amount of sales x to the money y earned in a week at each job.
b. How much would you need to sell in a week at each job to earn the same amount of money at both?
c. After talking with salespeople, you estimate weekly sales of about $600 at either job. At which job would you earn more money?

> **Sales Position**
> Salesperson Wanted
> Knowledge of Cellular Phones
> On-Site Sales
> $150/week + 20% commission

> **CAREER OPPORTUNITY**
> Sell Stereo Equipment in
> National Electronics Retail Chain!
> $200/week + 10% commission

Mixed Review

Lesson 9-8

Graph each equation and describe its translation from $y = |x|$.

47. $y = |x| + 2$ **48.** $y = |x + 3|$ **49.** $y = |x - 2| + 5$

Lesson 6-7

Find each percent of change. Describe the percent of change as an increase or decrease.

50. 4 cm to 5 cm   **51.** 12 in. to 8 in.   **52.** $20 to $24   **53.** 10 ft to 25 ft

54. $9 to $6   **55.** 12 cm to 15 cm   **56.** 50 m to 55 m   **57.** $48 to $42

1 ACTIVITY

Solve the system by using a table.

$$y = 3x - 6$$
$$y = -4x + 29$$

Step 1

Enter the equations in the **Y=** screen.

```
Plot1 Plot2 Plot3
\Y1 ▤ 3X–6
\Y2 ▤ -4X+29
\Y3 =
\Y4 =
\Y5 =
\Y6 =
\Y7 =■
```

Step 2

Use the **TBLSET** function. Set **TblStart** to 0 and **ΔTbl** to 1.

```
TABLE SETUP
  TblStart = 0
  △Tbl = 1
Indpnt:  Auto  Ask
Depend:  Auto  Ask
```

Step 3

Press 2nd GRAPH to access the **TABLE** screen.

X	Y1	Y2
0	-6	29
1	-3	25
2	0	21
3	3	17
4	6	13
5	9	9
6	12	5
X=0		

1. Which x-value gives the same value for **Y1** and **Y2**?

2. Complete the following statement:

The point (__, __) is a solution of each linear equation, so it is the solution of the system.

2 ACTIVITY

Solve the system by using a graph.

$$y = 4x + 14$$
$$y = -3x - 3.5$$

Step 1 Enter the equations in the **Y=** screen.

Step 2 Graph the equations. Use a standard graphing window.

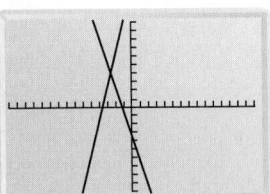

Step 3 Use the **CALC** feature, select **intersect** to find the point where the lines intersect.

3. Complete the following statement:

The lines intersect at (__, __), so it is the solution of the system.

EXERCISES

Choose Use a table or a graph to solve each system.

4. $y = 3x - 3$
$\ y = 2x - 1$

5. $y = -4.5x - 8.5$
$\ y = 4.5x + 18.5$

6. $y = -x - 2.5$
$\ y = 2.5x - 11.25$

7. $y = -\frac{1}{2}x - 1$
$\ y = 3x - 15$

8. $y = -2x - 7$
$\ y = 2x + 17$

9. $y = \frac{1}{2}x + \frac{9}{2}$
$\ y = 2x - 6$

Solving Systems Using Algebra Tiles

You can model and solve some linear systems using algebra tiles.

Solve the following system.
$$2x + y = 5$$
$$y = x - 1$$

Model the expression for y, which is $x - 1$.

To model the equation $2x + y = 5$,
substitute the expression for y, which is $x - 1$.

$$2x + y = 5$$
$$2x + x - 1 = 5$$
$$3x - 1 = 5$$

Using the Addition Property of Equality,
add 1 to each side. Simplify the model
by removing the zero pair.

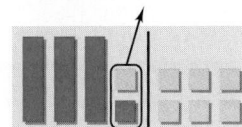

$$3x - 1 + 1 = 5 + 1$$
$$3x = 6$$

Divide each side into three
identical groups.

Solve for x.

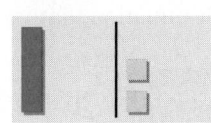

$x = 2$

To find y, substitute the value of x into the equation $y = x - 1$.

$$y = x - 1$$
$$= 2 - 1$$
$$= 1$$

The solution of the system is $(2, 1)$.

EXERCISES

Model and solve each system.

1. $y = x + 1$
$2x + y = 10$

2. $x + 4y = 1$
$x = y - 4$

3. $y = 2x - 1$
$y = x + 5$

4. $x = 3y + 2$
$2x = y + 9$

5. $x - 4y = 2$
$x = y + 1$

6. $y = x + 3$
$y = 2x + 6$

7. Open-Ended Let the equation $y = x + 2$ be part of a system. Write the second
equation of the system such that the system could be solved using algebra tiles.

Solving Systems Using Substitution

What You'll Learn

• To solve systems using substitution

. . . And Why

To solve problems involving transportation, as in Example 3

🔊 **New Vocabulary** • substitution method

---

1   Using Substitution

Vocabulary Tip

Substitution means one value or expression is used in place of another.

You can solve a system of equations by graphing when the solution contains integers or when you have a graphing calculator. Another method for solving systems of equations is the **substitution method.** By replacing one variable with an equivalent expression containing the other variable, you can create a one-variable equation that you can solve using methods shown in Chapter 3.

1 EXAMPLE   Using Substitution

Solve using substitution. $y = -4x + 8$
                     $y = x + 7$

Step 1   Write an equation containing only one variable, and solve it.

$y = -4x + 8$ **Start with one equation.**

$x + 7 = -4x + 8$ **Substitute x + 7 for y.**

$5x + 7 = 8$ **Add 4x to each side.**

$5x = 1$ **Subtract 7 from each side.**

$x = 0.2$ **Divide each side by 5.**

Step 2   Solve for the other variable in either equation.

$y = 0.2 + 7$ **Substitute 0.2 for x in y = x + 7.**

$y = 7.2$ **Simplify.**

Since $x = 0.2$ and $y = 7.2$, the solution is $(0.2, 7.2)$.

Check $7.2 \overset{?}{=} -4(0.2) + 8$ **Since y = x + 7 was used in step 2, see if (0.2, 7.2) solves y = -4x + 8.**

$7.2 = 7.2$ ✓   **Simplify.**

✓ **Quick Check** ❶ Solve using substitution. Check your solution. $y = 2x$
                                               $7x - y = 15$

To use the substitution method, you must have an equation that has already been solved for one of the variables.

2 EXAMPLE Using Substitution and the Distributive Property

Solve using the substitution method. $3y + 2x = 4$
$-6x + y = -7$

Step 1 Solve the second equation for y because it has a coefficient of 1.

$-6x + y = -7$

$y = 6x - 7$ **Add 6x to each side.**

Step 2 Write an equation containing only one variable and solve.

$3y + 2x = 4$	**Start with the other equation.**
$3(6x - 7) + 2x = 4$	**Substitute 6x − 7 for y. Use parentheses.**
$18x - 21 + 2x = 4$	**Use the Distributive Property.**
$20x = 25$	**Combine like terms and add 21 to each side.**
$x = 1.25$	**Divide each side by 20.**

Step 3 Solve for the other variable in either equation.

$-6(1.25) + y = -7$	**Substitute 1.25 for x in −6x + y = −7.**
$-7.5 + y = -7$	**Simplify.**
$y = 0.5$	**Add 7.5 to each side.**

Since $x = 1.25$ and $y = 0.5$, the solution is $(1.25, 0.5)$.

 **2** Solve using substitution. Check your solution. $6y + 8x = 28$
$3 = 2x - y$

3 EXAMPLE Real-World 🌐 Problem Solving

Transportation Your school is planning to bring 193 people to a competition at another school. There are eight drivers available and two types of vehicles, school buses and minivans. The school buses seat 51 people each, and the minivans seat 8 people each. How many buses and minivans will be needed?

Let b = number of school buses.   Let m = number of minivans.
    drivers $b + m = 8$ people $51b + 8m = 193$

Step 1 $b + m = 8$	**Solve the first equation for m.**
$m = -b + 8$	**Subtract b from each side.**
Step 2 $51b + 8(-b + 8) = 193$	**Substitute −b + 8 for m in the second equation.**
$51b - 8b + 64 = 193$	**Solve for b.**
$43b + 64 = 193$	
$43b = 129$	
$b = 3$	
Step 3 $(3) + m = 8$	**Substitute 3 for b in b + m = 8.**
$m = 5$	

Three school buses and five minivans will be needed to transport 193 people.

 **3** **Geometry** A rectangle is 4 times longer than it is wide. The perimeter of the rectangle is 30 cm. Find the dimensions of the rectangle.

EXERCISES

For more exercises, see *Extra Skill and Word Problem Practice*.

Practice and Problem Solving

 Practice by Example

Example 1
(page 558)

 **for Help**

Mental Math Match each system with its solution at the right.

1. $y = x + 1$
    $y = 2x - 1$

2. $y = \frac{1}{2}x + 4$
    $2y + 2x = 2$

A. $(3, 2)$

3. $2y = x + 3$
    $x = y$

4. $x - y = 1$
    $x = \frac{1}{2}y + 2$

B. $(3, 3)$

C. $(-2, 3)$

D. $(2, 3)$

Solve each system using substitution. Check your solution.

5. $y = 4x - 8$
    $y = 2x + 10$

6. $C(n) = -3n - 6$
    $C(n) = n - 4$

7. $m = 5p + 8$
    $m = -10p + 3$

8. $y = -4x + 12\frac{1}{2}$
    $y = \frac{1}{4}x + 4$

9. $h = 6g - 4$
    $h = -2g + 28$

10. $a = \frac{2}{5}b - 3$
    $a = 2b - 18$

Example 2
(page 559)

11. $y = x - 2$
    $2x + 2y = 4$

12. $c = 3d - 27$
    $4d + 10c = 120$

13. $3x - 6y = 30$
    $y = -6x + 34$

14. $m = 4n + 11$
    $-6n + 8m = 36$

15. $7x - 8y = 112$
    $y = -2x + 9$

16. $t = 0.2s + 10$
    $4s + 5t = 35$

Example 3
(page 559)

17. **Geometry** The length of a rectangle is 5 cm more than twice the width. The perimeter of the rectangle is 34 cm. Find the dimensions of the rectangle.

18. Suppose you have $28.00 in your bank account and start saving $18.25 every week. Your friend has $161.00 in his account and is withdrawing $15 every week. When will your account balances be the same?

 **Apply Your Skills**

Solve each system by substitution. Check your solution.

19. $a - 1.2b = -3$
    $0.2b + 0.6a = 12$

20. $0.5x + 0.25y = 36$
    $y + 18 = 16x$

21. $y = 0.8x + 7.2$
    $20x + 32y = 48$

For Exercises 22–24, define variables and write a system of equations for each situation. Solve using substitution.

22. Agriculture A farmer grows only sunflowers and flax on his 240-acre farm. This year he wants to plant 80 more acres of sunflowers than of flax. How many acres of each crop does the farmer need to plant?

23. Renting Videos Suppose you want to join a video store. Big Video offers a special discount card that costs $9.99 for one year. With the discount card, each video rental costs $2.49. A discount card from Main Street Video costs $20.49 for one year. With the Main Street Video discount card, each video rental costs $1.79. After how many video rentals is the cost the same?

24. Buying a Car Suppose you are thinking about buying one of two cars. Car A will cost $17,655. You can expect to pay an average of $1230 per year for fuel, maintenance, and repairs. Car B will cost about $15,900. Fuel, maintenance, and repairs for it will average about $1425 per year. After how many years are the total costs for the cars the same?

Real-World  **Connection**

Sunflower seeds are sold as snacks and as bird food, and they are a source of cooking oil.

25. Multiple Choice You have 28 coins that are all nickels n and dimes d. The value of the coins is \$2.05. Which system of equations can be used to find the number of nickels and the number of dimes?

   Ⓐ $n + d = 28$
      $10n + 5d = 2.05$

   Ⓑ $n + d = 205$
      $n + d = 28$

   Ⓒ $10n + 5d = 205$
      $n + d = 28$

   Ⓓ $n + d = 28$
      $5n + 10d = 205$

Estimation Graph each system to estimate the solution. Then use substitution to find the exact solution of the system.

26. $y = 2x$
    $y = -6x + 4$

27. $y = \frac{1}{2}x + 4$
    $y = -4x - 5$

28. $x + y = 0$
    $5x + 2y = -3$

29. $y = 2x + 3$
    $y = 0.5x - 2$

30. $y = -x + 4$
    $y = 2x + 6$

31. $y = 0.7x + 3$
    $y = -1.5x - 7$

32. Open-Ended Write a system of linear equations with exactly one solution. Use substitution to solve your system.

33. a. Solve each system below using substitution.

    $y = 0.5x + 4$
    $-x + 2y = 8$

    $6x - 2y = 10$
    $y = 3x + 1$

  b. Solve each system by graphing.

  c. Critical Thinking Make a general statement about the solutions you get when solving by graphing and the results you get when solving by substitution.

Solve each system using substitution.

34. $y = 2x$
    $6x - y = 8$

35. $y = 3x + 1$
    $x = 3y + 1$

36. $x - 3y = 14$
    $x - 2 = 0$

37. $2x + 2y = 5$
    $y = \frac{1}{4}x$

38. $4x + y = -2$
    $-2x - 3y = 1$

39. $3x + 5y = 2$
    $x + 4y = -4$

Ⓒ Challenge

40. There are 1170 students in a school. The ratio of girls to boys is 23 : 22. The system below describes relationships between the number of girls and the number of boys.

    $g + b = 1170$ $\frac{g}{b} = \frac{23}{22}$

  a. Solve the proportion for g.
  b. Solve the system.
  c. How many more girls are there than boys?

🌐 **41. Sprinting** The graph at the left represents the start of a 100-meter race between Joetta and Gail. The red line and blue line represent Joetta's and Gail's time and distance. Joetta averages 8.8 m/s. Gail averages 9 m/s but started 0.2 s after Joetta. At time 0.2 s, Gail's distance is 0 m. You can use point-slope form to write an equation that relates Gail's time t to her distance d.

    $y - y_1 = m(x - x_1)$
    $d - 0 = 9(t - 0.2)$
    $d = 9t - 1.8$

Since Joetta started at $t = 0$, the equation $d = 8.8t$ relates her time and distance.
  a. Solve the system using substitution.
  b. Will Gail overtake Joetta before the finish line?

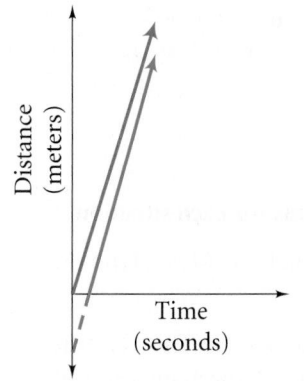

Distance (meters)

Time (seconds)

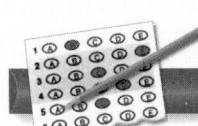

Gridded Response

42. Find the value of the y-coordinate of the solution to the given system. $5x + 5y = 179$ $x = 5y - 143$

43. Find the value of the y-coordinate of the solution to the given system. $y = 9x + 3480$ $y = 81x - 7104$

44. Tina has \$220 in her account. Cliff has \$100 in his account. Starting in July, Tina adds \$25 to her account on the first of each month, while Cliff adds \$35 to his. How many dollars will they have in their accounts when the amounts are the same?

Short Response

45. Is $(-2, -7)$ the solution of the following system? Justify your answer.
$7y - 4x = 29$
$x = y - 5$

Mixed Review

Lesson 10-1

Solve each system by graphing.

46. $y = x - 2$
$y = \frac{1}{2}x + 4$

47. $y = -2x + 5$
$y = -x + 3$

48. $y = \frac{3}{4}x - 1$
$y = \frac{1}{4}x + 1$

Lesson 8-3

Graph each function.

49. $y = 3x - 2$

50. $f(x) = x + 1$

51. $f(x) = -2x$

52. $y = |x| + 5$

53. $y = -2|x|$

54. $y = |x + 3| - 1$

 **Checkpoint Quiz 1**   **Lessons 10-1 through 10-2**

Solve each system by graphing.

1. $y = 3x - 4$
$y = -2x + 1$

2. $y = \frac{4}{3}x - 2$
$y = \frac{2}{3}x$

3. $y = \frac{1}{4}x - 1$
$y = -2x - 10$

Solve each system using substitution.

4. $y = 3x - 14$
$y = x - 10$

5. $y = 2x + 5$
$y = 6x + 1$

6. $x = y + 7$
$y = 8 + 2x$

7. $3x + 4y = 12$
$y = -2x + 10$

8. $4x + 9y = 24$
$y = -\frac{1}{3}x + 2$

In Exercises 9 and 10, write and solve a system of equations for each situation.

9. A rectangle is 3 times longer than it is wide. The perimeter is 44 cm. Find the dimensions of the rectangle.

10. A farmer grows only pumpkins and corn on her 420-acre farm. This year she wants to plant 250 more acres of corn than of pumpkins. How many acres of each crop does the farmer need to plant?

10-3

Solving Systems Using Elimination

What You'll Learn

- To solve systems by adding or subtracting
- To multiply first when solving systems

. . . And Why

To analyze a ticket-sales situation, as in Example 2

Solve each system using substitution.

1. $y = 4x - 3$
$y = 2x + 13$

2. $y + 5x = 4$
$y = 7x - 20$

3. $y = -2x + 2$
$3x - 17 = 2y$

◀)) **New Vocabulary** • elimination method

GO for Help Lesson 10-2

---

1 Adding or Subtracting to Solve Systems

Vocabulary Tip

<u>Addition Property of Equality</u>
If $a = b$,
then $a + c = b + c$.

<u>Subtraction Property of Equality</u>
If $a = b$,
then $a - c = b - c$.

The Addition and Subtraction Properties of Equality can be extended to state,

If $a = b$ and $c = d$, then $a + c = b + d$.   If $a = b$ and $c = d$, then $a - c = b - d$.

You can use the Addition and Subtraction Properties of Equality to solve a system by the **elimination method.** You can add or subtract equations to eliminate a variable.

1 EXAMPLE Adding Equations

Solve by elimination. $5x - 6y = -32$
$3x + 6y = 48$

Step 1 Eliminate y because the sum of the coefficients of y is zero.

$5x - 6y = -32$

$\underline{3x + 6y = 48}$ **Add the two equations.**

$8x + 0 = 16$ **Addition Property of Equality**

$x = 2$ **Solve for x.**

Step 2 Solve for the eliminated variable y using either of the original equations.

$3x + 6y = 48$ **Choose the second equation.**

$3(2) + 6y = 48$ **Substitute 2 for x.**

$6 + 6y = 48$ **Simplify. Then solve for y.**

$y = 7$

Since $x = 2$ and $y = 7$, the solution is $(2, 7)$.

Check $5(2) - 6(7) \stackrel{?}{=} -32$ **See if (2, 7) solves $5x - 6y = -32$.**

$10 - 42 \stackrel{?}{=} -32$

$-32 = -32$ ✓

 Quick Check ❶ Solve by elimination. $6x - 3y = 3$
$-6x + 5y = 3$

Real-World Connection

There are 188 basketball teams in 26 conferences in the National Wheelchair Basketball Association.

2 EXAMPLE Real-World Problem Solving

Ticket Sales Suppose your community center sells a total of 292 tickets for a basketball game. An adult ticket costs $3. A student ticket costs $1. The sponsors collect $470 in ticket sales. Write and solve a system to find the number of each type of ticket sold.

Define Let a = number of adult tickets.
Let s = number of student tickets.

Relate total number of tickets   total amount of sales
Write $a + s = 292$ $3a + 1s = 470$

Solve by elimination.

Step 1 Eliminate s because the difference of the coefficients of s is zero.

$$\begin{array}{ll} a + s = 292 & \\ 3a + s = 470 & \text{Subtract the two equations.} \\ \hline -2a + 0 = -178 & \text{Subtraction Property of Equality} \\ a = 89 & \text{Solve for } a. \end{array}$$

Step 2 Solve for the eliminated variable using either of the original equations.

$$\begin{array}{ll} a + s = 292 & \text{Choose the first equation.} \\ 89 + s = 292 & \text{Substitute 89 for } a. \\ s = 203 & \text{Solve for } s. \end{array}$$

There were 89 adult tickets sold and 203 student tickets sold.

Check Is the solution reasonable? The answers 89 and 203 are close to 90 and 200. The total number of tickets is about $90 + 200 = 290$, close to 292. The total sales is about $\$3(90) + \$1(200)$ or $\$470$. The solution is reasonable.

✓ Quick Check ❷ Your class sells a total of 64 tickets to a play. A student ticket costs $1, and an adult ticket costs $2.50. Your class collects $109 in total ticket sales. How many adult tickets did you sell? How many student tickets did you sell?

 **Multiplying First to Solve Systems**

From Examples 1 and 2 you can see that to eliminate a variable its coefficients must have a sum or difference of zero. Sometimes you may need to multiply one or both of the equations by a nonzero number first.

3 EXAMPLE Multiplying One Equation

Solve by the elimination method. $2x + 5y = -22$
                                    $10x + 3y = 22$

Step 1 Eliminate one variable.

Start with the given system.	To prepare for eliminating x, multiply the first equation by 5.	Subtract the equations to eliminate x.
$2x + 5y = -22$	$\rightarrow$ $5(2x + 5y = -22)$	$\rightarrow$ $10x + 25y = -110$
$10x + 3y = 22$	$\rightarrow$ $\underline{10x + 3y = 22}$	$\rightarrow$ $\underline{10x + 3y = 22}$
		$0 + 22y = -132$

Step 2 Solve for y.

$$22y = -132$$
$$y = -6$$

Step 3 Solve for the eliminated variable using either of the original equations.

$2x + 5y = -22$ **Choose the first equation.**

$2x + 5(-6) = -22$ **Substitute -6 for y.**

$2x - 30 = -22$ **Solve for x.**

$$2x = 8$$
$$x = 4$$

● The solution is $(4, -6)$.

✓ Quick Check   ❸ Solve by elimination. $-2x + 15y = -32$
                                                    $7x - 5y = 17$

To solve problems that arise from real-world situations, you can also use the elimination method.

4 EXAMPLE   **Real-World 🌐 Problem Solving**

Gridded Response Suppose your class sells gift wrap for $4 per package and greeting cards for $10 per package. Your class sells 205 packages in all and receives a total of $1084. Find the number of packages of gift wrap and the number of packages of greeting cards sold.

Define   Let w = number of packages of gift wrap sold.
           Let c = number of packages of greeting cards sold.

Relate   total number of packages   total amount of sales

Write $w + c = 205$ $4w + 10c = 1084$

Step 1 Eliminate one variable.

Start with the given system.	**To prepare for eliminating w, multiply the first equation by 4.**	**Subtract the equations to eliminate w.**
$w + c = 205$ →	$4(w + c = 205)$ →	$4w + 4c = 820$
$4w + 10c = 1084$ →	$4w + 10c = 1084$ →	$4w + 10c = 1084$
		$0 - 6c = -264$

Step 2 Solve for c.

$$-6c = -264$$
$$c = 44$$

Step 3 Solve for the eliminated variable using either of the original equations.

$w + c = 205$ **Use the first equation.**

$w + 44 = 205$ **Substitute 44 for c.**

$w = 161$ **Solve for w.**

● The class sold 161 packages of gift wrap and 44 packages of greeting cards.

✓ Quick Check   ❹ Suppose your younger brother's elementary school class sells a different brand of gift wrap, which costs $2 per package, and cards, which cost $5 per package. His class sells 220 packages in all and earns a total of $695. Find the number of each type of package sold.

If you are asked to grid one of the solutions of a system, such as the number of packages of gift wrap, be sure to select the correct variable.

Video Tutor Help

Visit: PHSchool.com
Web Code: ate-0775

To eliminate a variable, you may need to multiply both equations in a system by a nonzero number. Multiply each equation by values such that when you write equivalent equations, you can then add or subtract to eliminate a variable.

5 EXAMPLE **Multiplying Both Equations**

Solve by elimination. $4x + 2y = 14$
$7x - 3y = -8$

Step 1 Eliminate one variable.

| Start with the given system. | To prepare for eliminating *y*, multiply one equation by 3 and the other equation by 2. | Add the equations to eliminate *y*. |

$4x + 2y = 14 \rightarrow 3(4x + 2y = 14)$ $\rightarrow$ $12x + 6y = 42$
$7x - 3y = -8 \rightarrow \underline{2(7x - 3y = -8)}$ $\rightarrow$ $\underline{14x - 6y = -16}$
$26x + 0 = 26$

Step 2 Solve for *x*.

$26x = 26$
$x = 1$

Step 3 Solve for the eliminated variable *y* using either of the original equations.

$4x + 2y = 14$ **Use the first equation.**
$4(1) + 2y = 14$ **Substitute 1 for *x*.**
$2y = 10$
$y = 5$

• The solution is $(1, 5)$.

✓ **Quick Check** **5** Solve by elimination. $15x + 3y = 9$
$10x + 7y = -4$

When you solve systems using elimination, plan a strategy. A flowchart like the one below can help you to decide how to eliminate a variable.

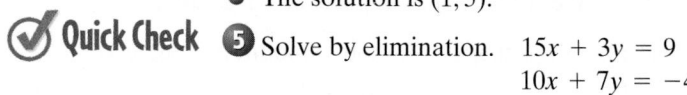

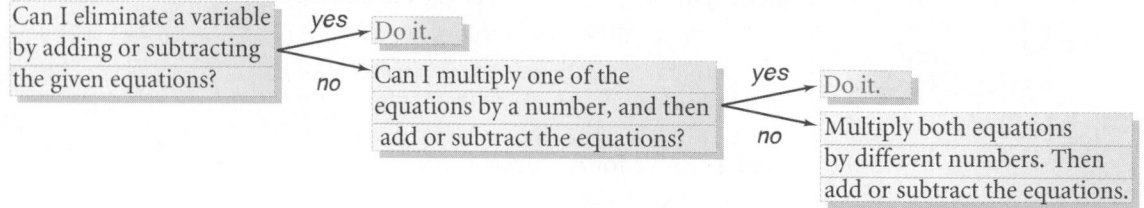

EXERCISES

For more exercises, see *Extra Skill and Word Problem Practice*.

Practice and Problem Solving

 Practice by Example

Solve by elimination.

Example 1
(page 563)

1. $2x + 5y = 17$
$6x - 5y = -9$

2. $7x + 2y = 10$
$-7x + y = -16$

3. $2x - 3y = 61$
$2x + y = -7$

GO for Help

4. $8x + 11y = 20$
$5x - 11y = -59$

5. $2x + 18y = -9$
$4x + 18y = -27$

6. $20x + 3y = 20$
$-20x + 5y = 60$

Example 2
(page 564)

7. The sum of two numbers is 20. Their difference is 4.
 a. Write a system of equations that describes this situation.
 b. Solve by elimination to find the two numbers.

8. Ticket Sales Your school sold 456 tickets for a high school play. An adult ticket cost $3.50. A student ticket cost $1. Total ticket sales equaled $1131. Let a equal the number of adult tickets sold, and let s equal the number of student tickets sold.
 a. Write a system of equations that relates the number of adult and student tickets sold to the total number of tickets sold and to the total ticket sales.
 b. Solve by elimination to find the number of each type of ticket sold.

Example 3
(page 564)

Solve by elimination.

9. $3x - 10y = -25$
  $4x + 40y = 20$

10. $7x + 15y = 32$
  $x - 3y = 20$

11. $x - 8y = 18$
  $-16x + 16y = -8$

12. $24x + 2y = 52$
  $6x - 3y = -36$

13. $88x - 5y = 39$
  $-8x + 3y = -1$

14. $2x + 4y = 8$
  $5x + y = -7$

Example 4
(page 565)

15. Sales A photo studio that takes school pictures offers several different packages. Let w equal the cost of a wallet-sized portrait, and let ℓ equal the cost of an 8×10 portrait.

Basic Package
30 wallet-sized photos
1 8" x 10" portrait
$17.65

Deluxe Package
20 wallet-sized photos
3 8" x 10" portraits
$25.65

 a. Write a system of equations that relates the cost of wallet-sized portraits and 8×10 portraits to the cost of the basic and deluxe packages.
 b. Find the cost of each type of portrait.

16. Two groups of students order burritos and tacos at a local restaurant. One order of 3 burritos and 4 tacos costs $11.33. The other order of 9 burritos and 5 tacos costs $23.56.
 a. Write a system of equations that describes this situation.
 b. Solve by elimination to find the cost of a burrito and the cost of a taco.

Example 5
(page 566)

Solve by elimination.

17. $3x + 2y = -9$
  $-10x + 5y = -5$

18. $4x + 5y = 15$
  $6x - 4y = 11$

19. $3x - 2y = 10$
  $2x + 3y = -2$

20. $-2x + 5y = 20$
  $3x - 7y = -26$

21. $10x + 8y = 2$
  $8x + 6y = 1$

22. $9x + 5y = 34$
  $8x - 2y = -2$

B **Apply Your Skills**

Solve each system using any method. Tell why you chose the method you used.

23. $y = 2x$
  $y = x - 1$

24. $7x + 8y = 25$
  $9x + 10y = 35$

25. $x = 12y - 14$
  $3y + 2x = 26$

26. $-20x + 7y = 137$
  $4x + 5y = 43$

27. $5y = x$
  $2x - 3y = 7$

28. $y = x + 2$
  $y = -2x + 3$

One weekend for
$195

One week for
$650

(per person,
double occupancy)

Beach
Bay
Hotel

29. Vacation A weekend at the Beach Bay Hotel in Florida includes 2 nights and 4 meals. A week includes 7 nights and 10 meals. Let n = the cost of 1 night and m = the cost of 1 meal. Find the cost of 1 night and the cost of 1 meal.

30. a. Business A company sells brass and steel machine parts. One shipment contains 3 brass and 10 steel parts and costs $48. A second shipment contains 7 brass and 4 steel parts and costs $54. Find the cost of each type of machine part.

    b. How much would a shipment containing 10 brass and 13 steel machine parts cost?

31. Error Analysis Beth is solving a system by elimination. Her work is shown below. What error did she make?

$$
\begin{aligned}
4x - 6y &= 1 \longrightarrow 20x - 30y = 5 \\
3x + 5y &= -8 \longrightarrow 18x + 30y = -8
\end{aligned}
$$

32. Open-Ended Write a system of equations that can be solved by elimination. Solve your system.

Solve by elimination.

33. $\frac{1}{2}x + y = -1$
$16x - \frac{1}{2}y = 163$

34. $\frac{1}{4}x - 6y = -70$
$5x + \frac{3}{4}y = 49$

35. $-0.2x + 4y = -1$
$x + 0.5y = -15.5$

36. $y = 0.5x + 2$
$1.5x + y = 42$

37. $\frac{1}{4}x + \frac{33}{2} = y$
$y - 12 = -2x$

38. $\frac{2}{3}x - y = 70$
$\frac{1}{3}x - \frac{2}{3}y = 43$

39. Critical Thinking Find a value of n such that the x-value of the solution of the system at the right is 4.

    $5x - 10y = 50$
    $nx + 10y = 6$

 40. Writing Explain how to solve a system using elimination. Give examples of when you use addition, subtraction, and multiplication.

41. Electricity Two batteries produce a total voltage of 4.5 volts ($B_1 + B_2 = 4.5$). The difference in their voltages is 1.5 volts ($B_1 - B_2 = 1.5$). Find the voltages of the two batteries.

 **Challenge**

Solve by elimination.

42. $\frac{6}{x} - \frac{4}{y} = -4$
$\frac{3}{x} + \frac{8}{y} = 3$

43. $ax + y = c$
$ax + by = c$

44. $x + y + z = 41$
$x - y + z = 15$
$3x - z = 4$

45. Music Suppose your band wants to sell CDs and cassette tapes of your music. You use a production company that offers two different production packages.

	CDs	Tapes	Mastering	Artwork	Total Cost
Package #1	300	400	✓	✓	$2080
Package #2	500	600	✓	✓	$3120

Both companies charge $100 to master your original recording and $240 to create cover artwork. Find the average production cost of each CD and cassette tape.

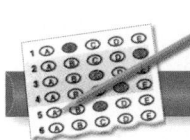
 46. Jewelry A ring is made out of gold and copper. Gold has a density of 19.3 g/cm³. Copper has a density of 9 g/cm³. Mass m, density d, and volume v are related by the formula $m = dv$. The ring has a volume of 4.2 cm³, and a mass of 52.22 g.

Let a = volume of gold.   mass of gold = dv = $19.3a$
Let c = volume of copper.   mass of copper = dv = $9c$

a. Solve the following system by elimination to find out how many grams of gold are in the ring.
$$a + c = 4.2$$
$$19.3a + 9c = 52.22$$

b. What is the percent of gold by mass?

Test Prep

Multiple Choice

47. Which of the following systems does NOT have the same solution as the system at the right?

$$7x - 4y = 5$$
$$6x + 7y = -11$$

A. $49x - 28y = 35$
    $24x + 28y = -44$
B. $42x - 24y = 30$
    $42x + 49y = -77$
C. $-14x + 8y = -10$
    $12x + 14y = -22$
D. $21x + 12y = 15$
    $-24x - 28y = 44$

48. Use the solution of the system below to find $x - y$.
$$4x - 2y = 11$$
$$3x - 4y = -6$$

F. 11.3   **G.** 0.1   **H.** −0.1   **J.** −11.3

Short Response

49. Solve the following system by elimination. Show your work.
$$y - x = 13$$
$$7y + x = 11$$

Extended Response

50. A trapezoid is formed by lines with the following equations.
$$2x + 4y = 16 \qquad x = 4 \qquad x = 0 \qquad y = 0$$
Find the area of the trapezoid.

Mixed Review

Lesson 10-2

Solve using substitution. Give the solutions in alphabetical order.

51. $y = 4x + 2$
    $y = 6x - 10$
52. $p = q - 5$
    $3p + q = 1$
53. $w + a = 4$
    $w + 2a = 13$

Lesson 5-7

You have a bag with two red marbles, three blue marbles, and five green marbles. You choose a marble at random. Without replacing the marble, you choose a second marble. Find each probability.

54. P(red then green)   **55.** P(two greens)   **56.** P(blue then red)

Lesson 4-6

Write and solve an equation to find the value of x.

57. 5, 7, 3, 4, 8, x; mean 5   **58.** 1.2, 1.4, 1.5, 1.1, x; mean 1.2

59. 10, 15, 9, 11, 8, x; mean 10.5   **60.** 4, 1, 3, x; mean 3.25

In Chapter 5, you learned how to add and subtract two matrices. You can also multiply matrices. You multiply the elements in a row of the first matrix by the corresponding elements in a column of the second matrix. Then you add the products.

3 elements in a row →

$$\begin{bmatrix} 2 & 5 & -3 \\ 3 & 1 & 6 \end{bmatrix}\begin{bmatrix} 7 \\ 2 \\ 1 \end{bmatrix} = \begin{bmatrix} 2 \cdot 7 + 5 \cdot 2 + (-3 \cdot 1) \\ 3 \cdot 7 + 1 \cdot 2 + 6 \cdot 1 \end{bmatrix} = \begin{bmatrix} 21 \\ 29 \end{bmatrix}$$

3 elements in a column

The second matrix can have more than one column.

first row and first column; first row and second column

$$\begin{bmatrix} 2 & 5 & -3 \\ 3 & 1 & 6 \end{bmatrix}\begin{bmatrix} 7 & 3 \\ 2 & 9 \\ 1 & 2 \end{bmatrix} = \begin{bmatrix} 2 \cdot 7 + 5 \cdot 2 + (-3 \cdot 1) & 2 \cdot 3 + 5 \cdot 9 + (-3 \cdot 2) \\ 3 \cdot 7 + 1 \cdot 2 + 6 \cdot 1 & 3 \cdot 3 + 1 \cdot 9 + 6 \cdot 2 \end{bmatrix} = \begin{bmatrix} 21 & 45 \\ 29 & 30 \end{bmatrix}$$

second row and first column; second row and second column

You can use a graphing calculator to multiply matrices. To enter matrices, you must know their dimensions. A matrix with two rows and three columns is a 2 × 3 matrix.

1 ACTIVITY

Use a graphing calculator to find $A \times B$.

$$A = \begin{bmatrix} 2 & 5 & -3 \\ 3 & 1 & 6 \end{bmatrix} \qquad B = \begin{bmatrix} 7 & 3 \\ 2 & 9 \\ 1 & 2 \end{bmatrix}$$

Step 1 Use the **MATRX** feature. Edit the dimensions and enter the values of the elements. You have to quit the first matrix screen before using the **MATRX** feature to enter the second matrix.

Matrix A

```
Matrix [A]  2×3
[2        5       -3]
[3        1        6]


2,3=6
```

Matrix B

```
Matrix [B]  3×2
[7        3       ]
[2        9       ]
[1        2       ]

3, 2=2
```

Step 2 Use the **NAMES** list on the matrix screen. Select [A]. Then use the name list on the matrix screen to select [B]. Press ENTER. The product matrix will appear on the main screen.

```
[A] [B]
          [[21    45]
           [29    30]]
```

You can use matrices to solve systems of equations. Start with equations in standard form.

System of Equations $\qquad$ Matrices for the System

$$2x + 6y = 80$$
$$4x + 5y = -1$$

$$\begin{bmatrix} 2 & 6 \\ 4 & 5 \end{bmatrix} \begin{bmatrix} x \\ y \end{bmatrix} = \begin{bmatrix} 80 \\ -1 \end{bmatrix}$$

$$A \quad \cdot X \; = \quad B$$

A is the matrix for the coefficients of the variables, X is a matrix for the variables, and B is a matrix for the constants. To solve the system you must use the inverse of A, which is A^{-1}. The product $A^{-1} \times B$ gives you X.

2 ACTIVITY

Solve the system at the right by using matrix multiplication.

$$2x + 6y = 80$$
$$4x + 5y = -1$$

$$A = \begin{bmatrix} 2 & 6 \\ 4 & 5 \end{bmatrix} \text{ and } B = \begin{bmatrix} 80 \\ -1 \end{bmatrix}$$

Step 1

Use the matrix feature. Edit the dimensions and enter the values of the elements for each matrix.

Step 2

Use the matrix feature. Select [A]. Then press x^{-1}. $[A]^{-1}$ will appear on the main screen.

Step 3

Use the matrix feature. Select [B]. Then press ENTER.

The values of matrix X will appear as shown at the right.

$[[-29]$
$[23]]$ corresponds to $\begin{bmatrix} x \\ y \end{bmatrix}$, so $x = -29$ and $y = 23$.

● The solution of the system is $(-29, 23)$.

```
[A]⁻¹ [B]



                        [[-29]
                         [23]]
```

EXERCISES

Find each product.

1. $[4 \quad 2 \quad 9] \begin{bmatrix} 3 \\ 1 \\ 7 \end{bmatrix}$

2. $\begin{bmatrix} 12 & 10 \\ 8 & -11 \end{bmatrix} \begin{bmatrix} 0 & 4 \\ 9 & -1 \end{bmatrix}$

3. $\begin{bmatrix} 44 & -12 \\ 27 & 35 \\ 25 & -16 \end{bmatrix} \begin{bmatrix} 21 & -41 \\ 25 & 17 \end{bmatrix}$

4. The table at the near right shows the number of three sizes of widgets made at a manufacturing plant on Monday and Tuesday. The table at the far right shows the production costs of each widget. Write each table as a matrix. Then multiply to find the total production cost each day.

Number of Widgets

Day	Size A	Size B	Size C
Monday	212	318	175
Tuesday	185	292	221

Cost of Widgets

Cost A	$.96
Cost B	$1.23
Cost C	$1.51

Solve each system using matrix multiplication.

5. $1x + 8y = 16$
$ 9x + 12y = 66$

6. $29x + 7y = 1012$
$ 8x - 25y = 737$

7. $76x + 18y = 86$
$ 189x + 47y = 132$

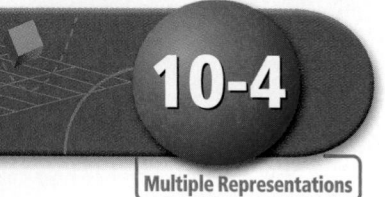

Applications of Linear Systems

What You'll Learn

• To write systems of linear equations

. . . And Why

To find average wind speed during an airplane flight, as in Example 3

✓ **Check Skills You'll Need**

**GO for Help** Lesson 6-6

1. Two trains run on parallel tracks. The first train leaves a city $\frac{1}{2}$ hour before the second train. The first train travels at 55 mi/h. The second train travels at 65 mi/h. How long does it take for the second train to pass the first train?

2. Carl drives to the beach at an average speed of 50 mi/h. He returns home on the same road at an average speed of 55 mi/h. The trip home takes 30 min less. What is the distance from his home to the beach?

---

1 Writing Systems of Linear Equations

Below is a summary of the methods you have used to solve systems of equations. You must choose a method before you solve a word problem.

 Key Concepts

Summary	Methods for Solving Systems of Linear Equations
Graphing	Use graphing for solving systems that are easily graphed. If the point of intersection does not have integers for coordinates, find the exact solution by using one of the methods below or by using a graphing calculator.
Substitution	Use substitution for solving systems when one variable has a coefficient of 1 or -1.
Elimination	Use elimination for solving any system.

Real-World Connection

The melting point of copper is 1083°C.

1 EXAMPLE **Real-World Problem Solving**

Metallurgy A metalworker has some ingots of metal alloy that are 20% copper and others that are 60% copper. How many kilograms of each type of ingot should the metalworker combine to create 80 kg of a 52% copper alloy?

Define Let g = the mass of the 20% alloy.
Let h = the mass of the 60% alloy.

Relate mass of alloys   mass of copper

Write $g + h = 80$ $0.2g + 0.6h = 0.52(80)$

Solve using substitution.

Step 1 Choose one of the equations and solve for a variable.

$g + h = 80$ **Solve for g.**

$g = 80 - h$ **Subtract h from each side.**

Step 2 Find h.

$$0.2g + 0.6h = 0.52(80)$$

$$0.2(80 - h) + 0.6h = 0.52(80)$$ **Substitute 80 − h for g. Use parentheses.**

$$16 - 0.2h + 0.6h = 0.52(80)$$ **Use the Distributive Property.**

$$16 + 0.4h = 41.6$$ **Simplify. Then solve for h.**

$$0.4h = 25.6$$

$$h = 64$$

Step 3 Find g. Substitute 64 for h in either equation.

$$g = 80 - 64$$

$$g = 16$$

To make 80 kg of 52% copper alloy, you need 16 kg of 20% copper alloy and 64 kg of 60% copper alloy.

 **Quick Check** **①** Suppose you combine ingots of 25% copper alloy and 50% copper alloy to create 40 kg of 45% copper alloy. How many kilograms of each do you need?

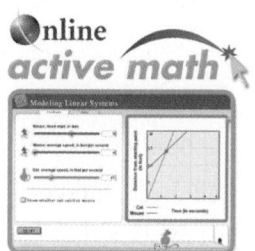

For: Linear System Activity
Use: Interactive Textbook, 10-4

When starting a business, people want to know the *break-even point*, the point at which their income equals their expenses. The graph at the right shows the break-even point for one business.

☐ Lose money   ▦ Make money

Notice that the values of y on the red line represent dollars spent on expenses, and the values of y on the blue line represent dollars received as income. So y is used to represent both expenses and income.

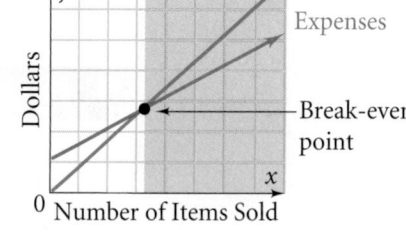

② **EXAMPLE** **Finding a Break-Even Point**

Publishing Suppose a model airplane club publishes a newsletter. Expenses are $.90 for printing and mailing each copy, plus $600 total for research and writing. The price of the newsletter is $1.50 per copy. How many copies of the newsletter must the club sell to break even?

Define Let x = the number of copies.
        Let y = the amount of dollars of expenses or income.

Relate Expenses are printing costs   Income is price
         plus research and writing.   times copies sold.

Write $y = 0.9x + 600$ $y = 1.5x$

Choose a method to solve this system. Use substitution since it is easy to substitute for y with these equations.

$$y = 0.9x + 600$$ **Start with one equation.**

$$1.5x = 0.9x + 600$$ **Substitute 1.5x for y.**

$$0.6x = 600$$ **Solve for x.**

$$x = 1000$$

To break even, the model airplane club must sell 1000 copies.

✓ Quick Check **2** Suppose an antique car club publishes a newsletter. Expenses are $.35 for printing and mailing each copy, plus $770 total for research and writing. The price of the newsletter is $.55 per copy. How many copies of the newsletter must the club sell to break even?

In Lesson 3-6, you modeled rate-time-distance problems using one variable. You can also model rate-time-distance problems using two variables. The steady west-to-east winds across the United States act as tail winds for planes traveling from west to east. The tail winds increase a plane's groundspeed. For planes traveling east to west, the head winds decrease a plane's groundspeed.

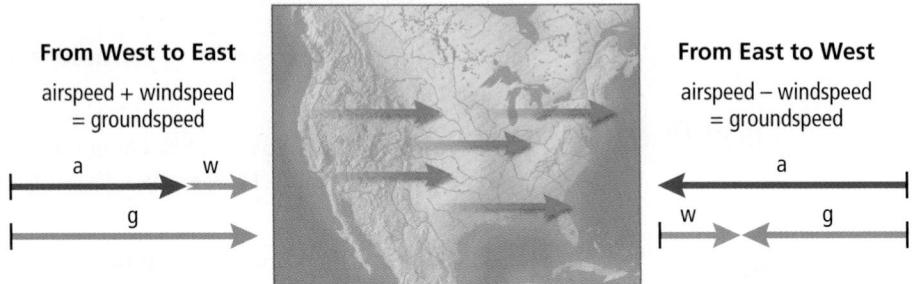

From West to East

airspeed + windspeed
= groundspeed

a   w

g

From East to West

airspeed − windspeed
= groundspeed

a

w   g

3 **EXAMPLE** **Real-World 🌐 Problem Solving**

Travel Suppose you fly from Miami, Florida, to San Francisco, California. It takes 6.5 hours to fly 2600 miles against a head wind. At the same time, your friend flies from San Francisco to Miami. Her plane travels at the same average airspeed, but her flight only takes 5.2 hours. Find the average airspeed of the planes. Find the average wind speed.

Define Let A = the airspeed. Let W = the wind speed.

Relate   with tail wind   with head wind
        (rate)(time) = distance   (rate)(time) = distance
        $(A + W)$(time) = distance $(A - W)$(time) = distance

Write $(A + W)5.2 = 2600$ $(A - W)6.5 = 2600$

Step 1 Divide to get the variables of each equation with coefficients of 1 or −1.
        $(A + W)5.2 = 2600 \rightarrow A + W = 500$ **Divide each side by 5.2.**
        $(A - W)6.5 = 2600 \rightarrow A - W = 400$ **Divide each side by 6.5.**

Step 2 Eliminate W.
        $A + W = 500$
        $\underline{A - W = 400}$ **Add the equations to eliminate W.**
        $2A + 0 = 900$

Step 3 Solve for A.
                $A = 450$ **Divide each side by 2.**

Step 4 Solve for W using either of the original equations.
            $A + W = 500$ **Use the first equation.**
            $450 + W = 500$ **Substitute 450 for A.**
                $W = 50$ **Solve for W.**

● The average airspeed of the planes is 450 mi/h. The average wind speed is 50 mi/h.

 **Quick Check** ❸ A plane takes about 6 hours to fly 2400 miles from New York City to Seattle, Washington. At the same time, your friend flies from Seattle to New York City. His plane travels with the same average airspeed, but his flight takes 5 hours. Find the average airspeed of the planes. Find the average wind speed.

EXERCISES

For more exercises, see *Extra Skill and Word Problem Practice.*

Practice and Problem Solving

 Practice by Example

Example 1
(page 572)

 **GO for Help**

1. Tyrel and Dalia bought some pens and pencils. Tyrel bought 4 pens and 5 pencils, which cost him $6.71. Dalia bought 5 pens and 3 pencils, which cost her $7.12. Let a equal the price of a pen. Let b equal the price of a pencil.
   a. Write an equation that relates the number of pens and pencils Tyrel bought to the amount he paid for them.
   b. Write an equation that relates the number of pens and pencils Dalia bought to the amount she paid for them.
   c. Solve the system you wrote for parts (a) and (b) to find the price of a pen and the price of a pencil.

2. Suppose you have just enough money, in coins, to pay for a loaf of bread priced at $1.95. You have 12 coins, all quarter and dimes. Let q equal the number of quarters and d equal the number of dimes. Which system models the given information?
   A. $q + d = 12$
   $\quad\;\; q + d = 1.95$
   B. $25q + 10d = 195$
   $\quad\;\; q + 12 = d$
   C. $10q + 25d = 12$
   $\quad\;\; q + d = 1.95$
   D. $q + d = 12$
   $\quad\;\; 25q + 10d = 195$

3. Suppose you want to combine two types of fruit drink to create 24 kilograms of a drink that will be 5% sugar by weight. Fruit drink A is 4% sugar by weight, and fruit drink B is 8% sugar by weight.
   a. Copy and complete the table below.

	Fruit Drink A 4% Sugar	Fruit Drink B 8% Sugar	Mixed Fruit Drink 5% Sugar
Fruit Drink (kg)	■	■	■
Sugar (kg)	■	■	■

   b. Write a system of equations that relates the amounts of fruit drink A and fruit drink B to the total amount of drink needed and to the total amount of sugar needed.
   c. Solve the system to find how much of each type of fruit drink you need to use.

4. You have $22 in your bank account and deposit $11.50 each week. At the same time your cousin has $218 but is withdrawing $13 each week.
   a. When will your accounts have the same balance?
   b. How much money will each of you have after 12 weeks?

Example 2
(page 573)

5. Business Suppose you invest $10,410 in equipment to manufacture a new board game. Each game costs $2.65 to manufacture and sells for $20. How many games must you make and sell before your business breaks even?

6. Business Several students decide to start a T-shirt company. After initial expenses of $280, they purchase each T-shirt wholesale for $3.99. They sell each T-shirt for $10.99. How many must they sell to break even?

Example 3
(page 574)

7. Travel A family is canoeing downstream (with the current). Their speed relative to the banks of the river averages 2.75 mi/h. During the return trip, they paddle upstream (against the current), averaging 1.5 mi/h relative to the riverbank.
  a. Write an equation for the rate of the canoe downstream.
  b. Write an equation for the rate of the canoe upstream.
  c. Solve the system to find the family's paddling speed in still water.
  d. Find the speed of the current of the river.

8. Travel John flies from Atlanta, Georgia, to San Francisco, California. It takes 5.6 hours to travel 2100 miles against the head wind. At the same time Debby flies from San Francisco to Atlanta. Her plane travels with the same average airspeed but, with a tail wind, her flight takes only 4.8 hours.
  a. Write a system of equations that relates time, airspeed, and wind speed to distance for each traveler.
  b. Solve the system to find the airspeed.
  c. Find the wind speed.

B   **Apply Your Skills**

Open-Ended **Without solving, what method would you choose to solve each system:** *graphing,* *substitution,* **or** *elimination?* **Explain your reasoning.**

9. $4s - 3t = 8$
   $t = -2s - 1$

10. $y = 3x - 1$
    $y = 4x$

11. $3m - 4n = 1$
    $3m - 2n = -1$

12. $y = -2x$
    $y = -\frac{1}{2}x + 3$

13. $2x - y = 4$
    $x + 3y = 16$

14. $u = 4v$
    $3u - 2v = 7$

15. Chemistry A piece of glass with an initial temperature of 99°C is cooled at a rate of 3.5 degrees Celsius per minute (°C/min). At the same time, a piece of copper with an initial temperature of 0°C is heated at a rate of 2.5°C/min. Let m = the number of minutes, and t = the temperature in degrees Celsius after m minutes.
  a. Write a system of equations that relates the temperature t of each material to the time m. Solve the system.
  b. Writing Explain what the solution means in this situation.

16. Geometry The perimeter of the rectangle is 34 cm. The perimeter of the triangle is 30 cm. Find the values of m and n.

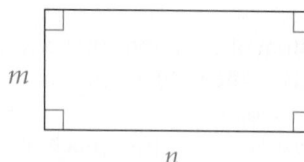
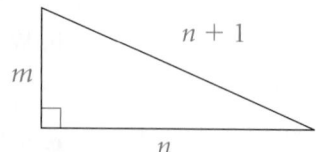

17. Open-Ended Write a problem for the total of two types of coins. Then solve the problem.

18. Sales A garden supply store sells two types of lawn mowers. Total sales of mowers for the year were $8379.70. The total number of mowers sold was 30. The small mower costs $249.99. The large mower costs $329.99. Find the number sold of each type of mower.

Real-World Connection

Glass can be drawn into optical fibers 16 km long. One fiber can carry 20 times as many phone calls as 500 copper wires.

GO for Help

For a guide to solving Exercise 18, see p. 579.

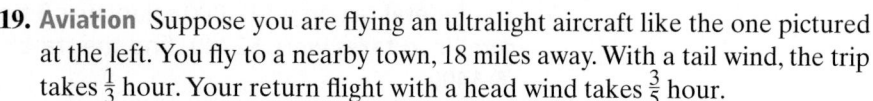

19. Aviation Suppose you are flying an ultralight aircraft like the one pictured at the left. You fly to a nearby town, 18 miles away. With a tail wind, the trip takes $\frac{1}{3}$ hour. Your return flight with a head wind takes $\frac{3}{5}$ hour.
  a. Find the average airspeed of the ultralight aircraft.
  b. Find the average wind speed.

20. Suppose the ratio of girls to boys in your school is 19 : 17. There are 1908 students altogether.
  a. Solve the proportion $\frac{g}{b} = \frac{19}{17}$ for g.
  b. Write and solve the system of equations to find the total number of boys b and girls g.

21. Consumer Decisions Suppose you are trying to decide whether to buy ski equipment. Typically, it costs you $60 a day to rent ski equipment and buy a lift ticket. You can buy ski equipment for about $400. A lift ticket alone costs $35 for one day.
  a. Find the break-even point.
  b. Critical Thinking If you expect to ski five days a year, should you buy the ski equipment? Explain.

22. Geometry Find the values of x and y.

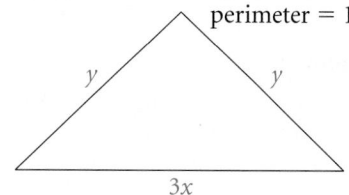

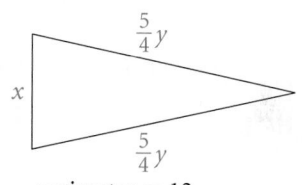

23. You can represent the value of any two-digit number with the expression $10a + b$, where a is the tens' place digit and b is the ones' place digit. If a is 5 and b is 7, then the value of the number is $10(5) + 7$, or 57.
Use a system of equations to find the two-digit number described below.

  • The ones' place digit is one more than twice the tens' place digit.
  • The value of the number is two more than five times the ones' place digit.

24. Sales An artist sells original hand-painted greeting cards. He makes $2.50 profit on a small card and $4.00 profit on a large card. He generally sells 5 large cards for every 2 small cards. He wants a profit of $10,000 from large and small cards this year.
  a. Find the quantity of each card the artist needs to sell to reach his goal.
  b. The artist can create a card every 12 minutes. How many hours will he need to make enough to reach his profit target if he sells them all?
  c. What is the artist's hourly rate of pay?

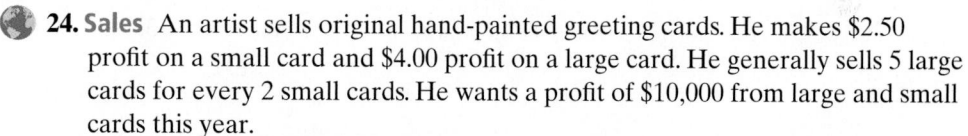

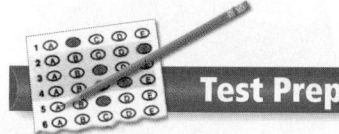

Multiple Choice

25. Which system describes the following situation: The sum of two numbers is 20. The difference between three times the larger and twice the smaller is 40.
  A. $x + y = 20$
      $3x + 2y = 40$
  B. $x - y = 20$
      $3x - 2y = 40$
  C. $x + y = 20$
      $3x - 2y = 40$
  D. $x - y = 20$
      $3x + 2y = 40$

Real-World  Connection

Ultralight aircraft like the one pictured above can weigh less than 400 lb.

GO Online

Homework Video Tutor
Visit: PHSchool.com
Web Code: ate-0704

C Challenge

26. The federal tax on a $12,000 salary was 8 times the state tax. If the combined taxes were $2700, find the state's share of taxes.
   F. $400   G. $150
   H. $300   J. $350

27. Which system describes the following situation? Craig has 80¢ in nickels n and dimes d. He has four more nickels than dimes.
   A. $d + n = 4$ B. $n - d = 4$
      $10d + 5n = 80$ $10d + 5n = 80$
   C. $d - n = 4$ D. $d + n = 4$
      $10d + 5n = 80$ $10d - 5n = 80$

Short Response

28. A large group of students wants to go to the movies. If the students take 3 vans and 1 car, they can transport 22 people. If they take 2 vans and 4 cars, they can transport 28 people. Write and solve a system of equations to find the number of people that can be transported in a van. Show your work.

Mixed Review

Lesson 10-3

Solve by elimination.

29. $2x + 5y = 13$ **30.** $4x + 2y = -10$ **31.** $7x + 6y = 30$
   $3x - 5y = 7$ $-2x + 3y = 33$ $9x - 8y = 15$

Lesson 9-1

Find the slope of the line that passes through each pair of points.

32. $(2, 4), (6, 10)$ **33.** $(-3, 1), (10, 14)$ **34.** $(8, -11), (5, -12)$

35. $(1.2, 7), (4.6, 0.2)$ **36.** $\left(5, -\frac{1}{2}\right), \left(-6, 3\frac{1}{2}\right)$ **37.** $(8, 0), (8, 5)$

Lesson 7-5

Solve each inequality and graph the solutions.

38. $6 < y < 10$ **39.** $-8 < n \leq 3$ **40.** $2 < k + 1 < 7$

41. $4 \leq 4p \leq 16$ **42.** $-13 < 3c + 2 \leq 17$ **43.** $21 > 5w - 4 > 1$

Algebra at Work

··· **Businessperson**

Some of the goals of a business are to minimize costs and maximize profits. People in business use systems of linear inequalities to analyze data in order to achieve these goals.

The illustration lists some of the variables involved in operating a small manufacturing company. To solve a problem, a businessperson must identify the variables and restrictions, and then search for the best of many possible solutions.

Restriction Polygon

— Advertising
— Raw Materials
— Transportation
— Packaging
— Equipment
— Labor

For: Information about a career in business
Web Code: atb-2031

Understanding Word Problems Read the exercise below and then follow along with what Bill thinks and writes. Check your understanding by solving the exercise at the bottom of the page.

A garden supply store sells two types of lawn mowers. Total sales of mowers for the year were $8379.70. The total number of mowers sold was 30. The small mowers cost $249.99. The large mowers cost $329.99. Find the number of each type of mower sold.

What Bill Thinks

I'll read the problem and write down the important information.

Where should I start? Well, it's always helpful to write sentences based on the information I'm given. Total sales include the sales for both the small mowers and the large mowers.

Total number of mowers is the number of small mowers *plus* the number of large mowers.

Now I'll define some variables. The problem asks for the number of small mowers and the number of large mowers. I'll use 2 variables.

Now I can write 2 equations.

Since the first equation has large numbers, it's probably easier to rewrite the second equation and substitute into the first equation. I'll then solve for w and s.

I'll write my answer in a sentence.

What Bill Writes

Total sales = $8379.70
Total number of mowers = 30
Small mowers cost $249.99.
Large mowers cost $329.99.

Total sales = sales from small mowers + sales from large mowers

Total number of mowers = number of small mowers + number of large mowers

Number of small mowers = s
Number of large mowers = w

Total sales: $8379.70 = 249.99s + 329.99w$
Total number: $30 = s + w$

$s = 30 - w$
$8379.70 = (249.99)(30 - w) + 329.99w$
$8379.70 = 7499.70 + 80w$
$\quad 880 = 80w$
$11 = w;\ s = 30 - 11 = 19$

The store sold 19 small mowers and 11 large mowers.

EXERCISE

A nursery sells small apple trees for $19.99 and large apple trees for $35.99. Total sales for the year were $1907.27. The total number of apple trees sold was 73. Find the number of each type of apple tree sold.

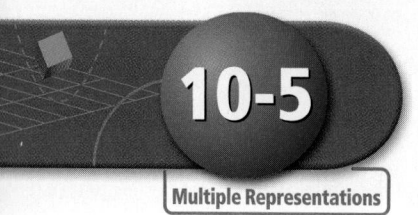
Linear Inequalities

What You'll Learn

- To graph linear inequalities
- To write and use linear inequalities when modeling real-world situations

. . . And Why

To analyze possible purchases within a budget, as in Example 3

✓ **Check Skills You'll Need**

GO **for Help** Lessons 7-1 and 9-2

Describe each statement as *always*, *sometimes*, or *never* true.

1. $-3 > -2$ **2.** $8 \leq 8$ **3.** $4n \geq n$

Write each equation in slope-intercept form.

4. $2x - 3y = 9$ **5.** $y + 3x = 6$ **6.** $4y - 3x = 1$

◀)) **New Vocabulary** • linear inequality • solutions of an inequality

---

1 · Graphing Linear Inequalities

> ### Activity: Graphing Inequalities
>
> **1.** Graph $y = x + 4$ on a coordinate plane.
>
> **2.** Test three points that lie above the graph of $y = x + 4$. Substitute the coordinates of each of the points for (x, y) in the inequality $y > x + 4$. If the results are true statements, mark the points on your graph.
>
> **3.** Test three points that lie below the graph of $y = x + 4$. Substitute the coordinates of each of the points for (x, y) in the inequality $y > x + 4$. If the results are true statements, mark the points on your graph.
>
> **4.** **Critical Thinking** To graph $y > x + 4$, would you choose points above or below $y = x + 4$?
>
> **5.** Determine whether you would graph points above or below the graph of $y = x - 2$ to graph the inequality $y < x - 2$.

Just as you have used inequalities to describe graphs on a number line, you can use inequalities to describe regions of a coordinate plane.

GO **for Help**

To review graphing inequalities in one variable see p. 196.

Number line
$x < 1$

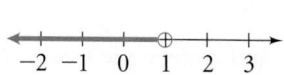

Coordinate plane
$x < 1$

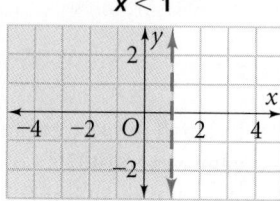

A **linear inequality** describes a region of the coordinate plane that has a boundary line. The **solutions of an inequality** are the coordinates of the points that make the inequality true.

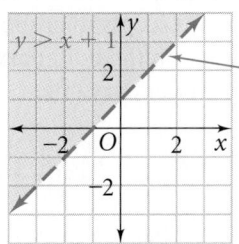

Each point on a *dashed* boundary line is not a solution.

Each point on a *solid* boundary line is a solution.

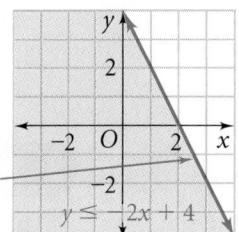

As you can see in the graphs above, you can tell from an inequality whether to shade above or below the boundary line. For an inequality written in the form of $y <$ or $y \le$, shade below the boundary line. For an inequality written in the form of $y >$ or $y \ge$, shade above the boundary line.

To do Example 1 with a graphing calculator, see page 757.

For: Linear Inequality Activity
Use: Interactive Textbook, 10-5

1 EXAMPLE **Graphing an Inequality**

Graph $y < 2x + 3$.

First graph the boundary line $y = 2x + 3$.

The coordinates of points on the boundary line do not make the inequality true. So, use a dashed line.

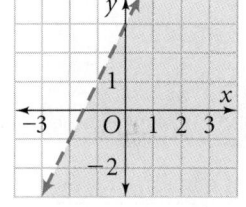

Shade below the boundary line.

Check The point $(0, 0)$ is in the region of the graph of the inequality. See if $(0, 0)$ satisfies the inequality.

$y < 2x + 3$
$0 < 2(0) + 3$ **Substitute (0, 0) for (x, y).**
$0 < 3$ ✓

 **Quick Check** **①** Graph $y \ge 3x - 1$.

In order to tell whether you shade above or below a boundary line, you may need to write the inequality in slope-intercept form.

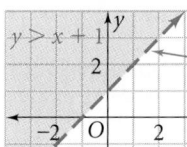

2 EXAMPLE **Rewriting to Graph an Inequality**

Graph $3x - 5y \le 10$.

Solve $3x - 5y \le 10$ for y.

$3x - 5y \le 10$
$\quad -5y \le -3x + 10$ **Subtract 3x from each side.**
$\quad\quad y \ge \frac{3}{5}x - 2$ **Divide each side by −5. Reverse the inequality symbol.**

Graph $y = \frac{3}{5}x - 2$.

The coordinates of points on the boundary line make the inequality true. So, use a solid line.

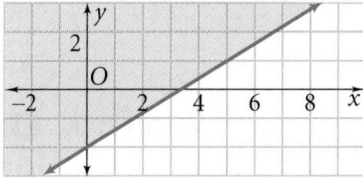

Since $y \ge \frac{3}{5}x - 2$, shade above the boundary line.

Quick Check **②** Graph $6x + 8y \ge 12$.

Many situations are modeled by inequalities that have a boundary line of the form $Ax + By = C$. You can use the intercepts to graph the boundary line of the inequality. Choose a test point not on the boundary line to determine whether the solutions are above or below the boundary line.

3 EXAMPLE   Real-World Problem Solving

Budget Suppose your budget for a party allows you to spend no more than $12 on peanuts and cashews. Peanuts cost $2/lb and cashews cost $4/lb. Find three possible combinations of peanuts and cashews you can buy.

Relate | cost of peanuts | plus | cost of cashews | is less than or equal to | total budget |

Define   Let x = the number of pounds of peanuts.

Let y = the number of pounds of cashews.

Write $2x$ + $4y$ $\leq$ 12

Graph $2x + 4y = 12$ by graphing the intercepts, $(6, 0)$ and $(0, 3)$.

The coordinates of points on the boundary line make the inequality true. So, use a solid line.

Graph only in Quadrant I, since you cannot buy a negative amount of peanuts or cashews.

Test the point $(1, 1)$.

$$2x + 4y \leq 12$$
$$2(1) + 4(1) \leq 12 \quad \textbf{Substitute (1, 1) for } (x, y).$$
$$6 \leq 12 \quad \textbf{Since the inequality is true, (1, 1) is a solution.}$$

Shade the region containing $(1, 1)$. The graph below shows all the possible solutions of the problem.

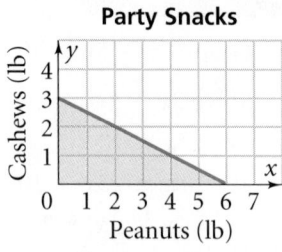

Party Snacks

Since the boundary line is included in the graph, the intercepts are also solutions of the inequality. The solution $(2, 2)$ means that if you buy 2 lb of peanuts, you can buy 2 lb of cashews. Three solutions are $(2, 2)$, $(3, 1)$, and $(1, 2)$.

 **Quick Check**   ❸ **Cooking** Suppose you plan to spend no more than $24 on meat for a cookout. At your local market, hamburger costs $3.00/lb and chicken wings cost $2.40/lb. Find three possible combinations of hamburger and chicken wings you can buy.

Real-World Connection

One ounce of peanuts has 9 g of protein. One ounce of cashews has 5.4 g of protein.

EXERCISES

For more exercises, see *Extra Skill and Word Problem Practice*.

Practice and Problem Solving

 Practice by Example

Example 1
(page 581)

 **GO for Help**

Determine whether point P is a solution of the linear inequality.

1. $y \le -2x + 1; P(2, 2)$ **2.** $x < 2; P(1, 0)$ **3.** $y \ge 3x - 2; P(0, 0)$

4. $y > x - 1; P(0, 1)$ **5.** $y \ge -\frac{2}{5}x + 4; P(0, 0)$ **6.** $y > \frac{5}{3}x - 4; P(0, 1)$

Choose the linear inequality that describes each graph.

7.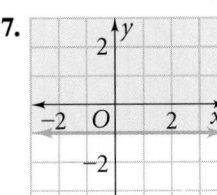
A. $y \ge -1$
B. $y \le -1$

8.
A. $y > \frac{1}{2}x$
B. $y < \frac{1}{2}x$

9.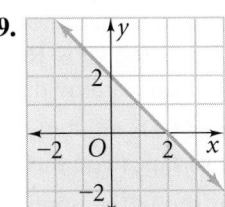
A. $y \ge -x + 2$
B. $y \le -x + 2$

10.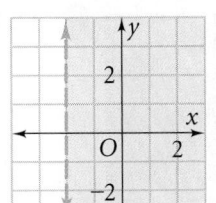
A. $x > -2$
B. $x < -2$

Graph each linear inequality.

11. $y \le \frac{1}{4}x - 1$ **12.** $y \ge \frac{1}{4}x - 1$ **13.** $y < -4x - 1$ **14.** $y \ge 4x - 1$

15. $y < 5x - 5$ **16.** $y \le \frac{2}{5}x - 3$ **17.** $y \le -3x$ **18.** $y \ge -\frac{1}{2}x$

Example 2
(page 581)

Write each linear inequality in slope-intercept form. Then graph the inequality.

19. $2x - 3y \ge 7$ **20.** $5x - 3y \le 6$ **21.** $4x - 6y \ge 16$ **22.** $-4y - 6x > 8$

Example 3
(page 582)

23. Budget Suppose you are shopping for crepe paper to decorate the school gym for a dance. Gold crepe paper costs $5 per roll, and blue crepe paper costs $3 per roll. Your budget allows you to spend at most $48 for crepe paper. How many rolls of gold and blue crepe paper can you buy without exceeding your budget?

Let x = the number of rolls of blue crepe paper.
Let y = the number of rolls of gold crepe paper.

a. Write a linear inequality that describes the situation.
b. Graph the linear inequality.
c. Write three possible solutions to the problem.
d. Critical Thinking The point $(-2, 5)$ is a solution of the inequality. Is it a solution of the problem? Explain.

24. Manufacturing A company makes nylon and canvas backpacks, as shown at the left. The profit on a nylon backpack is $3 and the profit on a canvas backpack is $10. How many backpacks must the company sell to make a profit of more than $250?
a. Write a linear inequality that describes the situation.
b. Graph the linear inequality.
c. Write three possible solutions to the problem.
d. Critical Thinking Which values are reasonable for the domain and for the range? Explain.

Real-World Connection

The American Academy of Orthopaedic Surgeons suggests that a backpack's weight should not be more than 20% of a student's body weight.

Apply Your Skills

Graph each linear inequality.

25. $y \leq \frac{2}{5}x + 2$ **26.** $y \geq -\frac{2}{5}x + 2$ **27.** $4x - 5y \leq 10$ **28.** $4x + 5y \leq 10$

29. $4y < 6x + 2$ **30.** $2x + 3y \leq 6$ **31.** $4x - 4y \leq 8$ **32.** $y - 2x < 2$

33. Writing Explain how you can tell from a linear inequality whether you will shade above or below the graph of the boundary line.

Write the linear inequality shown in each graph.

34. 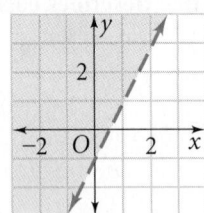   **35.** 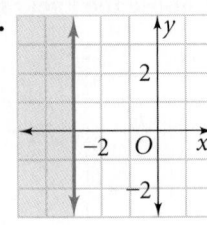   **36.**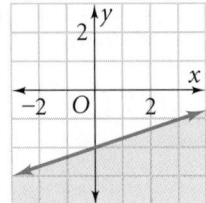

37. Budget Suppose you work at a local radio station. You are in charge of a $180 budget for new tapes and CDs. Record companies will give you 21 promotional (free) CDs. You can buy tapes for $8 and CDs for $12.

    Let x = the number of CDs you buy.
    Let y = the number of tapes you buy.

a. Write an inequality that shows the number of tapes and CDs you can buy.
b. Graph the inequality.
c. Is $(8, 9)$ a solution of the inequality? Explain what the solution means.
d. If you buy only tapes and you buy as many as possible, how many new recordings will the station get?

Write the linear inequality described. Then graph the inequality.

38. x is positive.   **39.** y is negative.

40. y is not negative.   **41.** x is less than y.

42. Error Analysis Jan's graph of the inequality $4x + 6y > 12$ is shown below. What is wrong with the graph?

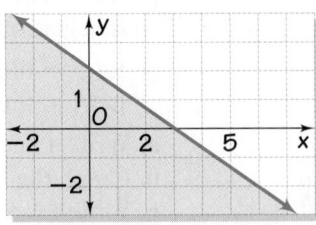

43. Critical Thinking Write an inequality that describes the entire part of the coordinate plane *not* included in the solution of $y \geq x + 2$.

44. Probability Suppose you play a carnival game. You toss one blue and one red number cube. If the number on the blue cube is greater than the number on the red cube, you win a prize. The graph at the left shows all the possible outcomes of tossing the cubes.

a. Copy and shade the graph to show the winning outcomes.
b. Write an inequality that describes the shaded region.
c. What is the probability that you will win a prize?

Comparing Cubes

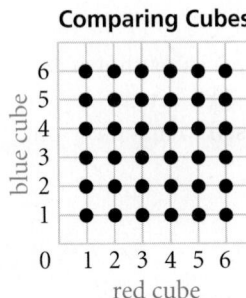

Real-World Connection

In 2000, there were about 12,900 licensed radio stations in the United States.

Problem Solving Hint

For Exercise 45, draw a diagram of a possible garden.

 45. Geometry You want to fence a rectangular area of your yard for a garden. You plan to use no more than 50 ft of fencing.
  a. Write and graph a linear inequality that describes this situation.
  b. Open-Ended What are two possible sizes for a square garden?
  c. Can you make the garden 12 ft by 15 ft? Justify your answer.

C Challenge

For Exercises 46–47, write the inequality that has the solution described.

46. The points $(0, -3)$ and $(8, 5)$ lie on the boundary line, but neither point is a solution. The point $(1, 1)$ is not a solution.

47. The points $(7, 12)$ and $(-3, -8)$ lie on the boundary line, and each point is a solution. The point $(1, 1)$ is also a solution.

48. a. Open-Ended Write and graph an inequality in the form $Ax + By > C$, where $A, B,$ and C are all positive.
  b. Write and graph an inequality in the form $Ax + By < C$, where $A, B,$ and C are all positive.
  c. Reasoning Both inequalities are in standard form. Make a conjecture about the inequality symbol and the region shaded.
  d. Would your conjecture in part (c) be different if B were negative?

GO nline

Homework Video Tutor

Visit: PHSchool.com
Web Code: ate-0705

49. a. Is the point $(4, 5)$ a solution of the inequality $y > x - 1$?
  b. Is the point $(4, 5)$ a solution of the inequality $y < 3x$?
  c. Find one other point that is a solution of both inequalities.
  d. Draw a graph that shows all the points that are solutions of both inequalities.

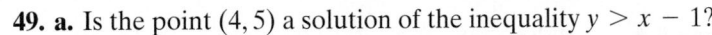

 **Test Prep**

Multiple Choice

50. Which of the following is true of the graph of $y \geq -x + 1$?
  A. The line is solid, and the shading is above the line.
  B. The line is dashed, and the shading is above the line.
  C. The line is solid, and the shading is below the line.
  D. The line is dashed, and the shading is below the line.

51. Which linear inequality describes the graph at the right?
  F. $y < -\frac{2}{3}x - 4$ **G.** $y > -\frac{2}{3}x - 4$
  H. $y \leq -\frac{2}{3}x - 4$ **J.** $y \geq -\frac{2}{3}x - 4$

52. The graph of which of the following is shaded above the line?
  A. $x + y < 9$ **B.** $x + y < -9$
  C. $y - x < 9$ **D.** $x - y < 9$

53. Which inequality below models the following situation?
  You want to spend less than $20 on asparagus and bananas. Asparagus is $3.00 per pound and bananas are $.50 per pound. Let a represent the weight of the asparagus and b represent the weight of the bananas.

  F. $3a + 0.5b < 20$ **G.** $3a + 0.5b > 20$
  H. $3a + 0.5b \leq 20$ **J.** $3a + 0.5b \geq 20$

Short Response

54. Explain how to graph $y \leq 3x - 4$. Then graph the inequality.

Lesson 10-4

For Exercises 55–56, define the variables and write a system of equations for each situation. Solve by any method.

55. Business Suppose you invest $12,000 in equipment to manufacture a new board game. Each game costs $2.50 to manufacture and sells for $18. How many games must you make and sell for your business to break even?

56. Suppose you are canoeing along a river with a steady current. Your average speed upstream is 2.5 mi/h. On the return trip you paddle with the current, and your average speed is 4 mi/h. Find the average speed of the current and your average speed if you were paddling in still water.

Lesson 8-7

Find the common difference of each arithmetic sequence.

57. $-8, -3, 2, \ldots$ **58.** $4, 11, 18, \ldots$ **59.** $13, 24, 35, \ldots$ **60.** $11, 5, -1, \ldots$

Find the second and fourth terms of each sequence.

61. $A(n) = 3 + (n - 1)(5)$ **62.** $A(n) = -9 + (n - 1)(2.3)$

Lesson 6-4

Solve each proportion.

63. $\frac{3}{4} = \frac{m}{16}$ **64.** $\frac{6}{7} = \frac{24}{g}$ **65.** $\frac{4}{w} = \frac{8}{22}$ **66.** $\frac{9}{10} = \frac{15}{a}$

67. $\frac{x+1}{3} = \frac{2}{9}$ **68.** $\frac{n-2}{5} = \frac{6}{15}$ **69.** $\frac{8}{r+1} = \frac{4}{7}$ **70.** $\frac{9}{x+3} = \frac{18}{19}$

Checkpoint Quiz 2   **Lessons 10-3 through 10-5**

For Exercises 1–5, solve each system using elimination.

1. $2x + 5y = 2$
$3x - 5y = 53$

2. $-8x - 3y = 69$
$8x + 7y = -65$

3. $4x + 2y = 34$
$10x - 4y = -5$

4. $11x - 13y = 89$
$-11x + 13y = 107$

5. $3x + 6y = 42$
$-7x + 8y = -109$

6. You have a total of 21 coins, all nickels and dimes. The total value is $1.70. Write and solve a system of equations to find the number of dimes d and the number of nickels n that you have.

7. Business Suppose you start an ice cream business. You buy a freezer for $200. It costs you $.35 to make each single-scoop ice cream cone. You sell each cone for $1.20. Write and solve a system of equations to find the break-even point for your business.

8. To go to a campsite 12 miles away, you paddle a canoe against the current of a river for 4 hours. During your return trip you paddle with the current, and you travel the same distance in 3 hours. Write and solve a system of equations to find your paddling speed in still water. Find the speed of the current of the river.

Graph each inequality.

9. $y \geq 2x - 4$ **10.** $3x + 4y < 18$

Systems of Linear Inequalities

What You'll Learn

- To solve systems of linear inequalities by graphing
- To model real-world situations using systems of linear inequalities

...And Why

To find the possible dimensions for a zoo habitat, as in Example 3

Solve each system by graphing.

1. $y = 3x - 6$
$y = -x + 2$

2. $y = -\frac{1}{2}x + 4$
$y = -\frac{1}{2}x + 3$

3. $x + y = 4$
$2x - y = 8$

Graph each inequality.

4. $y > 5$

5. $y \le \frac{2}{3}x - 1$

6. $4x - 8y \ge 4$

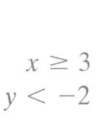 **New Vocabulary**
- system of linear inequalities
- solution of a system of linear inequalities

---

1 **Solving Systems of Linear Inequalities by Graphing**

Two or more linear inequalities together form a **system of linear inequalities.** The system below describes the lavender-shaded region of the graph. Notice that there are two boundary lines.

System of Linear Inequalities

$x \ge 3$
$y < -2$

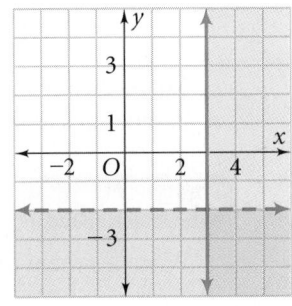

You can describe all the points of a quadrant with a system of linear inequalities.

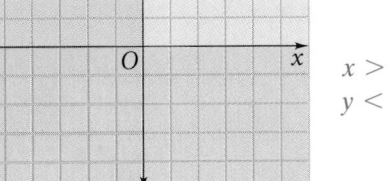

$x < 0$
$y > 0$

$x > 0$
$y > 0$

$x < 0$
$y < 0$

$x > 0$
$y < 0$

A **solution of a system of linear inequalities** makes each inequality in the system true. The graph of a system shows all of its solutions.

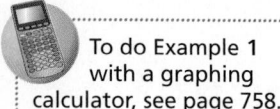
To do Example 1 with a graphing calculator, see page 758.

1 EXAMPLE Graphing a System of Inequalities

Solve by graphing. $y > 2x - 5$
                      $3x + 4y < 12$

Graph $y > 2x - 5$ and $3x + 4y < 12$.

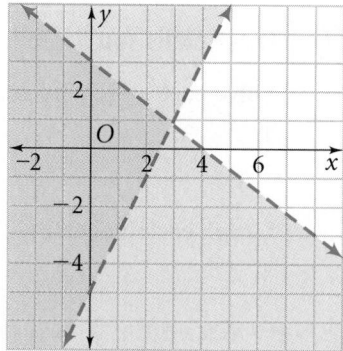

The coordinates of the points in the region where the graphs of the two inequalities overlap (shaded in lavender) are solutions of the system.

Check The point $(0, 0)$ is in the region graphed by both inequalities. See if $(0, 0)$ satisfies both inequalities.

$y > 2x - 5$ $3x + 4y < 12$
$0 > 2(0) - 5$ ⟵ **Substitute (0, 0) for (x, y).** ⟶ $3(0) + 4(0) < 12$
$0 > -5$ ✔ $0 < 12$ ✔

For: Systems of Inequalities Activity
Use: Interactive Textbook, 10-6

✓ Quick Check ❶ Solve by graphing. $y \geq -x + 2$
                                            $2x + 4y < 4$

You can combine your knowledge of linear equations with your knowledge of inequalities to describe a graph using a system of inequalities.

2 EXAMPLE Writing a System of Inequalities From a Graph

Write a system of linear inequalities from each shaded region below.

Video Tutor Help
Visit: PHSchool.com
Web Code: ate-0775

red region
boundary: $y = x - 2$
The region lies above the boundary line, so the inequality is $y > x - 2$.

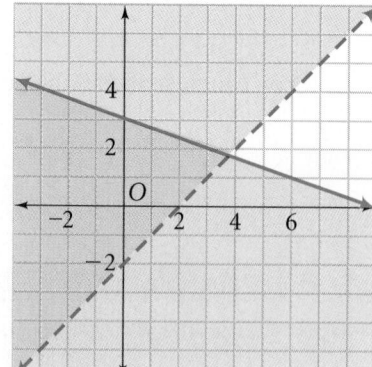

blue region
boundary: $y = -\frac{1}{3}x + 3$
The region includes the boundary line and the points lying below the boundary line, so the inequality is $y \leq -\frac{1}{3}x + 3$.

system for the lavender region: $y > x - 2$
                                   $y \leq -\frac{1}{3}x + 3$

✓ Quick Check **2** Write a system of inequalities for the lavender region in each of the following graphs.

a.

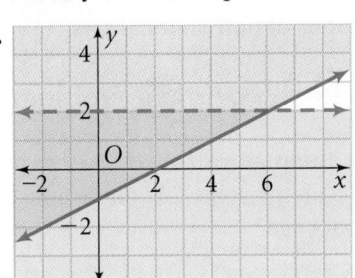

b.

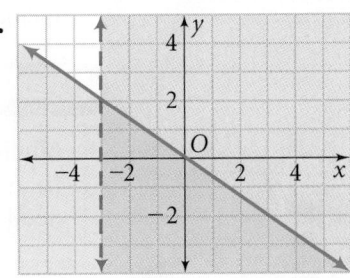

2 Writing and Using Systems of Linear Inequalities

You can model some real-world situations by graphing linear inequalities. When you graph real-world situations, you often need to plan how you will scale each axis. Use the values for the x- and y-intercepts to determine your scale.

3 EXAMPLE Real-World 🌎 Problem Solving

Animal Habitat A zoo keeper wants to fence a rectangular habitat for goats. The length of the habitat should be at least 80 ft, and the distance around it should be no more than 310 ft. What are the possible dimensions of the habitat?

Relate

the length	is at least	80 ft

the perimeter	is no more than	310 ft

Define Let x = width of the habitat.
Let y = length of the habitat.

Write

y	$\geq$	80		$2x + 2y$	$\leq$	310

Solve by graphing. $y \geq 80$
$2x + 2y \leq 310$.

$y \geq 80$
$m = 0$
$b = 80$

Shade above
$y = 80$.

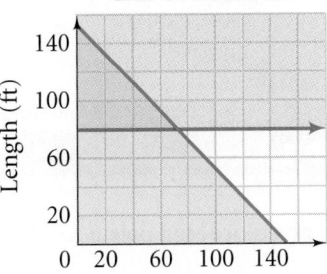

Size of Goat Pen

$2x + 2y \leq 310$

Graph the intercepts
$(155, 0)$ and $(0, 155)$.

Test $(0, 0)$.
$2(0) + 2(0) \leq 310$
$0 \leq 310$

Shade below
$2x + 2y = 310$.

The solutions are the coordinates of the points that lie in the region shaded lavender and on the parts of the lines $y = 80$ and $2x + 2y = 310$ that border the lavender region.

✓ Quick Check **3** Suppose you want to fence a rectangular garden plot. You want the length of the garden to be at least 50 ft and the perimeter to be no more than 140 ft. Solve by graphing to show all of the possible dimensions of the garden.

Real-World 🌎 Connection

Careers A zoologist studies individual animals and the processes that sustain an animal within its group and its environment. To adapt an animal to a zoo habitat, a zoologist must research ways to help an animal adapt to a restricted environment.

Some real-world situations have a domain and range that include only integers. In such cases, the solutions will be some, but not all, of the points in the region included in the graphs of both inequalities.

4 EXAMPLE   Real-World  Problem Solving

Mailing Packages Suppose you need $2.40 in postage to mail a package to a friend. You have 9 stamps, some 20¢ and some 34¢. How many of each do you need to mail the package?

Relate

the number of 20¢ and 34¢ stamps	is less than or equal to	9	the value of 20¢ and 34¢ stamps	is at least	240¢

Define Let a = the number of 20¢ stamps.
Let b = the number of 34¢ stamps.

Write

$a + b$	$\leq$	9	$20a + 34b$	$\geq$	240

Solve by graphing.
$a + b \leq 9$
$20a + 34b \geq 240$

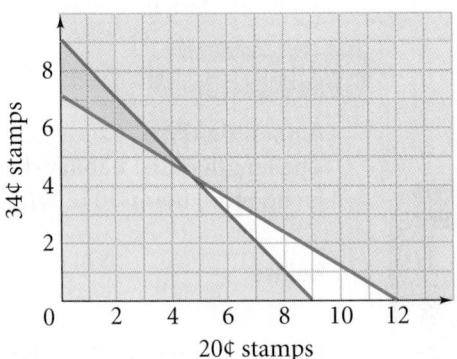

Real-World 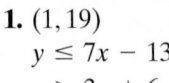 Connection

In 1932, you would have needed a 3¢ stamp to mail a letter. To mail the same letter in 2001 would have cost 34¢.

The solutions are all of the coordinates of points that are nonnegative integers lying in the region shaded lavender and on its boundary lines.

✓ Quick Check ④ **a.** Give two solutions from the graph in Example 4.
   b. Does either solution give you the exact postage needed to mail the package?
   c. Critical Thinking Why are the solutions to the problem only nonnegative integers?

EXERCISES
For more exercises, see *Extra Skill and Word Problem Practice.*

Practice and Problem Solving

A Practice by Example

Example 1
(page 588)

GO for Help

Is the given ordered pair a solution of the system of inequalities?

1. $(1, 19)$
   $y \leq 7x - 13$
   $y > 3x + 6$

2. $(4, 10)$
   $9x - y \geq 23$
   $5x + 0.2y \geq 20$

3. $(-2, 40)$
   $y > -13x + 29$
   $y \leq 9x + 11$

Solve each system of inequalities by graphing.

4. $y < 2x + 4$
   $-3x - 2y \geq 6$

5. $y < 2x + 4$
   $2x - y \leq 4$

6. $y > 2x + 4$
   $2x - y \leq 4$

7. $y > \frac{1}{4}x$
   $y \leq -x + 4$

8. $y < 2x - 3$
   $y > 5$

9. $y \leq -\frac{1}{3}x + 7$
   $y \geq -x + 1$

10. $x + 2y \le 10$
$x + 2y \ge 9$

11. $y \ge -x + 5$
$y \le 3x - 4$

12. $y \le 0.75x - 2$
$y > 0.75x - 3$

13. $8x + 4y \ge 10$
$3x - 6y > 12$

14. $2x - \frac{1}{4}y < 1$
$4x + 8y > 4$

15. $6x - 5y < 15$
$x + 2y \ge 7$

Example 2
(page 588)

Write a system of inequalities for each graph.

16.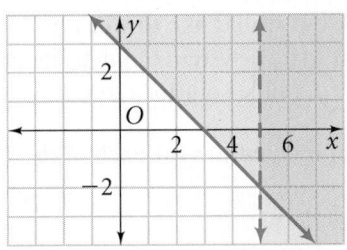

17.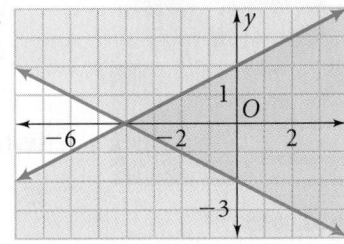

18.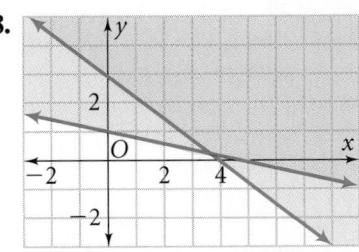

19.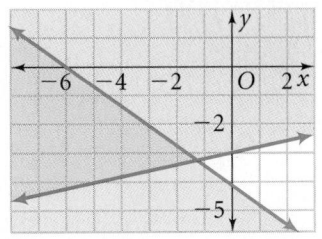

Example 3
(page 589)

20. Budget Suppose you buy flour and cornmeal in bulk to make flour tortillas and corn tortillas. Flour costs $1.50/lb. Cornmeal costs $2.50/lb. You want to spend less than $9.50 on flour and cornmeal, and you need at least 4 lb altogether.
a. Write a system of inequalities that describes this situation.
b. Graph the system to show all possible solutions.

21. Suppose you want to fence a rectangular area for your dog. You will use the house as one of the four sides. Since the house is 40 ft wide, the length ℓ needs to be no more than 40 ft. You plan to use at least 150 ft of fencing. Graph the following system to find possible dimensions for the rectangle.

$$\ell \le 40$$
$$\ell + 2w \ge 150$$

Example 4
(page 590)

22. Suppose you receive a $50 gift certificate to the Cityside Music and Books store. All CDs at the store cost $9.99, and all books cost $5.99. You want to buy some books and at least one CD.
a. Write a system of inequalities for x books and y CDs that describes this situation.
b. Graph the system to show all possible solutions.
c. What purchase does the ordered pair $(2, 6)$ represent? Is it a solution to your system? Explain.
d. Find a solution in which you spend almost all of the gift certificate.

 **Apply Your Skills**

23. Business A seafood restaurant owner orders perch and salmon. He wants to buy at least 50 pounds of fish but cannot spend more than $180. Write and graph a system of inequalities to show the possible combinations of perch and salmon he could buy.

24. Earnings Suppose you have a job in an ice cream shop that pays $6 per hour. You also have a babysitting job that pays $4 per hour. You want to earn at least $60 per week but would like to work no more than 12 hours per week.
 a. Graph and write a system of linear inequalities that describes this situation.
 b. Give three possible solutions to the system.

Perch $4.00/lb

Salmon $3.00/lb

Write a system of inequalities for each of the following graphs.

25.
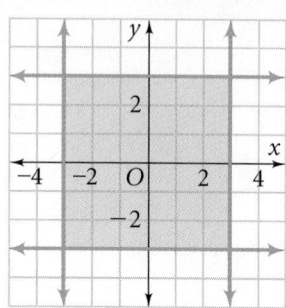

26.
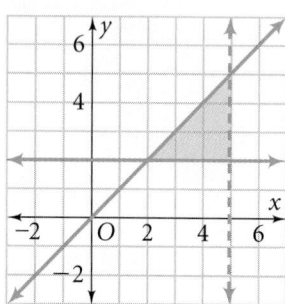

27.
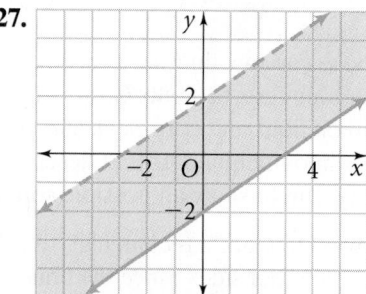

28.
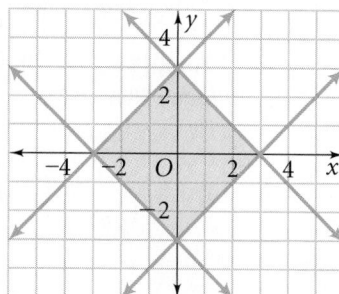

29. Open-Ended Write a system of four inequalities that describes a rectangle. Graph the system.

30. Geometry The following system of inequalities describes a right isosceles triangle.
 a. Find m.
 b. Find the area of the triangle.

$x > 0$
$y > 0$
$y < mx + 4$

Geometry **The solution region of each system of linear inequalities below forms a figure. (a) Describe the shape. (b) Find the vertices. (c) Find the area.**

31. $y \geq \frac{1}{2}x + 1$
 $y \leq 2$
 $x \geq -4$

32. $x \geq 1$
 $x \leq 5$
 $y \geq -1$
 $y \leq 3$

33. $x \geq 0$
 $x \leq 2$
 $y \geq -4$
 $y \leq -x + 2$

34. $x \geq 2$
 $y \geq -3$
 $x + y \leq 4$

35. a. Business A clothing store has a going-out-of-business sale. They are selling pants for $10.99 and shirts for $4.99. You can spend as much as $45 and want to buy at least one pair of pants. Write and graph a system of inequalities that describes this situation.
 b. Suppose you need to buy at least three pairs of pants. From your graph, find all the ordered pairs that are possible solutions.

GO Online
Homework Video Tutor
Visit: PHSchool.com
Web Code: ate-0706

36. a. Graph each inequality. $y > 4x + 1$
                                     $y < 4x - 2$

    b. Writing Will the boundary lines $y = 4x + 1$ and $y = 4x - 2$ ever intersect? Explain.

    c. Will the shaded regions you drew in part (a) overlap?

    d. Does the system of inequalities have any solutions?

37. a. Graph the system of inequalities. $y > 3x - 5$
                                        $y < 3x + 4$

    b. Will the boundary lines $y = 3x - 5$ and $y = 3x + 4$ ever intersect? Explain.

    c. Describe the shape of the overlapping region.

Open-Ended Write a system of linear inequalities with the given characteristics.

38. $(0, 0)$ is a solution.

39. Solutions are only in Quadrant II.

40. There is no solution.

41. $(3, 7)$ is not a solution.

42. Solutions are only in Quadrant IV.

43. Multiple Choice Which region represents the solution to the system?

$y \geq \frac{1}{2}x + 1$

$4x + 2y \leq 8$

   (A) I   (B) II

   (C) III   (D) IV

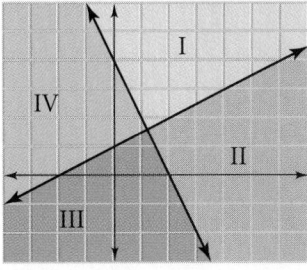

C Challenge 🌐 **44. Business** A jeweler plans to produce a ring made of silver and gold. The price of gold is approximately \$10/g. The price of silver is approximately \$.15/g. She considers the following in deciding how much gold and silver to use in the ring.

   • The total mass must be more than 10 g but less than 20 g.

   • The ring must contain at least 3 g of gold.

   • The total cost of the gold and silver must be less than \$60.

Let s = the mass of silver in grams and d = the mass of gold in grams.

a. Write and graph the four inequalities that describe this situation.

b. For one solution (s, d), find the mass of the ring and the cost of the gold and silver.

45. Solve $|y| \geq x$. (*Hint:* Write two inequalities; then graph them.)

Write a system of linear inequalities with the given characteristics.

46. $(2, 5)$ and $(5, 2)$ are not solutions; $(5, 5)$ is a solution.

47. $(-3, 2)$ and $(3, 2)$ are not solutions; $(-2, 6)$ is a solution.

🌐 **48. Business** A drum maker sells two sizes of frame drums like the ones at the left. A 14-in. drum sells for \$180 and an 18-in. drum sells for \$240. He is trying to decide how many drums to build and considers the following:

   • He wants to produce and sell at least \$2700 worth of drums.

   • He has materials to make no more than 17 drums.

   • He plans to make more 14-in. drums than 18-in. drums.

   • He wants to make at least four 18-in. drums.

a. Write and graph the four inequalities that describe this situation.

b. Give one possible solution to the system.

Multiple Choice

49. Which point is a solution of the following system? $y > x$
$$y < 3x - 4$$

   I. (1, 2)   **II.** (3, 4)   **III.** (3, 9)
   A. I only   **B.** I and II   **C.** I and III   **D.** II only

50. There are at most 12 bicycles and tricycles in a school playground. There are at least 17 wheels altogether. Let b equal the number of bicycles and t equal the number of tricycles. Which system describes this situation?

   F. $b + t < 12$ **G.** $b + t \le 12$
       $2b + 3t \ge 17$ $2b + 3t \ge 17$

   H. $b + t \le 12$ **J.** $b + t \le 12$
       $2b + 3t > 17$ $2b + 3t \le 17$

Short Response

51. Describe the solution to the following system. $3x + 4y \ge 12$
                                                $3x + 4y \le 12$

Extended Response

52. Suppose you and your friends are going out for pizza.

   a. Write a system of equations for the cost of a large pizza at each restaurant, based on the information at the right.
   b. Solve the system. Interpret your results.
   c. Where will you go for pizza? Explain your reasons.

Tony's Pizza	Maria's Pizza
Large cheese $7	Large cheese $8
Each topping $.75	Each topping $.50

Mixed Review

Lesson 10-5   **Graph each linear inequality.**

   53. $y > x - 5$ **54.** $y \le -2x + 4$ **55.** $y > -3$

   56. $y + x \le 7$ **57.** $3y - x \ge 6$ **58.** $4y + 2x < 8$

Lesson 9-6   **Find the slope of a line parallel to the graph of each equation.**

   59. $5x - 2y = 8$ **60.** $y - 17 = -3x$ **61.** $0.5y - 10 + 4x = 0$

   Find the slope of a line perpendicular to the graph of each equation.

   62. $y = 4x$ **63.** $y = 5x - 7$ **64.** $y = \frac{3}{8}x + 19$

   65. $y = -\frac{9}{10}x - 3$ **66.** $6y + 13x = 22$ **67.** $-4x - 15y = 74$

Lesson 8-4   **Write a function rule for each table.**

68.

x	f(x)
1	7
2	14
3	21
4	28
5	35

69.

x	f(x)
1	7
2	8
3	9
4	10
5	11

70.

x	f(x)
−2	4
−1	1
0	0
1	1
2	4

Graphing Linear Inequalities

You can use a graphing calculator to show the solutions of an inequality or a system of inequalities. The symbol before each Y in the [Y=] window indicates the graph style. You can use the graph style to shade above or below a line. The standard style, indicated by \, shows only the line.

Go Online
PHSchool.com
For: Graphing calculator procedures
Web Code: ate-2108

To change the graph style, select \ and press ENTER to rotate through the seven styles available. You can use ▼ to shade above the line and ▟ to shade below the line.

```
Plot1  Plot2  Plot3
▼Y₁ ▄ 2X−1          ← to graph above the line y = 2x − 1
▟Y₂ ▄ 3X+4          ← to graph below the line y = 3x + 4
 \Y₃ = ■
 \Y₄ =
 \Y₅ =
 \Y₆ =
 \Y₇ =
```

The graphing calculator does not make a distinction between a boundary line that is dotted ($y < 2x - 1$) and a boundary line that is solid ($y \leq 2x - 1$). You must decide whether a boundary line should be solid or dotted when you sketch the inequality.

1 ACTIVITY

Graph $y > -4x + 1$.

Enter the equation for the boundary line $y = -4x + 1$.
● Select ▼ to shade above the boundary line.

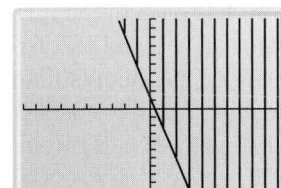

2 ACTIVITY

Graph the system: $y < -x + 4$
$\qquad\qquad\qquad y > 2x + 3$

Enter the equation of the first boundary line as Y_1.
Enter the equation of the second boundary line as Y_2.

Select ▟ to shade below $y = -x + 4$.
● Select ▼ to shade above $y = 2x + 3$.

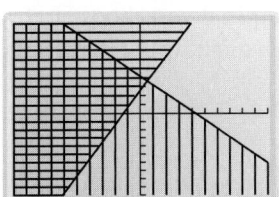

EXERCISES

Use a graphing calculator to graph each inequality. Sketch your graph.

1. $y < x$ **2.** $y > 2x - 3$ **3.** $y \geq -x + 3$ **4.** $y \leq 5$

Use a graphing calculator to graph each system of inequalities. Sketch your graph.

5. $y \geq -1$ **6.** $y \geq 0.5x - 2$ **7.** $y < x$ **8.** $y \geq -4x + 6$
$\quad\;\; y \geq 2x$ $y \leq x + 2$ $y \geq 1$ $y \geq -2x + 5$

In multiple correct answer questions, you have to determine the truth or falsehood of a number of statements. As you test each statement, mark it as true or false. Then choose the option with all those that are true.

1 EXAMPLE

Which system(s) of inequalities represent(s) the shaded region below?

I. $y \geq x$
$y \geq -x$
$y \leq 1$

II. $x + y \geq 0$
$x - y \geq 0$
$y \leq 1$

III. $y \geq |x|$
$y \leq 1$

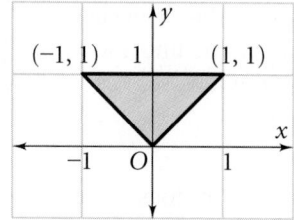

- Ⓐ I only
- Ⓒ I and II only
- Ⓔ II and III only
- Ⓑ I and III only
- Ⓓ I, II, and III

Method 1 Graph each system in I, II, and III to see which systems match the shaded region. The graphs of the systems in I and III match the shaded region. The correct answer is B.

Method 2 Choose a point, such as $(0, 0.5)$, inside the given shaded region. Test each of the three statements with the values $x = 0$ and $y = 0.5$. When $x = 0$ and $y = 0.5$, all the inequalities in I are true. The second inequality in II is $x - y = 0 - 0.5 \geq 0$, which is false. All the inequalities in III are true. The correct answer is B.

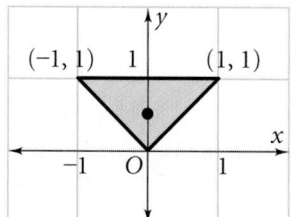

When you use Method 2, you should choose more than one point to test each system. This is because the point you choose may show a system to be true when it is really false. For example, if you choose to test the point $(1, 1)$, all the inequalities in II will be true, so you might think that II is a correct system.

EXERCISES

1. Choose another point in the shaded region and test each system.

2. **Writing** The point $(0, 0)$ is in the shaded region. Test each of the three statements with its coordinates to determine which are true. Explain why this point is not a good choice with which to answer this question.

3. Louis is selling lemonade for $.25 per cup. He bought the lemonade mix for $8.40 and the cups for $.05 each. Which statement(s) must be true?
   I. His break-even point is 42 cups.
   II. When he sells 20 cups, his income will be $13.40.
   III. His income is greater than his expenses when he sells 20 cups.
   - Ⓐ I and II only
   - Ⓒ I only
   - Ⓔ II and III only
   - Ⓑ I and III only
   - Ⓓ III only

Chapter Review

Vocabulary Review

🔊 elimination method (p. 563)
infinitely many solutions (p. 552)
linear inequality (p. 581)
no solution (p. 552)

solution of a system of linear
   equations (p. 550)
solution of a system of linear
   inequalities (p. 587)

solutions of an inequality (p. 581)
substitution method (p. 558)
system of linear equations (p. 550)
system of linear inequalities (p. 587)

Go Online
PHSchool.com

For: Vocabulary quiz
Web Code: atj-0751

Choose the vocabulary term that correctly completes each sentence.

1. _____?_____ is a method for solving a system of linear equations in which you multiply one or both equations by a nonzero number to get a variable term with coefficients that have a sum or difference of zero.

2. Any ordered pair that makes all equations in a system of equations true is a(n)_____?_____.

3. A(n)_____?_____ is formed by two or more linear inequalities.

4. Each point whose coordinates make an inequality true is a(n)_____?_____.

5. _____?_____ is a method for solving a system of linear equations in which at least one equation must first be solved for a single variable.

Skills and Concepts

10-1 Objectives

▼ To solve systems by graphing (p. 550)

▼ To analyze special types of systems (p. 552)

Two or more linear equations form a **system of linear equations.** You can solve a system of linear equations by graphing. A point where all the lines intersect is a **solution of the system.**

6. Which graph shows the solution of the following system? $y = x - 1$
$y = -x + 3$

A. 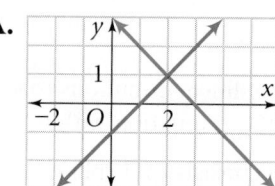   **B.**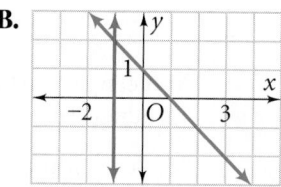

7. Is $(2, 5)$ a solution of the following system? Explain. $y = 2x + 1$
$2x - y = 8$

8. How many solutions does the following system have? Explain. $y = -\frac{1}{2}x + 2$
$3x + 6y = 12$

9. Critical Thinking What kinds of systems would be hard to solve by graphing?

Solve each system by graphing.

10. $y = 3x - 1$
$y = -x + 3$

11. $x - y = -3$
$3x + y = -1$

12. $-x + 2y = -2$
$y = \frac{1}{2}x + 3$

13. $y = -2x + 1$
$y = 2x - 3$

10-2 Objective

▼ To solve systems using substitution (p. 558)

You can also solve a system of linear equations using the **substitution method.** By replacing one variable with an equivalent expression containing the other variable, you create a one-variable equation to solve.

Solve each system using substitution.

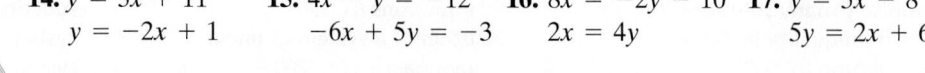

14. $y = 3x + 11$
$y = -2x + 1$

15. $4x - y = -12$
$-6x + 5y = -3$

16. $8x = -2y - 10$
$2x = 4y$

17. $y = 5x - 8$
$5y = 2x + 6$

18. Writing Explain how you determine if a system has no solution or infinitely many solutions when you solve a system using substitution.

19. There are 24 questions on a test. Each question is worth either 4 points or 5 points. The total is 100 points.
   a. Write a system of equations to find the number of each type of question.
   b. Solve the system by substitution.
   c. How many questions of each type are on the test?

10-3 Objectives

▼ To solve systems by adding or subtracting (p. 563)

▼ To multiply first when solving systems (p. 564)

You can solve a system of linear equations using the **elimination method.** You add or subtract the equations to eliminate one variable. You can multiply one or both of the equations by a nonzero number before adding or subtracting.

Solve each system using elimination. Check your solution.

20. $y = -3x + 5$
$y = -4x - 1$

21. $2x - 3y = 5$
$x + 2y = -1$

22. $x + y = 10$
$x - y = 2$

23. $x + 4y = 12$
$2x - 3y = 6$

24. Farming A farmer raises chickens and cows. There are 34 animals in all. The farmer counts 110 legs on these animals. Write a system of equations to find the number of each type of animal. Solve the system by elimination. How many of each animal does the farmer have?

10-4 Objective

▼ To write systems of linear equations (p. 572)

You can use systems of linear equations to solve word problems. First, define variables. Then model the situation with a system of linear equations.

25. A furniture finish consists of turpentine and linseed oil. It contains twice as much turpentine as linseed oil. If you plan to make 16 fluid ounces of furniture finish, how much turpentine do you need?

26. Geometry The difference between the measures of two complementary angles is 36°. Find both angle measures. (*Hint:* Two angles are complementary if the sum of their measures is 90°.)

27. Geometry The perimeter of a rectangle is 114 feet. Its length is three more than twice its width. Find the dimensions of the rectangle.

28. Supplies Marcella and Rupert bought some party supplies. Marcella bought 3 packages of balloons and 4 packages of favors for $14.63. Rupert bought 2 packages of balloons and 5 packages of favors for $16.03. Find the price of a package of balloons.

29. An airplane flew for 6 hours with a 22-km/h tail wind. The return flight against the same wind took 8 hours. Find the speed of the plane in still air.

10-5 Objectives

▼ To graph linear inequalities (p. 580)

▼ To use linear inequalities when modeling real-world situations (p. 582)

A **linear inequality** describes a region of the coordinate plane. The **solutions of the inequality** are the coordinates of the points that make the inequality true.

Graph each linear inequality.

30. $y < -3x + 8$ **31.** $y \geq 2x - 1$ **32.** $y \leq 0.5x + 6$ **33.** $y > -\frac{1}{4}x - 2$

Write the linear inequality shown in each graph.

34. 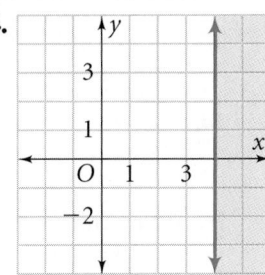   **35.** 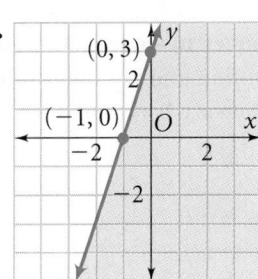   **36.**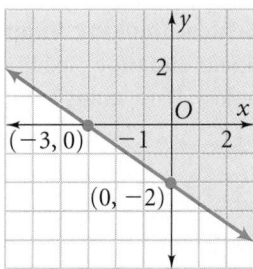

10-6 Objectives

▼ To solve systems of linear inequalities by graphing (p. 587)

▼ To model real-world situations using systems of linear inequalities (p. 589)

Two or more linear inequalities form a **system of linear inequalities.** To find the **solution of a system of linear inequalities,** graph each linear inequality. The solution region is where all the inequalities are true.

Solve each system of linear inequalities by graphing.

37. $y \geq -4x + 1$
$\quad\ y \leq \frac{5}{2}x - \frac{9}{2}$

38. $x - y < 10$
$\quad\ x + y \leq 8$

39. $y \leq x - 3$
$\quad\ y > x - 7$

40. $y < 5x$
$\quad\ y \geq 0$

Write the system of inequalities shown in each graph.

41. 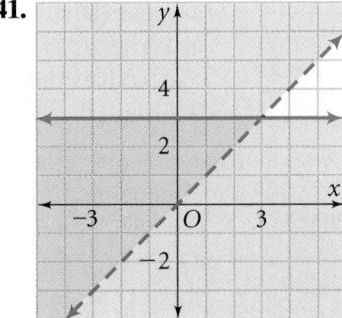   **42.**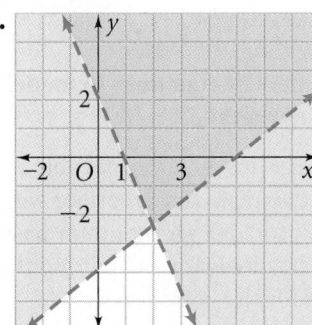

43. 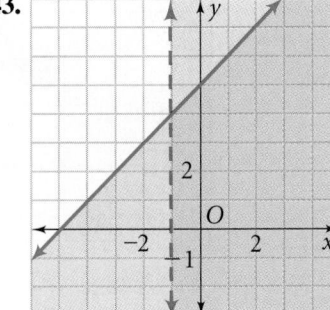   **44.**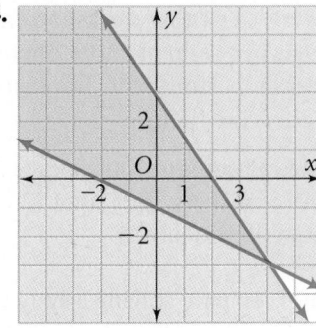

45. Open-Ended Write a system of linear inequalities for which the solution region is a pentagon.

Solve each system by graphing.

1. $y = 3x - 7$
   $y = -x + 1$

2. $4x + 3y = 12$
   $2x - 5y = -20$

Critical Thinking Suppose you try to solve systems of linear equations using substitution and get the results below. How many solutions does each system have?

3. $x = 8$

4. $5 = y$

5. $-7 = 4$

6. $x = -1$

7. $2 = y$

8. $9 = 9$

Solve each system using substitution.

9. $y = 4x - 7$
   $y = 2x + 9$

10. $y = -2x - 1$
    $y = 3x - 16$

11. $8x + 2y = -2$
    $y = -5x + 1$

12. $y + 6 = 2x$
    $4x - 10y = 4$

Solve each system using elimination.

13. $4x + y = 8$
    $-3x - y = 0$

14. $2x + 5y = 20$
    $3x - 10y = 37$

15. $x + y = 10$
    $-x - 2y = -14$

16. $3x + 2y = -19$
    $x - 12y = 19$

Write a system of equations to model each situation. Solve by any method.

17. **Cable Service** Your local cable television company offers two plans: basic service with one movie channel for $35 per month or basic service with two movie channels for $45 per month. What is the charge for the basic service and the charge for each movie channel?

18. **Education** A writing workshop enrolls novelists and poets in a ratio of 5 to 3. There are 24 people at the workshop. How many novelists are there? How many poets are there?

19. You have 15 coins in your pocket that are either quarters or nickels. They total $2.75. How many of each coin do you have?

20. **Writing** Compare solving a system of linear equations with solving a system of linear inequalities. What are the similarities? What are the differences?

21. Which point is *not* a solution of $y < 3x - 1$?
    A. $(2, -4)$ **B.** $(5, 7)$ **C.** $(0, -1)$ **D.** $(-2, -9)$

Solve each system by graphing.

22. $y > 4x - 1$
    $y \leq -x + 4$

23. $y \geq 3x + 5$
    $y > x - 2$

24. $x > -3$
    $-3x + y \geq 6$

25. $2x - y \leq 2$
    $y \geq 4$

26. **Open-Ended** Write a system of two linear equations. Solve by any method.

27. **Garage Sale** Leo held a garage sale. He priced all the items at a dime or a quarter. His sales totaled less than $5.
    a. Write a linear inequality that describes the situation. Graph the linear inequality.
    b. What is the maximum possible number of items that could have been sold for a dime?
    c. What is the maximum possible number of items that could have been sold for a quarter?

28. **Gardening** Mrs. Paulson bought chicken wire to enclose a rectangular garden. She is restricted to a width of no more than 30 ft. She would like to use at most 180 ft of chicken wire.
    a. Write a system of linear inequalities that describes this situation.
    b. Graph the system to show all possible solutions.

29. A chemist needs to mix a solution containing 30% insecticide with a solution containing 50% insecticide to make 200 L of a solution that is 42% insecticide. How much of each solution should she use?
    a. Complete the table below.

	30% Insecticide	50% Insecticide	42% Insecticide
Liters of Solution	■	■	■
Liters of Insecticide	■	■	■

   b. Write a system of equations that describes the situation. Solve the system.

When you conduct a survey, you collect *quantitative* or *qualitative* data.

Type of Data	Quantitative	Qualitative
Description	Has units, can be measured and numerically compared	Describes a category, cannot be measured or numerically compared
Examples	**Age:** 13 years **Weight:** 214 grams **Commute:** 23 minutes	**Hair color:** brown **Attitude:** optimistic **Zip code:** 02865

Notice that even though the zip code is a number, it is not a quantitative variable because it is not a measurement.

3 ACTIVITY

In this activity you will design and conduct a survey using sampling.

7. **Open-Ended** Select a topic for your survey.

8. **Writing** Write an unbiased question for your survey. Will you be collecting quantitative or qualitative data?

9. Choose a population and sampling method.

10. **Data Collection** Complete your survey.

11. **Writing** Summarize your results with a graph and a brief description.

EXERCISES

Tell whether each survey plan describes a good sample and, if so, which method of sampling is used.

12. A candidate calls every 50th name in the phone book to find out how the person likes the candidate.

13. A factory tests the quality of the last 25 out of 1000 shirts made.

14. A printer selects 10 of the 450 packages of inserts at random to see if all the inserts were printed properly.

Determine whether each question is biased or not. Explain.

15. What kind of meat toppings do you like on pizza?

16. Where would you most like to go for a vacation?

What You've Learned

- In Chapter 4 you learned how to use the order of operations to simplify expressions containing exponents.

- In Chapter 8 you studied number patterns and learned to recognize an arithmetic sequence. You also wrote equations for function rules.

- In Chapter 9 you found a line of best fit for a set of data.

  **for Help** to the Lesson in green.

Converting Fractions to Decimals (Skills Handbook page 791)

Write as a decimal.

1. $\frac{7}{10}$ **2.** $6\frac{2}{5}$ **3.** $\frac{8}{1000}$ **4.** $\frac{7}{2}$ **5.** $\frac{3}{11}$

Using the Order of Operations (Lesson 4-2)

Simplify each expression.

6. $(9 \div 3 + 4)^2$ **7.** $5 + (0.3)^3$ **8.** $3 - (1.5)^2$ **9.** $64 \div 2^4$

Evaluating Expressions (Lessons 5-1 to 5-3)

Evaluate each expression for $a = -2$ and $b = 5$.

10. $(ab)^2$ **11.** $(a - b)^2$ **12.** $a^3 + b^2$ **13.** $b - (3a)^2$

Finding Percent of Change (Lesson 6-7)

Find the percent of change.

14. \$15.00 to \$20.00   **15.** \$20.00 to \$15.00

Understanding Domain and Range (Lesson 8-2)

Find the range of each function with domain $\{-2, 0, 3.5\}$.

16. $f(x) = -2x^2$ **17.** $g(x) = 10 - x^3$ **18.** $y = 5x - 1$

Finding Terms of a Sequence (Lesson 8-7)

Find the next two terms of each sequence.

19. $1, 3, 5, 7, \ldots$ **20.** $-1, 0, 2, 5, 9, \ldots$ **21.** $7, 13, 19, 25, \ldots$

Exponents and Exponential Functions

🔊) **Key Vocabulary**

- common ratio (p. 636)
- compound interest (p. 652)
- decay factor (p. 654)
- exponential decay (p. 654)
- exponential function (p. 644)
- exponential growth (p. 651)
- geometric sequence (p. 636)
- growth factor (p. 651)
- interest period (p. 652)
- scientific notation (p. 612)

What You'll Learn Next

- In this chapter you will extend your knowledge about exponents to include zero and negative exponents.

- You will learn the properties of exponents, and how exponents are used to write a geometric sequence.

- By making a table of values, you will graph exponential functions.

Activity Lab Applying what you learn, you will use functions and graphs to do activities related to animals, on pages 490–491.

605

Zero and Negative Exponents

What You'll Learn

- To simplify expressions with zero and negative exponents
- To evaluate exponential expressions

. . . And Why

To find the size of a population, as in Example 4

✓ Check Skills You'll Need

GO for Help Lessons 4-2 and 5-3

Simplify each expression.

1. 2^3 **2.** $\frac{1}{4^2}$ **3.** $4^2 \div 2^2$

4. $(-3)^3$ **5.** -3^3 **6.** $6^2 \div 12$

Evaluate each expression for $a = 2$, $b = -1$, and $c = 0.5$.

7. $\frac{a}{2a}$ **8.** $\frac{bc}{c}$ **9.** $\frac{ab}{bc}$

---

1   Zero and Negative Exponents

Activity: Exponents

1. a. Copy the table below. Replace each blank with the value of the power in simplest form.

2^x	5^x	10^x
$2^4 = \blacksquare$	$5^4 = \blacksquare$	$10^4 = \blacksquare$
$2^3 = \blacksquare$	$5^3 = \blacksquare$	$10^3 = \blacksquare$
$2^2 = \blacksquare$	$5^2 = \blacksquare$	$10^2 = \blacksquare$

b. Look at the values that you used to replace the blanks. What pattern do you see as you go down each column?

2. Copy the table below. Use the pattern you described in Question 1 to complete the table.

2^x	5^x	10^x
$2^1 = \blacksquare$	$5^1 = \blacksquare$	$10^1 = \blacksquare$
$2^0 = \blacksquare$	$5^0 = \blacksquare$	$10^0 = \blacksquare$
$2^{-1} = \blacksquare$	$5^{-1} = \blacksquare$	$10^{-1} = \blacksquare$
$2^{-2} = \blacksquare$	$5^{-2} = \blacksquare$	$10^{-2} = \blacksquare$

3. Critical Thinking What pattern do you notice in the row with 0 as an exponent?

4. Copy and complete each expression.

     a. $2^{-1} = \frac{1}{2^{\blacksquare}}$ **b.** $2^{-2} = \frac{1}{2^{\blacksquare}}$ **c.** $2^{-3} = \frac{1}{2^{\blacksquare}}$

Consider 3^3, 3^2, and 3^1. Decreasing the exponent by one is the same as dividing by 3. Continuing the pattern, 3^0 equals 1 and 3^{-1} equals $\frac{1}{3}$.

Key Concepts

Property	Zero as an Exponent

For every nonzero number a, $a^0 = 1$.

Examples $5^0 = 1$ $(-2)^0 = 1$ $(1.02)^0 = 1$ $\left(\frac{1}{3}\right)^0 = 1$

Property	Negative Exponent

For every nonzero number a and integer n, $a^{-n} = \frac{1}{a^n}$.

Examples $6^{-4} = \frac{1}{6^4}$ $(-8)^{-1} = \frac{1}{(-8)^1}$

Why can't you use 0 as a base? By the first property, $3^0 = 1$, $2^0 = 1$, and $1^0 = 1$, which implies $0^0 = 1$. However, the pattern $0^3 = 0$, $0^2 = 0$, and $0^1 = 0$ implies $0^0 = 0$. Since both 1 and 0 cannot be the answer, 0^0 is undefined. In the second property, using 0 as a base results in division by zero, which you know is undefined.

1 EXAMPLE   Simplifying a Power

Vocabulary Tip

Read 4^{-3} as "four to the negative three".

Simplify.

a. $4^{-3} = \frac{1}{4^3}$ Use the definition of negative exponent.

  $= \frac{1}{64}$ Simplify.

b. $(-1.23)^0 = 1$ Use the definition of zero as an exponent.

✓ Quick Check ❶ Simplify each expression.
  a. 3^{-4} **b.** $(-7)^0$ **c.** $(-4)^{-3}$ **d.** 7^{-1} **e.** -3^{-2}

An algebraic expression is in simplest form when it is written with only positive exponents. If the expression is a fraction in simplest form, the only common factor of the numerator and denominator is 1.

2 EXAMPLE   Simplifying an Exponential Expression

Simplify each expression.

a. $4yx^{-3} = 4y\left(\frac{1}{x^3}\right)$ Use the definition of negative exponent.

  $= \frac{4y}{x^3}$ Simplify.

b. $\frac{1}{w^{-4}} = 1 \div w^{-4}$ Rewrite using a division symbol.

  $= 1 \div \frac{1}{w^4}$ Use the definition of negative exponent.

  $= 1 \cdot w^4$ Multiply by the reciprocal of $\frac{1}{w^4}$, which is w^4.

  $= w^4$ Identity Property of Multiplication

✓ Quick Check ❷ Simplify each expression.
  a. $11m^{-5}$ **b.** $7s^{-4}t^2$ **c.** $\frac{2}{a^{-3}}$ **d.** $\frac{n^{-5}}{v^2}$

When you evaluate an exponential expression, you can write the expression with positive exponents before substituting values.

3 **EXAMPLE** **Evaluating an Exponential Expression**

Evaluate $3m^2t^{-2}$ for $m = 2$ and $t = -3$.

Method 1 Write with positive exponents first.

$$3m^2t^{-2} = \frac{3m^2}{t^2} \qquad \text{Use the definition of negative exponent.}$$

$$= \frac{3(2)^2}{(-3)^2} \qquad \text{Substitute 2 for } m \text{ and } -3 \text{ for } t.$$

$$= \frac{12}{9} = 1\frac{1}{3} \qquad \text{Simplify.}$$

Method 2 Substitute first.

$$3m^2t^{-2} = 3(2)^2(-3)^{-2} \qquad \text{Substitute 2 for } m \text{ and } -3 \text{ for } t.$$

$$= \frac{3(2)^2}{(-3)^2} \qquad \text{Use the definition of negative exponent.}$$

$$= \frac{12}{9} = 1\frac{1}{3} \qquad \text{Simplify.}$$

 **Quick Check** **3** Evaluate each expression for $n = -2$ and $w = 5$.

a. $n^{-3}w^0$ **b.** $\dfrac{n^{-1}}{w^2}$ **c.** $\dfrac{w^0}{n^4}$ **d.** $\dfrac{1}{nw^{-2}}$

You can also evaluate exponential expressions that model real-world situations.

4 **EXAMPLE** **Real-World** **Problem Solving**

Population Growth A biologist is studying green peach aphids, like the one shown at the left. In the lab, the population doubles every week. The expression $1000 \cdot 2^w$ models an initial population of 1000 insects after w weeks of growth.

a. Evaluate the expression for $w = 0$. Then describe what the value of the expression represents in the situation.

$$1000 \cdot 2^w = 1000 \cdot 2^0 \qquad \text{Substitute 0 for } w.$$

$$= 1000 \cdot 1 \qquad \text{Simplify.}$$

$$= 1000$$

The value of the expression represents the initial population of insects. This makes sense because when $w = 0$, no time has passed.

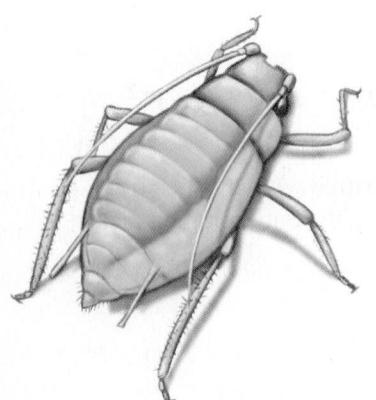

Real-World **Connection**

During the months of June and July, green peach aphids in a field of potato plants can double in population every three days.

b. Evaluate the expression for $w = -3$. Then describe what the value of the expression represents in the situation.

$$1000 \cdot 2^w = 1000 \cdot 2^{-3} \qquad \text{Substitute } -3 \text{ for } w.$$

$$= 1000 \cdot \frac{1}{8} \qquad \text{Simplify.}$$

$$= 125$$

There were 125 aphids 3 weeks before the present population of 1000 insects.

 **Quick Check** **4** A sample of bacteria triples each month. The expression $5400 \cdot 3^m$ models a population of 5400 bacteria after m months of growth. Evaluate the expression for $m = -2$ and $m = 0$. Describe what each value of the expression represents in the situation.

EXERCISES

For more exercises, see *Extra Skill and Word Problem Practice*.

Practice and Problem Solving

A Practice by Example

Example 1
(page 607)

GO for Help

Simplify each expression.

1. $-(2.57)^0$ **2.** 4^{-2} **3.** $(-5)^{-2}$ **4.** -5^{-2}

5. $(-4)^{-2}$ **6.** -3^{-4} **7.** 2^{-6} **8.** -12^{-1}

9. $\frac{1}{2^0}$ **10.** 78^{-1} **11.** $(-4)^{-3}$ **12.** -4^{-3}

Example 2
(page 607)

Copy and complete each equation.

13. $4n^{\blacksquare} = \frac{4}{n^2}$ **14.** $\frac{x^{\blacksquare}}{2y^{\blacksquare}} = \frac{1}{2x^{-3}y^4}$ **15.** $\frac{a^{\blacksquare}}{3b^{\blacksquare}} = \frac{b^3}{3}$ **16.** $3xy^{\blacksquare} = \frac{3x}{y^5}$

Simplify each expression.

17. $3ab^0$ **18.** $5x^{-4}$ **19.** $\frac{1}{x^{-7}}$ **20.** $\frac{1}{c^{-1}}$

21. $\frac{5^{-2}}{p}$ **22.** $a^{-4}c^0$ **23.** $\frac{3x^{-2}}{y}$ **24.** $\frac{7ab^{-2}}{3w}$

25. $x^{-5}y^{-7}$ **26.** $x^{-5}y^7$ **27.** $\frac{8}{2c^{-3}}$ **28.** $\frac{7s}{5t^{-3}}$

29. $\frac{6a^{-1}c^{-3}}{d^0}$ **30.** $2^{-3}x^2z^{-7}$ **31.** $9^0y^7t^{-11}$ **32.** $\frac{7s^0t^{-5}}{2^{-1}m^2}$

Example 3
(page 608)

Evaluate each expression for $r = -3$ and $s = 5$.

33. s^{-2} **34.** r^{-2} **35.** $-r^{-2}$ **36.** s^0

37. $3s^{-2}$ **38.** $(2s)^{-2}$ **39.** $r^{-4}s^2$ **40.** $\frac{1}{r^{-4}s^2}$

41. s^2r^{-3} **42.** r^0s^{-2} **43.** $5r^3s^{-1}$ **44.** $2^{-4}r^3s^{-2}$

Example 4
(page 608)

45. a. Suppose your allowance doubles every week. This week you receive $2.56. How much will your allowance be three weeks from now? How much was your allowance three weeks ago?

b. Critical Thinking From a parent's point of view, is doubling your allowance each week a good plan? Explain.

B Apply Your Skills

Mental Math Is the value of each expression *positive* or *negative*?

46. -2^2 **47.** $(-2)^2$ **48.** 2^{-2} **49.** $(-2)^3$ **50.** $(-2)^{-3}$

Write each number as a power of 10 using negative exponents.

51. $\frac{1}{10}$ **52.** $\frac{1}{100}$ **53.** $\frac{1}{1000}$ **54.** $\frac{1}{10,000}$ **55.** $\frac{1}{100,000}$

Write each expression as a decimal.

56. 10^{-3} **57.** 10^{-6} **58.** $7 \cdot 10^{-1}$ **59.** $3 \cdot 10^{-2}$ **60.** $5 \cdot 10^{-4}$

61. a. Patterns Complete the pattern using powers of 5.

$$\frac{1}{5^2} = \blacksquare \qquad \frac{1}{5^1} = \blacksquare \qquad \frac{1}{5^0} = \blacksquare \qquad \frac{1}{5^{-1}} = \blacksquare \qquad \frac{1}{5^{-2}} = \blacksquare$$

b. Write $\frac{1}{5^{-4}}$ using a positive exponent.

c. Rewrite $\frac{1}{a^{-n}}$ so that the power of a is in the numerator.

62. Multiple Choice Which expression is equivalent to $\frac{3x^{-2}y^3}{9x^3y^{-5}}$?

Ⓐ $\frac{3x^{-5}}{y^8}$ Ⓑ $\frac{xy^2}{3}$ Ⓒ $3xy^2$ Ⓓ $\frac{y^8}{3x^5}$

Simplify each expression.

63. $45 \cdot (0.5)^0$ **64.** $54 \cdot 3^{-2}$ **65.** $\dfrac{5^{-2}}{10^{-3}}$ **66.** $\dfrac{4^{-1}}{9^0}$ **67.** $\dfrac{(-3)^{-4}}{-3}$

Evaluate each expression for $a = 3$, $b = 2$, and $c = -4$.

68. c^b **69.** $a^{-b}b$ **70.** b^{-a} **71.** b^c **72.** $c^{-a}b^{ab}$

73. Copy and complete the table below.

a	4	■	■	$\frac{7}{8}$	■
a^{-1}	■	3	$\frac{1}{6}$	■	0.5

74. a. Critical Thinking Simplify $a^n \cdot a^{-n}$.
    b. What is the mathematical relationship of a^n and a^{-n}? Justify your answer.

75. Which expressions equal $\frac{1}{4}$?
    A. 4^{-1} **B.** 2^{-2} **C.** -4^1 **D.** $\frac{1}{2^2}$ **E.** 1^4 **F.** -2^{-2}

76. Open-Ended Choose a fraction to use as a value for the variable a. Find the values of a^{-1}, a^2, and a^{-2}.

77. Critical Thinking Are $3x^{-2}$ and $3x^2$ reciprocals? Explain.

78. Error Analysis A student simplified an expression as shown at the right. What error did the student make?

$$\frac{x^n}{a^{-n}b^0} = \frac{a^n x^n}{b^0}$$
$$= \frac{a^n x^n}{0} \text{ undefined}$$

79. Probability Suppose your history teacher gives a multiple-choice quiz. There are four questions, each with five answer choices. The probability p of guessing the answer to a question correctly is $\frac{1}{5}$. The probability q of guessing the answer to each question incorrectly is $\frac{4}{5}$.
    a. The table has expressions to find the probability of correctly guessing a certain number of answers on this quiz. Copy and complete the table.

Multiple-Choice Quiz

Number Correct	Expression	Probability
0	$p^0 q^4$	$\left(\frac{1}{5}\right)^0\left(\frac{4}{5}\right)^4 = 0.4096$
1	$4p^1 q^3$	■
2	$6p^2 q^2$	■
3	$4p^3 q^1$	■
4	$p^4 q^0$	■

    b. Which number of correct answers is most likely?

80. Communication Suppose you are the only person in your class who knows a certain story. After a minute you tell a classmate. Every minute after that, every student who knows the story tells another student (sometimes the person being told already will have heard it). In a class of 30 students, the expression $\dfrac{30}{1 + 29 \cdot 2^{-t}}$ predicts the approximate number of people who will have heard the story after t minutes. About how many students will have heard your story after 2 min? After 5 min? After 10 min?

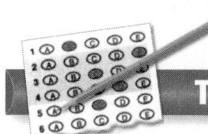 **Challenge**

Simplify each expression.

81. $2^3(5^0 - 6m^2)$ 　　**82.** $(-5)^2 - (0.5)^{-2}$ 　　**83.** $\frac{6}{m^2} + \frac{5m^{-2}}{3^{-3}}$

84. $(0.8)^{-3} + 19^0 - 2^{-6}$ 　**85.** $\frac{2r^{-5}y^3}{n^2} \div \frac{r^2y^5}{2n}$ 　　**86.** $2^{-1} - \frac{1}{3^{-2}} + 5\left(\frac{1}{2^2}\right)$

87. For what values of n is $n^{-3} = \left(\frac{1}{n}\right)^5$?

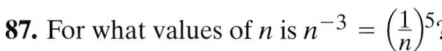

Test Prep

Gridded Response

88. Evaluate the expression xy^{-1} for $x = 2$ and $y = 3$.

89. Simplify $\frac{3^{-2}b^2}{a^0b^2}$.

90. Evaluate the expression $(4cd)^{-2}$ for $c = 2$ and $d = 1$.

91. Simplify $-6(-6)^{-1}$.

92. Write $26 \cdot 10^{-2}$ as a decimal.

93. Write $0.258 \cdot 10^2$ as a decimal.

Mixed Review

 **GO for Help**

Lesson 10-6

Solve each system by graphing.

94. $y > 3x + 4$　　　**95.** $y \le -2x + 1$　　　**96.** $y \ge 0.5x$
$y \le -3x + 1$　　　　　$y < 2x - 1$　　　　　　$y \le x + 2$

Lesson 9-7

97. Hat Sales Use the data in the table at the right.
　a. Make a scatter plot of the data. Use 87 for 1987.
　b. Draw a trend line.
　c. Write an equation for the trend line.
　d. Use your trend line to predict the retail sales of women's hats in 2005.

Lesson 9-2

Write an equation of the line with the given slope and y-intercept.

98. $m = -1, b = 4$

99. $m = 5, b = -2$

100. $m = \frac{2}{5}, b = -3$

101. $m = -\frac{3}{11}, b = -17$

102. $m = \frac{5}{9}, b = \frac{1}{3}$

103. $m = 1.25, b = -3.79$

Estimated Women's Retail Hat Sales

Year	Sales (millions of dollars)
1987	300
1988	345
1989	397
1990	457
1991	510
1992	587
1993	664
1994	700
1995	770
1996	792
1997	830
1998	872
1999	915

Source: Headwear Information Bureau

11-2

Scientific Notation

What You'll Learn

- To write numbers in scientific and standard notation
- To use scientific notation

...And Why

To order planets based on their masses, as in Example 4

Simplify each expression.

1. $6 \cdot 10^4$ **2.** $7 \cdot 10^{-2}$ **3.** $8.2 \cdot 10^5$

4. $3 \cdot 10^{-3}$ **5.** $3.4 \cdot 10^1$ **6.** $5.24 \cdot 10^2$

7. Simplify $3 \times 10^2 + 6 \times 10^1 + 7 \times 10^0 + 8 \times 10^{-1}$.

◄)) **New Vocabulary** • scientific notation

GO for Help Lesson 11-1

---

1 Writing Numbers in Scientific and Standard Notation

Calculator Hint

The *E* on a calculator readout means exponentiation. The EE or EXP keys let you input an exponent for a power of 10. So to enter 4×10^6, you can enter 4 EE 6.

The planet Jupiter has an average radius of 69,111 km. What is Jupiter's volume?

Since Jupiter is a sphere, to answer this question you use the formula for the volume of a sphere.

$$V = \frac{4}{3}\pi r^3$$
$$= \frac{4}{3}\pi (69{,}111)^3 \qquad \textbf{Substitute 69,111 for } r.$$
$$\approx \textit{1.382706933E15} \qquad \textbf{Use a calculator.}$$

In standard notation, you write the number above as 1,382,706,933,000,000. In scientific notation, you write the number as $1.382706933 \times 10^{15}$. Scientific notation is a shorthand way to write very large or very small numbers.

Key Concepts

Definition	**Scientific Notation**

A number in **scientific notation** is written as the product of two factors in the form $a \times 10^n$, where *n* is an integer and $1 \leq a < 10$.

Examples 3.4×10^6 5.43×10^{13} 2.1×10^{-10}

---

1 EXAMPLE **Recognizing Scientific Notation**

Is each number written in scientific notation? If not, explain.

a. 56.29×10^{12} No; 56.29 is greater than 10.

b. 0.84×10^{-3} No; 0.84 is less than 1.

c. 6.11×10^5 yes

 **Quick Check** ❶ Is each number written in scientific notation? If not, explain.

a. 3.42×10^{-7} **b.** 52×10^4 **c.** 0.04×10^{-5}

In scientific notation, you use positive exponents to write a number greater than 1. You use negative exponents to write a number between 0 and 1.

2 EXAMPLE Writing a Number in Scientific Notation

Write each number in scientific notation.

a. 56,900,000

$56,\!900,\!000. = 5.69 \times 10^7$ **Move the decimal point 7 places to the left and use 7 as an exponent. Drop the zeros after the 9.**

b. 0.00985

$0.00985 = 9.85 \times 10^{-3}$ **Move the decimal point 3 places to the right and use −3 as an exponent. Drop the zeros before the 9.**

✓ Quick Check

2 Write each number in scientific notation.
a. 267,000 **b.** 46,205,000 **c.** 0.0000325 **d.** 0.000000009
e. Critical Thinking You express 1 billion as 10^9. Explain why you express 436 billion as 4.36×10^{11} in scientific notation.

3 EXAMPLE Writing a Number in Standard Notation

Physical Science Write each number in standard notation.

a. temperature at the sun's core: 1.55×10^6 kelvins

$1.55 \times 10^6 = 1\,550000.$ **A positive exponent indicates a number greater than 10. Move the decimal point 6 places to the right.**
$= 1,\!550,\!000$

b. lowest temperature recorded in a lab: 2×10^{-11} kelvin

$2 \times 10^{-11} = 0.00000000002$ **A negative exponent indicates a number between 0 and 1. Move the decimal point 11 places to the left.**
$= 0.00000000002$

✓ Quick Check

3 Write each number in standard notation.
a. 3.2×10^{12} **b.** 5.07×10^4 **c.** 5.6×10^{-4} **d.** 8.3×10^{-2}

2 Using Scientific Notation

Masses of Planets (kilograms)

Jupiter
3.7×10^{27}
Uranus
8.7×10^{25}
Neptune
1.0×10^{26}
Saturn
5.7×10^{26}

You can compare and order numbers in scientific notation. First compare the powers of 10, and then compare the decimals.

4 EXAMPLE Real-World  Problem Solving

Astronomy List the planets in order from least to greatest mass.

Order the powers of 10. Arrange the decimals with the same power of 10 in order.

| 8.7×10^{25} | 1.0×10^{26} | 5.7×10^{26} | 3.7×10^{27} |
| Uranus | Neptune | Saturn | Jupiter |

From least to greatest mass, the order of the planets is Uranus, Neptune, Saturn, and Jupiter.

✓ Quick Check

4 The following masses of parts of an atom are measured in grams. Order the parts of an atom from least to greatest mass.
neutron: 1.6749×10^{-24}, electron: 9.1096×10^{-28}, proton: 1.6726×10^{-24}

You can write numbers like 815×10^5 and 0.078×10^{-2} in scientific notation.

$$815 \times 10^5 = 81,500,000 = 8.15 \times 10^7 \qquad 0.078 \times 10^{-2} = 0.00078 = 7.8 \times 10^{-4}$$

The examples above show this pattern: When you move a decimal n places left, the exponent of 10 increases by n; when you move a decimal point n places right, the exponent of 10 decreases by n.

5 EXAMPLE Using Scientific Notation to Order Numbers

Order $0.052 \times 10^7, 5.12 \times 10^5, 53.2 \times 10,$ and 534 from least to greatest.

Write each number in scientific notation.

$$
\begin{array}{cccc}
0.052 \times 10^7 & 5.12 \times 10^5 & 53.2 \times 10 & 534 \\
\downarrow & \downarrow & \downarrow & \downarrow \\
5.2 \times 10^5 & 5.12 \times 10^5 & 5.32 \times 10^2 & 5.34 \times 10^2
\end{array}
$$

> **Problem Solving Hint**
>
> Remember that
> 53.2×10 is 53.2×10^1.

Order the powers of 10. Arrange the decimals with the same power of 10 in order.

$$5.32 \times 10^2 \quad 5.34 \times 10^2 \quad 5.12 \times 10^5 \quad 5.2 \times 10^5$$

Write the original numbers in order.

$$53.2 \times 10 \quad 534 \quad 5.12 \times 10^5 \quad 0.052 \times 10^7$$

✓ Quick Check 5 Order $60.2 \times 10^{-5}, 63 \times 10^4, 0.067 \times 10^3,$ and 61×10^{-2} from least to greatest.

You can multiply a number that is in scientific notation by another number. If the product is less than one or greater than 10, rewrite the product in scientific notation.

6 EXAMPLE Multiplying a Number in Scientific Notation

Simplify. Write each answer using scientific notation.

a. $7(4 \times 10^5) = (7 \cdot 4) \times 10^5$ Use the Associative Property of Multiplication.

$\qquad\qquad\qquad = 28 \times 10^5$ Simplify inside the parentheses.

$\qquad\qquad\qquad = 2.8 \times 10^6$ Write the product in scientific notation.

b. $0.5(1.2 \times 10^{-3}) = (0.5 \cdot 1.2) \times 10^{-3}$ Use the Associative Property of Multiplication.

$\qquad\qquad\qquad\quad = 0.6 \times 10^{-3}$ Simplify inside the parentheses.

$\qquad\qquad\qquad\quad = 6 \times 10^{-4}$ Write the product in scientific notation.

✓ Quick Check 6 Simplify. Write each answer using scientific notation.
a. $2.5(6 \times 10^3)$ **b.** $0.4(2 \times 10^{-9})$

EXERCISES

For more exercises, see *Extra Skill and Word Problem Practice.*

Practice and Problem Solving

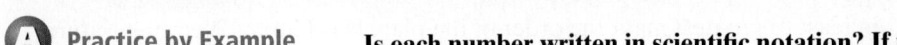

A Practice by Example

Example 1
(page 612)

GO for Help

Is each number written in scientific notation? If not, explain.

1. 55×10^4 **2.** 3.2×10^5 **3.** 0.9×10^{-2}

4. 7.3×10^{-5} **5.** 1.12×10^1 **6.** 46×10^7

Example 2
(page 613)

Write each number in scientific notation.

7. 9,040,000,000   **8.** 0.02   **9.** 9.3 million   **10.** 21,700

11. 0.00325   **12.** 8,003,000   **13.** 0.00092   **14.** 0.0156

Example 3
(page 613)

Write each number in standard notation.

15. 5×10^2 **16.** 5×10^{-2} **17.** 2.04×10^3 **18.** 7.2×10^5

19. 8.97×10^{-1} **20.** 1.3×10^0 **21.** 2.74×10^{-5} **22.** 4.8×10^{-3}

Examples 4, 5
(pages 613, 614)

Order the numbers in each list from least to greatest.

23. $10^5, 10^{-3}, 10^0, 10^{-1}, 10^1$

24. $9 \times 10^{-7}, 8 \times 10^{-8}, 7 \times 10^{-6}, 6 \times 10^{-10}$

25. $50.1 \times 10^{-3}, 4.8 \times 10^{-1}, 0.52 \times 10^{-3}, 56 \times 10^{-2}$

26. $0.53 \times 10^7, 5300 \times 10^{-1}, 5.3 \times 10^5, 530 \times 10^8$

27. Measuring instruments may have different degrees of precision. Instrument A is precise to 10^{-2} cm, Instrument B is precise to 5×10^{-2} cm, and Instrument C is precise to 8×10^{-3} cm. Order the instruments from most precise (least possible error) to least precise (greatest possible error).

Example 6
(page 614)

Simplify. Write each answer using scientific notation.

28. $8(7 \times 10^{-3})$ **29.** $8(3 \times 10^{14})$ **30.** $0.2(3 \times 10^2)$

31. $6(5.3 \times 10^{-4})$ **32.** $0.3(8.2 \times 10^{-3})$ **33.** $0.5(6.8 \times 10^5)$

 Apply Your Skills

For Exercises 34–39, find the missing value.

Selected Masses (kilograms)

		Standard Notation	Scientific Notation
34.	Elephant	▦	5.4×10^3
35.	Adult human	70	▦
36.	Dog	10	▦
37.	Golf ball	0.046	▦
38.	Paper clip	▦	5×10^{-4}
39.	Oxygen atom	0.000000000000000000000000003	▦

Real-World 🌐 **Connection**

Elephant calves weigh from 100 to 145 kilograms.

40. Critical Thinking Is the number 10^5 in scientific notation? Explain.

✏️ **41. Writing** Explain how to write 48 million and 48 millionths in scientific notation.

🌐 **42. Health Care** In 2010, the population in the United States will be about 3.09×10^8. Spending for health care will be about \$8754 per person. About how much will the United States spend on health care in 2010? Use scientific notation.

🌐 **43. Computers** A computer can perform 4.66×10^8 instructions per second. How many instructions is that per minute? Per hour? Use scientific notation.

44. Multiple Choice The national debt at the beginning of 2005 was about \$7,600,000,000,000. Which represents the debt in scientific notation?

Ⓐ 76×10^{11} Ⓑ 7.6×10^{12} Ⓒ 76×10^{12} Ⓓ 7.6×10^{13}

45. Math in the Media Use the cartoon below.

FOX TROT by Bill Amend

a. Write 500 trillion in scientific notation.

b. Since the 10-second length of the movie is off by a factor of 500 trillion, what time span does the movie actually represent?

C Challenge

46. World Population The world population in 2025 may reach 7.84×10^9 persons. This is about 3 times the world population in 1950. What was the world population in 1950?

47. Astronomy Use a calculator to find the volume of each planet with the given radius.
a. Mercury: 2439 km   **b.** Earth: 6378 km   **c.** Saturn: 60,268 km

48. Write $\frac{1}{300}$ using scientific notation.

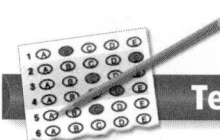

Test Prep

Multiple Choice

49. Simplify $90(1.2 \times 10^{-5})$. Write the answer in scientific notation.
A. 1.08×10^{-7} **B.** 108.0×10^{-5} **C.** 108.0×10^{-3} **D.** 1.08×10^{-3}

50. Which answer has the states in the table at the right ordered from least to greatest projected population?
F. New York, Florida, Virginia, Vermont
G. Vermont, Virginia, New York, Florida
H. Vermont, Virginia, Florida, New York
J. Florida, New York, Virginia, Vermont

Projected Population in 2025

State	Population
Florida	2.07×10^7
Virginia	8.47×10^6
Vermont	6.78×10^5
New York	1.98×10^7

51. Which equals 275 million?
A. 275×10^5 **B.** 2.75×10^6
C. 2.75×10^8 **D.** 275×10^9

Short Response

52. A microscope set on 1000X makes an object appear 1000 times its actual size. If a bacterium is 8×10^{-4} millimeters in diameter, how large will it appear under this microscope? Use scientific notation. Show your work.

Mixed Review

GO for Help

Lesson 11-1

Simplify each expression.
53. $4(1.8)^0$ **54.** $12 \cdot 2^{-2}$ **55.** $6 \cdot 3^{-2}$ **56.** $\frac{4^3}{7^2}$ **57.** $\frac{3^{-2}}{9^0}$

Lesson 10-5

Graph each linear inequality.
58. $y < -\frac{1}{4}x + 2$ **59.** $y \geq \frac{2}{3}x$ **60.** $y < 3x - 4$

11-3

Multiplication Properties of Exponents

What You'll Learn

- To multiply powers
- To work with scientific notation

. . . And Why

To find the number of red blood cells in the human body, as in Example 5

 **Check Skills You'll Need**

GO for Help Lesson 5-3

Rewrite each expression using exponents.

1. $t \cdot t \cdot t \cdot t \cdot t \cdot t \cdot t \cdot t$

2. $(6 - m)(6 - m)(6 - m)$

3. $(r + 5)(r + 5)(r + 5)(r + 5)(r + 5)$

4. $5 \cdot 5 \cdot 5 \cdot s \cdot s \cdot s$

Simplify.

5. -5^4
6. $(-5)^4$
7. $(-5)^0$
8. $(-5)^{-4}$

---

1 Multiplying

Activity: Exponents With the Same Base and Multiplication

1. Copy and complete the table.

2. What is true for $2^2 \cdot 2^2$ and $2^3 \cdot 2^1$?

3. **Patterns** What relationship do you see between the sum of the exponents of 2 in the first column and the exponent of 2 in the third column?

Factors	Product Using Repeated Factors	Power of 2
$2^1 \cdot 2^1$	$2 \cdot 2$	2^2
$2^2 \cdot 2^2$	■	■
$2^3 \cdot 2^1$	■	■
$2^4 \cdot 2^2$	■	■
$2^3 \cdot 2^3$	■	■

You can write the product of powers with the same base, like $2^4 \cdot 2^2$, using one exponent.

$$2^4 \cdot 2^2 = (2 \cdot 2 \cdot 2 \cdot 2) \cdot (2 \cdot 2) = 2^6$$

Notice that the sum of the exponents of the expression $2^4 \cdot 2^2$ equals the exponent of 2^6.

 Key Concepts

Property	**Multiplying Powers With the Same Base**

For every nonzero number a and integers m and n, $a^m \cdot a^n = a^{m + n}$.

Examples $3^5 \cdot 3^4 = 3^{5 + 4} = 3^9$ $h^2 \cdot h^9 = h^{2 + 9} = h^{11}$

1 EXAMPLE Multiplying Powers

Rewrite each expression using each base only once.

a. $11^4 \cdot 11^3 = 11^{4 + 3}$ **Add exponents of powers with the same base.**

             $= 11^7$ **Simplify the sum of the exponents.**

b. $5^{-2} \cdot 5^2 = 5^{-2 + 2}$ **Add exponents of powers with the same base.**

             $= 5^0$ **Simplify the sum of the exponents.**

             $= 1$ **Use the definition of zero as an exponent.**

 **Quick Check** **1** Rewrite each expression using each base only once.
   a. $5^3 \cdot 5^6$ **b.** $2^4 \cdot 2^{-3}$ **c.** $7^{-3} \cdot 7^2 \cdot 7^6$

When variable factors have more than one base, be careful to combine only those powers with the same base.

2 EXAMPLE Multiplying Powers in an Algebraic Expression

Simplify each expression.

a. $2n^5 \cdot 3n^{-2} = (2 \cdot 3)(n^5 \cdot n^{-2})$ **Commutative Property of Multiplication**

            $= 6(n^{5 + (-2)})$ **Add exponents of powers with the same base.**

            $= 6n^3$ **Simplify.**

> **Problem Solving Hint**
>
> Remember that $x = x^1$.

b. $5x \cdot 2y^4 \cdot 3x^8 = (5 \cdot 2 \cdot 3)(x \cdot x^8)(y^4)$ **Commutative and Associative Properties of Multiplication**

            $= 30(x^1 \cdot x^8)(y^4)$ **Multiply the coefficients. Write x as x^1.**

            $= 30(x^{1 + 8})(y^4)$ **Add exponents of powers with the same base.**

            $= 30x^9 y^4$ **Simplify.**

 **Quick Check** **2** Simplify each expression.
   a. $n^2 \cdot n^3 \cdot 7n$ **b.** $2y^3 \cdot 7x^2 \cdot 2y^4$ **c.** $m^2 \cdot n^{-2} \cdot 7m$

2   Working With Scientific Notation

In Lesson 11-2, you wrote numbers in scientific notation using patterns to move decimal points. You can now use the property for multiplying powers with the same base to write numbers and to multiply numbers in scientific notation.

3 EXAMPLE Multiplying Numbers in Scientific Notation

Simplify $(7 \times 10^2)(4 \times 10^5)$. Write the answer in scientific notation.

$(7 \times 10^2)(4 \times 10^5) = (7 \cdot 4)(10^2 \cdot 10^5)$ **Commutative and Associative Properties of Multiplication**

            $= 28 \times 10^7$ **Simplify.**

            $= 2.8 \times 10^1 \cdot 10^7$ **Write 28 in scientific notation.**

            $= 2.8 \times 10^{1 + 7}$ **Add exponents of powers with the same base.**

            $= 2.8 \times 10^8$ **Simplify the sum of the exponents.**

 **Quick Check** **3** Simplify each expression. Write each answer in scientific notation.
   a. $(2.5 \times 10^8)(6 \times 10^3)$ **b.** $(1.5 \times 10^{-2})(3 \times 10^4)$ **c.** $(9 \times 10^{-6})(7 \times 10^{-9})$

4 **EXAMPLE** <u>Real-World</u>  **Problem Solving**

Biology A human body contains about $3.2 \times 10^4 \ \mu L$ (microliters) of blood for each pound of body weight. Each microliter of blood contains about 5×10^6 red blood cells. Find the approximate number of red blood cells in the body of a 125-lb person.

red blood cells = pounds $\cdot$ $\dfrac{\text{microliters}}{\text{pound}}$ $\cdot$ $\dfrac{\text{cells}}{\text{microliter}}$	Use dimensional analysis.
$= 125 \text{ lb} \cdot \left(3.2 \times 10^4\right)\dfrac{\mu L}{\text{lb}} \cdot \left(5 \times 10^6\right)\dfrac{\text{cells}}{\mu L}$	Substitute.
$= (125 \cdot 3.2 \cdot 5) \times \left(10^4 \cdot 10^6\right)$	Commutative and Associative Properties of Multiplication
$= (2000) \times \left(10^{4 + 6}\right)$	Simplify.
$= 2000 \times 10^{10}$	Add exponents.
$= 2 \times 10^3 \cdot 10^{10}$	Write 2000 in scientific notation.
$= 2 \times 10^{13}$	Add the exponents.

There are about 2×10^{13} red blood cells in a 125-lb person.

  **④** About how many red blood cells are in the body of a 160-lb soccer player?

EXERCISES

For more exercises, see *Extra Skill, Word Problem, and Proof Practice.*

Practice and Problem Solving

A **Practice by Example**

GO for Help

Example 1
(page 618)

Rewrite each expression using each base only once.

1. $2^6 \cdot 2^4$
2. $5^{-13} \cdot 5^5 \cdot 2^5$
3. $10^{-6} \cdot 10^5 \cdot 10^1$
4. $(0.99)^3 \cdot (0.99)^0$
5. $6^6 \cdot 6^{-2} \cdot 6^5$
6. $(1.025)^2 (1.025)^{-2}$

Example 2
(page 618)

Simplify each expression.

7. $c^{-2} c^7$
8. $3r \cdot r^4$
9. $5t^{-2} \cdot 2t^{-5}$
10. $(7x^5)(8x)$
11. $3x^2 \cdot x^2$
12. $(-2.4n^4)(2n^{-1})$
13. $b^{-2} \cdot b^4 \cdot b$
14. $(-2m^3)(3.5m^{-3})$
15. $(15a^3)(-3a)$
16. $(x^5 y^2)(x^{-6} y)$
17. $(5x^5)(3y^6)(3x^2)$
18. $(4c^4)(ac^3)(3a^5 c)$
19. $x^6 \cdot y^2 \cdot x^4$
20. $a^6 b^3 \cdot a^2 b^{-2}$
21. $-m^2 \cdot 4r^3 \cdot 12r^{-4} \cdot 5m$

Example 3
(page 618)

Simplify each expression. Write each answer in scientific notation.

22. $(2 \times 10^3)(3 \times 10^2)$
23. $(2 \times 10^6)(3 \times 10^3)$
24. $(4 \times 10^6) \cdot 10^{-3}$
25. $(1 \times 10^3)(3.4 \times 10^{-8})$
26. $(8 \times 10^{-5})(7 \times 10^{-3})$
27. $(5 \times 10^7)(3 \times 10^{14})$

Example 4
(page 619)

Write each answer in scientific notation.

28. **Astronomy** The distance light travels in one year (one light-year) is about 5.88×10^{12} miles. The closest star to Earth (other than the sun) is Alpha Centauri, which is 4.35 light-years from Earth. About how many miles from Earth is Alpha Centauri?

Write each answer in scientific notation.

29. Geology Earth's crust contains approximately 120 trillion metric tons of gold. One metric ton of gold is worth about $9 million. What is the approximate value of the gold in Earth's crust?

30. Astronomy Light travels through space at a constant speed of about 3×10^5 km/s. Sunlight reflecting from the moon takes about 1.28×10^0 s to reach Earth. Find the distance from the moon to Earth.

B Apply Your Skills

Complete each equation.

31. $5^2 \cdot 5^{\blacksquare} = 5^{11}$ **32.** $5^7 \cdot 5^{\blacksquare} = 5^3$ **33.** $2^{\blacksquare} \cdot 2^4 = 2^1$

34. $c^{-5} \cdot c^{\blacksquare} = c^6$ **35.** $m^{\blacksquare} \cdot m^{-4} = m^{-9}$ **36.** $a \cdot a \cdot a^3 = a^{\blacksquare}$

37. $a^{\blacksquare} \cdot a^4 = 1$ **38.** $a^{12} \cdot a^{\blacksquare} = a^{12}$ **39.** $x^3 y^{\blacksquare} \cdot x^{\blacksquare} = y^2$

Geometry Find the area of each figure.

40.
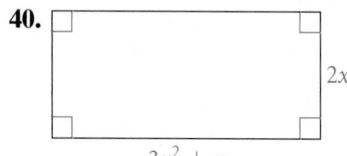
$2x$
$3x^2 + x$

41.

$2x^2$

GO Online
Homework Video Tutor
Visit: PHSchool.com
Web Code: ate-0803

42.
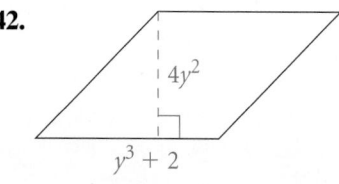
$4y^2$
$y^3 + 2$

43.
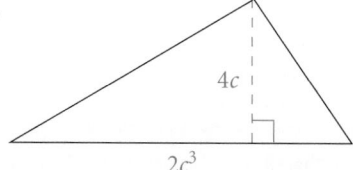
$4c$
$2c^3$

Error Analysis Correct each error.

44.
$$(3x^2)(-2x^4) = 3(-2)x^{2 \cdot 4}$$
$$= -6x^8$$

45.
$$4a^2 \cdot 3a^5 = (4 + 3)a^{2 + 5}$$
$$= 7a^7$$

46.
$$x^6 \cdot x \cdot x^3 = x^{6 + 3}$$
$$= x^9$$

47.
$$3^4 \cdot 2^2 = 6^{4 + 2}$$

Simplify each expression. Write each answer in scientific notation.

48. $(9 \times 10^7)(3 \times 10^{-16})$ **49.** $(8 \times 10^{-3})(0.1 \times 10^9)$

50. $(0.7 \times 10^{-12})(0.3 \times 10^8)$ **51.** $(0.4 \times 10^0)(3 \times 10^{-4})$

52. $(0.2 \times 10^5)(4 \times 10^{-12})$ **53.** $(0.5 \times 10^{13})(0.3 \times 10^{-4})$

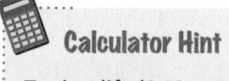
Calculator Hint

To simplify $(6.12 \times 10^5) \cdot (12.5 \times 10^8)$, press

6.12 [EE] 5 [ENTER]

[×] 12.5 [EE] 8 [ENTER].

54. Chemistry The term *mole* can be used in chemistry to refer to 6.02×10^{23} atoms of a substance. The mass of a single hydrogen atom is approximately 1.67×10^{-24} gram. What is the mass of 1 mole of hydrogen atoms?

55. a. Open-Ended Write y^8 as a product of two powers with the same base in four different ways. Use only positive exponents.
  b. Write y^8 as a product of two powers with the same base in four different ways using negative or zero exponents in each.
  c. Reasoning How many ways are there to write y^8 as the product of two powers? Explain your reasoning.

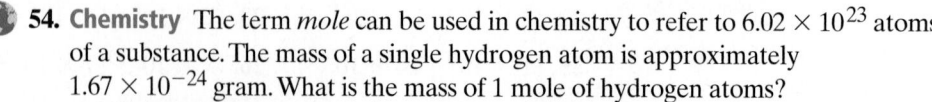

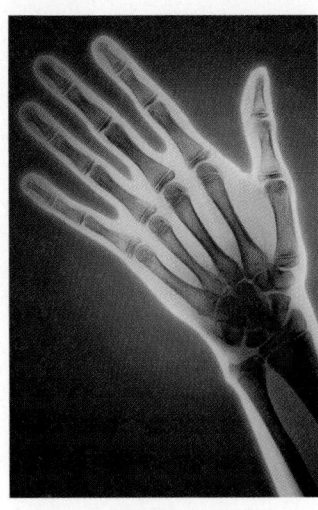

56. **Medicine** Medical X-rays, with a wavelength of about 10^{-10} meter, can penetrate your skin.
   a. Ultraviolet rays, which cause sunburn by penetrating only the top layers of skin, have a wavelength about 1000 times the wavelength of an X-ray. Find the wavelength of ultraviolet rays.
   b. **Critical Thinking** The wavelengths of visible light are between 4×10^{-7} meters and 7.5×10^{-7} meters. Are these wavelengths longer or shorter than those of ultraviolet rays? Explain.

57. **Writing** Explain why $x^3 \cdot y^5$ cannot be written with fewer bases.

58. 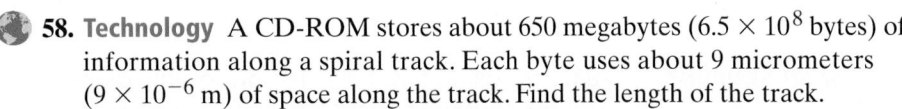 **Technology** A CD-ROM stores about 650 megabytes (6.5×10^8 bytes) of information along a spiral track. Each byte uses about 9 micrometers (9×10^{-6} m) of space along the track. Find the length of the track.

Use a calculator. Simplify each expression. Write each answer in scientific notation.

59. $(6.12 \times 10^5)(12.5 \times 10^8)$ 60. $(1.98 \times 10^{-3})(2.04 \times 10^{11})$

61. $(9.55 \times 10^7)(7.371 \times 10^{-15})$ 62. $(6.934 \times 10^{-9})(2.579 \times 10^{-4})$

63. **Measurement** There are about 3.35×10^{25} molecules in a liter of water. Pine Lake, in New York, has about 2×10^8 liters of water. About how many molecules of water are in Pine Lake?

64. **Measurement** About 8.4×10^{11} drops of water flow over Niagara Falls each minute. Each drop of water contains about 1.7×10^{21} molecules of water. About how many molecules of water flow over the falls each minute?

Simplify each expression.

65. $\dfrac{1}{x^2 \cdot x^{-5}}$ 66. $\dfrac{1}{a^3 \cdot a^{-2}}$ 67. $\dfrac{5}{c \cdot c^{-4}}$

68. $2a^2(3a + 5)$ 69. $8m^3(m^2 + 7)$ 70. $-4x^3(2x^2 - 9x)$

 Challenge

Simplify.

71. $3^x \cdot 3^{2-x} \cdot 3^2$ 72. $2^n \cdot 2^{n+2} \cdot 2$ 73. $3^x \cdot 2^y \cdot 3^2 \cdot 2^x$

74. $(a + b)^2(a + b)^{-3}$ 75. $(t + 3)^7(t + 3)^{-5}$ 76. $5^{x+1} \cdot 5^{1-x}$

77. a. **Geometry** Find the volume of a rectangular prism with length 1.3×10^{-3} km, width 1.5×10^{-3} km, and height 9.4×10^{-4} km. Write your answer in scientific notation.
   b. What is the volume of the prism in cubic meters?

78. **Science** An illustrator plans to draw a diagram of a protozoan for a science book. A protozoan is 1.1×10^{-4} meters long. The illustrator wants the diagram to be 7.7 centimeters long. The diagram will be how many times greater than the protozoan in length?

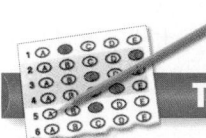

Test Prep

79. Simplify $(2x^2y^3)(4xy^{-2})$.
   A. $6x^3y^5$ B. $6x^2y^6$ C. $8x^2y$ D. $8x^3y$

80. In the 2000 Olympics, the winning time for the women's 100-meter race was 1.79×10^{-1} min. Which is another way of expressing this time in minutes?
   F. 0.179   G. 17.9   H. 179×10^1 J. 179×10^{-2}

81. Which is the product of (4.5×10^7) and (2.4×10^{-1}) in scientific notation?

    A. 1.08×10^7 **B.** 10.8×10^6

    C. 10.8×10^{-7} **D.** 1.08×10^{-8}

82. Which is an expression for the area of the triangle shown at the right?

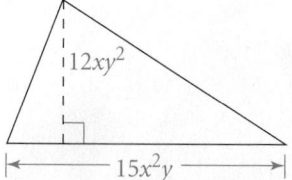

    F. $60x^2y^2$ **G.** $90x^3y^3$

    H. $180x^2y^2$ **J.** $180x^3y^3$

Short Response   **83.** Approximately 4.7×10^7 disposable diapers are thrown away each day in the United States. About how many are thrown away in one year? Write your answer in scientific notation. Show your work.

Extended Response   **84.** Sophie's Desserts packages its cheesecake in boxes with square bottoms, as shown below. Answer each of the following, showing all of your work.

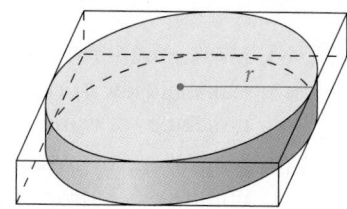

    a. Write an expression for the area of the bottom of the box.
    b. If the cheesecake has a radius of 5 in., what is the area of the bottom of the box?
    c. The area of the bottom of a second box is 144 in.^{2}. What is the diameter of the largest cheesecake the box can hold?

Mixed Review

 **for Help**

Lesson 11-2   **Write each number in scientific notation.**

    85. $1,280,000$ **86.** 0.0035 **87.** 0.00009 **88.** 6.2 million

    Write each number in standard form.

    89. 8.76×10^8 **90.** 1.052×10^{-3} **91.** 9.1×10^{11} **92.** 2.9×10^{-4}

Lesson 10-6   **Solve each system by graphing.**

    93. $y < 3x + 2$ **94.** $y < x + 6$ **95.** $y > x + 4$

        $2x + y \geq 4$ $x - 3y \leq 6$ $x + 2y \leq 6$

Lesson 8-7   **Find the third, seventh, and tenth terms of each sequence.**

    96. $A(n) = 10 + (n - 1)(4)$ **97.** $A(n) = -5 + (n - 1)(2)$

    98. $A(n) = 12 + (n - 1)(-4)$ **99.** $A(n) = 1.2 + (n - 1)(-4)$

11-4

More Multiplication Properties of Exponents

What You'll Learn

- To raise a power to a power
- To raise a product to a power

. . . And Why

To find the resting energy of an object, as in Example 5

✓ **Check Skills You'll Need**

GO for Help Lesson 11-3

Rewrite each expression using each base only once.

1. $3^2 \cdot 3^2 \cdot 3^2$

2. $2^3 \cdot 2^3 \cdot 2^3 \cdot 2^3$

3. $5^7 \cdot 5^7 \cdot 5^7 \cdot 5^7$

4. $7 \cdot 7 \cdot 7$

Simplify.

5. $x^3 \cdot x^3$

6. $a^2 \cdot a^2 \cdot a^2$

7. $y^{-2} \cdot y^{-2} \cdot y^{-2}$

8. $n^{-3} \cdot n^{-3}$

1 Raising a Power to a Power

Activity: Powers of Powers

You can use what you learned in the previous lesson to find a shortcut for simplifying expressions with powers. Copy and complete each statement.

1. $(3^6)^2 = 3^6 \cdot 3^6 = 3^{\blacksquare + \blacksquare} = 3^{6 \cdot \blacksquare} = 3^{\blacksquare}$

2. $(5^4)^3 = 5^4 \cdot 5^4 \cdot 5^4 = 5^{\blacksquare + \blacksquare + \blacksquare} = 5^{4 \cdot \blacksquare} = 5^{\blacksquare}$

3. $(2^7)^4 = 2^7 \cdot 2^7 \cdot 2^7 \cdot 2^7 = 2^{\blacksquare + \blacksquare + \blacksquare + \blacksquare} = 2^{7 \cdot \blacksquare} = 2^{\blacksquare}$

4. $(a^3)^2 = a^3 \cdot a^3 = a^{\blacksquare + \blacksquare} = a^{3 \cdot \blacksquare} = a^{\blacksquare}$

5. $(g^4)^3 = g^4 \cdot g^4 \cdot g^4 = g^{\blacksquare + \blacksquare + \blacksquare} = g^{4 \cdot \blacksquare} = g^{\blacksquare}$

6. $(c^3)^4 = c^3 \cdot c^3 \cdot c^3 \cdot c^3 = c^{\blacksquare + \blacksquare + \blacksquare + \blacksquare} = c^{3 \cdot \blacksquare} = c^{\blacksquare}$

7. a. Make a Conjecture What pattern do you see in your answers to Questions 1–6?

   b. Use your pattern to simplify $(8^6)^3$.

Raising a power to a power is the same as raising the base to the product of the exponents.

  Key Concepts

Property	Raising a Power to a Power

For every nonzero number a and integers m and n, $(a^m)^n = a^{mn}$.

Examples $(5^4)^2 = 5^{4 \cdot 2} = 5^8$ $(x^2)^5 = x^{2 \cdot 5} = x^{10}$

1 **EXAMPLE** **Simplifying a Power Raised to a Power**

Simplify $(x^3)^6$.

$(x^3)^6 = x^{3 \cdot 6}$ **Multiply exponents when raising a power to a power.**

$\qquad\quad = x^{18}$ **Simplify.**

✓ Quick Check **1** Simplify $(a^4)^7$ and $(a^{-4})^7$.

Be sure to use the order of operations. Simplify expressions in parentheses first.

Video Tutor Help
Visit: PHSchool.com
Web Code: ate-0775

2 **EXAMPLE** **Simplifying an Expression With Powers**

Simplify $c^5(c^3)^{-2}$.

$c^5(c^3)^{-2} = c^5 \cdot c^{3 \cdot (-2)}$ **Multiply exponents in $(c^3)^{-2}$.**

$\qquad\qquad = c^5 \cdot c^{-6}$ **Simplify.**

$\qquad\qquad = c^{5 + (-6)}$ **Add exponents when multiplying powers with the same base.**

$\qquad\qquad = c^{-1}$ **Simplify.**

$\qquad\qquad = \dfrac{1}{c}$ **Write using only positive exponents.**

✓ Quick Check **2** Simplify each expression.   **a.** $t^2(t^7)^{-2}$ **b.** $(a^4)^2 \cdot (a^2)^5$

---

2 Raising a Product to a Power

You can use repeated multiplication to simplify expressions like $(5y)^3$.

$$(5y)^3 = 5y \cdot 5y \cdot 5y$$
$$= 5 \cdot 5 \cdot 5 \cdot y \cdot y \cdot y$$
$$= 5^3 y^3$$
$$= 125 y^3$$

Notice that $(5y)^3 = 5^3 y^3$. This illustrates another property of exponents.

🔑 Key Concepts

Property	**Raising a Product to a Power**
For every nonzero number a and b and integer n, $(ab)^n = a^n b^n$.	
Example $(3x)^4 = 3^4 x^4 = 81 x^4$	

3 **EXAMPLE** **Simplifying a Product Raised to a Power**

Test-Taking Tip

When raising a product to a power, make sure each factor of the product is raised to the power.

Multiple Choice Which expression represents the area of the square?

   Ⓐ $8x^4$ Ⓑ $2x^8$ Ⓒ $4x^6$ Ⓓ $4x^8$

$(2x^4)^2 = 2^2(x^4)^2$ **Raise each factor to the 2nd power.**

$\qquad\quad\ = 2^2 x^8$ **Multiply exponents of a power raised to a power.**

$\qquad\quad\ = 4x^8$ **Simplify.**

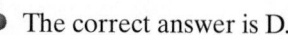

$2x^4$

The correct answer is D.

✓ Quick Check **3** Simplify each expression.   **a.** $(2z)^4$ **b.** $(4g^5)^{-2}$

Some expressions have more than one power raised to a power.

4 EXAMPLE **Simplifying a Product Raised to a Power**

Simplify $(x^{-2})^2(3xy^2)^4$.

$(x^{-2})^2(3xy^2)^4 = (x^{-2})^2 \cdot 3^4 x^4 (y^2)^4$ **Raise the three factors to the 4th power.**

$= x^{-4} \cdot 3^4 x^4 y^8$ **Multiply the exponents of a power raised to a power.**

$= 3^4 \cdot x^{-4} \cdot x^4 \cdot y^8$ **Use the Commutative Property of Multiplication.**

$= 3^4 x^0 y^8$ **Add exponents of powers with the same base.**

$= 81 y^8$ **Simplify.**

✓ Quick Check **4** Simplify each expression.

a. $(c^2)^3 (3c^5)^4$ **b.** $(2a^3)^5 (3ab^2)^3$ **c.** $(6mn)^3 (5m^{-3})^2$

You can use the property of raising a product to a power to solve problems involving scientific notation. For an expression like $(3 \times 10^8)^2$, raise both 3 and 10^8 to the second power.

5 EXAMPLE **Real-World Problem Solving**

Physical Science All objects, even resting ones, contain energy. A raisin has a mass of 10^{-3} kg. The expression $10^{-3} \cdot (3 \times 10^8)^2$ describes the amount of resting energy in joules the raisin contains. Simplify the expression.

$10^{-3} \cdot (3 \times 10^8)^2 = 10^{-3} \cdot 3^2 \cdot (10^8)^2$ **Raise each factor within parentheses to the second power.**

$= 10^{-3} \cdot 3^2 \cdot 10^{16}$ **Simplify $(10^8)^2$.**

$= 3^2 \cdot 10^{-3} \cdot 10^{16}$ **Use the Commutative Property of Multiplication.**

$= 3^2 \cdot 10^{-3+16}$ **Add exponents of powers with the same base.**

$= 9 \times 10^{13}$ **Simplify. Write in scientific notation.**

✓ Quick Check **5** **Energy** An hour of television use consumes 1.45×10^{-1} kWh (kilowatt-hour) of electricity. Each kilowatt-hour of electric use is equivalent to 3.6×10^6 joules of energy.

a. Simplify the expression $(1.45 \times 10^{-1})(3.6 \times 10^6)$ to find how many joules a television uses in 1 hour.

b. Critical Thinking Suppose you could release the resting energy in a raisin. About how many hours of television use could be powered by that energy?

EXERCISES

For more exercises, see *Extra Skill and Word Problem Practice.*

Practice and Problem Solving

A **Practice by Example**

Examples 1, 2
(page 624)

GO for Help

Simplify each expression.

1. $(c^5)^2$ **2.** $(c^2)^5$ **3.** $(n^8)^4$ **4.** $(q^{10})^{10}$

5. $(c^5)^3 c^4$ **6.** $(d^3)^5 (d^3)^0$ **7.** $(t^2)^{-2}(t^2)^{-5}$ **8.** $(x^3)^{-1}(x^2)^5$

Example 3
(page 624)

Simplify each expression.

9. $(5y)^4$ **10.** $(4m)^5$ **11.** $(7a)^2$ **12.** $(12g^4)^{-1}$

13. $(6y^2)^2$ **14.** $(3n^6)^4$ **15.** $(2y^4)^{-3}$ **16.** $(2p^6)^0$

Example 4
(page 625)

17. $(x^2)^5(x^3)^2$ **18.** $(2xy)^3x^2$ **19.** $(mg^4)^{-1}(mg^4)$

20. $(c^{-2})^3c^{-12}$ **21.** $(3b^{-2})^2(a^2b^4)^3$ **22.** $(2a^2c^4)^{-5}(c^{-1}a^7)^6$

Example 5
(page 625)

Simplify. Write each answer in scientific notation.

23. $(4 \times 10^5)^2$ **24.** $(3 \times 10^5)^2$ **25.** $(2 \times 10^{-10})^3$ **26.** $(2 \times 10^{-3})^3$

27. $(7 \times 10^4)^2$ **28.** $(6 \times 10^{12})^2$ **29.** $(4 \times 10^8)^{-2}$ **30.** $(3.5 \times 10^{-4})^3$

31. Geometry The length of one side of a cube is 9.5×10^{-4} m. What is the volume of the cube?

B **Apply Your Skills**

Complete each equation.

32. $(x^2)^{\blacksquare} = x^6$ **33.** $(m^{\blacksquare})^3 = m^{-12}$ **34.** $(b^2)^{\blacksquare} = b^8$

35. $(y^{-4})^{\blacksquare} = y^{12}$ **36.** $(n^9)^{\blacksquare} = 1$ **37.** $7(c^1)^{\blacksquare} = 7c^8$

38. $(5x^{\blacksquare})^2 = 25x^{-4}$ **39.** $(3x^3y^{\blacksquare})^3 = 27x^9$ **40.** $(m^2n^3)^{\blacksquare} = \dfrac{1}{m^6n^9}$

41. Error Analysis One student simplified $x^5 + x^5$ to x^{10}. A second student simplified $x^5 + x^5$ to $2x^5$. Which student is correct? Explain.

Simplify each expression.

42. $(4.1)^5 \cdot (4.1)^{-5}$ **43.** $3^2(3x)^3$ **44.** $(b^5)^3b^2$

45. $(-5x)^2 + 5x^2$ **46.** $(2x^{-3})^2 \cdot (0.2x)^2$ **47.** $(-2a^2b)^3(ab)^3$

48. $(3^7)^2 \cdot (3^{-4})^3$ **49.** $(10^3)^4(4.3 \times 10^{-8})$ **50.** $(4xy^2)^4(-y)^{-3}$

51. a. Geometry Write an expression for the surface area of each cube.
b. How many times greater than the surface area of the small cube is the surface area of the large cube?
c. Write an expression for the volume of each cube.
d. How many times greater than the volume of the small cube is the volume of the large cube?

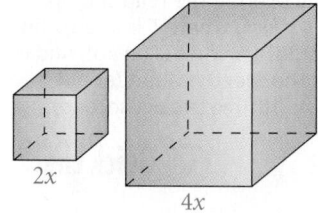

2x

4x

Write each expression with only one exponent. Use parentheses.

52. $m^4 \cdot n^4$ **53.** $(a^5)(b^5)(a^0)$ **54.** $49x^2y^2z^2$ **55.** $\dfrac{12x^2}{3y^2}$

56. Open-Ended Choose a value of n for the expression a^n. Express the power you wrote as a product of the form $(a^c)^d$ in four different ways.

57. Measurement Write each answer as a power of 10.
a. How many cubic centimeters are in a cubic meter?
b. How many cubic millimeters are in a cubic meter?
c. How many cubic meters are in a cubic kilometer?
d. How many cubic millimeters are in a cubic kilometer?

58. Computers Write each answer as a power of 2.

    a. Computer capacity is often measured in bits and bytes. A bit is the smallest unit, a 1 or 0 in the computer's memory. A byte is 2^3 bits. A megabyte (MB) is 2^{20} bytes. How many bits are in a megabyte?

    b. A gigabyte (GB) is 2^{10} megabytes. How many bytes are there in a gigabyte? How many bits are there in a gigabyte?

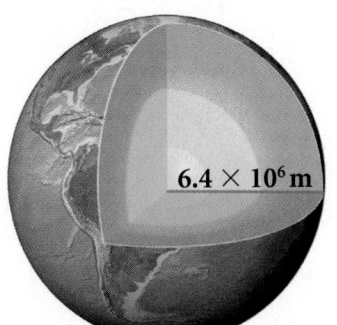 **59. a. Geography** Earth has a radius of about 6.4×10^6 m. Approximate the surface area of Earth using the formula for the surface area of a sphere, $S = 4\pi r^2$.

    b. Earth's surface is about 70% water, almost all of it in oceans. About how many square meters of Earth's surface are covered with water?

    c. The oceans have an average depth of 3795 m. Estimate the volume of water on Earth.

 6.4×10^6 m

60. Which expression or expressions do *not* equal 64?

    A. $2^5 \cdot 2$ **B.** 2^6 **C.** $2^2 \cdot 2^3$ **D.** $(2^3)^2$ **E.** $(2^2)(2^2)^2$

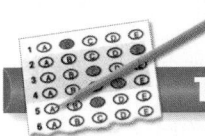 **61. Writing** Explain how you know when to add the exponents of powers and when to multiply the exponents.

C Challenge

Solve each equation.

Sample $25^3 = 5^x$

           $(5^2)^3 = 5^x$ **Write 25 as a power of 5.**

              $5^6 = 5^x$ **Simplify $(5^2)^3$.**

                $6 = x$ **Since the bases are the same, the exponents are equal.**

62. $5^6 = 25^x$ **63.** $8^2 = 2^x$ **64.** $3^x = 27^4$

65. $4^x = 2^6$ **66.** $3^{2x} = 9^4$ **67.** $2^x = \frac{1}{32}$

68. Critical Thinking Simplify $(x^3)^4$ and x^{3^4}. Are the expressions equivalent?

Test Prep

Multiple Choice

69. Which expression could you use for the area of the triangle at the right?

    A. $3x$ **B.** $4.5x^2$

    C. $9x^2$ **D.** $22.5x^2$

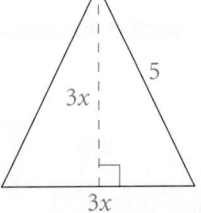

70. Evaluate $3a^2$ for $a = 5.1 \times 10^{-5}$.

    F. 1.53×10^{-10} **G.** 7.803×10^{-10}

    H. 1.53×10^{-9} **J.** 7.803×10^{-9}

71. If 7^{-2} is raised to the power of 3, which of the following describes the result?

    A. a number less than -7 **B.** a number between -1 and 0

    C. a number between 0 and 1   **D.** a number greater than 1

72. Which expression does NOT equal $25n^{12}$?

    F. $(5n^6)^2$ **G.** $(5n^3)(5n^9)$ **H.** $25(n^3)^9$ **J.** $5^2(n^2)^6$

Short Response

73. Does $(x^2 + 3y)^2$ equal $x^4 + 9y^2$? Substitute values for x and y to justify your answer.

Lesson 11-3

Simplify each expression.

74. $bc^{-6} \cdot b$ **75.** $(a^2b^3)(a^6)$ **76.** $9m^3(6m^2n^4)$ **77.** $2t(-2t^4)$

Lesson 10-2

Solve each system using substitution.

78. $y = 3x + 5$
$y = -4x + 12$

79. $y = 0.5x - 1$
$y = 0.2x + 0.4$

80. $y = 5x - 9$
$y = 3x + 5$

81. $y = x + 4$
$y = -5$

Lesson 9-1

Find the slope of the line that passes through each pair of points.

82. $(0, 3), (4, 0)$ **83.** $(2, -5), (3, 1)$ **84.** $(-3, 6), (1, 0)$ **85.** $(0, 0), (11, -9)$

Checkpoint Quiz 1   Lessons 11-1 through 11-4

Simplify each expression.

1. $5^{-1}(3^{-2})$ **2.** $(r^{-5})^{-4}$ **3.** $(2x^5)(3x^{12})$ **4.** $\dfrac{mn^{-4}}{p^0q^{-2}}$

5. $a^2b^0(a^{-3})$ **6.** $(3^2)^{-1}(4m^2)^3$ **7.** $(2m^3)(3m^6)$ **8.** $(3t^2)^3(2t^0)^{-3}$

9. A certain bacteria population doubles in size every day. Suppose a sample starts with 500 bacteria. The expression $500 \cdot 2^x$ models the number of bacteria in the sample after x days. Evaluate the expression for $x = 0, 2, 5$.

10. Astronomy The diameter of Mars is about 6800 km.
   a. Write this number in scientific notation.
   b. Approximate the surface area of Mars using the formula for the surface area of a sphere, $S = 4\pi r^2$. Write your answer in scientific notation.
   c. Write your answer from part (b) in standard form.

Algebra at Work

············· Dr. Jewel Plummer Cobb

Dr. Jewel Plummer Cobb was born in 1924 and obtained her master's and doctor's degrees in cell physiology from New York University. Dr. Cobb has concentrated on the study of normal and malignant skin cells and has published nearly 50 books, articles, and reports. Because the number of cancer cells grows exponentially, cell biologists often write cancer cell data in scientific notation.

Go Online
PHSchool.com

For: Information about a career in cancer research
Web Code: atb-2031

11-5

Division Properties of Exponents

What You'll Learn

- To divide powers with the same base
- To raise a quotient to a power

. . . And Why

To find the amount of paper recycled per person in the United States, as in Example 2

✓ **Check Skills You'll Need**

GO **for Help** Skills Handbook page 790

Write each fraction in simplest form.

1. $\frac{5}{20}$ 2. $\frac{125}{25}$ 3. $\frac{60}{100}$ 4. $\frac{124}{4}$

5. $\frac{6}{15}$ 6. $\frac{8}{30}$ 7. $\frac{10}{35}$ 8. $\frac{18}{63}$

9. $\frac{5xy}{15x}$ 10. $\frac{6y^2}{3x}$ 11. $\frac{3ac}{12a}$ 12. $\frac{24m}{6mn^2}$

---

1 Dividing Powers With the Same Base

You can use repeated multiplication to simplify fractions. Expand the numerator and the denominator using repeated multiplication. Then cancel like terms.

$$\frac{5^6}{5^2} = \frac{5 \cdot 5 \cdot 5 \cdot 5 \cdot 5 \cdot 5}{5 \cdot 5} = 5^4$$

This illustrates the following property of exponents.

 Key Concepts

Property	**Dividing Powers With the Same Base**

For every nonzero number a and integers m and n, $\frac{a^m}{a^n} = a^{m-n}$.

Example $\frac{3^7}{3^3} = 3^{7-3} = 3^4$

Since division by zero is undefined, assume that no base is equal to zero.

1 EXAMPLE Simplifying an Algebraic Expression

Simplify each expression.

a. $\frac{a^6}{a^{14}} = a^{6-14}$ Subtract exponents when dividing powers with the same base.

$= a^{-8}$ Simplify the exponents.

$= \frac{1}{a^8}$ Rewrite using positive exponents.

b. $\frac{c^{-1}d^3}{c^5 d^{-4}} = c^{-1-5}d^{3-(-4)}$ Subtract exponents when dividing powers with the same base.

$= c^{-6}d^7$ Simplify.

$= \frac{d^7}{c^6}$ Rewrite using positive exponents.

Video Tutor Help

Visit: PHSchool.com
Web Code: ate-0775

 **Quick Check** **1** Simplify each expression.

a. $\dfrac{b^4}{b^9}$ **b.** $\dfrac{z^{10}}{z^5}$ **c.** $\dfrac{a^2 b}{a^4 b^3}$ **d.** $\dfrac{m^{-1} n^2}{m^3 n}$ **e.** $\dfrac{x^2 y^{-1} z^4}{x y^4 z^{-3}}$

When you divide numbers that are in scientific notation, you can use the property of dividing powers with the same base. In real-world situations, decide whether to write the result in standard or scientific notation.

2 **EXAMPLE** **Real-World** 🌐 **Problem Solving**

Recycling In 2000, the total amount of paper and paperboard recycled in the United States was 37 million tons. The population of the United States in 2000 was 281.4 million. On average, how much paper and paperboard did each person recycle?

$\dfrac{37 \text{ million tons}}{281.4 \text{ million people}} = \dfrac{3.7 \times 10^7 \text{ tons}}{2.814 \times 10^8 \text{ people}}$ **Write in scientific notation.**

$\qquad = \dfrac{3.7}{2.814} \times 10^{7-8}$ **Subtract exponents when dividing powers with the same base.**

$\qquad = \dfrac{3.7}{2.814} \times 10^{-1}$ **Simplify the exponent.**

$\qquad \approx 1.3 \times 10^{-1}$ **Divide. Round to the nearest tenth.**

$\qquad = 0.13$ **Write in standard notation.**

● There was about 0.13 ton of paper and paperboard recycled per person in 2000.

Real-World 🌐 **Connection**

Worldwide, about 43% of the paper that is discarded is recovered for recycling.

 **Quick Check** **2** Find each quotient. Write each answer in scientific notation.

a. $\dfrac{2 \times 10^3}{8 \times 10^8}$ **b.** $\dfrac{7.5 \times 10^{12}}{2.5 \times 10^{-4}}$ **c.** $\dfrac{4.2 \times 10^5}{12.6 \times 10^2}$

d. In 2000 the total amount of glass recycled in the United States was 2.7 million tons. The population of the United States in 2000 was 281.4 million people. On average, about how many tons of glass were recycled per person?

2   Raising a Quotient to a Power

You can use repeated multiplication to simplify the expression $\left(\dfrac{x}{y}\right)^3$.

$\left(\dfrac{x}{y}\right)^3 = \dfrac{x}{y} \cdot \dfrac{x}{y} \cdot \dfrac{x}{y}$

$\qquad = \dfrac{x \cdot x \cdot x}{y \cdot y \cdot y}$

$\qquad = \dfrac{x^3}{y^3}$

This illustrates another property of exponents.

 Key Concepts

Property	**Raising a Quotient to a Power**
For every nonzero number a and b and integer n, $\left(\dfrac{a}{b}\right)^n = \dfrac{a^n}{b^n}$.	
Example $\left(\dfrac{4}{5}\right)^3 = \dfrac{4^3}{5^3} = \dfrac{64}{125}$	

3 EXAMPLE **Raising a Quotient to a Power**

Multiple Choice Which expression is equivalent to $\left(\frac{4}{x^2}\right)^3$?

A $\frac{12}{x^5}$ B $\frac{12}{x^6}$ C $\frac{64}{x^5}$ D $\frac{64}{x^6}$

$\left(\frac{4}{x^2}\right)^3 = \frac{4^3}{(x^2)^3}$ **Raise the numerator and the denominator to the third power.**

$= \frac{4^3}{x^6}$ **Multiply the exponents in the denominator.**

$= \frac{64}{x^6}$ **Simplify.**

● The correct answer is D.

✓ Quick Check ❸ Simplify each expression.   **a.** $\left(\frac{3}{x^2}\right)^2$ **b.** $\left(\frac{x}{y^2}\right)^3$

You can use what you know about exponents to rewrite an expression in the form $\left(\frac{a}{b}\right)^{-n}$ using positive exponents.

$\left(\frac{a}{b}\right)^{-n} = \frac{1}{\left(\frac{a}{b}\right)^n}$ **Use the definition of negative exponent.**

$= \frac{1}{\frac{a^n}{b^n}}$ **Raise the quotient to a power.**

$= \frac{1}{\frac{a^n}{b^n}} \cdot \frac{b^n}{b^n}$ **Use the Identity Property of Multiplication to multiply by $\frac{b^n}{b^n}$.**

$= \frac{b^n}{a^n}$ **Simplify.**

$= \left(\frac{b}{a}\right)^n$ **Write the quotient using one exponent.**

So, $\left(\frac{a}{b}\right)^{-n} = \left(\frac{b}{a}\right)^n$.

4 EXAMPLE **Simplifying an Exponential Expression**

Simplify each expression.

a. $\left(\frac{3}{5}\right)^{-2} = \left(\frac{5}{3}\right)^2$ **Rewrite using the reciprocal of $\frac{3}{5}$.**

$= \frac{5^2}{3^2}$ **Raise the numerator and denominator to the second power.**

$= \frac{25}{9}$ or $2\frac{7}{9}$ **Simplify.**

b. $\left(-\frac{2x}{y}\right)^{-4} = \left(-\frac{y}{2x}\right)^4$ **Rewrite using the reciprocal of $-\frac{2x}{y}$.**

$= \left(\frac{-y}{2x}\right)^4$ **Write the fraction with a negative numerator.**

$= \frac{(-y)^4}{(2x)^4}$ **Raise the numerator and denominator to the fourth power.**

$= \frac{y^4}{16x^4}$ **Simplify.**

✓ Quick Check ❹ Simplify each expression.

a. $\left(\frac{3}{4}\right)^{-3}$ **b.** $\left(\frac{-1}{2}\right)^{-5}$ **c.** $\left(\frac{2r}{s}\right)^{-1}$ **d.** $\left(\frac{7a}{m}\right)^{-2}$

EXERCISES

For more exercises, see *Extra Skill and Word Problem Practice*.

Practice and Problem Solving

 A Practice by Example

Example 1
(page 629)

 GO for Help

Copy and complete each equation.

1. $\frac{5^9}{5^2} = 5^{\blacksquare}$

2. $\frac{2^4}{2^3} = 2^{\blacksquare}$

3. $\frac{3^2}{3^5} = 3^{\blacksquare}$

4. $\frac{5^2 5^3}{5^3 5^2} = 5^{\blacksquare}$

Simplify each expression.

5. $\frac{2^5}{2^7}$

6. $\frac{2^7}{2^5}$

7. $\frac{c^{12}}{c^{15}}$

8. $\frac{m^{-2}}{m^{-5}}$

9. $\frac{3s^{-9}}{6s^{-11}}$

10. $\frac{x^{13}y^2}{x^{13}y}$

11. $\frac{c^2 d^{-3}}{c^3 d^{-1}}$

12. $\frac{3^2 m^3 t^6}{3^5 m^7 t^{-5}}$

Example 2
(page 630)

Simplify each quotient. Write each answer in scientific notation.

13. $\frac{6.5 \times 10^{15}}{1.3 \times 10^8}$

14. $\frac{2.7 \times 10^{-8}}{9 \times 10^{-4}}$

15. $\frac{4.2 \times 10^8}{7 \times 10^5}$

16. $\frac{8.4 \times 10^{-5}}{2 \times 10^{-8}}$

17. $\frac{4.65 \times 10^{-4}}{3.1 \times 10^2}$

18. $\frac{3.5 \times 10^6}{5 \times 10^8}$

19. Television In 2000, people in the United States over age 2 watched television a total of 386 billion hours. The population of the United States over age 2 was about 265 million people.
  a. Write each number in scientific notation.
  b. Find the average number of hours of TV viewing per person older than age 2 for 2000.
  c. On average, how many hours per day did each person older than age 2 watch television in 2000?

20. Computers The speed of computers is measured in number of calculations per picosecond. There are 3.6×10^{15} picoseconds per hour. What fraction of a second is a picosecond?

Example 3
(page 631)

Simplify each expression.

21. $\left(\frac{3}{5}\right)^2$

22. $\left(\frac{1}{x}\right)^3$

23. $\left(\frac{2x}{y}\right)^5$

24. $\left(\frac{3a}{2b}\right)^4$

25. $\left(\frac{2^2}{5}\right)^3$

26. $\left(\frac{3^3}{3^4}\right)^2$

27. $\left(\frac{6}{n^6}\right)^2$

28. $\left(\frac{2p}{5}\right)^3$

Example 4
(page 631)

29. $\left(\frac{2}{3}\right)^{-1}$

30. $\left(\frac{2}{3}\right)^{-2}$

31. $\left(-\frac{2}{3}\right)^{-2}$

32. $\left(-\frac{2}{3}\right)^{-3}$

33. $\left(\frac{3x^4}{15}\right)^2$

34. $\left(\frac{4n}{2n^2}\right)^3$

35. $\left(\frac{c^5}{c^9}\right)^3$

36. $\left(\frac{3b^2}{5}\right)^0$

B Apply Your Skills

Explain why each expression is *not* in simplest form.

37. $5^3 m^3$

38. $x^5 y^{-2}$

39. $(2c)^4$

40. $x^0 y$

41. $\frac{d^7}{d}$

Simplify each expression.

42. $\frac{3^2 \cdot 5^0}{2^3}$

43. $\left(\frac{2m^5}{m^2}\right)^{-4}$

44. $\frac{5x^3}{(5x)^3}$

45. $\frac{(2a^7)(3a^2)}{6a^3}$

46. $\left(\frac{7t^3}{21t}\right)^3$

47. $\left(\frac{n^4 n}{n^{-2}}\right)^{-4}$

48. $\left(\frac{2k^3}{3k^{-2}}\right)^{-2}$

49. $\frac{7^9 \cdot (10)^2}{7^7}$

1920's

1950's

Today

50. **Telecommunications** In 2000, there were 97.4 million households with telephones. The people in these households made 544 billion local calls and 97 billion long distance calls.
 a. Write each number in scientific notation.
 b. What was the average number of local calls placed per household? Round to the nearest whole number.
 c. What was the average number of long distance calls placed per household? Round to the nearest whole number.

51. a. **Writing** While simplifying the expression $\frac{c^4}{c^6}$, Kneale said, "I've found a property of exponents that's not in my algebra book!" Write an explanation of why Kneale's method works.
 b. **Open-Ended** Apply Kneale's method to an example you create.

Kneale

$$\frac{c^4}{c^6} = \frac{1}{c^{6-4}} = \frac{1}{c^2}$$

Simplify each expression.

52. $\left(\frac{2ab^6}{a^3b}\right)^{-2}$ 53. $\frac{a^3b^2c^{-4}}{a^{-2}b^5c^{-9}}$ 54. $\frac{\left(\frac{1}{3}\right)^{-3}}{\left(\frac{1}{6}\right)^{-2}}$ 55. $\frac{0.2^2 \cdot 0.2^3}{0.2^6}$

56. $\left(\frac{p^{-2}q^4r}{p^3q^5}\right)^5$ 57. $\left(\frac{(-3)^2}{(-2)^{-4}}\right)^2$ 58. $\left(\frac{(3x)^2y}{x^2y^4}\right)^{-2}$ 59. $\frac{(5a^2)(6b^3)}{(2a^3)(25b^{-2})}$

60. **Multiple Choice** The area of the rectangle is $60a^2b^5$. What is the width of the rectangle?

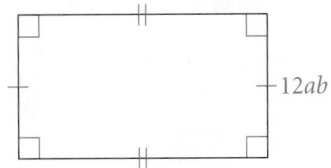
12ab

 F $\frac{a^2b^5}{5}$ G $\frac{5}{a^2b^5}$

 H $5ab^4$ J $5a^3b^6$

61. **Critical Thinking** Lena and Jared used different methods to simplify $\left(\frac{b^7}{b^3}\right)^2$. Why are both methods correct?

Lena

$$\left(\frac{b^7}{b^3}\right)^2 = \frac{b^{14}}{b^6}$$
$$= b^8$$

Jared

$$\left(\frac{b^7}{b^3}\right)^2 = (b^4)^2$$
$$= b^8$$

62. a. **Finance** In 1990, the United States government owed $3.23 trillion to its creditors. The population of the United States was 248.7 million people. How much did the government owe per person in 1990? Round to the nearest dollar.
 b. In 1999 the debt had grown to $5.66 trillion, with a population of 273 million. How much did the government owe per person? Round to the nearest dollar.
 c. What was the percent of increase in the average amount owed per person from 1990 to 1999?

63. a. **Error Analysis** What error did the student make in simplifying the expression at the right?
 b. What is the correct answer?

$$5^4 \div 5 = \frac{5^4}{5}$$
$$= 1^4$$
$$= 1$$

Write each expression with only one exponent. You may need to use parentheses.

64. $\dfrac{3^5}{5^5}$ **65.** $\dfrac{m^7}{n^7}$ **66.** $\dfrac{d^8}{d^5}$ **67.** $\dfrac{10^7 \cdot 10^0}{10^{-3}}$

68. $\dfrac{27x^3}{8y^3}$ **69.** $\dfrac{4m^2}{169m^4}$ **70.** $\dfrac{49m^2}{25n^2}$ **71.** $\dfrac{125c^7}{216c^4}$

🌐 **72. Medicine** If you donate blood regularly, the American Red Cross recommends a 56-day waiting period between donations. One pint of blood contains about 2.4×10^{12} red blood cells. Your body normally produces about 2×10^6 red blood cells per second.
  a. At its normal rate, in how many seconds will your body replace the red blood cells lost by giving one pint of blood?
  b. Convert your answer from part (a) to days.

73. a. Open Ended Write three numbers in scientific notation.
  b. Divide each number by 2.
  c. Critical Thinking Is the power of 10 divided by 2 when you divide a number in scientific notation by 2? Explain.

Which property or properties of exponents would you use to simplify each expression?

74. 2^{-3} **75.** $\dfrac{2^2}{2^5}$ **76.** $\left(\dfrac{1}{2}\right)^3$ **77.** $\dfrac{1}{2^{-4}2^7}$ **78.** $\dfrac{(2^4)^3}{2^{15}}$

C **Challenge** **Simplify each expression.**

79. $n^{x+2} \div n^x$ **80.** $n^{5x} \div n^x$ **81.** $\left(\dfrac{x^m}{x^{m-2}}\right)^2$ **82.** $\dfrac{\left(\dfrac{n^5}{n^4}\right)}{n^3}$

🌐 **83. Astronomy** The ratio of a planet's maximum to minimum distance from the sun is related to how circular its orbit is.
  a. Copy and complete the table below. Round decimals to the nearest hundredth.
  b. Reasoning How can you use the ratio maximum : minimum to determine whether a planet's orbit is close to circular?
  c. Which planet has the least circular orbit? The most circular orbit?

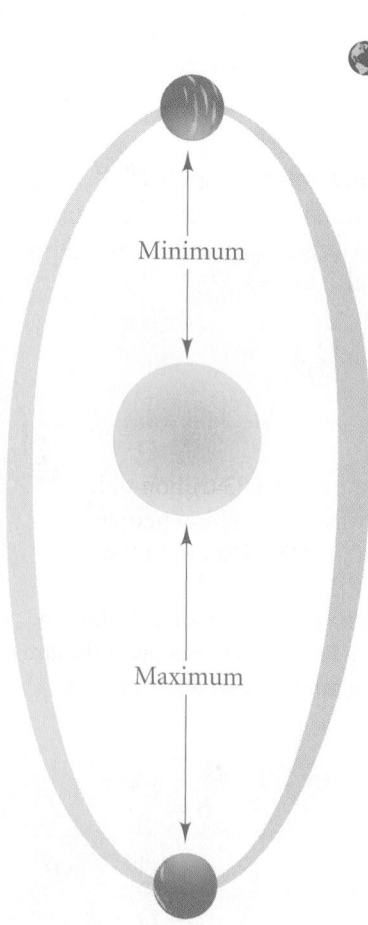

Minimum

Maximum

Distance From the Sun (kilometers)

Planet	Maximum	Minimum	Maximum : Minimum
Mercury	6.97×10^7	4.59×10^7	■ : ■ $= \dfrac{6.97 \times 10^7}{4.59 \times 10^7} = \dfrac{6.97}{4.59} \approx 1.52$
Venus	1.089×10^8	1.075×10^8	$1.089 \times 10^8 :$ ■ $\approx$ ■
Earth	1.521×10^8	1.471×10^8	■ $: 1.471 \times 10^8 \approx$ ■
Mars	2.491×10^8	2.067×10^8	■ : ■ $\approx$ ■
Jupiter	8.157×10^8	7.409×10^8	■ : ■ $\approx$ ■
Saturn	1.507×10^9	1.347×10^9	■ : ■ $\approx$ ■
Uranus	3.004×10^9	2.735×10^9	■ : ■ $\approx$ ■
Neptune	4.537×10^9	4.457×10^9	■ : ■ $\approx$ ■
Pluto	7.375×10^9	4.425×10^9	■ : ■ $\approx$ ■

Test Prep

Multiple Choice

84. Simplify the expression $\frac{(-6)^5}{6^5}$.

  A. -6^5 **B.** -1 **C.** 1 **D.** 6^7

85. Evaluate $\frac{-5x^3y^5}{15x^{-7}y^5z^{-2}}$ for $x = -1$, $y = 5$, and $z = 3$.

  F. -9 **G.** -3 **H.** -1 **J** 0

86. Which point on the number line below could be the graph of 2^n if n is a negative integer?

$$Y \quad W\ Z \qquad X$$
$$-2\,-1\ \ 0\ \ \ 1\ \ \ 2$$

  A. W **B.** X **C.** Y **D.** Z

87. Which of the following statements is true?

  F. Any number raised to the zero power equals zero.

  G. Any number raised to a negative power equals a negative number.

  H. Negative numbers can be written in scientific notation.

  J. The product of two powers with the same base equals the base raised to the sum of the exponents.

88. Find the quotient $\frac{1.8 \times 10^{-4}}{3.6 \times 10^3}$.

  A. 5×10^{-8} **B.** 5×10^{-6} **C.** 5×10^{-2} **D.** 5×10^{-1}

89. Which expression is NOT equivalent to $\left(\frac{4n}{3m^5}\right)^{-2}$?

  F. $\left(\frac{3m^5}{4n}\right)^2$ **G.** $\frac{4n^{-2}}{3m^3}$ **H.** $\frac{9m^{10}}{16n^2}$ **J** $\left(\frac{16n^2}{9m^{10}}\right)^{-1}$

Extended Response

90. At its closest, Saturn is about 743,000,000 miles from Earth. A deep-space probe travels from Earth to Saturn at an average speed of 25,000 miles per hour. Assume that the probe can go straight from Earth to Saturn. How many hours will it take the probe to get from Earth to Saturn? About how many years will it take? Show your work.

Mixed Review

Lesson 11-4   Simplify each expression.

91. $(3y^2)^3$ **92.** $(2m^{-7})^3$ **93.** $(r^2t^{-5})^{-4}$ **94.** $2(3s^{-2})^{-3}$

95. $(2^3c^2)^{-1}$ **96.** $(-3)^2(-r^3)^2$ **97.** $(7^0n^{-3})^2(n^5)^2$ **98.** $(7^2y^{12})^0$

Lesson 10-1   Solve each system by graphing.

99. $y = 3x$ **100.** $y = 2x + 1$ **101.** $y = 5$ **102.** $y = 7$
     $y = -2x$ $y = x - 3$ $x = 3$ $y = 8$

Lesson 9-8   **103.** Graph $y = |x|$ and its translation $y = |x| + 3$.

Geometric Sequences

What You'll Learn

- To form geometric sequences
- To use formulas when describing geometric sequences

... And Why

To find the height of a ball after a number of bounces, as in Example 5

GO for Help Lesson 8-7

✓ Check Skills You'll Need

Find the common difference of each sequence.

1. $1, 3, 5, 7, \ldots$ **2.** $19, 17, 15, 13, \ldots$

3. $1.3, 0.1, -1.1, -2.3, \ldots$ **4.** $18, 21.5, 25, 28.5, \ldots$

Use inductive reasoning to find the next two numbers in each pattern.

5. $2, 4, 8, 16, \ldots$ **6.** $4, 12, 36, \ldots$

7. $0.2, 0.4, 0.8, 1.6, \ldots$ **8.** $200, 100, 50, 25, \ldots$

◀)) New Vocabulary   • geometric sequence   • common ratio

---

1 Geometric Sequences

Recall that a number pattern is also called a sequence, and each number in a sequence is a term of the sequence.

Vocabulary Tip

When you write a ratio of one term to the previous term in a geometric sequence, the ratios are equal. Thus the name is <u>common ratio</u>.

In Chapter 5 you studied arithmetic sequences, where you found each new term by adding the same amount to each previous term. Another kind of number sequence is a geometric sequence. In a **geometric sequence,** the ratio between consecutive terms is constant. This ratio is called the **common ratio.**

$$
\begin{array}{cccc}
\text{Term} & 2, & 10, & 50, & 250 \\
\text{Common Ratio} & & \times 5 & \times 5 & \times 5 \\
\end{array}
$$

1 EXAMPLE   Finding the Common Ratio

Find the common ratio of each sequence.

a. $3, 12, 48, 192, \ldots$

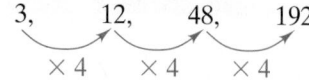

The common ratio is 4.

b. $80, 20, 5, \frac{5}{4}, \ldots$

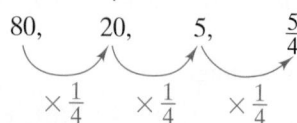

The common ratio is $\frac{1}{4}$.

✓ Quick Check

1 Find the common ratio of each sequence.

a. $750, 150, 30, 6, \ldots$ **b.** $-3, -6, -12, -24, \ldots$ **c.** $4, 6, 9, 13.5, \ldots$

2 EXAMPLE Finding the Next Terms in a Sequence

Find the next three terms of the sequence $2, -6, 18, -54, \ldots$

$$2, \qquad -6, \qquad 18, \qquad -54$$
$$\times (-3) \quad \times (-3) \quad \times (-3)$$

The common ratio is -3. The next three terms are $-54(-3) = 162$,
$162(-3) = -486$, and $-486(-3) = 1458$.

Quick Check ❷ Find the next three terms of each sequence.
    a. $1, 3, 9, 27, \ldots$ **b.** $120, -60, 30, -15, \ldots$ **c.** $1.1, 2.2, 4.4, 8.8, \ldots$

You can look for a common difference or common ratio to determine whether a sequence is arithmetic or geometric. If there is no common difference or common ratio, the sequence is neither arithmetic nor geometric.

3 EXAMPLE Arithmetic or Geometric Sequence

Determine whether each sequence is arithmetic or geometric.
  a. $-7, -5, -3, -1, \ldots$

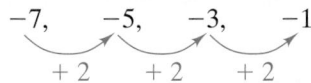
$$-7, \qquad -5, \qquad -3, \qquad -1$$
$$+ 2 \qquad + 2 \qquad + 2$$

The sequence has a common difference. The sequence is arithmetic.

  b. $56, 28, 14, 7, \ldots$

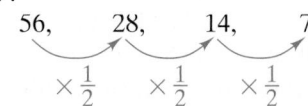
$$56, \qquad 28, \qquad 14, \qquad 7$$
$$\times \tfrac{1}{2} \quad \times \tfrac{1}{2} \quad \times \tfrac{1}{2}$$

The sequence has a common ratio. The sequence is geometric.

Quick Check ❸ Determine whether each sequence is arithmetic or geometric.
    a. $2, 4, 6, 8, \ldots$ **b.** $2, 4, 8, 16, \ldots$ **c.** $1, 3, 5, 7, \ldots$

2   Using a Formula

You can use the common ratio of a geometric sequence to write a function rule for the sequence. Consider the sequence $2, 6, 18, 54, \ldots$. Its common ratio is 3.

Let $n =$ the term number in a sequence.

Let $A(n) =$ the value of the nth term of the sequence.

$A(1) = 2$

$A(2) = 2 \cdot 3 = 2 \cdot 3^1$

$A(3) = 2 \cdot 3 \cdot 3 = 2 \cdot 3^2$ **Note that each exponent is one less than its term number.**

$A(4) = 2 \cdot 3 \cdot 3 \cdot 3 = 2 \cdot 3^3$

    (

$A(n) = 2 \cdot 3 \cdot 3 \cdot 3 \cdot 3 \ldots \cdot 3 = 2 \cdot 3^{n-1}$

In general, you can write a function rule using the first term, the term number, and the common ratio. For the sequence above, the rule is $A(n) = 2 \cdot 3^{n-1}$.

Key Concepts

Rule	Geometric Sequence

$$A(n) = a \cdot r^{n-1}$$

nth term   first term   common ratio   term number

4 EXAMPLE   **Finding Terms of a Sequence**

Find the first, fifth, and tenth terms of the sequence that has the rule $A(n) = 5(-2)^{n-1}$.

first term: $A(1) = 5$

fifth term: $A(5) = 5(-2)^{5-1} = 5(-2)^4 = 5(16) = 80$

tenth term: $A(10) = 5(-2)^{10-1} = 5(-2)^9 = 5(-512) = -2560$

✓ Quick Check   **4** Find the first, sixth, and twelfth terms of each sequence.

   a. $A(n) = 4 \cdot 3^{n-1}$ **b.** $A(n) = -2 \cdot 5^{n-1}$

You can write and evaluate a rule for a geometric sequence that models a real-world situation.

5 EXAMPLE   Real-World 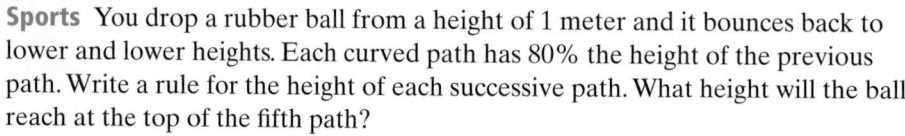 **Problem Solving**

Sports You drop a rubber ball from a height of 1 meter and it bounces back to lower and lower heights. Each curved path has 80% the height of the previous path. Write a rule for the height of each successive path. What height will the ball reach at the top of the fifth path?

Draw a diagram to help understand the problem.

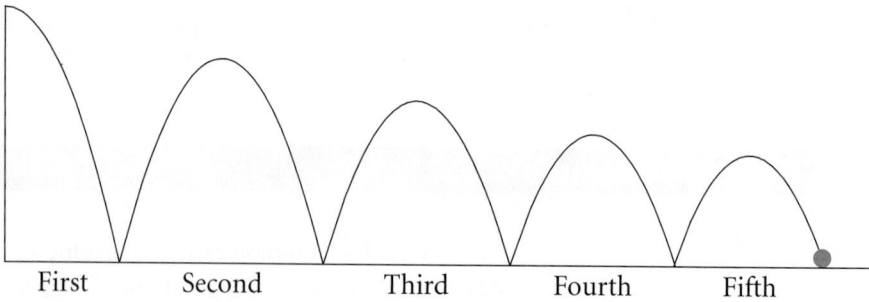

First   Second   Third   Fourth   Fifth

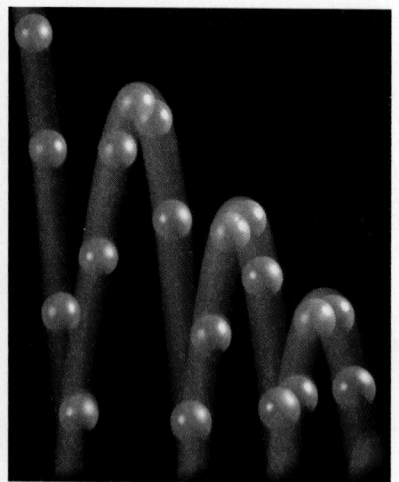

Real-World 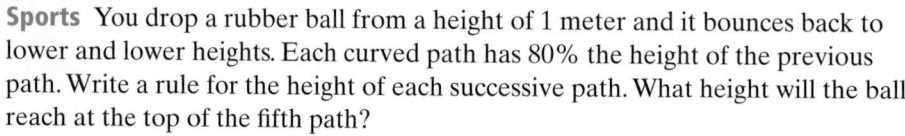 Connection

Strobe-light photography is often used to highlight details of the motion of objects.

The height of the first path is 100 cm. So the height is 100 cm for the first term, with $n = 1$. The height of the fifth path is given by the term $n = 5$. The common ratio is 80%, or 0.8.

A rule for the sequence is $A(n) = 100 \cdot 0.8^{n-1}$.

$A(n) = 100 \cdot 0.8^{n-1}$ **Use the sequence to find the height of the fifth path.**

$A(5) = 100 \cdot 0.8^{5-1}$ **Substitute 5 for n.**

$\quad\;\; = 100 \cdot 0.8^4$ **Simplify exponents.**

$\quad\;\; = 100 \cdot 0.4096$ **Evaluate powers.**

$\quad\;\; = 40.96$ **Simplify.**

● The height of the fourth bounce will be 40.96 cm.

 **Quick Check** **5** **Basketball** You drop a basketball from a height of 2 meters. Each curved path has 56% of the height of the previous path. Using the height in centimeters, write a rule for the sequence. What height will the basketball reach at the top of the fourth path (when $n = 4$)? Round to the nearest tenth of a centimeter.

EXERCISES

For more exercises, see *Extra Skill and Word Problem Practice.*

Practice and Problem Solving

A Practice by Example

Example 1
(page 636)

Find the common ratio of each sequence.

1. $2, 8, 32, 128, \ldots$ **2.** $-3, -12, -48, -192, \ldots$ **3.** $70, 7, 0.7, 0.07, \ldots$

4. $8, 20, 50, 125, \ldots$ **5.** $-80, 20, -5, 1.25, \ldots$ **6.** $0.45, 0.9, 1.8, 3.6, \ldots$

Example 2
(page 637)

Find the next three terms of each sequence.

7. $2.5, 5, 10, 20, \ldots$ **8.** $3, 6, 12, 24, \ldots$ **9.** $4, 6, 9, 13.5, \ldots$

10. $-8, 4, -2, 1, \ldots$ **11.** $225, 45, 9, 1.8 \ldots$ **12.** $-3, 6, -12, 24, \ldots$

Example 3
(page 637)

Determine whether each sequence is *arithmetic* or *geometric*.

13. $2, 14, 98, 686, \ldots$ **14.** $12, 8, 4, 0, \ldots$ **15.** $9, -36, 144, -576, \ldots$

16. $-5, -10, -15, -20, \ldots$ **17.** $0.6, 1.3, 2, 2.7, \ldots$ **18.** $9, 12, 16, 21\frac{1}{3}, \ldots$

Example 4
(page 638)

Find the first, fourth, and eighth terms of each sequence.

19. $A(n) = 5 \cdot 3^{n-1}$ **20.** $A(n) = -5 \cdot 3^{n-1}$ **21.** $A(n) = 5 \cdot (-3)^{n-1}$

22. $A(n) = 0.5 \cdot 3^{n-1}$ **23.** $A(n) = -2 \cdot 5^{n-1}$ **24.** $A(n) = -1.1 \cdot (-4)^{n-1}$

Example 5
(page 638)

Write a rule and find the given term in each geometric sequence described below.

25. What is the fifth term when the first term is 6 and the common ratio is 0.5?

26. What is the tenth term when the first term is -6 and the common ratio is 2?

27. What is the fourth term when the first term is 7 and the common ratio is 1.1?

28. What is the seventh term when the first term is 1 and the common ratio is -4?

29. You drop a handball from a height of 1 meter. Each curved path has 64% of the height of the previous path.
   a. Write a rule for the sequence using centimeters. The initial height is when $n = 1$.
   b. What height will the ball reach at the top of the sixth path?

B Apply Your Skills

Find the next three terms of each sequence. Then write a rule for each sequence.

30. $216, 72, 24, 8, \ldots$ **31.** $625, 125, 25, 5, \ldots$

32. $0.1, 0.9, 8.1, 72.9, \ldots$ **33.** $16, -8, 4, -2, \ldots$

Problem Solving Hint

For Exercises 30 and 31, making a list of the terms of a sequence, and their factors, can help you write a rule.

34. Open-Ended Write four terms of a geometric sequence. Then write a rule for your sequence.

35. Writing How can you determine whether a sequence is arithmetic or geometric?

Homework Video Tutor

Visit: PHSchool.com
Web Code: ate-0806

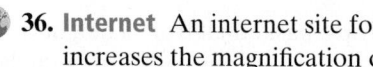 **36. Internet** An internet site for driving directions increases the magnification of a map 20% for each level of zoom.

a. Copy and complete the table to show the magnification at each level.

b. Write a rule for this situation using the decimal equivalents of the percent values.

Zoom Level	Magnification
0	100%
1	120%
2	▪
3	▪
4	▪

Determine whether each sequence is *arithmetic*, *geometric*, or *neither*. Find the next three terms of each sequence.

37. $11, 9, 7, 5, \ldots$

38. $7, 6, 4, 1, \ldots$

39. $18, 9, 4.5, 2.25, \ldots$

40. $12, 14, 16, 18, \ldots$

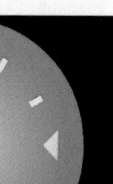

41. Physics On the first swing, a pendulum swings through an arc of length 36 centimeters. On each successive swing, the length of the arc is 90% of the length of the previous swing.

a. Write a rule to model this situation.

b. Critical Thinking What value of n would you use to find the length of the arc on the sixth swing? Explain.

c. Find the length of the arc on the sixth swing, to the nearest tenth of a centimeter.

42. a. Geometry What fraction of each figure is shaded?

b. Rewrite each fraction from part (a) in the form $2^{\blacksquare}$.

c. Write a rule that relates the figure number n to the shaded rectangle r.

d. What portion of the square would be shaded in Figure 10?

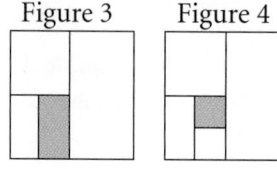

Figure 1   Figure 2

Figure 3   Figure 4

43. Reasoning Can zero be a term of a geometric sequence that has terms that are not zero? Explain.

C Challenge

44. Fractal Geometry The figures below show the first four steps in making Sierpinski's Triangle.

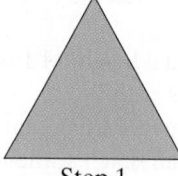 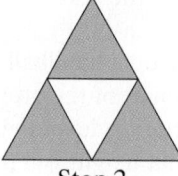 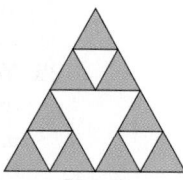 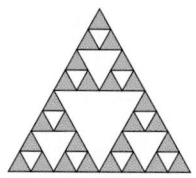

Step 1   Step 2   Step 3   Step 4

a. Patterns What fraction of each step is shaded?

b. Use your answer from part (a) to write a rule that relates the step number n to the fraction r of the figure that is shaded.

c. What fraction of Step 6 would be shaded?

d. Patterns What fraction of each step is *not* shaded?

e. Write a rule that relates the step number n to the fraction r of the figure that is *not* shaded.

f. What fraction of Step 8 would *not* be shaded?

Find each common ratio. Then find the next three terms in each sequence.

45. $x, x^2, x^3, x^4, \ldots$ **46.** $\frac{1}{3}, x, 3x^2, 9x^3, \ldots$ **47.** $xy, x^2y^3, x^3y^5, x^4y^7, \ldots$

48. $\frac{2}{b^2}, \frac{2a}{b}, 2a^2, 2a^3b, \ldots$ **49.** $2 \times 10^7, 1.2 \times 10^6, 7.2 \times 10^4, 4.32 \times 10^3, \ldots$

50. What term is 512 in the geometric sequence with the first term 2 and the common ratio 4?

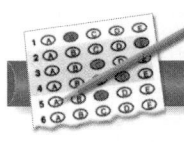

Test Prep

Multiple Choice

51. Which set of numbers continues the pattern 27, 9, 3, 1, ... ?

A. $-3, -9, -27$ **B.** $-\frac{1}{3}, -\frac{1}{6}, -\frac{1}{9}$

C. $\frac{1}{3}, \frac{1}{6}, \frac{1}{9}$ **D.** $\frac{1}{3}, \frac{1}{9}, \frac{1}{27}$

52. Charlie is stacking cans at a grocery store. The picture shows the first four layers. How many cans are there in 6 layers?

  F. 36 cans **G.** 61 cans
  H. 91 cans **J.** 729 cans

53. Which equation could you use to find the next term in the pattern 3, 6, 12, 24, 48, ... ?

A. $A(n) = 3^{n-1}$ **B.** $A(n) = 3(2)^{n-1}$
C. $A(n) = 3 \cdot 2n$ **D.** $A(n) = 3n^2$

Short Response

54. In a research laboratory, bacteria of a certain species double in number each day. If the number of bacteria at the beginning of a day is 350, how many bacteria will there be at the beginning of the 5th day? Show your work.

Mixed Review

Lesson 11-5

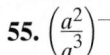

Simplify each expression.

55. $\left(\frac{a^2}{a^3}\right)^{-4}$ **56.** $\left(\frac{1}{2}\right)^{-4}$ **57.** $\left(\frac{x^2 z}{z^{-3}}\right)^{-5}$ **58.** $\left(\frac{m^{-3}}{n^4}\right)^0$

59. $\left(\frac{8}{9}\right)^{-2}$ **60.** $\left(\frac{m^4}{m^2}\right)^{-7}$ **61.** $\left(\frac{pq^0}{p^4}\right)^5$ **62.** $\left(\frac{c^2 d^{-2}}{d^3}\right)^{-1}$

Lesson 11-2

63. Write 0.002467 in scientific notation.

64. Water Conservation The Folsom Dam in California holds 1 million acre-feet of water in a reservoir. An acre-foot of water is the amount of water that covers an acre to the depth of one foot, or 326,000 gal. How many gallons are in the reservoir? Write your answer in scientific notation.

Lesson 8-5

Write an equation of the direct variation that includes the given point.

65. $(3, 8)$ **66.** $(-5, 2)$ **67.** $(6, -7)$ **68.** $(-3, -5)$

69. $(4, 7)$ **70.** $(-16, 4)$ **71.** $(9, 5)$ **72.** $(4, -2)$

In this Activity Lab, you will collect data from geometric situations and develop functions to model the situations.

1 ACTIVITY

1. Fold a piece of paper in half. How many layers are there?

2. Continue folding the paper. Copy and complete the table.

Number of Folds	Number of Layers
0	1
1	■
2	■
3	■
4	■
5	■
6	■

3. In the graphs below, the scale of the horizontal axis is from 0 to 6 and the scale of the vertical axis is from 0 to 10. Which graph best models the data in the table? Explain.

A.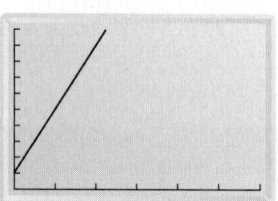

B.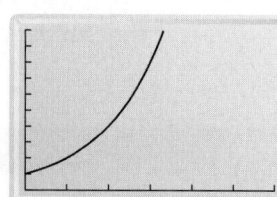

4. What kind of sequence is formed by the values in the column labeled "Number of Layers"?

5. Write a rule for this sequence.

6. Revise your sequence rule to write a function rule so that the number of layers $f(x)$ is a function of the number of folds x. The function rule should give $f(0) = 1$ and $f(1) = 2$.

7. Find the number of layers in 12 folds.

8. If there were 256 layers, how many folds would there be?

9. Is it physically possible to fold an $8\frac{1}{2}$ in. $\times$ 11 in. piece of paper in halves and get 144 layers? Explain.

10. Describe a reasonable domain for the function in Exercise 6.

11. Suppose the paper you were folding in Activity 1 measured 8 in. by 10 in. Complete the table for the area of a layer after each fold.

Number of Folds	Area of Layer
0	80 in.²
1	▨
2	▨
3	▨
4	▨
5	▨
6	▨

12. In the graphs below, the scale of the horizontal axis is from 0 to 6 and the scale of the vertical axis is from 0 to 80. Which graph best models the data in the table? Explain.

A.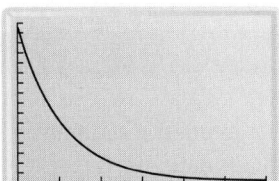

B.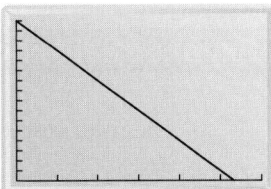

13. How is the graph you chose for Question 12 like the graph you chose for Question 3? How is it different?

14. What kind of sequence is formed by the values in the column labeled "Area of Layer"?

15. Write a rule for this sequence.

16. Revise your sequence rule to write a function rule so that the area of layer $g(x)$ is a function of the number of folds x. The function rule should give $f(0) = 80$.

17. Find the area of a layer after 8 folds.

EXERCISES

18. The rules you wrote for Questions 6 and 16 are examples of exponential functions. Why is "exponent" appropriate as part of the name for this type of function?

19. a. Copy the table below. Extend the table to $x = 5$.

x	f(x)
1	18
2	6
3	2

  b. Graph the data in your table.
  c. Write a function rule for the data in your table.
  d. Use the function rule to find $f(7)$.

Exponential Functions

What You'll Learn

- To evaluate exponential functions
- To graph exponential functions

... And Why

To use an exponential model for a population of rabbits, as in Example 2

 Check Skills You'll Need

Graph each function.

1. $y = 3x$ **2.** $y = 4x$ **3.** $y = -2x$

Simplify each expression.

4. 3^2 **5.** 5^{-3} **6.** $2 \cdot 3^4$

7. $2 \cdot 3^{-2}$ **8.** $3 \cdot 2^{-1}$ **9.** $10 \cdot 3^2$

GO for Help Lessons 9-2 and 11-1

New Vocabulary • exponential function

---

1   Evaluating Exponential Functions

The rules you wrote in Lesson 11-6 to describe geometric sequences, such as $A(n) = 3 \cdot 4^{n-1}$, are examples of exponential functions.

Key Concepts

Definition	Exponential Function

An **exponential function** is a function in the form $y = a \cdot b^x$, where a is a nonzero constant, b is greater than 0 and not equal to 1, and x is a real number.

Examples $y = 0.5 \cdot 2^x$ $f(x) = -2 \cdot 0.5^x$

You can evaluate an exponential function for given values of the domain to find the corresponding values of the range.

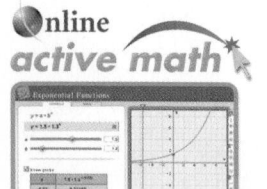

For: Exponential Functions Activity
Use: Interactive Textbook, 8-7

1 EXAMPLE   **Evaluating an Exponential Function**

Evaluate each exponential function.

a. $y = 5^x$ for $x = 2, 3, 4$ **b.** $t(n) = 4 \cdot 3^n$ for the domain $\{-3, 6\}$

x	5^x	y
2	$5^2 = 25$	25
3	$5^3 = 125$	125
4	$5^4 = 625$	625

n	$4 \cdot 3^n$	$t(n)$
-3	$4 \cdot 3^{-3} = 4 \cdot \frac{1}{27} = \frac{4}{27}$	$\frac{4}{27}$
6	$4 \cdot 3^6 = 4 \cdot 729 = 2916$	2916

 **Quick Check** ❶ Evaluate each exponential function for the domain $\{-2, 0, 3\}$.

     a. $y = 4^x$ **b.** $f(x) = 10 \cdot 5^x$ **c.** $g(x) = -2 \cdot 3^x$

You can evaluate exponential functions to solve real-world problems.

2 EXAMPLE Real-World Problem Solving

Gridded Response Suppose 20 rabbits are taken to an island. The rabbit population then triples every half year. The function $f(x) = 20 \cdot 3^x$, where x is the number of half-year periods, models this situation. How many rabbits would there be after 2 years?

$$f(x) = 20 \cdot 3^x$$

$= 20 \cdot 3^4$ **In 2 years, there are 4 half years. Evaluate the function for $x = 4$.**

$= 20 \cdot 81$ **Simplify powers.**

$= 1620$ **Simplify.**

● After two years, there would be 1620 rabbits.

✓ Quick Check **②** Suppose 10 animals are taken to an island, and then the population of these animals quadruples every year. Use the function $f(x) = 10 \cdot 4^x$. How many animals would there be after 6 years?

2 Graphing Exponential Functions

Here are two graphs that show what exponential functions generally look like.

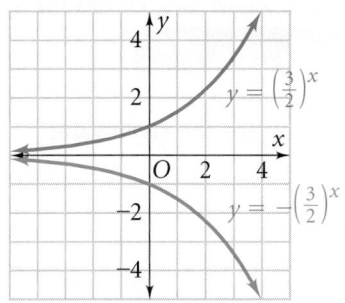

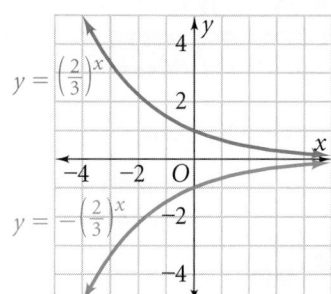

To graph an exponential function, make a table of values. Plot the points. Then join the points to form a smooth curve.

3 EXAMPLE Graphs of Exponential Functions

Graph $y = 3 \cdot 2^x$.

x	$3 \cdot 2^x$	(x, y)
-2	$3 \cdot 2^{-2} = \frac{3}{2^2} = \frac{3}{4}$	$\left(-2, \frac{3}{4}\right)$
-1	$3 \cdot 2^{-1} = \frac{3}{2^1} = 1\frac{1}{2}$	$\left(-1, 1\frac{1}{2}\right)$
0	$3 \cdot 2^0 = 3 \cdot 1 = 3$	$(0, 3)$
1	$3 \cdot 2^1 = 3 \cdot 2 = 6$	$(1, 6)$
2	$3 \cdot 2^2 = 3 \cdot 4 = 12$	$(2, 12)$

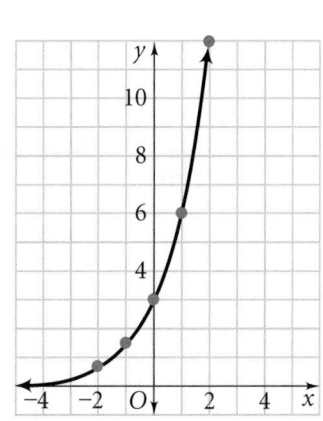

✓ Quick Check **③** Graph each exponential function.   **a.** $y = 0.5 \cdot 2^x$ **b.** $y = -0.5 \cdot 2^x$

You can graph exponential functions to model real-world situations.

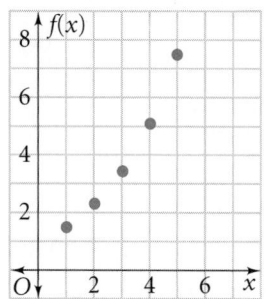 **4 EXAMPLE** Real-World Problem Solving

Photocopying Many photocopiers allow you to choose how large you want an image to be. The function $f(x) = 1.5^x$ models the new size of an image being copied over and over at 150%, where x is the number of enlargements. Graph the function.

x	1.5^x	(x, f(x))
1	$1.5^1 = 1.5$	(1, 1.5)
2	$1.5^2 = 2.25 \approx 2.3$	(2, 2.3)
3	$1.5^3 = 3.375 \approx 3.4$	(3, 3.4)
4	$1.5^4 = 5.0625 \approx 5.1$	(4, 5.1)
5	$1.5^5 = 7.59375 \approx 7.6$	(5, 7.6)

 **Quick Check** **4** **a.** You can also make images that are smaller than the original on a photocopier. The function $f(x) = 0.9^x$ models the new size of an image being copied over and over at 90%. Graph the function.

b. Critical Thinking Explain why the function in Example 4 models discrete data.

EXERCISES

For more exercises, see *Extra Skill and Word Problem Practice*.

Practice and Problem Solving

A Practice by Example

Example 1 (page 644)

GO for Help

Evaluate each function rule for the given value.

1. $f(x) = 6^x$ for $x = 3$

2. $g(t) = 2 \cdot 3^t$ for $t = -2$

3. $y = 20 \cdot (0.5)^x$ for $x = 3$

4. $h(w) = 0.5 \cdot 4^w$ for $w = 3$

5. $y = 50 \cdot (0.3)^x$ for $x = 2$

6. $f(x) = 1.8 \cdot 2^x$ for $x = 6$

7. $y = 100 \cdot \left(\frac{1}{2}\right)^x$ for $x = -4$

8. $y = 9 \cdot \left(\frac{5}{2}\right)^x$ for $x = -3$

Example 2 (page 645)

9. Finance Suppose an investment of $10,000 doubles in value every 13 years. How much is the investment worth after 52 years? After 65 years?

10. Finance Suppose an investment of $500 doubles in value every 15 years. How much is the investment worth after 30 years? After 45 years?

11. Finance Suppose an investment of $2000 doubles in value every 8 years. How much is the investment worth after 24 years? After 32 years?

Example 3 (page 645)

Match each table with the function that models the data.

12. $y = 3x$

13. $y = x^3$

14. $y = 3^x$

A.

x	y
1	3
2	6
3	9
4	12

B.

x	y
1	3
2	9
3	27
4	81

C.

x	y
1	1
2	8
3	27
4	64

Match each function rule with the graph of the function.

15. $y = 2^x$ **16.** $y = -(2^x)$ **17.** $y = \left(\frac{1}{2}\right)^x$ **18.** $y = -\left(\frac{1}{2}\right)^x$

A. 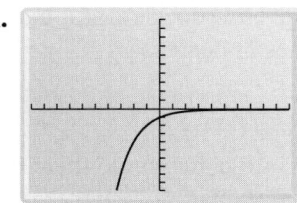 **B.**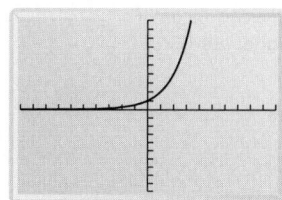

C. 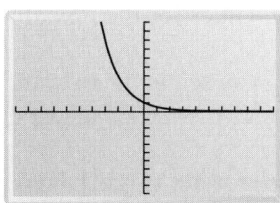 **D.**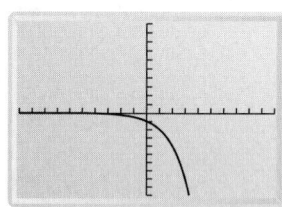

Graph each function.

19. $y = 10 \cdot 2^x$ **20.** $y = 0.1 \cdot 2^x$ **21.** $y = \frac{1}{4} \cdot 2^x$ **22.** $y = 4^x$

Example 4
(page 646)

23. Photocopying Suppose you are photocopying an image, reducing it to 85% its original size. The function $y = 0.85^x$ models the size of an image after x number of times it is reduced. Graph the function.

24. Science A population of 100 insects triples in size every month. The function $y = 100 \cdot 3^x$ models the population after x months. Graph the function.

 Apply Your Skills

Evaluate each function for the domain {−2, −1, 0, 1, 2, 3}. As the values of the domain increase, do the values of the range *increase* or *decrease*?

25. $f(x) = 5^x$ **26.** $y = 2.5^x$ **27.** $h(x) = 0.1^x$ **28.** $f(x) = 5 \cdot 4^x$

29. $y = 0.5^x$ **30.** $y = \left(\frac{2}{3}\right)^x$ **31.** $g(x) = 4 \cdot 10^x$ **32.** $y = 100 \cdot 0.3^x$

33. Multiple Choice The population of Texas in 2000 was about 20.852 million people. The function $p(n) = 20.852(1.02071)^n$ estimates the population where $n = 0$ corresponds to the year 2000. Which is a reasonable estimate in millions of the population of Texas in 2020?

  (A) 21.284 (B) 31.420 (C) 41.740 (D) 49.842

34. Biology A certain species of bacteria in a laboratory culture begins with 75 cells and doubles in number every 20 min.

a. Copy, complete, and extend the table to find when there will be more than 5,000 bacteria cells.

Time (min)	Number of 20-min Time Periods	Pattern	Number of Bacteria Cells
Initial	0	75	75
20	1	$75 \cdot 2$	$75 \cdot 2^{\blacksquare} = \blacksquare$
40	■	$75 \cdot 2 \cdot 2$	$75 \cdot 2^{\blacksquare} = \blacksquare$
60	■	■	$75 \cdot 2^{\blacksquare} = \blacksquare$
■	■	■	■

b. Write a function rule to model the situation.

Homework Video Tutor

Visit: PHSchool.com
Web Code: ate-0807

35. a. Graph $y = 2^x$, $y = 4^x$, and $y = (0.25)^x$.
  b. What point is on each graph?
  c. Does the graph of an exponential function intersect the x-axis? Explain.
  d. Critical Thinking How does the graph of an exponential function change as the base increases or decreases?

 36. Ecology In 50 days, a water hyacinth can generate 1000 offspring (the number of plants is multiplied by 1000).
  a. How many hyacinth plants could there be after 150 days?
  b. How many hyacinth plants could there be after 200 days?

37. a. Make a table of values for the domain $\{1, 2, 3, 4, 5\}$ of the function $y = (-2)^x$.
  b. What pattern do you see in the outputs?
  c. Critical Thinking Is $y = (-2)^x$ an exponential function? Justify your answer.

Which function is greater at the given value?

38. $y = 5^x$ or $y = x^5$ at $x = 3$ **39.** $f(t) = 10 \cdot 2^t$ or $f(t) = 200 \cdot t^2$ at $t = 7$

40. $y = 3^x$ or $y = x^3$ at $x = 4$ **41.** $f(x) = 2^x$ or $f(x) = 100x^2$ at $x = 10$

 42. Writing Analyze the range of the function $f(x) = 500 \cdot 1^x$ using the domain $\{1, 2, 3, 4, 5\}$. Explain why the definition of *exponential function* includes the restriction that $b \neq 1$.

 43. a. Graphing Calculator Graph the functions $y = x^2$ and $y = 2^x$.
  b. What happens to the graphs between $x = 1$ and $x = 3$?
  c. Critical Thinking How do you think the graph of $y = 6^x$ would compare to the graphs of $y = x^2$ and $y = 2^x$?

 **Challenge**

Solve each equation.

44. $3^x = 9$ **45.** $3^x = \frac{1}{27}$ **46.** $2^x = 64$

47. $3 \cdot 2^x = 24$ **48.** $2 \cdot 3^x = 162$ **49.** $5 \cdot 2^x - 152 = 8$

50. Suppose $(0, 4)$ and $(2, 36)$ are on the graph of an exponential function.
  a. Use $(0, 4)$ in the general form of an exponential function $y = a \cdot b^x$ to find the value of the constant a.
  b. Use your answer from part (a) along with $(2, 36)$ to find the value of the constant b.
  c. Write a rule for the function.
  d. Evaluate the function for $x = -2$ and $x = 4$.

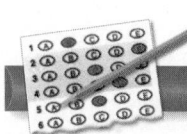

Test Prep

Multiple Choice

51. For the function $y = -3^x$, what is the value of y when $x = -2$?
  A. -9 **B.** $-\frac{1}{9}$ **C.** $\frac{1}{9}$ **D.** 9

52. Which function contains the points $(1, 3)$ and $(3, 6.75)$?
  F. $y = 1.675x + 1.325$ **G.** $y = 2 \cdot 1.5^x$
  H. $y = 1.5 \cdot 2^x$ **J.** $y = 1.325x + 1.675$

53. Which function has the same y-intercept as $y = 2^x$?
  A. $y = x + 1$ **B.** $y = 2x$ **C.** $y = x$ **D.** $y = 2(x + 1)$

54. A population of 6000 doubles in size every 10 years. Which equation relates the size of the population y to the number of 10-year periods x?

  F. $y = 6000 \cdot 10^x$ **G.** $y = 10 \cdot 2^x$

  H. $y = 6000 \cdot 2^x$ **J.** $y = 2 \cdot 100^x$

Short Response   **55.** Between what two integer values of x do the graphs of $y = 20(0.5)^x$ and $y = 0.5 \cdot 4^x$ intersect? Show your work.

Mixed Review

Lesson 11-6   **Find each common ratio. Then find the next three terms in each sequence.**

56. $2, 10, 50, 250, \ldots$ **57.** $7, -21, 63, -189, \ldots$

58. $-0.2, -0.4, -0.8, -1.6, \ldots$ **59.** $27, -9, 3, -1, \ldots$

60. $450, 45, 4.5, 0.45, \ldots$ **61.** $7168, 1792, 448, 112, \ldots$

Lesson 9-6   **Write an equation for the line that passes through the given point and is parallel to the given line.**

62. $y = 5x + 1; (0, 0)$ **63.** $y = 3x - 2; (0, 1)$

64. $y = -2x + 5; (4, 0)$ **65.** $y = 0.4x + 5; (2, -3)$

 **Checkpoint Quiz 2**   **Lessons 11-5 through 11-7**

Simplify each expression.

1. $\left(\dfrac{3^2}{3^{-1}}\right)^4$ **2.** $\left(\dfrac{x^2}{y^3}\right)^{-5}$ **3.** $\left(\dfrac{10m^{-3}}{25n^{-6}}\right)^2$ **4.** $\left(\dfrac{6^2 t^{-3}}{6^2 r^0 t^2}\right)^2$

Determine whether each sequence is *arithmetic* or *geometric*.

5. $22, 11, 5.5, 2.75, \ldots$ **6.** $5, 10, 20, 40, 80, \ldots$ **7.** $5, 10, 15, 20, 25, \ldots$

8. Use the sequence $-100, 20, -4, \ldots$.
  a. What is the first term?
  b. What is the common ratio?
  c. Write a rule for the sequence.
  d. Use your rule to find the fifth and seventh terms in the sequence.

9. Physics On the first swing, a pendulum swings through an arc of length 40 cm. On each successive swing, the length of the arc is 85% of the length of the previous swing.
  a. Write a rule to model this situation.
  b. Find the length of the arc on the fifth swing. Round your answer to the nearest millimeter.

10. Commuting Refer to the information at the left.
  a. Write the number of vehicles that crossed the George Washington Bridge in scientific notation.
  b. The Port Authority collected about $249 million in tolls from this bridge. Write this number in scientific notation.
  c. What was the average toll per vehicle?

Real-World Connection

About 108 million vehicles cross the George Washington Bridge between New York and New Jersey in a year.

Fitting Exponential Curves to Data

Go Online
PHSchool.com

For: Graphing calculator procedures
Web Code: ate-2122

In Chapter 6 you learned how to find a line of best fit for a set of data. You can model some data better using an exponential function. To graph an exponential function, you may need to adjust your viewing window. Use your data to choose appropriate Xmax and Ymax values.

EXAMPLE

The table at the right shows the estimated number of customers downloading music files. Use a graphing calculator to find the best-fitting exponential function for the data. Then graph the function.

Digital Download

Year	Customers (millions)
2000	0.4
2001	1.0
2002	2.2
2003	4.4

Step 1 Use your calculator's STAT feature. Enter the data. Let $x = 0$ correspond to 2000.

Step 2 To get the equation of the best-fitting exponential function, press STAT ▶ 0 ENTER .

```
ExpReg
 y=a*b^x
 a=.4236368467
 b=2.221570366
 r²=.9960912309
 r=.9980437019
```

Step 3 To view the graph of the function press Y= CLEAR VARS 5 ▶ ▶ 1 GRAPH .

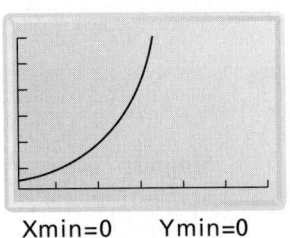

Xmin=0   Ymin=0
Xmax=6   Ymax=6

EXERCISES

Use a graphing calculator to find the exponential function that fits each set of data. Then (a) write a function for the data rounding decimals to the nearest hundredth, (b) sketch a graph of the function, and (c) use your answer from part (a) to predict the value of the function in the year 2010.

1. Shipment of Record Singles Let $x = 0$ correspond to 1990.

Year	1990	1995	2000	2001	2002	2003	2004
Record Singles (millions)	27.6	10.2	4.8	5.5	4.4	3.8	3.5

Source: Record Industry Association of America

2. U.S. Energy Consumption Let $x = 0$ correspond to 1990.

Year	1990	1995	2000	2001	2002	2003	2004
Btu (quadrillions)	84.7	91.2	98.9	96.4	97.8	98.2	99.7

Source: U.S. Department of Energy

3. U.S. Homes Heated by Coal Let $x = 0$ correspond to 1950.

Year	1950	1960	1970	1980	1991	2001
Percent of Homes	34.6	12.2	2.9	0.6	0.3	0.1

Source: U.S. Department of Energy

Exponential Growth and Decay

What You'll Learn

- To model exponential growth
- To model exponential decay

. . . And Why

To find the balance of a bank account, as in Examples 2 and 3

✓ **Check Skills You'll Need**

 **for Help** Lesson 6-7

Find each percent of change. Describe the percent of change as an increase or decrease. If necessary, round to the nearest percent.

1. The original cost of a shirt is $25. On sale the shirt costs $22.
2. In one week, a plant's height went from 15 cm to 18 cm.
3. The population of a town went from 38,356 in 1990 to 40,481 in 2000.
4. A computer that cost $1450 last year costs $999 this year.
5. An elephant that weighed 220 lb at birth weighed 300 lb at one month.

🔊 **New Vocabulary** • **exponential growth** • **growth factor** • **compound interest** • **interest period** • **exponential decay** • **decay factor**

---

1 ▸ Exponential Growth

Real-World 🌐 **Connection**

In 2000, Florida's population was about 16 million. Roughly 23% of the population was under the age of 18.

In 2000, Florida's population was about 16 million. Since 2000, the state's population has grown about 2% each year. This means that Florida's population is growing exponentially.

To find Florida's population in 2001, multiply the 2000 population by 2% and add this to the 2000 population. So the population in 2001 is (2% + 100%) of the 2000 population, or 102% of the 2000 population. Here is a function that models Florida's population since 2000.

population in millions
↓
$$y = 16(1.02)^x \quad \leftarrow \text{number of years since 2000}$$
↑
102% as a decimal

The following is a general rule for modeling exponential growth.

 Key Concepts

> **Rule**   **Exponential Growth**
>
> **Exponential growth** can be modeled with the function $y = a \cdot b^x$ for $a > 0$ and $b > 1$.
>
>   starting amount (when $x = 0$)
>   ↓
> $y = a \cdot b^x \quad \leftarrow \text{exponent}$
>   ↑
>   The base, which is greater than 1, is the **growth factor.**

1 EXAMPLE Modeling Exponential Growth

Medical Care Since 1995, the daily cost of patient care in community hospitals in the United States has increased about 4% per year. In 1995, such hospital costs were an average of $968 per day.

a. Write an equation to model the cost of hospital care since 1995.

Relate $y = a \cdot b^x$ Use an exponential function.

Define Let x = the number of years since 1995.
Let y = the cost of community hospital care at various times.
Let a = the initial cost in 1995, $968.
Let b = the growth factor, which is 100% + 4% = 104% = 1.04.

Write $y = 968 \cdot 1.04^x$

Calculator Hint

To evaluate
$968 \cdot 1.04^{15}$, press

968 ✕ 1.04 ∧

15 ENTER .

b. Use your equation to estimate the approximate cost per day in 2010.

$y = 968 \cdot 1.04^x$

$y = 968 \cdot 1.04^{15}$ **2010 is 15 years after 1995, so substitute 15 for x.**

≈ 1743 **Use a calculator. Round to the nearest dollar.**

● The average cost per day in 2010 will be about $1743.

✓ Quick Check **1** **a.** Suppose your community has 4512 students this year. The student population is growing 2.5% each year. Write an equation to model the student population.
b. What will the student population be in 3 years?

When a bank pays interest on both the principal *and* the interest an account has already earned, the bank is paying **compound interest.** An **interest period** is the length of time over which interest is calculated.

2 EXAMPLE Compound Interest

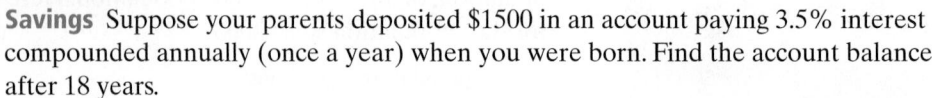

Savings Suppose your parents deposited $1500 in an account paying 3.5% interest compounded annually (once a year) when you were born. Find the account balance after 18 years.

BANK 1

Deposit **$1500**

Interest compounded
annually **3.5%**

Balance after 18 years
$2786.23

Relate $y = a \cdot b^x$ Use an exponential function.

Define Let x = the number of interest periods.
Let y = the balance.
Let a = the initial deposit, $1500.
Let b = 100% + 3.5% = 103.5% = 1.035.

Write $y = 1500 \cdot 1.035^x$

$= 1500 \cdot 1.035^{18}$ **Once a year for 18 years is 18 interest periods. Substitute 18 for x.**

≈ 2786.23 **Use a calculator. Round to the nearest cent.**

● The balance after 18 years will be $2786.23.

✓ Quick Check **2** **a.** Suppose the interest rate on the account in Example 2 was 4%. How much would be in the account after 18 years?
b. Another formula for compound interest is $B = p(1 + r)^x$, where B is the balance, p is the principal, and r is the annual interest rate in decimal form. Use this formula to find the balance in the account in part (a).
c. Critical Thinking Explain why the two formulas for finding compound interest are actually the same.

When interest is compounded quarterly (four times per year), you divide the interest rate by 4, the number of interest periods per year. To find the number of payment periods, you multiply the number of years by the number of interest periods per year.

Annual Interest Rate of 8%

Compounded	Periods per Year	Interest Rate per Period
annually	1	8% every year
semi-annually	2	$\frac{8\%}{2}$ = 4% every 6 months
quarterly	4	$\frac{8\%}{4}$ = 2% every 3 months
monthly	12	$\frac{8\%}{12}$ = $0.\overline{6}$% every month

3 EXAMPLE **Compound Interest**

Savings Suppose the account in Example 2 paid interest compounded quarterly instead of annually. Find the account balance after 18 years.

Relate $y = a \cdot b^x$ **Use an exponential function.**

Define Let x = the number of interest periods.
Let y = the balance.
Let a = the initial deposit, $1500.

Let b = 100% + $\frac{3.5\%}{4}$ **There are 4 interest periods in 1 year, so divide the interest into 4 parts.**

     = 1 + 0.00875 = 1.00875

Write $y = 1500 \cdot 1.00875^x$

     = $1500 \cdot 1.00875^{72}$ **Four interest periods a year for 18 years is 72 interest periods. Substitute 72 for x.**

     ≈ 2808.71   **Use a calculator. Round to the nearest cent.**

● The balance after 18 years will be $2808.71.

BANK 2

Deposit **$1500**

Interest compounded quarterly **3.5%**

Balance after 18 years **$2808.71**

✓ **Quick Check** ❸ **a.** Suppose the account in Example 3 paid interest compounded monthly. How much money would be in the account after 18 years?
b. You deposit $200 into an account earning 5%, compounded monthly. How much will be in the account after 1 year? After 2 years? After 5 years?

2 Exponential Decay

The graphs at the right show exponential growth and exponential decay. For exponential growth, as x increases, y increases exponentially. For exponential decay, as x increases, y decreases exponentially.

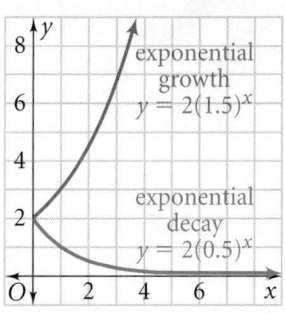

exponential growth $y = 2(1.5)^x$

exponential decay $y = 2(0.5)^x$

A real-world example of exponential decay is radioactive decay, in which radioactive elements break down by releasing particles and energy.

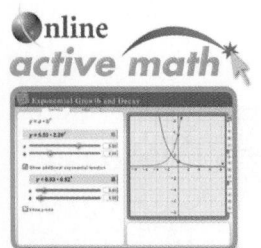
Online active math

For: Exponential Functions Activity
Use: Interactive Textbook, 8-8

4 **EXAMPLE** <u>Real-World</u> Problem Solving

Medicine The half-life of a radioactive substance is the length of time it takes for one half of the substance to decay into another substance. To treat some forms of cancer, doctors use radioactive iodine. The half-life of iodine-131 is 8 days. A patient receives a 12-mCi (millicuries, a measure of radiation) treatment. How much iodine-131 is left in the patient 16 days later?

In 16 days, there are two 8-day half-lives.

After one half-life, there are 6 mCi left in the patient.

After two half-lives, there are 3 mCi left in the patient.

 Quick Check **4** **a.** How many half-lives of iodine-131 occur in 32 days?
b. Suppose you start with a 50-mCi sample of iodine-131. How much iodine-131 is left after one half-life? After two half-lives?
c. **Chemistry** Cesium-137 has a half-life of 30 years. Suppose a lab stored a 30-mCi sample in 1973. How much of the sample will be left in 2003? In 2063?

The function $y = a \cdot b^x$ can model exponential decay as well as exponential growth.

 **Key Concepts**

Rule	**Exponential Decay**

The function $y = a \cdot b^x$ models exponential decay for $a > 0$ and $0 < b < 1$.

starting amount (when $x = 0$)

$$y = a \cdot b^x \longleftarrow \text{exponent}$$

The base, which is between 0 and 1, is the **decay factor.**

When a number is decreased by 5%, the result is 95% of the original number. So when you find the decay factor, think 100% minus the percent a number is decreasing.

5 **EXAMPLE** **Modeling Exponential Decay**

Milk Consumption Since 1980, the number of gallons of whole milk each person in the United States drinks each year has decreased 4.1% each year. In 1980, each person drank an average of 16.5 gallons of whole milk per year.

a. Write an equation to model the gallons of whole milk drunk per person.

Relate $y = a \cdot b^x$ **Use an exponential function.**

Define Let $x =$ the number of years since 1980.
Let $y =$ the consumption of whole milk, in gallons.
Let $a = 16.5$, the initial number of gallons in 1980.
Let $b =$ the decay factor, which is $100\% - 4.1\% = 95.9\% = 0.959$.

Write $y = 16.5 \cdot 0.959^x$

Real-World Connection

One cup of milk contains 300 mg of calcium. The body absorbs about 32% of the calcium in milk.

b. Use your equation to find the approximate consumption per person of whole milk in 2000.

$y = 16.5 \cdot 0.959^x$

$y = 16.5 \cdot 0.959^{20}$ **2000 is 20 years after 1980, so substitute 20 for *x*.**

≈ 7.1 **Use a calculator. Round to the nearest tenth of a gallon.**

The average annual consumption of whole milk in 2000 was about 7 gal/person.

✓ **Quick Check** **5** **Statistics** In 1990, the population of Washington, D.C., was about 604,000 people. Since then the population has decreased about 1.8% per year.
   a. What is the initial number of people?
   b. What is the decay factor?
   c. Write an equation to model the population of Washington, D.C., since 1990.
   d. Suppose the current trend in population change continues. Predict the population of Washington, D.C., in 2010.

EXERCISES

For more exercises, see *Extra Skill and Word Problem Practice*.

Practice and Problem Solving

A **Practice by Example**

Example 1
(page 652)

GO for Help

Identify the initial amount *a* and the growth factor *b* in each exponential function.

1. $g(x) = 20 \cdot 2^x$ **2.** $y = 200 \cdot 1.0875^x$ **3.** $y = 10{,}000 \cdot 1.01^x$ **4.** $f(t) = 1.5^t$

5. Suppose the population of a city is 50,000 and is growing 3% each year.
   a. The initial amount *a* is ■.
   b. The growth factor *b* is 100% + 3%, which is 1 + ■ = ■.
   c. To find the population after one year, you multiply 50,000 · ■.
   d. Complete the equation $y = ■ \cdot ■^■$ to find the population after *x* years.
   e. Use your equation to predict the population after 25 years.

Examples 2, 3
(pages 652, 653)

Each percent is an annual interest rate. In the formula $y = a \cdot b^x$, what value would you use for *b*?

6. 4%   **7.** 5%   **8.** 3.7%   **9.** 8.75%   **10.** 0.5%

Assume each interest rate below is an annual interest rate. Find the interest rate for an account that is compounded quarterly and monthly.

11. 3%   **12.** 4%   **13.** 4.5%   **14.** 7.6%   **15.** 6.25%

Find the balance in each account.

16. $4000 principal earning 6% compounded annually, after 5 years

17. $12,000 principal earning 4.8% compounded annually, after 7 years

18. $500 principal earning 4% compounded quarterly, after 6 years

19. $20,000 deposit earning 3.5% compounded quarterly, after 10 years

Example 4
(page 654)

20. Chemistry The half-life of iodine-124 is 4 days. A technician measures a 40-mCi sample of iodine-124.
   a. How many half-lives of iodine-124 occur in 16 days?
   b. How much iodine-124 is in the sample 16 days after the technician measures the original sample?

21. Chemistry The half-life of carbon-11 is 20 min. A sample of carbon-11 has 25 mCi.
  a. How many half-lives of carbon-11 occur in 1 hour?
  b. How much carbon-11 is in the sample 1 hour after the original sample is measured?

Example 5
(page 654)

Identify the decay factor in each function.

22. $y = 5 \cdot 0.5^x$ **23.** $f(x) = 10 \cdot 0.1^x$

24. $g(x) = 100 \cdot \left(\frac{2}{3}\right)^x$ **25.** $y = 0.1 \cdot 0.9^x$

Identify each function as *exponential growth* or *exponential decay*.

26. $y = 0.68 \cdot 2^x$ **27.** $y = 2 \cdot 0.68^x$ **28.** $y = 68 \cdot 2^x$ **29.** $y = 68 \cdot 0.2^x$

30. Cars The value of a new car decreases exponentially. Suppose your mother buys a new car for $22,000. The value of the car decreases by 20% each year.
  a. What is the initial price of the car? The decay factor?
  b. Write an equation to model the value of the car x years after she buys it.
  c. Find the value of the car after 6 years.

B Apply Your Skills

Write an exponential function to model each situation. Find each amount after the specified time.

31. A population of 130,000 grows 1% per year for 9 years.

32. A population of 3,000,000 decreases 1.5% annually for 10 years.

33. A $2400 principal earns 7% compounded annually for 10 years.

34. A $2400 principal earns 7% compounded monthly for 10 years.

35. Education Since 1985, the average annual cost y (in dollars) for tuition and fees at public two-year colleges in the United States has increased about 6.5% per year. In 1985, tuition and fees were an average of $584 per year.
  a. Write an equation to model the cost of two-year colleges. Predict the average annual cost for 2015.
  b. Open-Ended Predict the average annual cost for the year you plan to graduate from high school.

Tell whether each graph shows a *linear function*, an *exponential function*, or *neither*. Justify your reasoning.

36.
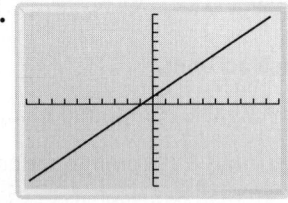

37.
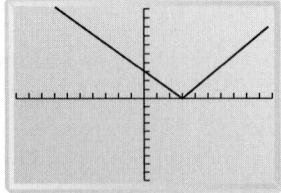

38.
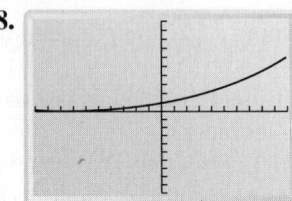

39.
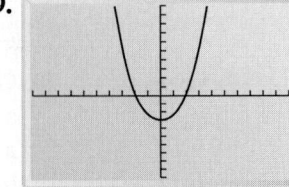

GO Online
Homework Video Tutor
Visit: PHSchool.com
Web Code: ate-0808

Graph the function represented in each table. Then tell whether the table represents a *linear function* or an *exponential function*.

40.

x	y
1	20
2	40
3	60
4	80

41.

x	y
1	3
2	9
3	27
4	81

42.

x	y
1	3
2	9
3	15
4	21

43. **Writing** Would you rather have $500 in an account paying 6% interest compounded quarterly or $600 in an account paying 5% compounded annually? Summarize your reasoning.

For a guide to solving Exercise 46 see p. 659.

How many half-lives occur in each period of time?

44. 2 days (1 half-life = 8 h)

45. 300 years (1 half-life = 75 yr)

46. **Medicine** The function $y = 15 \cdot 0.84^x$ models the amount y of a 15-mg dose of antibiotic remaining in the bloodstream after x hours.

   a. Estimation Use the graphing calculator screen to estimate the half-life of this antibiotic in the bloodstream.

   b. Use your estimate to predict the amount of antibiotic that will remain in the bloodstream after 8 hours.

   c. Verify your prediction by using the function to find the amount of antibiotic remaining after 8 hours.

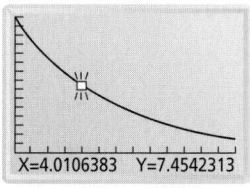

Antibiotic Decay in the Bloodstream

X=4.0106383 Y=7.4542313
Xmin=0   Ymin=0
Xmax=13 Ymax=15

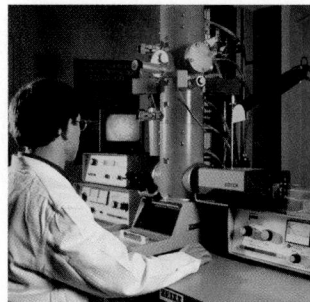

Real-World Connection

Careers A medical researcher may use equipment such as a scanning electron microscope.

47. **Population Growth** Since 1990, the population of Virginia has grown at an average annual rate of about 1%. In 1990, the population was about 6,284,000.

   a. Write an equation to model the population growth in Virginia since 1990.

   b. Suppose this rate of growth continues. Predict Virginia's population in 2010.

By which percent would you multiply a number to decrease it by the given amount?

48. 6%   49. 12%   50. 3.5%   51. 53.9%

52. **Multiple Choice** Use the graph at the right. What is a reasonable estimate of the half-life of cesium-134?

   Ⓐ $\frac{1}{2}$ year   Ⓑ 2 years

   Ⓒ $3\frac{1}{2}$ years   Ⓓ 4 years

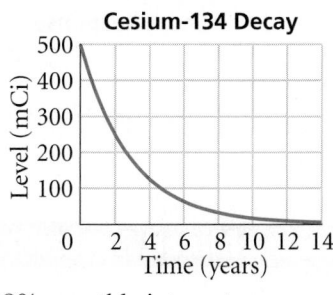

Cesium-134 Decay

Level (mCi) / Time (years)

C Challenge 53. **Credit Card Balances** Suppose you charge $250 for a new suit. If you do not pay the whole amount the first month, you are charged 1.8% monthly interest on your account balance. Suppose you can make a $30 payment each month.

   a. What is your balance after your first payment?

   b. How much interest are you charged after your first payment?

   c. What is your balance just before you make your second payment?

   d. What is your balance after your second payment?

   e. How many months will it take for you to pay off the entire bill?

   f. How much interest will you have paid in all?

54. Data Collection Complete the table at the right using any ball. The height 0 is the starting height. Record the maximum height after the first, second, and third bounce.
a. Graph your data.
b. Write an exponential decay function that models your data.

Bounce	Height (centimeters)
0	7
1	7
2	7
3	7

55. On January 1, 2000, Chessville had a population of 40,000 people. Its population increases 7% each year. On the same day, Checkersville had a population of 60,000 people. Its population decreases 4% each year. During what year will the population of Chessville exceed that of Checkersville?

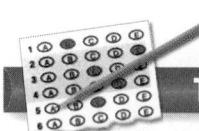

Test Prep

Multiple Choice

56. For which function will values of y decrease as values of x increase?
A. $y = 12.5(1.325)^x$
B. $y = 300(1.06)^x$
C. $y = 5000(0.98)^x$
D. $y = 1.02^x$

57. Suppose you deposit $1000 in an account earning 6% interest. You make no further deposits to the account and interest is compounded semi-annually. What is the balance after 5 years?
F. $538.62
G. $1006.00
H. $1343.92
J. $1790.85

58. Read the passage below and answer the following problem.

Manhattan, Then and Now

In 1626, the Dutch landed on the island we now call Manhattan. They bought the island for $24 worth of merchandise. Today Manhattan is one of the most expensive places in the world to live. Rent for a one-bedroom apartment averages $2000 a month.

Suppose $24 had been invested in 1626 in an account paying 4.5% interest compounded annually. Which amount is closest to the balance in 2000?
A. $339 million
B. $89 million
C. $9400
D. $8900

Short Response

59. Which is greater, the amount in an account that pays 5% interest compounded quarterly for 5 years or the amount in an account that pays 5.5% compounded annually for 5 years? Assume the accounts start with the same amount. Show your work.

Mixed Review

GO for Help

Lesson 11-7

Graph each function.

60. $y = 2 \cdot 10^x$
61. $f(x) = 100 \cdot 0.9^x$
62. $g(x) = \frac{1}{10} \cdot 0.1^x$

Lesson 11-2

63. Geography In 2000, about 1.4×10^4 ships passed through the Panama Canal. About 5.2×10^7 gallons of water flow out of the canal with each ship. About how many gallons of water flowed out of the canal with ships in 2000? Write your answer in scientific notation.

Guided Problem Solving

Understanding Math Problems Read the exercise below, and then learn how to use a graphing calculator to solve it. Check your understanding by solving the exercise at the bottom of the page.

Medicine The function $y = 15 \cdot 0.84^x$ models the amount y of a 15-mg dose of antibiotic remaining in the bloodstream after x hours.

a. Estimation Use the graphing calculator screen to estimate the half-life of this antibiotic in the bloodstream.

b. Use your estimate to predict the amount of antibiotic that will remain in the bloodstream after 8 hours.

c. Verify your prediction by using the function to find the amount of antibiotic remaining after 8 hours.

Antibiotic Decay in the Bloodstream

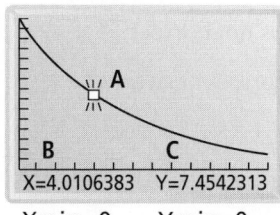

X=4.0106383   Y=7.4542313

D Xmin=0 E Ymin=0
  Xmax=13   Ymax=15

To solve this problem, use the graphing calculator screen shown at the left. Parts of this screen are explained below.

A   The point shown on the screen is a point (x, y) on the graph.

B and C   These are the x-coordinates and y-coordinates of the highlighted point. The coordinates of the point are $(4.0106383, 7.4542313)$.

D and E   These give the viewable range for the x- and y-values. The screen displays the graph for x-values from 0 to 13 and y-values from 0 to 15.

a. *Half-life* is the time required for the body to eliminate half of the initial dose. How do the coordinates $(4.0106383, 7.4542313)$ relate to the half-life of the antibiotic? At time $x = 0$, the amount in the bloodstream is $y = 15$. When $y = \frac{15}{2} = 7.5$, the corresponding value of x represents the half-life. When $y \approx 7.5, x \approx 4$, so the half-life is about 4 hours.

b. If 7.5 mg remain after 4 hours, then $\frac{7.5}{2} = 3.75$ mg will remain after 8 hours.

c. $y = 15 \cdot 0.84^x$
$y = 15 \cdot 0.84^8$ **Substitute 8 for x.**
$y \approx 3.72$ **Use a calculator.**

The amount of antibiotic remaining after 8 hours will be about 3.72 mg.

EXERCISE

Memory Suppose the function $y = 40 \cdot 0.75^x$ models the number y of foreign-language words recalled from a list of 40 words after x weeks (without additional practice or study).

a. Estimation Use the graphing calculator to estimate the number of vocabulary words recalled after 5 weeks.

b. Verify your prediction by using the function to find the number of vocabulary words recalled after 5 weeks.

c. Critical Thinking What does 0.75 represent in the function?

Testing Multiple Choices

One advantage of multiple-choice tests is that the correct answer is among the choices. A strategy is to work backward by taking answers and testing them in the original problem.

1 EXAMPLE

Find the value of x if x, $x + 2$, and $4x$ are three consecutive terms of a geometric sequence.

  (A) 0   (B) 1   (C) 2   (D) 3   (E) 4

The ratios of consecutive terms of a geometric sequence are the same. So $\frac{x + 2}{x}$ must equal $\frac{4x}{x + 2}$. Find the number for which this is true by substituting each answer choice for x.

Let $x = 0$. The sequence 0, 2, 0 is not a geometric sequence because $\frac{2}{0} \neq \frac{0}{2}$. So A is not correct.

Let $x = 1$. The sequence 1, 3, 4 is not a geometric sequence because $\frac{3}{1} \neq \frac{4}{3}$. So B is not correct.

Let $x = 2$. The sequence 2, 4, 8 is a geometric sequence because $\frac{4}{2} = \frac{8}{4}$.   The correct answer is C.

● You do not need to try choice D or E.

2 EXAMPLE

Find the value of x if $2x^{-3} = \frac{1}{4}$.

  (A) 1   (B) 2   (C) 3   (D) 4   (E) 5

Solve by substituting each answer choice into the original equation.

Let $x = 1$. ⟶ $2(1)^{-3} = 2(1) = 2$ ⟶ $2 \neq \frac{1}{4}$.   A is not the answer.

Let $x = 2$. ⟶ $2(2)^{-3} = 2\left(\frac{1}{8}\right) = \frac{2}{8}$ ⟶ $\frac{1}{4} = \frac{1}{4}$.   B is the answer.

● You do not have to test answer choices C, D, and E.

EXERCISES

Solve each of the following by working backward.

1. Find the value of x if $x - 2$, x, and $x + 3$ are three consecutive terms of a geometric sequence.

  (A) 4   (B) 6   (C) 8   (D) 10   (E) 12

2. Find the value of x if $x^{-1} + x^{-2} = 0$.

  (A) -2 (B) -1 (C) 1   (D) 2   (E) 4

3. The area of a square is 1.21×10^{-4}. What is its perimeter?

  (A) 0.00044   (B) 0.0044   (C) 0.044   (D) 0.44   (E) 4.4

4. Find the value of x if x, $3x + 1$, and $6x - 1$ are three consecutive terms of an arithmetic sequence.

  (A) -3 (B) -1 (C) 1   (D) 3   (E) 4

Chapter Review

Vocabulary Review

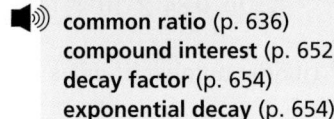

common ratio (p. 636)
compound interest (p. 652)
decay factor (p. 654)
exponential decay (p. 654)

exponential function (p. 644)
exponential growth (p. 651)
geometric sequence (p. 636)
growth factor (p. 651)

interest period (p. 652)
scientific notation (p. 612)

PHSchool.com

For: Vocabulary quiz
Web Code: atj-0851

Choose the correct term to complete each sentence.

1. The function $y = a \cdot b^x$ models __?__ for $a > 0$ and $b > 1$.

2. For the function $y = a \cdot b^x$, where $a > 0$ and $b > 1$, b is the __?__.

3. __?__ is a shorthand way to write very large and very small numbers.

4. The function rule $y = a \cdot b^x$ models __?__ for $a > 0$ and $0 < b < 1$.

5. For the function $y = a \cdot b^x$, where $a > 0$ and $0 < b < 1$, b is the __?__.

6. __?__ is calculated using both the principal and the interest that an account has already earned.

7. Each term of a geometric sequence is found by multiplying the previous term by a fixed number called the __?__.

8. The length of time over which interest is calculated is the __?__.

9. When a sequence has a common ratio, it is a(n) __?__.

10. The rule $y = 7^x$ is a(n) __?__.

Skills and Concepts

11-1 Objectives

▼ To simplify expressions with zero and negative exponents (p. 606)

▼ To evaluate exponential expressions (p. 608)

You can use zero and negative integers as exponents. For every nonzero number a, $a^0 = 1$. For every nonzero number a and any integer n, $a^{-n} = \frac{1}{a^n}$.

Simplify each expression.

11. $b^{-4}c^0d^6$

12. $\frac{x^{-2}}{y^{-8}}$

13. $7k^{-8}h^3$

14. $\frac{1}{p^2q^{-4}r^0}$

15. $\left(\frac{2}{5}\right)^{-4}$

16. $(-2)^{-3}$

17. -2^{-3}

18. $7^{-2}y^{-4}$

19. $\frac{9w^{-4}}{x^{-2}y^7}$

Evaluate each expression for $p = 2$, $q = -3$, and $r = 0$.

20. p^2q^2

21. $(-p)^2q^{-2}$

22. $p^q q^p$

23. $p^r q^r$

24. $-p^2q^3$

25. Which expression has the greatest value for $a = 4$, $b = -3$, and $c = 0$?

    A. a^b **B.** b^c **C.** $\frac{1}{b^{-a}}$ **D.** $\frac{a^c}{b^c}$ **E.** $\frac{c}{a^{-b}}$

26. **Critical Thinking** Is $(-3b)^4 = -12b^4$? Explain why or why not.

11-2 Objectives

▼ To write numbers in scientific and standard notation (p. 612)

▼ To use scientific notation (p. 613)

You can use **scientific notation** to express very large or very small numbers. A number is in scientific notation if it is in the form $a \times 10^n$, where $1 \leq a < 10$, and n is an integer.

Is each number written in scientific notation? If not, explain.

27. 950×10^5 **28.** 72.35×10^8 **29.** 1.6×10^{-6} **30.** 0.84×10^{-5}

31. The space probe Voyager 2 traveled 2,793,000 miles. Write the number of miles in scientific notation.

32. There are 189 million passenger cars and trucks in use in the United States. Write the number of passenger cars and trucks using scientific notation.

11-3 and 11-4 Objectives

▼ To multiply powers (p. 617)

▼ To work with scientific notation (p. 618)

▼ To raise a power to a power (p. 623)

▼ To raise a product to a power (p. 624)

To multiply powers with the same base, add the exponents.

$$a^m \cdot a^n = a^{m+n}$$

To raise a power to a power, multiply the exponents.

$$(a^m)^n = a^{mn}$$

To raise a product to a power, raise each factor in the product to the power.

$$(ab)^n = a^n b^n$$

Simplify each expression.

33. $2d^2 d^3$ **34.** $(q^3 r)^4$ **35.** $(5c^{-4})(-4m^2 c^8)$

36. $(1.34^2)^5 (1.34)^{-8}$ **37.** $(12x^2 y^{-2})^5 (4xy^{-3})^{-8}$ **38.** $(-2r^{-4})^2 (-3r^2 z^8)^{-1}$

39. Estimation Each square inch of your body has about 6.5×10^2 pores. Suppose the back of your hand has an area of about 0.12×10^2 in.^{2}. About how many pores are on the back of your hand?

40. Open-Ended Write and solve a problem that involves multiplying exponents.

11-5 Objectives

▼ To divide powers with the same base (p. 629)

▼ To raise a quotient to a power (p. 630)

To divide powers with the same base, subtract the exponents.

$$\frac{a^m}{a^n} = a^{m-n}$$

To raise a quotient to a power, raise the dividend and the divisor to the power.

$$\left(\frac{a}{b}\right)^n = \frac{a^n}{b^n}$$

Simplify each expression.

41. $\frac{w^2}{w^5}$ **42.** $(8^3) \cdot 8^{-5}$ **43.** $\left(\frac{21x^3}{3x}\right)$ **44.** $\left(\frac{n^5}{v^3}\right)^7$ **45.** $\frac{e^{-6} c^3}{e^5}$

Simplify each quotient. Give your answer in scientific notation.

46. $\frac{4.2 \times 10^8}{2.1 \times 10^{11}}$ **47.** $\frac{3.1 \times 10^4}{12.4 \times 10^2}$ **48.** $\frac{4.5 \times 10^3}{9 \times 10^7}$ **49.** $\frac{5.1 \times 10^5}{1.7 \times 10^2}$

50. Writing List the steps that you would use to simplify $\left(\frac{5a^8}{10a^6}\right)^{-3}$.

11-6 Objectives

▼ To use geometric sequences (p. 636)

▼ To use formulas when describing geometric sequences (p. 637)

You find each term of a **geometric sequence** by multiplying the previous term by a fixed number called the common ratio.

Find the common ratio in each geometric sequence.

51. $750, 75, 7.5, 0.75, \ldots$ **52.** $0.04, 0.12, 0.36, 1.08, \ldots$ **53.** $20, -10, 5, -\frac{5}{2}, \ldots$

Determine whether each sequence is *arithmetic*, *geometric*, or *neither*. Find the next three terms.

54. $1600, 400, 100, 25, \ldots$ **55.** $-40, -39, -37, -34, \ldots$ **56.** $14, 21, 28, 35, \ldots$

11-7 Objectives

▼ To evaluate exponential functions (p. 644)

▼ To graph exponential functions (p. 645)

You can use exponents to show repeated multiplication. An **exponential function** involves repeated multiplication of an initial amount by the same positive number.

Evaluate each function for the given values.

57. $f(x) = 3 \cdot 2^x$ for the domain $\{1, 2, 3, 4\}$

58. $y = 10 \cdot (0.75)^x$ for the domain $\{1, 2, 3\}$

59. a. One kind of bacteria in a laboratory culture triples in number every 30 minutes. Suppose a culture is started with 30 bacteria cells. How many bacteria will there be after 2 hours?

  b. After how many minutes will there be more than 20,000 bacteria cells?

11-8 Objectives

▼ To model exponential growth (p. 651)

▼ To model exponential decay (p. 653)

The general form of an exponential function is $y = a \cdot b^x$.

When $a > 0$ and $b > 1$, the function increases, and the function shows **exponential growth.** The base of the exponent, b, is called the **growth factor.** An example of exponential growth is **compound interest**.

When $a > 0$ and $0 < b < 1$, the function decreases, and the function shows **exponential decay.** Then the base of the exponent b is called the **decay factor.** An example of exponential decay is the half-life model.

Identify the initial amount a and the growth or decay factor b in each exponential function.

60. $y = 100 \cdot 1.025^x$ **61.** $y = 32 \cdot 0.75^x$ **62.** $y = 0.4 \cdot 2^x$

Identify each function as *exponential growth* or *exponential decay*. Then identify the growth or decay factor.

63. $y = 5.2 \cdot 3^x$ **64.** $y = 0.15 \cdot \left(\frac{3}{2}\right)^x$ **65.** $y = 7 \cdot 0.32^x$ **66.** $y = 1.3 \cdot \left(\frac{1}{4}\right)^x$

Graph each function.

67. $f(x) = 2.5^x$ **68.** $y = 0.5 \cdot (0.5)^x$ **69.** $f(x) = \left(\frac{1}{2}\right) \cdot 3^x$ **70.** $y = 0.1^x$

71. The function $y = 25 \cdot 0.80^x$ models the amount y of a 25-mg dose of medicine remaining in the bloodstream after x hours. How many milligrams of medicine remain in the bloodstream after 5 hours?

Chapter Test

Go Online
PHSchool.com
For: Chapter Test
Web Code: ata-0852

Simplify each expression.

1. $\dfrac{r^3 t^{-7}}{t^5}$

2. $\left(\dfrac{a^3}{m}\right)^{-4}$

3. $\dfrac{t^{-8} m^2}{m^{-3}}$

4. $c^3 v^9 c^{-1} c^0$

5. $h^2 k^{-5} d^3 k^2$

6. $9 y^4 j^2 y^{-9}$

7. $(w^2 k^0 p^{-5})^{-7}$

8. $2y^{-9} h^2 (2y^0 h^{-4})^{-6}$

9. $(1.2)^5 (1.2)^{-2}$

10. $(-3q^{-1})^3 \, q^2$

11. If $n = -3$, which expression has the least value?

A. $n^2 n^0$
B. n^n
C. $n^8 n^{-5}$
D. $-n^n n^{-4}$

Write each number in scientific notation.

12. **History** There were about 62,041,000 votes cast for George Bush in the 2004 presidential election.

13. **Pets** More than 450,000 households in the United States have reptiles as pets.

Is each number written in scientific notation? If not, explain.

14. 76×10^{-9}

15. 7.3×10^5

16. $4.05 \times 10 \times 10^{-8}$

17. 32.5×10^{13}

18. **a. Astronomy** The speed of light in a vacuum is about 186,300 mi/s. Use scientific notation to express how far light travels in one hour.
    b. At its farthest, Saturn is about 1.03×10^9 mi from Earth. About how many hours does it take for light to travel from Earth to Saturn?

19. Use the sequence $-32, 16, -8, 4, \ldots$.
    a. What is the common ratio?
    b. What are the next three terms?
    c. Write a rule for the sequence.
    d. What is the ninth term of the sequence?

20. You drop a ball from a height of 12 ft. Each bounce has $\frac{3}{5}$ the height of the previous bounce.
    a. Write a rule for the sequence. The initial height is given by the term $n = 1$.
    b. What height will the ball reach at the top of the fourth path ($n = 4$)?

21. Find the fifth term of the sequence $A(n) = -3(-2)^{n+1}$.

Evaluate each function for $x = 1, 2,$ and 3.

22. $y = 3 \cdot 5^x$

23. $f(x) = \frac{1}{2} \cdot 4^x$

24. $f(x) = 4(0.95)^x$

25. $g(x) = 5\left(\frac{3}{4}\right)^x$

Graph each function.

26. $y = \frac{1}{2} \cdot 2^x$

27. $y = 2 \cdot \left(\frac{1}{2}\right)^x$

28. $f(x) = 3^x$

29. **Open-Ended** Write and solve a problem involving exponential decay.

30. **Writing** Explain when the function $y = a \cdot b^x$ shows exponential growth and when it shows exponential decay.

31. **Banking** A customer deposits $1000 in a savings account that pays 4% interest compounded quarterly. How much money will the customer have in the account after 2 years? After 5 years?

32. The function $y = 1.3 \cdot (1.07)^x$ models a city's annual electrical consumption for x years since 1985, where y is kilowatt-hours.
    a. Determine whether the function models exponential growth or decay, and find the growth or decay factor.
    b. According to the model, what will be the annual electrical usage in 2010?
    c. According to the model, what was the annual electrical usage in 1975?
    d. What value of x should you substitute to find the value of y now? Use this value for x to find y.

33. **Automobiles** Suppose a new car is worth $20,000. You can use the function $y = 20{,}000(0.85)^x$ to estimate the car's value after x years.
    a. What is the decay factor? What does it mean?
    b. Estimate the car's value after one year.
    c. Estimate the car's value after four years.

34. The function $y = 10 \cdot 1.08^x$ models the cost of annual tuition (in thousands of dollars) at a local college x years after 1997.
    a. What is the annual percent increase?
    b. How much was tuition in 1997? In 2000?
    c. How much will the tuition be the year you plan to graduate from high school?

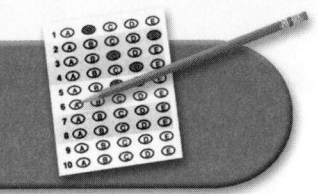

Standardized Test Prep

Multiple Choice

For Exercises 1–12, choose the correct letter.

1. If a is positive and b is negative, which of the following is negative?
   - Ⓐ $a + |b|$
   - Ⓑ $a|b|$
   - Ⓒ $|a|b$
   - Ⓓ $|a| - b$

2. The scores on your first five algebra tests are 88, 78, 81, 83, and 90. What score must you get on your next test to raise the mean to 85?
   - Ⓕ 90
   - Ⓖ 87
   - Ⓗ 86
   - Ⓙ 85

3. Which value of x is NOT a solution to the inequality $5 - 6x < -x + 2$?
   - Ⓐ -1
   - Ⓑ 1
   - Ⓒ 3
   - Ⓓ 5

4. You earn a commission of 6% on your first $500 of sales and 10% on all sales above $500. If you earn $130 in commission, what are your total sales?
   - Ⓕ $800
   - Ⓖ $1000
   - Ⓗ $1300
   - Ⓙ $1500

5. Find the solution of the system of equations.
$$\frac{1}{3}x - y = 4$$
$$x + 3y = 0$$
   - Ⓐ $(9, -1)$
   - Ⓑ $(-6, 2)$
   - Ⓒ $(6, -2)$
   - Ⓓ $(-9, 1)$

6. You flip a coin and roll a number cube. What is the probability of getting a head and a multiple of three?
   - Ⓕ $\frac{1}{12}$
   - Ⓖ $\frac{1}{6}$
   - Ⓗ $\frac{1}{4}$
   - Ⓙ $\frac{3}{2}$

7. Which number has the least value?
   - Ⓐ 2.8×10^{-5}
   - Ⓑ 5.3×10^{-4}
   - Ⓒ 8.3×10^{-7}
   - Ⓓ 1.6×10^{-8}

8. Potassium-42 has a half-life of 12.5 h. How many half-lives are in 75 h?
   - Ⓕ 6
   - Ⓖ 8
   - Ⓗ 25
   - Ⓙ 150

9. Simplify $-3a^8 \cdot cb^{-3} \cdot b^{12} \cdot 9c^5$.
   - Ⓐ $6a^9b^5c^6$
   - Ⓑ $-27a^8b^9c^6$
   - Ⓒ $-27a^8b^{15}c^6$
   - Ⓓ $-3abc$

10. Which statement is true for every solution of the following system?
$$y > x + 4$$
$$y + x > 4$$
   - Ⓕ $x \le -3$
   - Ⓖ $y < 5$
   - Ⓗ $x > 4$
   - Ⓙ $y > 4$

11. What value for k makes the equation true?
$$\begin{bmatrix} 6 & 1 \\ 0 & 3 \end{bmatrix} + \begin{bmatrix} 1 & k \\ -5 & 3 \end{bmatrix} = \begin{bmatrix} 7 & -2 \\ -5 & 6 \end{bmatrix}$$
   - Ⓐ -3
   - Ⓑ -2
   - Ⓒ 2
   - Ⓓ 3

12. Which system of equations is shown in the graph below?

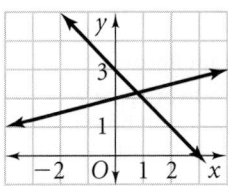

   - Ⓕ $3x + 2y = 6$
        $y = \frac{1}{4}x + 2$
   - Ⓖ $2x + 3y = 12$
        $y = -\frac{1}{4}x + 2$
   - Ⓗ $3x + 3y = 9$
        $y = \frac{1}{4}x + 2$
   - Ⓙ $3x - 2y = 12$
        $y = 4x + 2$

Gridded Response

13. A cafeteria charges $.21/oz for frozen yogurt. How many dollars would a 9-oz serving cost?

14. For a spinner numbered from 1 to 6, the outcomes are equally likely. What is the probability of getting an odd number?

Short Response

Show all work.

15. On April 1, 2000, the day of the 2000 national census, the population of the United States was 281,421,906 people. This was a 13.2% increase from the 1990 census. What was the 1990 population of the United States?

16. Graph the inequality $|x - 2| \le 9$ on a number line.

Extended Response

17. The slopes of four different lines are $\frac{3}{5}, -\frac{10}{6}, -\frac{5}{3}$, and $\frac{9}{15}$. Do these lines determine a rectangle? Explain why or why not.
    book.

How Fast Can You Run?

Applying Linear Equations Animals run to escape predators and to chase prey. The display below compares animals as if they were able to sprint along at their top velocities or speeds for a whole hour. Linear equations and graphs are good tools for describing and comparing motion at constant velocities.

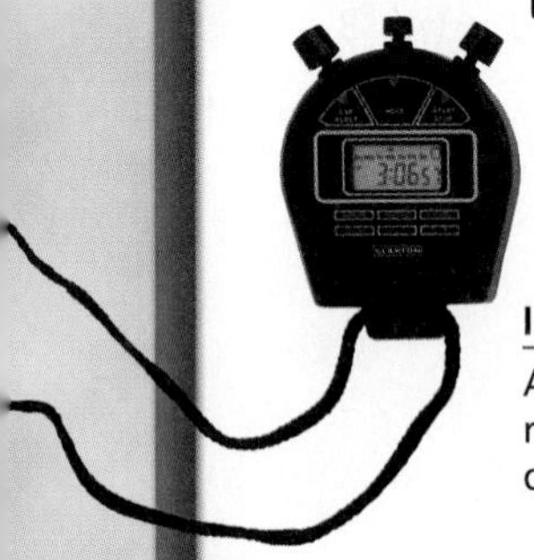

Instant Records

A stopwatch is a watch used to time races. It can be started and stopped quickly for accurate timing.

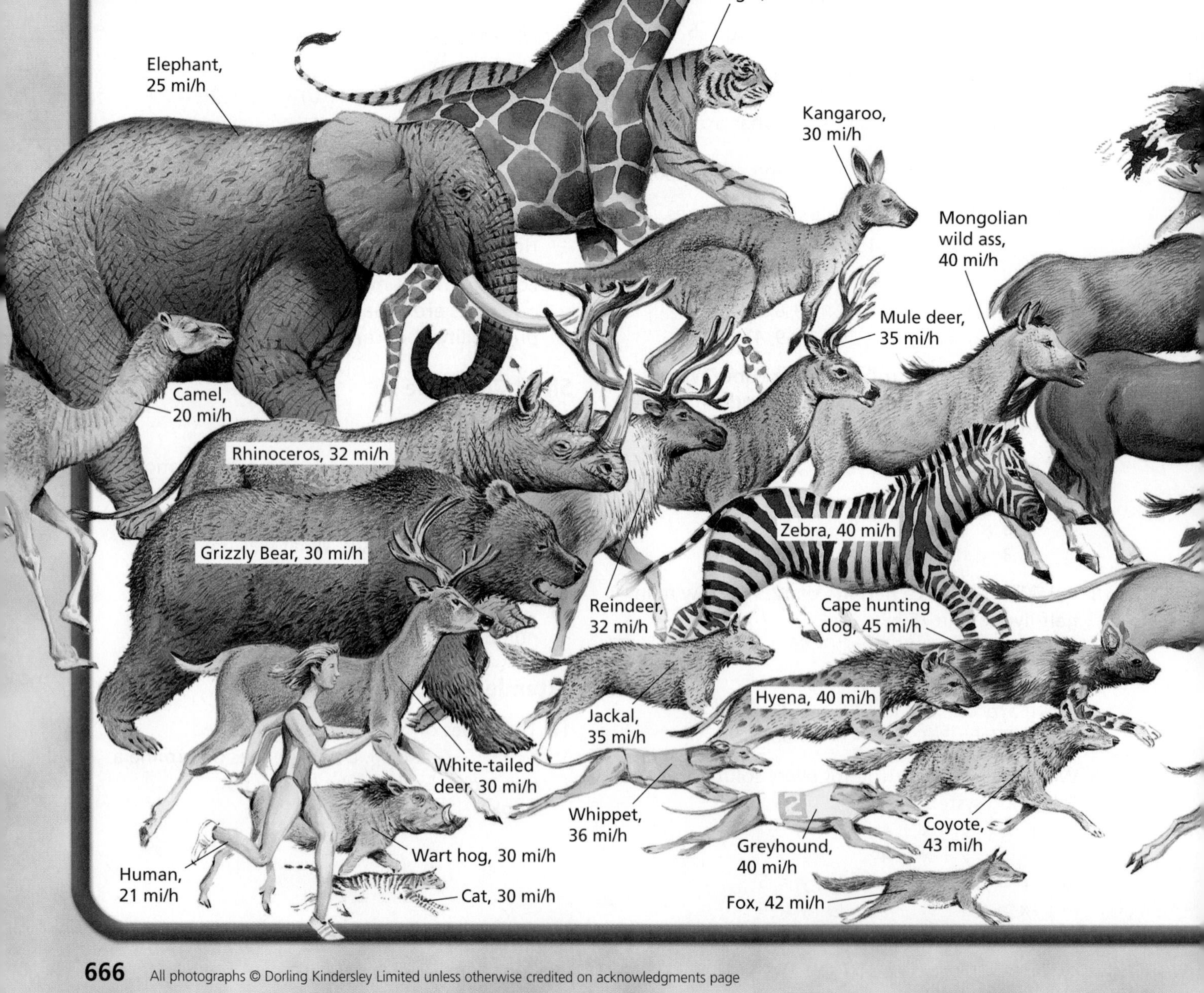

Giraffe, 32 mi/h

Tiger, 35 mi/h

Kangaroo, 30 mi/h

Mongolian wild ass, 40 mi/h

Mule deer, 35 mi/h

Elephant, 25 mi/h

Camel, 20 mi/h

Rhinoceros, 32 mi/h

Grizzly Bear, 30 mi/h

Zebra, 40 mi/h

Reindeer, 32 mi/h

Cape hunting dog, 45 mi/h

Hyena, 40 mi/h

Jackal, 35 mi/h

White-tailed deer, 30 mi/h

Whippet, 36 mi/h

Greyhound, 40 mi/h

Coyote, 43 mi/h

Human, 21 mi/h

Wart hog, 30 mi/h

Cat, 30 mi/h

Fox, 42 mi/h

Car Racing
Formula 1 cars compete at speeds as high as 200 mi/h. The speed limit on most U.S. highways and interstates is 65 mi/h.

Activity 1

Materials: graph paper, pencil

a. Suppose two animals are in a race. Choose the two animals and calculate the speed of each animal in yards per second.

b. Decide how much of a head start (in yards) the faster animal offers the slower animal. For each animal, write an equation relating distance from the starting line to time.

c. Graph the two equations on the same coordinate plane.

d. How long will it take the faster animal to overtake the slower animal? How many yards from the starting line are the animals when the faster animal overtakes the slower animal?

e. Reduce the head start by half and repeat parts (c) and (d).

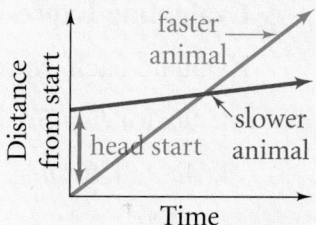

Activity 2

a. Choose a third animal. Calculate its speed in yards per second. Compare its speed with the speed of the two animals you chose in Activity 1.

b. Decide which two animals should get head starts and how much of a head start each should get. Write three equations relating distance from the starting line to time.

c. Graph all three equations on the same coordinate plane.

Ostrich, 45 mi/h

Moose, 45 mi/h

Horse, 43 mi/h

Wildebeest, 50 mi/h

Lion, 50 mi/h

Thomson's gazelle, 50 mi/h

Cheetah, 70 mi/h

Go Online
PHSchool.com

For: Information about speeds
Web Code: ate-0853

667

What You've Learned

In Chapter 1, you wrote rules for patterns using inductive reasoning.

● In Chapter 2, you learned to simplify variable expressions by combining like terms.

● In Chapter 4, you learned how to multiply powers in the same base by adding the exponents.

● In Chapter 8, you graphed linear functions by making a table of values to show ordered-pair solutions.

 **Check Your Readiness**   **for Help** to the Lesson in green.

Evaluating Expressions (Lesson 4-3)

Evaluate each expression.

1. $8b$, for $b = 5$ **2.** $(-h)^5$, for $h = 2$ **3.** $19 - (n - 6)$, for $n = 8$

4. $4a + 4$, for $a = 6$ **5.** n^2, for $n = 0.8$ **6.** $55 - 3mn$, for $m = 2, n = 5$

7. $\frac{120}{s + r}$, for $s = 25$ and $r = 35$ **8.** $\frac{j - k}{9}$, for $j = 75$ and $k = 12$

Using the Distributive Property (Lesson 5-2)

Simplify each expression.

9. $(d - 4)3$ **10.** $5(3x + 1)$ **11.** $3(u - 8)$ **12.** $-4(-2y - 7)$

13. $4(-3d + 1)$ **14.** $10(5 - 3s)$ **15.** $-3(7 - 2w)$ **16.** $(9 - 2b)3$

Simplifying Variable Expressions (Lesson 5-3)

Simplify each expression.

17. $5a - 4 + 6a$ **18.** $x - 4x + 3x + 5$ **19.** $g + 4 - 3g + g$

20. $5t + 5s + 5t$ **21.** $9b - 3d + 7d - 2b$ **22.** $-4(9c) + 2(-4c) - c$

Equations With Two Variables (Lesson 11-2)

Find the y values of each equation for $x = -2, 0$, and 2.

23. $y = 3x - 4$ **24.** $y = -3x$ **25.** $y = 4x - 2$ **26.** $y = \frac{3}{5}x - 5$

27. $y = 6 - 2x$ **28.** $y = -\frac{1}{4}x - 8$ **29.** $y = \frac{1}{2}x$ **30.** $y = -3x - 1$

Nonlinear Functions and Polynomials

Chapter

12

Key Vocabulary

- absolute value function (p. 677)
- arithmetic sequence (p. 670)
- binomial (p. 686)
- common difference (p. 670)
- common ratio (p. 671)
- geometric sequence (p. 671)
- monomial (p. 686)
- polynomial (p. 686)
- quadratic function (p. 676)
- sequence (p. 670)
- term (p. 670)
- trinomial (p. 686)

What You'll Learn Next

In this chapter, you will learn how to

- Use arithmetic and geometric sequences.
- Graph nonlinear functions.
- Perform operations with polynomials.
- Solve a problem using multiple strategies.

Activity Lab Applying what you learn, on pages 716–717 you will learn to solve problems about carbon-14 dating.

669

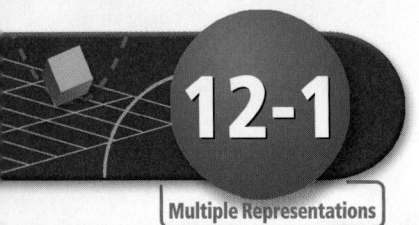

Patterns and Sequences

What You'll Learn

- To describe number patterns with arithmetic sequences
- To describe number patterns with geometric sequences

. . . And Why

To use sequences in making predictions

 Check Skills You'll Need

Write a rule for each number pattern.

1. 60, 48, 36, 24, . . .

2. 7, 12, 17, 22, . . .

3. 6, 18, 54, 162, . . .

4. 60, 30, 15, $7\frac{1}{2}$, . . .

GO for Help
Lesson 1-7

New Vocabulary

- sequence
- term
- arithmetic sequence
- common difference
- geometric sequence
- common ratio

1 Arithmetic Sequences

ctivity

Discovering a Pattern

You win a contest and can choose one of two options for 30 days.

Option A	**Option B**
You receive $500 the first day, $550 the second, $600 the third, $650 the fourth, and so on.	You receive $1 the first day, $2 the second, $4 the third, $8 the fourth, and so on.

1. Make a table of values for both options for the first 10 days.
   a. Which option gives you more money in 10 days?
   b. Which option would you choose for 30 days? Explain.

A **sequence** is a set of numbers that follow a pattern. Each number in the sequence is a **term** of the sequence. You find a term of an **arithmetic sequence** by *adding* a fixed number to the previous term. This fixed number is called the **common difference.**

Term Number	1st	2nd	3rd	4th
Arithmetic Sequence	2	6	10	14
Common Difference		+4	+4	+4

You can find the common difference for an arithmetic sequence by subtracting any term from the next term in the sequence.

1 EXAMPLE Finding the Common Difference

What is the common difference in the sequence 4, 2, 0, –2, . . .?

$$4 \quad 2 \quad 0 \quad -2$$
$$\quad -2 \quad -2 \quad -2$$

Find the common difference.

The common difference is −2.

 Quick Check

1. What is the common difference in each sequence?
   a. 8, 13, 18, 23, . . .   **b.** 12, 9, 6, 3, . . .

You can continue a sequence and write a rule to describe it.

During a
two-mile run,
a runner's feet strike the
ground about 3,000 times.

2 EXAMPLE <u>Real-World</u> 🌐 <u>Problem Solving</u>

A runner training for a race runs 2 mi the first day, $2\frac{1}{4}$ mi the second day, $2\frac{1}{2}$ mi the third day, and so on. Find the next three terms of the sequence. Then write a rule to describe the sequence.

Ⓐ $2, 2\frac{1}{4}, 2\frac{1}{2}$; *Start with 2 and add $\frac{1}{4}$ repeatedly.*

Ⓑ $2\frac{3}{4}, 3, 3\frac{1}{4}$; *Start with 2 and add $\frac{1}{4}$ repeatedly.*

Ⓒ $2\frac{3}{4}, 3, 3\frac{1}{4}$; *Start with 3 and add $\frac{1}{4}$ repeatedly.*

Ⓓ $3, 3\frac{1}{4}, 3\frac{1}{2}$; *Start with 3 and add $\frac{1}{4}$ repeatedly.*

$$2 \quad 2\frac{1}{4} \quad 2\frac{1}{2} \quad 2\frac{3}{4} \quad 3 \quad 3\frac{1}{4}$$
$$+\frac{1}{4} \quad +\frac{1}{4} \quad +\frac{1}{4} \quad +\frac{1}{4} \quad +\frac{1}{4}$$

Find the common difference. Use it to find the next three terms.

The next three terms are $2\frac{3}{4}$, 3, and $3\frac{1}{4}$. The rule for the sequence is *Start with 2 and add $\frac{1}{4}$ repeatedly*. The answer is B.

✔ **Quick Check**

2. Find the next three terms of each sequence. Then write a rule to describe the sequence.

   a. $23, 19, 15, 11, \ldots$ b. $-6, -4\frac{2}{3}, -3\frac{1}{3}, -2, \ldots$

2 Geometric and Other Sequences

You find a term of a **geometric sequence** by *multiplying* the previous term by a fixed number called the **common ratio.**

Term Number	1st	2nd	3rd	4th
Geometric Sequence	2	6	18	54
Common Ratio		×3	×3	×3

You can find the common ratio for a geometric sequence by dividing any term by the previous term in the sequence.

3 EXAMPLE **Finding the Common Ratio**

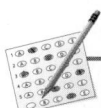
Find the common ratio in the sequence $4, 8, 16, 32, \ldots$ Find the next three terms of the sequence. Then write a rule to describe the sequence.

$$4 \quad 8 \quad 16 \quad 32 \quad 64 \quad 128 \quad 256$$
$$\times 2 \quad \times 2 \quad \times 2 \quad \times 2 \quad \times 2 \quad \times 2$$

Find the common ratio. Use it to find the next three terms.

The next three terms are 64, 128, and 256. The rule for the sequence is *Start with 4 and multiply by 2 repeatedly.*

3. Find the common ratio and the next three terms of each sequence. Then write a rule to describe the sequence.

a. 4, 12, 36, 108, . . .   **b.** 4, 2, 1, 0.5, . . .

Not every sequence is arithmetic or geometric. You can determine whether any sequence of numbers is arithmetic or geometric by looking for a common difference or a common ratio. For other sequences, you can look for patterns.

4 EXAMPLE   **Finding the Type of Sequence**

Tell whether each sequence is *arithmetic*, *geometric*, or *neither*. Find the next three terms of each sequence.

a. 4, 6, 8, 10, . . .

4   6   8   10   12   14   16
 +2 +2 +2 +2 +2 +2

There is a common difference of 2. The sequence is arithmetic. The next three terms are 12, 14, and 16.

b. 4, 6, 9, $13\frac{1}{2}$, . . .

4   6   9 $13\frac{1}{2}$ $20\frac{1}{4}$ $30\frac{3}{8}$ $45\frac{9}{16}$
 $\times\frac{3}{2}$ $\times\frac{3}{2}$ $\times\frac{3}{2}$ $\times\frac{3}{2}$ $\times\frac{3}{2}$ $\times\frac{3}{2}$

The ratios for the first four terms are $\frac{6}{4}, \frac{9}{6}$, and $\frac{27}{18}$. These equal $\frac{3}{2}$, which is the common ratio. The sequence is geometric. The next three terms are $20\frac{1}{4}, 30\frac{3}{8}$, and $45\frac{9}{16}$.

c. 4, 6, 9, 13, . . .

4   6   9   13   18   24   31
 +2 +3 +4 +5 +6 +7

The sequence is neither arithmetic nor geometric. Following the pattern above, the next three terms are 18, 24, and 31.

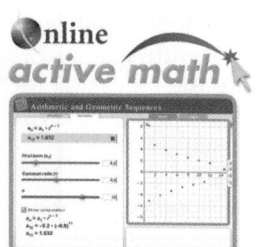

For: Sequences Activity
Use: Interactive Textbook, 12-1

✓ **Quick Check**

4. Tell whether each sequence is *arithmetic*, *geometric*, or *neither*. Then find the next three terms of the sequence.

a. 3, 9, 27, 81, . . .   **b.** 10, 13, 18, 25, . . .
c. −12, 12, −12, 12, . . .   **d.** 50, 200, 350, 500, . . .

EXERCISES

For more exercises, see *Extra Skill and Word Problem Practice*.

Practice and Problem Solving

A Practice by Example

GO for Help

Example 1
(page 670)

What is the common difference of each arithmetic sequence?

1. $5, 4, 3, 2, \ldots$ **2.** $4, 11, 18, 25, \ldots$ **3.** $7, 1, -5, -11, \ldots$

4. $80, 60, 40, 20, \ldots$ **5.** $3, 9, 15, 21, \ldots$ **6.** $-6, -5, -4, -3, \ldots$

Example 2
(page 671)

Find the next three terms of each sequence. Then write a rule to describe the sequence.

7. $0, 5, 10, 15, \ldots$ **8.** $21, 15, 9, 3, \ldots$ **9.** $-11, -8, -5, -2, \ldots$

🌐 **10. Exercising** You begin doing 20 sit-ups every day in November. You do 32 sit-ups every day in December, 44 sit-ups every day in January, and so on. Find the next three terms of the sequence. Then write a rule to describe the sequence.

Example 3
(page 686)

Find the common ratio and the next three terms of each sequence. Then write a rule to describe the sequence.

11. $3, 6, 12, 24, \ldots$ **12.** $5, 1, \frac{1}{5}, \frac{1}{25}, \ldots$ **13.** $45, 90, 180, 360, \ldots$

14. $2, 3, 4\frac{1}{2}, 6\frac{3}{4}, \ldots$ **15.** $12, 4, 1\frac{1}{3}, \frac{4}{9}, \ldots$ **16.** $8, 40, 200, 1{,}000, \ldots$

Example 4
(page 687)

Tell whether each sequence is *arithmetic*, *geometric*, or *neither*. Find the next three terms of the sequence.

17. $1, 3, 9, 27, \ldots$ **18.** $10, 5, 0, -5, \ldots$ **19.** $4.5, 4, 3.5, 3, \ldots$

20. $2, 2, 4, 6, \ldots$ **21.** $-1, 3, -9, 27, \ldots$ **22.** $0, 5, 12, 21, \ldots$

23. Multiple Choice Is the sequence $4, 3\frac{1}{2}, 3, 2\frac{1}{2}, \ldots$ *arithmetic* or *geometric*? Find the common difference or common ratio.

   Ⓐ arithmetic; $\frac{1}{2}$ Ⓑ arithmetic; $-\frac{1}{2}$

   Ⓒ geometric; 2 Ⓓ geometric; $\frac{1}{2}$

B Apply Your Skills

Tell whether each sequence is *arithmetic* or *geometric*. If arithmetic, give the common difference. If geometric, give the common ratio.

24. $1, 1\frac{1}{2}, 2, 2\frac{1}{2}, \ldots$ **25.** $-3, -15, -75, \ldots$ **26.** $-4, 12, -36, 108, \ldots$

27. $5, 6.4, 7.8, 9.2, \ldots$ **28.** $5, 15, 45, 135, \ldots$ **29.** $8.3, 5.7, 3.1, 0.5, \ldots$

Find the next three terms of each sequence. Then write a rule to describe the sequence.

30. $1, 4, 16, 64, \ldots$ **31.** $3, 1, -1, -3, \ldots$ **32.** $2, 20, 200, 2{,}000, \ldots$

33. $9, 18, 36, 72, \ldots$ **34.** $25, 50, 75, 100, \ldots$ **35.** $6.5, 6.7, 6.9, 7.1, \ldots$

Tell whether each sequence is *arithmetic*, *geometric*, or *neither*. Find the next three terms of each sequence.

GO 🌐 **nline**
Homework Video Tutor
Visit: PHSchool.com
Web Code: ade-1301

36. $\frac{1}{2}, \frac{5}{6}, 1\frac{1}{6}, 1\frac{1}{2}, \ldots$ **37.** $1, 10, 2, 20, \ldots$ **38.** $13, 12, 10, 7, \ldots$

39. $7, 7.03, 7.06, 7.09, \ldots$ **40.** $-\frac{1}{5}, -\frac{1}{10}, -\frac{1}{20}, -\frac{1}{40}, \ldots$

12-1 Patterns and Sequences   **673**

41. Savings You open a savings account with $2,000. The account earns 4% interest compounded semiannually.
   a. Write the balance in the savings account after each interest payment for two years.
   b. **Writing in Math** Does the pattern of balances form an arithmetic or geometric sequence? Explain.

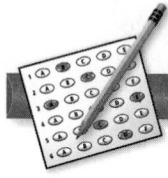 Challenge

Evaluate each expression for $n = -2, -1, 0$, and 1. Is the sequence formed *arithmetic*, *geometric*, or *neither*?

42. $3n$ **43.** $n(n + 1)$ **44.** 2^n **45.** n^2

46. Patterns In the Fibonacci sequence $1, 1, 2, 3, 5, 8, \ldots$, you find each term (after the first two terms) by adding the two previous terms. Write the next three terms of the sequence.

Test Prep

Multiple Choice

47. If the first term of an arithmetic sequence is 35 and the fifth term is 67, what is the third term?
   A. 43   **B.** 51   **C.** 59   **D.** 75

48. If the rule for a sequence is "start with -7 and multiply by -2 repeatedly," what is the fourth term in the sequence?
   F. -112 **G.** -56 **H.** 56   **J.** 112

Short Response

Read the passage below before doing Exercises 49 and 50.

Population Watch

The population of the United States in 1980 was about 226 million, in 1985 it was about 238 million, in 1990 it was about 250 million, and in 1995 it was about 263 million.

49. What intervals of time are used with the given population data?

50. Which type of sequence, arithmetic or geometric, could you use to model the United States population data? Explain.

Mixed Review

51. Surveys You want to find out which presidential candidate is most popular in your city. You plan to interview people who visit the city's art museum. State whether the survey plan describes a good sample. Explain your reasoning.

Find the circumference of each circle rounded to the nearest tenth.

52. radius = 8.5 m   **53.** radius = 5 in.   **54.** diameter = 14 cm

Displaying Sequences

You can model rules for sequences mathematically and then display the sequences using graphing calculator tables. You can use the tables to find any term in a sequence.

1 ACTIVITY

Model the rule "Start with 23 and add −4 repeatedly" mathematically and then display the sequence in a calculator table.

Model: $23 + (-4)x$, or $23 - 4x$, with $x = 0, 1, 2, \ldots$

Display Method 1

Press $\boxed{Y=}$ and enter $Y_1 = 23 - 4x$.

- In **TBLSET,** set TblStart = 0 and ΔTbl = 1, then press **TABLE.**

X	Y_1	
0	23	
1	19	
2	15	
3	11	
4	7	
5	3	
6	−1	
X=6		

Move down in either column to see more terms of the sequence.

2 ACTIVITY

Model the rule "Start with 4 and multiply by 2 repeatedly" mathematically and then display the sequence in a calculator table. Find the sixth term.

Model: $4(2)^x$, with $x = 0, 1, 2, \ldots$

Display Method 2

Clear your home screen. In **STAT,** use the **OPS** menu. Select the **seq** operator, and $\boxed{\text{ENTER}}$. Then

enter seq(X,X,0,10) $\boxed{\text{STO}\blacktriangleright}$ **STAT L$_1$** $\boxed{\text{ENTER}}$. In similar fashion,

enter seq(4(2)^X,X,0,10) $\boxed{\text{STO}\blacktriangleright}$ **STAT L$_2$** $\boxed{\text{ENTER}}$.

Press $\boxed{\text{LIST}}$.

- The sixth term is when $x = 6$, or 256.

L1	L2	L3	1
0	4		
1	8		
2	16		
3	32		
4	64		
5	128		
6	256		
L1(7)=6			

This list ends at 10.

EXERCISES

Use a graphing calculator table to display the first 11 terms of each sequence. Find the 11th term. Use Display Method 1 for some exercises and Display Method 2 for the others.

1. Start with 0 and add 5 repeatedly.

2. Start with 80 and subtract 30 repeatedly.

3. Start with 3 and add 6 repeatedly.

4. Start with −4 and multiply by −3 repeatedly.

5. 7, 7.3, 7.6, 7.9, . . .

6. 3, 1, −1, −3, . . .

7. $18 - 3x; x = 0, 1, 2, \ldots$

8. $6(3)^x$

9. In Activity 1, the model gives the desired sequence for x having values $0, 1, 2, \ldots$ Find a model using x that gives the same sequence for x having values $1, 2, 3, \ldots$

Graphing Nonlinear Functions

What You'll Learn

• To graph quadratic functions

• To graph absolute value functions

. . . And Why

To use nonlinear functions in modeling real-world situations, such as finding the area of an enclosed space

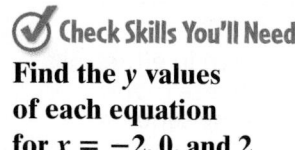 **Check Skills You'll Need**

Find the y values of each equation for $x = -2, 0,$ and 2.

1. $y = 5x - 1$

2. $y = \frac{1}{2}x + 3$

3. $y = 3x + 2$

4. $y = \frac{1}{4}x - 5$

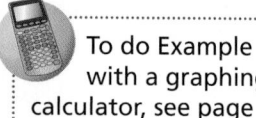 **New Vocabulary**

• quadratic function

• absolute value function

 **1** ▸ Graphing Quadratic Functions

Activity

Graphing Data

You can graph the area of a square as a function of the length of a side of the square.

1. Copy and complete the table at the right.

2. Draw a graph of the data. Does your graph appear to be a linear function? Explain.

Side x	Area $f(x)$
1	1
2	
3	
4	
5	
6	36

In a **quadratic function,** the input variable is squared. The graph of a quadratic function is a U-shaped curve called a *parabola*. The curve may open upward or downward.

1 **EXAMPLE** **Graphing a Quadratic Function**

For the function $y = 2x^2$, make a table with integer values of x from -2 to 2. Then graph the function.

Make a table.

x	$2x^2 = y$	(x, y)
-2	$2(-2)^2 = 8$	$(-2, 8)$
-1	$2(-1)^2 = 2$	$(-1, 2)$
0	$2(0)^2 = 0$	$(0, 0)$
1	$2(1)^2 = 2$	$(1, 2)$
2	$2(2)^2 = 8$	$(2, 8)$

Make a graph.

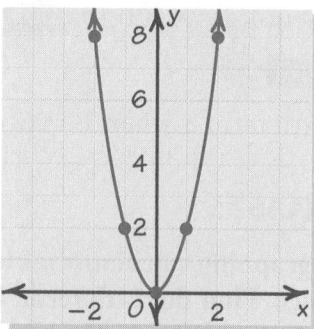

To do Example 1 with a graphing calculator, see page 759.

Quick Check

1. For each function, make a table with integer values of x from -2 to 2. Then graph each function.

  a. $y = -2x^2$ **b.** $y = -x^2 + 3$

---

2 EXAMPLE   Using a Graph to Solve a Problem

The function $A = 10x - x^2$, where x is the width in yards, gives the area A of a goat pen in square yards. Graph the function. Use the graph to find the width that gives the greatest area.

x	$10x - x^2 = y$	(x, y)
0	$10(0) - 0^2 = 0$	$(0, 0)$
1	$10(1) - 1^2 = 9$	$(1, 9)$
2	$10(2) - 2^2 = 16$	$(2, 16)$
3	$10(3) - 3^2 = 21$	$(3, 21)$
4	$10(4) - 4^2 = 24$	$(4, 24)$
5	$10(5) - 5^2 = 25$	$(5, 25)$
6	$10(6) - 6^2 = 24$	$(6, 24)$

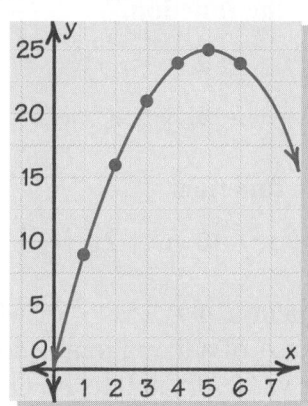

A goat pen with width 5 yd and area 25 yd^2 must have length 5 yd.

The ordered pair $(5, 25)$ shows what appears to be the highest point. So the width 5 yards gives the greatest area.

✓ Quick Check

2. Graph each function.

   a. $y = 3x + x^2$　　　　**b.** $y = 6x - x^2$

---

2   Graphing Absolute Value Functions

The equation $y = |x|$ is an **absolute value function.** The graph of $y = |x|$ is V-shaped.

3 EXAMPLE   Graphing an Absolute Value Function

Graph the function $y = |x|$.

x	$|x| = y$	(x, y)
-2	$|-2| = 2$	$(-2, 2)$
-1	$|-1| = 1$	$(-1, 1)$
0	$|0| = 0$	$(0, 0)$
1	$|1| = 1$	$(1, 1)$
2	$|2| = 2$	$(2, 2)$

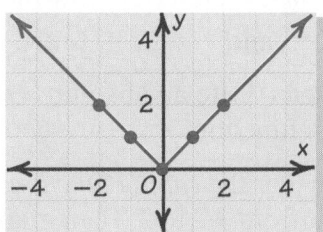

✓ Quick Check

3. Graph each function.

   a. $y = -|x| + 1$　　　　**b.** $y = 2|x|$

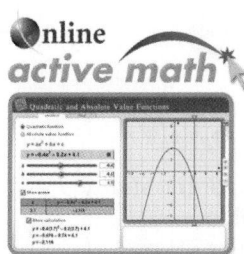

🌐nline
active math

For: Nonlinear Functions Activity
Use: Interactive Textbook, 12-2

EXERCISES

For more exercises, see *Extra Skill and Word Problem Practice*.

Practice and Problem Solving

A Practice by Example

for Help

Example 1
(page 676)

For each function, make a table with integer values of x from -2 to 2. Then graph the function.

1. $y = 4x^2$ **2.** $y = -x^2$ **3.** $y = -3x^2$ **4.** $y = x^2 + 1$

5. $y = -x^2 + 2$ **6.** $y = x^2 - 2$ **7.** $y = x^2 + 4$ **8.** $y = -x^2 + 3$

Example 2
(page 677)

Graph each function.

9. $y = x - x^2$ **10.** $y = 2x - x^2$ **11.** $y = 5x - x^2$ **12.** $y = 8x - x^2$

13. The function $A = 15x - x^2$, where x is the width in yards, gives the area A of a llama pen in square yards. Make a table with integer values from 0 to 10. Graph the function. Use the graph to find the width that gives the greatest area.

Example 3
(page 677)

For each function, make a table with integer values of x from -2 to 2. Then graph the function.

14. $y = 3|x|$ **15.** $y = |x| + 3$ **16.** $y = -3|x|$

17. $y = |x| - 4$ **18.** $y = -|x| - 1$ **19.** $y = -2|x|$

B Apply Your Skills

State whether the graph of the function has a U shape or a V shape. Make a table with integer values of x from -2 to 2. Then graph the function.

20. $y = |x| + 1$ **21.** $y = x^2 - 8$ **22.** $y = 3x - x^2$

23. $y = -4x^2$ **24.** $y = -|x| - 3$ **25.** $y = 2x^2 - 2$

26. $y = -\frac{1}{2}|x|$ **27.** $y = |x| - 2$ **28.** $y = -x^2 + 5$

Visit: PHSchool.com
Web Code: ade-1302

29. a. Graph $y = x^2$, $y = 2x^2$, and $y = \frac{1}{2}x^2$ on the same coordinate plane.
   b. Describe how the coefficients of x^2 affect the graphs.

GO for Help

For a guide to reading and solving Exercise 29, see page 680.

30. Writing in Math Describe how the graphs of the functions $y = x^2$, $y = 2x + x^2$, and $y = 2x - x^2$ are alike and how they are different.

31. Open-Ended Write an absolute value function of your own. Graph the function.

C Challenge

32. Reasoning For the *cubing function*, $y = x^3$, make a table with integer values of x from -2 to 2. Then graph the function. Is the cubing function a quadratic function? Explain.

33. a. Geometry Make a table to show edge lengths and volumes of four cubes. Let the edge lengths be 1 m, 2 m, 3 m, and 4 m.
   b. Graph the ordered pairs from your table.
   c. Using your graph from part (b), estimate the volume of a cube with edge length 3.5 m.

Writing in Math

How are quadratic and absolute value functions alike? How are they different?

Test Prep

Multiple Choice

For Exercises 34–36, use the graph at the right.

34. The graph shows what type of function?
    A. quadratic   **B.** linear
    C. area   **D.** absolute value

35. Which point is NOT on the graph?
    F. $(1, -2)$ **G.** $(-2, 0)$
    H. $(0, -2)$ **J.** $(1, -1)$

36. Which function matches the graph?
    A. $y = -2|x|$ **B.** $y = x^2 - 2$
    C. $y = |x - 2|$ **D.** $y = |x| - 2$

Short Response

37. For the function $y = -3x^2$, **(a)** make a table with integer values of x from -2 to 2. **(b)** Graph the function.

Mixed Review

Lesson 12-1

Find the next three terms of each sequence. Then write a rule to describe the sequence.

38. $8, 4, 2, 1, \ldots$ **39.** $12, 27, 42, 57, \ldots$ **40.** $3, 4, 6, 9, \ldots$

41. Statistics The table shows the prices of evening movies at 18 different theaters. Use the data to make a frequency table.

Costs of Movie Tickets

$7.00, $6.50, $7.50, $7.00, $7.50, $8.00,
$7.00, $8.50, $8.00, $6.00, $7.00, $7.50,
$8.00, $7.00, $7.50, $8.50, $7.50, $6.50

Math at Work

Systems Analyst

Systems analysts are responsible for upgrading hardware and designing and installing new software. They also respond to problems users have with hardware or software. Logic skills are necessary for writing programs and solving problems.

Systems analysts have backgrounds in computer programming. Since computer technology is constantly changing, they must continue their education throughout their careers.

For: Information about systems analysts
PHSchool.com **Web Code:** adb-2031

Understanding Math Problems Read the problem below. Then let Lily's thinking guide you through the solution. Check your understanding with the exercises at the bottom of the page.

a. Graph $y = x^2$, $y = 2x^2$, and $y = \frac{1}{2}x^2$ on the same coordinate plane.
b. Describe how the coefficients of x^2 affect the graphs.

What Lily Thinks

What Lily Writes

To graph the three functions, I need to make a table. Then I need to draw the graphs. That's part (a).

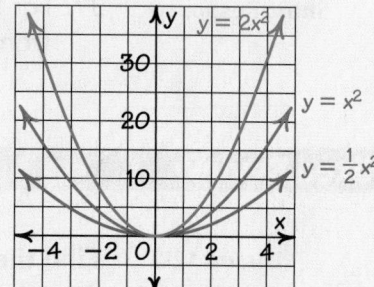

Now I need to describe how the coefficients of x^2 affect the graphs. First I'll tell how the graphs are alike. Then I'll describe how the graphs are different.

Graphs alike: All three graphs are parabolas. All contain $(0, 0)$. All open upward.
Graphs differ: From the top down, they get wider.

Now I'll tell how the functions are alike. And how the functions are different.

Functions alike: All contain x^2.
Functions differ: x^2 has different coefficients.

OK, I know the graphs get wider as the coefficients of x^2 decrease in value. That's what I'll write.

As the coefficients of x^2 decrease in value, the parabolas get wider.

EXERCISES

1. For $y = -x^2$, $y = -2x^2$, and $y = -\frac{1}{2}x^2$, describe how the coefficients of x^2 affect the graphs of the functions.

2. a. Graph $y = x^2$, $y = x^2 + 2$, and $y = x^2 - 3$ on the same coordinate plane.
   b. Describe how the constants affect the graphs of the functions.

3. For $y = k|x|$, describe how the values of k affect the graphs.

Exponential Growth and Decay

1 Exponential Growth

A function like $y = 2^x$ has input, or domain, values that are exponents. It models *exponential growth.* Its graph curves upward as input values increase.

1 EXAMPLE   Real-World ● Problem Solving

Biology A warren of rabbits starts with one male and one female. The number of rabbits then doubles each month. The function $y = 2^x$ models the number of rabbits in the warren.

For the function $y = 2^x$, make a table with integer values of x from 2 to 5. Then graph the function.

x	2^x	y	(x, y)
2	2^2	4	(2, 4)
3	2^3	8	(3, 8)
4	2^4	16	(4, 16)
5	2^5	32	(5, 32)

✓ Quick Check

1. For the function $y = 3^x$, make a table with integer values of x from 1 to 4. Then graph the function.

You can multiply the power in a function by a number. For example, in $y = 0.25(4^x)$, the power 4^x is multiplied by 0.25.

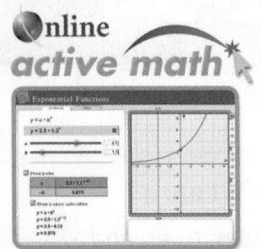

Online
active math

For: Functions Activity
Use: Interactive Textbook, 12-3

2 EXAMPLE   **Graphing Exponential Growth**

For the function $y = 0.25(4)^x$, make a table with integer values of x from 0 to 4. Then graph the function.

x	$0.25(4)^x$	y	(x, y)
0	$0.25(4)^0$	0.25	(0, 0.25)
1	$0.25(4)^1$	1	(1, 1)
2	$0.25(4)^2$	4	(2, 4)
3	$0.25(4)^3$	16	(3, 16)
4	$0.25(4)^4$	64	(4, 64)

✓ **Quick Check**

2. For the function $y = 0.5(2)^x$, make a table with integer values of x from 0 to 5. Then graph the function.

2   **Exponential Decay**

A function like $y = \left(\frac{1}{2}\right)^x$ models *exponential decay*. Its graph slopes downward as input values increase.

To do Example 3 with a graphing calculator, see page 760.

Real-World Connection

Doctors use the element technetium to make bone scans. Technetium decays exponentially. After 6 hours, only 15 mg of a 30-mg dose remain. After 12 hours, only 7.5 mg remain.

3 EXAMPLE   **Graphing Exponential Decay**

For $y = 60\left(\frac{1}{2}\right)^x$, make a table with integer values of x from 0 to 5. Then graph the function.

x	$60(\frac{1}{2})^x$	y	(x, y)
0	$60(\frac{1}{2})^0$	60	(0, 60)
1	$60(\frac{1}{2})^1$	30	(1, 30)
2	$60(\frac{1}{2})^2$	15	(2, 15)
3	$60(\frac{1}{2})^3$	7.5	(3, 7.5)
4	$60(\frac{1}{2})^4$	3.75	(4, 3.75)
5	$60(\frac{1}{2})^5$	1.875	(5, 1.875)

✓ **Quick Check**

3. For the function $y = 90\left(\frac{1}{3}\right)^x$, make a table with integer values of x from 0 to 5. Then graph the function.

EXERCISES

Practice and Problem Solving

A Practice by Example

Examples 1 and 2
(pages 681 and 682)

Make a table with integer values of x from 0 to 4. Then graph the function.

1. $y = 4^x$ **2.** $y = 5^x$ **3.** $y = 6^x$

4. $y = 0.4(2)^x$ **5.** $y = 0.5(4)^x$ **6.** $y = 0.2(5)^x$

7. Biology A bacteria culture starts with ten cells and doubles every hour. The function $y = 10(2)^x$ models the number of cells y in the culture after x hours. Make a table with integer values of x from 0 to 3. Then graph the function.

Example 3
(page 682)

Make a table with integer values of x from 0 to 5. Then graph the function.

8. $y = \left(\frac{1}{2}\right)^x$ **9.** $y = 30\left(\frac{1}{3}\right)^x$ **10.** $y = 100\left(\frac{1}{5}\right)^x$

B Apply Your Skills

Match each graph with an equation.

11.

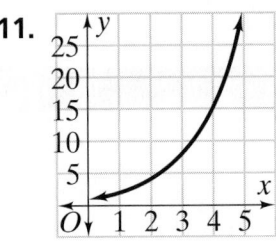

A. $y = 3^x$ **B.** $y = 2^x$

12.

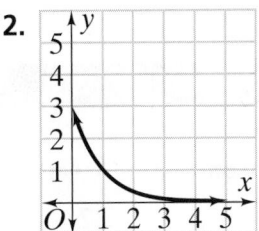

A. $y = 3\left(\frac{1}{3}\right)^x$ **B.** $y = 2\left(\frac{1}{2}\right)^x$

13. Multiple Choice You put $100 in a stock that increases in value by 20% each year. The function $v = 100(1.2)^x$ describes the value of the stock after x years. Evaluate the function for $x = 2$. What does the value represent?

   Ⓐ 103.2; the value of the stock after 2 years

   Ⓑ 120; the number of shares you own after 2 years

   Ⓒ 144; the value of the stock after 2 years

   Ⓓ 240; the number of shares you own after 2 years

Make a table with integer values of x from 0 to 4. Then graph the function.

14. $y = 2 \cdot 3^x$ **15.** $y = \frac{1}{5} \cdot 5^x$ **16.** $y = 6(0.5)^x$

17. $f(x) = \frac{1}{2} \cdot 2^x$ **18.** $g(x) = 20\left(\frac{1}{2}\right)^x$ **19.** $g(x) = 3 \cdot 2^x$

GO Online
Homework Video Tutor
Visit: PHSchool.com
Web Code: ade-1303

Is the point (4, 16) on the graph of each function? Explain.

20. $y = 4x$ **21.** $y = 2^x$ **22.** $y = x^2$ **23.** $y = \left(\frac{1}{2}\right)^x$

 **Challenge**

24. a. For the functions $y = 2x$, $y = x^2$, and $y = 2^x$, make tables with integer values of x from 0 to 5. Then graph the functions.

   b. Writing in Math Describe how the graphs are similar. Describe how they are different.

25. Reasoning Without graphing, predict whether each function shows exponential growth or exponential decay. Justify your prediction.

   a. $y = 5^x$ **b.** $y = \left(\frac{1}{2}\right)^x$ **c.** $y = 3(0.2)^x$ **d.** $y = 3(2)^x$

Test Prep

Gridded Response   For the given equation, what is the value of y for $x = 2$?

26. $y = 0.2(3)^x$ **27.** $y = 3\left(\frac{1}{3}\right)^x$ **28.** $y = 3x^2 - 6$ **29.** $y = 4|x| - 1$

For Exercises 30 and 31, use the formula $B = p(1.03)^n$ to find the balance B (in dollars and cents) for a principal p invested at a compound interest rate of 3% for n years.

30. \$5 invested for 5 years   **31.** \$2 invested for 10 years

Mixed Review

 **Lesson 12-2**

Graph each function.

32. $y = |x| + 2$ **33.** $f(x) = 3|x|$ **34.** $g(x) = -x^2 + 1$

 **35. Shopping** Janelle is buying a sweatshirt. She has a choice of red, purple, or green; zipper or no zipper; and hooded or not hooded. How many different sweatshirt choices does she have?

Find the midpoint of each segment with the given endpoints.

36. $A(4, -6)$ and $B(-2, 5)$ **37.** $X(-3, -8)$ and $Y(1, 6)$

✓ Checkpoint Quiz 1   Lessons 12-1 through 12-3

Find the next three terms of each sequence. Then write a rule to describe the sequence.

   1. $100, 85, 70, 55, \ldots$ **2.** $17, 24, 31, 38, \ldots$ **3.** $13, 26, 52, 104, \ldots$

   4. A geometric sequence begins with 3 and has common ratio 2. Write its first five terms.

For each function, make a table with integer values of x. (Use –2 to 2 for Ex. 5 and 6; use 0 to 4 for Ex. 7.) Then graph the function.

   5. $y = \frac{1}{4}x^2$ **6.** $f(x) = \frac{1}{4}|x|$ **7.** $f(x) = 0.5(3)^x$

Nonlinear Functions and Graphing Calculators

For Use With Lesson 12-3

You can use a graphing calculator to graph nonlinear functions. For the exponent 2, you can use the x^2 key or press $\wedge$ 2.

ACTIVITY

Graph $y = |3x|$.

Step 1 Press Y= CLEAR . Press MATH . In the **NUM** menu, select **abs** then ENTER . Enter Y_1 = abs (3x).

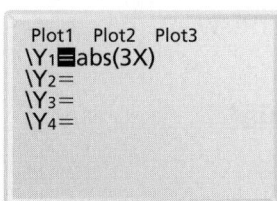

Step 2 Set your viewing window.

```
WINDOW
 Xmin=-5
 Xmax=5
 ΔX=
 Xscl=1
 Ymin=-5
 Ymax=5
 Yscl=1
```

Step 3 Press GRAPH .

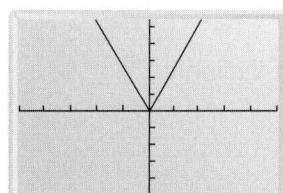

Step 4 Press **TABLE** to see solutions.

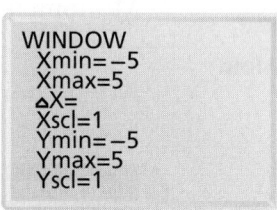

EXERCISES

Graph each equation using a graphing calculator. For each function, use TABLE and make a table on paper for integer values of x from -5 to 5. Then sketch the graph.

1. $y = |2x|$ 　　　　**2.** $y = -|2x|$ 　　　　**3.** $y = |2x| + 1$

4. $y = x^2 - 1$ 　　　**5.** $y = -x^2 - 1$ 　　　**6.** $y = 3(2)^x$

7. $y = -3(2)^x$ 　　　**8.** $y = 3\left(\frac{1}{2}\right)^x$ 　　　**9.** $y = -3\left(\frac{1}{2}\right)^x$

10. Compare your graphs for Exercises 1 and 2.
   a. Explain how they are related and why this is so.
   b. Compare the equations in Exercises 6 and 7. Should their graphs be related in the same way as in part (a)? Explain. Then check.

11. Open-Ended Write a nonlinear function that you can graph using a graphing calculator. Graph your function. Make a table of values and sketch your graph.

Polynomials

What You'll Learn

- To Identify polynomials
- To evaluate polynomials

. . . And Why

To model real-world applications in science

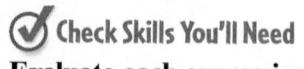 **Check Skills You'll Need**

Evaluate each expression.

1. $5n$ for $n = -8$

2. mn for $m = 6$ and $n = -4$

3. $x - 9$ for $x = 7$

4. $63 - 5x$ for $x = 7$

 **for Help**
Lesson 1-3

New Vocabulary

- monomial
- polynomial
- binomial
- trinomial

1 Identifying Polynomials

You have seen how mathematics uses algebraic expressions to represent real-world situations. Some of these expressions are monomials. A **monomial** is a real number, a variable, or a product of a real number and variables with whole-number exponents.

Monomials: $\qquad 3 \qquad m \qquad 5xy \qquad 0.35bc^3 \qquad \frac{w}{9} \qquad \frac{1}{4}p^2q$

Not monomials: $\qquad a - 8 \qquad \sqrt{m} \qquad y^{-1} \text{ (or } \frac{1}{y}) \qquad \frac{ab}{c}$

1 EXAMPLE **Recognizing a Monomial**

Is the expression a monomial? Explain.

a. $7x^2y$ — Yes, the expression is the product of the real number 7 and the variables x and y.

b. $8 + a$ — No, the expression is a sum.

c. $\frac{a}{7y}$ — No, the denominator contains a variable.

d. $\frac{5x}{4}$ — Yes, the expression is the product of the real number $\frac{5}{4}$ and the variable x.

✓ **Quick Check**

1. Is the expression a monomial? Explain.

a. $\frac{6}{m}$ b. $\frac{m}{6}$ c. 45   d. $mx + b$

A **polynomial** is a monomial or a sum or difference of monomials. We call the monomials that make up a polynomial its *terms*. You can name a polynomial by the number of its terms.

Polynomial	Number of terms	Examples
Monomial	1	$4, 32, x, 2x^2$
Binomial	2	$x - 3, 5x + 1, x^3 - x$
Trinomial	3	$x^2 + x + 1, x^4 - 2x - 5$

2 EXAMPLE Naming a Polynomial

State whether the polynomial is a *monomial*, a *binomial*, or a *trinomial*.

a. $x - y$

binomial

b. $8xyz$

monomial

c. $y^2 + 8y + 18$

trinomial

✓ Quick Check

2. Is the polynomial a monomial, a binomial, or a trinomial?

a. 10   b. $9x^2 + xy$ c. $8 - y$ d. $5 + x - 3y$

---

2 Evaluating Polynomials

You evaluate polynomials by substituting values for the variables.

3 EXAMPLE Evaluating a Polynomial

Evaluate each polynomial for $m = 8$ and $p = -3$.

a. $2mp$

$2mp = 2(8)(-3)$ **Replace m with 8 and p with −3.**

$= -48$ **Simplify.**

b. $3m - 2p$

$3m - 2p = 3(8) - 2(-3)$
$= 24 + 6$
$= 30$

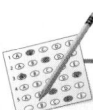
Test-Taking Tip

When you simplify a long polynomial, apply the properties one at a time. Record your work clearly, so you can check your answer easily.

✓ Quick Check

3. Evaluate each polynomial for $x = -2$ and $y = 5$.

a. $5xy$ b. $x + 3y$ c. $y^2 - 2y + x$

4 EXAMPLE Real-World 🌐 Problem Solving

Gridded Response The polynomial $-16t^2 + 140t$ gives the height, in feet, reached by fireworks in t seconds. If the fireworks explode 4 seconds after launch, at what height do they explode?

$-16t^2 + 140t$
$-16(4)^2 + 140(4)$ **Replace t with 4.**
304 **Simplify.**

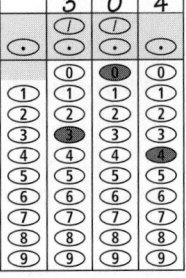

The fireworks explode at 304 feet.

Real-World 🌐 Connection

During a twenty-minute show, fireworks technicians can set off as many as 6,000 different fireworks.

✓ Quick Check

4. Fireworks are set to explode 6 seconds after launch. At what height will they explode?

EXERCISES

For more exercises, see *Extra Skill and Word Problem Practice.*

Practice and Problem Solving

 A Practice by Example

Example 1
(page 686)

 **GO for Help**

Is the expression a monomial? Explain.

1. $2 + x$ **2.** $18ab^2$ **3.** $\frac{a}{3}$ **4.** $\frac{4}{b}$

5. 1 **6.** $0.82k$ **7.** $2x$ **8.** $-0.3y$

Example 2
(page 687)

State whether the polynomial is a *monomial*, a *binomial*, or a *trinomial*.

9. $3xy + 4y^2$ **10.** $5c - 2 + a$ **11.** $7y^2 + 2y - 9$

12. 658 **13.** $3x^2 + 2x$ **14.** 21

15. $7p^2$ **16.** $56 - x$ **17.** $a^2 + 7b - 3c$

Example 3
(page 687)

Evaluate each polynomial for $a = 2$ and $b = -4$.

18. $2ab$ **19.** $-4ab$ **20.** $7a + b$

21. $a - 3b$ **22.** $5a + 7b$ **23.** $ab^2 + 5$

24. $a^2 + 2b - 3$ **25.** $2a^2 - b + 4$ **26.** $10a + b^2 - 7$

Example 4 **27. Sports** The polynomial $-16t^2 + 32t + 4$ gives the height, in feet,
(page 687) that a tossed ball reaches in t seconds. If the ball reaches a
maximum height after one second, what is that height?

B Apply Your Skills

Is the expression a monomial? Explain.

28. pq^{-3} **29.** 0 **30.** $\frac{3}{p}$ **31.** $10bc + b$

State whether the polynomial is a *monomial*, a *binomial*, a *trinomial* or *none* of these.

32. $4.5 + 3.7m$ **33.** $2x - 4^{-1}$ **34.** -42 **35.** $x^2 + 7x + 4$

36. $3a^2 - 6a^{-3}$ **37.** $15 + w$ **38.** abc **39.** $b^2 + \frac{2}{b} - 3$

40. Open-Ended Write a polynomial with four terms.

41. Geometry You can write the formula for the area of a trapezoid
as $A = \frac{1}{2}b_1h + \frac{1}{2}b_2h$. What kind of polynomial is $\frac{1}{2}b_1h + \frac{1}{2}b_2h$?

42. a. Writing in Math Name other words with the prefixes *mono*, *bi*,
tri, and *poly*. How do the prefixes help you understand the
meanings of the words?
b. What would you call a polynomial with four terms?

 **GO Online
Homework Video Tutor**
Visit: PHSchool.com
Web Code: ade-1304

Evaluate each polynomial for $x = -5$ and $y = 3$.

43. $2x + 2y$ **44.** $7 + x^2y$ **45.** $7y^2 + 6x - 20$

46. $xy - y$ **47.** $x^2 + 2x - 3$ **48.** $\frac{x^2}{5} + x$

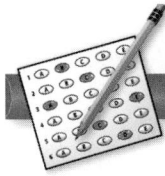

C Challenge

Reasoning Tell why each expression is not a polynomial.

49. $x^2 + 2x + \frac{1}{x}$ **50.** $2ab + b^2 + \sqrt{a}$ **51.** $(y^2 + 4) \div y$

52. a. Public Schools The polynomial $34x^2 - 945x + 46{,}971$ models U.S. public school enrollment, in thousands, from 1970 to 1998. The value of x for 1970 is 1 and the value of x for 1998 is 29. How many students were enrolled in public schools in 1970? In 1998?

   b. Use the polynomial to predict enrollment in 2010.

53. Geometry A polygon is convex if no diagonal has points outside the polygon. The polynomial $\frac{n^2}{2} - \frac{3n}{2}$ gives the number of diagonals that you can draw in a convex polygon with n sides. How many diagonals does a 20-sided convex polygon have?

Test Prep

Multiple Choice

54. Which of the following statements is NOT true?
   A. A monomial is a polynomial.
   B. A binomial is a sum or difference of two monomials.
   C. A polynomial must have more than one term.
   D. An integer is a monomial.

55. The area of a trapezoid is $\frac{1}{2}b_1h + \frac{1}{2}b_2h$, where h is the height and b_1 and b_2 are the lengths of the bases. What is the area of a trapezoid with height 13 in., one base 4 in., and the other base twice as long?
   F. 39 in.^{2} **G.** 52 in.^{2} **H.** 78 in.^{2} **J.** 130 in.^{2}

Short Response

56. Is $\frac{4}{x}$ a monomial? Explain.

57. a. Write an example of a monomial, a binomial, and a trinomial.
   b. Explain why each is that type of polynomial.

Mixed Review

GO for Help

Lesson 12-3

For each function make a table with integer values of x from 1 to 4. Then graph each function.

58. $y = 2 \cdot 2^x$ **59.** $f(x) = \frac{1}{3} \cdot 3^x$ **60.** $y = 18(0.2)^x$

61. Navigation A plane is flying 6.3 mi above the ground. The angle of depression to an airport is 14°. How far is the plane from the airport (in ground distance)?

Simplify each expression.

62. $m + 5 + 3m$ **63.** $2y - 1 + 6x + 5$ **64.** $4a + 10b - 7a - 2$

Just as you can get information about a polynomial by counting the number of terms, you can get other information by looking at the exponents. The *degree of a term* is the sum of the exponents of the variables in the term. The *degree of a polynomial* is the greatest degree of its terms.

polynomial $\longrightarrow x^3 + 4x^2 + xy - 5x + 9 \longleftarrow$ The degree of a nonzero constant is zero.

degree of $\longrightarrow$ 3   2   2   1   0
each term

Degree of the polynomial is 3.

1 EXAMPLE

Identify each polynomial by name and by degree.

a. $2 - a$

   0   1 $\longleftarrow$ degree of each term

   Greatest degree of the two terms is 1.

   The polynomial is a binomial of degree 1.

b. $3y^3x$

   4 $\longleftarrow$ Add the exponents: $3 + 1 = 4$.

   Degree of the one term is 4.

   The polynomial is a monomial of degree 4.

c. $5x^2 + x + 4$

   2   1   0 $\longleftarrow$ degree of each term

   Greatest degree of the three terms is 2.

   The polynomial is a trinomial of degree 2.

When you write a polynomial with the terms in order of decreasing degree, the polynomial is in *standard form*. If you need to move terms to do this, you can first write subtractions as additions and then use the Commutative Property of Addition. For example, first write $4 - x^2$ as $4 + (-x^2)$. Then rewrite the polynomial as $-x^2 + 4$.

2 EXAMPLE

Write each polynomial in standard form.

a. $x^4 + 2 - x^2$

$\quad\uparrow\quad\uparrow\quad\uparrow$

$\quad 4\quad 0\quad 2$ ← degree of each term

standard form: $x^4 - x^2 + 2$

b. $-2y + y^3 + y^2 - 3$

$\quad\uparrow\quad\uparrow\quad\uparrow\quad\uparrow$

$\quad 1\quad 3\quad 2\quad 0$ ← degree of each term

standard form: $y^3 + y^2 - 2y - 3$

When you simplify a polynomial, write your result in standard form.

3 EXAMPLE

Simplify each polynomial.

a. $5a + a^2 + 3a^2 + 2$

$\quad 5a + (1 + 3)a^2 + 2$ **Combine like terms.**

$\quad 5a + 4a^2 + 2$ **Simplify.**

$\quad 4a^2 + 5a + 2$ **Write in standard form.**

b. $3x - 8x + 2x^2 + 4x^2$

$\quad (3 - 8)x + (2 + 4)x^2$

$\quad -5x + 6x^2$

$\quad 6x^2 - 5x$

EXERCISES

Identify each polynomial by name and by degree.

1. $9c + 5$

2. $12a^2b$

3. $6x^2 - 3x + 2$

4. p^2q^3

5. $d^4 + 6d$

6. $4a^3 + 8a^2 - 11$

7. $24x^3yz$

8. $15x - 2x^2$

Write each polynomial in standard form.

9. $8 + 5a$

10. $3y^2 + 16 + y$

11. $2c + 4c^2 - 7$

12. $5x - 4x^2 + 3$

13. $2b^2 - 2 + b^3 - b$

14. $11 + 6y^2 - y$

15. $4x^4 + 4x^5 + x^2 + 2x^3$

16. $p^6 - 4 + p + p^2 - 7p^3$

17. $9a - 5 + 6a^3 - 5a^2$

Simplify each polynomial.

18. $x + 3x^2 + x^2$

19. $3a + 5a^2 + 2a + 6$

20. $4m^2 + m^2 + 10 + 4m$

21. $6p - 5p^2 + 4p + 3p^2$

22. $c + 9c^2 - 7c - 8$

23. $-2x^2 + 5 + 3x^2 + 2x + 3$

24. $3b + 1 + 7b^2 - 3b - 2b^2$

25. $5m^3 + 8m^2 + 11m + 14$

26. $3a^4 - 5a^6 - 9a + 6$

27. $-11 - y^2 - 8y + 2y$

28. $6p + 8p^2 + 5p + 7p^2$

29. $22x + 18x^2 + 6 + 4x$

Extension Degree of a Polynomial **691**

Adding and Subtracting Polynomials

What You'll Learn

• To add polynomials
• To subtract polynomials

. . . And Why

To solve problems involving area and volume

✓ Check Skills You'll Need

Simplify each expression.

1. $5x - 7 - 3x$

2. $a + 3b + 4a - 7b$

3. $8m - 4n - 7m - 8n$

4. $2x + 3y - 7 - 8x + 2$

 **for Help**
Lesson 2-3

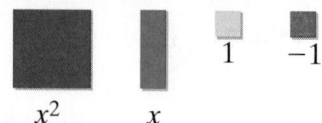 **Adding Polynomials**

In Chapter 2, you saw models for variables and numbers. You can also model the square, x^2, of a variable x.

x^2 x 1   −1

You can use models or properties to add polynomials.

1 EXAMPLE   **Adding Polynomials**

Simplify $(2x^2 + 3x - 1) + (x^2 + x - 3)$.

Method 1 Add using tiles.

$2x^2 + 3x \;\; - 1$

$x^2 + x \;\; - 3$

The sum is $3x^2$ + $4x$ − 4

Method 2 Add by combining like terms.

$(2x^2 + 3x - 1) + (x^2 + x - 3)$

$= (2x^2 + x^2) + (3x + x) - 1 - 3$ **Use the Commutative and Associative Properties of Addition to group like terms.**

$= (2 + 1)x^2 + (3 + 1)x - 1 - 3$ **Use the Distributive Property to combine like terms.**

$= 3x^2 + 4x - 4$ **Simplify.**

✓ Quick Check

1. Simplify.

   a. $(7d^2 + 7d) + (2d^2 + 3d)$
   b. $(x^2 + 2x + 5) + (3x^2 + x + 12)$

Vocabulary Tip

Like <u>terms</u> are terms with the same variable(s), raised to the same power(s). You combine like terms by adding coefficients.

$3b + 12b = (3 + 12)b$
$\qquad\qquad = 15b$

You can also add polynomials in a column by aligning like terms and then adding their coefficients.

GO **O**nline

Video Tutor Help
Visit: PHSchool.com
Web Code: ada-0775

2 EXAMPLE **Aligning Like Terms**

Find the sum of $z^2 + 5z + 4$ and $2z^2 - 5$.

Align like terms.

$$
\begin{array}{r}
z^2 + 5z + 4 \\
+\quad 2z^2 \qquad - 5 \\
\hline
3z^2 + 5z - 1
\end{array}
$$

Add the terms in each column.

✓ Quick Check

2. Simplify each sum.

   a. $\begin{array}{r} 4x + 9y \\ +\quad 3x - 5y \\ \hline \end{array}$

   b. $\begin{array}{r} a^2 + 6a - 4 \\ +\quad 8a^2 - 8a \\ \hline \end{array}$

   c. $(4g^2 - 2g + 2) + (2g^2 - 3)$
   d. $(-2t^2 + t + 5) + (2t + 4)$

---

2 **Subtracting Polynomials**

You subtract polynomials by adding the opposite of each term in the second polynomial.

3 EXAMPLE **Subtracting Polynominals**

Simplify $(5x^2 + 10x) - (3x - 12)$.

$(5x^2 + 10x) - (3x - 12)$

$= 5x^2 + 10x - 3x + 12$ Write the opposite of each term in the second polynomial.

$= 5x^2 + (10x - 3x) + 12$ Group like terms.

$= 5x^2 + (10 - 3)x + 12$ Use the Distributive Property.

$= 5x^2 + 7x + 12$ Simplify.

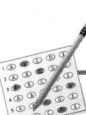

Test-Taking Tip

After you have written the sum or difference of two polynomials, make a mental check of your work, term by term.

✓ Quick Check

3. Simplify each difference.

   a. $(7a^2 - 2a) - (5a^2 + 3a)$
   b. $(10z^2 + 6z + 5) - (z^2 - 8z + 7)$
   c. $(3w^2 + 8 + v) - (5w^2 - 3 - 7v)$

EXERCISES

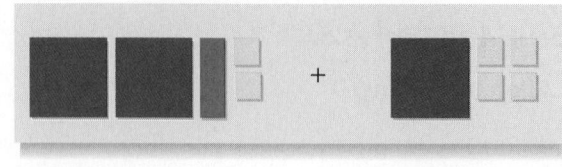

For more exercises, see *Extra Skill and Word Problem Practice.*

Practice and Problem Solving

A Practice by Example

Example 1
(page 692)

Write the sum modeled in each exercise. Then simplify the sum.

1.

2.

Add by combining like terms.

3. $(x^2 + 3x + 1) + (x^2 + x + 6)$ **4.** $(x^2 + 5x + 2) + (3x^2 + x + 1)$

5. $(3x + 2) + (-4x + 3)$ **6.** $(5x^2 + 3x + 7) + (7x - 2)$

Example 2
(page 693)

Simplify each sum.

7. $\begin{array}{r} 5a + 7b \\ + -3a + 2b \\ \hline \end{array}$

8. $\begin{array}{r} x^2 + 4x - 2 \\ + 8x^2 - 3x + 7 \\ \hline \end{array}$

9. $\begin{array}{r} x^4 + 3x^3 - x^2 + x - 2 \\ + 7x^3 + x^2 - 5x - 9 \\ \hline \end{array}$

10. $\begin{array}{r} xy + 5x - 2y + 4 \\ + 2xy - 3x - 3y - 8 \\ \hline \end{array}$

11. $\begin{array}{r} x^3 + 5x^2 + 3x - 2 \\ + x^3 - 2x + 6 \\ \hline \end{array}$

12. $\begin{array}{r} 4x^2 - 5xy + 7 \\ + 8x^2 + 3xy - 3y - 4 \\ \hline \end{array}$

Example 3
(page 693)

Simplify each difference.

13. $(5x + 9) - (2x + 1)$ **14.** $(-11a^2 + 2a - 1) - (7a^2 + 4a)$

15. $(3x - 2y) - (5x + 4y)$ **16.** $(2x^2 + 3x - 7) - (x^2 - 6x - 9)$

17. $(ab - 4) - (3ab - 6)$ **18.** $(-4x^2 + x - 1) - (x^2 - x + 8)$

B Apply Your Skills

Simplify each sum or difference.

19. $(x^2 - 3x - 9) - (5x - 4)$ **20.** $(13a^2 - 3a) + (2a^2 + 5a)$

21. $(2x^2 + 3x) + (x^2 + 2x)$ **22.** $(8j - 3k + 6m) - (-2j + 3m)$

23. $(w^2 + 5w) + (2w - 6)$ **24.** $(3x^2 + x + 7) - (2x^2 + x + 2)$

25. $(6y - 8) - (2y + 7)$ **26.** $(x^2 + 3x + 5) + (x^2 + x + 2)$

27. a. Write an expression for the sum of three consecutive integers.
Let x be the first integer. Then simplify the expression.
b. What three consecutive integers have the sum 108?

Geometry Write the perimeter of each figure as a polynomial. Simplify.

28.

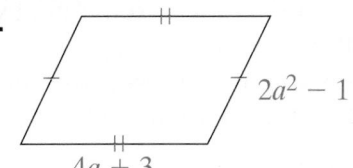

$4a + 3$

$2a^2 - 1$

29.

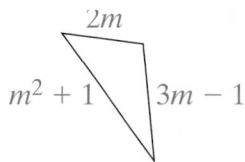

$2m$

$m^2 + 1$ $3m - 1$

30.

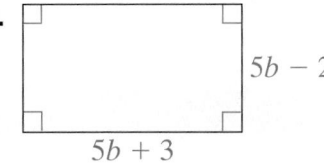

$5b - 2$

$5b + 3$

31.

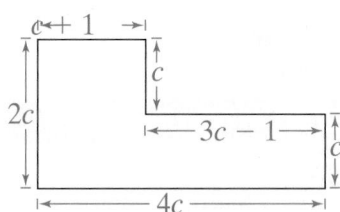

$c + 1$

c

$2c$

$3c - 1$

c

$4c$

$$5x^2 + 4x - 3$$
$$-\ \ 2x^2 - x$$
$$\overline{\ \ 3x^2 + 3x - 3}$$

32. Error Analysis Tian simplified $(5x^2 + 4x - 3) - (2x^2 - x)$ as shown at the left. What is his error?

33. The perimeter of a triangle is $11y - 2$. Two of the sides are represented by the expressions $3y - 1$ and $3y + 1$. Write an expression for the third side.

Geometry Find each missing length.

34. perimeter $= 11x + 6$

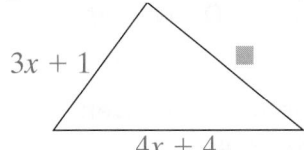

$3x + 1$

$4x + 4$

35. perimeter $= 12b - 2$

$2b$

36. perimeter $= 5m^2 + 3m$

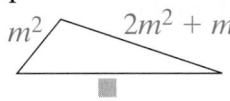

m^2 $2m^2 + m$

37. perimeter $= 6a + 3$

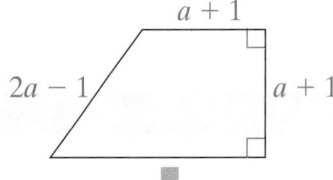

$a + 1$

$2a - 1$ $a + 1$

38. Writing in Math How is the process for adding two polynomials like the process for adding two integers? How is it different?

C Challenge

39. Reasoning Justify each step.
$$(x^2 + 2x + 1) - (2x^2 - 3x - 4)$$
$$(x^2 + 2x + 1) + (-2x^2) + 3x + 4$$
$$(x^2 + -2x^2) + (2x + 3x) + (1 + 4)$$
$$(1 + -2)x^2 + (2 + 3)x + (1 + 4)$$
$$-x^2 + 5x + 5$$

40. Do Exercise 27 by letting x be the second integer.

41. a. Geometry The volume of a cube is $(3x^3 + 9)$ in.^{3}. A smaller
   cube with volume $(x^3 - 3)$ in.^{3} is cut out of the cube. Write a
   polynomial for the remaining volume.
   b. Evaluate your polynomial for $x = 2$.
   c. Reasoning When $x = 2$, will the large cube fit into a 5 in.-by-4 in.-
   by-6 in. box? Explain. (*Hint:* Recall cube roots, p. 591.)

42. a. What polynomial is the opposite of $2x^2 + 3x - 5$?
   b. What is the sum of $2x^2 + 3x - 5$ and its opposite?

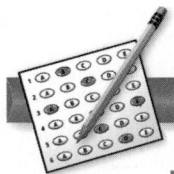

Test Prep

Multiple Choice
For Exercises 43 and 44 assume x is an integer.
43. What is the sum of x and the next two integers?
   A. $x + 2x + 3x$ **B.** $x + x + 1 + x + 2$
   C. $x^3 + x^2 + x$ **D.** $x + y + 1 + z + 2$

44. What is the sum of x and the previous two integers?
   F. $x + x - 1 + x - 2$ **G.** $x - x - 1 - x - 2$
   H. $x + x + 1 + x + 2$ **J.** $x + 2x + 3x$

45. What is the perimeter of the
   given figure?
   A. $4a + 4b$ **B.** $4a + 3b$
   C. $7a + 4b$ **D.** $6a + 4b$

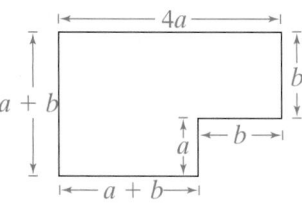

Short Response
46. The perimeter of the given
   figure is $8x^2 + 4$.
   a. What is the missing length?
   b. If $x = 3$ cm, what is the
   perimeter of the figure?

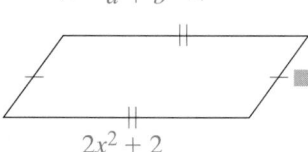

Mixed Review

Lesson 12-4
Evaluate each polynomial for $a = 2$, $b = -1$, and $c = \frac{1}{2}$.
   47. $8ab + 1$ **48.** $5 + 4ab - c$ **49.** $a^2 + ab + b^2$

Find the area of each figure.
   50. 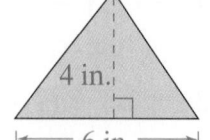   **51.** 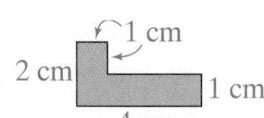   **52.**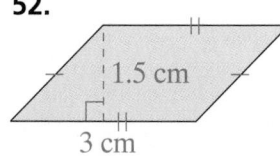

53. Charity A student participated in a walk for charity. His friends
   pledged a total of $3.20 for each mile he walked. The student
   earned $22.40 for the charity. How many miles did he walk?

Multiplying a Polynomial by a Monomial

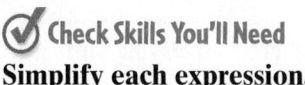

1 Using an Area Model

You can model the product of a monomial and a polynomial using algebra tiles. You can find the area of a rectangle that is $2x$ units long and $(x + 4)$ units wide by counting the tiles.

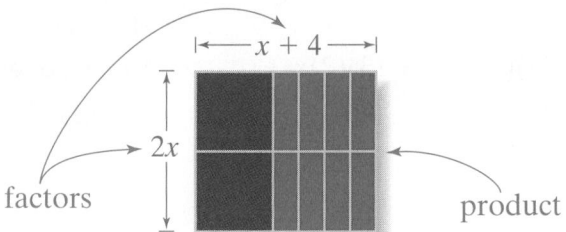

factors — product

The area is $2x^2 + 8x$. So $2x(x + 4) = 2x^2 + 8x$.

You can also use the Distributive Property to simplify a product of a monomial and a polynomial. Multiply each term of the polynomial by the monomial.

1 EXAMPLE   Real-World Problem Solving

Multiple Choice **What is the area of the garden? All measurements are in feet.**

Ⓐ $(3x - 5)$ ft^2
Ⓑ $(2x^2 - 10x)$ ft^2
Ⓒ $(2x^2 - 5)$ ft^2
Ⓓ $(x^3 - 10x)$ ft^2

$x - 5$

$2x$

$$A = \ell w = 2x(x - 5) \qquad \textbf{Substitute.}$$
$$= 2x(x) - 2x(5) \qquad \textbf{Use the Distributive Property.}$$
$$= 2x^2 - 10x \qquad \textbf{Simplify.}$$

The area of the garden is $(2x^2 - 10x)$ ft^2. The answer is B.

✓ Quick Check

1. Simplify each product.
   a. $3x(x + 4)$ **b.** $-x(2x - 3)$

What You'll Learn

• To use an area model for multiplication

• To write a polynomial as the product of a monomial and a polynomial

. . . And Why

To use area formulas with polynomials

✓ **Check Skills You'll Need**

Simplify each expression.

1. $7(v + 3)$

2. $3(u - 8)$

3. $-5(6 - 3t)$

4. $(p + 8)9$

GO for Help

Lesson 2-3

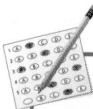 **Test-Taking Tip**

When you multiply a polynomial by a monomial with a negative sign, remember to distribute the negative sign to each term of the polynomial.

Video Tutor Help
Visit: PHSchool.com
Web Code: ada-0775

Problem Solving Hint
To multiply powers with the same base, add exponents.

You can often use other properties to simplify the product of a monomial and a polynomial.

2 EXAMPLE **Simplifying a Product**

Simplify $3x^2(8x^2 - 5x + 2)$.

$3x^2(8x^2 - 5x + 2)$

$= 3x^2(8x^2) + 3x^2(-5x) + 3x^2(2)$ Use the Distributive Property.

$= (3)(8)x^{2+2} + (3)(-5)x^{2+1} + (3)(2)x^2$ Use the Commutative Property of Multiplication.

$= (3)(8)x^4 + (3)(-5)x^3 + (3)(2)x^2$ Add exponents.

$= 24x^4 - 15x^3 + 6x^2$ Simplify.

✓ Quick Check

2. Simplify each product.

   a. $x(x^2 + 2x + 4)$ **b.** $2a^2(2a^3 - 3a^2 + 3)$

---

2   Writing a Polynomial as a Product

You can sometimes use the Distributive Property to write a polynomial as the product of two factors. First, find the GCF of all the terms of the polynomial and then use it as one of the factors.

3 EXAMPLE **Finding Factors of a Polynomial**

Write $6x^3 + 3x^2 + 9x$ as a product of two factors.

$\left.\begin{array}{l} 6x^3 = 2 \cdot 3 \cdot x \cdot x \cdot x \\ 3x^2 = 3 \cdot x \cdot x \\ 9x = 3 \cdot 3 \cdot x \end{array}\right\}$ Write the prime factorization of each term.

$\text{GCF} = 3x$ Find the GCF.

Write each term as the product of $3x$ and another factor.

$6x^3 = 3x \cdot 2x^2$ $3x^2 = 3x \cdot x$ $9x = 3x \cdot 3$

$6x^3 + 3x^2 + 9x = 3x(2x^2 + x + 3)$ Use the Distributive Property.

✓ Quick Check

3. Use the GCF of the terms to write each polynomial as the product of two factors.

   a. $2x^2 + x$ **b.** $2b^3 + 6b^2 - 12b$

EXERCISES

Practice and Problem Solving

A Practice by Example

Example 1
(page 697)

GO for Help

Simplify each product. Use an area model as needed.

1. $3x(x + 1)$ **2.** $x(x + 5)$ **3.** $2x(x + 3)$

4. $3y(y + 7)$ **5.** $2x(3x + 1)$ **6.** $2x(x + 6)$

7. $3x(3x - 1)$ **8.** $3x(2x + 4)$ **9.** $7c(4 + c)$

🌐 **10. City Property** Find the area of the city lot shown. All measurements are in feet.

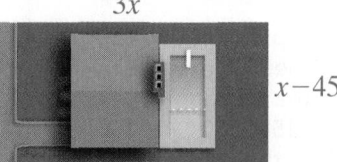

🌐 **11. Sports** The length of an Olympic-size pool is 50 meters. If x represents the width of one lane, what is the area of a pool with five lanes?

Example 2
(page 698)

Simplify each product.

12. $5x(-3x^2 + 2x)$ **13.** $x(5x^2 + x - 4)$ **14.** $3a(a^2 + 2a + 1)$

15. $3b(2b^2 - b + 4)$ **16.** $a^3(a + a^2 + 5)$ **17.** $-3(2c^2 - 3c - 1)$

18. $5c(c + 5 - c^2)$ **19.** $4x^2(x^3 + x^2 - x)$ **20.** $7b^2(2b^2 + b - 3)$

Example 3
(page 698)

Use the GCF of the terms to write each polynomial as the product of two factors.

21. $3d^4 + d^2$ **22.** $4y^3 - 8y^2 - 12y$ **23.** $10x^5 - 5x^3 + 10x$

24. $7x^2 - 14x$ **25.** $14a^2 + 7a - 7$ **26.** $24y^3 + 6y^2 - 20y$

27. $7p^2 + p$ **28.** $5z^2 - 20z$ **29.** $15x^3 + 4x^2 - 7x$

B Apply Your Skills

Simplify each product.

30. $3y(4y - 1)$ **31.** $a(a^2 + 3)$ **32.** $-14a(a^2 + 3a - 4)$

33. $\frac{1}{2}b(b - 8)$ **34.** $-8y(2y + 3)$ **35.** $6y^2\left(y^2 - 2y - \frac{1}{3}\right)$

36. $12x^2(5x + 2)$ **37.** $x(2x - 5)$ **38.** $17y(2y^2 - 8y + 9)$

39. Open-Ended Write a monomial and a polynomial with 4 terms. Multiply them and then simplify the product.

40. Open-Ended Write a polynomial whose terms have a GCF ≠ 1. Then write the polynomial as the product of two factors.

41. Multiple Choice Write the polynomial $2m^3n - 6m^2n^2 + 8mn$ as the product of two factors.

  Ⓐ $-2mn(m + 3mn - 4)$ Ⓑ $-2(m^3n + 3m^2n^2 - 4mn)$

  Ⓒ $2mn(m - 3mn + 4)$ Ⓓ $2mn(m^2 - 3mn + 4)$

GO Online
Homework Video Tutor
Visit: PHSchool.com
Web Code: ade-1306

Write each polynomial as the product of two factors.

42. $-9b^2 - 3b$ **43.** $4x^5 - 4x^4 + 8x^2$ **44.** $18g^7 - 6g^4 + 3g^2$

45. $2a^3 - 6a^2 - 4a$ **46.** $6y^6 + 32y^4 - y^3$ **47.** $4m^9 + 6m^5 - 2m^2$

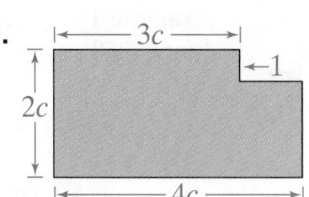

C Challenge

Simplify each product.

48. $4z(2z^6 - 3z^5 - 12z^2 + 8)$ **49.** $-3xy(2x^2y + xy + y^2 - 3)$

Geometry In Exercises 50–55, write an expression to represent the area of each figure. Then simplify the expression.

50.

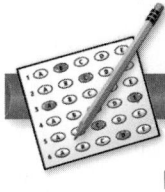

51.

52. The width of a rectangle is 7 more than $\frac{1}{2}$ its length.

53. The length of a rectangle is 5 less than 4 times its width.

54. The base length of a triangle is $8x$. The triangle's height is twice the base length plus 5.

55. The height of an isosceles triangle is 3 less than $\frac{1}{3}$ its base.

Writing in Math

Explain how to use the GCF to write the polynomial
$15a^3 + 20a^2 + 45a$
as the product of two factors.

Test Prep

Multiple Choice

56. The length of a rectangular table is 35 inches greater than twice the width. If x is the width, what is the area of the table?
  A. $2x^2 + 35x$ **B.** $x + 35$ **C.** $2x + 35$ **D.** $2x^2 + 35$

57. Which polynomial is the simplified form of $-3y(-6y^2 - 5y + 1)$?
  F. $18y^3 - 15y^2 - 3y$ **G.** $18y^2 + 15y - 3$
  H. $18y^3 + 15y^2 - 3y$ **J.** $18y^2 - 15y - 3$

Extended Response

58. The length of a rectangle is 2 inches more than the width w.
(a) What expression in terms of w could you use for the length of the rectangle?   **(b)** Explain.   **(c)** Draw a diagram of the rectangle and label it.   **(d)** Find the area.

Mixed Review

Lesson 12-5

GO for Help

Find each sum or difference.

59. $(2x + 8) + (3x^2 + 5x - 2)$

60. $(-7x^2 - 8x + 4) - (2x^2 - 3x - 9)$

Display each set of data in a line plot.

61. 1.7, 2.1, 1.9, 2.1, 2.2, 2.4,   **62.** 13, 17, 15, 14, 12, 14,
2.3, 2.1, 1.9   11, 13, 15

63. Banking A college student received a bank statement. The new balance was $200. It showed deposits of $400, interest of $1, and checks totaling $650. What was the beginning balance?

Multiplying Binomials

1 Using Models

You can use tiles to model the product of two binomials.

1 EXAMPLE Using a Model

Simplify $(x + 2)(x + 4)$.

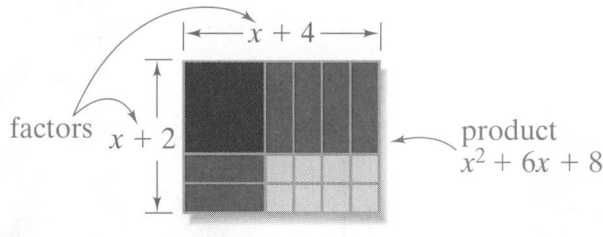

$(x + 2)(x + 4) = x^2 + 6x + 8$

The area is $x^2 + 6x + 8$.

Quick Check

1. Simplify each product using models.

    a. $(x + 2)(x + 3)$ **b.** $(y + 1)(y + 4)$

Check Skills You'll Need

Simplify each expression.

1. $-2(2x + 1)$

2. $3(7 + 4y)$

3. $(2a - b)5$

4. $(3m - 2n)4$

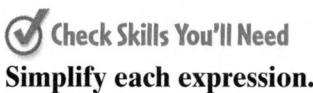
GO for Help
Lesson 2-2

2 Multiplying Binomials

To simplify the product of two binomials, you can think of one binomial as a single expression and use the Distributive Property. Then you use the Distributive Property a second time.

2 EXAMPLE Multiplying Two Binomials

Simplify $(x + 4)(x - 3)$.

$(x + 4)(x - 3)$

    $= x(x - 3) + 4(x - 3)$ **Use the Distributive Property.**

    $= x^2 - 3x + 4x - 12$ **Use the Distributive Property again!**

    $= x^2 + x - 12$ **Simplify.**

Check $(x + 4)(x - 3) = (x + 4)x - (x + 4)3$

                     $= x^2 + 4x - 3x - 12$

                     $= x^2 + x - 12$

2. Simplify each product.

   a. $(x + 2)(x - 5)$ **b.** $(m + 2)(2m + 3)$

More Than One Way

Write a polynomial to express the area of the square at the right.

$(2x + 1)$ in.

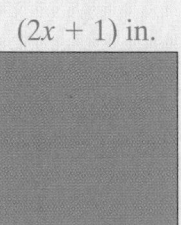

Eric's Method

Use a model.

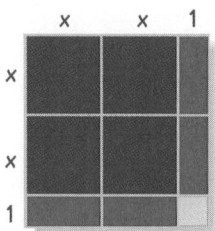

The area of the square is $(4x^2 + 4x + 1)$ in.^{2}.

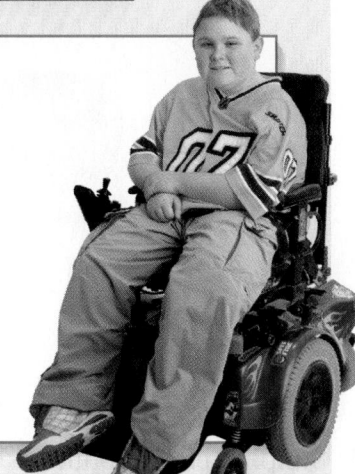

Jasmine's Method

Use the formula for the area of a square and the Distributive Property.

$$\text{Area} = \text{side}^2$$
$$A = (2x + 1)^2$$
$$= (2x + 1)(2x + 1)$$
$$= 2x(2x + 1) + 1(2x + 1)$$
$$= 2x(2x) + 2x(1) + 1(2x) + 1(1)$$
$$= 4x^2 + 2x + 2x + 1$$
$$= 4x^2 + 4x + 1$$

The area of the square is $(4x^2 + 4x + 1)$ in.^{2}.

Choose a Method

1. Which method do you prefer to use? Explain.
2. Which method would you use to simplify $(3x + 4)(3x + 4)$?

EXERCISES

For more exercises, see *Extra Skill and Word Problem Practice*.

Practice and Problem Solving

 **Practice by Example**

Example 1
(page 701)

 **for Help**

Simplify each product using models. Sketch and label your models.

1. $(x + 2)(x + 1)$ **2.** $(y + 2)(y + 2)$ **3.** $(w + 3)(w + 1)$

4. $(k + 3)(k + 4)$ **5.** $(x + 4)(x + 5)$ **6.** $(m + 9)(m + 3)$

7. $(s + 3)(s + 6)$ **8.** $(t + 2)(t + 5)$ **9.** $(m + 1)(m + 6)$

Example 2
(page 701)

Simplify each product using the Distributive Property.

10. $(x + 2)(x - 1)$ **11.** $(c + 7)(c + 9)$ **12.** $(x - 5)(x + 3)$

13. $(a - 4)(a - 2)$ **14.** $(x + 5)(x + 5)$ **15.** $(b + 6)(b - 6)$

16. $(c + 3)(c - 4)$ **17.** $(x + 3)(x - 2)$ **18.** $(y + 3)(y + 8)$

B **Apply Your Skills**

19. Multiple Choice What is the area of the rectangle at the right?

Ⓐ $7n - 4$ Ⓑ $12n - 5$
Ⓒ $12n^2 - 11n - 5$ Ⓓ $12n^2 - 5$

$4n - 5$

$3n + 1$

Find the area of each rectangle.

20.

$2c + 4$

$5c + 3$

21.

$3x + 3$

$3x - 3$

GO Online
Homework Video Tutor
Visit: PHSchool.com
Web Code: ade-1307

Simplify each product.

22. $(x + 4)(2x + 1)$ **23.** $(n - 16)(n + 20)$ **24.** $(x + 2)(x + 8)$

25. $(b + 1)^2$ **26.** $(m - 8)(m - 3)$ **27.** $(2a + b)(4c - 2d)$

28. $(3c + 1)(2c - 4)$ **29.** $(3 + x)(5 - x)$ **30.** $\left(\frac{1}{2}x + 9\right)(4x + 8)$

31. Error Analysis A student simplifies $(x + 5)(x - 3)$ as shown at the right. Find the error in the student's work.

$(x + 5)(x - 3)$
$x(x - 3) + 5(x - 3)$
$x^2 - 3x + 5x - 3$
$x^2 + 2x - 3$

32. Writing in Math Explain the similarities between multiplying two binomials and multiplying a polynomial by a monomial.

C **Challenge**

Patterns **Simplify the expressions. What pattern do you see?**

33. $(y + 2)^2, (y + 3)^2, (y + 4)^2$

34. $(y + 1)(y - 1), (y + 2)(y - 2), (y + 5)(y - 5)$

35. Geometry The base of a parallelogram is $(w + 5)$ cm. The height is 2 cm less than the base. Find the area of the parallelogram.

36. Suppose x is an odd integer. What is the product of x and the next two odd integers?

12-7 Multiplying Binomials **703**

Multiple Choice

37. Suppose m is an even integer. What is the product of the next two consecutive even integers?

  A. $m^2 + 3m + 2$ **B.** $m^2 + 6m + 8$
  C. $m^2 + 2m$ **D.** $2m + 6$

38. If the length of a rectangular picture is $(2x + 3)$ inches and the width is $(x - 4)$ inches, which expression represents the area of the picture?

  F. $(2x^2 + 5x - 12)$ in.^{2} **G.** $(2x^2 + 3x - 12)$ in.^{2}
  H. $(2x^2 - 8x - 12)$ in.^{2} **J.** $(2x^2 - 5x - 12)$ in.^{2}

Short Response

39. a. Simplify $(3c - 1)(4c + 2)$ using the Distributive Property.
   b. Justify each step in part (a).

 **Mixed Review**

Lesson 12-6

GO **for Help**

Find each product.

40. $7a(a + 5b + 2c)$ **41.** $-3xy(2x + 9y - 6)$

42. $8m^2(-4m^3 + mp + 2p^4)$ **43.** $2pq(5p + 8pq + 2)$

44. Does the problem below require *permutations* or *combinations?* Explain.
   You select three colors from a choice of eight colors to paint a picture. How many 3-color choices are possible?

Make a box-and-whisker plot for the data.

45. $8, 9, 27, 39, 14, 17, 13, 25, 15, 8, 11, 29, 36, 10, 15, 25$

 **Checkpoint Quiz 2**   **Lessons 12-4 through 12-7**

Tell whether each polynomial is a *monomial*, a *binomial*, or a *trinomial*.

  1. 178 **2.** $x + 15y$ **3.** $7pq$ **4.** $m^2 + 4m - 12$

Evaluate each polynomial for $x = -1$ and $y = 3$.

  5. $5x - y$ **6.** $x + 3y$ **7.** $-7x + x^2y$ **8.** $4y^2 + 11x - 16$

Simplify each expression.

  9. $(4a - b) + (3a - 5b)$ **10.** $(x^2 + 7x - 4) + (x^2 + 9)$

  11. $(g + 6)(g + 4)$ **12.** $3m(-6m - 2m^2p - 10p)$

13. Open-Ended Write a binomial expression for the length of a side of a square. Use it to write a polynomial for the area of the square.

You can sometimes write a trinomial as the product of two binomial factors. You can use algebra tiles to find the factors. Use tiles to form a rectangle. The lengths of the sides of the rectangle are the factors of the trinomial.

EXAMPLE

Write $x^2 + 4x + 3$ as the product of two binomial factors.

$x^2 \quad + \quad 4x \quad + \quad 3$

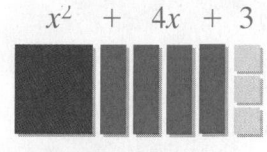

Model the trinomial.

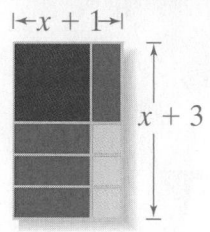

$\leftarrow x + 1 \rightarrow$

$x + 3$

Use the tiles to form a rectangle. The length is $(x + 3)$ and the width is $(x + 1)$.

• $x^2 + 4x + 3 = (x + 3)(x + 1)$

EXERCISES

Use tiles to find binomial factors of each trinomial.

1. $x^2 + 2x + 1$ **2.** $x^2 + 5x + 6$ **3.** $x^2 + 7x + 10$

4. $x^2 + 6x + 5$ **5.** $x^2 + 4x + 4$ **6.** $x^2 + 5x + 4$

7. $x^2 + 9x + 8$ **8.** $2x^2 + 5x + 3$ **9.** $2x^2 + 7x + 3$

10. $2x^2 + 9x + 4$ **11.** $2x^2 + 9x + 9$ **12.** $2x^2 + 9x + 10$

13. Reasoning Complete $x^2 + \blacksquare x + 12$ with three different integers so that each trinomial has two binomial factors. For each trinomial, write the binomial factors.

14. a. What two numbers have a sum of 11 and a product of 30?
   b. Reasoning Use your answer to part (a) to find the binomial factors of $x^2 + 11x + 30$.

15. $(x + 3)^2 = x^2 + 6x + 9$ is a *perfect-square trinomial*. What properties of a trinomial would reveal it as a perfect-square trinomial? Show how a perfect-square trinomial can be factored.

Use Multiple Strategies

What You'll Learn

- To solve problems by combining strategies

. . . And Why

To solve problems about building a kite

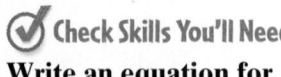 **Check Skills You'll Need**

Write an equation for each statement.

1. Seven times the opposite of twelve is negative 84.

2. Eleven times a number is 132.

3. A number divided by 45 is three.

4. A number squared is 64.

 **for Help**
Lesson 2-4

---

1 **Combining Strategies**

Math Strategies in Action
After a natural disaster such as an earthquake, a tornado, or a flood, relief workers help to rescue survivors. They also bring food, clothing, and blankets to people who need them. Relief organizers use multiple strategies as they plan and coordinate their efforts.

In many situations in your own life, you have already combined multiple strategies. Remember when you learned how to ride a bike or fly a kite. The more you practiced, the less you had to think about the steps required to be successful.

In mathematics, you can combine strategies to solve problems. The more strategies you learn and the more you use them, the better problem solver you will be. Solving problems can become as easy as riding a bike or flying a kite!

EXAMPLE **Real-World** **Problem Solving**

Hobbies Suppose you receive instructions for building a kite. The writer of the instructions presents them as a puzzle:

> I fly above the clouds with my tail flowing behind me. My tail is 12 ft plus twice my length. Together, our length is 21 ft. How long am I? How long is my tail?

Understand the Problem

Read the problem carefully.

1. What do you want to find?

2. What is the relationship between the length of the kite's tail and the length of the kite's body?

To get a visual picture of the problem, draw a diagram. Then write an equation to solve the problem.

Carry Out the Plan

Draw a diagram.

Let b = length of the body of the kite.

Write an equation.

$3b + 12 = 21$	Use the diagram to write an equation.
$3b + 12 - 12 = 21 - 12$	Subtract 12 from each side.
$3b = 9$	Simplify.
$\dfrac{3b}{3} = \dfrac{9}{3}$	Divide each side by 3.
$b = 3$	

The kite is 3 ft long. Now find the length of the tail.

length of tail $= 2b + 12$	Use the diagram to write an expression for the length of the tail.
$= 2(3) + 12$	Replace b with the length of the kite's body.
$= 18$	Simplify.

The tail is 18 ft long.

Check the Answer

It is always good procedure to check your result in the context of the original problem.

✓ Quick Check

3. The original problem says that the tail must be 12 ft plus twice the length of the kite's body. Show that the lengths found meet this condition.

4. The length of the kite's body plus the length of its tail must be 21 ft. Show that the lengths found meet this condition.

EXERCISES

For more exercises, see *Extra Skill and Word Problem Practice*.

Practice and Problem Solving

A Practice by Example

Combine multiple strategies to solve each problem.

Example
(page 706)

GO for Help

1. **Travel** A bus traveling 40 mi/h left Freetown at noon. A car following the bus at 60 mi/h left Freetown at 1:30 P.M.
   a. At what time did the car catch up with the bus?
   b. How many miles were the car and the bus from Freetown when the car caught up with the bus?

2. **Chess** A student playing a computer chess game gets 5 points every time he wins a round. The computer gets 3 points every time it wins a round. They play 64 rounds and end with a tied score. How many rounds did the computer win?

3. **Algebra** A kite and its tail total 36 ft in length. The tail is five times the length of the body. How long is the kite's tail?

B Apply Your Skills

Solve using any strategy.

4. A student has $8 to spend on a phone call. The cost of a call is $.34 for the first minute and $.24 for each additional minute. How long can the student talk on the phone?

5. **Painting** A painter places an 8.5-ft-long ladder against a wall. The bottom of the ladder is 4 ft from the base of the wall. How high up the wall does the ladder reach?

6. **Geometry** A room has a floor area of 1,025 ft^2 and a 10-ft-high ceiling. The Housing Code requires at least 200 ft^3 per person. What is the maximum number of people allowed in the room?

7. **Pets** A student weighs her hamsters two at a time. Sandy and White Ears weigh 209 g together. White Ears and Sport weigh 223 g together. Sandy and Sport weigh 216 g together. How much does each hamster weigh?

8. **Geometry** There are 27 white cubes assembled to form a large cube. The outside surface of the large cube is painted red. The large cube is then separated into the 27 smaller cubes. How many of the small cubes will have red paint on exactly the following number of faces?
   a. three faces   b. two faces   c. one face   d. no face

9. You decide to purchase a new telephone. You can choose from 8 different models, 2 different cord lengths, and 4 different colors. How many possible choices do you have?

10. **Geometry** A lot measures 50 ft by 100 ft. The house on the lot measures 25 ft by 50 ft. What is the area of the lawn?

11. **Algebra** A student spends $\frac{1}{3}$ of her money on a movie and $\frac{1}{4}$ of the remaining amount on a snack after the movie. She now has $12 left. How much money did she have originally?

Strategies

- Act It Out
- Draw a Diagram
- Guess, Check, Revise
- Look for a Pattern
- Make a Model
- Make a Table
- Simulate the Problem
- Solve by Graphing
- Use Multiple Strategies
- Work a Simpler Problem
- Work Backward
- Write an Equation
- Write a Proportion

 **12. Salaries** A clerk starts working at a beginning salary of $10,400 with an annual increase of $400. An assistant clerk who starts at the same time has a starting salary of $9,600 per year with an annual increase of $600.

a. Who earns more after 3 years?

b. After how many years will the assistant be earning more money than the clerk?

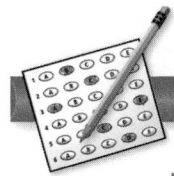 **Challenge**

13. Geometry You have three pieces of string, each 60 cm long. You form a circle with one piece, a square with another, and an equilateral triangle with the third piece. How do the areas of the three figures compare? Explain.

14. Each face of a cube can be painted either red or yellow. How many different ways can you paint the cube?

Test Prep

Multiple Choice

15. What is the product of $(x - 3)(x + 3)$?

A. $x^2 + 6x - 9$ **B.** $x^2 - 6x + 9$

C. $x^2 - 9$ **D.** $x^2 + 9$

16. A house lot measures 75 ft by 100 ft. It is all lawn except for the house on the lot. The house measures 30 ft by 50 ft. What is the area of the lawn?

F. 1,500 ft^2 **G.** 6,000 ft^2 **H.** 7,500 ft^2 **J.** 8,000 ft^2

Short Response

17. A square has a perimeter of 24 inches and a rectangle has an area of 36 sq. inches. **(a)** Which figure has the greater area? **(b)** Explain.

18. Aaron receives his allowance of $25. He spends $\frac{1}{5}$ of it on food, $\frac{1}{4}$ of it on magazines, and $\frac{11}{20}$ of it on movies. **(a)** How much of his allowance does Aaron have left? **(b)** Show your work.

Mixed Review

GO for Help

Lesson 12-7

Simplify each product.

19. $(x + 1)(x - 3)$ **20.** $(d + 2)(2d + 5)$ **21.** $(x + 3)^2$

Make a list to find the number of two-letter combinations you can form from each group of letters.

22. G, O, A, T   **23.** A, P, E   **24.** H, Y, E, N, A

25. Jogging A boy jogs in the park every other day. His sister jogs every third day. They both jogged together on April 2. On how many more of the 30 days in April will they jog together if they maintain this schedule?

Using Mental Math

You can solve many problems quickly using mental math and proven "shortcut" methods. One well-known shortcut is the FOIL method for multiplying binomials. With it, you multiply each term of the first binomial with each term of the second binomial, just as you did when you used the Distributive Property in Lesson 12-7.

EXAMPLE

Simplify the product $(2x + 3)(x + 6)$.

Think First terms, Outer terms,
Inner terms, Last terms.
Notice that the first letters spell FOIL.

First Last

$(2x+3)(x+6)$

Inner

Outer

Identify the *First* terms in each binomial. Multiply them.	$2x$ and x $2x \cdot x =$	$2x^2$
Identify the *Outer* terms. Multiply them. Identify the *Inner* terms. Multiply them.	$2x$ and 6 $2x \cdot 6 = 12x$ 3 and x $3 \cdot x = 3x$	
Add the outer and inner products.	$12x + 3x =$	$15x$
Identify the *Last* terms in each binomial. Multiply them.	3 and 6 $3 \cdot 6 =$	18

● Your FOIL result will look like this: $(2x + 3)(x + 6) = 2x^2 + 15x + 18$

EXERCISES

Use FOIL and mental math to simplify the following.

1. $(x + 2)(x + 3)$ **2.** $(x + 6)(x + 6)$ **3.** $(x + 3)(x + 4)$

4. $(x + 2)^2$ **5.** $(x - 8)(x - 2)$ **6.** $(x - 6)(x - 3)$

7. $(x - 5)(x - 5)$ **8.** $(x - 4)^2$ **9.** $(x - 9)(x + 9)$

10. $(x + 4)(x - 7)$ **11.** $(x - 5)(x + 8)$ **12.** $(x + 6)(x - 6)$

13. $(2x + 2)(x + 6)$ **14.** $(7x + 7)(x + 3)$ **15.** $(6x - 5)(4x - 10)$

16. $(3x + 1)^2$ **17.** $(5x - 2)(4x + 3)$ **18.** $(8x + 5)(3x - 1)$

19. $(6x + 5)(4x - 10)$ **20.** $(3x - 2)(4x + 3)$ **21.** $(4x + 6)(4x - 6)$

22. $(3 - 3x)(5 + 4x)$ **23.** $(7 + 2x)(1 - x)$ **24.** $\left(\frac{1}{2}x + 5\right)(4x + 10)$

Chapter 12

Chapter Review

Vocabulary Review

absolute value function (p. 677)   common ratio (p. 671)   quadratic function (p. 676)
arithmetic sequence (p. 670)   geometric sequence (p. 671)   sequence (p. 670)
binomial (p. 686)   monomial (p. 686)   term (p. 670)
common difference (p. 670)   polynomial (p. 686)   trinomial (p. 686)

Match the vocabulary terms on the right with their descriptions on the left.

1. A monomial or a sum or difference of monomials

2. The graph of this is a parabola.

3. A sequence in which you find the terms by adding a fixed number to previous terms

4. An equation of the type $y = |x|$

5. A polynomial with two terms

6. A polynomial with three terms

7. Each number in a sequence

8. A set of numbers that follow a pattern

9. A real number, a variable, or a product of a real number and variables with whole-number exponents

a. arithmetic sequence
b. binomial
c. monomial
d. polynomial
e. quadratic function
f. absolute value function
g. term
h. trinomial
i. sequence

Go Online
PHSchool.com
For: Vocabulary quiz
Web Code: adj-1351

Skills and Concepts

12-1 Objectives

▼ To describe number patterns with arithmetic sequences (p. 670)

▼ To describe number patterns with geometric sequences (p. 671)

A **sequence** is a set of numbers that follow a pattern. Each number in the sequence is a **term** of the sequence. You find a term of an **arithmetic sequence** by adding a fixed number, called the **common difference,** to the previous term.

You find a term of a **geometric sequence** by multiplying the previous term by a fixed number. This fixed number is the **common ratio.**

Find the next three terms of each sequence. Then write a rule to describe the sequence.

10. $1, 5, 9, 13, \ldots$

11. $-60, -30, -15, -7.5, \ldots$

12. $100, 107, 114, 121, \ldots$

13. $0, -5, -10, -15, \ldots$

14. $26, 15, 4, -7, \ldots$

15. $\frac{1}{10}, \frac{1}{2}, 2\frac{1}{2}, 12\frac{1}{2}, \ldots$

**Tell whether each sequence is *arithmetic, geometric,* or *neither.*
Find the next three terms of the sequence.**

16. $9, 13, 17, 21, \ldots$ **17.** $-8, -4, -2, -1, \ldots$

18. $3, 4, 5, 6, \ldots$ **19.** $-22, -11, 0, 11, \ldots$

20. $10, 1, 20, 2, \ldots$ **21.** $\frac{1}{200}, \frac{1}{100}, \frac{1}{50}, \frac{1}{25}, \ldots$

22. Open-Ended Describe a situation that you can represent with an arithmetic sequence. Write a sequence of numbers for that situation and identify the common difference.

12-2 and 12-3 Objectives

▼ To graph quadratic functions (p. 676)

▼ To graph absolute value functions (p. 677)

▼ To use tables, rules, and graphs with functions modeling growth (p. 681)

▼ To use tables, rules, and graphs with functions modeling decay (p. 682)

Two types of nonlinear functions are **quadratic functions** and **absolute value functions.** The graph of a quadratic function is a U-shaped curve called a *parabola* that opens upward or downward. The graph of an absolute value function is V-shaped.

A function like $y = 2^x$ models *exponential growth.* Its graph curves upward as input values increase. A function like $y = \left(\frac{1}{2}\right)^x$ models *exponential decay.* Its graph slopes downward as input values increase.

For each function, make a table with integer values of x from -2 to 2. Then graph the function.

23. $y = \frac{1}{2}x^2$ **24.** $y = 2|x|$ **25.** $y = |x| + 1$ **26.** $y = x^2 + 5$

27. $y = -|x|$ **28.** $y = \frac{1}{2}|x|$ **29.** $y = -x^2 - 3$ **30.** $y = -x^2 + 4$

For each function, make a table with integer values of x from 0 to 4. Then graph the function.

31. $y = \left(\frac{1}{4}\right)^x$ **32.** $y = \frac{1}{2} \cdot 2^x$ **33.** $y = 3^x$ **34.** $y = \left(\frac{1}{2}\right)^x$

12-4 Objectives

▼ To identify polynomials (p. 686)

▼ To evaluate polynomials (p. 687)

A **monomial** is a real number, a variable, or a product of a real number and variables with whole-number exponents. A **polynomial** is a monomial or a sum or difference of monomials. You can name a polynomial by the number of its terms. A **binomial** has two terms and a **trinomial** has three terms.

Tell whether each polynomial is a *monomial,* a *binomial,* or a *trinomial.*

35. $3x$ **36.** $2x^2 - 1$ **37.** $\frac{2}{3}x$ **38.** $x^4 - x^3 + 2$ **39.** 15

40. mn **41.** $z^2 + z$ **42.** $7d + f$ **43.** $-2x^2 - 12$ **44.** $3 + 2x - x^2$

Evaluate each polynomial for $x = -3$ and $y = 2$.

45. y^5 **46.** $x^2 - y$ **47.** $y^2 - x - 1$ **48.** $2xy$ **49.** $3 - xy$

You can add polynomials by using models, combining like terms, or aligning like terms vertically and then adding their coefficients. You can subtract polynomials by adding the opposite of each term in the second polynomial.

Simplify each sum or difference.

50. $(a^2 + a + 1) + (2a^2 + a + 7)$

51. $(m^2 - 5m - 2) + (3m^2 + 3m - 10)$

52. $(3x^2 - 4) + (x^2 - 2x + 6)$

53. $(7p - 5q + 2) - (3p + 2q + 4)$

54. $(10w^2 + 6w) - (7w^2 - 3w + 5)$

55. $(9x - 3y) - (3x - 9y)$

You can use properties to simplify the product of a monomial and a polynomial. You can sometimes use the Distributive Property to write a polynomial as the product of two factors.

You can use tiles to model the product of two binomials. When you use the Distributive Property to find the product of two binomials, you use the Distributive Property twice.

Simplify each product.

56. $a(2a + 5)$ **57.** $4c(3c - 7)$ **58.** $-6y(5y + 3)$

59. $3x(x^2 - x - 5)$ **60.** $x^2(x + 7)$ **61.** $2x^2(x^2 - 3x - 6)$

62. $(x + 3)(x + 4)$ **63.** $(x + 1)(x - 5)$ **64.** $(x - 2)(x - 4)$

Use the GCF of the terms to write each expression as the product of two factors.

65. $x^2 - x$ **66.** $9p^2 + 27$ **67.** $3x^3 - 9x^2 + 6x$

68. $5b^5 + 20b^3 - 30$ **69.** $8x^3 + 2x^2 + 4x$ **70.** $28a^2 - 4ab$

You can combine multiple strategies to solve problems.

71. A gardener plans to use 196 feet of fencing to enclose a garden. What is the largest possible area of the garden?

72. Explain your choice of strategies for Exercise 71.

Chapter Test

Find the next three terms of each sequence. Then write a rule to describe the sequence.

1. $5, 8, 11, 14, \ldots$ **2.** $-1.5, -3, -6, \ldots$

3. $50, 10, 2, 0.4, \ldots$ **4.** $100, 93, 86, 79, \ldots$

Tell whether each sequence is *arithmetic*, *geometric*, or *neither*. Find the next three terms of the sequence.

5. $5, 2, -1, -4, \ldots$ **6.** $1, 1, 2, 3, 5, \ldots$

7. $15, 13, 11, 9, \ldots$ **8.** $-48, -12, -3, \ldots$

9. $2, 4, 8, 16, \ldots$ **10.** $0, 7, 14, 21, \ldots$

For each function, make a table with integer values of x from -2 to 2. Then graph the function.

11. $y = x^2$ **12.** $y = x^2 - 1$

13. $y = -x^2 + 1$ **14.** $y = -x^2 - 2$

15. $y = |x| - 1$ **16.** $y = \frac{1}{2}|x|$

For each function, make a table with integer values of x from 0 to 4. Then graph the function.

17. $y = 2^x$ **18.** $y = 3^x$

19. $y = 2\left(\frac{1}{2}\right)^x$ **20.** $y = \left(\frac{1}{3}\right)^x$

Tell whether each polynomial is a *monomial*, a *binomial*, or a *trinomial*.

21. $4x - 1$ **22.** $c^2 + c + 1$

23. xyz **24.** $a^5 - 7$

25. $h^4 - h^3 - h$ **26.** ab

Evaluate each polynomial for $x = 4$ and $y = 10$.

27. $x + y$ **28.** $y - x^2$

29. $xy - 15$ **30.** $x^2 + xy - y^2$

31. Open-Ended Write a polynomial with two different variables. Assign a value to each variable. Evaluate your polynomial for those values.

Simplify each sum or difference.

32. $(x^2 + 4x + 3) + (x^2 - 3x + 7)$

33. $(2x^2 - 3) + (x + 4)$

34. $(3x^2 + 2x + 4) + (x^2 + 3)$

35. $(x^2 + 10x + 9) - (x^2 + x + 1)$

36. $(3x^2 - x + 3) - (2x^2 - 2x - 4)$

37. $(2x^2 - 4x) - (x^2 - 3x - 5)$

Simplify each product.

38. $x(x - 4)$

39. $2x(x^2 - x + 2)$

40. $x^2(3x^2 + 2x - 5)$

41. $(x + 2)(x + 4)$ **42.** $(x + 1)(x + 5)$

43. $(x + 3)(x - 1)$ **44.** $(x + 2)(x - 4)$

45. $(x - 1)(x - 6)$ **46.** $(x - 2)(x - 3)$

Write each expression as the product of a monomial and a polynomial.

47. $2x^3 + 4x^2 + 12x$

48. $x^2 - x$

49. $9x^3 - 18x^2 - 3x$

50. Writing in Math Explain how you can use the Distributive Property to write the expression $3x^2 + 6x$ as the product of a monomial and a polynomial.

51. A customer gives a clerk a $100 bill for a $76 purchase. In how many ways can the clerk give change using $20, $10, $5, and $1 bills?

Carbon Dating

Applying Algebra Have you ever wondered how a scientist can estimate the age of a fossil? When an organism is alive, it maintains carbon-14 in the same proportion as the atmosphere. When the organism dies, it stops replenishing its carbon-14. A scientist finds the amount of carbon-14 currently present in the fossil and calculates how long the amount that was present at death has been decaying.

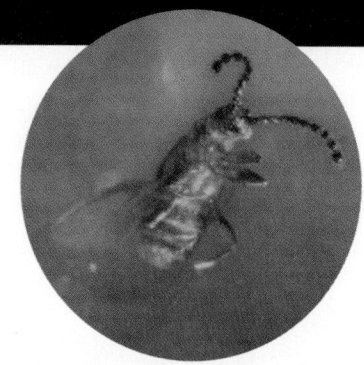

Amber Insects
Sometimes bees, flies, and other insects get stuck in the sap from a tree. Over time, the sap hardens and turns into amber.

How Old Is That?
Carbon-14 has a half-life of 5,730 years. Scientists use it to determine the age of bone, cloth, wood, and plant fibers.

Mammoth Model
The "woolly mammoth" was about 11 ft tall and weighed 4 to 6 tons, the same as an African elephant today, but had very small ears, a sloping back, and much longer tusks.

Shoulder hump

Mammoth hair was up to 3 ft long.

Activity

1. Copy and complete the table.

2. **Estimation** About how old is a fossil that has 40% carbon-14 present?

3. **Estimation** What percent of carbon-14 would you hope to find in a fossil that you think is 20,000 years old?

4. **Reasoning** Why do you think carbon-14 dating works only on fossils less than 60,000 years old?

Carbon-14 Dating

Percent of Carbon-14 Present	Age of Fossil (years)
100	0
50	5,730
■	11,460
12.5	■
■	22,920
3.125	■
■	34,380
0.78125	■

Remains of the Mammoth

Scientists have found several frozen mammoths, complete with hide and hair, in the frozen ground of Siberia and Alaska.

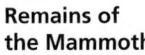

Go Online
PHSchool.com

For: Information about fossils
Web Code: ade-1353

Chapter Projects

Cure for the Common Code

A special sculpture stands outside the headquarters of the United States Central Intelligence Agency (CIA) in Langley, Virginia. Carved in the copper sculpture is a message in secret code. The code is so complex that for many years even CIA agents could not figure it out. The sculptor, James Sandborn, provided the secret agents with a challenge they could appreciate.

Chapter 1 *Algebraic Expressions and Integers*

Invent a Secret Code For the chapter project, you will decode computer writing and write in a code used by Julius Caesar. Then you'll invent a code of your own.

Go Online
PHSchool.com

For: Information about secret codes
Web Code: add-0161

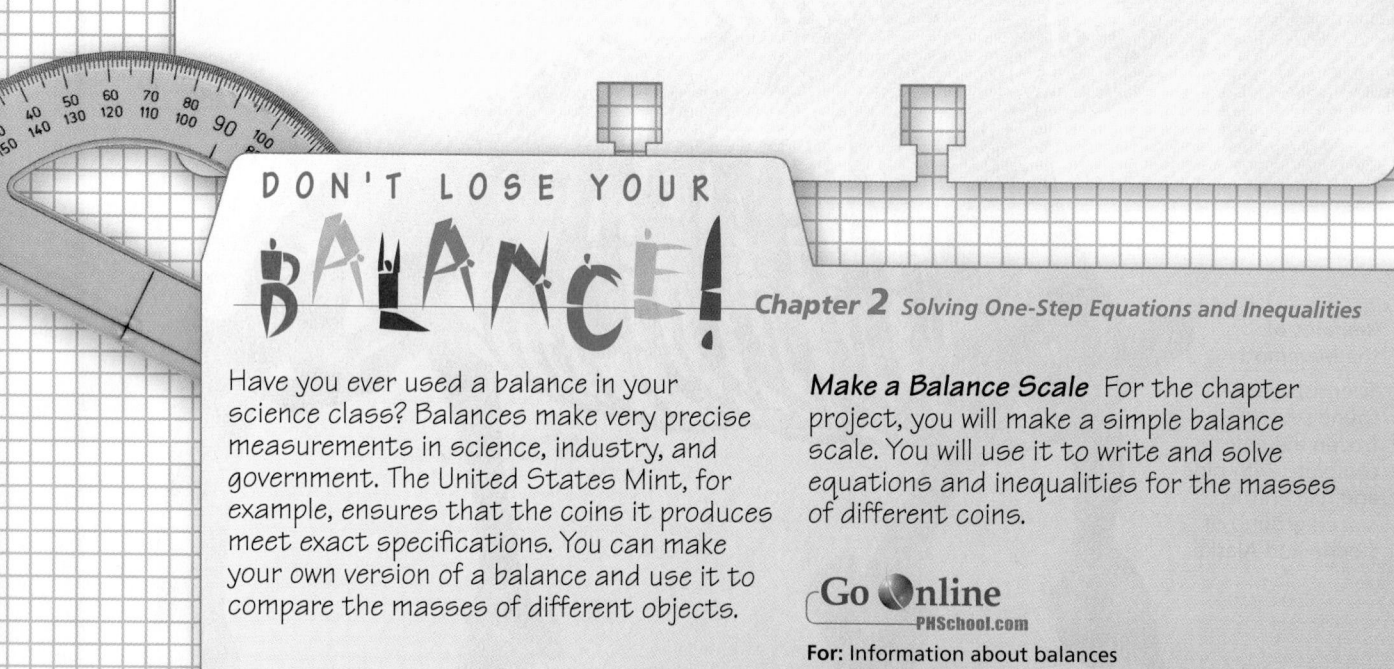

DON'T LOSE YOUR BALANCE!

Have you ever used a balance in your science class? Balances make very precise measurements in science, industry, and government. The United States Mint, for example, ensures that the coins it produces meet exact specifications. You can make your own version of a balance and use it to compare the masses of different objects.

Chapter 2 *Solving One-Step Equations and Inequalities*

Make a Balance Scale For the chapter project, you will make a simple balance scale. You will use it to write and solve equations and inequalities for the masses of different coins.

Go Online
PHSchool.com

For: Information about balances
Web Code: add-0161

CURRENCY EVENTS

Chapter 3 *Decimals and Equations*

When you are shopping, of course you want to know how much an item costs before you decide to buy it! When you travel in another country, you need to "translate" the cost into its value in U.S. dollars.

Compare Currencies For the chapter project, you will research currency exchange rates and calculate prices in different currencies. You will make a poster that shows prices in U.S. dollars and in the currencies of three other countries.

PHSchool.com

For: Information about currencies
Web Code: add-0161

PRISM BUILDING

Chapter 12 *Nonlinear Functions and Polynomials*

The prismatic shapes of tall buildings can be described using mathematical expressions such as $(a + b)^3$. Is $(a + b)^3$ equal to $a^3 + b^3$? No, but many students make that mistake. Sometimes it helps to have a concrete representation of a mathematical expression.

Make a 3-D Polynomial Model For the chapter project, you will make a three-dimensional model of a polynomial. You will analyze the model and its parts. You will use the model to see how polynomials can represent real-world objects.

PHSchool.com

For: Information about polynomials
Web Code: add-0161

Chapter 1 Extra Practice: Skills and Word Problems

Lesson 1-1 Write a variable expression for each word phrase.

1. 6 less than x

2. y less than 12

3. the sum of z and 2

4. a number m increased by 34

5. the product of 8 and p

6. t divided by 5 $\frac{t}{5}$

Lesson 1-2 Simplify each expression.

7. $15 + 20 \cdot 3$

8. $46 - 4(2 + 8)$

9. $16 \div 4 + 10 \div 2$

10. $100 \div (30 + 20)$

11. $5(8 + 4) \div 6 \div 2$

12. $9 \cdot 6 - 12 \div 2$

Lesson 1-3 Evaluate each expression.

13. $3x + 6$, for $x = 12$

14. $15a - 2a$, for $a = 20$

15. $38 - 3y$, for $y = 9$

16. $25 - (t + 18)$, for $t = 7$

17. $\frac{x + y}{10}$, for $x = 35$ and $y = 65$

Lesson 1-4 Compare. Use $>$, $<$, or $=$ to complete each statement.

18. $-12 \ \blacksquare \ -9$

19. $|-4| \ \blacksquare \ |4|$

20. $-|-7| \ \blacksquare \ |-7|$

21. $0 \ \blacksquare \ -100$

Lessons 1-5 and 1-6 Simplify each expression.

22. $-56 + 60$

23. $18 + (-25)$

24. $-34 + (-36)$

25. $19 - (-5)$

26. $80 - (-125)$

27. $-82 - (-50)$

28. $-7 + 35 + (-22)$

29. $-44 - 20 - 80$

30. $-8 + (-13) - (24)$

Lesson 1-7 Write a rule for continuing each pattern. Find the next three numbers in the pattern.

31. $-12, -3, 6, 15, 24, \ldots$

32. $0.15, 0.3, 0.45, 0.6, \ldots$

33. $1, 1, 2, 3, 5, 8, 13, \ldots$

Lesson 1-9 Simplify each expression.

34. $-4 \cdot 12$

35. $-15(-8)$

36. $30 \cdot (-5)$

37. $-1(-2)(-3)(-4)$

38. $-78 \div (-3)$

39. $-150 \div 25$

40. $\frac{120}{-15}$

41. $-1{,}125 \div (-125)$

Lesson 1-10 Draw a coordinate plane. Graph each point.

42. $A(0, 9)$

43. $B(-3, -5)$

44. $C(-9, 5)$

45. $D(7, 2)$

46. $E(0, 0)$

47. $F(8, 0)$

48. $G(7, -8)$

49. $H(1, 1)$

50. $K(-2, -2)$

● **Lesson 1-1** **Write an expression for each statement.**

51. Shari has *g* gel pens, and Jennifer has 8 fewer gel pens.

52. A stock starts Friday at a price *p*, and ends the day $2.50 higher.

● **Lesson 1-2** **Write and simplify a numerical expression for the phrase.**

53. the quotient of twenty-eight and seven, minus two

● **Lesson 1-3** **Write an expression for each statement. Then evaluate it for the given value.**

54. A video store pays $30 for each movie *m* that it purchases. How much does it pay for 15 movies?

55. A pizza store charges $3 for delivery and $10 per pizza *p*. How much does it cost to have three pizzas delivered?

● **Lesson 1-4** **Write an expression to represent each quantity.**

56. a payment of *d* dollars on a credit card with a balance of $165

57. The temperature on top of a mountain is 4°C lower than the temperature *t* at the base of the mountain.

● **Lessons 1-5 and 1-6** **Write a numerical expression for each statement. Then find the sum or difference.**

58. Your savings account had a balance of $175 before you deposited $250.

59. A hot-air balloon descends 450 ft from a height of 1,000 ft.

● **Lesson 1-7** **Is each conjecture correct or incorrect? If incorrect, give a counterexample.**

60. The difference of two numbers is always less than their sum.

61. The sum of two numbers is always greater than zero.

● **Lesson 1-8** **Look for a pattern to help you solve the problem.**

62. You owe a friend $42. You repay the friend $2 the first day, $4 the second day, $6 the third day, and so on. How many days will you take to pay your friend back?

● **Lesson 1-9** **Simplify each expression.**

63. thirty-six divided by three   **64.** four times six, divided by twelve

● **Lesson 1-10** **Write the coordinates of each point.**

65. three units left of the *y*-axis and six units below the *x*-axis

66. five units right of the *y*-axis and two units above the *x*-axis

Chapter 2 Extra Practice: Skills and Word Problems

● **Lesson 2-1** Simplify each expression. Justify each step.

1. $99 + (-46) + (-99) + 45$
2. $225 + 320 + 75$
3. $18 + 12 + (-25) + 13$
4. $5 \cdot 678 \cdot 2$
5. $58 \cdot 2 \cdot 50$
6. $20 \cdot 4 \cdot 5 \cdot 25$

● **Lessons 2-2 and 2-3** Use the Distributive Property to simplify.

7. $7(5) - 3(5)$
8. $3 \cdot 6 + 7 \cdot 6$
9. $15 \cdot 32 - 12 \cdot 32$
10. $7b + 25 - 4b$
11. $3(a - 2c)$
12. $3q + 2(q + 1)$
13. $-3(4y - 1) + 5(7 - y)$
14. $41 - 2(m + 1) - m$
15. $12 + 5x - 2(3x + 5)$

● **Lesson 2-4** Write an equation for each sentence. Is each equation *true*, *false*, or an *open sentence*?

16. Twice the sum of a number and one is twenty-two.

17. Negative three divided by negative one is three. $\frac{-3}{-1}$

18. Forty-five plus five equals negative fifty.

● **Lessons 2-5 and 2-6** Solve each equation.

19. $40 + x = 25$
20. $-5 = y - 12$
21. $z + (-23) = -47$
22. $14 = a - 9$
23. $t - 453 = -520$
24. $78 = b + 100$
25. $4k = 96$
26. $300 = -15j$
27. $-12c = 180$
28. $\frac{d}{7} = -14$
29. $-4 = \frac{w}{6}$
30. $\frac{k}{-9} = -20$

● **Lesson 2-8** Graph the solutions of each inequality.

31. $x > -12$
32. $y \leq 3$
33. $0 \geq z$
34. $p < -9$
35. $7 < n$
36. $f \leq -3$

● **Lessons 2-9 and 2-10** Solve each inequality.

37. $a + 3 < -1$
38. $-2 > b - 4$
39. $5 + x > -8$
40. $-12 < -2 + y$
41. $w - 32 \leq 15$
42. $-20 \geq z - 13$
43. $\frac{c}{5} \leq -3$
44. $8p \geq -96$
45. $0 < 8r$
46. $\frac{t}{-6} < -3$
47. $\frac{a}{11} > -22$
48. $-12k \geq -144$

● **Lesson 2-1 Name each property shown.**

49. Seven plus twelve equals twelve plus seven.

50. Thirty-four times one is thirty-four.

● **Lesson 2-2 Use the Distributive Property to solve each problem.**

51. A sports stadium holds 14,600 people. There are eight home games in a season. Find the total number of people who could attend home games in one season.

52. Janet drives 36 miles Monday through Friday to work and back. How many miles does she drive in one week?

● **Lesson 2-3 Write and simplify a variable expression.**

53. A family ordered four dinners at d dollars each and a $7 side dish from a local restaurant. There is a $3 delivery charge.

● **Lesson 2-4 Write an equation to solve each problem.**

54. Michelle wants to run a total of 15 miles per week. She runs 3 miles each day d that she runs. Will she meet her goal by running 5 days per week?

55. Suppose you want to save $105. You put $15 per week w into a savings account. Will you have $105 in 6 weeks?

● **Lessons 2-5 and 2-6 Write and solve an equation.**

56. Jake bought five books at a yard sale. He now has 44 books. How many books did Jake have before?

57. A painter pays $15 per can of paint. How many cans of paint can she buy with $165?

● **Lesson 2-7 Use *Guess, Check, and Revise* to solve each problem.**

58. Sara bought some tapes for $8 each and some books for $5 each. She paid a total of $39. How many of each did she buy?

59. The sum of the ages of two brothers is 22 and the product of their ages is 120. How old are the brothers?

● **Lesson 2-8 Write and graph an inequality for each sentence.**

60. A number d plus fifteen is no more than 12.

61. Seven times a number p is more than forty-two.

● **Lessons 2-9 and 2-10 Write and solve an inequality.**

62. Four times a number r is no more than sixty-five.

63. You want to save at least $100. How much do you need to save if you start with $37?

Chapter 3

Extra Practice: Skills and Word Problems

● **Lesson 3-1** Estimate. State the method you used.

1. $5.35 + 7.953$

2. $25.68 - 3.7$

3. $6.877 + 3.521 + 8.5$

4. $103.890 - 25.6$

5. $42.875 + 36.982 + 45.7$

6. $42.651 - 12.8$

● **Lesson 3-2** Estimate each product or quotient.

7. $9.5(12.31)$

8. $24.8 \div 5.03$

9. $2.8 \cdot 6.11$

10. $-5.78 \div 1.95$

11. $(-2.468)(-9.031)$

12. $-19.32 \div 4.025$

● **Lesson 3-3** Find the mean, median, and mode. When the answer is not an integer, round to the nearest tenth. Identify any outliers.

13. 10 13 10 15 12 11 12 19 14

14. 85 86 80 85 90 90 50 88

15. \$25 \$30 \$32 \$28 \$30 \$15 \$28 \$30

16. 6.2 4.5 4.8 12.3 5.7 4.8 6.0

● **Lesson 3-4** Evaluate each formula for the values given.

17. perimeter of a rectangle: $P = 2\ell + 2w$ when $\ell = 45$ yd and $w = 20$ yd

18. circumference of a circle: $C = 2\pi r$ when $r = 6.8$ in.; use 3.14 for π

19. distance traveled: $d = rt$ when $r = 50$ mi/h and $t = 3.5$ h

20. perimeter of a square: $P = 4s$ when $s = 12$ cm

● **Lessons 3-5 and 3-6** Solve each equation.

21. $t + 4.5 = 17.2$

22. $15.5 + y = 10.5$

23. $x - 70.2 = 23.6$

24. $1.2b = 6$

25. $c \div 5.3 = 12$

26. $-21.2 = p - 12.7$

27. $f \div 5.25 = 7.8$

28. $6.4m = 38.4$

29. $-3.1 = -31a$

30. $h + 25.8 = 76$

31. $101.5 = j - 82.8$

32. $-50.8 = d + 36.2$

33. $4.5v = 13.5$

34. $s \div 10.5 = 42$

35. $26.2 = z - 6.55$

● **Lesson 3-7** Complete each statement.

36. 0.95 m = ▉ cm

37. 250 mL = ▉ L

38. 2.5 kg = ▉ g

39. 60 g = ▉ kg

40. 0.54 L = ▉ mL

41. 5.62 m = ▉ cm

42. 58 cm = ▉ m

43. 564 mm = ▉ m

44. 345 g = ▉ mg

45. 36 mg = ▉ g

46. 234 cm = ▉ m

47. 567 mg = ▉ g

● **Lessons 3-1 and 3-2** **Estimate each amount.**

48. Four packages of ground beef weigh 1.94 lb, 1.82 lb, 2.21 lb, and 2.03 lb.

49. You buy three items that cost $4.85, $7.45, and $8.99.

50. Your class is on a field trip. Thirty students buy lunches that cost $4.95 each.

51. A car holds 12 gallons of gasoline. Gas costs $2.29/gal. About how much will it cost to fill the car up?

52. A fund drive for a charity raised $2,450. If 120 people donated, about how much did each person donate on average?

● **Lesson 3-3** **Find the mean, median, mode, and range of each group of data. Then identify which measure of central tendency best describes the data set.**

53. The daily balance in a checking account for 5 days is $30, $42, $25, $25, $34.

54. The heights in centimeters of ten people are 168, 160, 164, 166, 180, 178, 165, 166, 160, and 166.

● **Lesson 3-4** **Use the distance formula $d = rt$ (where d is the distance, r is rate, or speed, and t is time spent traveling) to answer each question.**

55. The length of Michelle's commute to work is 35 mi. It takes her 54 min to get to work. What is her average speed?

56. Sam runs 6 mi/h. How many minutes will it take him to run 4 mi?

57. A train travels 70 mi/h. How far does it travel in 45 min?

● **Lesson 3-5 and 3-6** **Write and solve an equation.**

58. Karenna spent $8.75 at a video store. She had $16.65 when she left the video store. How much money, m, did she start with?

59. At the deli, 1.5 lb of turkey cost $5.64. What is the cost per pound, c, of the turkey?

● **Lesson 3-7** **Convert each unit.**

60. A bag of potato chips has 400 mg of sodium per serving. How many grams of sodium does it have?

61. Julius is training to run a 10-km race. How many meters long is the race?

● **Lesson 3-8** **Solve the problem by *Acting It Out*.**

62. A class has 15 students. How many handshakes are there if each person in the class shakes hands once with everyone else?

Chapter 4

Extra Practice: Skills and Word Problems

● **Lesson 4-1 Define variables and write an equation to model each situation.**

1. The total length of the edges of a cube is 12 times the length of an edge.

2. The total cost of lunch is $5.50 times the number of people at the table.

3. The area of a rectangle is 12 cm times the length of the rectangle.

4. The cost of a telephone call is 75 cents plus 25 cents times the number of minutes.

● **Lesson 4-2 Simplify each expression.**

5. $4 + 3 \cdot 8$
6. $2 \cdot 3^2 - 7$
7. $6 \cdot (5 - 2) - 9$
8. $2 - 12 \div 3$

9. $4^2 + 8 \div 2$
10. $\frac{1}{2} \div \frac{4}{3}$
11. $-6 \cdot 4.2 - 5 \div 2$
12. $9 - (3 + 1)^2$

13. $2 + 6 \cdot 8 \div 4$
14. $6 + 8 \div 2 - 3$
15. $10 \div 5 \cdot 2 + 6$
16. $5 + 4 \cdot (8 - 6)^2$

● **Lesson 4-3 Use <, =, or > to compare.**

17. $0.45 \ \blacksquare \ 0.54$
18. $-1.08 \ \blacksquare \ -1.008$
19. $\frac{3}{7} \ \blacksquare \ \frac{11}{25}$
20. $1.4 \ \blacksquare \ \frac{18}{11}$

21. $0.444\ldots \ \blacksquare \ \frac{4}{9}$
22. $\frac{4}{13} \ \blacksquare \ \frac{4}{15}$
23. $0.101101110\ldots \ \blacksquare \ \frac{1}{9}$
24. $\pi \ \blacksquare \ \frac{22}{7}$

● **Lesson 4-4 The relationships in the tables are functions. Write a function rule for each.**

25.

Ears of Corn	Total Cost
1	$0.20
2	$0.40
3	$0.60
4	$0.80

26.

Time (hours)	Cost of Canoe Rental
1	$12
2	$19
3	$26
4	$33

27.

Number of Tickets	Total Cost
1	$9
2	$18
3	$27
4	$36

● **Lesson 4-5**

28. Make a scatter plot of the data. Describe the trend of the data.

Cover Price and Number of Pages of Some Magazines

Cover Price	$2.25	$2.50	$3.75	$3.00	$4.95	$1.95	$2.95	$2.50
Number of Pages	208	68	122	124	234	72	90	90

● **Lesson 4-6 Find the mean, median, and mode for each set of data.**

29. 36, 42, 35, 40, 35, 51, 41, 35
30. 1.2, 0.9, 0.7, 1.1, 0.8, 1.3, 0.6
31. 5, 8, 6, 8, 3, 5, 8, 6, 5, 9

32. A student surveyed the members of the drama club. She included a question about age. Her results are shown at the right.
a. Make a stem-and-leaf plot for the data.
b. What is the median age of the drama club members?

Ages of Drama Club Members
14 18 16 15 17 14 15 18 15
13 14 15 18 14 17 16 14 16

● **Lesson 4-1 Define variables and write an equation for each phrase.**

33. The total cost of gas is the number of gallons times $2.25.

34. The length of the trip is 35 minutes plus extra time spent in traffic.

35. The number of tickets available is 4200 minus the number of tickets sold.

● **Lesson 4-2 Use the formula for the area of a trapezoid $A = h\left(\frac{b_1 + b_2}{2}\right)$, where A is area, b_1 and b_2 are the length of the bases and h is the height, to answer each question.**

36. What is the area of a trapezoidal pool with and a height of 15 yd and bases of 14 yd and 26 yd?

37. How many square feet of grass are there on a trapezoidal field with a height of 75 ft and bases of 125 ft and 81 ft?

● **Lesson 4-3 Is each statement *true* or *false*? If the statement is false, give a counterexample.**

38. The product of a rational number and an integer is not an integer.

39. The quotient of two integers is an integer.

40. The sum of two rational numbers is a rational number.

● **Lesson 4-4 Identify the independent and dependent quantity in each situation.**

41. A museum charges $10 admission for each person.

42. Marta is reimbursed $.20 for each mile that she drives on company business.

43. Each acre of cropland takes a farmer 90 minutes to plow.

44. Tom earns $12 for each lawn he cuts. He can cut up to seven lawns working on Saturday and Sunday. Identify the independent and dependent quantities for this situation. Then find reasonable domain and range values.

● **Lesson 4-5 Would you expect a *positive correlation,* a *negative correlation,* or *no correlation* between the two data sets? Explain why.**

45. the population of a town and the length of its name

46. the temperature during a lacrosse game and the amount of water the players need to drink

47. the number of computers sold and the price of the computer

● **Lesson 4-6 Make a stem-and-leaf plot for each set of data. Then find the mean, median, and mode.**

48. Students' grades on a test:

95, 62, 68, 72, 88, 75, 78, 81, 88, 91, 72, 68, 75, 78, 82, 88, 88, 76, 93

49. Amount of precipitation for the past 12 months in inches:

0.4, 0.6, 1.2, 1.0, 0.9, 1.4, 1.6, 1.1, 0.9, 1.1, 0.2, 0.3, 0.5

Extra Practice: Skills and Word Problems

● **Lessons 5-1 to 5-3** Simplify each expression.

1. $22 + (-33)$

2. $45 + (-54)$

3. $-\frac{4}{3} - \frac{4}{5}$

4. $\frac{4}{13} - \frac{4}{13}$

5. $|12 - 21|$

6. $|12| - |-21|$

7. $-(-(11 - 22))$

8. $\left|\frac{2}{3} + \frac{4}{5}\right|$

9. $(-2)(44)$

10. $(-3)^2$

11. -3^2

12. $\left(\frac{3}{2}\right)\left(-\frac{22}{33}\right)$

13. $\frac{3^2}{2^3}$

14. $\frac{-5^2}{(-5)^2}$

15. $81 \div (-9)$

16. $\frac{4^2}{5^2}$

17. $\frac{2 \cdot 3 + 4}{2(3 + 4)}$

18. $1 + \dfrac{1}{2 + \frac{1}{3}}$

19. $\left(\frac{5}{7}\right)^2$

20. $\frac{2}{3} \div \frac{4}{9}$

21. $\begin{bmatrix} -3 & 0 \\ 11 & -5 \end{bmatrix} + \begin{bmatrix} -4 & 6 \\ -8 & 13 \end{bmatrix}$

22. $\begin{bmatrix} 6 & 12 \\ -9 & 7 \end{bmatrix} - \begin{bmatrix} 8 & -6 \\ 15 & 0 \end{bmatrix}$

23. $\begin{bmatrix} 4.2 & 0.6 \\ 1.7 & 9.5 \end{bmatrix} + \begin{bmatrix} 5.8 & -3.5 \\ 0.2 & 4.9 \end{bmatrix}$

● **Lessons 5-4 and 5-5** Simplify each expression.

24. $-4(a + 3)$

25. $-12\left(\frac{4}{3}x - 1\right)$

26. $5 + 6(m + 1)$

27. $\frac{4}{9}(18 - 9t)$

28. $1 + 3 + 5 + 7$

29. $1 - 3 + 5 - 7$

30. $-3(7w) + 7(3w)$

31. $2(1 - d) - (2d + 1)$

32. $6c + 2(4c - 3)$

33. $5(2 - j) + (2j - 3)$

34. $\frac{1}{3}(12 - 6r)$

35. $6\left(\frac{1}{2} - \frac{2}{3}y\right)$

● **Lesson 5-6** The results of rolling a number cube 54 times are shown below. Use the results to find each probability.

```
6 3 4 5 1 1 5 5 5 3 6 3 2 1 3 3 3 2 1
2 3 6 3 3 4 5 1 2 2 6 3 3 6 5 4 5 3
2 5 1 4 5 2 6 2 5 2 1 2 5 3 2 4 6 3
```

36. $P(3)$

37. $P(4)$

38. $P(\text{not } 5)$

39. $P(7)$

40. $P(\text{even number})$

41. $P(\text{not } 1)$

42. $P(1)$

43. $P(\text{odd number})$

● **Lesson 5-7** You roll a blue number cube and a red number cube. Find each probability.

44. $P(\text{blue 3 and red 2})$

45. $P(\text{blue odd and red 6})$

46. $P(\text{blue 5 and red less than 4})$

47. $P(\text{same number})$

48. $P(\text{both numbers less than three})$

49. $P(\text{both numbers greater than 5})$

You have 3 green marbles, 5 red marbles, and 1 yellow marble in a bag. You pick two marbles from the bag. You pick the second one without replacing the first one. Find each probability.

50. $P(\text{red then green})$

51. $P(\text{yellow then red})$

52. $P(\text{two greens})$

Lessons 5-1 to 5-3 Use addition, subtraction, multiplication, or division to answer each question.

53. A pot of water has a temperature of 25°C. How many degrees should you raise the temperature to boil the water at 100°C?

54. Romana is 68 in. tall and Sophie is 73 in. tall. How much taller is Sophie than Romana?

55. Your goal is to save $50. So far, you have saved $34. How much more do you need to save?

56. A company buys 1500 small items from a manufacturer for $.02 apiece. What is the total cost of the items?

57. If 36 people are at a pizza party, how many eight-piece pizzas need to be ordered so each person can get two pieces of pizza?

58. Your parents drove the family car 462 miles on 14 gallons of gas. On average, how many miles did the car travel on each gallon of gas?

Lesson 5-4 Use the Distributive Property to find each price.

59. Cereal is on sale for $3.95 per box. What is the cost of seven boxes?

60. The school drama club is putting on a play. If there will be five shows and the auditorium holds 480 people, how many people can see the show?

61. What is the total cost of four CDs on sale for $12.15 each?

Lesson 5-5 Identify the property of real numbers shown in each situation.

62. The cost of one item sold for $14.50 is $14.50.

63. You can find the cost of fish by multiplying the price per pound by the amount or by multiplying the amount by the price per pound.

64. To find total time spent doing homework in a week, you add the amount from each day. You find that the total is the same no matter what order you use.

Lesson 5-6 Find the theoretical probability of each event.

65. What is the probability of rolling an even number on a number cube?

66. Tiles with the letters from the word PROBABILITY are placed in a bag. Include the letter *y* as a vowel. What is the probability of selecting a vowel at random?

67. A spinner has four equal sections. Two are red, one is blue, and one is yellow. What is the probability of spinning yellow?

Lesson 5-7 A bag contains 5 green marbles, 15 purple marbles, and 10 yellow marbles.

68. What is the probability of selecting a green marble, replacing it, and then selecting another green marble?

69. What is the probability of selecting a yellow marble, not replacing it, and then selecting a green marble?

● **Lessons 6-1 to 6-2** Solve each equation.

1. $8p - 3 = 13$ **2.** $8j - 5 + j = 67$ **3.** $-n + 8.5 = 14.2$ **4.** $6(t + 5) = -36$

5. $m - 9 = 11$ **6.** $\frac{1}{2}(s + 5) = 7.5$ **7.** $7h + 2h - 3 = 15$ **8.** $\frac{7}{12}x = \frac{3}{14}$

9. $3r - 8 = -32$ **10.** $8g - 10g = 4$ **11.** $-3(5 - t) = 18$ **12.** $3(c - 4) = -9$

Define a variable and write an equation for each situation. Then solve.

13. Your test scores for the semester are 87, 84, and 85. Can you raise your test average to 90 with your next test?

14. You spend $\frac{1}{2}$ of your allowance each week on school lunches. Each lunch costs $1.25. How much is your weekly allowance?

● **Lesson 6-3** Solve each equation. If the equation is an identity, write *identity*. If it has no solution, write *no solution*.

15. $4h + 5 = 9h$ **16.** $2(3x - 6) = 3(2x - 4)$ **17.** $7t = 80 + 9t$

18. $m + 3m = 4$ **19.** $-b + 4b = 8b - b$ **20.** $6p + 1 = 3(2p + 1)$

21. $10z - 5 + 3z = 8 - z$ **22.** $3(g - 1) + 7 = 3g + 4$ **23.** $17 - 20q = (-13 - 5q)4$

● **Lessons 6-4 and 6-5** Solve each proportion.

24. $\frac{3}{4} = \frac{-6}{m}$ **25.** $\frac{t}{7} = \frac{3}{21}$ **26.** $\frac{9}{j} = \frac{3}{16}$ **27.** $\frac{2}{5} = \frac{w}{65}$

28. $\frac{s}{15} = \frac{4}{45}$ **29.** $\frac{9}{4} = \frac{x}{10}$ **30.** $\frac{10}{q} = \frac{8}{62}$ **31.** $\frac{3}{2} = \frac{18}{y}$

32. The scale on a map is 1 in. : 15 mi. The distance between two cities is 25 mi. Find the distance in inches between the cities on the map.

● **Lesson 6-6**

33. Transportation A bus traveling 40 mi/h and a car traveling 50 mi/h cover the same distance. The bus travels 1 h more than the car. How many hours did each travel?

● **Lesson 6-7** Find each percent of change. Describe each as a percent of increase or decrease. Round to the nearest percent.

34. $4.50 to $5.00   **35.** 56 in. to 65 in.   **36.** 18 oz to 12 oz

37. 1 s to 3 s   **38.** 8 lb to 5 lb   **39.** 6 km to 6.5 km

● **Lesson 6-8** Find the square roots of each number.

40. 25   **41.** $\frac{4}{9}$ **42.** 64   **43.** $\frac{25}{36}$ **44.** 0.81   **45.** 900

● **Lesson 6-9** Determine whether the given lengths are sides of a right triangle.

46. 15, 36, 39   **47.** 3, 7, 10   **48.** 8, 15, 17   **49.** $\sqrt{3}, \sqrt{4}, \sqrt{5}$

For the values given, *a* and *b* are legs of a right triangle. Find the length of the hypotenuse. If necessary, round to the nearest tenth.

50. $a = 6, b = 8$ **51.** $a = 5, b = 9$ **52.** $a = 4, b = 10$ **53.** $a = 9, b = 1$

● **Lessons 6-1 to 6-3** **Write an equation to model each situation. Then solve.**

54. A DVD club charges a monthly membership fee of $4.95 and $11.95 for each DVD purchased. If a customer's bill for the month was $64.70, how many DVDs did the customer purchase?

55. A lawyer charges $100 per month to be put on retainer for a client. The lawyer also charges an hourly rate of $75 for work done. How many hours does the lawyer have to work for a client, in one month, to charge $625?

56. A rectangular pool is twice as long as it is wide. What are the dimensions of the pool if the perimeter is 42 yd?

57. Two friends rent an apartment together. They agree that one person will pay 1.5 times what the other person pays. If the rent is $850, how much will each friend pay?

58. A shopper's discount club charges a monthly fee of $15 and sells gasoline for $2.05 per gallon. The gas station across the street sells gasoline for $2.35 per gallon and charges no fee. How many gallons of gasoline would you have to buy in one month to spend the same amount at either store?

59. Michael and Kevin are running. Kevin gets a 3-mile head start and runs at a rate of 5.5 mi/h. Michael runs at a rate of 7 mi/h. How many hours will it take Michael to catch up with Kevin?

● **Lessons 6-4 and 6-5**

60. A 12-ounce can of green beans is sold for $1.45. What is the price per pound?

61. A sailboat is traveling at a speed of 10 nautical miles per hour. If 1 nautical mile is 6076 ft, what is the speed of the sailboat in feet per second?

62. A 40 : 1 scale model of an airplane is being used to conduct wind-tunnel tests. If the model is 4.5 feet long, how long is the actual airplane?

● **Lesson 6-6**

63. Joe and Gayna live 3 miles apart. They both leave their houses at the same time and walk to meet each other. Joe walks at 2.5 mi/h and Gayna walks at 3.5 mi/h. How far will Joe walk before he meets Gayna?

● **Lesson 6-7** **Find the percent of change. Describe the percent of change as an increase or decrease.**

64. A $1500 computer is on sale for $1275.

65. The value of a stamp collection increases from $160 to $180 in one year.

● **Lesson 6-8**

66. What is the length of each side of a square garden with an area of 70 ft^2?

● **Lesson 6-9** **Use the Pythagorean Theorem to answer each question.**

67. A 20-ft ladder is placed 5 ft from the base of a building. How high on the building will the ladder reach?

68. A soccer field is 80 yd long and 35 yd wide. What is the diagonal distance across the field?

● **Lessons 7-1 to 7-4** Solve each inequality. Graph and check your solution.

1. $-8w < 24$

2. $9 + p \leq 17$

3. $\frac{r}{4} > -1$

4. $7y + 2 \leq -8$

5. $t - 5 \geq -13$

6. $9h > -108$

7. $8w + 7 > 5$

8. $\frac{s}{6} \leq 3$

9. $\frac{6c}{5} \geq -12$

10. $-8\ell + 3.7 \leq 31.7$

11. $9 - t \leq 4$

12. $m + 4 \geq 8$

13. $y + 3 < 16$

14. $n - 6 \leq 8.5$

15. $12b - 5 > -29$

16. $4 - a > 15$

17. $4 - x \leq 3$

18. $1 - 4d \geq 4 - d$

19. $n + 7 \leq 3n - 1$

20. $\frac{s}{2} + 1 < s + 2$

21. $3 - \frac{2x}{3} > 5$

22. $8r - \frac{r}{6} > \frac{1}{6} - 8$

23. $1.4 + 2.4x < 0.6$

24. $x - 2 < 3x - 4$

25. The booster club raised $102 in their car wash. They want to buy $18 soccer balls for the soccer team. Write and solve an inequality to find how many soccer balls they can buy.

26. You earn $7.50 per hour and need to earn $35. Write and solve an inequality to find how many hours you must work.

● **Lesson 7-5** Solve each compound inequality.

27. $8 < w + 3 < 10$

28. $-6 < t - 1 < 6$

29. $6m - 15 \leq 9$ or $10m > 84$

30. $9j - 5j \geq 20$ and $8j > -36$

31. $37 < 3c + 7 < 43$

32. $3 < 5 + 6h < 10$

33. $1 + t < 4 < 2 + t$

34. $2 + 3w < -1 < 3w + 5$

35. $2x - 3 \leq x$ and $2x + 1 \geq x + 3$

36. $3n - 7 > n + 1$ or $4n - 5 < 3n - 3$

● **Lesson 7-6** Choose a variable and write an absolute value inequality that represents each set of numbers.

37. all real numbers less than 2 units from 0

38. all real numbers more than 0.5 units from 4.5

39. all real numbers less than 1 unit from -4

40. all real numbers 3 or more units from -1

41. all real numbers less than or equal to 5 units from 3

Solve each inequality. Graph and check your solution.

42. $|x| < 5$

43. $|t| > 1$

44. $|t| - 5 \leq 3$

45. $|-6m + 2| > 20$

46. $|3c| - 1 \geq 11$

47. $|8 - w| \leq 8$

48. $|2b + 3| < 7$

49. $|c - 5| \leq 6$

50. $|n| + 4 \leq 5$

51. Write an absolute value inequality that has numbers between 2 and 3 as the solutions.

52. Holes with radius 3 cm must be drilled in sheets of metal. The radius must have an error no more than 0.01 cm. Write an absolute value inequality whose solutions are acceptable radii.

Lesson 7-1 **Define a variable and write an inequality for each situation.**

53. A car dealership sells at least 35 cars each week.

54. No more than 425 tickets to a musical will be sold.

55. You must be at least 18 years old to vote.

56. The party store sold more than 720 balloons in July.

Lessons 7-2 to 7-4 **Write and solve an inequality for each situation.**

57. Suppose you are trying to increase your coin collection to at least 500 coins. How many more coins do you need if you already have a collection of 375 coins?

58. Janet has a balance of $125 on a credit card. On her next statement, she wants to reduce her balance to no more than $60. How much does she need to pay off?

59. A homeroom class with 25 students is holding a fund-raiser to support school sports. Their goal is to raise at least $200. On average, how much money does each student need to contribute to meet or exceed the goal?

60. You are reading a book with 19 chapters. How many chapters should you read each week if you want to finish the book in 5 weeks or less?

61. The sophomore class is putting on a variety show to raise money. It costs $700 to rent the banquet hall they are going to use. If they charge $15 for each ticket, how many tickets do they need to sell in order to raise at least $1000?

62. A technical-support company charges $10 per month plus $35 per hour of phone support. If you need to spend less than $100 per month on support, how many hours can you get?

Lesson 7-5 **Write a compound inequality for each situation. Graph your solution.**

63. Water will not be in liquid form when it is colder than 32°F or warmer than 212°F.

64. The width of a parking space needs to be at least 8 feet and no more than 11 feet.

65. A car salesman has been told to sell a particular car for more than $14,500 and up to the sticker price of $15,755.

Lesson 7-6 **Write and solve an absolute value inequality for each situation.**

66. The ideal diameter of an aircraft tire is 105 inches. The acceptable error for each tire is 0.175 inches. Find the range of acceptable tire diameters.

67. A tractor crankshaft is designed to have a radius of 4.25 cm. The acceptable error for the radius is 0.005 cm. Find the range of acceptable radii for the crankshaft.

68. The ideal weight of an exercise ball is 175 ounces. Each ball can have an error of 0.35 ounces. What is the range of acceptable weights?

Extra Practice: Skills and Word Problems

Lesson 8-1 Sketch a graph to describe each situation. Label each section of the graph.

1. the number of apples on a tree over one year

2. the amount of milk in your bowl as you eat cereal

3. the energy you use in a 24-h period

4. your distance from home plate after your home run

Lesson 8-2 Find the range of each function when the domain is $\{-4, -1, 0, 3\}$.

5. $y = 6x - 5$ **6.** $y = |x| - 2$ **7.** $y = x^2 + 3x + 1$

8. $y = \frac{1}{2}x + 8$ **9.** $y = -x^2 - x$ **10.** $y = \frac{2}{3}x$

Use a mapping diagram to determine whether each relation is a function.

11. $\{(1, 2), (2, 3), (3, 4), (4, 5), (5, 6)\}$ **12.** $\{(5, 2), (1, 3), (4, 7), (5, 6), (0, 4)\}$

13. $\{(3.4, 2), (5.6, 2), (0.1, 2), (2.8, 2)\}$ **14.** $\{(6, 7), (5, 2), (7, 7), (4, 3), (0, 0)\}$

Lesson 8-3 Graph each function.

15. $y = 2x + 1$ **16.** $y = 4 - x$ **17.** $y = |x| - 3$

Lesson 8-4 Write a function rule for each table.

18.

x	f(x)
−3	−1
−1	1
1	3
3	5

19.

x	f(x)
0	0
3	6
6	12
9	18

20.

x	f(x)
21	14
25	18
29	22
33	26

21.

x	f(x)
−8	−4
−6	−3
−4	−2
−2	−1

Lesson 8-5 Graph the direct variation that includes the given point. Write the equation of the line.

22. $(5, 4)$ **23.** $(7, 7)$ **24.** $(-3, -10)$ **25.** $(4, -8)$ **26.** $(-2, 9)$

Lesson 8-6 Find the constant of variation k for each inverse variation.

27. $y = 10$ when $x = 7$ **28.** $y = -8$ when $x = 12$ **29.** $y = 0.2$ when $x = 4$

Each pair of points is on the graph of an inverse variation. Find the missing value.

30. $(5.4, 3)$ and $(2, y)$ **31.** $(x, 4)$ and $(5, 6)$ **32.** $(3, 6)$ and $(9, y)$

33. $(100, 2)$ and $(x, 25)$ **34.** $(6, 1)$ and $(x, -2)$ **35.** $(8, y)$ and $(-2, 4)$

Lesson 8-7 Find the second and fifth terms of each sequence.

36. $A(n) = 22 + (n - 1)11$ **37.** $A(n) = -2 + (n - 1)(-2)$

38. $A(n) = -2 + (n - 1)$ **39.** $A(n) = 1 + 4(n - 1)$

● **Lesson 8-1** **Sketch a graph to represent each situation.**

40. the speed of a bus as it makes its last stop to pick up students and then continues until it arrives at school

41. the temperature of a lake from January through December

42. the height of a roller coaster during a ride

● **Lesson 8-2** **Evaluate each function rule to find the range for the domain {1, 4, 9}.**

43. The function $f(x) = 20 - x$ represents the amount of change you receive after paying for an item that costs x dollars with a $20 bill.

44. The function $f(x) = x^2$ represents the area of a square with a side length of x.

45. The function $f(x) = 8x$ represents the number of pieces of pizza from x eight-piece pizzas.

● **Lesson 8-3** **Make a table of values and graph each function.**

46. The function $f(x) = 175 + x$ represents the amount of money in a savings account that started with $175 after a deposit of x dollars.

47. The function $f(x) = 4x$ represents the perimeter of a square with side length x.

● **Lesson 8-4** **Write a function rule for each situation.**

48. the circumference of a circle $C(r)$ when you know the radius r

49. the area of a 100-yard-long field $A(w)$ when you know the width w

50. the distance run in feet $D(m)$ when you know the distance in miles m

51. the number of pounds $P(n)$ when you know the number of ounces n

● **Lessons 8-5 and 8-6** **Write a direct or inverse variation to model each situation. Then answer the question.**

52. After 30 minutes a car moving at a constant speed has traveled 25 miles. Moving at the same speed, how far will it travel in 140 minutes?

53. The perimeter of a square depends on the length of a side of the square. What is the perimeter of a square with side length 13.4 in.?

54. Two rectangular fields have the same area. One measures 75 yd by 60 yd. If the other has a length of 72 yd, what is its width?

55. Kevin is training to run in a half marathon. Initially, he could run 6 miles per hour for 2 hours. Two months later he ran the same distance in 1 hour and 45 minutes. What is his new speed?

● **Lesson 8-7** **Use inductive reasoning to answer the question.**

56. A train arrives at a subway station at 9:05 A.M. Another train arrives at 9:12 A.M. and a third arrives at 9:19 A.M. If the trains keep running on the same schedule, at what times will each of the next three trains arrive?

57. The balance of a car loan starts at $9,200 and decreases by $180 each month. What will the balance be at the end of the next three months?

Extra Practice: Skills and Word Problems

● **Lesson 9-1** **Find the rate of change for each situation.**

1. growing from 1.4 m to 1.6 m in one year

2. bicycling 3 mi in 15 min and 7 mi in 55 min

3. growing 22.4 mm in 14 s

4. reading 8 pages in 9 min and 22 pages in 30 min

● **Lessons 9-2 and 9-3** **Find the slope and y-intercept.**

5. $y = 6x + 8$

6. $3x + 4y = -24$

7. $2y = 8$

8. $y = \frac{-3}{4}x - 8$

Graph each equation.

9. $y = 2x - 3$

10. $y = \frac{2}{3}x - 4$

11. $y = -\frac{1}{2}x + 4$

12. $y = -\frac{5}{4}x$

● **Lessons 9-4 and 9-5** **Find the x- and y-intercepts for each equation.**

13. $6x + y = 12$

14. $y = -7x$

15. $y = \frac{1}{2}x + 3$

16. $-2y = 5x - 12$

Write the equation in point-slope form for the line through the given point with the given slope.

17. $(4, 6); m = -5$

18. $(3, -1); m = 1$

19. $(8, 5); m = \frac{1}{2}$

20. $(0, -6); m = \frac{4}{3}$

Graph each equation.

21. $x + 4y = 8$

22. $y - 5 = -2(x + 1)$

23. $x + 3 = 0$

24. $4x - 3y = 12$

25. $y = -1$

26. $y + 1 = -\frac{1}{2}(x + 2)$

A line passes through the given points. Write an equation for the line in slope-intercept form.

27. $(2, 5)$ and $(4, 8)$

28. $(1, 6)$ and $(7, 3)$

29. $(-2, 4)$ and $(3, 9)$

30. $(1, 6)$ and $(9, -4)$

31. $(0, -7)$ and $(-1, 0)$

32. $(7, 0)$ and $(3, -4)$

33. $(0, 0)$ and $(-7, 1)$

34. $(10, 0)$ and $(0, 7)$

● **Lesson 9-5** **Write an equation in standard form that satisfies the given conditions.**

35. parallel to $y = 4x + 1$, through $(-3, 5)$

36. perpendicular to $y = -x - 3$, through $(0, 0)$

37. perpendicular to $3x + 4y = 12$, through $(7, 1)$

38. parallel to $2x - y = 6$, through $(-6, -9)$

39. parallel to the x-axis and through $(4, -1)$

40. through $(4, 44)$ and parallel to the y-axis

● **Lesson 9-6**

41. a. Graph the (ages, grades) data of some students in a school at the right.
   b. Draw a trend line.
   c. Find the equation of the line of best fit.

$(10, 6), (16, 10), (15, 10), (18, 12), (17, 11),$
$(17, 12), (19, 12), (16, 11), (11, 7), (15, 9), (13, 8)$

● **Lesson 9-7** **Graph each equation by translating $y = |x|$ or $y = -|x|$.**

42. $y = |x| + 1$

43. $y = |x + 2|$

44. $y = |x - 2|$

45. $y = -|x - 1|$

46. $y = -|x + 1|$

47. $y = -|x| + 1$

48. $y = |x + 0.5|$

49. $y = |x| - 4$

● **Lesson 9-1** **Find the rate of change for each situation.**

50. The cost of four movie tickets is $30 and the cost of seven tickets is $52.50.

51. Five seconds after jumping out of the plane, a sky diver is 10,000 ft above the ground. After 30 seconds, the sky diver is 3,750 ft above the ground.

● **Lesson 9-2** **Write an equation in slope-intercept form for each situation.**

52. A skateboard ramp is 5 ft high and 12 ft long from end to end.

53. An airplane with no fuel weighs 2575 lbs. Each gallon of gasoline added to the fuel tanks weighs 6 lbs.

● **Lesson 9-3** **Write a function for each situation and then determine a reasonable range for the function.**

54. You plan to buy no more than three gallons of milk. Each gallon costs $3.75.

55. The amount of time spent in line at a grocery store depends on how many people are in line ahead of you. Each person takes about two minutes to check out at the cash register.

● **Lesson 9-4** **Write an equation in standard form for each situation.**

56. Juan can ride his bike at 12 mi/h and walk at 4 mi/h. Write an equation that relates the amount of time he can spend riding or walking combined, to travel 20 miles.

57. You have $25 to buy supplies for a class party. Juice costs $3 per bottle and chips cost $2 per bag. Write an equation that relates the amount of juice and chips you can buy using $25.

● **Lesson 9-5** **Write an equation in point-slope form for each situation.**

58. A train travels at a rate of 70 mi/h. Two hours after leaving the station it was 210 miles from its destination.

59. An escalator has a slope of $\frac{3}{4}$. After traveling forward 32 feet, the escalator is 24 feet above the floor.

● **Lesson 9-6** **Tell whether each statement is *true* or *false*. Explain your choice.**

60. Two airplanes traveling at the same rate leave an airport 1 hour apart. The graphs of the distance each plane travels will be parallel.

61. Two lines with negative slopes can be perpendicular.

● **Lesson 9-7**

62. Use a calculator to find a line of best fit for the data. Find the value of the correlation coefficient *r*. Let $x = 0$ correspond to 1960.

Total U.S. Vehicle Production (millions)

1960	1970	1980	1990	2000
7.9	8.8	8.0	9.8	12.8

● **Lesson 9-8**

63. A car traveling at a rate of 50 mi/h passes a rest area 30 minutes after the beginning of the trip. Write an absolute value equation that represents the car's distance from the rest area.

● **Lesson 10-1** Solve each system by graphing.

1. $x - y = 7$
$3x + 2y = 6$

2. $y = 2x + 3$
$y = -\frac{3}{2}x - 4$

3. $y = -2x + 6$
$3x + 4y = 24$

● **Lesson 10-2** Solve each system by using substitution.

4. $x - y = 13$
$y - x = -13$

5. $3x - y = 4$
$x + 5y = -4$

6. $x + y = 4$
$y = 7x + 4$

● **Lesson 10-3** Solve each system by elimination.

7. $x + y = 19$
$x - y = -7$

8. $-3x + 4y = 29$
$3x + 2y = -17$

9. $3x + y = 3$
$-3x + 2y = -30$

10. $6x + y = 13$
$y - x = -8$

11. $4x - 9y = 61$
$10x + 3y = 25$

12. $4x - y = 105$
$x + 7y = -10$

● **Lesson 10-4** Write a system of equations to model each problem and solve.

13. Suppose you have 12 coins that total 32 cents. Some of the coins are nickels and the rest are pennies. How many of each coin do you have?

14. Claire bought three bars of soap and five sponges for $2.31. Steve bought five bars of soap and three sponges for $3.05. Find the cost of each item.

15. The perimeter of a rectangular lot is 74 feet. The cost of fencing along the two lengths is $1 per foot, and the cost of fencing along the two widths is $3.50 per foot. Find the dimensions of the lot if the total cost of the fencing is $159.

16. A chemist wants to make a 10% solution of fertilizer. How much water and how much of a 30% solution should the chemist mix to get 30 L of a 10% solution?

17. Fruit drink A consists of 6% pure fruit juice and drink B consists of 15% pure fruit juice. How much of each kind of drink should you mix together to get 4 L of a 10% concentration of fruit juice?

18. A motor boat traveled 12 miles with the current, turned around, and returned 12 miles against the current to its starting point. The trip with the current took 2 hours and the trip against the current took 3 hours. Find the speed of the boat and the speed of the current.

● **Lesson 10-5** Graph each linear inequality.

19. $y < x$

20. $y < x - 4$

21. $y > -6x + 5$

22. $y \leq 14 - x$

23. $y \geq \frac{1}{4}x - 3$

24. $2x + 3y \leq 6$

● **Lesson 10-6** Solve each system by graphing.

25. $y \leq 5x + 1$
$y > x - 3$

26. $y > 4x + 3$
$y \geq -2x - 1$

27. $y > -x + 2$
$y > x - 4$

28. $y < -2x + 1$
$y > -2x - 3$

29. $y \leq 5$
$y \geq -x + 1$

30. $y \leq 5x - 2$
$y > 3$

● **Lesson 10-1 Write and solve a system of equations by graphing.**

31. One calling card has a $.50 connection fee and charges $.02 per minute. Another card has a $.25 connection fee and charges $.03 per minute. After how many minutes would a call cost the same amount using either card?

32. Suppose that you have $75 in your savings account and you save an additional $5 per week. Your friend has $30 in his savings account and saves an additional $10 per week. In how many weeks will you both have the same amount of money in your accounts?

● **Lesson 10-2 Write and solve a system of equations by substitution.**

33. A farmer grows corn and soybeans on her 300-acre farm. She wants to plant 110 more acres of soybeans than corn. How many acres of each crop does she need to plant?

34. The perimeter of a rectangle is 34 cm. The length is 1 cm longer than the width. What are the dimensions of the rectangle?

● **Lesson 10-3 Write and solve a system of equations using elimination.**

35. Two groups of people order food at a restaurant. One group orders 4 hamburgers and 7 chicken sandwiches for $34.50. The other group orders 8 hamburgers and 3 chicken sandwiches for $30.50. Find the cost of each item.

36. The sum of two numbers is 25. Their difference is 9. What are the two numbers?

● **Lesson 10-4 Write and solve a system of equations for each situation by any method. Explain why you chose the method.**

37. The ratio of boys to girls at a college is 4 : 5. How many boys and girls are there if the total number of students is 3321?

38. A boat travels 18 miles downstream in 1.5 hours. It then takes the boat 3 hours to travel upstream the same distance. Find the speed of the boat in still water and the speed of the current.

● **Lesson 10-5 Write and graph a linear inequality for each situation.**

39. Suppose you can spend up to $10 on bananas and apples. Apples cost $3 per pound and bananas cost $1 per pound. List three possible combinations of apples and bananas you can buy.

40. Trenton is going to make a rectangular garden in his yard. He wants the perimeter to be no larger than 40 ft. What are three possible sets of dimensions that the garden can have?

● **Lesson 10-6**

41. Hideo plans to spend no more than $60 at an entertainment store on DVDs and CDs. DVDs cost $17 each and CDs cost $14 each. He wants to buy at least two items. Write and graph a system of linear inequalities that describes the situation. What are three possible combinations of CDs and DVDs that he can buy? Write and graph a system of inequalities that describes the situation.

Extra Practice: Skills and Word Problems

● **Lessons 11-1 to 11-5** Simplify each expression. Use only positive exponents.

1. $(2t)^{-6}$

2. $5m^5 m^{-8}$

3. $(4.5)^4 (4.5)^{-2}$

4. $(m^7 t^{-5})^2$

5. $(x^2 n^4)(n^{-8})$

6. $(w^{-2} j^{-4})^{-3}(j^7 j^3)$

7. $(t^6)^3 (m)^2$

8. $(3n^4)^2$

9. $\dfrac{r^5}{g^{-3}}$

10. $\dfrac{1}{a^{-4}}$

11. $\dfrac{w^7}{w^{-6}}$

12. $\dfrac{6}{t^{-4}}$

13. $\dfrac{a^2 b^{-7} c^4}{a^5 b^3 c^{-2}}$

14. $\dfrac{(2t^5)^3}{4t^8 t^{-1}}$

15. $\left(\dfrac{a^6}{a^7}\right)^{-3}$

16. $\left(\dfrac{c^5 c^{-3}}{c^{-4}}\right)^{-2}$

Evaluate each expression for $m = 2$, $t = -3$, $w = 4$, and $z = 0$.

17. t^m

18. t^{-m}

19. $(w \cdot t)^m$

20. $w^m \cdot t^m$

21. $(w^z)^m$

22. $w^m w^z$

23. $z^{-t}(m^t)^z$

24. $w^{-t} t^t$

Write each number in scientific notation.

25. 34,000,000

26. 0.00063

27. 1500

28. 0.0002

29. 360,000

30. 6,200,000,000

31. 0.05

32. 0.000000000891

Write each number in standard notation.

33. 8.05×10^6

34. 3.2×10^{-7}

35. 9.0×10^8

36. 4.25×10^{-4}

37. 2.35×10^2

38. 6.3×10^4

39. 2.001×10^{-5}

40. 5.2956×10^3

● **Lesson 11-6** Find the common ratio of each sequence. Then find the next two terms.

41. $12, 18, 27, \ldots$

42. $2, 1, 0.5, \ldots$

43. $-1, -0.2, -0.04, \ldots$

44. $-2, -4, -8, \ldots$

45. $2, 6, 18, \ldots$

46. $1.2, -0.6, 0.3, \ldots$

47. $30, 10, \frac{10}{3}, \ldots$

48. $-2.25, -9, -36, \ldots$

● **Lesson 11-7** Evaluate each function for the domain $\{-1, 0, 1, 2\}$. As the values of the domain increase, do the values of the function *increase* or *decrease*?

49. $y = 3^x$

50. $y = \left(\frac{3}{4}\right)^x$

51. $y = 1.5^x$

52. $y = \frac{1}{2} \cdot 3^x$

53. $y = -3 \cdot 7^x$

54. $y = -(4)^x$

55. $y = 3 \cdot \left(\frac{1}{5}\right)^x$

56. $y = 2^x$

57. $y = 2 \cdot 3^x$

58. $y = (0.8)^x$

59. $y = 2.5^x$

60. $y = -4 \cdot (0.2)^x$

● **Lesson 11-8** Identify each function as *exponential growth* or *exponential decay*. Then identify the growth factor or decay factor.

61. $y = 8^x$

62. $y = \frac{3}{4} \cdot 2^x$

63. $y = 9 \cdot \left(\frac{1}{2}\right)^x$

64. $y = 4 \cdot 9^x$

65. $y = 0.65^x$

66. $y = 3 \cdot 1.5^x$

67. $y = \frac{2}{5} \cdot \left(\frac{1}{4}\right)^x$

68. $y = 0.1 \cdot 0.9^x$

Write an exponential function to model each situation. Find each amount after the specified time.

69. \$200 principal, 4% compounded annually for 5 years

70. \$1000 principal, 3.6% compounded monthly for 10 years

71. \$3000 investment, 8% loss each year for 3 years

● **Lesson 11-1**

72. Suppose an investment doubles in value every 5 years. This year the investment is worth $12,480. How much will it be worth 10 years from now? How much was it worth 5 years ago?

● **Lesson 11-2 Write each number in scientific notation.**

73. A bacteria culture has a population of approximately 7,500,000,000.

74. The diameter of a blood cell is about 0.0000082 m.

● **Lessons 11-3 and 11-4 Write each answer in scientific notation.**

75. A light-year is the distance light travels in one year. If the speed of light is about 3×10^5 km/s, how long is a light-year in kilometers? (Use 365 days for the length of a year).

76. The radius of Earth is approximately 6.4×10^6 m. Use the formula $V = \frac{4}{3}\pi r^3$ to find the volume of Earth.

77. A spherical cell has a radius of 2.75×10^{-6} m. Use the formula for the surface area of a sphere $S.A. = 4\pi r^2$ to find the surface area of a cell.

● **Lesson 11-5**

78. What is the volume of a cube with a side length of $\frac{4}{5}$ m?

79. The speed of sound is approximately 1.2×10^3 km/h. How long does it take for sound to travel 7.2×10^2 km? Write your answer in minutes.

● **Lesson 11-6 Write a rule and find the given term in each geometric sequence described below.**

80. What is the ninth term when the first term is 4 and the common ratio is -6?

81. What is the sixth term when the first term is 60 and the common ratio is 0.4?

● **Lesson 11-7 Write and solve an exponential equation to answer each question.**

82. Suppose an investment of $5,000 doubles every 12 years. How much is the investment worth after 36 years? After 48 years?

83. Suppose 15 animals are taken to an island, and then their population triples every 8 months. How many animals will there be in 4 years?

● **Lesson 11-8 Find the balance in each account.**

84. You deposit $2500 in a savings account with 3% interest compounded annually. What is the balance in the account after 6 years?

85. You deposit $750 in an account with 7% interest compounded semiannually. What is the balance in the account after 4 years?

86. You deposit $520 in an account with 4% interest compounded monthly. What is the balance in the account after 5 years?

● **Lesson 12-1** Find the next three terms of each sequence. Then write a rule to describe each sequence.

1. $100, 80, 60, 40, \ldots$ **2.** $6, 12, 18, 24, \ldots$

3. $8, 16, 24, 32, \ldots$ **4.** $50, 500, 5,000, 50,000, \ldots$

5. $-5, 25, -125, 625, \ldots$ **6.** $50, 10, -30, -70, \ldots$

● **Lesson 12-2** Graph each function, for x values from -2 to 2.

7. $y = x^2 - 1$ **8.** $y = -x^2 + 6$ **9.** $y = |x| - 3$ **10.** $y = -|x| + 2$

11. $y = -3x^2$ **12.** $y = -3|x| - 1$ **13.** $y = 2x^2 - 2$ **14.** $y = \frac{1}{2}|x|$

● **Lesson 12-3** For each function, make a table with integer values of x from 0 to 4. Then graph each function.

15. $y = 4^x$ **16.** $y = \frac{1}{2} \cdot 10^x$ **17.** $y = 10(0.5)^x$ **18.** $y = 2^x$

● **Lesson 12-4** Tell whether each polynomial is a *monomial*, a *binomial*, or a *trinomial*.

19. $2x^2 - 3x - 1$ **20.** $3xy$ **21.** $5x^3 - 15$ **22.** $10 - 2x + 5y$

23. xyz^2 **24.** $56 - y$ **25.** $3ab - a^2 - b$ **26.** 80

● **Lesson 12-5** Simplify each sum or difference.

27. $(5y - 12) + (2y + 10)$ **28.** $(x^2 + 3x + 4) + (2x^2 + x + 6)$

29. $(x^2 - 7x + 2) + (-x^2 + 6x - 2)$ **30.** $(4a^2 - 3a - 2) - (2a^2 + 5a + 10)$

31. $(5x - 3) + (6x^2 - 9)$ **32.** $(15y^2 + 12y) - (12y^2 - 20)$

33. $(3ab + a^2 + b^2) - (a^2 - 3b^2 - 5ab)$ **34.** $(10t - t^2 - 15) + (3t^2 + 12)$

● **Lessons 12-6 and 12-7** Simplify each product.

35. $2x(5x^2 + 6)$ **36.** $y^2(x + y)$ **37.** $6t^2(2t^2 - 3 + 8t)$

38. $(x - 8)(x + 1)$ **39.** $(y + 6)(2y + 4)$ **40.** $3b(5ab + 2ab^2 + 6b)$

Use the GCF of the terms to write each expression as the product of two factors.

41. $4x^2 - 12$ **42.** $5z^2 - 20z + 30$ **43.** $2a^2b - 4a + 6b$

44. $t^2 - 3t$ **45.** $6xy + 2x + 3x^2y$ **46.** $5w^3 + 6w^2 - 3w$

● **Lesson 12-1** **Find the next three terms of each sequence.**

47. Eduardo does 10 push-ups per day one week, 15 push-ups per day the next week, and 20 push-ups per day the following week.

48. You save $8 in January, $12 in February, and $18 in March.

● **Lesson 12-2** **Graph the function to answer each question.**

49. The formula $A = 12x - x^2$ models the area of a garden with a width of x ft. What width gives the greatest area?

50. The formula $h = -16t^2 + 200$ models the height h of a dropped ball that takes t seconds to reach the ground. Suppose you drop a ball from 200 feet. In approximately how many seconds will the ball hit the ground?

● **Lesson 12-3** **Graph each function.**

51. The formula $y = 25(2)^x$ models the number of cells y in a bacteria culture after x days.

52. You deposit $500 in a savings account earning 5% interest each year. The formula $b = 500(1.05)^y$ models the balance b in the account after y years.

● **Lesson 12-4** **Evaluate the polynomial.**

53. The polynomial $x^2 + 10x$ models the area of a greenhouse 10 m longer than it is wide. The greenhouse is 8 m wide. Find its area.

● **Lesson 12-5** **Write and simplify a polynomial expression.**

54. To make a flying ring, Lily cut out a circle with area $(2x + 4)$ cm^2 from the center of a plastic circle with area $(5x - 6)$ cm^2. Find the surface area of her flying ring.

● **Lessons 12-6 and 12-7** **Find each area. Use 3.14 for π.**

55. A rectangular soccer field is $4x$ m long and $(2x + 12)$ m wide.

56. A cornfield is shaped like a trapezoid with bases of $(5p + 2)$ m and $(2p - 4)$ m and a height of $3p$ m.

57. A circular pool has a radius of $(4c - 2)$ ft.

● **Lesson 12-8** **Solve by using multiple strategies.**

58. A rectangular playing field is three times as long as it is wide. Its area is 507 m^2. Find the perimeter of the playing field.

Using TI Technology for Selected Examples

This section includes calculator activities using the TI-83/84 Plus and TI-83/84 Plus Silver Edition. All activities are tied to specific examples found in lessons throughout this course. These activities provide an alternate way to complete these examples using technology.

Using Grouping Symbols

See Lesson 1-2, Example 3

There are three different grouping symbols: brackets, [ ], parentheses, ( ), and braces, { }. However, you cannot use brackets on the graphing calculator to simplify an expression. As you enter an expression, you can use braces or parentheses instead of brackets.

EXAMPLE Simplifying With Grouping Symbols

Simplify the expression $24 \div [6 - (2 \cdot 2)]$.

Enter the expression using braces instead of brackets. Press:

24 ÷ 2nd (6 − (2 × 2) 2nd).

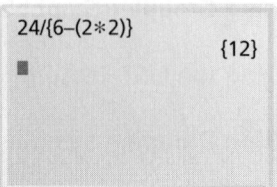

Check the expression for accuracy. Do all of the grouping symbols appear in matching pairs?

To simplify, press ENTER .

> Calculator Tip: Do not confuse the subtraction key, −, and the negative key, (-) , when entering expressions.

Enter the expression using parentheses instead of brackets.

24 ÷ (6 − (2 × 2)) ENTER .

```
24/(6−(2*2))
                       12
■
```

Regardless if braces or parentheses were used, the expression $24 \div [6 - (2 \cdot 2)]$ simplifies to 12.

Try again, omitting the outer pair of grouping symbols entirely.

```
24/6−(2*2)
              0
```

Entered like this, 24 is divided by 6 before the subtraction is done.

The answer shown, 0, is NOT the correct simplification for $24 \div [6 - (2 \cdot 2)]$. The grouping symbols are essential.

EXERCISES

Use your calculator to simplify each expression.

1. $[(16 \div 4) - 2] + (-3)$

2. $2[13 + (10 \div 2)] \div (-6)$

3. $1 + \dfrac{10 - 2}{4}$

4. $2(6) + \dfrac{7 + 8}{3}$

Using the LIST Feature

See Lesson 3-3, Example 1

EXAMPLE Real-World 🌐 Problem Solving

Find the mean and median of this group of data: 45, 50, 48, 59, 50, and 40.

Store the data as a list. Press $\boxed{\text{STAT}}$ and select **1: Edit** by pressing $\boxed{\text{ENTER}}$. With the cursor under L1, store the data as List 1. After each number is keyed in, you must press $\boxed{\text{ENTER}}$ to move it into the list.

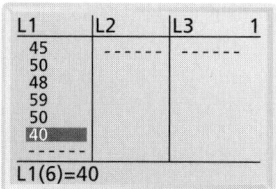

Line L1(6) = 40 tells you that the value of 40 has been entered for List 1, item 6.

> **Calculator Tip:** To clear any previously entered lists, use $\boxed{\blacktriangle}$ to select the list number (L1, L2, etc.) Once highlighted, press $\boxed{\text{CLEAR}}$ $\boxed{\text{ENTER}}$.

Return to the home screen by pressing $\boxed{\text{2nd}}$ $\boxed{\text{MODE}}$. Press $\boxed{\text{CLEAR}}$ to delete any previous work. Clearing the home screen does NOT clear the lists.

To find the mean of L1, enter the LIST menu by pressing $\boxed{\text{2nd}}$ $\boxed{\text{STAT}}$. Under MATH, select **3:mean(**. Enter L1 by pressing $\boxed{\text{2nd}}$ $\boxed{1}$ $\boxed{)}$ and press $\boxed{\text{ENTER}}$ to find the answer.

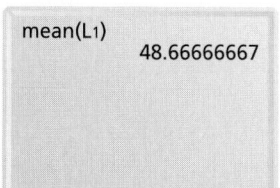

Notice the calculator rounds the last digit displayed.

Similar steps are followed to find the median of L1.

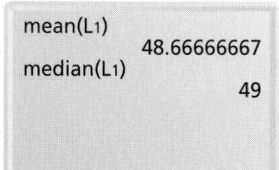

Under MATH, select 4:median(to find the median.

EXERCISES

Find the mean and median. Round to the nearest tenth.

1. 23.3, 56.9, 64.0, 17.6, 9.2, 81.7, 35.5, 29.8, 93.1, 101.4

2. **Error Analysis** A student entered the following data: 2, 3, 6, 8, 8, 10, 11, 12, 14, 14, 18, 20. Is the list entered correctly as shown at the right? Explain the student's error.

Technology Examples

Using Grouping Symbols

See Lesson 4-2, Example 6

When simplifying expressions on the graphing calculator, parentheses, ( ), and braces, { }, may be used as grouping symbols. However, brackets, [ ], can only be used for matrices.

EXAMPLE Simplifying an Expression

Simplify the expression $2[\,(13-7)^2 \div 3]$.
Enter the expression by pressing these keys:

2 `2nd` `{(` `(` 13 `—` 7 `)` `x²` `÷` 3 `2nd` `)}` .

> **Special Calculator Feature:** To square a value you may press `x²`. To raise a value to any other exponent, you can use `▲`.

Check that all grouping symbols appear in pairs. To simplify, press `ENTER`.

It is easy to confuse the subtraction key, `—`, and the negative key, `(-)`. Double check to make sure you use the one you want.

Enter the expression again, but this time use parentheses to show both sets of grouping symbols:

2 `(` `(` 13 `—` 7 `)` `x²` `÷` 3 `)` .

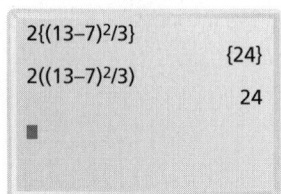

The calculator simplifies the expression correctly regardless of which grouping symbols you use, ( ) or { }.

● The expression $2[\,(13-7)^2 \div 3]$ simplifies to 24.

EXERCISES

Use your calculator to simplify each expression.

1. $5[4 + 3\,(2^2 + 1)]$ **2.** $12 + 3[18 - 5\,(16 - 13)]$

3. $5 + [\,(2 + 1)^3 - 3]$ **4.** $4[\,(9 - 7)^3 \div 2]$

5. A student was asked to simplify the expression $17 - 5^2 \div (2^4 + 3^2)$. The student pressed

1 7 `(-)` 5 `x²` `÷` `(` 2 `▲` 4 `+` 3 `x²` `)`

and received an error message. Explain the student's error.

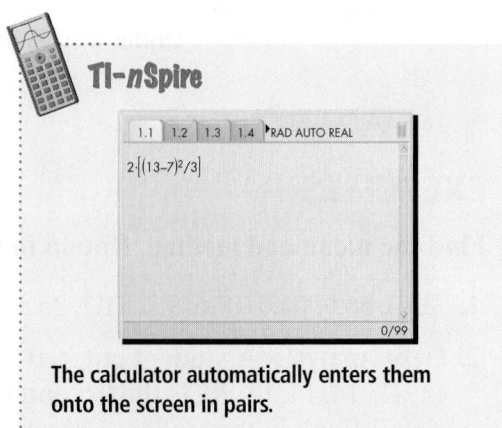

TI-*n*Spire

The calculator automatically enters them onto the screen in pairs.

Sorting a List

See Lesson 4-6, Example 4

EXAMPLE Making a Stem-and Leaf Plot

Make a stem-and-leaf plot for the data at the right.

Press **STAT**, under the **EDIT** menu, select **1: Edit**.

Enter the data as L1. After each number is keyed in, you must press **ENTER** to move it into the list.

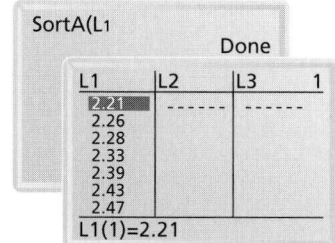

The entire list will not fit on one screen. Use ▲ and ▲ to see the entire list. Check that all of the data is correct.

The calculator can sort the list for you in ascending order. Press **STAT** again. In the **EDIT** menu, press **2** to select **SortA(**. Press **2nd 1 ENTER** to sort L1 in ascending order. The screen will say "Done".

Press **STAT**, highlight **1:Edit** and press **ENTER**.

SortA(L₁

Done

L1	L2	L3	1
2.21	------	------	
2.26			
2.28			
2.33			
2.39			
2.43			
2.47			

L1(1)=2.21

The list is in ascending order. Use ▲ and ▲ to find the minimum and maximum values.

With a minimum of 2.21 and a maximum of 2.57, the stems should be 2.2, 2.3, 2.4, and 2.5. Now add the leaves.

Gasoline Prices

2.2	1 6 8
2.3	3 9
2.4	3 7
2.5	7

Key: 2.5 | 7 means 2.57

EXERCISES

Make a stem-and-leaf plot for each set of data.

1. 4.5, 4.3, 0.8, 3.5, 2.6, 1.4, 0.2, 0.8, 4.3, 6.0

2. 17.8, 16.3, 19.1, 15.9, 16.3, 18.5, 15.2, 19.1

Gasoline Prices (cost/gallon)
$2.39
$2.47
$2.43
$2.21
$2.33
$2.28
$2.57
$2.26

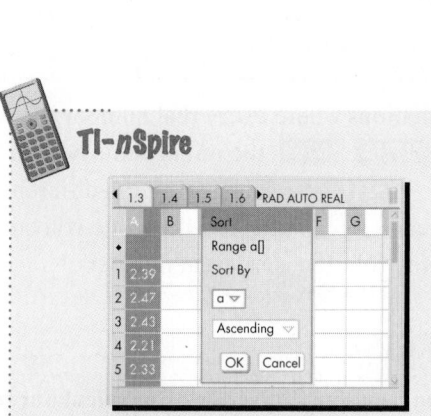

TI-*n*Spire

A list can be sorted in ascending or descending order without leaving the screen where the data is displayed.

Using the Equation Solver

See Lesson 6-3, Example 3

EXAMPLE Solving an Equation

Solve the equation $\frac{3}{4}m = 8 - \frac{1}{2}m$.

Rewrite the equation to equal zero by moving all terms to one side: $0 = 8 - \frac{1}{2}m - \frac{3}{4}m$. To use Equation Solver, press **MATH** and select **0: Solver**. "0=" is automatically displayed.

> EQUATION SOLVER
> eqn:0=8–1/2X–3/4
> X

You can enter the equation using any variable you choose. You could use *M* (press **ALPHA** **÷**) or *X* (press **X,T,θ,n**).

Press **ENTER**.

> 8–1/2X–3/4X=0
>   X=0
>   bound={–1ᴇ99,1...

The value next to "X=" is NOT the solution. "Bound=" indicates the upper and lower bound values for the solution.

Place the cursor on the "X=" line. Press **ALPHA** **ENTER** to solve the equation.

> 8–1/2X–3/4X=0
> •X=6.4
>   bound={–1ᴇ99,1...
> •left–rt=0

After you select **ALPHA** **ENTER**, "X=" changes to the solution.

● The solution to $0 = 8 - \frac{1}{2}m - \frac{3}{4}m$ is $x = 6.4$.

> **Calculator Tip:** For equations with no solution, you will receive an error message.

For equations where every real number is a solution, after you press **ALPHA** **ENTER**, the initial value next to "X=" does not change. Enter a different value next to "X=" and press **ALPHA** **ENTER**. If the value you entered does not change again, the solution is "all real numbers."

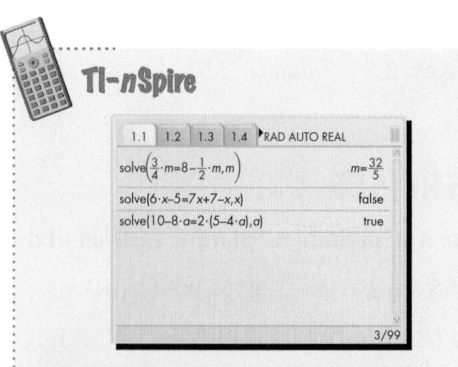

TI-nSpire

You do not need to rearrange the equation to get the solution. This calculator displays "false" for equations with no solution or "true" for identities.

EXERCISES

Use the Equation Solver on your calculator to solve the equations.

1. $4 + \frac{1}{2}x = x - 1$

2. $\frac{3}{5}x - \frac{1}{10}x = \frac{1}{2}x + 1$

3. $x = 0.98x + 0.02x$

4. $3x + 6 = 5x - 10$

Using the GeoMaster Application

See Lesson 6-5, Example 2

To use Geomaster, press APPS and find **:GeoMastr**.

- Use the keys beneath the screen to enter a tool menu in GeoMaster.

- If the GeoMaster tools are not visible, press GRAPH.

- To hide the GeoMaster tools, press CLEAR.

EXAMPLE Dilating a Figure

Quadrilateral _PQRS_ has vertices _P_(−2,4), _Q_(4, 4), _R_(4, −2), and _S_(−4, −4). It is dilated by a scale factor of $\frac{1}{2}$, and the origin is the center of dilation. Graph the original figure and its dilation.

Select the GeoMaster tool **DRAW**. Press **6** to draw a polygon. Move the cursor to (−2, 4). Press ENTER. Move to the other three points in the order they were given. Press ENTER at each coordinate to place a vertex. Press **DRAW** and select **1:Point**. Move to (0, 0) and press ENTER twice.

Press ZOOM **2** to **Zoom In**. Place the cursor at the origin and press ENTER.

Enter the **FILE** menu and press **3** to save. Select **1:New File Name** and type in the name of your choice. For example, type "FIGURE". Press ENTER.

In the **TRFM** menu, press **4** for **Dilation**. Select the item being dilated by placing the cursor anywhere on the polygon and pressing ENTER.

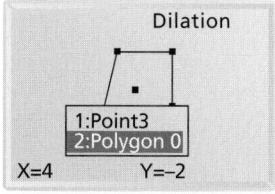

If you placed the cursor on a vertex, you will be asked to choose between the point or the polygon. Choose 2:Polygon. Press ENTER.

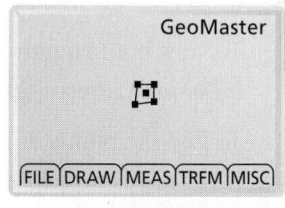

GeoMaster

FILE DRAW MEAS TRFM MISC

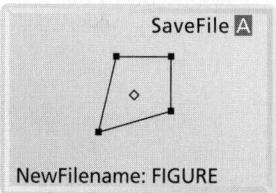

SaveFile A

NewFilename: FIGURE

Place the cursor at the center of dilation, (0, 0). Press ENTER. Key in the scale factor, .5. Press ENTER. The only visible figure is the dilation.

In the **FILE** menu, press **4** for **Append File**. Select **1** for No. Find "FIGURE" and press ENTER. You now have both figures graphed, the original and its dilation.

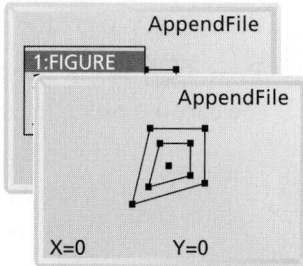

AppendFile

1:FIGURE

AppendFile

X=0   Y=0

EXERCISE

ΔMNP has vertices _M_(3, −2), _N_(3, 5), and _P_(−4, 1). Graph the triangle and its image after a dilation with a scale factor of 2 and center of dilation at the origin.

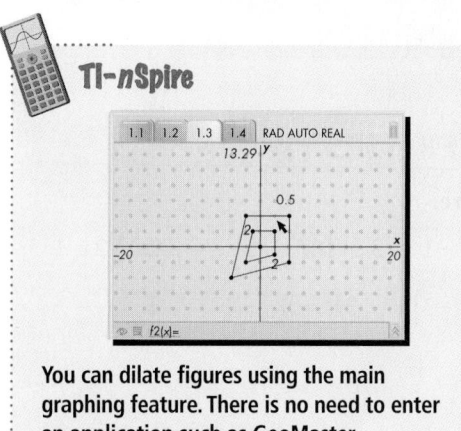

TI-_n_Spire

You can dilate figures using the main graphing feature. There is no need to enter an application such as GeoMaster.

Using the Y= Feature to Graph Absolute Value

See Lesson 7-6, Example 2

EXAMPLE Solving an Absolute Value Equation

Solve $|2p + 5| = 11$.

Press Y= . Next to Y_1 enter the left side of the equation by pressing MATH ▶ and press **1** to select **abs(**. Enter **2** X,T,θ,*n* **+** **5** **)** and press ENTER . Enter **11** for Y_2.

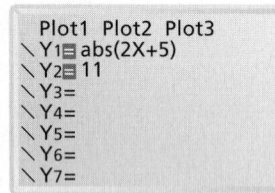

You must use *X* instead of the variable *P* in order for the absolute value equation to be graphed.

To view both equations on the same screen, press ZOOM . Use ▲ or ▼ to highlight **0:ZoomFit**. Press ENTER .

To find the points of intersection, press 2nd TRACE . Press **5** for **intersect.**

Place the cursor close to one point of intersection and press ENTER .	Again, place the cursor close to the point of Intersection. Press ENTER .	The *y*-value, Y=11, is given. Use the *x*-value 2.765 . . . to guess the actual value. Press **3**.

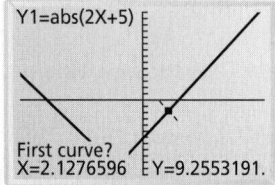 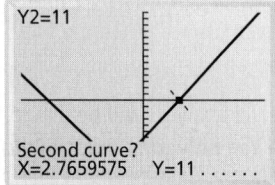 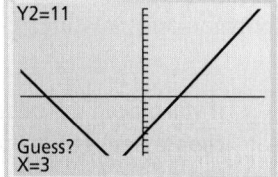

Press ENTER to get the intersection point (3, 11). The guess was correct.

Press 2nd TRACE **5** to find the second point of intersection. Use ◀ and ▶ to move the cursor close to the second point of intersection. The coordinate is $(-8, 11)$.

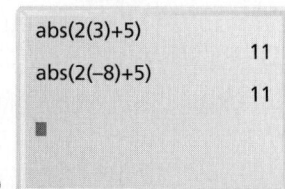

Check these values by evaluating the original equation for $x = 3$ and $x = -8$.

EXERCISES

Solve.

1. $-1 = 3 - \left|\dfrac{x}{2}\right|$

2. $\dfrac{4}{3}\left|2x + 3\right| = 4x$

3. $-3\left|x - 3\right| = 9$

4. $\left|x - 8\right| = 1$

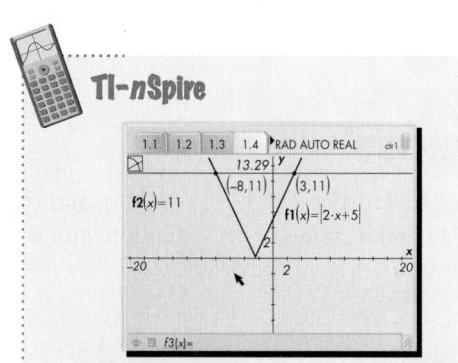

When finding intersection points, you only need to select the two equations. The intersection points are calculated at the same time.

Using the TBLSET Feature

See Lesson 8-2, Example 4

EXAMPLE Finding the Range

Evaluate the function rule $f(a) = -3a + 5$ to find the range of the function for the domain $\{-3, 1, 4\}$.

Press **Y=** and enter the function, $-3x + 5$. Use **X,T,θ,n** instead of the variable A.

Press **2nd** **WINDOW** to see the TABLE SETUP.

Use the arrow keys to highlight **Ask** next to **Indpnt:**. Press **ENTER**. For the independent variable, x, you can enter your own values. Highlight **Auto** next to **Depend:**.

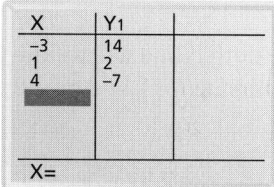

The calculator will give you matching *y*-values for each *x*-value you enter.

> **Calculator Tip:** **TblStart=** and △**Tbl=** do not need to be set to any particular value when **Ask** is selected next to **Indpnt:**.

Press **2nd** **GRAPH** to view the table. Under the X-column enter -3. Press **ENTER**. Notice that in the Y-column, the number 9 appears. Enter 1 and 4. Press **ENTER** after each value.

X	Y₁	
–3	14	
1	2	
4	–7	

X=

To make a table of *x*-values that automatically increase by 1, select Auto for both variables.

● The range of the function rule $f(a) = -3a + 5$ is $\{14, 2, -7\}$.

EXERCISES

Find the range of each function rule for the given domain.

1. $y = -4x$
   $\{-2, 0, 5\}$

2. $g(t) = t^2 + 1$
   $\{-7, 1, 11\}$

3. $f(x) = 0.5x + 1$
   $\{1, 2, 3, 4, 5, 6, 7\}$

4. $f(x) = 3x^2 - 5$
   $\{2, 4, 6, 8, 10, 12\}$

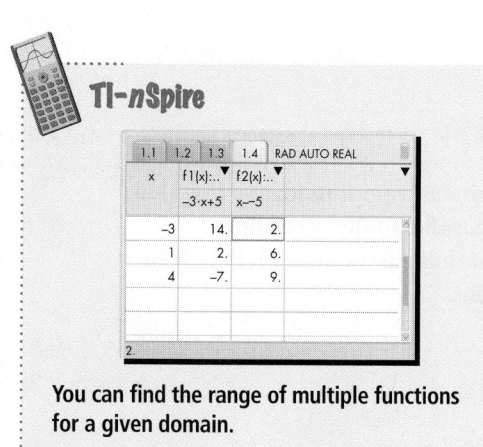

TI-*n*Spire

1.1	1.2	1.3	1.4	RAD AUTO REAL
x	f1(x):..▼	f2(x):..▼		▼
	−3·x+5	x−5		
−3	14.	2.		
1	2.	6.		
4	−7.	9.		

You can find the range of multiple functions for a given domain.

Using the Cabri Jr.® Application

See Lesson 9-6, Example 2

To enter the Cabri Jr. application, press APPS, find :CabriJr, and press ENTER.

How do I ...?

choose a menu	Use F1, F2, F3, F4, and F5. There is no need to press ALPHA.
use a tool	Select a tool from the menu. Press CLEAR to quit a tool.
label coordinates or equations	In the F5 menu, select **Coord. & Eq.** Animate the coordinate or line. Press ENTER. Press ENTER again to set the location.
move an object	Make sure no tool is active. Animate the object and press ALPHA. The hand cursor will appear. Press ENTER to set the location.

EXAMPLE Writing Equations of Parallel Lines

Write an equation for the line that contains (5, 1) and is parallel to $y = \frac{3}{5}x - 4$.

In the F5 menu, highlight **Hide/Show,** press ▶ and select **Axes.** Press ENTER.

The line $y = \frac{3}{5}x - 4$ has points $(5, -1)$ and $(0, -4)$. Notice the dashed lines on both of the axes. Each line represents 1 unit. The point $(0, -4)$ is not visible.

Step 1 Move the origin. Make sure point (5, 1) can be plotted.

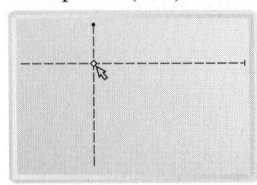

Step 2 Enter the F2 menu and select **Line.** Move the cursor to $(0, -4)$ and press ENTER. Move the cursor to $(5, -1)$ and press enter. Label both of these points. If a coordinate is not correct, you can move the point.

Step 3 In the F2 menu, select **Point.** Move to $(5, -1)$ and press ENTER. Label the point.

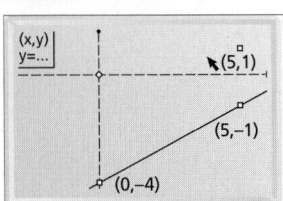

Step 4 Enter the F3 menu and select **Parallel.** Animate the line and press ENTER.

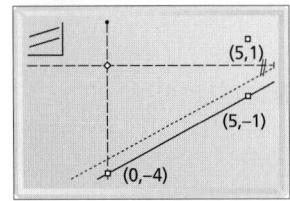

Step 5 A dotted line will follow the cursor. Animate (5, 1) and press ENTER.

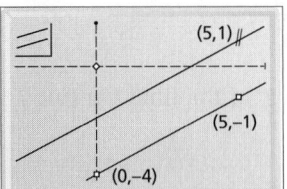

● Once it is labeled, the new line $y = 0.6x - 2$ is displayed.

EXERCISES

Write an equation for the line that is parallel to the given line and that passes through the given point.

1. $y = 3x + 9$; $(2, -6)$

2. $y = 0.5x - 8$; $(8, -5)$

3. $y = -\frac{2}{3}x + 12$; $(5, -3)$

4. $y = -2x + 3$; $(5, -1)$

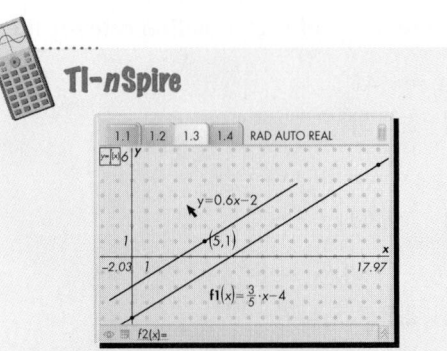

The Graphs & Geometry application allows you to make and label parallel lines.

Making a Trend Line

See Lesson 9-7, Example 1

EXAMPLE Trend Line

Make a scatter plot of the data shown at the right. Draw the trend line and find its equation. Find the wingspan of a hawk that is 28 in. long.

Step 1 Use your calculator's STAT feature. Enter the data for Length in L1 and the data for Wingspan in L2.

Step 2 Press 2nd Y= 1 for **Plot1** and choose the settings shown below. You can choose the mark each coordinate will be.

Step 3 Press ZOOM, find **ZoomStat** and press ENTER.

```
Plot1 Plot2 Plot3
On  Off
Type: ▪▪▪  ⸌⸜  ⼝
      ⼐  ⼑  ⼕
Xlist:L1
Ylist:L2
Mark: ▫ + ·
```

Step 4 Press STAT and in the **CALC** menu select **Manual–Fit**. Move the cursor to a point that will be on your trend line and press ENTER. Move the cursor to a second point on your trend line and press ENTER. A trend line is drawn and its equation is given, Y=1.9376X+1.6297.

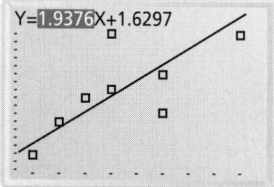

Step 5 Press Y=. The equation of your trend line appears automatically next to Y_1=. Press 2nd GRAPH to view a table of the trend line. X represents length and Y_1 represents wingspan. Under X, scroll down to 28. The corresponding Y_1 value is 55.883.

● A hawk measuring 28 in. will have a wingspan of about 56 in.

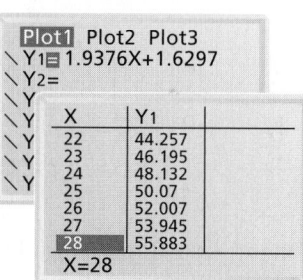

Hawks	
Length (in.)	Wingspan (in.)
21	36
21	41
18	38
24	46
16	31
19	39
17	35
19	46

EXERCISES

Use your graphing calculator and the data below.

Average Temperatures in Northern Latitudes

Latitude (°N)	0	10	20	30	40	50	60	70	80
Temp. (°F)	79.2	80.1	77.5	68.7	57.4	42.4	30.0	12.7	1.0

1. Graph the data for the latitude and average temperature.

2. Find the equation of a trend line.

3. Use your equation to predict the average temperature at 32°N.

TI-nSpire

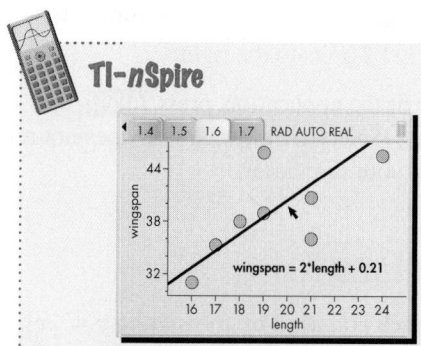

The x-axis, y-axis, and equation of a trend line can be labeled directly on the scatter plot.

Using the Transformation Graphing Application

See Lesson 9-8, Example 4

To open the Transformation Graphing application, press APPS ALPHA 4, highlight **Transfrm** and press ENTER . The Transformation Graphing application shows you how a change in a coefficient affects a parent function. A parent function and its translations can be set to a play type by pressing WINDOW and viewing the **SETTINGS** menu.

>|| (Play-Pause)	Allows you to set the coefficient and control when a function is graphed by pressing either ◄ or ► .
> (Play)	The settings for the coefficient are stored and the functions are displayed as a continuous slide show.
>> (Play-Fast)	Similar to > (Play) except the slide show is played faster.

EXAMPLE   Graphing a Horizontal Translation

Graph each equation, $y = |x + 2|$ **and** $= 5|x - 2|$ **, by translating** $y = |x|$ **.**
Press Y= . Enter $y = |x + A|$. Press WINDOW and view the **SETTINGS** menu. Enter the settings as shown below.

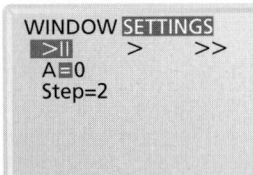

The function will first be graphed where A= 0.
Step= 2 means that the graph can be translated in increments of 2. You can find the function at A= 2, A= −2, or any other increment of 2.

Press ZOOM **6**. To see the *x*-intercept more clearly, press ZOOM **2**. With the cursor at the origin, press ENTER . Press GRAPH to exit the **Zoom In** tool.

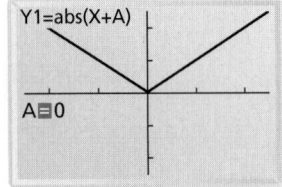

The function $y = |x + 0|$ or $y = |x|$ is displayed.

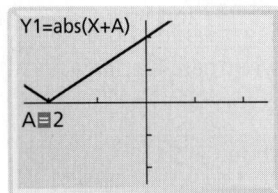

Press ► so that **A=2**.
The function $y = |x + 2$ translates $y = |x|$ 2 units to the left.

Press ◄ so that **A=−2**. The function $y = |x - 2|$ translates $y = |x|$ 2 units to the right.

To exit the application, press APPS , find **Transfrm**, and press ENTER . Select **1:Uninstall**. This does not remove the application from your calculator.

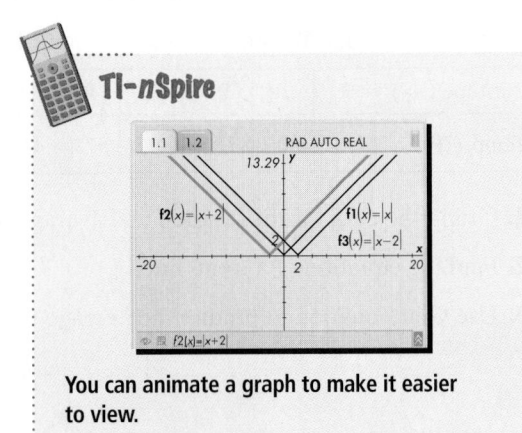

TI-*n*Spire

You can animate a graph to make it easier to view.

EXERCISES

Graph each equation by translating $y = |x|$.

1. $y = |x - 4|$ **2.** $y = |x + 1|$

3. $y = |x + 6|$ **4.** $y = |x - 3|$

Using Y= to Graph an Inequality

See Lesson 10-5, Example 1

In the Y= feature of the graphing calculator, you can change the style of your graph. Move the cursor on top of the equals sign. Press ◄. The symbol to the left of Y_1 will become animated. Press ENTER repeatedly to change the icon. Below is a list of each icon and the type of graph it represents.

Icon	Style
	regular graph, a solid thin line
	the graph will be a solid thick line
	the area above the graph will be shaded, use with $>$ or $\geq$
	the area below the graph will be shaded, use with $<$ or $\leq$
	a circular cursor traces the path of the graph as its displayed
	a circular cursor traces the path of the graph, but no graph is displayed
	the graph will be a dotted line

EXAMPLE Graphing an Inequality

Graph $y < 2x + 3$.

Press Y= and enter the expression $2x + 3$. Change the icon to appropriately graph the inequality.

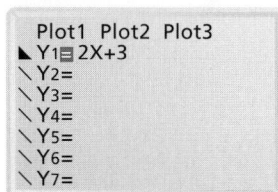

The area beneath the graph should be shaded.

Press ZOOM 6 to select **ZStandard**.

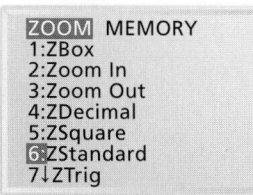

The ZStandard window has minimum and maximum values of -10 and 10.

Once you press **6** in the Zoom menu, the graph will automatically be displayed.

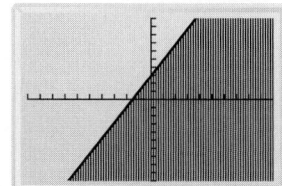

The calculator displays a solid boundary line. Remember that a graph with $<$ or $>$ has a dashed boundary line to make the inequality true.

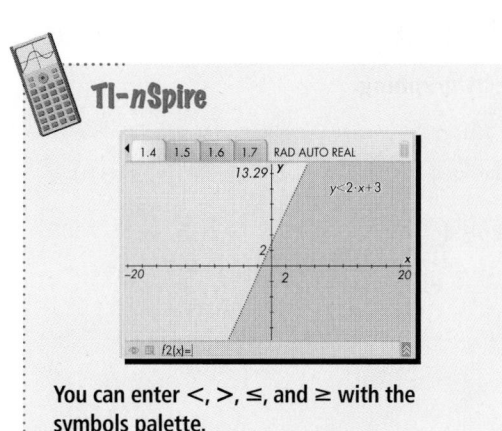

TI-nSpire

You can enter $<$, $>$, $\leq$, and $\geq$ with the symbols palette.

EXERCISES

Graph each inequality. Write whether the boundary line should be dashed or solid.

1. $y \geq 3x - 1$

2. $6x + 8y \geq 12$

3. $y > \frac{5}{3}x - 4$

4. $5x - 3y \leq 6$

Using the Inequality Graphing Application

See Lesson 10-6, Example 1

EXAMPLE Graphing a System of Inequalities

Solve by graphing. $\begin{array}{l} y > 2x - 5 \\ 3x + 4y < 12 \end{array}$

Press [APPS]. From the menu, highlight **Inequalz** and press [ENTER]. To graph in this application, inequalities need to be rewritten so that y is isolated. Therefore,

$3x + 4y < 12$ needs to be rewritten as $y < 3 - \frac{3}{4}x$.

Step 1

Press [ALPHA] [TRACE] to select F4, the $>$ symbol.

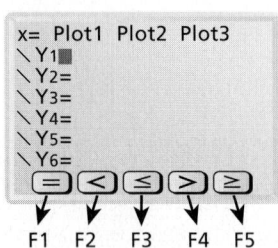

F1 F2 F3 F4 F5

Step 2

Move to the right of the $>$ symbol. Enter the expression $2x - 5$.

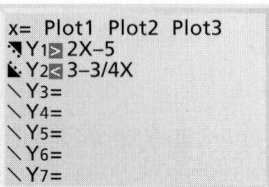

Step 3

Enter $y < 3 - \frac{3}{4}x$ as Y_2.

Press [ALPHA] [WINDOW] to insert the $<$ symbol.

The icon next to Y_1 was changed to a dotted line with the area above shaded. This is the proper graph style for a $>$ symbol.

Step 4

Press [GRAPH]. Any point in the overlap is a solution of the system.

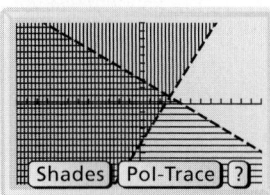

Step 5

Press [ALPHA] [WINDOW].
Press **1** for **Ineq Intersection** to shade only the solution.

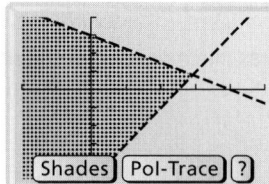

EXERCISES

Solve by graphing.

1. $\begin{array}{l} y \geq -x + 2 \\ 2x + 4y < 4 \end{array}$

2. $\begin{array}{l} y \geq 80 \\ 2x + 2y \leq 310 \end{array}$

3. $\begin{array}{l} y < 2x + 4 \\ 2x - y \leq 4 \end{array}$

4. $\begin{array}{l} y > 6 - x \\ 2x + 7 \leq y \end{array}$

TI-*n*Spire

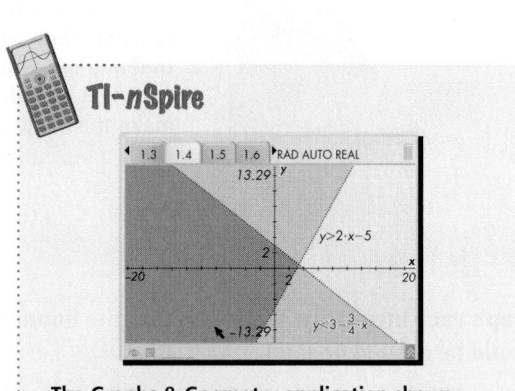

The Graphs & Geometry application shows the boundary line as dashed or solid.

Graphing a Quadratic Function

See Lesson 12-2, Example 1

EXAMPLE **Graphing a Quadratic Function**

Graph the function $y = 2x^2$ and make a table with integer values of x from -2 to 2.

Press Y= and enter the right side of the equation. Press GRAPH to view the parabola.

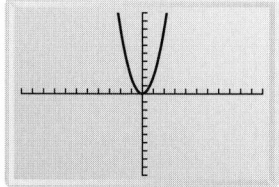

You can use ZOOM to get a better view of the graph.

Press 2nd WINDOW to change the table setup. Use the arrow keys to move to the **Indpnt:** row, highlight **Ask**, and press ENTER . **Depend:** should be set to **Auto**.

```
TABLE SETUP
  TblStart=-5
  ΔTbl=1
Indpnt: auto ask
Depend: auto ask
```

When Indpnt: is set to Ask, you can enter your own values for Δ.

> **Calculator Tip:** You are entering your own x-values. Therefore, it does not matter what TblStart= or ΔTbl= are set to.

Press 2nd GRAPH to view the table for the function. With the cursor in the x-column, enter your first x-value, -2, by pressing (-) 2 ENTER . Enter the rest of the x-values, $-1, 0, 1$, and 2. Press ENTER after each number has been keyed.

```
 X  | Y₁
-2  | 8
-1  | 2
 0  | 0
 1  | 2
 2  | 8

X=
```

For each x-value you entered, the calculator generates the corresponding y-value. Each pair of values is a point on the parabola.

The graph of the function $y = 2x^2$ contains the coordinates $(-2, 8)$, $(-1, 2)$, $(0, 0)$, $(1, 2)$, and $(2, 8)$.

EXERCISES

Graph each function. Make a table of integer values from -2 to 2.

1. $y = -2x^2$ **2.** $y = -x^2 + 9$ **3.** $y = x^2 - 4$

Graphing an Exponential Function

See Lesson 12-3, Example 3

EXAMPLE Graphing Exponential Decay

Graph the function $y = 60 \left(\frac{1}{2}\right)^x$ and make a table with integer values of x from 0 to 5.

Press $\boxed{Y=}$ and enter $60 \left(\frac{1}{2}\right)^x$ by pressing $\boxed{6}$ $\boxed{0}$ $\boxed{\times}$ $\boxed{(}$ $\boxed{1}$ $\boxed{\div}$ $\boxed{2}$ $\boxed{)}$ $\boxed{\wedge}$ $\boxed{X,T,\theta,n}$ $\boxed{ENTER}$.

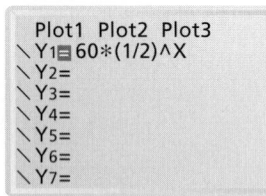

The value $\frac{1}{2}$ is being raised to the x power, so it was placed in parentheses.

Method 1

Press $\boxed{GRAPH}$. It is difficult to view any details of the graph. A table will provide you with exact coordinates of the function. For more information on creating a table for the x-values 0 to 5, see p. 793.

X	Y1
0	60
1	30
2	15
3	7.5
4	3.75
5	1.875

X=

Method 2

While viewing the graph of the exponential function, press $\boxed{2nd}$ $\boxed{TRACE}$ to enter the **CALCULATE** menu. Select **1:value**.

On the bottom left of the graph, you are asked to enter a value for x.

Press **0** $\boxed{ENTER}$.

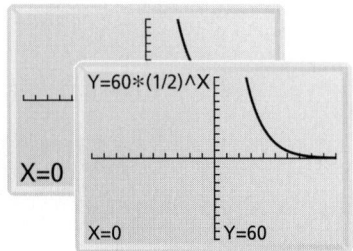

You now have the first row of your table, where $x = 0$ and $y = 60$. The function appears in the upper left corner of the screen.

Press $\boxed{2nd}$ $\boxed{TRACE}$ **1** and enter **1** after **X=**. Continue these steps for the other integer values through 5. The calculator will find the corresponding y-values to complete your table.

EXERCISES

Graph each function and make a table with integer values of x from 0 to 5.

1. $y = \left(\frac{1}{4}\right)^x$ **2.** $y = 6 \left(\frac{1}{3}\right)^x$ **3.** $y = \left(\frac{1}{3}\right) \cdot 3^x$

4. Error Analysis Carla was asked to graph the function $y = 60 \left(\frac{2}{3}\right)^x$. Her calculator screen is shown at the right.
   a. What is her error?
   b. Correctly graph the function. Use a table of values from 0 to 5.

Plot1 Plot2 Plot3
\Y1◻60*2/3^X∎
\Y2=
\Y3=
\Y4=
\Y5=
\Y6=
\Y7=

Skills Handbook

Comparing and Ordering Whole Numbers

The numbers on a number line are in order from least to greatest.

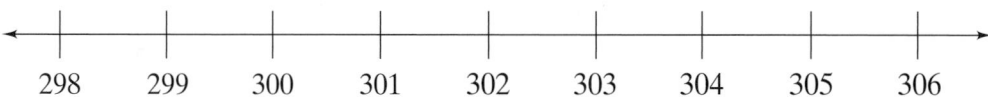

298   299   300   301   302   303   304   305   306

You can use a number line to compare whole numbers. Use the symbols > (is greater than) and < (is less than).

1 EXAMPLE

Use > or < to compare the numbers.

a. **303 ▇ 299**
303 is to the right of 299.
303 > 299

b. **301 ▇ 305**
301 is to the left of 305.
301 < 305

The value of a digit depends on its place in a number. Compare digits starting from the left.

2 EXAMPLE

Use > or < to compare the numbers.

a. **12,060,012,875 ▇ 12,060,012,675**
8 hundreds > 6 hundreds, so
12,060,012,875 > 12,060,012,675.

b. **465,320 ▇ 4,653,208**
0 millions < 4 millions, so
465,320 < 4,653,208.

EXERCISES

Use > or < to compare the numbers.

1. 3,660 ▇ 360
2. 74,328 ▇ 74,238
3. 88,010 ▇ 8,101
4. 87,524 ▇ 9,879
5. 295,286 ▇ 295,826
6. 829,631 ▇ 842,832
7. 932,401 ▇ 932,701
8. 60,000 ▇ 500,009
9. 1,609,372,002 ▇ 609,172,002
10. 45,248,315,150 ▇ 45,283,718,150

Write the numbers from least to greatest.

11. 3,747; 3,474; 3,774; 3,347; 3,734
12. 70,903; 70,309; 73,909; 73,090
13. 32,056,403; 302,056,403; 30,265,403; 30,256,403
14. 884,172; 881,472; 887,142; 881,872

Rounding Whole Numbers

You can use number lines to help you round numbers.

1 EXAMPLE

a. Round 7,510 to the nearest thousand.

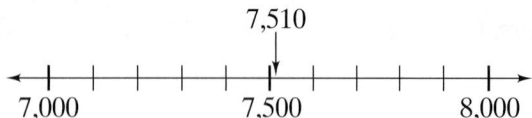

7,510 is between 7,000 and 8,000
and closer to 8,000.
7,510 rounds to 8,000.

b. Round 237 to the nearest ten.

237 is between 230 and 240
and closer to 240.
237 rounds to 240.

To round a number to a particular place, look at the digit to the right of that place. If the digit is less than 5, round down. If the digit is 5 or greater, round up.

2 EXAMPLE

Round to the place of the underlined digit.

a. 3,4<u>6</u>3,280
The digit to the right of the 6 is 3, so
3,463,280 rounds down to 3,460,000.

b. 28<u>9</u>,543
The digit to the right of the 9 is 5, so
289,543 rounds up to 290,000.

EXERCISES

Round to the nearest ten.

1. 42   **2.** 89   **3.** 671   **4.** 3,482   **5.** 7,029   **6.** 661,423

Round to the nearest thousand.

7. 5,800   **8.** 3,100   **9.** 44,280   **10.** 9,936   **11.** 987   **12.** 313,591

13. 5,641   **14.** 37,896   **15.** 82,019   **16.** 808,155   **17.** 34,501   **18.** 650,828

Round to the place of the underlined digit.

19. 68,<u>8</u>52   **20.** <u>4</u>51,006   **21.** 3,40<u>7</u>,481   **22.** 2<u>8</u>,512,030   **23.** 71,2<u>2</u>5,003

24. 96,<u>4</u>49   **25.** 4<u>0</u>1,223   **26.** <u>8</u>,902   **27.** 3,6<u>7</u>7   **28.** 2,551,<u>7</u>50

29. 6<u>8</u>,663   **30.** 70<u>1</u>,803,229   **31.** 56<u>5</u>,598   **32.** 32,<u>8</u>10   **33.** 1,<u>4</u>46,300

Multiplying Whole Numbers

When you multiply by a two-digit number, first multiply by the ones and then multiply by the tens. Add the products.

1 EXAMPLE

Multiply 62 × 704.

Step 1	Step 2	Step 3
704	704	704
× 62	× 62	× 62
1408	1408	1 408
	42240	+ 42 240
		43,648

2 EXAMPLE

Find each product.

a. **93 × 6**

```
   93
 ×  6
  558
```

b. **25 × 48**

```
    48
 ×  25
   240
 + 960
 1,200
```

c. **80 × 921**

```
    921
 ×   80
 73,680
```

EXERCISES

Find each product.

1. 74 × 6	**2.** 35 × 9	**3.** 53 × 7	**4.** 80 × 8	**5.** 98 × 4	**6.** 65 × 8
7. 512 × 3	**8.** 407 × 9	**9.** 225 × 6	**10.** 340 × 5	**11.** 816 × 7	**12.** 603 × 3
13. 70 × 36	**14.** 41 × 55	**15.** 38 × 49	**16.** 601 × 87	**17.** 271 × 34	**18.** 450 × 67

19. 6×82 **20.** 405×5 **21.** 81×9 **22.** 3×274 **23.** 552×4

24. 60×84 **25.** 52×17 **26.** 31×90 **27.** 78×52 **28.** 43×66

29. 826×3 **30.** 702×4 **31.** 8×180 **32.** 6×339 **33.** 781×7

Dividing Whole Numbers

First estimate the quotient by rounding the divisor, the dividend, or both. When you divide, after you bring down a digit, you must write a digit in the quotient.

EXAMPLE

Find each quotient.

a. $741 \div 8$

Estimate:

$720 \div 8 \approx 90$

```
   92 R5
8)741
  -72
   21
  -16
    5
```

b. $838 \div 43$

Estimate:

$800 \div 40 \approx 20$

```
    19 R21
43)838
  -43
   408
  -387
    21
```

c. $367 \div 9$

Estimate:

$360 \div 9 \approx 40$

```
    40 R7
9)367
  -360
    7
```

EXERCISES

Divide.

1. $4\overline{)61}$

2. $8\overline{)53}$

3. $7\overline{)90}$

4. $3\overline{)84}$

5. $6\overline{)81}$

6. $6\overline{)469}$

7. $3\overline{)653}$

8. $8\overline{)645}$

9. $9\overline{)231}$

10. $4\overline{)415}$

11. $60\overline{)461}$

12. $40\overline{)213}$

13. $70\overline{)517}$

14. $30\overline{)432}$

15. $80\overline{)276}$

16. $43\overline{)273}$

17. $52\overline{)281}$

18. $69\overline{)207}$

19. $38\overline{)121}$

20. $81\overline{)433}$

21. $94\overline{)1,368}$

22. $62\overline{)1,147}$

23. $55\overline{)2,047}$

24. $85\overline{)1,450}$

25. $46\overline{)996}$

26. $94 \div 4$

27. $66 \div 9$

28. $90 \div 5$

29. $69 \div 6$

30. $58 \div 8$

31. $323 \div 5$

32. $849 \div 7$

33. $404 \div 8$

34. $934 \div 3$

35. $619 \div 6$

36. $777 \div 50$

37. $528 \div 20$

38. $443 \div 70$

39. $312 \div 40$

40. $335 \div 60$

41. $382 \div 72$

42. $580 \div 68$

43. $279 \div 43$

44. $232 \div 27$

45. $331 \div 93$

46. $614 \div 35$

47. $423 \div 28$

48. $489 \div 15$

49. $1,134 \div 51$

50. $1,103 \div 26$

Decimals and Place Value

Each digit in a whole number or a decimal has both a place and a value. The value of any place is one tenth the value of the place to its left. The chart below can help you read and write decimals.

Billions	Hundred millions	Ten millions	Millions	Hundred thousands	Ten thousands	Thousands	Hundreds	Tens	Ones	.	Tenths	Hundredths	Thousandths	Ten-thousandths	Hundred-thousandths	Millionths
2	4	0	1	2	6	2	8	3	0	.	7	5	0	1	9	1

EXAMPLE

a. **What is the value of the digit 8 in the number above?**
The digit 8 is in the hundreds place. So, its value is 8 hundreds.

b. **Write 2.006 in words.**
The digit 6 is in the thousandths place. So, 2.006 is read two and six thousandths.

c. **Write five and thirty-four ten-thousandths as a decimal.**
Ten-thousandths is 4 places to the right of the decimal point. So, the decimal will have 4 places after the decimal point. The answer is 5.0034.

EXERCISES

Use the chart above. Write the value of each digit.

1. the digit 9
2. the digit 7
3. the digit 5
4. the digit 6
5. the digit 4
6. the digit 3

Write a decimal for the given words.

7. forty-one ten-thousandths
8. eighteen and five hundred four thousandths
9. eight millionths
10. seven and sixty-three hundred-thousandths
11. thirteen thousandths
12. sixty-five and two hundred one thousandths

Write each decimal in words.

13. 0.06
14. 4.7
15. 0.00011
16. 0.9
17. 0.012
18. 0.000059
19. 0.0042
20. 6.020

Comparing and Ordering Decimals

To compare two decimals, use the symbols > (is greater than),
< (is less than), or = (is equal to). When you compare, start at the left
and compare the digits.

① EXAMPLE

Use >, <, or = to compare the decimals.

a. 0.1 ▧ 0.06

1 tenth > 0 tenths, so
0.1 > 0.06.

b. 2.4583 ▧ 2.48

5 hundredths < 8 hundredths,
so 2.4583 < 2.48.

c. 0.30026 ▧ 0.03026

3 tenths > 0 tenths, so
0.30026 > 0.03026.

② EXAMPLE

Draw number lines to compare the decimals.

a. 0.1 ▧ 0.06

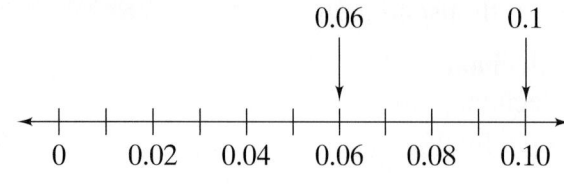

0.1 > 0.06

b. 2.4583 ▧ 2.48

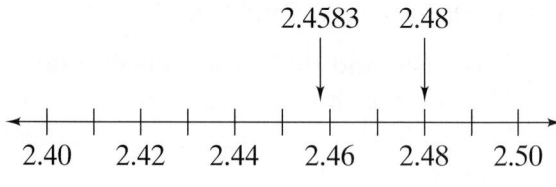

2.4583 < 2.48

EXERCISES

Use >, <, or = to compare the decimals. Draw number
lines if you wish.

1. 0.003 ▧ 0.02
2. 84.2 ▧ 842
3. 0.162 ▧ 0.106
4. 0.0659 ▧ 0.6059

5. 2.13 ▧ 2.99
6. 3.53 ▧ 3.529
7. 2.01 ▧ 2.010
8. 0.00072 ▧ 0.07002

9. 0.458 ▧ 0.4589
10. 8.627 ▧ 8.649
11. 0.0019 ▧ 0.0002
12. 0.19321 ▧ 0.19231

Write the decimals in order from least to greatest.

13. 2.31, 0.231, 23.1, 0.23, 3.21
14. 1.02, 1.002, 1.2, 1.11, 1.021

15. 0.02, 0.002, 0.22, 0.222, 2.22
16. 55.5, 555.5, 55.555, 5.5555

17. 0.07, 0.007, 0.7, 0.71, 0.72
18. 2.78, 2.7001, 2.701, 2.71, 2.7

19. 7, 7.3264, 7.3, 7.3246, 7.0324
20. 0.0101, 0.0099, 0.011, 0.00019

Rounding

When you round to a particular place, look at the digit to the right of that place. If it is 5 or greater, you increase the digit in the place you are rounding to by 1. If it is less than 5, you leave the digit in the place you are rounding to unchanged.

EXAMPLE

a. **Round 1.627 to the nearest whole number.**
The digit to the right of the units place is 6, so 1.627 rounds up to 2.

b. **Round 12,034 to the nearest thousand.**
The digit to the right of the thousands place is 0, so 12,034 rounds down to 12,000.

c. **Round 2.7195 to the nearest hundredth.**
The digit to the right of the hundredths place is 9, so 2.7195 rounds up to 2.72.

d. **Round 0.060521 to the nearest thousandth.**
The digit to the right of the thousandths place is 5, so 0.060521 rounds up to 0.061.

EXERCISES

Round to the nearest thousand.

1. 105,099 **2.** 10,400 **3.** 79,527,826 **4.** 79,932 **5.** 4,312,349

Round to the nearest whole number.

6. 135.91 **7.** 3.001095 **8.** 96.912 **9.** 101.167 **10.** 299.9

Round to the nearest tenth.

11. 82.01 **12.** 4.67522 **13.** 20.397 **14.** 399.95 **15.** 129.98

Round to the nearest hundredth.

16. 13.458 **17.** 96.4045 **18.** 0.699 **19.** 4.234 **20.** 12.09531

Round to the place of the underlined digit.

21. 7.0$\underline{6}$15 **22.** $\underline{5}$.77125 **23.** 1,5$\underline{2}$2 **24.** 0.919$\underline{5}$2 **25.** 4.$\underline{2}$43

26. 2$\underline{3}$6.001 **27.** $\underline{3}$52 **28.** 3.4953$\underline{6}$6 **29.** 8.0$\underline{7}$092 **30.** $\underline{0}$.6008

31. 4$\underline{0}$9 **32.** 23,9$\underline{5}$1,888 **33.** 2.5$\underline{7}$84 **34.** 8$\underline{6}$2 **35.** 1$\underline{9}$.32

36. $\underline{9}$18 **37.** 7,$\underline{7}$35 **38.** 25.66$\underline{0}$47 **39.** 9$\underline{8}$3,240,631 **40.** $\underline{2}$7

41. 0.0037$\underline{7}$1 **42.** 0.$\underline{0}$649 **43.** 12.$\underline{7}$77 **44.** 1,759,$\underline{2}$30 **45.** 20,$\underline{9}$08

Adding and Subtracting Decimals

You add or subtract decimals just as you do whole numbers. You line up the decimal points and then add or subtract. If you wish, you can use zeros to make the columns even.

EXAMPLE

Find each sum or difference.

a. **37.6 + 8.431**

$$\begin{array}{r} 37.6 \\ + 8.431 \\ \hline \end{array} \rightarrow \begin{array}{r} 37.600 \\ + 8.431 \\ \hline 46.031 \end{array}$$

b. **8 − 4.593**

$$\begin{array}{r} 8 \\ - 4.593 \\ \hline \end{array} \rightarrow \begin{array}{r} 8.000 \\ - 4.593 \\ \hline 3.407 \end{array}$$

c. **8.3 + 2.99 + 17.5**

$$\begin{array}{r} 8.3 \\ 2.99 \\ + 17.5 \\ \hline \end{array} \rightarrow \begin{array}{r} 8.30 \\ 2.99 \\ + 17.50 \\ \hline 28.79 \end{array}$$

EXERCISES

Find each sum or difference.

1. $\begin{array}{r} 39.7 \\ - 36.03 \\ \hline \end{array}$
2. $\begin{array}{r} 1.08 \\ - 0.9 \\ \hline \end{array}$
3. $\begin{array}{r} 6.784 \\ + 0.528 \\ \hline \end{array}$
4. $\begin{array}{r} 5.01 \\ - 0.87 \\ \hline \end{array}$
5. $\begin{array}{r} 13.02 \\ + 23.107 \\ \hline \end{array}$

6. $\begin{array}{r} 8.634 \\ + 1.409 \\ \hline \end{array}$
7. $\begin{array}{r} 2.1 \\ - 0.5 \\ \hline \end{array}$
8. $\begin{array}{r} 8.23 \\ - 3.1 \\ \hline \end{array}$
9. $\begin{array}{r} 1.05 \\ + 12.9 \\ \hline \end{array}$
10. $\begin{array}{r} 2.6 \\ + 0.003 \\ \hline \end{array}$

11. $\begin{array}{r} 0.1 \\ 58.21 \\ + 1.9 \\ \hline \end{array}$
12. $\begin{array}{r} 12.2 \\ 3.06 \\ + 0.5 \\ \hline \end{array}$
13. $\begin{array}{r} 9.42 \\ 3.6 \\ + 21.003 \\ \hline \end{array}$
14. $\begin{array}{r} 15.22 \\ 7.4 \\ + 8.125 \\ \hline \end{array}$
15. $\begin{array}{r} 3.7 \\ 20.06 \\ + 16.19 \\ \hline \end{array}$

16. 76.39 − 8.47
17. 8.7 + 17.03
18. 32.403 + 12.06
19. 20.5 + 11.45

20. 8.9 − 4.45
21. 1.245 + 5.8
22. 3.9 + 6.57
23. 14.81 − 8.6

24. 11.9 − 2.06
25. 3.45 + 4.061
26. 8.29 + 4.3
27. 7.06 − 4.235

28. 6.02 + 4.005
29. 7.05 − 3.5
30. 1.18 + 3.015
31. 2.304 − 0.87

32. 5.002 − 3.45
33. 6.8 + 3.57
34. 0.23 + 0.091
35. 0.5 − 0.18

36. 8.3 + 2.99 + 17.52
37. 9.5 + 12.32 + 6.4
38. 4.521 + 1.8 + 3.07

39. 3.602 + 9.4 + 24
40. 11.6 + 8.05 + 5.13
41. 7.023 + 1.48 + 3.9

42. 57 + 0.6327 + 189.007
43. 741 + 6.08 + 0.0309
44. 0.045 + 16.32 + 8.6

45. 4.27 + 6.18 + 0.91
46. 3.856 + 14.01 + 1.72
47. 11.45 + 3.79 + 23.861

Multiplying Decimals

Multiply decimals as you would whole numbers. Then place the decimal point in the product. To do this, add the number of decimal places in the factors.

1 EXAMPLE

Multiply 0.068 × 2.3.

Step 1 Multiply.

$$
\begin{array}{r}
0.068 \\
\times\ 2.3 \\
\hline
204 \\
+\ 1360 \\
\hline
1564
\end{array}
$$

Step 2 Place the decimal point.

$$
\begin{array}{r}
0.068 \\
\times\ 2.3 \\
\hline
204 \\
+\ 1360 \\
\hline
0.1564
\end{array}
$$

←three decimal places
←one decimal place

←four decimal places

2 EXAMPLE

Find each product.

a. 3.12 × 0.9

$$
\begin{array}{r}
3.12 \\
\times\ 0.9 \\
\hline
2.808
\end{array}
$$

b. 5.75 × 42

$$
\begin{array}{r}
5.75 \\
\times\ 42 \\
\hline
11\ 50 \\
+\ 230\ 00 \\
\hline
241.50
\end{array}
$$

c. 0.964 × 0.28

$$
\begin{array}{r}
0.964 \\
\times\ 0.28 \\
\hline
7712 \\
+\ 19280 \\
\hline
0.26992
\end{array}
$$

EXERCISES

Multiply.

1. $\begin{array}{r} 1.48 \\ \times\ 3.6 \\ \hline \end{array}$

2. $\begin{array}{r} 191.2 \\ \times\ 3.4 \\ \hline \end{array}$

3. $\begin{array}{r} 0.05 \\ \times\ 43 \\ \hline \end{array}$

4. $\begin{array}{r} 0.27 \\ \times\ 5 \\ \hline \end{array}$

5. $\begin{array}{r} 1.36 \\ \times\ 3.8 \\ \hline \end{array}$

6. $\begin{array}{r} 6.23 \\ \times\ 0.21 \\ \hline \end{array}$

7. $\begin{array}{r} 0.512 \\ \times\ 0.76 \\ \hline \end{array}$

8. $\begin{array}{r} 0.04 \\ \times\ 7 \\ \hline \end{array}$

9. $\begin{array}{r} 0.136 \\ \times\ 8.4 \\ \hline \end{array}$

10. $\begin{array}{r} 3 \\ \times\ 0.05 \\ \hline \end{array}$

11. 2.07×1.004

12. 0.12×6.1

13. 3.2×0.15

14. 0.74×0.23

15. 2.6×0.14

16. 0.77×51

17. 9.3×0.706

18. 71.13×0.4

19. 0.42×98

20. 6.3×85

21. 45×0.028

22. 76×3.3

23. 9×1.35

24. 4.56×7

25. 5×2.41

26. 704×0.3

27. 8.003×0.6

28. 42.2×0.9

29. 0.6×30.02

30. 0.05×11.8

Zeros in a Product

When you multiply with decimals, you may have to write one or more zeros to the left of a product before you can place the decimal point.

1 EXAMPLE

Multiply 0.06 × 0.015.

Step 1 Multiply.

```
  0.015
× 0.06
─────
    90
```

Step 2 Place the decimal point.

```
  0.015
× 0.06
─────
0.00090
```

← **The product should have 5 decimal places, so you must write three zeros before placing the decimal point.**

2 EXAMPLE

a. 0.02 × 1.3

```
   1.3
× 0.02
─────
 0.026
```

b. 0.012 × 2.4

```
    2.4
× 0.012
──────
     48
+  240
──────
 0.0288
```

c. 0.022 × 0.051

```
   0.051
× 0.022
───────
     102
+ 1020
───────
0.001122
```

EXERCISES

Multiply.

1.
```
  0.03
× 0.9
```

2.
```
  0.06
× 0.5
```

3.
```
   2.4
× 0.03
```

4.
```
      7
× 0.01
```

5.
```
  0.05
× 0.05
```

6.
```
  0.016
× 0.12
```

7.
```
  0.031
× 0.08
```

8.
```
  0.03
× 0.2
```

9.
```
   0.27
× 0.033
```

10.
```
  0.014
× 0.25
```

11. 0.003 × 0.55 **12.** 0.01 × 0.74 **13.** 0.47 × 0.08 **14.** 0.76 × 0.1

15. 0.3 × 0.27 **16.** 0.19 × 0.05 **17.** 0.018 × 0.04 **18.** 0.43 × 0.2

19. 0.03 × 0.03 **20.** 4.003 × 0.02 **21.** 0.5 × 0.08 **22.** 0.06 × 0.7

23. 0.047 × 0.008 **24.** 0.05 × 0.06 **25.** 0.03 × 0.4 **26.** 0.05 × 0.036

27. 0.4 × 0.23 **28.** 0.3 × 0.017 **29.** 0.3 × 0.24 **30.** 0.67 × 0.09

31. 3.02 × 0.006 **32.** 0.31 × 0.08 **33.** 0.14 × 0.05 **34.** 0.07 × 0.85

Dividing Decimals by Whole Numbers

When you divide a decimal by a whole number, the decimal point in the quotient goes directly above the decimal point in the dividend. You may need extra zeros to place the decimal point.

1 EXAMPLE

Divide 2.432 ÷ 32.

Step 1 Divide.

$$\begin{array}{r} 76 \\ 32\overline{)2.432} \\ -2\,24 \\ \hline 192 \\ -192 \\ \hline 0 \end{array}$$

Step 2 Place the decimal point.

$$\begin{array}{r} 0.076 \\ 32\overline{)2.432} \\ -2\,24 \\ \hline 192 \\ -192 \\ \hline 0 \end{array}$$

← **Put extra zeros to the left. Then place the decimal point.**

2 EXAMPLE

a. **37.6 ÷ 8**

$$\begin{array}{r} 4.7 \\ 8\overline{)37.6} \\ -32 \\ \hline 5\,6 \\ -5\,6 \\ \hline 0 \end{array}$$

b. **39.33 ÷ 69**

$$\begin{array}{r} 0.57 \\ 69\overline{)39.33} \\ -34\,5 \\ \hline 4\,83 \\ -4\,83 \\ \hline 0 \end{array}$$

c. **4.482 ÷ 54**

$$\begin{array}{r} 0.083 \\ 54\overline{)4.482} \\ -4\,32 \\ \hline 162 \\ -162 \\ \hline 0 \end{array}$$

EXERCISES

Divide.

1. $7\overline{)17.92}$ **2.** $5\overline{)16.5}$ **3.** $9\overline{)6.984}$ **4.** $6\overline{)91.44}$ **5.** $4\overline{)35.16}$

6. $56\overline{)8.848}$ **7.** $22\overline{)2.42}$ **8.** $26\overline{)1,723.8}$ **9.** $83\overline{)15.272}$ **10.** $39\overline{)26.91}$

11. $14.49 \div 7$ **12.** $10.53 \div 9$ **13.** $17.52 \div 2$ **14.** $37.14 \div 6$

15. $0.1352 \div 8$ **16.** $0.0324 \div 9$ **17.** $0.0882 \div 6$ **18.** $0.8682 \div 6$

19. $12.342 \div 22$ **20.** $29.792 \div 32$ **21.** $22.568 \div 26$ **22.** $11.340 \div 36$

23. $45.918 \div 18$ **24.** $79.599 \div 13$ **25.** $58.5 \div 15$ **26.** $74.664 \div 12$

27. $21.0 \div 84$ **28.** $89.378 \div 67$ **29.** $0.0672 \div 48$ **30.** $171.031 \div 53$

Multiplying and Dividing by Powers of Ten

You can use shortcuts to multiply or divide by powers of ten.

When you multiply by	Move the decimal point	When you divide by	Move the decimal point
10,000	4 places to the right	10,000	4 places to the left
1,000	3 places to the right	1,000	3 places to the left
100	2 places to the right	100	2 places to the left
10	1 place to the right	10	1 place to the left
0.1	1 place to the left	0.1	1 place to the right
0.01	2 places to the left	0.01	2 places to the right
0.001	3 places to the left	0.001	3 places to the right

EXAMPLE

Multiply or divide.

a. 0.7×0.001

Move the decimal point 3 places to the left.
0.000.7

$0.7 \times 0.001 = 0.0007$

b. $0.605 \div 100$

Move the decimal point 2 places to the left.
0.00.605

$0.605 \div 100 = 0.00605$

EXERCISES

Multiply or divide.

1. $10,000 \times 0.056$
2. 0.001×0.09
3. 5.2×10
4. $0.03 \times 1,000$
5. $236.7 \div 0.1$
6. $45.28 \div 10$
7. $0.9 \div 1,000$
8. $1.07 \div 0.01$
9. 100×0.08
10. $1.03 \times 10,000$
11. 1.803×0.001
12. 4.1×100
13. $13.7 \div 0.001$
14. $203.05 \div 0.01$
15. $4.7 \div 10$
16. $0.05 \div 100$
17. 23.6×0.01
18. $1,000 \times 0.12$
19. 0.41×0.001
20. 0.01×6.2
21. $42.3 \div 0.1$
22. $0.4 \div 10,000$
23. $5.02 \div 0.01$
24. $16.5 \div 100$
25. $0.27 \div 0.01$
26. 1.05×0.001
27. 10×0.04
28. $2.09 \div 100$
29. 0.65×0.1
30. $0.03 \div 100$
31. $2.6 \div 0.1$
32. $12.6 \times 10,000$
33. $0.3 \div 1,000$
34. 0.01×6.7
35. 100×0.158
36. $23.1 \div 10$

Dividing Decimals by Decimals

To divide with a decimal divisor, multiply it by the smallest power of ten that will make the divisor a whole number. Then multiply the dividend by that same power of ten.

EXAMPLE

Find each quotient.

a. 3.348 ÷ 6.2
   Multiply by 10.

$$
\begin{array}{r}
0.54 \\
6.2.\overline{)3.3.48} \\
-3\ 1\ 0 \\
\hline
2\ 48 \\
-2\ 48 \\
\hline
0
\end{array}
$$

b. 2.4885 ÷ 0.35
   Multiply by 100.

$$
\begin{array}{r}
7.11 \\
0.35.\overline{)2.48.85} \\
-2\ 45 \\
\hline
3\ 8 \\
-3\ 5 \\
\hline
35 \\
-35 \\
\hline
0
\end{array}
$$

c. 0.0576 ÷ 0.012
   Multiply by 1,000.

$$
\begin{array}{r}
4.8 \\
0.012.\overline{)0.057.6} \\
-48 \\
\hline
96 \\
-96 \\
\hline
0
\end{array}
$$

EXERCISES

Divide.

1. $3.2\overline{)268.8}$ **2.** $1.9\overline{)123.5}$ **3.** $0.3\overline{)135.6}$ **4.** $2.3\overline{)170.2}$ **5.** $7.9\overline{)252.8}$

6. $5.7\overline{)10.26}$ **7.** $2.3\overline{)71.53}$ **8.** $3.1\overline{)16.12}$ **9.** $7.8\overline{)24.18}$ **10.** $6.3\overline{)14.49}$

11. $134.42 \div 5.17$ **12.** $89.96 \div 3.46$ **13.** $160.58 \div 5.18$ **14.** $106.59 \div 6.27$

15. $62.4 \div 3.9$ **16.** $260.4 \div 8.4$ **17.** $316.8 \div 7.2$ **18.** $162.4 \div 2.9$

19. $1.512 \div 0.54$ **20.** $3.225 \div 0.43$ **21.** $2.484 \div 0.69$ **22.** $511.5 \div 5.5$

23. $0.992 \div 0.8$ **24.** $4.53 \div 0.05$ **25.** $3.498 \div 0.06$ **26.** $59.2 \div 0.8$

27. $2.198 \div 0.07$ **28.** $14.28 \div 0.7$ **29.** $1.98 \div 0.5$ **30.** $26.36 \div 0.04$

31. $3.922 \div 7.4$ **32.** $23.52 \div 0.98$ **33.** $71.25 \div 7.5$ **34.** $114.7 \div 3.7$

35. $0.832 \div 0.52$ **36.** $1.125 \div 0.09$ **37.** $9.666 \div 2.7$ **38.** $1.456 \div 9.1$

39. $0.4374 \div 1.8$ **40.** $2.3414 \div 0.46$ **41.** $0.07224 \div 0.021$ **42.** $0.1386 \div 0.18$

43. $0.16926 \div 0.091$ **44.** $0.6042 \div 5.3$ **45.** $2.3374 \div 0.62$ **46.** $1.0062 \div 0.078$

Zeros in Decimal Division

When you are dividing by a decimal, sometimes you need to use extra zeros in the dividend or the quotient, or both.

1 EXAMPLE

Divide 0.045 ÷ 3.6.

Step 1 Multiply by 10.

$$3.6.\overline{)0.0.45}$$

Step 2 Divide.

$$\begin{array}{r} 125 \\ 3.6.\overline{)0.0.4500} \\ -36 \\ \hline 90 \\ -72 \\ \hline 180 \\ -180 \\ \hline 0 \end{array}$$

Step 3 Place the decimal point.

$$\begin{array}{r} 0.0125 \\ 3.6.\overline{)0.0.4500} \\ -36 \\ \hline 90 \\ -72 \\ \hline 180 \\ -180 \\ \hline 0 \end{array}$$

2 EXAMPLE

Find each quotient.

a. **0.4428 ÷ 8.2**
   Multiply by 10.
$$\begin{array}{r} 0.054 \\ 8.2.\overline{)0.4.428} \end{array}$$

b. **0.00434 ÷ 0.07**
   Multiply by 100.
$$\begin{array}{r} 0.062 \\ 0.07.\overline{)0.00.434} \end{array}$$

c. **0.00306 ÷ 0.072**
   Multiply by 1,000.
$$\begin{array}{r} 0.0425 \\ 0.072.\overline{)0.003.0600} \end{array}$$

EXERCISES

Divide.

1. $0.05\overline{)0.0023}$

2. $0.02\overline{)0.000162}$

3. $0.12\overline{)0.009}$

4. $2.5\overline{)0.021}$

5. $0.0019 \div 0.2$

6. $0.9 \div 0.8$

7. $0.000175 \div 0.07$

8. $0.142 \div 0.04$

9. $0.0017 \div 0.02$

10. $0.003 \div 0.6$

11. $0.0105 \div 0.7$

12. $0.034 \div 0.05$

13. $0.00056 \div 0.16$

14. $0.0612 \div 7.2$

15. $0.217 \div 3.1$

16. $0.052 \div 0.8$

17. $0.000924 \div 0.44$

18. $0.05796 \div 0.63$

19. $0.00123 \div 8.2$

20. $0.0954 \div 0.09$

21. $0.0084 \div 1.4$

22. $0.259 \div 3.5$

23. $0.00468 \div 0.52$

24. $0.104 \div 0.05$

25. $0.00063 \div 0.18$

26. $0.011 \div 0.25$

27. $0.3069 \div 9.3$

28. $0.00045 \div 0.3$

Writing Equivalent Fractions

If you multiply or divide both the numerator and the denominator of a fraction by the same number, you get an equivalent fraction.

1 EXAMPLE

a. Find the missing number in $\frac{5}{6} = \frac{20}{\blacksquare}$.

$$\overset{\curvearrowright \times 4 \curvearrowleft}{\frac{5}{6} = \frac{20}{\blacksquare}}$$

$$\underset{\curvearrowright \times 4 \curvearrowleft}{\frac{5}{6} = \frac{20}{24}}$$

b. Find the missing number in $\frac{12}{30} = \frac{\blacksquare}{15}$.

$$\overset{\curvearrowright \div 2 \curvearrowleft}{\frac{12}{30} = \frac{\blacksquare}{15}}$$

$$\underset{\curvearrowright \div 2 \curvearrowleft}{\frac{12}{30} = \frac{6}{15}}$$

To write a fraction in simplest form, divide both the numerator and the denominator by the greatest common factor.

2 EXAMPLE

a. Write $\frac{6}{15}$ in simplest form.

3 is the greatest common factor.

$$\frac{6}{15} = \frac{6 \div 3}{15 \div 3} = \frac{2}{5}$$

The simplest form of $\frac{6}{15}$ is $\frac{2}{5}$.

b. Write $\frac{36}{42}$ in simplest form.

6 is the greatest common factor.

$$\frac{36}{42} = \frac{36 \div 6}{42 \div 6} = \frac{6}{7}$$

The simplest form of $\frac{36}{42}$ is $\frac{6}{7}$.

EXERCISES

Find each missing number.

1. $\frac{1}{3} = \frac{\blacksquare}{6}$

2. $\frac{3}{4} = \frac{\blacksquare}{16}$

3. $\frac{18}{30} = \frac{6}{\blacksquare}$

4. $\frac{2}{3} = \frac{\blacksquare}{21}$

5. $\frac{3}{4} = \frac{9}{\blacksquare}$

6. $\frac{3}{10} = \frac{9}{\blacksquare}$

7. $\frac{4}{5} = \frac{\blacksquare}{30}$

8. $\frac{2}{3} = \frac{8}{\blacksquare}$

9. $\frac{33}{55} = \frac{\blacksquare}{5}$

10. $\frac{27}{72} = \frac{9}{\blacksquare}$

11. $\frac{2}{3} = \frac{\blacksquare}{24}$

12. $\frac{11}{12} = \frac{55}{\blacksquare}$

13. $\frac{3}{5} = \frac{18}{\blacksquare}$

14. $\frac{60}{72} = \frac{10}{\blacksquare}$

15. $\frac{7}{8} = \frac{\blacksquare}{24}$

Write each fraction in simplest form.

16. $\frac{12}{36} \quad \frac{1}{3}$

17. $\frac{25}{30} \quad \frac{5}{6}$

18. $\frac{14}{16} \quad \frac{7}{8}$

19. $\frac{27}{36} \quad \frac{3}{4}$

20. $\frac{21}{35} \quad \frac{3}{5}$

21. $\frac{40}{50} \quad \frac{4}{5}$

22. $\frac{24}{40} \quad \frac{3}{5}$

23. $\frac{32}{64} \quad \frac{1}{2}$

24. $\frac{15}{45} \quad \frac{1}{3}$

25. $\frac{27}{63} \quad \frac{3}{7}$

26. $\frac{44}{77} \quad \frac{4}{7}$

27. $\frac{45}{75} \quad \frac{3}{5}$

28. $\frac{60}{72} \quad \frac{5}{6}$

29. $\frac{77}{84} \quad \frac{11}{12}$

30. $\frac{12}{24} \quad \frac{1}{2}$

31. $\frac{24}{32} \quad \frac{3}{4}$

32. $\frac{7}{21} \quad \frac{1}{3}$

33. $\frac{18}{42} \quad \frac{3}{7}$

Mixed Numbers and Improper Fractions

A fraction, such as $\frac{10}{7}$, in which the numerator is greater than or equal to the denominator is an improper fraction. You can write an improper fraction as a mixed number that shows the sum of a whole number and a fraction.

Sometimes it is necessary to do the opposite and write a mixed number as an improper fraction.

EXAMPLE

a. Write $\frac{11}{5}$ as a mixed number.

$$\frac{11}{5} \rightarrow 5\overline{)11} \quad \begin{array}{l} 2 \leftarrow \text{whole number} \\ \underline{-10} \\ 1 \leftarrow \text{remainder} \end{array}$$

$$\frac{11}{5} = 2\frac{1}{5} \quad \leftarrow \text{whole number} + \frac{\text{remainder}}{\text{denominator}}$$

b. Write $2\frac{5}{6}$ as an improper fraction.

$$2\frac{5}{6} = 2 + \frac{5}{6}$$

$$= \frac{12}{6} + \frac{5}{6} \quad \leftarrow \text{Write 2 as } \frac{12}{6}.$$

$$= \frac{12 + 5}{6} \quad \leftarrow \text{Add the numerators.}$$

$$2\frac{5}{6} = \frac{17}{6}$$

EXERCISES

Write each improper fraction as a mixed number.

1. $\frac{7}{5}$ $1\frac{2}{5}$ 2. $\frac{9}{2}$ $4\frac{1}{2}$ 3. $\frac{13}{4}$ $3\frac{1}{4}$ 4. $\frac{21}{5}$ $4\frac{1}{5}$ 5. $\frac{13}{10}$ $1\frac{3}{10}$ 6. $\frac{49}{5}$ $9\frac{4}{5}$

7. $\frac{21}{8}$ $2\frac{5}{8}$ 8. $\frac{13}{7}$ $1\frac{6}{7}$ 9. $\frac{17}{5}$ $3\frac{2}{5}$ 10. $\frac{49}{6}$ $8\frac{1}{6}$ 11. $\frac{17}{4}$ $4\frac{1}{4}$ 12. $\frac{5}{2}$ $2\frac{1}{2}$

13. $\frac{27}{5}$ $5\frac{2}{5}$ 14. $\frac{12}{9}$ $1\frac{1}{3}$ 15. $\frac{30}{8}$ $3\frac{3}{4}$ 16. $\frac{37}{12}$ $3\frac{1}{12}$ 17. $\frac{8}{6}$ $1\frac{1}{3}$ 18. $\frac{19}{12}$ $1\frac{7}{12}$

19. $\frac{45}{10}$ $4\frac{1}{2}$ 20. $\frac{15}{12}$ $1\frac{1}{4}$ 21. $\frac{11}{2}$ $5\frac{1}{2}$ 22. $\frac{20}{6}$ $3\frac{1}{3}$ 23. $\frac{34}{8}$ $4\frac{1}{4}$ 24. $\frac{21}{9}$ $2\frac{1}{3}$

Write each mixed number as an improper fraction.

25. $1\frac{1}{2}$ $\frac{3}{2}$ 26. $2\frac{2}{3}$ $\frac{8}{3}$ 27. $1\frac{1}{12}$ $\frac{13}{12}$ 28. $3\frac{1}{5}$ $\frac{16}{5}$ 29. $2\frac{2}{7}$ $\frac{16}{7}$ 30. $4\frac{1}{2}$ $\frac{9}{2}$

31. $2\frac{7}{8}$ $\frac{23}{8}$ 32. $1\frac{2}{9}$ $\frac{11}{9}$ 33. $5\frac{1}{5}$ $\frac{26}{5}$ 34. $4\frac{7}{9}$ $\frac{43}{9}$ 35. $9\frac{1}{4}$ $\frac{37}{4}$ 36. $2\frac{3}{8}$ $\frac{19}{8}$

37. $7\frac{7}{8}$ $\frac{63}{8}$ 38. $1\frac{5}{12}$ $\frac{17}{12}$ 39. $3\frac{3}{7}$ $\frac{24}{7}$ 40. $6\frac{1}{2}$ $\frac{13}{2}$ 41. $3\frac{1}{10}$ $\frac{31}{10}$ 42. $4\frac{6}{7}$ $\frac{34}{7}$

Factors and Multiples

A common factor is a number that is a factor of two or more numbers. The greatest common factor (GCF) is the greatest number that is a common factor of two or more numbers.

1 EXAMPLE

Find the GCF of 24 and 64.

Method 1 List all the factors of each number.

Factors of 24 $1, 2, 3, 4, 6, 8, 12, 24$ **Find the common factors: 1, 2, 4, 8.**

Factors of 64 $1, 2, 4, 8, 16, 32, 64$ **The greatest common factor is 8.**

$GCF(24, 64) = 8$

Method 2 Use the prime factorization of each number.

$24 = 2 \cdot 2 \cdot 2 \cdot 3$ **Find the prime factorization of each number.**

$64 = 2 \cdot 2 \cdot 2 \cdot 2 \cdot 2 \cdot 2$

$GCF = 2 \cdot 2 \cdot 2 = 8$ **Use each factor the number of times it appears as a common factor.**

A common multiple is a number that is a multiple of two or more numbers. The least common multiple (LCM) is the least number that is a common multiple of two or more numbers.

2 EXAMPLE

Find the LCM of 12 and 18.

Method 1 List the multiples of each number.

Multiples of 12 $12, 24, 36, \ldots$ **List a number of multiples until you find**

Multiples of 18 $18, 36, \ldots$ **the first common multiple.**

$LCM(12, 18) = 36$

Method 2 Use the prime factorization of each number.

$12 = 2 \cdot 2 \cdot 3$

$18 = 2 \cdot 3 \cdot 3$

$LCM = 2 \cdot 2 \cdot 3 \cdot 3 = 36$ **Use each prime factor the greatest number of times it appears in either number.**

EXERCISES

Find the GCF of each set of numbers.

1. 12 and 22   **2.** 7 and 21   **3.** 24 and 48   **4.** 17 and 51

5. 9 and 12   **6.** 10 and 25   **7.** 21 and 49   **8.** 27 and 36

9. 10, 30, and 25   **10.** 56, 84, and 140   **11.** 42, 63, and 105   **12.** 20, 28, and 40

Find the LCM of each set of numbers.

13. 16 and 20   **14.** 14 and 21   **15.** 11 and 33   **16.** 8 and 9

17. 5 and 12   **18.** 54 and 84   **19.** 48 and 80   **20.** 25 and 36

21. 10, 15, and 25   **22.** 6, 7, and 12   **23.** 5, 8, and 20   **24.** 18, 21, and 36

Divisibility

An integer is divisible by another integer if the remainder is zero. You can use the following tests to determine whether a number is divisible by the numbers below.

Number	Divisibility Test
2	The ones digit is 0, 2, 4, 6, or 8.
3	The sum of the digits is divisible by 3.
4	The number formed by the last two digits is divisible by 4.
5	The ones digit is 0 or 5.
6	The number is divisible by 2 and by 3.
8	The number formed by the last three digits is divisible by 8.
9	The sum of the digits is divisible by 9.
10	The ones digit is 0.

EXAMPLE

Use the divisibility tests to determine the numbers by which 2116 is divisible.

2: Yes; the ones digit is 6.
3: No; the sum of the digits is $2 + 1 + 1 + 6 = 10$, which is *not* divisible by 3.
4: Yes; the number formed by the last two digits is 16, which is divisible by 4.
5: No; the ones digit is 6, *not* 0 or 5.
6: No; 2116 is *not* divisible by 3.
8: No; the number formed by the last three digits is 116, which is *not* divisible by 8.
9: No; the sum of the digits is $2 + 1 + 1 + 6 = 10$, which is *not* divisible by 9.
10: No; the ones digit is 6, *not* 0.

● 2116 is divisible by 2 and 4.

EXERCISES

Determine whether each number is divisible by 2, 3, 4, 5, 6, 8, 9, or 10.

1. 236   **2.** 72   **3.** 105   **4.** 108   **5.** 225   **6.** 364

7. 1234   **8.** 4321   **9.** 7848   **10.** 3366   **11.** 1421   **12.** 1071

13. 78,765   **14.** 30,303   **15.** 4104   **16.** 700   **17.** 868   **18.** 1155

19. Reasoning Since 435 is divisible by both 3 and 5, it is also divisible by what number?

20. Find a number greater than 1000 that is divisible by 4, 5, and 9.

21. Critical Thinking If a is divisible by 2, what can you conclude about $a + 1$? Justify your answer.

Using Estimation

To make sure the answer to a problem is reasonable, you can estimate before you calculate. If the answer is close to your estimate, the answer is probably correct.

1 EXAMPLE

Estimate to find whether each answer is reasonable.

a. Calculation   Estimate

$$
\begin{array}{rcr}
\$126.91 & \approx & \$130 \\
\$14.05 & \approx & \$10 \\
+\,\$25.14 & \approx & +\,\$30 \\
\hline
\$266.10 & & \$170
\end{array}
$$

The answer is not close to the estimate. It is *not* reasonable. The calculation is *incorrect*.

b. Calculation   Estimate

$$
\begin{array}{rcr}
372.85 & \approx & 370 \\
-227.31 & \approx & -230 \\
\hline
145.54 & & 140
\end{array}
$$

The answer is close to the estimate. It *is* reasonable. The calculation is *correct*.

For some situations, like estimating a grocery bill, you may not need an exact answer. A *front-end estimate* will give you a good estimate that is usually closer to the exact answer than an estimate you would get by rounding. Add the front-end digits, estimate the sum of the remaining digits by rounding, and then combine sums.

2 EXAMPLE

Tomatoes cost $3.54, squash costs $2.75, and lemons cost $1.20. Estimate the total cost of the produce.

$$
\begin{array}{lccc}
\textbf{Add the} & 3.54 & \rightarrow & 0.50 \qquad \textbf{Estimate by rounding.}\\
\textbf{front-end digits.} & 2.75 & \rightarrow & 0.80 \\
& +1.20 & \rightarrow & +\;0.20 \\
\cline{2-2}\cline{4-4}
& 6 & + & 1.50 = 7.50
\end{array}
$$

The total cost is about $7.50.

EXERCISES

Estimate by rounding.

1. the sum of $15.70, $49.62, and $278.01

2. $563 - 125$

3. the sum of $163.90, $107.21, and $33.56

4. $824 - 467$

Use front-end estimation.

5. $1.65 + $5.42 + $9.89

6. $1.369 + 7.421 + 2.700$

7. $9.563 - 2.480$

8. $1.17 + 3.92 + 2.26$

9. $8.611 - 1.584$

10. $2.52 + $3.04 + $5.25

Estimate using a method of your choice.

11. Ticket prices at an amusement park cost $11.25 for adults and $6.50 for children under 12. Estimate the cost for three children and one adult.

12. Esmeralda has a new checking account. So far, she has deposited $177, $250, and $193. She has also written a check for $26.89. Estimate her current balance.

Simplifying Fractions

A fraction can name a part of a group or region. The region below is divided into 10 equal parts and 6 of the equal parts are shaded.

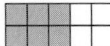 $\dfrac{6}{10}$ ← Numerator
← Denominator   **Read: six tenths**

A fraction can have many names. Different names for the same fraction are called equivalent fractions. You can find an equivalent fraction for any given fraction by multiplying the numerator and denominator of the given fraction by the same number.

1 EXAMPLE

Write five equivalent fractions for $\dfrac{3}{5}$.

$$\dfrac{3}{5} = \dfrac{3 \cdot 2}{5 \cdot 2} = \dfrac{6}{10} \qquad \dfrac{3}{5} = \dfrac{3 \cdot 3}{5 \cdot 3} = \dfrac{9}{15} \qquad \dfrac{3}{5} = \dfrac{3 \cdot 4}{5 \cdot 4} = \dfrac{12}{20} \qquad \dfrac{3}{5} = \dfrac{3 \cdot 5}{5 \cdot 5} = \dfrac{15}{25} \qquad \dfrac{3}{5} = \dfrac{3 \cdot 6}{5 \cdot 6} = \dfrac{18}{30}$$

The fraction $\dfrac{3}{5}$ is in simplest form because its numerator and denominator are relatively prime, that is, their only common factor is the number 1. To write a fraction in simplest form, divide its numerator and denominator by their greatest common factor (GCF).

2 EXAMPLE

Write $\dfrac{6}{24}$ in simplest form.

Step 1 Find the GCF of 6 and 24.

$6 = 2 \cdot 3$ **Multiply the common prime factors.**

$24 = 2 \cdot 2 \cdot 2 \cdot 3$ **GCF = 2 · 3 = 6.**

Step 2 Divide the numerator and denominator of $\dfrac{6}{24}$ by the GCF, 6.

$$\dfrac{6}{24} = \dfrac{6 \div 6}{24 \div 6} = \dfrac{1}{4} \quad \text{simplest form}$$

EXERCISES

Write five equivalent fractions for each fraction.

1. $\dfrac{4}{7}$ 2. $\dfrac{9}{16}$ 3. $\dfrac{3}{8}$ 4. $\dfrac{8}{17}$ 5. $\dfrac{5}{6}$ 6. $\dfrac{7}{10}$

Complete each statement.

7. $\dfrac{3}{7} = \dfrac{\blacksquare}{21}$ 8. $\dfrac{5}{8} = \dfrac{20}{\blacksquare}$ 9. $\dfrac{11}{12} = \dfrac{44}{\blacksquare}$ 10. $\dfrac{12}{16} = \dfrac{\blacksquare}{4}$ 11. $\dfrac{50}{100} = \dfrac{1}{\blacksquare}$

12. $\dfrac{5}{9} = \dfrac{\blacksquare}{27}$ 13. $\dfrac{3}{8} = \dfrac{\blacksquare}{24}$ 14. $\dfrac{5}{6} = \dfrac{20}{\blacksquare}$ 15. $\dfrac{12}{20} = \dfrac{\blacksquare}{5}$ 16. $\dfrac{75}{150} = \dfrac{1}{\blacksquare}$

Which fractions are in simplest form?

17. $\dfrac{4}{12}$ 18. $\dfrac{3}{16}$ 19. $\dfrac{5}{30}$ 20. $\dfrac{9}{72}$ 21. $\dfrac{11}{22}$ 22. $\dfrac{24}{25}$

Write in simplest form.

23. $\dfrac{8}{16}$ 24. $\dfrac{7}{14}$ 25. $\dfrac{6}{9}$ 26. $\dfrac{20}{30}$ 27. $\dfrac{8}{20}$ 28. $\dfrac{12}{40}$

29. $\dfrac{15}{45}$ 30. $\dfrac{14}{56}$ 31. $\dfrac{10}{25}$ 32. $\dfrac{9}{27}$ 33. $\dfrac{45}{60}$ 34. $\dfrac{20}{35}$

Fractions and Decimals

You can write a fraction as a decimal.

1 EXAMPLE

Write $\frac{3}{5}$ as a decimal.

$$\begin{array}{r} 0.6 \\ 5\overline{)3.0} \\ -3.0 \end{array}$$ **Divide the numerator by the denominator.**

The decimal for $\frac{3}{5}$ is 0.6.

You can write a decimal as a fraction.

2 EXAMPLE

Write 0.38 as a fraction.

$0.38 = 38$ hundredths $= \frac{38}{100} = \frac{19}{50}$

Some fractions have decimal forms that do not end, but do repeat.

3 EXAMPLE

Write $\frac{3}{11}$ as a decimal.

Divide the numerator by the denominator. The remainders 8 and 3 keep repeating. Therefore 2 and 7 will keep repeating in the quotient.

$\frac{3}{11} = 0.2727\ldots = 0.\overline{27}$

$$\frac{3}{11} = 11\overline{)3.0000\ldots} \begin{array}{r} 0.2727 \\ \underline{22} \\ 80 \\ \underline{77} \\ 30 \\ \underline{22} \\ 80 \\ \underline{77} \\ 3 \end{array}$$

You can write a repeating decimal as a fraction.

4 EXAMPLE

Write 0.363636 . . . as a fraction.

Let $x = 0.363636\ldots$

Then $100x = 36.36363636\ldots$ **When 2 digits repeat, multiply by 100.**

$99x = 36$ **Subtract the first equation from the second.**

$x = \frac{36}{99}$ or $\frac{4}{11}$ **Divide each side by 99.**

EXERCISES

Write as a decimal.

1. $\frac{3}{10}$ 2. $\frac{13}{12}$ 3. $\frac{4}{20}$ 4. $\frac{25}{75}$ 5. $\frac{5}{7}$ 6. $4\frac{3}{25}$

7. $\frac{5}{9}$ 8. $5\frac{7}{8}$ 9. $\frac{2}{7}$ 10. $\frac{3}{15}$ 11. $\frac{16}{100}$ 12. $2\frac{2}{5}$

Write as a fraction in simplest form.

13. 0.07   14. 0.25   15. 0.875   16. 0.4545 . . .   17. 6.333 . . .   18. 7.2626 . . .

19. 0.77 . . .   20. 3.1313 . . .   21. 0.375   22. 0.8333 . . .   23. 6.48   24. 0.8

Adding and Subtracting Fractions

You can add and subtract fractions when they have the same denominator. Fractions with the same denominator are called like fractions.

1 EXAMPLE

a. Add $\frac{4}{5} + \frac{3}{5}$.

b. Subtract $\frac{5}{9} - \frac{2}{9}$.

$\frac{4}{5} + \frac{3}{5} = \frac{4+3}{5} = \frac{7}{5} = 1\frac{2}{5}$ ← Add or subtract the numerators and keep the same denominator. → $\frac{5}{9} - \frac{2}{9} = \frac{5-2}{9} = \frac{3}{9} = \frac{1}{3}$

Fractions with unlike denominators are called unlike fractions. To add or subtract fractions with unlike denominators, find the least common denominator (LCD) and write equivalent fractions with the same denominator. Then add or subtract the like fractions.

2 EXAMPLE

Add $\frac{3}{4} + \frac{5}{6}$.

$\frac{3}{4} + \frac{5}{6} = \frac{9}{12} + \frac{10}{12}$ Find the LCD. The LCD is the same as the least common multiple (LCM). The LCD of 4 and 6 is 12.

$= \frac{9+10}{12} = \frac{19}{12}$ or $1\frac{7}{12}$ Write equivalent fractions with the same denominator.

To add or subtract mixed numbers, add or subtract the fractions. Then add or subtract the whole numbers. Sometimes when subtracting mixed numbers you may have to regroup.

3 EXAMPLE

Subtract $5\frac{1}{4} - 3\frac{2}{3}$.

$5\frac{1}{4} - 3\frac{2}{3} = 5\frac{3}{12} - 3\frac{8}{12}$ Write equivalent fractions with the same denominator.

$= 4\frac{15}{12} - 3\frac{8}{12}$ Write $5\frac{3}{12}$ as $4\frac{15}{12}$ so you can subtract the fractions.

$= 1\frac{7}{12}$ Subtract the fractions. Then subtract the whole numbers.

EXERCISES

Add. Write each answer in simplest form.

1. $\frac{2}{7} + \frac{3}{7}$

2. $\frac{3}{8} + \frac{7}{8}$

3. $\frac{6}{5} + \frac{9}{5}$

4. $\frac{4}{9} + \frac{8}{9}$

5. $6\frac{2}{3} + 3\frac{4}{5}$

6. $1\frac{4}{7} + 2\frac{3}{14}$

7. $4\frac{5}{6} + 1\frac{7}{18}$

8. $2\frac{4}{5} + 3\frac{6}{7}$

9. $4\frac{2}{3} + 1\frac{6}{11}$

10. $3\frac{7}{9} + 5\frac{4}{11}$

11. $8 + 1\frac{2}{3}$

12. $8\frac{1}{5} + 3\frac{3}{4}$

13. $11\frac{3}{8} + 2\frac{1}{16}$

14. $9\frac{1}{12} + 8\frac{3}{4}$

15. $33\frac{1}{3} + 23\frac{2}{5}$

Subtract. Write each answer in simplest form.

16. $\frac{7}{8} - \frac{3}{8}$

17. $\frac{9}{10} - \frac{3}{10}$

18. $\frac{17}{5} - \frac{2}{5}$

19. $\frac{11}{7} - \frac{2}{7}$

20. $\frac{5}{11} - \frac{4}{11}$

21. $8\frac{5}{8} - 6\frac{1}{4}$

22. $3\frac{2}{3} - 1\frac{8}{9}$

23. $8\frac{5}{6} - 5\frac{1}{2}$

24. $12\frac{3}{4} - 4\frac{5}{6}$

25. $17\frac{2}{7} - 8\frac{2}{9}$

26. $7\frac{3}{4} - 3\frac{3}{8}$

27. $4\frac{1}{12} - 1\frac{11}{12}$

28. $5\frac{5}{8} - 2\frac{7}{16}$

29. $11\frac{2}{3} - 3\frac{5}{6}$

30. $25\frac{5}{8} - 17\frac{15}{16}$

Multiplying and Dividing Fractions

To multiply two or more fractions, multiply the numerators, multiply the denominators, and simplify the product, if necessary.

1 EXAMPLE

Multiply $\frac{3}{7} \cdot \frac{5}{6}$.

$\frac{3}{7} \cdot \frac{5}{6} = \frac{3 \cdot 5}{7 \cdot 6} = \frac{15}{42} = \frac{15 \div 3}{42 \div 3} = \frac{5}{14}$

Sometimes you can simplify before multiplying.

$\frac{3^1}{7} \cdot \frac{5}{6_2} = \frac{5}{14}$ **Divide a numerator and a denominator by a common factor.**

To multiply mixed numbers, change the mixed numbers to improper fractions and multiply the fractions. Write the product as a mixed number.

2 EXAMPLE

Multiply $2\frac{4}{5} \cdot 1\frac{2}{3}$.

$2\frac{4}{5} \cdot 1\frac{2}{3} = \frac{14}{{}_1 5} \cdot \frac{5^1}{3} = \frac{14}{3} = 4\frac{2}{3}$

To divide fractions, change the division problem to a multiplication problem. Remember that $8 \div \frac{1}{4}$ is the same as $8 \cdot 4$.

To divide mixed numbers, change the mixed numbers to improper fractions and divide the fractions.

3 EXAMPLE

a. Divide $\frac{4}{5} \div \frac{3}{7}$.

$\frac{4}{5} \div \frac{3}{7} = \frac{4}{5} \cdot \frac{7}{3}$ ⟵ Multiply by the reciprocal ⟶
                                         of the divisor.

$= \frac{28}{15}$ ⟵ Simplify the answer. ⟶

$= 1\frac{13}{15}$ ⟵ Write as a mixed number.

b. Divide $4\frac{2}{3} \div 7\frac{3}{5}$.

$4\frac{2}{3} \div 7\frac{3}{5} = \frac{14}{3} \div \frac{38}{5}$

$= \frac{14^7}{3} \cdot \frac{5}{38_{19}}$

$= \frac{35}{57}$

EXERCISES

Multiply. Write your answers in simplest form.

1. $\frac{2}{5} \cdot \frac{3}{4}$

2. $\frac{3}{7} \cdot \frac{4}{3}$

3. $1\frac{1}{2} \cdot 5\frac{3}{4}$

4. $3\frac{4}{5} \cdot 10$

5. $5\frac{1}{4} \cdot \frac{2}{3}$

6. $4\frac{1}{2} \cdot 7\frac{1}{2}$

7. $3\frac{2}{3} \cdot 6\frac{9}{10}$

8. $6\frac{1}{2} \cdot 7\frac{2}{3}$

9. $2\frac{2}{5} \cdot 1\frac{1}{6}$

10. $4\frac{1}{9} \cdot 3\frac{3}{8}$

11. $3\frac{1}{5} \cdot 1\frac{7}{8}$

12. $7\frac{5}{6} \cdot 4\frac{1}{2}$

13. $1\frac{2}{3} \cdot 5\frac{9}{10}$

14. $3\frac{3}{4} \cdot 5\frac{1}{3}$

15. $1\frac{2}{3} \cdot 3\frac{9}{16}$

Divide. Write your answers in simplest form.

16. $\frac{3}{5} \div \frac{1}{2}$

17. $\frac{4}{5} \div \frac{9}{10}$

18. $2\frac{1}{2} \div 3\frac{1}{2}$

19. $1\frac{4}{5} \div 2\frac{1}{2}$

20. $3\frac{1}{6} \div 1\frac{3}{4}$

21. $5 \div \frac{3}{8}$

22. $\frac{4}{9} \div \frac{3}{5}$

23. $\frac{5}{8} \div \frac{3}{4}$

24. $2\frac{1}{5} \div 2\frac{1}{2}$

25. $6\frac{1}{2} \div \frac{1}{4}$

26. $1\frac{3}{4} \div 4\frac{3}{8}$

27. $\frac{8}{9} \div \frac{2}{3}$

28. $\frac{1}{5} \div \frac{1}{3}$

29. $2\frac{2}{5} \div 7\frac{1}{5}$

30. $7\frac{2}{3} \div \frac{2}{9}$

Fractions, Decimals, and Percents

Percent means per hundred. 50% means 50 per hundred. $50\% = \frac{50}{100} = 0.50$

You can write fractions as percents by writing the fractions as decimals first. Then move the decimal point two places to the right and write a percent sign.

1 EXAMPLE

Write each number as a percent.

a. $\frac{3}{5}$

$\frac{3}{5} = 0.6$

b. $\frac{7}{20}$

$\frac{7}{20} = 0.35$

c. $\frac{2}{3}$

$\frac{2}{3} = 0.66\overline{6}$

Move the decimal point two places to the right and write a percent sign.

$0.6 = 60\%$ 　　　　　 $0.35 = 35\%$ 　　　　　 $0.66\overline{6} = 66.\overline{6}\% \approx 66.7\%$

You can write percents as decimals by moving the decimal point two places to the left and removing the percent sign.

You can write a percent as a fraction with the denominator of 100. You then simplify it, if possible.

2 EXAMPLE

Write each number as a decimal and as a fraction or mixed number.

a. 25%

$25\% = 0.25$

$25\% = \frac{25}{100} = \frac{1}{4}$

$\frac{1}{200}$

b. $\frac{1}{2}\%$

$\frac{1}{2}\% = 0.5\% = 0.005$

$\frac{1}{2}\% = \frac{\frac{1}{2}}{100} = \frac{1}{2} \div 100$

c. 360%

$360\% = 3.6$

$360\% = \frac{360}{100} = \frac{18}{5} = 3\frac{3}{5}$
$= \quad \cdot \quad = \frac{1}{2} \quad \frac{1}{100}$

EXERCISES

Write each number as a percent. If necessary, round to the nearest tenth.

1. 0.56 　　　　 **2.** 0.09 　　　　 **3.** 6.02 　　　　 **4.** 5.245

5. 8.2 　　　　 **6.** 0.14 　　　　 **7.** $\frac{1}{7}$ 　　　　 **8.** $\frac{9}{20}$

9. $\frac{1}{9}$ 　　　　 **10.** $\frac{5}{6}$ 　　　　 **11.** $\frac{3}{4}$ 　　　　 **12.** $\frac{7}{8}$

Write each number as a decimal.

13. 7% 　　 **14.** 8.5% 　　 **15.** 0.9% 　　 **16.** 250% 　　 **17.** 83% 　　 **18.** 110%

19. 15% 　　 **20.** 72% 　　 **21.** 0.03% 　　 **22.** 36.2% 　　 **23.** 365% 　　 **24.** 101%

Write each number as a fraction or mixed number in simplest form.

25. 19% 　　 **26.** $\frac{3}{4}\%$ 　　 **27.** 450% 　　 **28.** $\frac{4}{5}\%$ 　　 **29.** 64% 　　 **30.** $\frac{2}{3}\%$

31. 24% 　　 **32.** 845% 　　 **33.** $\frac{3}{8}\%$ 　　 **34.** 480% 　　 **35.** 60% 　　 **36.** 350%

37. 2% 　　 **38.** 16% 　　 **39.** 66% 　　 **40.** $\frac{4}{7}\%$ 　　 **41.** 125% 　　 **42.** 84%

Exponents

You can express $2 \cdot 2 \cdot 2 \cdot 2 \cdot 2$ as 2^5. The raised number 5 shows the number of times 2 is used as a factor. The number 2 is the base. The number 5 is the exponent.

$2^5 \leftarrow$ **exponent**
$\uparrow$ **base**

Factored Form	Exponential Form	Standard Form
$2 \cdot 2 \cdot 2 \cdot 2 \cdot 2$	2^5	32

A number with an exponent of 1 is the number itself: $8^1 = 8$.
Any number, except 0, with an exponent of 0 is 1: $5^0 = 1$.

1 EXAMPLE

Write using exponents.

a. $8 \cdot 8 \cdot 8 \cdot 8 \cdot 8$ **b.** $2 \cdot 9 \cdot 9 \cdot 9 \cdot 9 \cdot 9 \cdot 9$ **c.** $6 \cdot 6 \cdot 10 \cdot 10 \cdot 10 \cdot 6 \cdot 6$

Count the number of times the number is used as a factor.

$= 8^5$ $= 2 \cdot 9^6$ $= 6^4 \cdot 10^3$

2 EXAMPLE

Write in standard form.

a. 2^3 **b.** $8^2 \cdot 3^4$ **c.** $10^3 \cdot 15^2$

Write in factored form and multiply.

$2 \cdot 2 \cdot 2 = 8$ $8 \cdot 8 \cdot 3 \cdot 3 \cdot 3 \cdot 3 = 5184$ $10 \cdot 10 \cdot 10 \cdot 15 \cdot 15 = 225{,}000$

In powers of 10, an exponent tells how many zeros are in the equivalent standard form.

$10^1 = 10$ $10^4 = 10 \cdot 10 \cdot 10 \cdot 10 = 10{,}000$
$10^2 = 10 \cdot 10 = 100$ $10^5 = 10 \cdot 10 \cdot 10 \cdot 10 \cdot 10 = 100{,}000$
$10^3 = 10 \cdot 10 \cdot 10 = 1000$ $10^6 = 10 \cdot 10 \cdot 10 \cdot 10 \cdot 10 \cdot 10 = 1{,}000{,}000$

You can use exponents to write numbers in expanded form.

3 EXAMPLE

Write 739 in expanded form using exponents.

$739 = 700 + 30 + 9 = (7 \cdot 100) + (3 \cdot 10) + (9 \cdot 1) = (7 \cdot 10^2) + (3 \cdot 10^1) + (9 \cdot 10^0)$

EXERCISES

Write using exponents.

1. $6 \cdot 6 \cdot 6 \cdot 6$ **2.** $7 \cdot 7 \cdot 7 \cdot 7 \cdot 7$ **3.** $5 \cdot 2 \cdot 2 \cdot 2 \cdot 2$

4. $3 \cdot 3 \cdot 3 \cdot 3 \cdot 3 \cdot 14 \cdot 14$ **5.** $4 \cdot 4 \cdot 3 \cdot 3 \cdot 2$ **6.** $3 \cdot 5 \cdot 5 \cdot 7 \cdot 7 \cdot 7$

Write in standard form.

7. 4^3 **8.** 9^4 **9.** 12^2 **10.** $6^2 \cdot 7^1$ **11.** $11^2 \cdot 3^3$

Write in expanded form using exponents.

12. 658   **13.** 1254   **14.** 7125   **15.** 83,401   **16.** 294,863

Measuring and Classifying Angles

An angle is a geometric figure formed by two rays with a common endpoint. The rays are sides of the angle and the endpoint is the vertex of the angle. An angle is measured in degrees. The symbol for an angle is ∠.

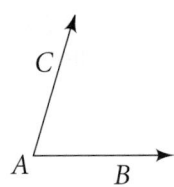

The angle picture at the right can be named in three different ways: ∠A, ∠BAC, or ∠CAB.

Angles can be classified by their measures.

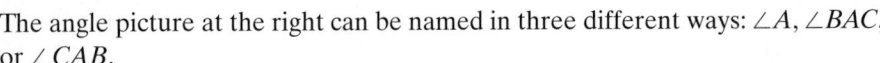

Acute angle less than 90°	**Right angle** 90°	**Obtuse angle** greater than 90° but less than 180°	**Straight angle** 180°

EXAMPLE

Measure the angle. Is it *acute, right, obtuse* or *straight*?

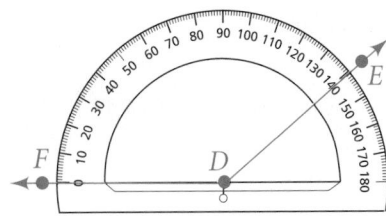

Line up side *DF* through 0° with the vertex at the center of the protractor. Read the scale number through which side *DE* passes.

The measure of the angle is 140°. The angle is obtuse.

EXERCISES

Measure each angle. Is the angle *acute, right, obtuse,* or *straight*?

1.

A

2.

B

3.

C

4.

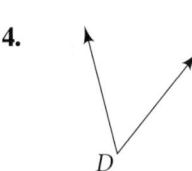

D

Draw an angle with the given measure.

5. 45°   **6.** 95°   **7.** 120°   **8.** 170°

9. 20°   **10.** 85°   **11.** 150°   **12.** 160°

13. Open-Ended Draw a triangle. Use a protractor to find the measure of each angle of your triangle.

Perimeter, Area, and Volume

The perimeter of a figure is the distance around the figure. The area of a figure is the number of square units contained in the figure. The volume of a space figure is the number of cubic units contained in the space figure.

1 EXAMPLE

Find the perimeter of each figure.

a.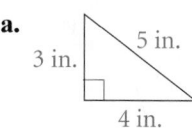
Add the measures of the sides.
$3 + 4 + 5 = 12$
The perimeter is 12 in.

b.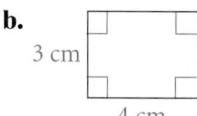
Use the formula $P = 2\ell + 2w$.
$P = 2(3) + 2(4)$
$= 6 + 8 = 14$
The perimeter is 14 cm.

2 EXAMPLE

Find the area of each figure.

a.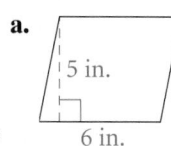
Use the formula $A = bh$.
$A = 6 \cdot 5 = 30$
The area is 30 in.^{2}.

b.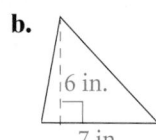
Use the formula $A = \frac{1}{2}(bh)$.
$A = \frac{1}{2}(7 \cdot 6) = 21$
The area is 21 in.^{2}.

3 EXAMPLE

Find the volume of each figure.

a.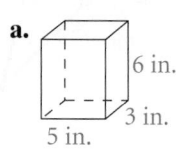
Use the formula $V = Bh$.
(B = area of the base
$= 3 \cdot 5 = 15$).
$V = 15 \cdot 6 = 90$ in.^{3}
The volume is 90 in.^{3}.

b.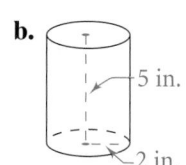
Use the formula $V = \pi r^2 h$.
$V = 3.14 \cdot 2^2 \cdot 5$
$= 3.14 \cdot 4 \cdot 5 = 62.8$ in.^{3}
The volume is 62.8 in.^{3}.

EXERCISES

For Exercises 1–2, find the perimeter of each figure. For Exercises 3–4, find the area of each figure.

1.

2.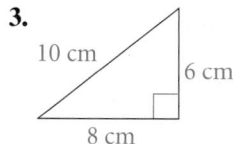

3.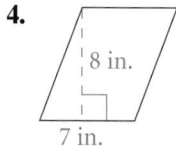

4.

Find the volume of each figure.

5.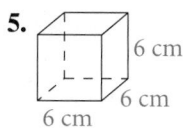

6.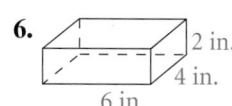

7.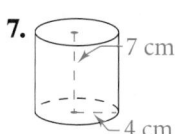

Translations

A translation is a transformation that moves a figure so that every point in the figure moves the same direction and the same distance. Each translated figure is an image of the original figure. If point A is on the original figure, the corresponding point on the image is A'.

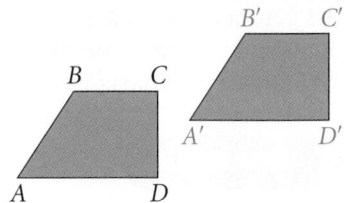

1 EXAMPLE

Graph the image of $\triangle ABC$ after a translation of 4 units right and 2 units down.

To get from $A(-6, 1)$ to $A'(-2, -1)$ by a translation, move
4 units to the right: add 4 to the x-value, $-6 + 4 = -2$,
and 2 units down: add -2 to the y-value, $1 + (-2) = -1$.

● Similarly, the coordinates of B' are $(3, 3)$ and of C' are $(2, 0)$.

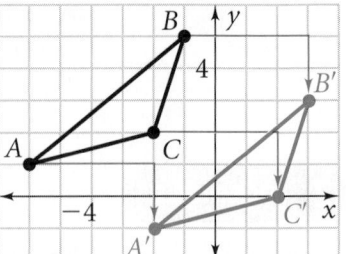

You can describe a translation using arrow ($\rightarrow$) notation. The translation from A to A' in Example 1 can be written $A(-6, 1) \rightarrow A'(-2, -1)$.

2 EXAMPLE

Write a rule to describe the translation of $\triangle PQR$ to $\triangle P'Q'R'$.

Use any point on the figure and its image to find the horizontal and vertical translations. Try $P(3, 2)$ and its image $P'(-2, 5)$.

horizontal translation: $-2 - 3 = -5$ 5 units left
vertical translation: $5 - 2 = 3$ 3 units up

● The rule for the translation is $(x, y) \rightarrow (x - 5, y + 3)$.

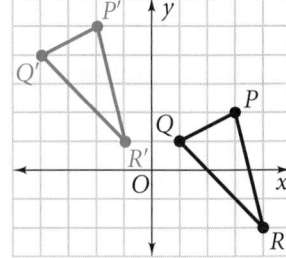

EXERCISES

The vertices of a triangle are given. Graph the triangle and its image after a translation of the specified number of units in each direction.

1. $P(2, 5)$, $Q(5, 6)$, $R(5, 0)$; 4 units right, 5 units down

2. $U(0, 0)$, $V(-5, -3)$, $W(-6, 0)$; 2 units left, 2 units up

Write a rule to describe each translation.

3. $A(4, -4) \rightarrow A'(2, -5)$

4. $G(-1, 9) \rightarrow G'(1, -9)$

5. $M(-2, 0) \rightarrow M'\left(2, \frac{1}{2}\right)$

6. $D(2, 4) \rightarrow D'(-3, 5)$

7. $Q(7, -3) \rightarrow Q'(9, 2)$

8. $W(6, -4) \rightarrow W'(2, 2)$

9.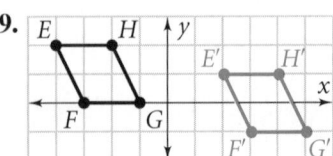

10.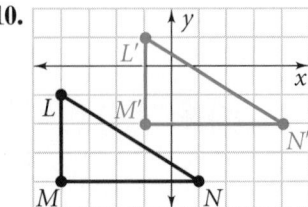

11.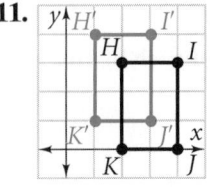

Reflections

A reflection is a transformation that flips a figure over a line, called a line of reflection. The picture at the right shows $\triangle DEF$ and its reflection over the line of reflection ℓ. The image is $\triangle D'E'F'$.

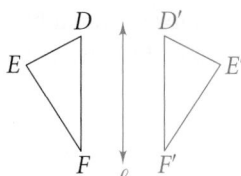

1 EXAMPLE

Reflect the point $P(2, 5)$ over the line $y = 2$. What are the coordinates of its image P'?

● The coordinates of P' are $(2, -1)$.

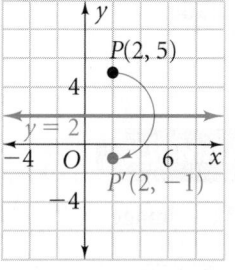

2 EXAMPLE

The vertices of $\triangle ABC$ are $A(-7, 0)$, $B(-5, 6)$, and $C(-3, 4)$. Graph the image of the triangle after a reflection over the line $x = 1$.

To get from $A(-7, 0)$ to $A'(9, 0)$, point A is reflected the same distance on the other side of the line $x = 1$. The coordinates of the other two vertices in the
● reflected image are $B'(7, 6)$ and $C'(5, 4)$.

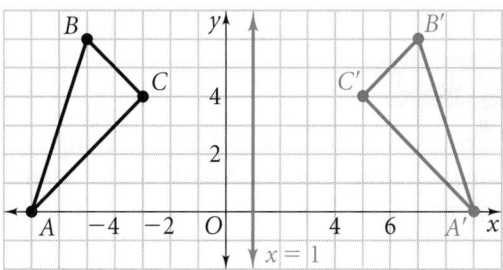

EXERCISES

Graph each point and its image after a reflection over the specified line.

1. $K(2, 3); x = 1$

2. $D(-3, 1); y = -2$

3. $Z(2, 5); x\text{-axis}$

The vertices of various figures are given. Graph both the figure and its image after a reflection over the specified line.

4. $R(2, 4), S(-1, 3), T(2, 0); y = -2$

5. $C(1, 4), D(1, 7), E(-2, 7); x = 3$

6. $H(-5, 5), \ I(6, 0), \ J(0, 0); y\text{-axis}$

7. $K(-2, -3), L(-7, -3), M(-7, -5), N(-2, -5); x\text{-axis}$

The reflected image of each figure is shown in red. Identify the line of reflection.

8.
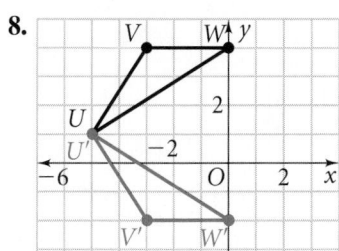

9.
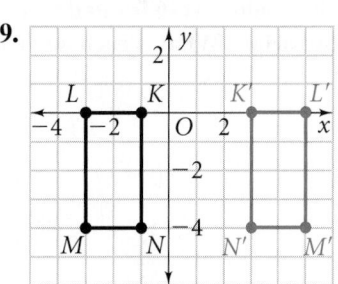

Rotations

A rotation is a transformation that turns a figure about a fixed point, called the *center of rotation*. You can rotate a figure up to 360°. All rotations shown on this page are counterclockwise.

90°   180°   270°   360°

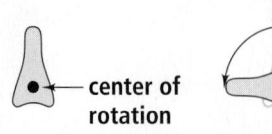 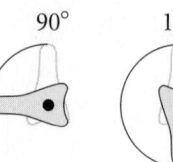 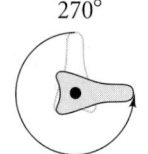 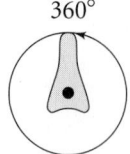

center of rotation

1 EXAMPLE

Find the image of $P(1, 2)$ after a rotation of 90° about the origin.

● The coordinates of P' are $(-2, 1)$.

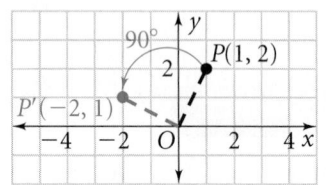

2 EXAMPLE

The vertices of $\triangle ABC$ are $A(0, 2)$, $B(-2, 0)$, and $C(2, 2)$. Find the coordinates of the image of $\triangle ABC$ after a rotation of 180° about the origin.

● The vertices of the image are $A'(0, -2)$, $B'(2, 0)$, and $C'(-2, -2)$.

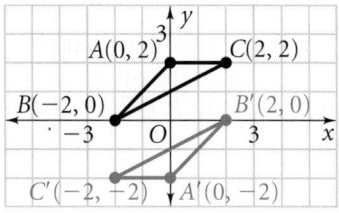

EXERCISES

Graph each point. Then rotate it the given number of degrees counterclockwise about the given center of rotation and graph the new point.

1. $D(2, 4)$; 90° about the origin

2. $G(-3, -1)$; 180° about $(0, 0)$

3. $Z(4, -2)$; 90° about $(2, 0)$

4. $M(-3, 2)$; 180° about $(2, 3)$

The vertices of a triangle are given. On separate coordinate planes, graph each triangle and its image after a rotation of (a) 90° and (b) 180° about the origin.

5. $A(2, 0)$, $B(7, 2)$, $C(7, 0)$

6. $E(0, 3)$, $F(-5, 4)$, $G(-3, 0)$

7. $L(-2, -1)$, $M(-5, -1)$, $N(-2, -5)$

8. $Q(0, -2)$, $R(0, 0)$, $S(2, 0)$

The triangles in the exercises below were formed by rotating the triangle at the left counterclockwise about the origin. What is each angle of rotation?

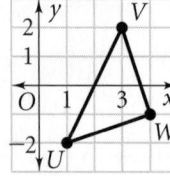

9.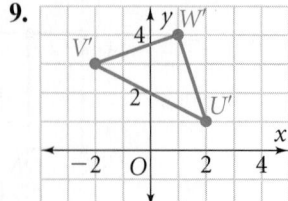

10.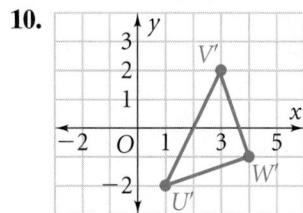

Line Plots

A line plot is created by placing a mark above a number line corresponding to the location of each data item. Line plots have two main advantages:

- You can see the frequency of data items.

- You can see how the data items compare.

EXAMPLE

The table at the right gives the heights (in inches) of a group of twenty-five adults. Display the data in a line plot. Describe the data shown in the line plot.

Height of Adults (inches)

59	60	63	63	64
64	64	65	65	65
67	67	67	67	68
68	68	69	70	70
71	72	73	73	77

The data are graphed on a number line.

The title describes the data.

An *X* represents one element of the data set.

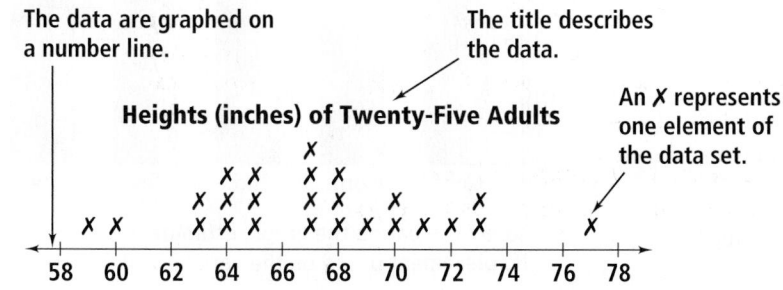

The line plot shows that most of the heights are concentrated around 67 inches, the maximum value is 77, and the minimum value is 59.

EXERCISES

Display each set of data in a line plot.

1. 3, 6, 4, 3, 6, 0, 4, 5, 0, 4, 6, 1, 5, 1, 0, 5, 5, 6, 5, 3

2. 19, 18, 18, 18, 19, 20, 19, 18, 18, 17, 18, 20, 19, 17

Draw a line plot for each frequency table.

3.

Number	1	2	3	4	5	6
Frequency	4	1	0	5	7	2

4.

Number	12	13	15	16	18	19
Frequency	2	5	1	3	6	3

5. Olympics Here are the numbers of gold medals won by different countries during the 1998 Winter Olympics (Bulgaria had the least with 1 gold medal and Germany had the most with 12 gold medals).
1, 1, 2, 2, 2, 2, 3, 3, 5, 5, 6, 6, 9, 10, 12
Display the data in a line plot. Describe the data shown in the line plot.

Bar Graphs

Bar graphs are used to compare amounts. The horizontal axis shows the categories and the vertical axis shows the amounts. A multiple bar graph includes a key.

EXAMPLE

Draw a bar graph for the data in the table below.

Median Household Income

State	1995	1997	1999
Calif.	$40,457	$41,203	$43,744
Conn.	$43,993	$45,657	$50,798
Ind.	$36,496	$40,367	$40,929
Tex.	$35,024	$36,408	$38,978
Utah	$39,879	$44,401	$46,094

SOURCE: U.S. Census Bureau

The categories (in the first column) are placed on the horizontal scale. The amounts (in the second, third, and fourth columns) are placed on the vertical scale.

Graph the data for each state. Use the values in the top row to create the key.

The highest projected income is $50,798. So a reasonable range for the vertical scale is 0 to $55,000.

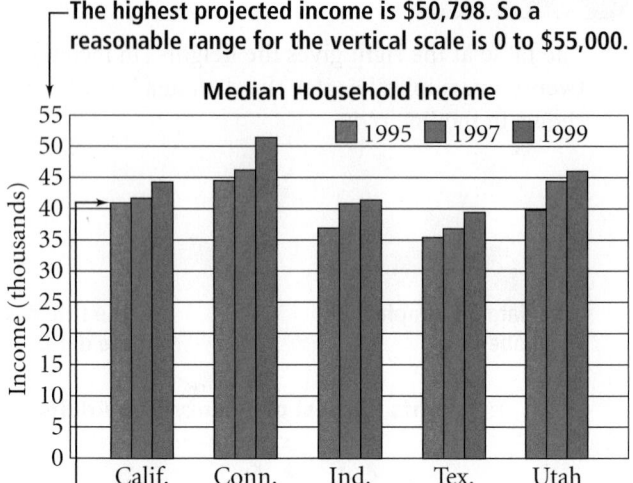

To draw a bar on the graph, estimate its placement based on the vertical scale.

EXERCISES

1. Draw a bar graph for the data in the table below.

Highest Temperatures (°F)

City	March	June	August
Juneau, AK	61	86	83
Denver, CO	84	104	101
Atlanta, GA	89	101	102
Honolulu, HI	88	92	93
Detroit, MI	81	104	100
Buffalo, NY	81	96	99
Houston, TX	91	103	107

2. a. Critical Thinking If one more column of data were added to the table in the example, how would the bar graph be different?

b. If one more row of data were added to the table in the example, how would the bar graph be different?

Histograms

A histogram is a bar graph that shows the frequency, or number of times, a data item occurs. Histograms often combine data into intervals of equal size. The intervals do not overlap.

 **EXAMPLE**

The data at the right show the number of hours of battery life for different brands of batteries used in portable CD players. Use the data to make a histogram.

Hours of Battery Life

12 9 10 14 10 11
10 18 21 10 14 22

Step 1 Decide on an interval size.

The data start at 9 hours and go to 22 hours. Use equal-sized intervals of 4 hours, beginning with 8 hours. So the first interval will be 8–11.

Step 2 Make a frequency table.

Battery Life

Hours	Tally	Frequency
8–11	JHT I	6
12–15	III	3
16–19	I	1
20–23	II	2

Step 3 Make a histogram.

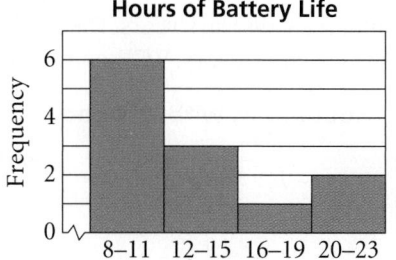

EXERCISES

1. Students answered a survey question about how long it takes to get ready in the morning. The histogram at the right shows the survey results.

   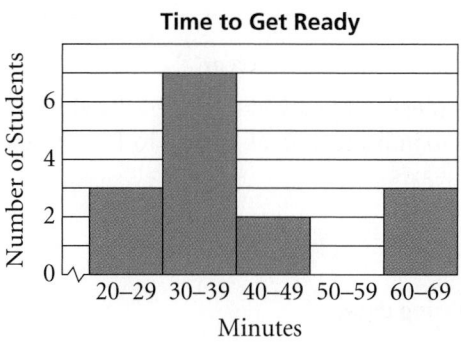

   a. Which interval indicates the answers most students gave?

   b. How many students answered the survey question?

   c. Why might no students have given an answer in the interval 50–59?

   d. **Critical Thinking** With the information you have, could you redraw the histogram with intervals half their current size? Explain why or why not.

2. a. An Internet company surveyed its users. The first 25 people who responded gave the ages shown at the right. What intervals would you use to make a histogram?

   b. Make a frequency table for the data.

   c. Make a histogram.

   Age of Internet Users

   25, 43, 65, 12, 8, 30, 44, 68, 18, 21,
   25, 33, 37, 54, 61, 29, 31, 38, 22, 48,
   19, 34, 55, 14, 21

3. a. **Data Collection** Survey your class to find out what day of the month they were born. For example, 12 if a student's birthday is August 12th.

   b. What intervals would you use to make a histogram?

   c. Make a frequency table for the data.

   d. Make a histogram.

Line Graphs

Line graphs are used to display the change in a set of data over a period of time. A multiple-line graph shows change in more than one category of data over time. You can use a line graph to look for trends and make predictions.

EXAMPLE

Graph the data in the table below.

Households with VCR and Cable TV (millions)

Year	1985	1990	1995	1996	1997	1998
VCR	18	63	77	79	82	83
Cable TV	36	52	60	63	64	66

SOURCE: Television Bureau of Advertising, Inc., *Trends in Television*

Since the data show changes over time for two sets of data, use a double line graph. The horizontal scale displays years. The vertical scale displays the number of households for each category, VCR and cable TV.

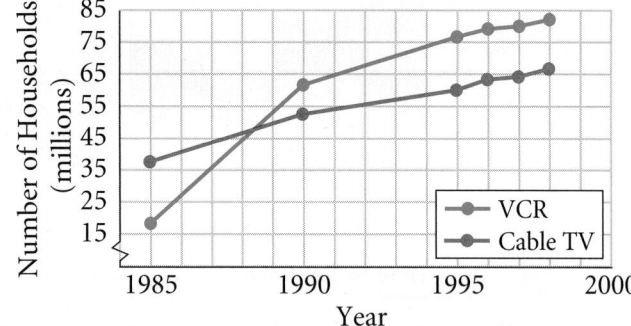

Notice that there is a *break* in the vertical scale, which goes from 0 to 85. A zigzag line is used to indicate a break from 0 to 15 since there is no data to graph in this part of the *y*-axis.

EXERCISES

Graph the following data.

1.

Market Shares (percent)

Year	1994	1995	1996	1997	1998	1999	2000
Rap/Hip Hop	7.9	6.7	8.9	10.1	9.7	10.8	12.9
Pop	10.3	10.1	9.3	9.4	10.0	10.3	11.0

SOURCE: The Recording Industry of America

2.

Percents of Schools with Internet Access

Year	1995	1996	1997	1998	1999
Elementary	46	61	75	88	94
Secondary	65	77	89	94	98

SOURCE: U.S. National Center for Education Statistics

Circle Graphs

A circle graph is an efficient way to present certain types of data. The graphs show data as percents or fractions of a whole. The total must be 100% or 1. Circle graphs are used to show the parts of the whole. The angles at the center are central angles, and each angle is proportional to the percent or fraction of the total.

What Do You Think Is the Number One Problem in the World Today?

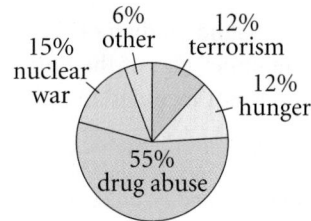

SOURCE: *The Second Kids' World Almanac*

EXAMPLE

The table below shows the number of people in the United States who have at least one grandchild under the age of 18. Draw a circle graph for the data.

Ages of U.S. Grandparents

Age	People (millions)
44 and under	3.6
45–54	10.3
55–64	15.0
65 and over	18.2

Step 1 Add to find the total number.

$3.6 + 10.3 + 15.0 + 18.2 = 47.1$ (million)

Step 2 For each central angle, set up a proportion to find the measure. Use a calculator to solve each proportion.

$$\frac{3.6}{47.1} = \frac{a}{360°} \qquad \frac{10.3}{47.1} = \frac{b}{360°} \qquad \frac{15.0}{47.1} = \frac{c}{360°} \qquad \frac{18.2}{47.1} = \frac{d}{360°}$$
$$a \approx 27.5° \qquad b \approx 78.7° \qquad c \approx 114.6° \qquad d \approx 139.1°$$

Step 3 Use a compass to draw a circle. Draw the approximate central angles with a protractor.

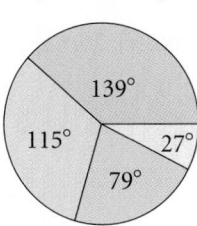

Step 4 Label each sector. Add any necessary information.

Ages of U.S. Grandparents

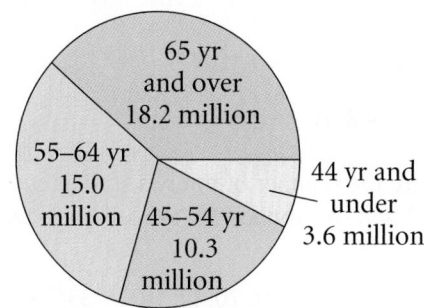

EXERCISES

1. a. Use the data in the table to draw a circle graph.
   b. Approximately what percent of students ride the bus?
   c. Approximately how many times more students walk than ride in a car?

Transportation Mode	Walk	Bicycle	Bus	Car
Number of Students	252	135	432	81

2. Data Collection Survey your class to find out how they get to school. Use the data to draw a circle graph.

Box-and-Whisker Plots

To show how data items are spread out, you can arrange a set of data in order from least to greatest. The maximum, minimum, and median give you some information about the data. You can better describe the data by dividing it into fourths.

The lower quartile is the median of the lower half of the data. The upper quartile is the median of the upper half of the data. If the data set has an odd number of items, the median is not included in either the upper half or the lower half.

The data below describe the highway gas mileage (mi/gal) for several cars.

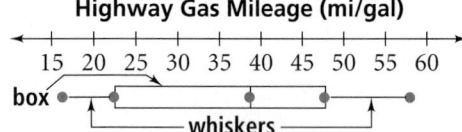

minimum | median = 38.5 | | maximum

17   19   27   37   40   42   52   58

lower quartile $\frac{19 + 27}{2} = 23$ upper quartile $\frac{42 + 52}{2} = 47$

A box-and-whisker plot is a visual representation of data. The box-and-whisker plot below displays the gas mileage information.

Highway Gas Mileage (mi/gal)

15 20 25 30 35 40 45 50 55 60

box

whiskers

The box represents the data from the lower quartile to the upper quartile. The vertical line segment represents the median. Horizontal line segments called whiskers show the spread of the data to the minimum and to the maximum.

EXERCISES

Create a box-and-whisker plot for each data set.

1. {3, 2, 3, 4, 6, 6, 7}

2. {1, 1.5, 1.7, 2, 6.1, 6.2, 7}

3. {1, 2, 5, 6, 9, 12, 7, 10}

4. {65, 66, 59, 61, 67, 70, 67, 66, 69, 70, 63}

5. {29, 32, 40, 31, 33, 39, 27, 42}

6. {3, 3, 5, 7, 1, 10, 10, 4, 4, 7, 9, 8, 6}

7. {1, 1.2, 1.3, 4, 4.1, 4.2, 7}

8. {1, 3.8, 3.9, 4, 4.3, 4.4, 7, 5}

9. Jobs Below are the number of hours a student worked each week at her summer job. When she applied for the job, she was told that the typical work week was 29 hours.

29, 25, 21, 20, 17, 16, 15, 33, 33, 30, 15

a. Make a box-and-whisker plot for the data.
b. How many weeks are above the upper quartile? What are the numbers of hours worked?
c. What is the median number of hours she worked? What is the mean? Compare them to the typical work week.

10. Writing In what ways are histograms and box-and-whisker plots alike, and in what ways are they different?

Choosing an Appropriate Graph

The type of data you want to display can suggest an appropriate graph. You can have data by categories (qualitative data), such as states, years, or mode of transportation. You may also have measurement data (quantitative data), such as height, time to get ready in the morning, or gas mileage.

The table below lists some common types of graphs and how they are frequently used.

Graph	Use
Bar Graph	To display frequency of categories
Circle Graph	To show categories as part of a whole
Line Graph	To show trends over time
Line Plot, Histogram, Stem-and-Leaf Plot	To display frequency distribution of measurement data
Box-and-Whisker Plot	To summarize the distribution of measurement data
Scatter Plot	To display possible relationships in data pairs

EXAMPLE

Would you use a line graph or a circle graph to display the percent of fiction books published each year for the last ten years?

A circle graph shows percents, but it would not allow you to show the change over time. A line graph would be more appropriate.

EXERCISES

Choose the appropriate graph to display each set of data. Explain your choice.

1. circle graph or bar graph
   how much the average family spends on rent, food, transportation, utilities, and entertainment in October

2. bar graph or line graph
   the number of runners in the Olympic marathon for each of the last five Olympic games

3. scatter plot or double bar graph
   the ages of twelve cars and their levels of emissions

4. double box-and-whisker plot or scatter plot
   the heights of men and women playing professional basketball in 2004

Open-Ended **For each type of graph, describe a set of data that would be appropriate.**

5. stem-and-leaf plot

6. double line graph

7. circle graph

Misleading Graphs

There are many ways to graph data that show the data accurately. There are also ways to graph data that are misleading. One way that is misleading is graphing data that has less than the whole vertical axis, but doesn't point this out with the use of a break symbol on the axis.

1 EXAMPLE

What impression does the graph at the right give? What is actually true about the data?

Company Revenues

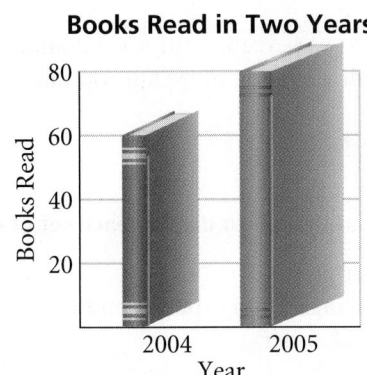

The graph implies that company revenues are growing quickly. Actually, company revenues are increasing more slowly.

Another way a graph can mislead is by using shapes that increase in both height and width, which implies a much bigger increase has happened, since the area increases much more than the height alone.

2 EXAMPLE

What makes the graph at the right misleading? Explain.

Books Read in Two Years

Looking at the vertical axis, you can see that the number of books read increased by one third. However, the bar on the right increased not only in height, but width. The area of the second bar is more than two times the area of the first bar. This gives the impression that the increase was much greater than it really was.

EXERCISES

For each graph below, (a) explain how the graph is misleading, and (b) explain how to redraw the graph so it is not misleading.

1. **Times for 10-Mile Run**

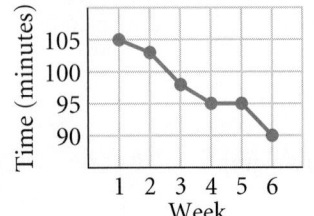

2. **Towels Sold**

3. Choose one of the graphs on this page. Redraw the graph to display the data accurately.

Spreadsheets

You can use a spreadsheet to evaluate formulas. Spreadsheets use the symbols
$+$ for addition and $-$ for subtraction, but different symbols for other operations.

Multiplication:	$* \rightarrow$	$10 * 2 = 10 \cdot 2 = 20$
Division:	$/ \rightarrow$	$10 / 2 = 10 \div 2 = 5$
Exponent:	$\wedge \rightarrow$	$10 \wedge 2 = 10^2 = 100$

EXAMPLE

Evaluate the formula $P = 2\ell + 2w$ for $\ell = 3$ and for whole-number values of w from 8 to 11.

Enter the values of ℓ and w into the first two columns. Cell A2 has the value of ℓ. Cell B2 has the first value of w. In cell C2, enter the expression $= 2*A2 + 2*B2$ to find the perimeter of a figure with length 3 and width 8.

Column names

	A	B	C
1	L	W	2L + 2W
2		3	8	= 2*A2 + 2* B2
3		3	9	
4		3	10	
5		3	**11**	

Row numbers

└ Cell B5

The spreadsheet evaluates the expression automatically.

Copy the expression in cell C2 into cells C3, C4, and C5. The spreadsheet automatically updates for the values of ℓ and w in rows 3, 4, and 5.

✗	✓	= 2*A2 + 2* B2	
	A	B	C
1	L	W	2L + 2W
2		3	8	**22**
3		3	9	24
4		3	10	26
5		3	11	28

EXERCISES

Suppose the values of a, b, and c are in cells A2, B2, and C2 of a spreadsheet. Write the expression you would use to enter each formula in the spreadsheet.

1. $P = a + b + c$ **2.** $T = \dfrac{3a + 5b}{8}$ **3.** $R = \frac{1}{2}bc$ **4.** $A = c^2$

5. You deposit \$200 in an account that earns 6% compounded annually for three years. The spreadsheet below shows the balance at the end of each year.

	A	B	C	D	E
1	Year	Start of Year	Rate	Interest	End of Year
2	1st	\$200.00	0.06	\$12.00	\$212.00
3	2nd	\$212.00	0.06	\$12.72	\$224.72
4	3rd	\$224.72	0.06	\$13.48	\$238.20

a. In which cell of the spreadsheet would you find the formula $= B3 * C3$?
b. In which cell of the spreadsheet would you find the formula $= B4 + D4$?

SAT® PREP ACT®

Preparing for the SAT and the ACT

Introduction

The SAT and the ACT are standardized tests used nationally for college admissions. This appendix provides you with test-taking strategies and sample problems to help you with the Mathematics portions of these tests. You can find SAT-specific strategies on pages 814 and 815, and ACT-specific strategies on pages 816 and 817.

The SAT Test

One of the three parts of the SAT is Mathematics. You will be tested on numbers and operations, algebra and functions, geometry, statistics, probability, and data analysis.

The Mathematics portion contains these three sections

- 20 multiple-choice (25 minutes)

- 8 multiple-choice and 10 student-produced response (25 minutes)

- 16 multiple-choice (20 minutes)

On the 10 student-produced response questions, also called "grid-ins", you bubble in your answer on a four-column grid. The questions of the same type are ordered by difficulty, starting with the easiest.

Scoring The multiple-choice questions count the same—you are awarded 1 point for each correct answer and deducted $\frac{1}{4}$ point for each incorrect answer. No points are awarded or deducted for omitted answers. There is no penalty for an incorrect grid-in, so you should always answer these. Your raw score is rounded to the nearest whole number and then a conversion chart is used to find your official score from 200 to 800.

All multiple-choice answers are in an A, B, C, D, E format. Be careful when omitting answers that you do not incorrectly complete your answer sheet.

The ACT Test

The ACT test has four subject tests, one of which is Mathematics. You will be tested on pre-algebra, elementary algebra, intermediate algebra, coordinate geometry, geometry, and elementary trigonometry. The Mathematics section consists of 60 multiple-choice questions to be answered in 60 minutes. All of the questions count the same, and there is no penalty for guessing.

Scoring The total number of correct answers is counted to get your raw score. No points are deducted for an incorrect answer. This raw score is then converted to the test score ranging from 1 (low) to 36 (high).

SAT and ACT Strategy: Time Management

Time management plays a very important role in your success. It is important that you do not spend extended periods of time on any one question. You may skip questions that are too difficult or time consuming. You can mark your booklet, so circle questions that you have skipped.

On the SAT *only*, the questions are arranged from easy to hard. To manage your time properly, you may want to omit the last 2 or 3 questions at the end of a section. They will be the most difficult and time consuming to complete. Use this time to look back over the section and redo any skipped questions. If there is time remaining once you are finished looking over the section, try to answer the last few questions.

On the ACT *only*, when you hear the announcement of five minutes remaining, go back and answer any skipped questions, even if it is only a guess. Put an answer for *every* question on the ACT, because there is no penalty for answering incorrectly.

EXERCISES

You have 5 minutes to complete the questions below. Next to each problem, write the time you started.

1. The number .009 is equivalent to the ratio of 9 to what number?

   A. .1   B. 1   C. 10   D. 100   E. 1,000

2. Which of the following is not a solution to $3n + 8 > 26$?

   A. 10   B. 9   C. 8   D. 7   E. 6

3. The mean of x, x, x, and 57 is 24. What is the value of x?

   A. 17   B. 15   C. 13   D. 11   E. 9

4. Find the slope of the line containing the points $(1, -5)$ and $(-4, -2)$.

   A. $-\frac{5}{3}$ B. $-\frac{3}{5}$ C. $\frac{3}{5}$ D. $\frac{5}{7}$ E. $\frac{5}{3}$

5. The gauge of a gas tank shows $\frac{1}{4}$ full. After 8 gallons are added, the tank is $\frac{3}{4}$ full. What is the capacity, in gallons, of the tank?

   A. 8   B. 16   C. 24   D. 32   E. 40

After you've completed the exercises, answer the following questions.

6. Which problem was the most difficult for you?

7. Which problem took you the longest?

8. Was there a problem you did not answer because you ran out of time?

SAT and ACT Strategy: Eliminating Answers

You may solve a multiple-choice question by eliminating some of the answer choices. One way to eliminate answers is to use estimation. You may also use the answer choices to work backward through the problem. Each method requires less work and increases your chances of answering the question correctly.

In the figure at the right, the shaded region is symmetrical about the *x*- and *y*-axes. Which of the following is the approximate area of the shaded region?

(A) 7   (B) 10   (C) 14   (D) 22   (E) 29

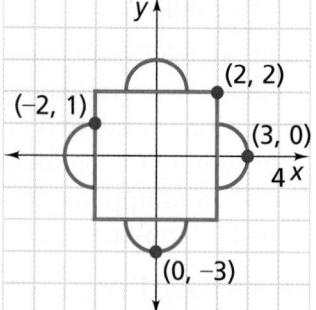

The area of the square is $4 \times 4 = 16$.

→ The figure has an area of *at least* 16. **Eliminate answer choices A, B, and C.**

The area of the 4 semi-circles or 2 full circles is $2 \times \pi r^2$.

→ $2 \times \pi(1^2) = 2 \times \pi$ **Estimate: $\pi \approx 3$.**
≈ 6

Add the two areas; $16 + 6$. The area is about 22.

→ **The correct answer is (D).**

If *x* and *y* are positive integers and $x^2 - y^2 = 5$, what is the value of *x*?

(A) 1   (B) 2   (C) 3   (D) 4   (E) 5

Work backward by placing each answer choice into the equation.

→ (A); $(1)^2 - y^2 = 5$ (D); $(4)^2 - y^2 = 5$
(B); $(2)^2 - y^2 = 5$ (E); $(5)^2 - y^2 = 5$
(C); $(3)^2 - y^2 = 5$

x^2 must be greater than 5.

→ **Eliminate answer choices A and B.**
(C); $9 - 5 = 4$ √

If *y* is an integer, then the difference between x^2 and 5 must be a perfect square.

→ (D); $16 - 5 = 11$ ✕
(E); $25 - 5 = 20$ ✕

EXERCISES

1. If k is a positive integer, for which of the following is the least possible value of *k* for which $\frac{7k}{2}$ is an integer?

(A) 3   (B) 5   (C) 15   (D) 30   (E) 60

2. The area of a rectangle is 48 in.². If the area is increased by 25%, which of the following could be the dimensions of the new rectangle?

(A) 2 in. by 6 in.   (B) 4 in. by 6 in.   (C) 4 in. by 8 in.   (D) 6 in. by 8in.   (E) 6 in. by 10 in.

SAT and ACT Strategy: Using a Variable

When you are solving a problem with unknown values, you may need to use variables. Choose letters that characterize the unknown value, for example d for distance or a for age.

You should know what the variables in common formulas represent. For example, the variables in the formula $V = \pi r^2 h$ stand for Volume, radius, and height. Often, the value of one or more of the variables needed for a formula is given in the problem. You can substitute given values into the formula to find the unknown variable.

1 EXAMPLE

In a class, the ratio of the number of boys to the number of girls is 4 to 5. If there are 16 boys in the class, what is the total number of students in the class?

(A) 24
(B) 28
(C) 32
(D) 36
(E) 40

Write the ratio of boys (b) to girls (g).	$\dfrac{b}{g} = \dfrac{4}{5}$
Write a proportion using the information given; There are 16 boys.	$\dfrac{4}{5} = \dfrac{16}{g}$
Write the cross products and solve the proportion.	$4g = 5(16)$ $4g = 80$ $g = 20$
Find the total number of students, $b + g$.	$b = 16,\ g = 20;\ b + g = 36$ **The correct answer is (D).**

EXERCISES

1. If 6 more than 3 times a number is 4 more than the number, what is the number?

(A) -3 (B) -1 (C) 0   (D) 2   (E) 4

2. A 20-foot ladder is placed against a wall. The bottom of the ladder is standing 12 feet from the base of the wall. At what height does the top of the ladder touch the wall?

(A) 13   (B) 14   (C) 15   (D) 16   (E) 17

SAT Strategy: Writing Gridded Responses

Your score for the 10 gridded-response questions on the SAT test is based on the number of questions you answer correctly. Your answer must be gridded properly to count as a correct response. There is no penalty for incorrect answers so answer every question, even if you need to make a guess.

1 EXAMPLE

If the right triangle on the right has a hypotenuse of $27.2x$, what is the value of x?

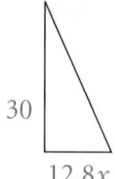

30

12.8x

Use the Pythagorean Theorem to solve the problem.

$$a^2 + b^2 = c^2$$

$$(12.8x)^2 + (30)^2 = (27.2x)^2$$

$$1.25 = x$$

To enter the 1.25 into the grid, start at the left placing each digit or symbol into one column only. Then, fill the corresponding circle with the digit or symbol at the top of the column.

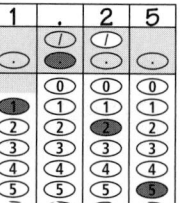

Fractions can be placed in the grid. However, mixed numbers should NOT be gridded. For example, 1.25 can be written as $1\frac{1}{4}$. If entered into the grid, $1\frac{1}{4}$ would be interpreted as $\frac{11}{4}$, making the answer incorrect. Mixed numbers must be changed into an improper fraction. $1\frac{1}{4} = \frac{5}{4}$.

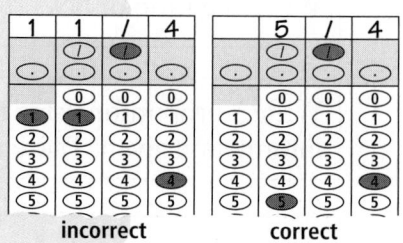

incorrect   correct

A decimal answer may have more digits than the grid allows. When recording these decimals, the grid must be filled to the thousandths place. For example, a repeating decimal such as .363636...., can be placed in the grid as either $\frac{11}{4}$, .363, or .364.

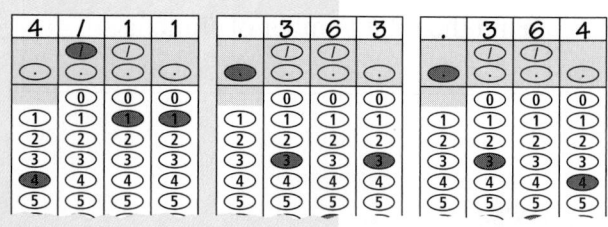

EXERCISES

Rewrite each answer to properly fit the grid.

1. $7\frac{1}{2}$

2. .3232

3. 2.745

4. $2\frac{1}{2}$

SAT Strategy: Finding Multiple Correct Answers

You will find that some multiple-choice questions ask you to select one or more correct answers from a group of possibilities. For these problems, figure out whether each possibility is correct. Then you will be able to select the answer choice that includes all of the correct possibilities.

1 EXAMPLE

A group of children have the following ages: 2, 3, 7, 5, 2, 2, 4, 5, 6. Which of the following must be true?

  I. The mean of the ages is equal to the age of at least one child.

 II. The mean of the ages is equal to the median, and both are greater than the mode.

III. If a 4-year old child is added to the group, the mean, median, and mode will not change.

(A) I only
(B) II only
(C) III only
(D) I and II only
(E) I, II, and III

I. Find the mean age of the group and compare it to the ages of each child.	→	$\dfrac{2 + 3 + 7 + 5 + 2 + 2 + 4 + 5 + 6}{9} = \dfrac{36}{9}$ Mean = 4 and there is a 4-year old child. **I is true.**
II. Find the median and the mode. Compare all three values; mean, median, and mode.	→	2, 2, 2, 3, 4, 5, 5, 6, 7; Median = 4, Mode = 2 Both mean and median are 4 and greater than the mode, 2. **II is true.**
III. Find the mean, median, and mode for the group with an added 4-year old child.	→	$\dfrac{2 + 3 + 7 + 5 + 2 + 2 + 4 + 5 + 6 + 4}{10} = \dfrac{40}{10}$ Mean = 4 2, 2, 2, 3, 4, 4, 5, 5, 6, 7; Median = 4, Mode = 2 **III is true.** **The correct answer is (E).**

EXERCISES

1. If $2x + 1 > -3$, which of the following could be a possible value of x?

   I. -3
  II. -2
 III. 0

(A) I only
(B) II only
(C) III only
(D) I and II only
(E) II and III only

2. If $x < -1$, which of the following statements must be true?

   I. $x^2 > x^4$
  II. $x^2 < x^3$
 III. $x > x - 2$

(A) I only
(B) II only
(C) III only
(D) I and II only
(E) I and III only

ACT Strategy: Answering the Question Asked

Many test questions require more than one step. As you solve these multiple-step problems, make sure you complete all of the steps necessary to solve the final question. As you read a problem, it may be helpful to underline the question being asked. After you solve, check over your work to ensure that you answered the final question.

1 EXAMPLE

If a is 40 percent of 200, b is 25 percent of 120, and c is 10 percent of $a + b$, what is the value of $(a + b) - c$?

A. 11
B. 30
C. 80
D. 99
E. 110

To solve for $(a + b) - c$, you must first calculate the values of a, b, and c.

$a = 40$ percent of 200	$b = 25$ percent of 120	$c = 10$ percent of $a + b$
$= 0.40 \times 200$	$= 0.25 \times 120$	$= 0.10 \times (80 + 30)$
$= 80$	$= 30$	$= 0.10 \times 110 = 11$

Choice C is the value of a.

Choice B is the value of b.

Choice A is the value of c.
Choice E is the value of $a + b$.

Thus, choices A, B, C, and E do not answer the final question; what is the value of $(a + b) - c$?

Choice D is correct, $(80 + 30) - 11 = 99$.

EXERCISES

Answer the question asked.

1. Three business partners share the company profits in the ratio of 8:3:1. If the yearly profits were $54,000, what is the greatest amount one of the partners would earn?

   A. $49,500   B. $40,500   C. $36,000   D. $13,500   E. $4,500

2. If $3x - 10 = 2 - x$ and $\frac{1}{2}y - 3 = -1$, then $x^2 y = ?$

   F. 3   G. 4   H. 9   J. 36   K. 144

3. If $2x - 4$, $x + 2$, and $3x - 7$ are all integers and $x + 2$ is the median of these integers, which of the following could be a value of x?

   A. 1   B. 2   C. 3   D. 4   E. 5

ACT Strategy: Drawing a Diagram

Sometimes it is helpful to solve a problem by drawing a diagram. It is very important to follow the criteria given in the problem to ensure that your drawing is accurate.

Some problems may already provide you with a diagram. Do NOT assume that the diagram is drawn to scale. You are allowed to mark your booklet, so label information that has not been labeled for you.

1 EXAMPLE

A rectangle is three times as long as it is wide. If the length of the rectangle is 12 inches, what is the rectangle's perimeter, in inches?

A. 16
B. 20
C. 24
D. 28
E. 32

Draw a diagram that has a length that is three times longer than the width.	*length* → *width* ▭
Label the diagram with the information given. The length is 12 inches. The width is 4 inches because the length is three times the width.	*length* = 12 inches → *width* = 4 inches ▭
Use the diagram to find the perimeter of the rectangle.	length + length + width + width = 12 in. + 12 in. + 4 in. + 4 in. = 32 in.

The correct answer is E.

EXERCISES

1. If $\overline{AB} = 3\,\overline{BC}$, what is the value of $\dfrac{\overline{BC}}{\overline{AC}}$?

A—●——B—●——C—●

A. 1   B. $\dfrac{1}{2}$ C. $\dfrac{1}{3}$ D. $\dfrac{1}{4}$ E. $\dfrac{1}{9}$

2. The total surface area of a rectangular box is the sum of the areas of the 6 sides. If the length is 2 inches, the width is 3 inches, and the height is 5 inches, what is the box's total surface area, in square inches?

F. 50   G. 62   H. 74   J. 82   K. 96

Tables

Table 1 Measures

United States Customary	Metric
Length	
12 inches (in.) = 1 foot (ft) 36 in. = 1 yard (yd) 3 ft = 1 yard 5280 ft = 1 mile (mi) 1760 yd = 1 mile	10 millimeters (mm) = 1 centimeter (cm) 100 cm = 1 meter (m) 1000 mm = 1 meter 1000 m = 1 kilometer (km)
Area	
144 square inches (in.^2) = 1 square foot (ft^2) 9 ft^2 = 1 square yard (yd^2) 43,560 ft^2 = 1 acre (a) 4840 yd^2 = 1 acre	100 square millimeters (mm^2) = 1 square centimeter (cm^2) 10,000 cm^2 = 1 square meter (m^2) 10,000 m^2 = 1 hectare (ha)
Volume	
1728 cubic inches (in.^3) = 1 cubic foot (ft^3) 27 ft^3 = 1 cubic yard (yd^3)	1000 cubic millimeters (mm^3) = 1 cubic centimeter (cm^3) 1,000,000 cm^3 = 1 cubic meter (m^3)
Liquid Capacity	
8 fluid ounces (fl oz) = 1 cup (c) 2 c = 1 pint (pt) 2 pt = 1 quart (qt) 4 qt = 1 gallon (gal)	1000 milliliters (mL) = 1 liter (L) 1000 L = 1 kiloliter (kL)
Weight or Mass	
16 ounces (oz) = 1 pound (lb) 2000 pounds = 1 ton (t)	1000 milligrams (mg) = 1 gram (g) 1000 g = 1 kilogram (kg) 1000 kg = 1 metric ton
Temperature	
32°F = freezing point of water 98.6°F = normal body temperature 212°F = boiling point of water	0°C = freezing point of water 37°C = normal body temperature 100°C = boiling point of water
Time	
60 seconds (s) = 1 minute (min) 60 minutes = 1 hour (h) 24 hours = 1 day (d) 7 days = 1 week (wk) 4 weeks (approx.) = 1 month (mo)	365 days = 1 year (yr) 52 weeks (approx.) = 1 year 12 months = 1 year 10 years = 1 decade 100 years = 1 century

Table 2 Reading Math Symbols

Symbol	Meaning
$>$	is greater than
$<$	is less than
$\geq$	is greater than or equal to
$\leq$	is less than or equal to
$=$	is equal to
$\neq$	is not equal to
$\approx$	is approximately equal to
$\stackrel{?}{=}$	is this statement true?
$+$	plus (addition)
$-$	minus (subtraction)
$\times, \cdot$	times (multiplication)
$\div, \overline{)}$	divide (division)
$\sqrt{x}$	nonnegative square root of x
$^\circ$	degrees
$\%$	percent
$(\ )$	parentheses for grouping
$\lvert a \rvert$	absolute value of a
$a:b, \frac{a}{b}$	ratio of a to b
(a, b)	ordered pair with x-coordinate a and y-coordinate b
$\cong$	is congruent to
$\sim$	is similar to
$\parallel$	is parallel to
π	pi, an irrational number approximately equal to 3.14
$f(n)$	function value at n, f of n
b	y-intercept
m	slope of a line
$-a$	opposite of a
$\frac{1}{a}$	reciprocal of a
a^n	nth power of a
d	diameter distance
A'	image of A, A prime

Symbol	Meaning
A	Area
b_1, b_2	base lengths of a trapezoid
b	base length
h	height
p or P	perimeter
ℓ	length slant height
w	width
C	circumference
S.A.	surface area
L.A.	lateral area
B	area of a base
V	volume
r	rate radius
$\overline{AB}$	segment AB
$\overrightarrow{AB}$	ray AB
$\overleftrightarrow{AB}$	line AB
$\triangle ABC$	triangle with vertices A, B, and C
$\angle A$	angle with vertex A
$\angle ABC$	angle with sides $\overrightarrow{BA}$ and $\overrightarrow{BC}$
$m\angle ABC$	measure of angle ABC
AB	length of segment $\overline{AB}$
$\sin A$	sine of $\angle A$
$\cos A$	cosine of $\angle A$
$\tan A$	tangent of $\angle A$
$P(\text{event})$	probability of an event
$_nP_r$	number of permutations of n things taken r at a time
$_nC_r$	number of combinations of n things taken r at a time
$\wedge$	raised to a power (in software or a calculator)

Table 3 Squares and Square Roots

Number n	Square n^2	Positive Square Root $\sqrt{n}$	Number n	Square n^2	Positive Square Root $\sqrt{n}$	Number n	Square n^2	Positive Square Root $\sqrt{n}$
1	1	1.000	51	2601	7.141	101	10,201	10.050
2	4	1.414	52	2704	7.211	102	10,404	10.100
3	9	1.732	53	2809	7.280	103	10,609	10.149
4	16	2.000	54	2916	7.348	104	10,816	10.198
5	25	2.236	55	3025	7.416	105	11,025	10.247
6	36	2.449	56	3136	7.483	106	11,236	10.296
7	49	2.646	57	3249	7.550	107	11,449	10.344
8	64	2.828	58	3364	7.616	108	11,664	10.392
9	81	3.000	59	3481	7.681	109	11,881	10.440
10	100	3.162	60	3600	7.746	110	12,100	10.488
11	121	3.317	61	3721	7.810	111	12,321	10.536
12	144	3.464	62	3844	7.874	112	12,544	10.583
13	169	3.606	63	3969	7.937	113	12,769	10.630
14	196	3.742	64	4096	8.000	114	12,996	10.677
15	225	3.873	65	4225	8.062	115	13,225	10.724
16	256	4.000	66	4356	8.124	116	13,456	10.770
17	289	4.123	67	4489	8.185	117	13,689	10.817
18	324	4.243	68	4624	8.246	118	13,924	10.863
19	361	4.359	69	4761	8.307	119	14,161	10.909
20	400	4.472	70	4900	8.367	120	14,400	10.954
21	441	4.583	71	5041	8.426	121	14,641	11.000
22	484	4.690	72	5184	8.485	122	14,884	11.045
23	529	4.796	73	5329	8.544	123	15,129	11.091
24	576	4.899	74	5476	8.602	124	15,376	11.136
25	625	5.000	75	5625	8.660	125	15,625	11.180
26	676	5.099	76	5776	8.718	126	15,876	11.225
27	729	5.196	77	5929	8.775	127	16,129	11.269
28	784	5.292	78	6084	8.832	128	16,384	11.314
29	841	5.385	79	6241	8.888	129	16,641	11.358
30	900	5.477	80	6400	8.944	130	16,900	11.402
31	961	5.568	81	6561	9.000	131	17,161	11.446
32	1024	5.657	82	6724	9.055	132	17,424	11.489
33	1089	5.745	83	6889	9.110	133	17,689	11.533
34	1156	5.831	84	7056	9.165	134	17,956	11.576
35	1225	5.916	85	7225	9.220	135	18,225	11.619
36	1296	6.000	86	7396	9.274	136	18,496	11.662
37	1369	6.083	87	7569	9.327	137	18,769	11.705
38	1444	6.164	88	7744	9.381	138	19,044	11.747
39	1521	6.245	89	7921	9.434	139	19,321	11.790
40	1600	6.325	90	8100	9.487	140	19,600	11.832
41	1681	6.403	91	8281	9.539	141	19,881	11.874
42	1764	6.481	92	8464	9.592	142	20,164	11.916
43	1849	6.557	93	8649	9.644	143	20,449	11.958
44	1936	6.633	94	8836	9.695	144	20,736	12.000
45	2025	6.708	95	9025	9.747	145	21,025	12.042
46	2116	6.782	96	9216	9.798	146	21,316	12.083
47	2209	6.856	97	9409	9.849	147	21,609	12.124
48	2304	6.928	98	9604	9.899	148	21,904	12.166
49	2401	7.000	99	9801	9.950	149	22,201	12.207
50	2500	7.071	100	10,000	10.000	150	22,500	12.247

Table 4 Trigonometric Ratios

Angle	Sine	Cosine	Tangent
1°	0.0175	0.9998	0.0175
2°	0.0349	0.9994	0.0349
3°	0.0523	0.9986	0.0524
4°	0.0698	0.9976	0.0699
5°	0.0872	0.9962	0.0875
6°	0.1045	0.9945	0.1051
7°	0.1219	0.9925	0.1228
8°	0.1392	0.9903	0.1405
9°	0.1564	0.9877	0.1584
10°	0.1736	0.9848	0.1763
11°	0.1908	0.9816	0.1944
12°	0.2079	0.9781	0.2126
13°	0.2250	0.9744	0.2309
14°	0.2419	0.9703	0.2493
15°	0.2588	0.9659	0.2679
16°	0.2756	0.9613	0.2867
17°	0.2924	0.9563	0.3057
18°	0.3090	0.9511	0.3249
19°	0.3256	0.9455	0.3443
20°	0.3420	0.9397	0.3640
21°	0.3584	0.9336	0.3839
22°	0.3746	0.9272	0.4040
23°	0.3907	0.9205	0.4245
24°	0.4067	0.9135	0.4452
25°	0.4226	0.9063	0.4663
26°	0.4384	0.8988	0.4877
27°	0.4540	0.8910	0.5095
28°	0.4695	0.8829	0.5317
29°	0.4848	0.8746	0.5543
30°	0.5000	0.8660	0.5774
31°	0.5150	0.8572	0.6009
32°	0.5299	0.8480	0.6249
33°	0.5446	0.8387	0.6494
34°	0.5592	0.8290	0.6745
35°	0.5736	0.8192	0.7002
36°	0.5878	0.8090	0.7265
37°	0.6018	0.7986	0.7536
38°	0.6157	0.7880	0.7813
39°	0.6293	0.7771	0.8098
40°	0.6428	0.7660	0.8391
41°	0.6561	0.7547	0.8693
42°	0.6691	0.7431	0.9004
43°	0.6820	0.7314	0.9325
44°	0.6947	0.7193	0.9657
45°	0.7071	0.7071	1.0000

Angle	Sine	Cosine	Tangent
46°	0.7193	0.6947	1.0355
47°	0.7314	0.6820	1.0724
48°	0.7431	0.6691	1.1106
49°	0.7547	0.6561	1.1504
50°	0.7660	0.6428	1.1918
51°	0.7771	0.6293	1.2349
52°	0.7880	0.6157	1.2799
53°	0.7986	0.6018	1.3270
54°	0.8090	0.5878	1.3764
55°	0.8192	0.5736	1.4281
56°	0.8290	0.5592	1.4826
57°	0.8387	0.5446	1.5399
58°	0.8480	0.5299	1.6003
59°	0.8572	0.5150	1.6643
60°	0.8660	0.5000	1.7321
61°	0.8746	0.4848	1.8040
62°	0.8829	0.4695	1.8807
63°	0.8910	0.4540	1.9626
64°	0.8988	0.4384	2.0503
65°	0.9063	0.4226	2.1445
66°	0.9135	0.4067	2.2460
67°	0.9205	0.3907	2.3559
68°	0.9272	0.3746	2.4751
69°	0.9336	0.3584	2.6051
70°	0.9397	0.3420	2.7475
71°	0.9455	0.3256	2.9042
72°	0.9511	0.3090	3.0777
73°	0.9563	0.2924	3.2709
74°	0.9613	0.2756	3.4874
75°	0.9659	0.2588	3.7321
76°	0.9703	0.2419	4.0108
77°	0.9744	0.2250	4.3315
78°	0.9781	0.2079	4.7046
79°	0.9816	0.1908	5.1446
80°	0.9848	0.1736	5.6713
81°	0.9877	0.1564	6.3138
82°	0.9903	0.1392	7.1154
83°	0.9925	0.1219	8.1443
84°	0.9945	0.1045	9.5144
85°	0.9962	0.0872	11.4301
86°	0.9976	0.0698	14.3007
87°	0.9986	0.0523	19.0811
88°	0.9994	0.0349	28.6363
89°	0.9998	0.0175	57.2900
90°	1.0000	0.0000	

Tables

Formulas and Properties

Geometric Formulas

Perimeter and Circumference

Rectangle

$P = 2\ell + 2w$

Circle

$C = \pi d$ or $C = 2\pi r$

Area

Square

$A = s^2$

Parallelogram and Rectangle

$A = bh$

Triangle

$A = \frac{1}{2}bh$

Trapezoid

$A = \frac{1}{2}h(b_1 + b_2)$

Circle

$C = \pi r^2$

Triangle Formulas

Pythagorean Theorem

In a right triangle with legs of lengths a and b and hypotenuse of length c, $a^2 + b^2 = c^2$.

Trigonometric Ratios

$\text{sine of } \angle A = \dfrac{\text{length of leg opposite } \angle A}{\text{length of hypotenuse}}$

$\text{cosine of } \angle A = \dfrac{\text{length of leg adjacent to } \angle A}{\text{length of hypotenuse}}$

$\text{tangent of } \angle A = \dfrac{\text{length of leg opposite } \angle A}{\text{length of leg adjacent to } \angle A}$

Triangle Angle Sum

For any $\triangle ABC$,

$m\angle A + m\angle B + m\angle C = 180°$.

Surface Area

Rectangular Prism

$\text{L.A.} = ph$

$\text{S.A.} = \text{L.A.} + 2B$

Cylinder

$\text{L.A.} = 2\pi rh$

$\text{S.A.} = \text{L.A.} + 2B$

Pyramid

$\text{L.A.} = \frac{1}{2}p\ell = n\left(\frac{1}{2}b\ell\right)$, where n is the number of faces

$\text{S.A.} = \text{L.A.} + B$

Cone

$\text{L.A.} = \pi r\ell$

$\text{S.A.} = \text{L.A.} + B$

Sphere

$\text{S.A.} = 4\pi r^2$

Volume

Prism

$V = Bh$

Cylinder

$V = Bh$, or $\pi r^2 h$

Pyramid

$V = \frac{1}{3}Bh$

Cone

$V = \frac{1}{3}Bh$, or $\frac{1}{3}\pi r^2 h$

Sphere

$V = \frac{4}{3}\pi r^3$

Properties of Real Numbers

Unless otherwise stated, $a, b, c,$ and d are real numbers.

Identity Properties

Addition $a + 0 = a$ and $0 + a = a$

Multiplication $a \cdot 1 = a$ and $1 \cdot a = a$

Commutative Properties

Addition $a + b = b + a$

Multiplication $a \cdot b = b \cdot a$

Associative Properties

Addition $(a + b) + c = a + (b + c)$

Multiplication $(a \cdot b) \cdot c = a \cdot (b \cdot c)$

Inverse Properties

Addition

$a + (-a) = 0$ and $-a + a = 0$

Multiplication

$a \cdot \frac{1}{a} = 1$ and $\frac{1}{a} \cdot a = 1 (a \neq 0)$

Distributive Properties

$a(b + c) = ab + ac$ $(b + c)a = ba + ca$

$a(b - c) = ab - ac$ $(b - c)a = ba - ca$

Properties of Equality

Addition   If $a = b$, then $a + c = b + c$.

Subtraction   If $a = b$, then $a - c = b - c$.

Multiplication If $a = b$, then $a \cdot c = b \cdot c$.

Division   If $a = b$, and $c \neq 0$, then $\frac{a}{c} = \frac{b}{c}$.

Substitution   If $a = b$, then b can replace a in any expression.

Reflexive $a = a$

Symmetric   If $a = b$, then $b = a$.

Transitive   If $a = b$ and $b = c$, then $a = c$.

Zero-Product Property

If $ab = 0$ then $a = 0$ or $b = 0$.

Zero Property of Multiplication

$a \cdot 0 = 0 \cdot a = 0$

Cross Product Property

$\frac{a}{b} = \frac{c}{d}$ is equivalent to $ad = bc$.

Closure Properties

$a + b$ is a unique real number.

ab is a unique real number.

Density Property

Between any two rational numbers, there is at least one other rational number.

Properties of Inequality

Addition   If $a > b$, then $a + c > b + c$.
                    If $a < b$, then $a + c < b + c$.

Subtraction   If $a > b$, then $a - c > b - c$.
                    If $a < b$, then $a - c < b - c$.

Multiplication

If $a > b$ and $c > 0$, then $ac > bc$.

If $a < b$ and $c > 0$, then $ac < bc$.

If $a > b$ and $c < 0$, then $ac < bc$.

If $a < b$ and $c < 0$, then $ac > bc$.

Division

If $a > b$ and $c > 0$, then $\frac{a}{c} > \frac{b}{c}$.

If $a < b$ and $c > 0$, then $\frac{a}{c} < \frac{b}{c}$.

If $a > b$ and $c < 0$, then $\frac{a}{c} < \frac{b}{c}$.

If $a < b$ and $c < 0$, then $\frac{a}{c} > \frac{b}{c}$.

Transitive   If $a > b$ and $b > c$, then $a > c$.

Comparison   If $a = b + c$ and $c > 0$, then $a > b$.

Properties of Exponents

For $a \neq 0$ and any integers m and n:

Zero Exponent $a^0 = 1$

Negative Exponent $a^{-n} = \frac{1}{a^n}$

Product of Powers $a^m \cdot a^n = a^{m+n}$

Quotient of Powers $\frac{a^m}{a^n} = a^{m-n}$

Power of a Power $(a^m)^n = a^{m \cdot n}$

Formulas of Geometry

You will use a number of geometric formulas as you work through your algebra book. Here are some perimeter, area, and volume formulas.

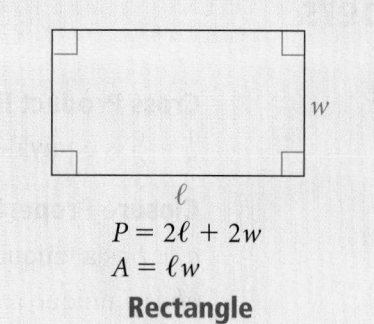

$P = 2\ell + 2w$
$A = \ell w$
Rectangle

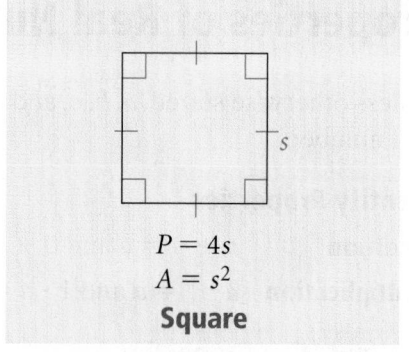

$P = 4s$
$A = s^2$
Square

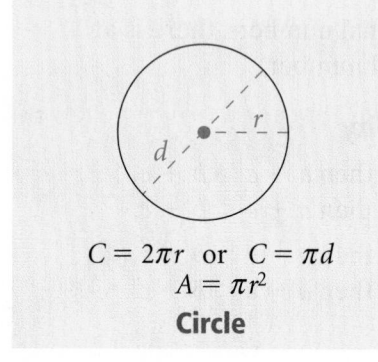

$C = 2\pi r$ or $C = \pi d$
$A = \pi r^2$
Circle

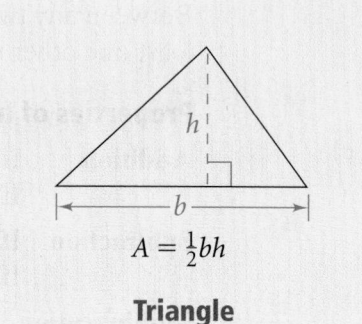

$A = \frac{1}{2}bh$
Triangle

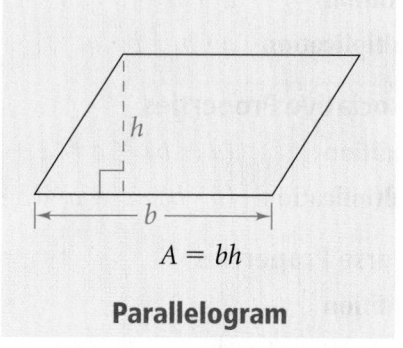

$A = bh$
Parallelogram

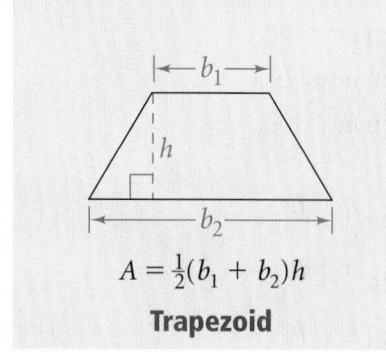

$A = \frac{1}{2}(b_1 + b_2)h$
Trapezoid

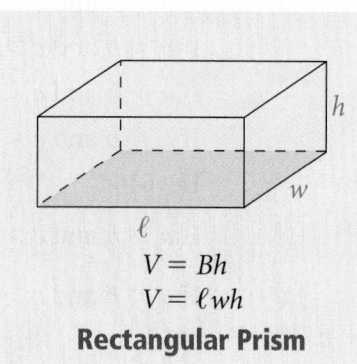

$V = Bh$
$V = \ell wh$
Rectangular Prism

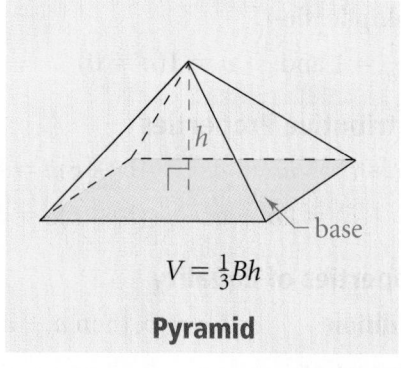

$V = \frac{1}{3}Bh$
Pyramid

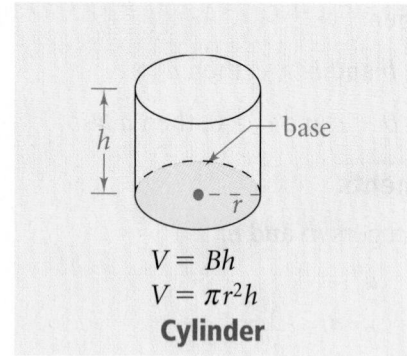

$V = Bh$
$V = \pi r^2 h$
Cylinder

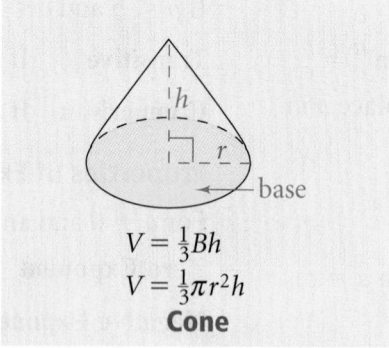

$V = \frac{1}{3}Bh$
$V = \frac{1}{3}\pi r^2 h$
Cone

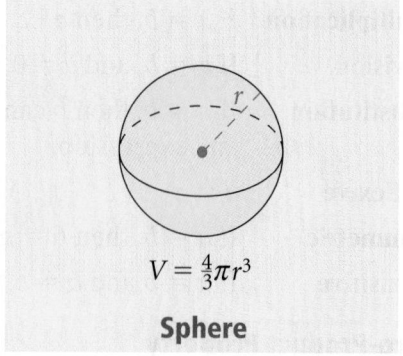

$V = \frac{4}{3}\pi r^3$
Sphere

English/Spanish Illustrated Glossary

Absolute value (p. 19)   Absolute value is the distance of a number from zero on a number line. You write *the absolute value* of -3 as $|-3|$.

Valor absoluto (p. 19)   El valor absoluto de un número es la distancia desde cero hasta ese número en una recta numérica. Escribe "el valor absoluto de 23" como $|-3|$.

The absolute value of -3 is 3 because -3 is 3 units from zero on a number line.

Absolute value equation (p. 535)   Equation whose graph forms a V that opens up or down.

Ecuación de valor absoluto (p. 535)   La ecuación cuya gráfica forma una V que se abre hacia arriba o hacia abajo.

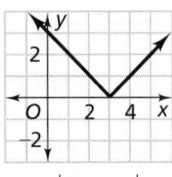

$$y = |3 - x|$$

Addition Property of Equality (p. 90)   If $a = b$ then $a + c = b + c$.

Propiedad aditiva de la igualdad (p. 90)   Si $a = b$, entonces $a + c = b + c$.

$8 = 2(4)$, so $8 + 3 = 2(4) + 3$

Addition Property of Inequality (p. 109)   If $a > b$, then $a + c > b + c$. If $a < b$, then $a + c < b + c$.

Propiedad aditiva de la desigualdad (p. 109)   Si $a > b$, entonces $a + c > b + c$. Si $a < b$, entonces $a + c < b + c$.

$7 > 3$, so $7 + 4 > 3 + 4$
$2 < 5$, so $2 + 6 < 5 + 6$

Additive identity (p. 69)   The additive identity is zero. When you add a number and 0, the sum equals the original number.

Identidad aditiva (p. 69)   La identidad aditiva es cero. Cuando se suman un número y 0, la suma es idéntica al número original.

$a + 0 = a$

Additive inverses (p. 24)   Additive inverses are two numbers with a sum of zero.

Inversos aditivos (p. 24)   Se llaman inversos aditivos a los números cuya suma es igual a cero.

23 and -23 are additive inverses because $-23 + 23 = 0$.

Algebraic expression (p. 180)   A mathematical phrase that can include numbers, variables, and operation symbols.

Expresión algebraica (p. 180)   Proposición matemática que incluye números, variables y símbolos de operaciones.

$7 + x$ is an algebraic expression.

English/Spanish Glossary

Arithmetic sequence (p. 469)   A number sequence formed by adding a fixed number to each previous term.

$4, 7, 10, 13, \ldots$ is an arithmetic sequence.

Progresión aritmética (p. 469)   Sucesión numérica que se obtiene al sumar un número constante a cada término consecutivo.

Associative Properties of Addition and Multiplication (p. 68)
For any numbers $a, b,$ and $c, (a + b) + c = a + (b + c)$ and $(ab)c = a(bc)$.

$(2 + 7) + 3 = 2 + (7 + 3)$
$(9 \cdot 4)5 = 9(4 \cdot 5)$

Propiedad asociativa de la suma y de la multiplicación (p. 68)   Para cualesquiera números a, b y $c, (a + b) + c = a + (b + c)$ y $(ab)c = a(bc)$.

Base (p. 185)   A number that is multiplied repeatedly.

$4^5 = 4 \cdot 4 \cdot 4 \cdot 4 \cdot 4$. The base 4 is used as a factor 5 times.

Base (p. 185)   El número que se multiplica repetidas veces.

Bar graph (p. 103)   A bar graph is a graph that compares amounts.
EXAMPLE This bar graph compares the numbers of students in grades 6, 7, and 8.

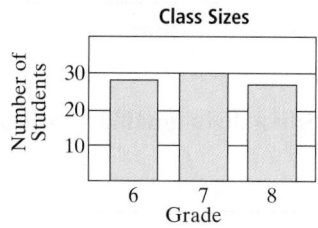

Gráfica de barras (p. 103)   Una gráfica de barras es una gráfica que compara cantidades.

Binomial (p. 686)   A binomial is a polynomial with two terms.

$3x^2 - 1$ is a binomial.

Binomio (p. 686)   Un binomio es un polinomio con dos términos.

Coefficient (p. 78)   A coefficient is a number that multiplies a variable.

In the expression $2x + 3y - 16$, 2 is the coefficient of x and 3 is the coefficient of y.

Coeficiente (p. 78)   Coeficiente es el número que multiplica una variable.

Common difference (p. 469)   The fixed number added to each term of an arithmetic sequence.

The common difference is 3 in the arithmetic sequence $4, 7, 10, 13, \ldots$

Diferencia común (p. 469)   Número constante que se usa a cada término para formar una progresión aritmética.

Common ratio (p. 636)   The fixed number used to find terms in a geometric sequence.

The common ratio is $\frac{1}{3}$ in the geometric sequence $9, 3, 1, \frac{1}{3}, \ldots$

Razón común (p. 636)   Número constante que se usa para hallar los términos en una progresión geométrica.

Commutative Properties of Addition and Multiplication (p. 68) For any numbers a and b, $a + b = b + a$ and $ab = ba$.

$6 + 4 = 4 + 6$
$9 \cdot 5 = 5 \cdot 9$

Propiedad conmutativa de la suma (p. 68) Para cualquier número a y b, $a + b = b + a$, y $ab = ba$.

Compatible numbers (p. 135) Compatible numbers are numbers that are close in value to the numbers you want to add, subtract, multiply, or divide, and for which the operation is easy to perform mentally. Estimating sums, differences, products, and quotients is easy to do mentally when you use compatible numbers.

Estimate $151 \div 14.6$.
$151 \approx 150$
$14.6 \approx 15$
$150 \div 15 = 10$
$151 \div 14.6 \approx 10$
For $155 \div 14.6$, 150 and 15 are compatible numbers.

Números compatibles (p. 135) Los números compatibles son aquéllos con un valor cercano a los números que deseas sumar, restar, multiplicar o dividir, y con los cuales es fácil hacer los cáculos mentalmente. Cuando calculas sumas, diferencias, productos y cocientes, te resulta más fácil utilizar números compatibles.

Complement of an event (p. 270) All possible outcomes that are not in the event.

$P(\text{complement of event}) = 1 - P(\text{event})$

The complement of rolling a 1 or a 2 on a number cube is rolling a 3, 4, 5, or 6.

Complemento de un suceso (p. 270) Todos los resultados posibles que no se dan en el suceso.

$P(\text{complemento de un suceso}) = 1 - P(\text{suceso})$

Compound inequalities (p. 403) Two inequalities that are joined by *and* or *or*.

$5 < x$ and $x < 10$
$14 < x$ or $x \geq -3$

Desigualdades compuestas (p. 403) Dos desigualdades que están enlazadas por medio de una *y* o una *o*.

Compound interest (p. 652) Interest paid on both the principal and the interest that has already been paid.

For an initial deposit of $1000 at a 6% interest rate with interest compounded quarterly, the function $y = 1000\left(\frac{0.06}{4}\right)^{4x}$ gives the account balance y after x years.

Interés compuesto (p. 652) Interés calculado tanto sobre el capital como sobre los intereses ya pagados.

Conclusion (p. 359) In a conditional, the part following *then*. *See* **conditional**.

In the conditional "If an animal has four legs, then it is a horse," the conclusion is "it is a horse."

Conclusión (p. 359) En un enunciado condicional, la parte que sigue a *entonces*. *Ver* **conditional**.

Conditional (p. 359) An "if-then" statement.

If an animal has four legs, then it is a horse.

Condicional (p. 359) Un enunciado de la forma "si-entonces".

Conjecture (p. 35)   A conjecture is a conclusion reached through inductive reasoning.

Conjectura (p. 35)   Una conjectura es una conclusión obtenida usando el razonamiento inductivo.

A dropped piece of toast always lands with its buttered side down.

Consecutive integers (p. 335)   Integers that differ by one.

Números enteros consecutivos (p. 335)   Número enteros cuya diferencia es 1.

$-5, -4,$ and -3 are three consecutive integers.

Constant (p. 78)   A constant is a term that has no variable.

Constante (p. 78)   Constante es un término que no tiene variable.

In the expression $4x - 13y + 17$, 17 is the constant.

Constant of variation for direct variation (p. 454)   The nonzero constant k in the function $y = kx$.

Constante de variación en variaciones directas (p. 454)   La constante k cuyo valor no es cero en la función $y = kx$.

For the function $y = 24x$, 24 is the constant of variation.

Constant of variation for inverse variation (p. 461)   The nonzero constant k in the function $y = \frac{k}{x}$.

Constante de variación en variaciones inversas (p. 461)   La constante k cuyo valor no es cero en la función $y = \frac{k}{x}$.

For the equation $y = \frac{8}{x}$, 8 is the constant of variation.

Continuous Data (p. 440)   Data where numbers between any two data values have meaning.

Datos continuos (p. 440)   Datos en los cuales los números entre dos valores cualesquiera tienen un significado.

temperature, length, or weight

Converse (p. 359)   The statement obtained by reversing the *if* and *then* parts of an if-then statement.

Expresión recíproca (p. 359)   La que se obtiene al invertir los componentes *si* y *entonces* de un enunciado condicional.

The converse of "If I was born in Houston, then I am a Texan," would be "If I am a Texan, then I was born in Houston."

Coordinate plane (p. 52)   The coordinate plane is the plane formed by two number lines that intersect at their zero points. The horizontal number line is called the x-axis. The vertical number line is called the y-axis. The two axes meet at the origin, $O(0,0)$, and divide the coordinate plane into four quadrants.

Plano de coordenadas (p. 52)   El plano de coordenadas está formado por la intersección de una recta numérica horizontal, llamada el eje de x, y una recta numérica vertical, llamada el eje de y. Los dos ejes se intersecan en el origen, $O(0,0)$, y divide el plano de coordenadas en cuatro cuadrantes.

Coordinates (p. 52) Coordinates are ordered pairs (x, y) that identify points in a coordinate plane. The x-coordinate (the first coordinate) shows the horizontal position. The y-coordinate (the second coordinate) shows the vertical position.

Coordenadas (p. 52) Las coordenadas son pares ordenados (x, y), que identifican puntos en el plano de coordenadas. La coordenada x, (la primera coordenada) muestra la posición horizontal. La coordenada y (la segunda coordenada) muestra la posición vertical.

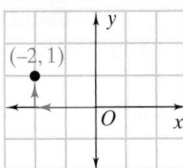

The ordered pair $(-2, 1)$ describes the point that is found by moving 2 units to the left from the origin and one unit up from the x-axis.

Correlation coefficient (p. 527) A number that tells how closely the equation of best fit models the data. The value r of the correlation coefficient is in the range $-1 \le r \le 1$.

Coeficiente de correlación (p. 527) Valor que indica qué tan bien la ecuación más adecuada expresa los datos. El valor r del coeficiente de correlación está dentro del rango $-1 \le r \le 1$.

```
LinReg
 y=ax+b
 a=.0134039132
 b=-.3622031627
 r²=.886327776
 r=.9414498267
■
```

The correlation coefficient for the data points $(68, 0.5)$, $(85, 0.9)$, $(100, 0.9)$, and $(108, 1.1)$ is approximately 0.94.

Counterexample (p. 37) A counterexample is an example that proves a statement false.

Contraejemplo (p. 37) Contraejemplo es todo ejemplo que pruebe la falsedad de un enunciado.

Statement: Motor vehicles have four wheels.

Counterexample: A motorcycle is a motor vehicle with two wheels.

Cross products (p. 320) In a proportion, $\frac{a}{b} = \frac{c}{d}$, the products ad and bc. These products are equal.

Productos cruzados (p. 320) En una proporción, $\frac{a}{b} = \frac{c}{d}$, los productos ad y bc. Estos productos son iguales.

$\frac{3}{4} = \frac{6}{8}$

The cross products are $3 \cdot 8$ and $4 \cdot 6$. $3 \cdot 8 = 24$ and $4 \cdot 6 = 24$

Decay factor (p. 654) The base b in the exponential function $y = ab^x$, where $0 < b < 1$.

Factor de decremento (p. 654) La base b en la función exponencial $y = ab^x$ donde $0 < b < 1$.

The decay factor of the function $y = 5(0.3)^x$ is 0.3.

Deductive reasoning (p. 79) Deductive reasoning is the process of reasoning logically from given facts to a conclusion.

EXAMPLE Deductive reasoning is used to simplify the expression $4c + 3(3 + c)$.

Razonamiento deductivo (p. 79) El razonamiento deductivo es el proceso de razonar lógicamente para llegar a una conclusión a partir de datos dados.

$$\begin{aligned} 4c + 3(3 + c) &= 4c + 9 + 3c \\ &= 4c + 3c + 9 \\ &= (4 + 3)c + 9 \\ &= 7c + 9 \end{aligned}$$

English/Spanish Glossary

Dependent events (p. 279) Two events in which the occurrence of one event affects the probability of the second event.

Sucesos dependientes (p. 279) Cuando el resultado de un suceso influye en la probabilidad de que ocurra el segundo suceso, los sucesos son dependientes.

You have a bag with marbles of different colors. If you pick a marble from the bag and pick another without replacing the first, the events are dependent events.

Dependent variable (p. 204) A variable that provides the output values of a function.

Variable dependiente (p. 204) Variable de la que dependen los valores de salida de una función.

In the equation $y = 3x$ the value of y depends upon the value of x.

Dilation (p. 326) A transformation in which a figure and its image are similar.

Dilatación (p. 326) Transformación en la cual una figura y su imagen son semejantes.

Quadrilateral $PQRS$ is dilated by a scale factor of $\frac{1}{2}$.

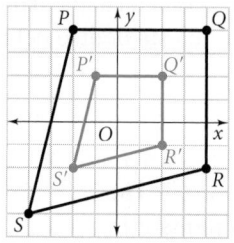

Direct variation (p. 454) A linear function that can be expressed in the form $y = kx$, where $k \neq 0$.

Variación directa (p. 454) Función lineal que puede expresarse como $y = kx$, donde $k \neq 0$.

$y = 18x$ is a direct variation.

Discrete data (p. 440) Data that involve a count of items.

Datos discretos (p. 440) Datos que implican un conteo de objetos.

number of people or number of cars

Distance Formula (p. 362) The distance d between any two points (x_1, y_1) and (x_2, y_2) is
$d = \sqrt{(x_2 - x_1)^2 + (y_2 - y_1)^2}$.

Fórmula de distancia (p. 362) La distancia d entre dos puntos cualesquiera (x_1, y_1) y (x_2, y_2) es
$d = \sqrt{(x_2 - x_1)^2 + (y_2 - y_1)^2}$.

The distance between $(-2, 4)$ and $(4, 5)$ is
$d = \sqrt{(4 - (-2))^2 + (5 - 4)^2}$
$ = \sqrt{(6)^2 + (1)^2}$
$ = \sqrt{37}$

Distributive Property (p. 73) For any numbers a, b, and c,
$a(b + c) = ab + ac$ and $a(b - c) = ab - ac$.

Propiedad distributiva (p. 73) Para cualquier número a, b y c,
$a(b + c) = ab + ac$ y $a(b - c) = ab - ac$

$2\left(3 + \frac{1}{2}\right) = 2 \cdot 3 + 2 \cdot \frac{1}{2}$
$8(5 - 3) = 8(5) - 8(3)$

Division Property of Equality (p. 94)   If $a = b$ and $c \neq 0$,
then $\frac{a}{c} = \frac{b}{c}$.

$6 = 3(2)$, so $\frac{6}{3} = \frac{3(2)}{3}$

Propiedad de igualdad en la división (p. 94)   Si $a = b$ y $c \neq 0$,
entonces $\frac{a}{c} = \frac{b}{c}$.

Division Properties of Inequality (p. 112)   If $a < b$ and c is
positive, then $\frac{a}{c} < \frac{b}{c}$. If $a > b$ and c is positive, then $\frac{a}{c} > \frac{b}{c}$.
If you divide each side of an inequality by a negative number, you
reverse the inequality symbol.

$3 < 6$, so $\frac{3}{3} < \frac{6}{3}$

$8 > 2$, so $\frac{8}{2} > \frac{2}{2}$

If $a < b$ and c is negative, then $\frac{a}{c} > \frac{b}{c}$.

$6 < 12$, so $\frac{6}{-3} > \frac{12}{-3}$

If $a > b$ and c is negative, then $\frac{a}{c} < \frac{b}{c}$.

$16 > 8$, so $\frac{16}{-4} < \frac{8}{-4}$

Propiedad de división de la desigualdad (p. 112)   Si $a < b$ y c es
positivo, entonces $\frac{a}{c} < \frac{b}{c}$. Si $a > b$ y c es positivo, entonces $\frac{a}{c} > \frac{b}{c}$.
Si se divide cada lado de una desigualdad por un número negativo, se
invierte la dirección del símbolo de desigualdad.

Si $a < b$, y c es negativo, entonces $\frac{a}{c} > \frac{b}{c}$.

Si $a > b$, y c es negativo, entonces $\frac{a}{c} < \frac{b}{c}$.

Domain (of a function) (p. 205)   The possible values for the input,
or the independent variable, of a function.

In the function $f(x) = x + 22$, the
domain is all real numbers.

Dominio (p. 205)   Todos los valores posibles para la entrada, o
variable independiente, de una función.

Element (p. 235)   An item in a matrix.

$\begin{bmatrix} 5 & -2 \\ 7 & 3 \end{bmatrix}$ $5, 7, -2,$ and 3 are the four
elements of the matrix.

Elemento (p. 235)   Componente de una matriz.

Elements (of a set) (p. 409)   Members of a set.

Cats and dogs are elements of the set of
mammals.

Elementos (p. 409)   Partes integrantes de un conjunto.

Elimination method (p. 563)   A method for solving a system of
linear equations. You add or subtract the equations to eliminate
a variable.

$3x + y = 19$

$\underline{2x - y = 1}$

$x + 0 = 18 \qquad x = 18$

Eliminación (p. 563)   Método para resolver un sistema de
ecuaciones lineales. Se suman o se restan las ecuaciones para
eliminar una variable.

$2(18) - y = 1 \rightarrow$ Substitute 18 for x

$36 - y = 1 \qquad$ in the second
equation.

$y = 35 \rightarrow$ Solve for y.

English/Spanish Glossary

Equation (p. 82)   An equation is a mathematical sentence with an equal sign, =. An equation says that the side to the left of the equal sign has the same value as the side to the right of the equal sign.

$2(6 + 17) = 46$

Ecuación (p. 82)   Una ecuación es un enunciado matemático que contiene un signo igual, =. Una ecuacíon dice que el lado izquierdo del signo igual tiene el mismo valor que el lado derecho del signo igual.

Equivalent equations (p. 294)   Equations that have the same solution.

$\frac{9}{3} = 3$ and $\frac{9}{3} + a = 3 + a$ are equivalent equations.

Ecuaciones equivalentes (p. 294)   Ecuaciones que tienen la misma solución.

Equivalent inequalities (p. 382)   Equivalent inequalities have the same set of solutions.

$x + 4 < 7$ and $x < 3$ are equivalent inequalities.

Desigualdades equivalentes (p. 382)   Las desigualdades equivalentes tienen el mismo conjunto de soluciones.

Evaluate (p. 186)   Substitute a given number for each variable, and then simplify.

To evaluate $3x + 4$ for $x = 2$, substitute 2 for x and simplify.
$3(2) + 4$
$6 + 4$
10

Evaluar (p. 186)   Método de sustitair cada variable por un número dado para luego simplificar la expresión.

Evaluate an expression (p. 14)   To evaluate an expression is to replace each variable with a number, and then follow the order of operations.

To evaluate the expression $3x + 2$ for $x = 4$, substitute 4 for x.
$3x + 2 = 3(4) + 2 = 12 + 2 = 14$

Evaluación de una expresión (p. 14)   Una expresión se evalúa, sustituyendo cada variable con un número. Luego se sigue el órden de las operaciones.

Event (p. 269)   Any group of outcomes in a situation involving probability.

When rolling a number cube, there are six possible outcomes. Rolling an even number is an event with three possible outcomes, 2, 4, and 6.

Suceso (p. 269)   En la probabilidad, cualquier grupo de resultados.

Experimental probability (p. 270)   The ratio of the number of times an event actually happens to the number of times the experiment is done.

A baseball player's batting average shows how likely it is that a player will get a hit, based on previous times at bat.

$$P(\text{event}) = \frac{\text{number of times an event happens}}{\text{number of times the experiment is done}}$$

Probabilidad experimental (p. 270)   La razón entre el número de veces que un suceso sucede en la realidad y el número de veces que se hace el experimento.

$$P(\text{suceso}) = \frac{\text{número de veces que sucede un suceso}}{\text{número de veces que se hace el experimento}}$$

Exponent (p. 185)   A number that shows repeated multiplication.

Exponente (p. 185)   Denota el número de veces que debe multiplicarse.

$3^4 = 3 \cdot 3 \cdot 3 \cdot 3$

The exponent 4 indicates that 3 is used as a factor four times.

Exponential decay (p. 654)   A situation modeled with a function of the form $y = ab^x$, where $a > 0$ and $0 < b < 1$.

Decremento exponencial (p. 654)   Para $a > 0$ y $0 < b < 1$, la función $y = ab^x$ representa el decremento exponencial.

$y = 5(0.1)^x$

Exponential function (p. 644)   A function that repeatedly multiplies an initial amount by the same positive number. You can model all exponential functions using $y = ab^x$, where a is a nonzero constant, $b > 0, b \neq 1$.

Función exponencial (p. 644)   Función que multiplica repetidas veces una cantidad inicial por el mismo número positivo. Todas las funciones exponenciales se pueden representar mediante $y = ab^x$, donde a es una constante con valor distinto de cero, $b > 0$ y $b \neq 1$.

$y = 4.8(1.1)^x$

Exponential growth (p. 651)   A situation modeled with a function of the form $y = ab^x$, where $a > 0$ and $b > 1$.

Incremento exponencial (p. 651)   Para $a > 0$ y $b > 1$, la función $y = ab^x$ representa el incremento exponencial.

$y = 100(2)^x$

Extremes of a proportion (p. 319)   In the proportion, $\frac{a}{b} = \frac{c}{d}$, a and d are the extremes.

Valores extremos de una proporción (p. 319)   En la proporción $\frac{a}{b} = \frac{c}{d}$, a y d son los valores extremos.

The product of the extremes of $\frac{x}{4} = \frac{x + 3}{2}$ is $2x$.

F

Formula (p. 145)   A formula is an equation that shows a relationship between quantities that are represented by variables.

Fórmula (p. 145)   Una fórmula es una ecuación que muestra una relación entre las cantidades que representan las variables.

The formula $P = 4s$ gives the perimeter of a square in terms of the length s of a side.

Front-end estimation (p. 130)   Front-end estimation is a way to estimate a sum. First add the front-end digits. Round to estimate the sum of the remaining digits. Then combine estimates.

Estimación por la izquierda (p. 130)   La estimación por la izquierda se emplea para estimar sumas. Primero, se suman los dígitos delanteros. Luego, se redondea para estimar la suma de los dígitos restantes. Por último se combinan las estimaciones.

Estimate $3.49 + $2.29.
$3 + 2 = 5$
$0.49 + 0.29 \approx 0.50 + 0.30 = 0.80$
$3.49 + $2.29 \approx $5 + $0.80 = 5.80

English/Spanish Glossary

Function (p. 203)   A relation that assigns exactly one value in the range to each value of the domain.

Función (p. 203)   La relación que asigna exactamente un valor del rango a cada valor del dominio.

Earned income is a function of the number of hours worked. If you earn $4.50/h, then your income is expressed by the function $f(h) = 4.5h$.

Function notation (p. 434)   To write a rule in function notation, you use the symbol $f(x)$ in place of y.

Notación de una función (p. 434)   Para expresar una regla en notación de función se usa el símbolo $f(x)$ en lugar de y.

$f(x) = 3x - 8$ is in function notation.

Function rule (p. 203)   An equation that describes a function.

Regla de una función (p. 203)   Ecuación que describe una función.

$y = 4x + 1$ is a function rule.

Geometric sequence (p. 636)   A number sequence formed by multiplying a term in a sequence by a fixed number to find the next term.

Progresión geométrica (p. 636)   Tipo de sucesión numérica formada al multiplicar un término de la secuencia por un número constante, para hallar el siguiente término.

$9, 3, 1, \frac{1}{3}, \ldots$ is an example of a geometric sequence.

Greatest possible error (p. 345)   One half of the measuring unit, for any measurement.

Máximo error posible (p. 345)   Para una medición dada, la mitad de la unidad de medida.

The mass of a rock is measured as 3.8 g. The greatest possible error is one half 0.1 g, or 0.05 g.

Growth factor (p. 651)   The number b in an exponential growth function of the form $y = ab^x$, where $b > 1$.

Factor incremental (p. 651)   Para la función exponencial incremental $y = ab^x$, donde $b > 1$, b es el factor incremental.

The growth factor of $y = 7(1.3)^x$ is 1.3.

Hypotenuse (p. 357)   The side opposite the right angle in a right triangle. It is the longest side in the triangle.

Hipotenusa (p. 357)   En un triángulo rectángulo, el lado opuesto al ángulo recto. Es el lado más largo del triángulo.

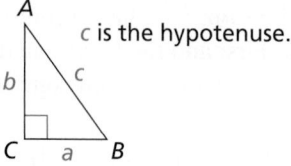

c is the hypotenuse.

Hypothesis (p. 359) The part following *if* in a conditional. *See* **conditional**.

In the conditional "If an animal has four legs, then it is a horse," the hypothesis is "an animal has four legs."

Hipótesis (p. 359) En un enunciado condicional, la parte que sigue a *si*. *Ver* **conditional**.

Identity (p. 312) An equation that is true for every value.

$5 - 14x = 5\left(1 - \frac{14}{5}x\right)$ is an identity because it is true for any value of x.

Identidad (p. 312) Una ecuación que es verdadera para todos los valores.

Identity Properties of Addition and Multiplication (p. 69) For any number a, the sum of a and 0 is a. The product of a and 1 is 1.

$a + 0 = a$
$a \cdot 1 = a$

Propiedad de identidad de la suma y de la multiplicación (p. 69) La suma de cero y cualquier número a es a. El producto de cualquier número a y uno es a.

Independent events (p. 278) Two events for which the outcome of one does not affect the other.

Picking a colored marble from a bag, and then replacing it and picking another marble, are two independent events.

Sucesos independientes (p. 278) Dos sucesos son independientes si el resultado de uno de ellos no influye en el resultado del otro.

Independent variable (p. 204) A variable that provides the input values of a function.

In the equation $y = 3x$, x is the independent variable.

Variable independiente (p. 204) Variable de la que dependen los valores de entrada de una función.

Inductive reasoning (p. 35) Inductive reasoning is making conclusions based on patterns you observe.

By inductive reasoning, the next number in the pattern 2, 4, 6, 8, . . . is 10.

Razonamiento inductivo (p. 35) El razonamiento inductivo es sacar conclusiones a partir de patrones observados.

Inequality (p. 104) An inequality is a sentence that uses one of the symbols $>, <, \geq, \leq,$ or $\neq$.

$0 \leq 2, k > -3, 10 < t$

Desigualdad (p. 104) Una desigualdad es un enunciado que usa uno de los siguientes símbolos $>, <, \geq, \leq,$ o $\neq$.

Infinitely many solutions (p. 522) The number of solutions of a system of equations in which the graphs of the equations are the same line.

The system $2x + 4y = 8$ and $y = -\frac{1}{2}x + 2$ has infinitely many solutions.

Infinitamente muchas soluciones (p. 522) El número de soluciones de un sistema de ecuaciones cuyas gráficas son la misma recta.

English/Spanish Glossary

Integer (p. 19)   The integers are the whole numbers and their opposites.

−45, 0, and 289 are integers.

Números enteros (p. 19)   Los números enteros son el conjunto de los números enteros positivos (naturales) y sus opuestos.

Interest period (p. 652)   The length of time over which interest is calculated.

Período de interés (p. 652)   Plazo para el cual se calcula el interés a pagar.

Intersection (p. 409)   The set of elements that are common to two or more sets.

If $C = \{1, 2, 3, 4\}$ and $D = \{2, 4, 6, 8\}$ then the intersection of C and D, or $C \cap D$, equals $\{2, 4\}$.

Intersección (p. 409)   El conjunto de elementos que son comunes a dos o más conjuntos.

Inverse operations (p. 88)   Inverse operations are operations that undo each other.

Multiplication and division are inverse operations.

Operaciones inversas (p. 88)   Operaciones inversas son las operaciones que se cancelan una a la otra.

Inverse variation (p. 461)   A function that can be written in the form $xy = k$ or $y = \frac{k}{x}$. The product of the quantities remains constant, so as one quantity increases, the other decreases.

The length x and the width y of a rectangle with a fixed area vary inversely. If the area is 40, $xy = 40$.

Variación inversa (p. 461)   Función que puede expresarse como $xy = k$ ó $y = \frac{k}{x}$. El producto de las cantidades permanece constante, de modo que al aumentar una cantidad, disminuye la otra.

Irrational number (p. 194)   A number that cannot be written as a ratio of two integers. Irrational numbers in decimal form are nonterminating and nonrepeating.

$\sqrt{11}$ and π are irrational numbers.

Número irracional (p. 194)   Número que no puede expresarse como razón de dos números enteros. Los números irracionales en forma decimal no tienen término y no se repiten.

Leg (p. 357)   Each of the sides that form the right angle of a right triangle.

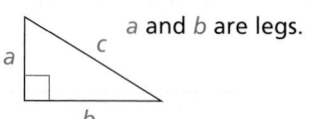

a and b are legs.

Cateto (p. 357)   Cada uno de los dos lados que forman el ángulo recto en un triángulo rectángulo.

Like terms (p. 78) Like terms are terms with the same variable(s), raised to the same power(s).

EXAMPLE $3b$ and $12b$ are like terms. Like terms can be combined by using the Distributive Property.

$$3b + 12b = (3 + 12)b$$
$$= 15b$$

Términos semejantes (p. 78) Términos semejantes son aquellos que tienen la o las mismas variables elevadas a las mismas potencias.

Line graph (p. 102) A line graph is a graph that shows a relationship between two quantities.

EXAMPLE This line graph shows the change in the number of listeners to station KLZR during the day.

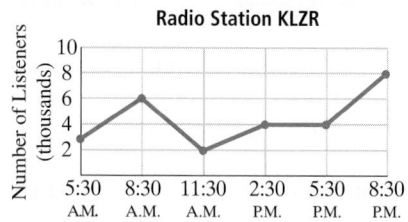

EXAMPLE This multiple line graph represents seasonal air conditioner and snowblower sales (in thousands) for a large chain of stores.

Gráfica lineal (p. 102) Una gráfica lineal representa la relación que existe entre dos cantidades.

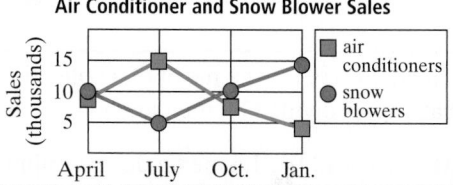

Line of best fit (p. 527) The most accurate trend line on a scatter plot showing the relationship between two sets of data.

Recta de mayor aproximación (p. 527) La línea de tendencia en un diagrama de puntos que más se acerca a los puntos que representan la relación entre dos conjuntos de datos.

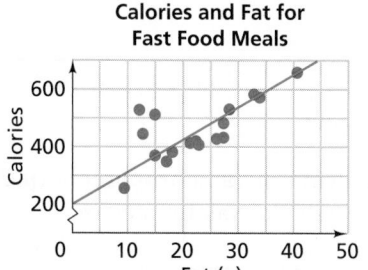

Linear equation (p. 493) An equation whose graph forms a straight line.

Ecuación lineal (p. 493) Ecuación cuya gráfica es una línea recta.

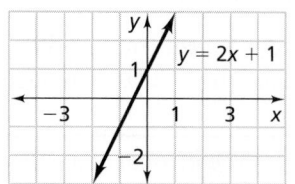

Linear inequality (p. 581) A mathematical sentence that describes a region of the coordinate plane having a boundary line. Each point in the region is a solution of the inequality.

Desigualdad lineal (p. 581) Expresión matemática que describe una región del plano de coordenadas que tiene una recta límite. Cada punto de la región es una solución de la desigualdad.

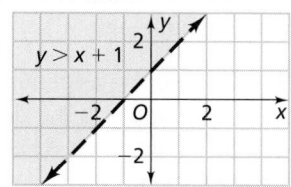

Linear parent function (p. 493) The simplest form of a linear function.

$$y = x$$

Función lineal elemental (p. 493) La forma más simple de una función lineal.

English/Spanish Glossary

Literal equation (p. 316) An equation involving two or more variables.

$4x + 2y = 18$ is a literal equation.

Ecuación literal (p. 316) Ecuación que incluye dos o más variables.

Matrix (p. 235) A rectangular arrangement of numbers. The number of rows and columns of a matrix determines its size. Each item in a matrix is an element.

$\begin{bmatrix} 2 & 5 & 6.3 \\ -8 & 0 & -1 \end{bmatrix}$ is a 2 × 3 matrix.

Matriz (p. 235) Conjunto de números dispuestos en forma de rectángulo. La cantidad de filas y columnas de una matriz determina su tamaño. Cada cifra de la matriz es un elemento.

Mean (p. 139) The mean of a collection of data is the sum of the data items divided by the number of data items.

The mean temperature (°F) for the temperatures 44, 52, 48, 55, 61, 67, and 58 is 55.

Media (p. 139) La media de un conjunto de datos resulta de la suma de los datos dividida entre el número de componentes de los datos.

Means of a proportion (p. 319) In the proportion, $\frac{a}{b} = \frac{c}{d}$, b and c are the means.

The product of the means of $\frac{x}{4} = \frac{x+3}{2}$ is $4(x + 3)$ or $4x + 12$.

Valores medios de una proporción (p. 319) En la proporción, $\frac{a}{b} = \frac{c}{d}$, b y c son los valores medios.

Measures of central tendency (p. 139) Measures of central tendency in statistics are *mean*, *median*, and *mode*.

See *Mean*, *Median*, and *Mode*.

Medidas de tendencia central (p. 139) En estadistia, la *media*, la *mediana* y la *moda* son medidas de tendencia central en la estadística.

Median (p. 139) The median of a collection of data is the middle number when there is an odd number of data items and they are written in order. For an even number of data items, the median is the mean of the two middle numbers.

The median temperature (°F) for the temperatures 44, 48, 52, 55, 58, 61, and 67 is 55.

Mediana (p. 139) La mediana es el número central de un conjunto de datos, cuando hay un número impar de datos y éstos están dispuestos en orden. Si hay un número par de datos, la mediana es la media de los dos números centrales.

Midpoint (p. 201) The point M that divides a segment $\overline{AB}$ into two equal segments, $\overline{AM}$ and $\overline{MB}$.

M is the midpoint of $\overline{XY}$.

X   M   Y

Punto medio (p. 201) El punto M que divide un segmento $\overline{AB}$ en dos segmentos iguales, $\overline{AM}$ y $\overline{MB}$.

Midpoint Formula (p. 201)   The midpoint M of a line segment with endpoints $A(x_1, y_1)$ and $B(x_2, y_2)$ is $\left(\dfrac{x_1 + x_2}{2}, \dfrac{y_1 + y_2}{2}\right)$.

The midpoint of a segment with endpoints $A(3, 5)$ and $B(7, 1)$ is $(5, 3)$.

Fórmula del punto medio (p. 201)   El punto medio M de un segmento con puntos extremos $A(x_1, y_1)$ y $B(x_2, y_2)$ es $\left(\dfrac{x_1 + x_2}{2}, \dfrac{y_1 + y_2}{2}\right)$.

Mode (p. 139)   The mode of a collection of data is the data item that occurs most often. There can be no mode, one mode, or more than one mode.

The mode of the collection of numbers $3, 4, 1, 3, 2, 2, 5, 3$ is 3.

Moda (p. 139)   La moda de un conjunto de datos es el dato que se presenta con mayor frecuencia. Puede no haber moda, una moda o más de una moda.

Monomial (p. 686)   A monomial is a real number, a variable, or a product of a real number and variables with whole number exponents.

$5x$, -4, and y^3 are all monomials.

Monomio (p. 686)   Un monomio es un número real, una variable o el producto de un número real y variables con exponentes que sean números enteros.

Multiple line graph (p. 102)   A multiple line graph is a graph that shows more than one data set changing over time.

See *Line graph*.

Gráfica multilineal (p. 102)   Una gráfica multilineal representa las variaciones de más de un conjunto de datos en el tiempo.

Multiplication Property of Equality (p. 95)   If $a = b$, then $ac = bc$.

$12 = 3(4)$, so $12 \cdot 2 = 3(4) \cdot 2$

Propiedad multiplicativa de la igualdad (p. 95)   Si $a = b$, entonces $ac = bc$.

Multiplication Properties of Inequality (p. 113)   If $a < b$, and c is positive, then $ac < bc$. If $a > b$, and c is positive, then $ac > bc$.

$3 < 4$, so $3(5) < 4(5)$
$7 > 2$, so $7(6) > 2(6)$

If you multiply each side of an inequality by a negative number, you reverse the inequality symbol.

If $a < b$, and c is negative, then $ac > bc$. If $a > b$, and c is negative, then $ac < bc$.

$6 < 9$, so $6(-2) > 9(-2)$
$7 > 5$, so $7(-3) < 5(-3)$

Propiedad multiplicativa de la desigualdad (p. 113)   Si $a < b$, y c es positivo, entonces $ac < bc$. Si $a > b$, y c es positivo, entonces $ac > bc$. Si se multiplica cada lado de una desigualdad por un número negativo, se invierte la dirección del signo de la desigualdad. Si $a < b$, y c es negativo, entonces $ac > bc$. Si $a > b$, y c es negativo, entonces $ac < bc$.

English/Spanish Glossary

Multiplicative identity (p. 69)   The multiplicative identity is 1. For any number *a*, the product of *a* and 1 is *a*.

$a \cdot 1 = a$

Identidad multiplicativa (p. 69)   La identidad multiplicativa es 1. Cuando se multiplica un número por uno, el producto es igual al número original.

Multiplicative inverse (p. 248)   Given a nonzero rational number $\frac{a}{b}$, the multiplicative inverse, or reciprocal, is $\frac{b}{a}$. The product of a nonzero number and its multiplicative inverse is 1.

$\frac{3}{4}$ is a multiplicative inverse of $\frac{4}{3}$ because $\frac{3}{4} \times \frac{4}{3} = 1$.

Inverso multiplicativo (p. 248)   Dado un número racional $\frac{a}{b}$ distinto de cero, el inverso multiplicativo, o recíproco, es $\frac{b}{a}$. El producto de un número distinto de cero y su inverso multiplicativo es 1.

Natural numbers (p. 193)   The counting numbers.

$1, 2, 3, \ldots$

Números naturales (p. 193)   Los números que se emplean para contar.

Negative correlation (p. 210)   The relationship between two sets of data, in which one set of data decreases as the other set of data increases.

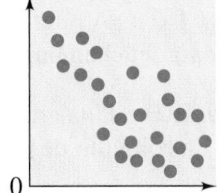

Correlación negativa (p. 210)   Relación entre dos conjuntos de datos en la que uno de los conjuntos disminuye a medida que el otro aumenta.

Negative reciprocal (p. 520)   A number of the form $-\frac{b}{a}$, where $\frac{a}{b}$ is a nonzero rational number. The product of a number and its negative reciprocal is -1.

$\frac{2}{5}$ and $-\frac{5}{2}$ are negative reciprocals because $\left(\frac{2}{5}\right)\left(-\frac{5}{2}\right) = -1$.

Recíproco negativo (p. 520)   El recíproco negativo de un número racional $\frac{a}{b}$ cuyo valor no es cero es $-\frac{b}{a}$. El producto de un número y su recíproco negativo es -1.

Negative square root (p. 352)   A number of the form $-\sqrt{b}$, which is the negative square root of *b*.

-7 is the negative square root of $\sqrt{49}$.

Raíz cuadrada negativa (p. 352) $-\sqrt{b}$ es la raíz cuadrada negativa de *b*.

No correlation (p. 210)   There does not appear to be a relationship between two sets of data.

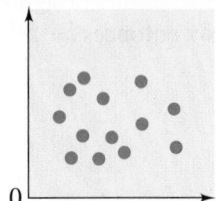

Sin correlación (p. 210)   No hay relación entre dos conjuntos de datos.

No solution (p. 552) When the graphs of the equations in a system are parallel with no point of intersection.

There is no solution to the system of equations $x + y = 5$ and $x + y = -3$.

Sin solución (p. 552) Cuando las gráficas de las ecuaciones de un sistema son paralelas y no existe entre ellas ningún punto de intersección.

Null set (p. 409) A set that has no elements.

$\{\}$ or $\varnothing$

Conjunto vacío (p. 409) Conjunto que no tiene elementos.

Odds (p. 270) A ratio that describes the likelihood of an event. Odds in favor of an event are number of favorable outcomes : number of unfavorable outcomes.

You have 3 red marbles and 5 blue marbles. The odds in favor of selecting red are 3 : 5.

Probabilidad a favor (p. 270) Razón que describe la posibilidad de que se produzca un suceso. La probabilidad a favor de que se produzca determinado resultado es la razón del número de resultados favorables : número de resultados no favorables.

Open sentence (p. 82) An open sentence is an equation with one or more variables.

$3a = 5a + 8$

Proposición abierta (p. 82) Una proposición abierta es una ecuación con una o más variables.

Opposites (p. 19) Opposites are numbers that are the same distance from zero on the number line but in opposite directions.

-17 and 17 are opposites because they are both 17 units from zero on the number line.

Números opuestos (p. 19) Números opuestos son los números que se hallan a la misma distancia de cero en una recta, numérica pero en direcciones opuestas.

Order of operations (pp. 9, 186)
1. Work inside grouping symbols.
2. Simplify any terms with exponents.
3. Multiply and divide in order from left to right.
4. Add and subtract in order from left to right.

$2^3(7 - 4) = 2^3(3) = 8 \cdot 3 = 24$

Orden de las operaciones (pp. 9, 186)
1. Efectúa las operaciones que están dentro de los signos de agrupación.
2. Trabaja con los exponentes.
3. Multiplica y divide en orden de izquierda a derecha.
4. Suma y resta en orden de izquierda a derecha.

Ordered pair (p. 52)   An ordered pair is a pair of numbers that gives the location of a point in a coordinate plane. The first number is the *x*-coordinate and the second number is the *y*-coordinate.

See *Coordinates.*

Par ordenado (p. 52)   Un par ordenado es un par de números que describe la localización de un punto en un plano de coordenadas. El primer número es la coordenada *x* y el segundo número es la coordenada *y.*

Origin (p. 52)   The origin is the intersection of the *x*-axis and the *y*-axis in a coordinate plane. The ordered pair $(0, 0)$ describes the origin.

See *Coordinate plane.*

Origen (p. 52)   El origen el punto de intersección de los ejes de *x* y de *y* en un plano de coordenadas. El par ordenado $(0, 0)$ describe el origen.

Outcome (p. 269)   The result of a single trial in a probability experiment.

The outcomes of rolling a number cube are 1, 2, 3, 4, 5, and 6.

Resultado (p. 269)   Lo que se obtiene al hacer una sola prueba en un experimento de probabilidad.

Outlier (p. 140)   An outlier is a data value that is much higher or lower than the other data values in a collection of data.

An outlier in the data 1, 1, 2, 3, 4, 4, 6, 7, 7, 52 is 52.

Extremo (p. 140)   Un extremo es el valor de un conjunto de datos que es mucho mayor o menor que el resto de los datos.

Parabola (p. 680)   A parabola is the graph of a quadratic function. It is U-shaped.

EXAMPLE   This parabola is the graph of the equation $y = x^2 - 2$.

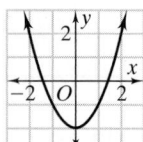

Parábola (p. 680)   Una parábola es la gráfica de una ecuación cuadrática. Tiene la forma de U.

Parallel lines (p. 519)   Two lines in the same plane that never intersect. Parallel lines have the same slope.

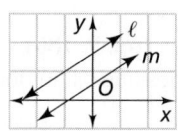

Rectas paralelas (p. 519)   Dos rectas situadas en el mismo plano que nunca se cortan. Las rectas paralelas tienen la misma pendiente.

Lines ℓ and *m* are parallel.

Parent function (p. 493)   A family of functions is a group of functions with common characteristics. A parent function is the simplest function with these characteristics.

Función elemental (p. 493)   Una familia de functiones es un grupo de funciones con características en común. La función elemental es la función más simple que reúne esas características.

$y = x^2$ is the parent function for the family of quadractic equations of the form $y = ax^2 + bx + c$.

Percent error (p. 346)   The ratio of the greatest possible error to the measurement.

Error porcentual (p. 346)   La razón del máximo error posible a la medida obtenida.

The diameter of a CD is measured as 12.1 cm. The greatest possible error is 0.05 cm. The percent error is $\frac{0.05}{12.1} \approx 0.4\%$.

Percent of change (p. 344)   The ratio of the amount of change to the original amount expressed as a percent.

Porcentaje de cambio (p. 344)   La razón de la cantidad de cambio la cantidad original, expresada como un porcentaje.

The price of a sweater was $20. The price increases $2. The percent of change is $\frac{2}{20} = 10\%$.

Percent of decrease (p. 344)   The percent of change found when the original amount decreases.

Porcentaje de disminución (p. 344)   El porcentaje de cambio que resulta cuando la cantidad original disminuye.

The price of a sweater was $22. The price decreases $2. The percent of change is $\frac{2}{22} \approx 9\%$.

Percent of increase (p. 344)   The percent of change found when the original amount increases.

Porcentaje de aumento (p. 344)   El porcentaje de cambio que resulta cuando la cantidad original aumenta.

See example for percent of change.

Perfect squares (p. 353)   Numbers whose square roots are integers.

Cuadrado perfecto (p. 353)   Número cuya raíz cuadrada es un número entero.

The numbers $1, 4, 9, 16, 25, 36, \ldots$ are perfect squares because they are the squares of integers.

Perimeter (p. 146)   The perimeter of a figure is the distance around the figure. To find the perimeter of a rectangle, find the sum of the lengths of all its sides, or use the formula $P = 2\ell + 2w$.

EXAMPLE   The perimeter of $ABCD$ is 12 ft.

Perímetro (p. 146)   El perímetro de una figura es la suma de las longitudes de sus lados. Para hallar el perímetro de un rectángulo, halla la suma de los largos de todos los lados o usa la fórmula $P = 2\ell + 2w$.

English/Spanish Glossary

Perpendicular lines (p. 520) Lines that intersect to form right angles. Two lines are perpendicular if the product of their slopes is −1.

Rectas perpendiculares (p. 520) Rectas que forman ángulos rectos en su intersección . Dos rectas son perpendiculares si el producto de sus pendientes es −1.

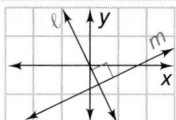

Lines ℓ and m are perpendicular.

Point-slope form (p. 512) A linear equation of a nonvertical line written as $y - y_1 = m(x - x_1)$. The line passes through the point (x_1, y_1) with slope m.

Forma punto-pendiente (p. 512) La ecuación lineal de una recta no vertical que pasa por el punto (x_1, y_1) con pendiente m está dada por $y - y_1 = m(x - x_1)$.

An equation with a slope of $-\frac{1}{2}$ passing through $(2, -1)$ would be written $y + 1 = -\frac{1}{2}(x - 2)$ in point-slope form.

Polynomial (p. 686) A polynomial is a monomial or a sum or difference of monomials.

Polinomio (p. 686) Un polinomio es un monomio o la suma o la diferencia de dos o más monomios.

$4x^2 - 3x + 7$ is a polynomial.

Positive correlation (p. 210) The relationship between two sets of data in which both sets of data increase together.

Correlación positiva (p. 210) La relación entre dos conjuntos de datos en la que ambos conjuntos incrementan a la vez.

Power (p. 185) The base and the exponent of an expression of the form a^n.

Potencia (p. 185) La base y el exponente de una expresión de la forma a^n.

5^4

Precision in measurement (p. 164) The precision of a measurement is its exactness. A measurement cannot be more precise than the precision of the measuring tool used.

Precisión de una medición (p. 164) La precisión de una medición se refiere a su grado de exactitud. Una medida no puede ser más precisa que la precisión del instrumento de medida utilizado.

A hundredth of a meter is a smaller unit than a tenth of a meter. So, 2.72 m is more precise than 2.7 m.

Principal square root (p. 352) A number of the form $\sqrt{b}$. The expression $\sqrt{b}$ is called the principal (or positive) square root of b.

Raíz cuadrada principal (p. 352) La expresión $\sqrt{b}$ se llama raíz cuadrada principal (o positiva) de b.

5 is the principal square root of $\sqrt{25}$.

Probability (p. 269) How likely it is that an event will occur (written formally as P (event)).

Probabilidad (p. 269) La posibilidad de que un suceso ocurra, escrita formalmente P (suceso).

You have 4 red marbles and 3 white marbles. The probability that you select one red marble, and then, without replacing it, randomly select another red marble is $P(\text{red}) = \frac{4}{7} \cdot \frac{3}{6} = \frac{2}{7}$.

Properties of equality (p. 294) For all real numbers a, b, and c:

Addition: If $a = b$, then $a + c = b + c$.

Subtraction: If $a = b$, then $a - c = b - c$.

Multiplication: If $a = b$, then $a \cdot c = b \cdot c$.

Division: If $a = b$, and $c \neq 0$, then $\frac{a}{c} = \frac{b}{c}$.

Propiedades de la igualdad (p. 294) Para todos los números reales a, b y c:

Suma: Si $a = b$, entonces $a + c = b + c$.

Resta: Si $a = b$, entonces $a - c = b - c$.

Multiplicación: Si $a = b$, entonces $a \cdot c = b \cdot c$.

División: Si $a = b$, y $c \neq 0$, entonces $\frac{a}{c} = \frac{b}{c}$.

Since $\frac{2}{4} = \frac{1}{2}$, $\frac{2}{4} + 5 = \frac{1}{2} + 5$.

Since $\frac{9}{3} = 3$, $\frac{9}{3} - 6 = 3 - 6$.

Proportion (p. 319) An equation that states that two ratios are equal.
$$\frac{a}{b} = \frac{c}{d} \text{ where } b \neq 0 \text{ and } d \neq 0$$

Proporción (p. 319) Es una ecuación que establece que dos razones son iguales.
$$\frac{a}{b} = \frac{c}{d} \text{ por } b \neq 0 \text{ y } d \neq 0$$

$\frac{7.5}{9} = \frac{5}{6}$

Pythagorean Theorem (p. 357) In any right triangle, the sum of the squares of the lengths of the legs is equal to the square of the length of the hypotenuse: $a^2 + b^2 = c^2$.

Teorema de Pitágoras (p. 357) En un triángulo rectángulo, la suma de los cuadrados de los catetos es igual al cuadrado de la hipotenusa: $a^2 + b^2 = c^2$.

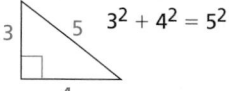

$3^2 + 4^2 = 5^2$

Quadrants (p. 52) Quadrants are the four regions determined by the x- and y-axes of the coordinate plane.

Cuadrantes (p. 52) El eje de x y el eje de y dividen el plano de coordenadas en cuatro regiones llamadas cuadrantes.

See *Coordinate plane.*

English/Spanish Glossary

Quadratic function (p. 676)   A quadratic function is a function based on squaring the input variable. The graph of a quadratic function is a parabola.

See *Parabola*.

Función cuadrática (p. 676)   Una función cuadrática es la función que tiene una variable elevada a la segunda potencia. La gráfica de una función cuadrática es una párabola.

R

Radicand (p. 352)   The expression under the radical sign.

The radicand of the radical expression $\sqrt{x + 2}$ is $x + 2$.

Radicando (p. 352)   La expresión que aparece debajo del signo radical.

Random event (p. 283)   An event in which you cannot predict individual outcomes.

Suceso aleatorio (p. 283)   Suceso para el cual no se pueden predecir resultados individuales.

Range (p. 218)   The difference between the greatest and the least data values for a set of data.

For the set 2, 5, 8, 12, the range is $12 - 2 = 10$.

Rango (p. 218)   Diferencia entre el valor mayor y el menor en un conjunto de datos.

Range (p. 205)   The possible values of the output, or dependent variable, of a function.

In the function $y = |x|$, the range is the set of all nonnegative numbers.

Rango (p. 205)   El conjunto de todos los valores posibles de salida, o variable dependiente, de una función.

Range of a set of data (p. 139)   The range is the difference between the greatest and least values in a set of data.

The range of the data 7 9 15 3 18 2 16 14 14 20 is $20 - 2 = 18$.

Amplitud de un conjunto de datos (p. 139)   La amplitud es la diferencia entre los valores mayor y menor de un conjunto de datos.

Rate (p. 318)   A ratio of a to b where a and b represent quantities measured in different units.

Traveling 125 miles in 2 hours results in the rate $\frac{125 \text{ miles}}{2 \text{ hours}}$ or 62.5 mi/h.

Razón (p. 318)   La relación que existe entre a y b cuando a y b son cantidades medidas con distintas unidades.

Rate of change (p. 484) The relationship between two quantities that are changing. The rate of change is also called slope.

rate of change = $\dfrac{\text{change in the dependent variable}}{\text{change in the independent variable}}$

Tasa de cambio (p. 484) La relación entre dos cantidades que cambian. La tasa de cambio se llama también pendiente.

tasa de cambio = $\dfrac{\text{cambio en la variable dependiente}}{\text{cambio en la variable independiente}}$

Video rental for 1 day is $1.99. Video rental for 2 days is $2.99.

rate of change = $\dfrac{2.99 - 1.99}{2 - 1}$

$= \dfrac{1.00}{1}$

$= 1$

Ratio (p. 318) A comparison of two numbers by division.

Razón (p. 318) Comparación de dos números por división.

$\dfrac{5}{7}$ and $7:3$ are ratios.

Rational number (p. 193) A real number that can be written as a ratio of two integers. Rational numbers in decimal form are terminating or repeating.

Número racional (p. 193) Número real que puede expresarse como la razón de dos números enteros. Los números racionales en forma decimal son exactos o periódicos.

$\dfrac{2}{3}$, 1.548, and 2.292929 . . . are all rational numbers.

Real number (p. 194) A number that is either rational or irrational.

Número real (p. 194) Un número que no es racional ni irracional.

$5, -3, \sqrt{11}, 0.666\ldots, 5\frac{4}{11}, 0,$ and π are all real numbers.

Reciprocal (p. 249) Given a nonzero rational number $\frac{a}{b}$, the reciprocal, or multiplicative inverse, is $\frac{b}{a}$. The product of a nonzero number and its reciprocal is 1.

Recíproco (p. 249) El recíproco, o inverso multiplicativo, de un número racional $\frac{a}{b}$ cuyo valor no es cero es $\frac{b}{a}$. El producto de un número que no es cero y su valor recíproco es 1.

$\frac{2}{5}$ and $\frac{5}{2}$ are reciprocals because $\frac{2}{5} \times \frac{5}{2} = 1$.

Relation (p. 433) Any set of ordered pairs.

Relación (p. 433) Cualquier conjunto de pares ordenados.

$\{(0, 0), (2, 3), (2, -7)\}$ is a relation.

Sample space (p. 269) All possible outcomes of an event.

Espacio de muestra (p. 269) Todos los resultados posibles de un suceso.

When tossing two coins one at a time, the sample space is $(H, H), (T, T),$ $(H, T), (T, H)$.

Scale (p. 327) The ratio of a distance in a drawing to the actual distance.

Escala (p. 327) La razón entre la distancia expresada en un dibujo y la distancia real.

For a drawing in which a 2-in. length represents an actual length of 18 ft, the scale is 1 in. : 9 ft.

Scale drawing (p. 327) An enlarged or reduced drawing similar to an actual object or place.

Dibujo a escala (p. 327) Dibujo que muestra de mayor o menor tamaño un objeto o lugar dado.

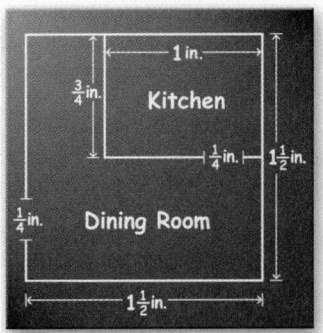

Scale factor (p. 326) The ratio of the dimensions of a similar image of a figure to its original dimensions.

Factor de escala (p. 326) La razón de las dimensiones de una imagen semejante de una figura a sus dimensiones originales.

Scatter plot (p. 209) A graph that relates data of two different sets. The two sets of data are displayed as ordered pairs.

Diagrama de puntos (p. 209) Gráfica que muestra la relación entre dos conjuntos. Los datos de ambos conjuntos se presentan como pares ordenados.

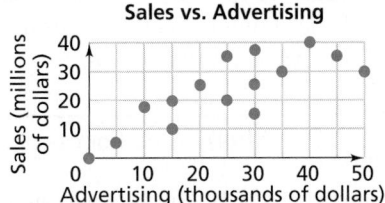

The scatter plot displays the amount spent on advertising (in thousands of dollars) versus product sales (in millions of dollars).

Scientific notation (p. 612) A number expressed in the form $a \times 10^n$, where n is an integer and $1 < a < 10$.

Notación científica (p. 612) Un número expresado en forma de $a \times 10^n$, donde n es un número entero y $1 < a < 10$.

3.4×10^6

Sequence (p. 469) A number pattern.

Progresión (p. 469) Sucesión de números.

$-4, 5, 14, 23$ is a sequence.

Set (p. 409) A well-defined collection of elements.

Conjunto (p. 409) Un grupo bien definido de elementos.

The set of integers:
$Z = \{ \ldots, -3, -2, -1, 0, 1, 2, 3, \ldots \}$

Significant digits (p. 164) Significant digits are the digits that represent an actual measurement.

Dígitos significativos (p. 164) Dígitos significativos son los dígitos que representan una medida real.

Similar figures (p. 326) Figures that have the same shape, but not necessarily the same size.

Figuras semejantes (p. 326) Figuras que tienen la misma forma pero no necesariamente el mismo tamaño.

$\triangle DEF$ and $\triangle GHI$ are similar.

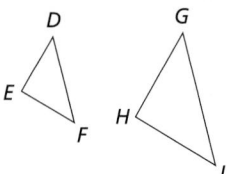

Simple interest (p. 343) Interest paid only on the principal.

Interés simple (p. 343) Intéres basado en el capital solamente.

The interest on $1000 at 6% for 5 years is $1000(0.06)5 = \$300$.

Simplify (p. 185) Replace an expression with its simplest name or form.

Simplificar (p. 185) Reemplazar una expresión por su versión o forma más simple.

$$\underbrace{\frac{3 + 5}{8}}$$

Simplify a variable expression (p. 78) To simplify a variable expression is to replace it with an equivalent expression having as few terms as possible.

Simplificar una expresión variable (p. 78) Se simplifica una expresión variable al reemplazarla con una expresión equivalente que tiene el menor número posible de términos.

$2x + 5 + 4x$ simplifies to $6x + 5$.

Simulation (p. 276) A simulation is a model of a real-world situation used to find probability.

Simulación (p. 276) Una simulación es un modelo de una situación real que se usa para hallar la probabilidad.

A baseball team has an equal chance of winning or losing its next game. You can toss a coin to simulate the situation.

Slope (p. 486) The ratio of the vertical change to the horizontal change.

slope $= \dfrac{\text{vertical change}}{\text{horizontal change}} = \dfrac{y_2 - y_1}{x_2 - x_1}$, where $x_2 - x_1 \neq 0$

Pendiente (p. 486) La razón del cambio vertical al cambio horizontal.

pendiente $= \dfrac{\text{cambio vertical}}{\text{cambio horizontal}} = \dfrac{y_2 - y_1}{x_2 - x_1}$, donde $x_2 - x_1 \neq 0$

The slope of the line below is $\frac{2}{4} = \frac{1}{2}$.

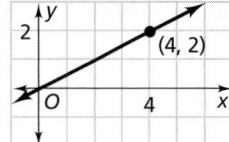

Slope-intercept form (p. 494) A linear equation of a nonvertical line written as $y = mx + b$, where m is the slope and b is the y-intercept.

Forma pendiente-intercepto (p. 494) La ecuación lineal de una recta no vertical expresada como $y = mx + b$, donde m es la pendiente y b es el intercepto en y.

$y = 8x + 2$

Solution (p. 83)   A solution is any value or values that make an equation or an inequality true.

Solución (p. 83)   Una solución es cualquier valor o valores que hacen verdadera una ecuación o una desigualdad.

4 is the solution of $x + 5 = 9$.

$(8, 4)$ is a solution of $y = -1x + 12$ because $4 = -1(8) + 12$.

-4 is a solution of $2x < -3$, because $2 \cdot -4 < -3$.

$(-1, 3)$ is a solution of $y > x - 4$, because $3 > -1 - 4$.

Solution of a system of linear equations (p. 550)   Any ordered pair in a system that makes all the equations of that system true.

Solución de un sistema de ecuaciones lineales (p. 550)   Todo par ordenado de un sistema que hace verdaderas todas las ecuaciones de ese sistema.

$(2, 1)$ is a solution of the system
$y = 2x - 3$
$y = x - 1$
because the ordered pair makes each equation true.

Solution of a system of linear inequalities (p. 587)   Any ordered pair that makes all of the inequalities in the system true.

Solución de un sistema de desigualdades lineales (p. 587)   Todo par ordenado que hace verdaderas todas las desigualdades del sistema.

The shaded purple area shows the solution of the system
$y > 2x - 5$
$3x + 4y < 12$.

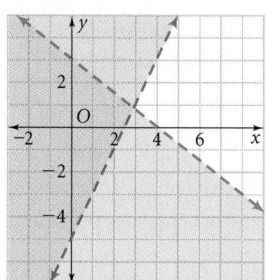

Solution of an equation (p. 294)   Any value or values that make an equation true.

Solución de una ecuación (p. 294)   Cualquier valor o valores que hagan verdadera una ecuación.

In the equation $y + 22 = 11$, -11 is the solution.

Solution of an inequality (one variable) (p. 376)   Any value or values of a variable in the inequality that makes an inequality true.

Solución de una desigualdad (una variable) (p. 376)   Cualquier valor o valores de una variable de la desigualdad que hagan verdadera la desigualdad.

The solution of the inequality $x < 9$ is all numbers less than 9.

Solution of an inequality (two variables) (p. 581)   Any ordered pair that makes the inequality true.

Solución de una desigualdad (dos variables) (p. 581)   Cualquier par ordenado que haga verdadera la desigualdad.

Each ordered pair in the pink area and on the solid pink line is a solution of $3x - 5y \le 10$.

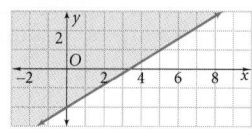

Square root (p. 352) A number b such that $a^2 = b$. $\sqrt{b}$ is the principal square root. $-\sqrt{b}$ is the negative square root.

-3 and 3 are square roots of 9.

Raíz cuadrada (p. 352) Si $a^2 = b$, entonces a es la raíz cuadrada de b. $\sqrt{b}$ es la raíz cuadrada principal. $-\sqrt{b}$ es la raíz cuadrada negativa.

Standard form (p. 690) Standard form of a polynomial is the form in which the terms are in order of decreasing degree.

$3y^2 + 8y - 2$ is in standard form.

Forma general de un polinomio (p. 690) Un polinomio está en forma general cuando sus términos están en orden descendente.

Standard form of a linear equation (p. 506) The form of a linear equation $Ax + By = C$, where A, B, and C are real numbers and A and B are not both zero.

$6x - y = 12$

Forma normal de una ecuación lineal (p. 506) La forma normal de una ecuación lineal es $Ax + By = C$, donde A, B y C son números reales, y donde A y B no son iguales a cero.

Stem-and-leaf plot (p. 218) A display of data made by using the digits of the values.

Diagrama de tallo y hojas (p. 218) Un arreglo de los datos que use los dígitos de los valoves.

Substitution method (p. 558) A method of solving a system of equations by replacing one variable with an equivalent expression containing the other variable.

$y = 2x + 5$
$x + 3y = 7$
$x + 3(2x + 5) = 7$

Método de sustitución (p. 558) Método para resolver un sistema de ecuaciones en el que se reemplaza una variable por una expresión equivalente que contenga la otra variable.

Subtraction Property of Equality (p. 88) If $a = b$, then $a - c = b - c$.

$10 = 2(5)$, so $10 - 5 = 2(5) - 5$

Propiedad sustrativa de la igualdad (p. 88) Si $a = b$, entonces $a - c = b - c$.

Subtraction Property of Inequality (p. 108) If $a > b$, then $a - c > b - c$. If $a < b$, then $a - c < b - c$.

$7 > 4$, so $7 - 3 > 4 - 3$
$6 < 9$, so $6 - 2 < 9 - 2$

Propiedad sustractiva de la desigualdad (p. 108) Si $a > b$, entonces $a - c > b - c$. Si $a < b$, entonces $a - c < b - c$.

System of linear equations (p. 550) Two or more linear equations using the same variables.

$y = 5x + 7$, $y = \frac{1}{2}x - 3$

Sistema de ecuaciones lineales (p. 550) Dos o más ecuaciones lineales que usen las mismas variables.

English/Spanish Glossary

System of linear inequalities (p. 587) Two or more linear inequalities using the same variables.

Sistema de desigualdades lineales (p. 587) Dos o más desigualdades lineales que usen las mismas variables.

$y \le x + 11, y < 5x$

Term (p. 257) A number, variable, or the product or quotient of a number and one or more variables.

Término (p. 257) Un número, una variable o el producto o cociente de un número y una o más variables.

The expression $5x + \frac{y}{2} - 8$ has three terms: $5x, \frac{y}{2}$, and -8.

Term of a sequence (p. 469) Any number in a sequence.

Término de una progresión (p. 469) Todos los números de una progresión.

-4 is the first term of the sequence $-4, 5, 14, 23$.

Term of an expression (p. 78) A term is a number, a variable, or the product of a number and variable(s).

Término de una expresión (p. 78) Un término es un número, una variable o el producto de un número y una o mas variables.

The expression $7x + 12 + (-9y)$ has three terms: $7x, 12$, and $-9y$.

Theoretical probability (p. 269) The ratio of the number of favorable outcomes to the number of possible outcomes if all outcomes have the same chance of happening.

$P(\text{event}) = \frac{\text{number of favorable outcomes}}{\text{number of possible outcomes}}$

Probabilidad teórica (p. 269) Si cada resultado tiene la misma probabilidad de darse, la probabilidad teórica de un suceso se calcula como la razón del número de resultados favorables al número de resultados posibles.

$P(\text{suceso}) = \frac{\text{número de resultados favorables}}{\text{número de resultados posibles}}$

In tossing a coin, the probabilities of getting a head or tail are equally likely. The likelihood of getting a head is $P(\text{head}) = \frac{1}{2}$.

Translation (p. 535) A transformation that shifts a graph horizontally, vertically, or both.

Traslación (p. 535) Proceso de mover una gráfica horizontalmente, verticalmente o en ambos sentidos.

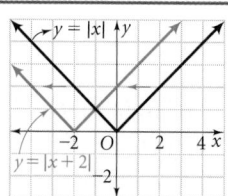

$y = |x + 2|$ is a translation of $y = |x|$.

Trend line (p. 517) A line on a scatter plot drawn near the points. It shows a correlation.

Línea de tendencia (p. 517) Línea de un diagrama de puntos que se traza cerca de los puntos para mostrar una correlación.

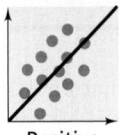 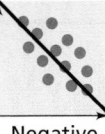

Positive   Negative

Trinomial (p. 686) A trinomial is a polynomial with three terms.

Trinomio (p. 686) Un trinomio es un polinomio compuesto de tres términos.

$x^2 - 5x + 6$ is a trinomial.

Uniform motion (p. 335) The motion of an object moving at a constant rate.

Movimiento uniforme (p. 335) El movimiento de un objeto que se mueve a una velocidad constante.

Union (p. 409) The set that contains all of the elements of two or more sets.

Unión (p. 409) El conjunto que contiene todos los elementos de dos o más conjuntos.

If $A = \{1, 3, 6, 9\}$ and $B = \{1, 5, 10\}$, then the union of A and B, or $A \cup B$, equals $\{1, 3, 5, 6, 9, 10\}$

Unit analysis (p. 318) The process of selecting conversion factors to produce the appropriate units.

Análisis de unidades (p. 318) Proceso de seleccionar factores de conversión para producir las unidades apropiadas.

To change ten feet to yards, multiply by the conversion factor $\frac{1\ \text{yd}}{3\ \text{ft}}$.

$10\ \text{ft}\left(\frac{1\ \text{yd}}{3\ \text{ft}}\right) = 3\frac{1}{3}\ \text{yd}$

Unit rate (p. 318) A rate with a denominator of 1.

Razón en unidades (p. 318) Razón cuyo denominador es 1.

The unit rate for 120 miles driven in 2 hours is 60 mi/h.

Variable (p. 4) A variable is a letter that stands for a number.

Variable (p. 4) Una variable es una letra que representa a un número.

x is a variable in the equation $9 - x = 3$.

Vertical-line test (p. 434) A method used to determine if a relation is a function or not. If a vertical line passes through a graph more than once, the graph is not the graph of a function.

Prueba de la recta vertical (p. 434) Método que permite determinar si una relación es o no es una función. Si una recta vertical corta la gráfica más de una vez, la gráfica no es de función.

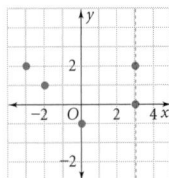

A line would pass through $(3, 0)$ and $(3, 2)$, so the relation is not a function.

Whole numbers (p. 193)   The nonnegative integers.

$0, 1, 2, 3, \ldots$

Números enteros positivos (p. 193)   Todos los números enteros que no son negativos.

***x*-axis (p. 52)**   The *x*-axis is the horizontal number line that, together with the *y*-axis, establishes the coordinate plane.

See *Coordinate plane.*

Eje de *x* (p. 52)   El eje de *x* es la recta numérica horizontal que, junto al eje de *y*, forma el plano de coordenadas.

***x*-coordinate (p. 52)**   The *x*-coordinate is the horizontal position of a point in the coordinate plane.

See *Coordinates.*

Coordenada *x* (p. 52)   La coordenada *x* muestra la ubicación horizontal de un punto en el plano de coordenadas.

***x*-intercept (p. 506)**   The *x*-coordinate of the point where a line crosses the *x*-axis.

The *x*-intercept of $3x + 4y = 12$ is 3.

Intercepto en *x* (p. 506)   La coordenada *x* del punto donde una recta corta el eje *x*.

***y*-axis (p. 52)**   The *y*-axis is the vertical number line that, together with the *x*-axis, forms the coordinate plane.

See *Coordinate plane.*

Eje de *y* (p. 52)   El eje de *y* es la recta numérica vertical que, junto al eje de *x*, forma el plano de coordenadas.

***y*-coordinate (p. 52)**   The *y*-coordinate is the vertical position of a point in the coordinate plane.

See *Coordinates.*

Coordenada *y* (p. 52)   La coordenada *y* muestra la ubicación vertical de un punto en el plano de coordenadas.

y-intercept (p. 493)   The *y*-coordinate of the point where a line crosses the *y*-axis.

The *y*-intercept of $y = 5x + 2$ is 2.

Intercepto en *y* (p. 493)   La coordenada *y* del punto donde una recta corta el eje *y*.

Zero pair (p. 23)   A zero pair is a positive algebra tile paired with a negative algebra tile.

Par cero (p. 23)   Un par cero es un ficha de álgebra positiva que se empareja con una ficha de álgebra negativa.

Answers to Instant Check System™

Chapter 1

Check Your Readiness   p. 2

1. 1 **2.** 11 **3.** 11 **4.** 19 **5.** 13 **6.** 40 **7.** 17 **8.** 44
9. 176 **10.** 28 **11.** 166 **12.** 75 **13.** > **14.** >
15. < **16.** < **17.** < **18.** = **19.** 12 **20.** 30 **21.** 28
22. 5 **23.** 96 **24.** 5 **25.** 200 **26.** 80 **27.** 31
28. 13 **29.** 480 **30.** 12 **31.** 1 **32.** 4 **33.** 7 **34.** 10

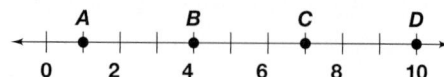

Lesson 1-1   pp. 4–7

Check Skills You'll Need 1. 7 **2.** 12 **3.** 5 **4.** 4 **5.** 3

Quick Check 1a. Variable expression; x is the
variable. **b.** numerical expression **c.** Variable
expression.; d is the variable **2a.** $0.50b$ **b.** $\frac{m}{60}$

Lesson 1-2   pp. 8–12

Check Skills You'll Need 1. 82 **2.** 43 **3.** 71 **4.** 19 **5.** 14
6. 26

Quick Check 1a. 17 **b.** 3 **c.** 3 **2a.** 4 **b.** 12 **3.** 3

Lesson 1-3   pp. 14–17

Check Skills You'll Need 1. 60 **2.** 18 **3.** 29 **4.** 32

Quick Check 1a. 28 **b.** 45 **2a.** 90 **b.** 23 **c.** 12
3. $29c$; $145 **4.** $146

Lesson 1-4   pp. 18–22

Check Skills You'll Need 1. −7 **2.** 9 **3.** 8 **4.** 3 **5.** −5

Quick Check 1. −2

2.
$$-6, 0, 2$$
−6, 0, 2 **3.** the absolute value of negative ten; 10

Checkpoint Quiz 1 1. $f + 23$ **2.** $\frac{g}{34}$ **3.** $9p$ **4.** 20 **5.** 2
6. 19 **7.** 0 **8.** 54 **9.** 15

10a.

b. Tuesday, Wednesday, Monday, Thursday

Lesson 1-5   pp. 24–29

Check Skills You'll Need 1. < **2.** > **3.** < **4.** = **5.** > **6.** >

Quick Check 1a. 3 **b.** 4 **c.** −4 **2a.** −4 **b.** 5
c. −6 **3a.** −38 **b.** 47 **c.** −90 **4.** 1,280 m **5a.** −10
b. 70

Lesson 1-6   pp. 30–34

Check Skills You'll Need 1. −1 **2.** −29 **3.** −10 **4.** 11
5. 0 **6.** −23

Quick Check 1a. −5 **b.** −1 **c.** −3 **2a.** −4
b. −6 **c.** 5 **3a.** 35 **b.** −106 **c.** −46 **3d.** −81°C

Lesson 1-7   pp. 35–39

Check Skills You'll Need 1. −7 **2.** −11 **3.** −15 **4.** −19

Quick Check 1. A six-sided figure with all vertices
on a circle. **2a.** Start with 4 and add 5 repeatedly.
b. Start with 3 and multiply by 3 repeatedly
c. Start with 1, 1. Then each number is the sum
of the previous two numbers. **3.** Start with 1 and
add 2 repeatedly; 9, 11. **4.** No; if the coin is fair,
the coin can come up tails on any toss.
5a. correct **b.** Incorrect; 8 and |8| are not
opposites. **c.** correct

Lesson 1-8   pp. 40–43

Check Skills You'll Need 1. Start with 8 and add 3
repeatedly; 20, 23, 26 **2.** Start with 1, then
alternately add 4 and subtract 1; 11, 10, 14
3. Start with 3, then alternately add 2 and multiply
by 2; 26, 52, 54 **4.** Start with 1, then add 3
repeatedly; 13, 16, 19

Quick Check 8. 127 students

Lesson 1-9   pp. 44–49

Check Skills You'll Need 1. 20 **2.** 24 **3.** 25 **4.** 28 **5.** 30
6. 140

Quick Check 1a. −12 **b.** −12 **c.** −14 **2.** 12 **3a.** 64
b. −90 **c.** 0 **4a.** −4 **b.** 8 **c.** 14 **d.** −2

Checkpoint Quiz 2 1. −8 **2.** 20 **3.** −45 **4.** 8 **5.** −12
6. 72 **7–9.** Answers may vary. Samples are given.
7. $3 + (-10) = -7$ **8.** $2 - (-20) = 22$
9. $8 \cdot (-5) = -40$ **10.** 13, 18, 23 **11.** 81, 243, 729

Lesson 1-10   pp. 52–56

Check Skills You'll Need

1.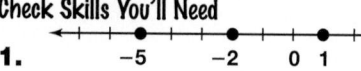

2.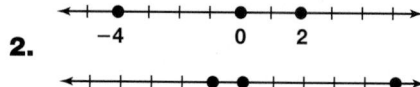

3.

4.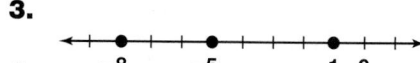

Quick Check 1a. (2, −3); (3, 3) **b.** Quadrant IV; Quadrant I

2a–b.

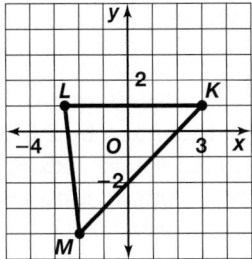

b. a triangle

Chapter 2

1. 1.1, 1.1 **2.** 0.3, 0.3 **3.** 0.7, 0.7 **4.** 5.8, 5.8
5. 2.5, 2.5 **6.** 6, 6 **7.** 0.6, 0.6 **8.** 0.07, 0.07 **9.** <
10. > **11.** < **12.** > **13.** < **14.** = **15.** = **16.** <
17. > **18.** < **19.** < **20.** > **21.** 25 **22.** 28 **23.** 15
24. −110 **25.** 36 **26.** 16 **27.** −24 **28.** 45
29. −20 **30.** −27 **31.** −5 **32.** −45

Lesson 2-1   pp. 68–72

Check Skills You'll Need 1. −25 **2.** 35 **3.** −7 **4.** −46

Quick Check
1. $18; 6 + 8 + 4
    $= 6 + (8 + 4)$ Assoc. Prop. of Add.
    $= 6 + (4 + 8)$ Comm. Prop. of Add.
    $= (6 + 4) + 8$ Assoc. Prop. of Add.
    $= 10 + 8$ Add within parentheses.
    $= 18$ Add.
2a. Comm. Prop. of Add **b.** Ident. Prop. of Mult.
c. Assoc. Prop. of Mult. **3a.** 27 **b.** 3 **c.** 40 **d.** 10
4. $6.30 **5a.** 300 **b.** −120 **c.** 240 **d.** 540

Lesson 2-2   pp. 73–77

Check Skills You'll Need 1. 12 **2.** 24 **3.** 20 **4.** 6 **5.** 8
6. 4

Quick Check 1. 1,791 **2.** $1,428 **3a.** 210 **b.** −120
c. 35 **4a.** $8x − 12$ **b.** $3x + 12$ **c.** $6x + 2$ **5a.** $14 − 6d$
b. $18m + 3$ **c.** $−15t + 6$

Lesson 2-3   pp. 78–81

Check Skills You'll Need 1. $5b + 20$ **2.** $−6x − 15$
3. $−32 − 12q$ **4.** $−12b + 42$

Quick Check 1a. 2, 4; 2s, 4s; 6 **b.** −4; none; none
c. 9, 2, −2, 1; 9m and −2m, 2r and r; none
2. $7a + 1$ **3a.** $2b$ **b.** $−13m$ **c.** $3p$ **4a.** $−y + 5m$
b. $2x − 7$

Comm. Prop of Mult.
2. Assoc. Prop. of Mult. **3.** Ident. Prop. of Mult.
4. Comm. Prop. of Add. **5.** Comm. Prop. of Mult.
6. Dist. Prop. **7.** $9a$ **8.** $18y$ **9.** $16w − 6$

Lesson 2-4   pp. 82–85

Check Skills You'll Need 1. $x + 46$ **2.** $g − 4$ **3.** $t − 5$
4. $\frac{z}{26}$

Quick Check 1a. false; $2 \neq 3$ **b.** open; has a variable
c. true; $20 = 20$ **2.** $20 − x = 3$; open because
there is a variable **3a.** no **b.** yes
4. $b + 6 = 33$; $27 + 6 = 33$; Yes, the backpack
weighs 27 lb.

Lesson 2-5   pp. 88–92

Check Skills You'll Need 1. 3 **2.** 9 **3.** 8 **4.** 6

Quick Check 1a. −5 **b.** 4 **c.** −1 **2.** $123 = r + 55$;
68 beats/min **3a.** 13 **b.** 72 **c.** 112 **4.** $17 ≈ $15;
$9 ≈ $10; $10 ≈ n − 15$; $25

Lesson 2-6   pp. 94–97

Check Skills You'll Need 1. 1 **2.** −1 **3.** −1 **4.** 1

Quick Check 1a. 21 **b.** 13 **c.** 9 **2a.** −8
b. −12 **c.** 14 **3a.** −50 **b.** 324 **c.** −600

Lesson 2-7   pp. 98–101

Check Skills You'll Need 1. 178 **2.** 188 **3.** 183 **4.** 180
5. 180 (Ex. 4)

Quick Check 6. 53 adult tickets, 80 student tickets

Lesson 2-8   pp. 104–107

Check Skills You'll Need

1. −9, −3, 7

2. −10, −8, −2

3. −5, 0, 3

4. −6, 3, 10

Quick Check

1a.

b.

c.

d.

2. $x ≥ 3$ **3.** $n < 5$

Lesson 2-9   pp. 108–111

Check Skills You'll Need **1.** −2 **2.** 19 **3.** 9 **4.** 29

Quick Check **1a.** $m > 3$

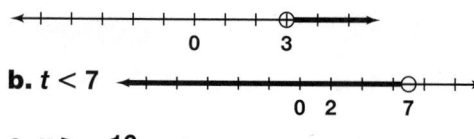

b. $t < 7$

c. $x \geq -10$

2. ≤ 28 lb **3a.** $m > 42$ **b.** $v \leq 11$ **c.** $t \geq 16$

Checkpoint Quiz 2 **1.** true; 19 = 19 **2.** open; variable
3. false; 1 ≠ −1 **4.** −4 **5.** 4 **6.** 6 **7.** −32 **8.** −9
9. $a \geq 6$ **10.** $r < 19$ **11.** $m > -19$
12. 1 quarter, 5 dimes, 2 pennies

Lesson 2-10   pp. 112–116

Check Skills You'll Need **1.** 4 **2.** −9 **3.** −20 **4.** 288

Quick Check **1a.** $x > 10$ **b.** $m < -7$
c. $t > -4$ **2a.** $m \geq 8$ **b.** $t > -21$ **c.** $r > 35$

Chapter 3

Check Your Readiness   p. 126

1. 40 **2.** 10 **3.** 0 **4.** 600 **5.** 830 **6.** 6,010 **7.** <
8. > **9.** < **10.** < **11.** > **12.** > **13.** 8,349, 8.35,
8.351, 9.25 **14.** 0.017, 0.02, 0.0201, 0.201
15. −14.1, −1.401, −1.4, −1.04 **16.** −3.2, −3.19,
−2.8, −2.3 **17.** 11.49 **18.** 3.07 **19.** 3.65 **20.** 1.206
21. 6.7067 **22.** 6.9 **23.** 55.12 **24.** 10.6 **25.** 98.7
26. 532 **27.** 300 **28.** 154,070 **29.** 0.08 **30.** 0.0842
31. 0.0161 **32.** 0.001209

Lesson 3-1   pp. 129–133

Check Skills You'll Need **1.** 2 tens **2.** 3 tenths
3. 8 hundredths **4.** 6 thousandths

Quick Check **1a.** tenths; 38.4 **b.** ones; 1
c. tenths; 7,098.6 **d.** thousandths; 274.943
e. tenths; 5.0 **f.** hundredths; 9.85 **2a.** about 560
b. about 220 **3a.** about 18.6 **b.** about $11
4a. about $15 **b.** about 125

Lesson 3-2   pp. 134–137

Check Skills You'll Need **1.** 146 **2.** 199 **3.** 101 **4.** 28

Quick Check **1a.** about 10 **b.** about 68
c. about 160 **2.** about $40 **3a.** about 20
b. about 6 **c.** about 20 **4a.** Yes; 0.68 is close to
an estimate of 0.8. **b.** No; 52.3 is not close to an
estimate of 5.

Lesson 3-3   pp. 139–143

Check Skills You'll Need **1.** 3, 4, 5, 6, 6, 8, 9
2. 68, 69, 71, 72, 72 **3.** 98, 101, 101, 112, 120
4. 3, 3.3, 3.7, 3.74, 37

Quick Check **1.** 2.95, 2.8, 2.3, 2 **2a.** 3 modes
b. 1 mode **3a.** 31; raises the mean by 2.6
b. 1; lowers the mean by 2.8 **4a.** $25.25, $23.50,
$20 **b.** Answers may vary. Sample: Median; the
mode is equal to two of the smaller data values,
and the outlier ($42) affects the mean too much.

Lesson 3-4   pp. 145–148

Check Skills You'll Need **1.** 14 **2.** 10 **3.** 14 **4.** 3.5

Quick Check **1a.** $r = 28$ mi/h **b.** $t = 51.5$ yr
2a. 61°F **b.** 59°F **c.** 53.5°F **3a.** 88.2 cm **b.** 52 in.

Checkpoint Quiz 1 **1.** 15.66 **2.** 0.891 **3.** 7,023 **4.** 345.7
5. about 32 **6.** about 24 **7.** about −1 **8.** about 6
9. 56, 57, no mode **10.** 2, 2, 1 **11.** 8.5 h

Lesson 3-5   pp. 150–153

Check Skills You'll Need **1.** 9.86 **2.** 2.45 **3.** 2.04 **4.** 3.08

Quick Check **1a.** 13.9 **b.** 38.96
2. $35.48 + m = 70$; $34.52 **3a.** 21.1 **b.** −7.4
4. $x - 14.95 = 12.48$; $27.43

Lesson 3-6   pp. 154–157

Check Skills You'll Need **1.** 11.7 **2.** 0.48 **3.** 6.618
4. 4.8018

Quick Check **1a.** −2 **b.** 0.5 **c.** 90.9
2. $5.5p = 7.70$; $1.40 **3a.** −3 **b.** 12.5 **c.** −360
4. 12 hits

Lesson 3-7   pp. 158–163

Check Skills You'll Need **1.** 500 **2.** 0.01406 **3.** 2.94
4. 0.009

Quick Check **1a.** Centimeter; a meter is too large
unless you use fractional parts of a meter;
millimeters are too small. **b.** Gram; an energy bar
has a mass of several grams, but it is much less
than 1 kilogram. **c.** Kilogram; a horse is very
heavy, so grams are too small. **d.** Liter; a gas tank
holds several liters, so milliliters are too small.
2a. 50 km; millimeters are used to measure very
small lengths. **b.** 10 mL; the eyedropper holds
several drops of water but much less than a quart.
3a. 0.035 **b.** 250,000 **c.** 6,000 **4a.** 3,800 m
b. 250 mL

Checkpoint Quiz 2 1. 0.25 **2.** 8.55 **3.** 130 **4.** 3.05
5. 6.5 **6.** 129.6 **7.** 1.5 m; 1.5 cm is a little wider
than the width of a thumbnail. **8.** 500 mL; 500 L
would be about 500 qt. **9.** 0.095 **10.** 7,650,000 **11.**
0.675 **12.** 7,100 **13.** 9,100 g

Lesson 3-8   pp. 166–169

Check Skills You'll Need 1. Start with 0 and add 6
repeatedly; 24, 30, 36 **2.** Start with −18 and add 9
repeatedly; 18, 27, 36 **3.** Start with 0. Alternately
add 2 and subtract 1; 5, 4, 6 **4.** Start with 7.
Alternately subtract 1 and add 2; 9, 11, 10

Quick Check

5.

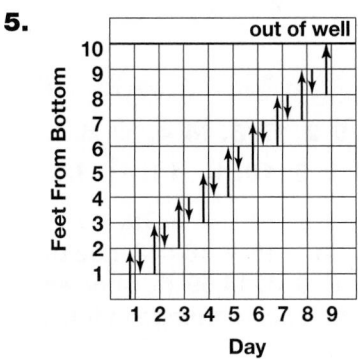

Chapter 4

Check Your Readiness   p. 2

1. $\frac{4}{5}$ **2.** $\frac{5}{7}$ **3.** $\frac{3}{7}$ **4.** $\frac{1}{7}$ **5.** $\frac{12}{13}$ **6.** $\frac{7}{24}$ **7.** $\frac{6}{11}$ **8.** $1\frac{9}{20}$ **9.** $\frac{23}{39}$
10. $12\frac{23}{40}$ **11.** $4\frac{7}{12}$ **12.** $1\frac{5}{6}$ **13.** $13\frac{13}{28}$ **14.** 9^5 **15.** $5 \cdot 7^6$
16. $2^2 \cdot 3^6$ **17.** ≈2,650,000 voters **18.** Texas;
≈1,000,000 voters

Lesson 4-1   pp. 4–6

Check Skills You'll Need 1. Reasonable **2.** Incorrect
3. Incorrect **4.** Reasonable

Quick Check 1a. $\frac{4.2}{c}$ **b.** $t - 15$ **2.** Let n be
the number. **a.** $n - 9$ **b.** $2n + 31$
3a. $c = 15n$ **b.** Each CD costs $10.99.
4. Answers may vary. Sample: e = money earned,
s = money saved, $s = \frac{1}{2}e$

Lesson 4-2   pp. 9–12

Check Skills You'll Need 1. 4 **2.** 3 **3.** 1 **4.** 4 **5.** 7 **6.** 4
7. 8 **8.** 60 **9.** 35 **10.** 9 **11.** 18 **12.** 36

Quick Check 1a. 4 **b.** 10 **c.** 29 **d.** 134
2a. 3 **b.** 8 **c.** 6 **d.** 45

3.

Price p	$p + 0.05p$	Cost c
$5	5 + 0.05(5)	$5.25
$10	10 + 0.05(10)	$10.50
$15	15 + 0.05(15)	$15.75
$20	20 + 0.05(20)	$21.00

$5.25, $10.50, $15.75, $21.00
4a. 26 **b.** 10.5 **5a.** 1764 **b.** 1134 **c.** 15,876 **6a.** 95
b. 21 **c.** 29 **7.** 63,000 ft^2

Lesson 4-3   pp. 17–20, 23

Check Skills You'll Need 1. $\frac{1}{2}$ **2.** $\frac{1}{20}$ **3.** $\frac{13}{4}$ **4.** $\frac{13}{40}$ **5.** 0.4
6. 0.375 **7.** $0.\overline{6}$ **8.** $3.\overline{5}$

Quick Check 1a. integers, rational numbers
b. rational numbers **c.** rational numbers
d. natural numbers, whole numbers, integers,
rational numbers **2.** rational numbers **3a.** true
b. False; answers may vary. Sample: $\frac{3}{1} = 3$ is a
whole number. **4.** $-\frac{2}{3}, -\frac{5}{8}, \frac{1}{12}$ **5a.** 5 **b.** 4 **c.** 3.7
d. $\frac{5}{7}$

Checkpoint Quiz 2 1. 6 + 4 **2.** $\frac{c}{2}$ **3.** 4.3a **4.** $b + c +$
$2a$ **5.** 28 **6.** 58 **7.** 60 **8.** 252 **9.** False; answers
may vary. Sample: The opposite of −2 is 2, but
−2 > 2. **10.** natural numbers or whole numbers

Lesson 4-4   pp. 27–29

Check Skills You'll Need

1. $2x + 10$ **2.** $\frac{t}{4}$ **3.** $8 - 6n$ **4.** $7 - 2p$

Quick Check 1. $m = 60h$ **2a.** 36 **b.** No; you need 11
toothpicks to make 2 houses and 16 toothpicks
to make 3 houses. **c.** $y = 2 + 3x$ **3.** independent:
weight of turkey; dependent: cooking time
4. independent: the amount of money he can
spend; dependent: number of songs he can
download. domain: $3.00 to $6.00; range: 4 to 8
songs.

Lesson 4-5 pp. 33–34, 37

Check Skills You'll Need

1–4.

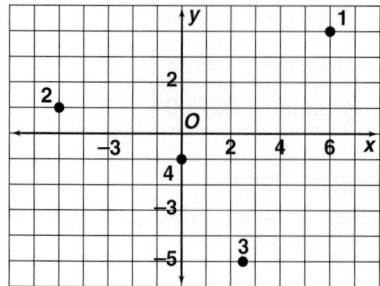

Quick Check 1.

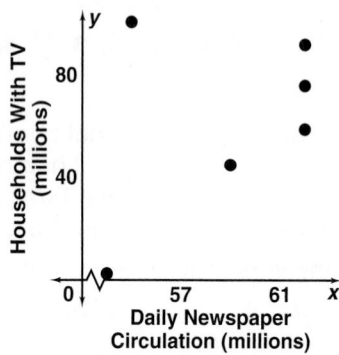

2a. 4-year-old car with an asking price of $14,900 **b.** $5000

Checkpoint Quiz 2 1. $w = 35m$ **2.** depth below sea level; pressure **3.** money in the account; time in account **4.** number of papers delivered; money earned

5a.

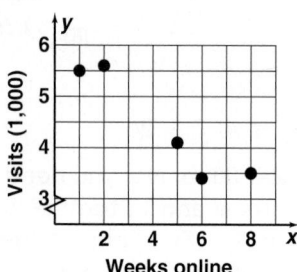

b. negative correlation

c. {1, 2, 5, 6, 8}

Lesson 4-6 pp. 40–43

Check Skills You'll Need 1. 1.9, 2.4, 3.6, 7.5, 9.8 **2.** 58, 72, 98, 144, 195, 235 **3.** −12, −8, −3, 0, 7, 14 **4.** $-4\frac{3}{8}, -3\frac{2}{3}, -2\frac{5}{8}, 2\frac{1}{2}, 4\frac{1}{2}, 6\frac{1}{4}$ **5.** 5 **6.** 7

Quick Check 1a. about $6.53/h; about $6.38/h; $6.25/h **b.** Median; the mean is still larger than 8 of 10 wages. **2.** No; you would need at least a 104 to have a 92 average. **3.** Maine: mean = 0.4°F, range = 13°F; Michigan: mean = 4.4°F, range = 34°F. On average, Maine was colder. The temperatures for Michigan were more spread out.

4.

```
0 | 2 8 8
1 | 4
2 | 6
3 | 5
4 | 3 3 5
6 | 0
4 | 3 means 4.3
```

5a. city: 28 mi/gal; highway: 32 mi/gal **b.** city: 23 mi/gal; 31 mi/gal; highway: 32 mi/gal; 38 mi/gal **c.** city: 15 mi/gal; highway: 14 mi/gal

Chapter 5

Check Your Readiness p. 230

1. $0.45n = 3.60$ **2.** $3s = 124$ **3.** 34 **4.** 10 **5.** 5 **6.** 30 **7.** 33 **8.** 63 **9.** 140 **10.** 1 **11.** 18 **12.** 39 **13.** < **14.** < **15.** > **16.** = **17.** $m = 55h$ **18.** $t = 0.8c + 0.4$ **19.** $l = 2 + 2w$

Lesson 5-1 pp. 232–235

Check Skills You'll Need 1. 6 **2.** 17 **3.** 14 **4.** 59 **5.** 1.3 **6.** 5.2 **7.** 10.9 **8.** 17.1 **9.** $\frac{4}{5}$ **10.** $1\frac{2}{9}$ **11.** $1\frac{1}{4}$ **12.** $\frac{5}{8}$

Quick Check 1a. −2 **b.** −2 **c.** −11 **d.** 6 **2a.** −11 **b.** −17.4 **c.** $-1\frac{1}{4}$ **d.** $\frac{1}{18}$ **3.** $-15 + 18 = 3$, rise of 3° **4a.** −11.4 **b.** −9.1 **c.** 15.6 **d.** 14.59 **5.** Choices of variable may vary. Sample: c = change in temp., $-14 + c$; −25°F

6a. $\begin{bmatrix} -4 \\ 1.5 \\ -16 \end{bmatrix}$ **b.** $\begin{bmatrix} -9 & \frac{1}{8} \\ 1\frac{1}{4} & -1 \end{bmatrix}$

Lesson 5-2 pp. 240–242

Check Skills You'll Need 1. −6 **2.** 7 **3.** −3.79 **4.** $\frac{7}{19}$ **5.** 1 **6.** 6 **7.** 5 **8.** $\frac{1}{2}$

Quick Check 1a. −4 **b.** −5 **c.** −11 **d.** 5 **2a.** −1 **b.** 14 **c.** 4 **d.** 3 **3a.** −8 **b.** 12 **c.** 8.0 **d.** $-\frac{1}{18}$ **4a.** 1 **b.** 1 **c.** 6 **d.** 6 **5a.** −5 **b.** 5 **c.** 9 **d.** 5 **6.** ABC: $32.47; PQR: $15.46

Lesson 5-3 pp. 245–249

Check Skills You'll Need 1. −8 **2.** −25 **3.** −24 **4.** −72 **5.** 8, 10, 12 **6.** 0, −2, −4 **7.** 3, 0, −3 **8.** 0, 6, 12

Quick Check 1a. −24 **b.** 50 **c.** 39.2 **d.** $-\frac{1}{2}$ **2a.** −56 **b.** 336 **c.** −56 **3a.** −24.75°F **b.** 15.25°F **4a.** −64 **b.** 16 **c.** 0.09 **d.** $-\frac{9}{16}$ **5a.** −6 **b.** 4 **c.** −1 **d.** 13 **6a.** $-4\frac{1}{2}$ **b.** $-\frac{1}{5}$ **c.** $29\frac{1}{2}$ **7.** −10

Lesson 5-4   pp. 255–257, 261

Check Skills You'll Need **1.** 33 **2.** −22 **3.** 1 **4.** −1 **5.** 3t
6. −4m

Quick Check **1a.** 1339 **b.** 2121 **c.** 2352
d. 1485 **2.** $17.70 **3a.** 6 − 14t
b. 1.2 + 3.3c **4a.** −2x − 1 **b.** −3 + 8a **5a.** 13y
b. 2t **c.** −12w^3 **d.** 9d
6a. −2(t + 7) **b.** 14(8 + w)

Checkpoint Quiz 1 **1.** $-\frac{1}{9}$ **2.** −20 **3.** 5 **4.** $\begin{bmatrix} 0 & -5 \\ -2.1 & 8 \\ -23 & 11 \end{bmatrix}$

5. 120 **6.** 1 **7.** −1.6 **8.** t = temperature change;
−5 + t; 8°F **9.** 8x − 12 **10.** 49t

Lesson 5-5   pp. 262–264

Check Skills You'll Need **1.** 19 **2.** −30 **3.** 26 **4.** 140
5. −1 **6.** 3 **7.** 1 + x **8.** 5t − 8 **9.** −7m

Quick Check **1a.** Ident. Prop. of Mult.; m is
mult. by the mult. identity, 1. **b.** Assoc. Prop. of
Add.; the grouping of the terms changes.
c. Assoc. Prop. of Mult.; the grouping of the
factors changes. **d.** Ident. Prop. of Add.; the
ident. for add., 0, is added. **e.** Comm. Prop. of
Mult.; the order of the factors changes.
f. Comm. Prop. of Add.; the order of the terms
changes. **2.** $8.80
3a. 5a + 6 + a
   = 5a + a + 6   Comm. Prop. of Add.
   = (5a + a) + 6   Assoc. Prop. of Add.
   = (5a + 1a) + 6   Ident. Prop. of Mult.
   = (5 + 1)a + 6   Dist. Prop.
   = 6a + 6   addition
b. 2(3t − 1) + 2
   = 6t − 2 + 2   Dist. Prop.
   = 6t + (−2) + 2   def. of subtr.
   = 6t + [(−2) + 2]   Assoc. Prop. of Add.
   = 6t + 0   Inv. Prop. of Add.
   = 6t   Ident. Prop. of Add.

Lesson 5-6   pp. 269–271, 275

Check Skills You'll Need **1.** 32% **2.** 9% **3.** 22.5% **4.** 18%

Quick Check **1.** $\frac{2}{7}$ **2.** increases **3.** 6:2 or 3:1 **4.** 98%
5. about 35,260 light bulbs

Checkpoint Quiz 2 **1.** Dist. Prop. **2.** Comm. Prop. of
Add. **3.** Assoc. Prop. of Add. **4.** Simplify. **5.** Dist.
Prop. **6.** Simplify. **9.** $\frac{2}{7}$ **10.** 2352 bicycles

Lesson 5-7   pp. 277–279

Check Skills You'll Need **1.** $\frac{1}{3}$ **2.** $\frac{1}{3}$ **3.** $\frac{1}{6}$ **4.** 0 **5.** $\frac{1}{6}$ **6.** $\frac{1}{4}$
7. $1\frac{3}{5}$

Quick Check **1.** $\frac{1}{18}$ **2.** $\frac{4}{225}$ **3.** $\frac{4}{105}$ **4a.** $\frac{2}{39}$ **b.** $\frac{2}{39}$
c. No; according to the Comm. Prop. of Mult., the
order of the terms does not change the result.

Chapter 6

Check Your Readiness   p. 292

1. m = 7.5n **2.** t = 200 − 13w **3.** 3 **4.** −10 **5.** 8
6. −8 **7.** 7.14 **8.** 16.4 **9.** $-\frac{9}{20}$ **10.** $-\frac{7}{15}$ **11.** 17
12. −3 **13.** 576 **14.** −2.75 **15.** 16k^2 **16.** 13xy
17. 2t + 2 **18.** 12x − 4

Lesson 6-1   pp. 295–297

Check Skills You'll Need **1.** 19; Add. Prop. of Eq.
2. 5.2; Subtr. Prop. of Eq. **3.** 14; Add. Prop. of Eq.
4. 33; Add. Prop. of Eq. **5.** 32; Mult. Prop. of Eq.
6. 3; Div. Prop. of Eq. **7.** $\frac{1}{5}$; **8.** −9; **9.** $3\frac{3}{4}$

Quick Check **1a.** 5 **b.** 243 **c.** 3 **2.** 2
3a. 29 **b.** Let t = total weekly salary and
s = weekly sales; t = 125 + $\frac{1}{12}$s; $1560

4. −9 − 4m = 3   Original equation
  −9 + 9 −4m = 3 + 9   Add. Prop. of Eq.
        −4m = 12   Simplify.
      $\frac{-4m}{-4} = \frac{12}{-4}$ Div. Prop. of Eq.
         m = −3   Simplify.

Lesson 6-2   pp. 302–304

Check Skills You'll Need **1.** −n **2.** 8b − 2 **3.** 9w − 45
4. −10b + 120 **5.** −3x + 12 **6.** 30 − 5w **7.** 43
8. 26 **9.** −45 **10.** −35

Quick Check **1a.** 8 **b.** 3 **c.** 3 **d.** 4 **2.** 135 ft
3a. −1 **b.** −1 **4a.** $\frac{5}{6}$ **b.** 624 **5a.** 28 **b.** 4

Lesson 6-3   pp. 310–312

Check Skills You'll Need **1.** 4x **2.** −4x **3.** 0 **4.** 0 **5.** −2
6. −5 **7.** −7 **8.** $\frac{1}{3}$

Quick Check **1a.** $-\frac{4}{7}$ **b.** −2 **c.** $-\frac{5}{2}$ **d.** 10
2. at least 15 bottles **3.** 10 **4a.** no solution
b. identity

Lesson 6-4   pp. 318–321

Check Skills You'll Need **1.** $\frac{7}{12}$ **2.** $\frac{4}{7}$ **3.** $\frac{3}{4}$ **4.** 4 **5.** $\frac{3}{4}$ **6.** $\frac{1}{2}$

Quick Check **1.** $1.025/rose; $1.25 rose; Main Street Florist **2a.** about 3.4 mi/h; $d = 3.4t$
b. about 3.4 mi **3.** 13.2 ft/min **4a.** $6\frac{2}{3}$ **b.** $6\frac{6}{7}$ **c.** 5.4
5a. $8\frac{1}{3}$ **b.** 33.6 **c.** 48 **6a.** 5 **b.** −8.75 **c.** −21

Lesson 6-5   pp. 325–327, 331

Check Skills You'll Need **1.** $\frac{6}{7}$ **2.** $\frac{3}{4}$ **3.** $\frac{1}{2}$ **4.** $2\frac{4}{5}$ **5.** $2\frac{2}{15}$
6. $6\frac{2}{3}$ **7.** $1\frac{1}{9}$ **8.** 10 **9.** $\frac{3}{5}$

Quick Check **1.** 10.5 cm

2.

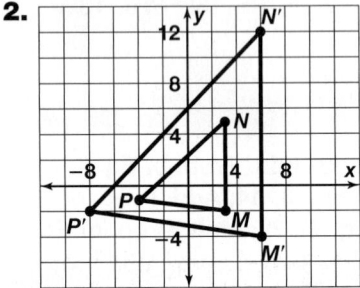

3a. 9.75 ft **b.** 42 ft **4a.** about 21 mi **b.** 3.5 in.

Checkpoint Quiz 1 **1.** 2.5 **2.** 2 **3.** no solution
4. $6\frac{3}{4}$ **5.** −20 **6.** 4.4 **7.** 33.6 min **8.** 3.125 cm
9. 4.5 ft **10.** 35 ft

Lesson 6-6   pp. 334–338

Check Skills You'll Need **1.** $25q$ **2.** 2ℓ **3.** $34h$ **4.** $5x$
5. $3.99n$

Quick Check **1.** 5 cm **2a.** Let $x =$ the first integer.
b. $x + 1$ is the second integer and $x + 2$ is the third integer. **c.** $3x + 3 = 48$; 15, 16, 17
3a. $3\frac{2}{3}$ h **b.** $1\frac{2}{3}$ h **4.** 1h **5.** John: 38 mi/h; Sarah: 50 mi/h

Lesson 6-7   pp. 344–346

Check Skills You'll Need **1.** $\frac{x}{20} = \frac{20}{100}$, 4 **2.** $\frac{8}{20} = \frac{x}{100}$, 40%
3. $\frac{18}{x} = \frac{90}{100}$, 20 **4.** $\frac{27}{x} = \frac{90}{100}$, 30 **5.** 16 **6.** 32

Quick Check **1a.** 8% **b.** 7% **2.** 1899%
3. 0.5 cm **4.** 86.25 ft², 106.25 ft² **5a.** about 0.3%
b. about 0.03% **6.** about 66%

Lesson 6-8   pp. 352–354, 356

Check Skills You'll Need **1.** 121 **2.** 144 **3.** −144 **4.** 2.25
5. 0.36 **6.** $\frac{1}{4}$ **7.** $\frac{4}{9}$ **8.** $\frac{16}{25}$

Quick Check **1a.** 7 **b.** ±6 **c.** −11 **d.** $\frac{1}{5}$
2a. irrational **b.** rational **c.** irrational **d.** rational
3. −11 and −10 **4.** 4.22 **5.** 156.5 ft

Checkpoint Quiz 2 **1.** 14 cm **2.** 153, 155, 157
3. Beth: 63 mi/h; Marcus: 50 mi/h **4.** about 0.2%
5. 2 **6.** 303.75 cm²; 340.75 cm² **7.** −16 **8.** $\frac{8}{11}$
9. ±0.05 **10.** 7 and 8

Lesson 6-9   pp. 357–360

Check Skills You'll Need **1.** 61 **2.** 65 **3.** $25t^2$ **4.** 14
5. $\frac{5}{7}$ **6.** 1.2

Quick Check **1.** 25 cm **2.** 6.9 mi **3.** yes **4.** no

Chapter 7

Check Your Readiness   p. 374

1. > **2.** = **3.** > **4.** < **5.** 7 **6.** −4 **7.** 1 **8.** 2 **9.** 3
10. −12 **11.** 32.4 **12.** 23 **13.** 29.5 **14.** −28
15. −12 **16.** 48 **17.** 5 **18.** −24 **19.** −10 **20.** 1.85
21. −24 **22.** −2 **23.** 3 **24.** −4 **25.** 3 **26.** $\frac{1}{2}$ **27.** $\frac{5}{2}$
28. 4.1 **29.** 48

Lesson 7-1   pp. 376–378

Check Skills You'll Need 1–5.
$$\xleftarrow{\quad}\!\!\bullet\!\!\xrightarrow{\quad}$$
−4 −3 −2 −1 0 1 2 3 4

6. > **7.** < **8.** = **9.** = **10.** > **11.** <

Quick Check **1a.** no **b.** yes **c.** yes **d.** yes **2a.** no **b.** no **c.** yes **d.** yes

3a. (number line from −2 to 2, open circle) **b.** (number line from −5 to 1, closed dot)
c. (number line from −1 to 5, open circle) **4a.–b.** Choice of variable may vary. **a.** $x \geq 2$ **b.** $x < 0$ **5a.** No; speeds cannot be negative, so you can't use all real numbers. **b.** No; answers may vary. Sample: Hourly wages are not likely to be in hundreds of dollars.

Lesson 7-2 — pp. 382–384

Check Skills You'll Need **1.** > **2.** < **3.** > **4.** 9 **5.** −2
6. −9 **7.** $\frac{1}{6}$

Quick Check **1.** $m > 2$;

2. $n \le 5$;

3. $t \ge 5$;

4. $b \ge 53$

Lesson 7-3 — pp. 388–391, 393

Check Skills You'll Need **1.** 16 **2.** $-\frac{2}{3}$ **3.** −6 **4.** 6.4
5. −18 **6.** 18 **7.** $x \le -1$ **8.** $x > 3$

Quick Check **1a.** $b > 2$;

b. $d \ge 2\frac{1}{2}$;

c. $y \le -1.5$;

2a. $k < 4$;

b. $t > -\frac{1}{2}$;

c. $w \le -10$;

3a. $t > 4$;

b. $w \le -4$;

c. $n > -3$;

4. $0.4c > 327$; $c > 317.5$; 818 calendars

Checkpoint Quiz 1 **1.** $c > 5$;

2. $x < -6$;

3. $p \le -6$;

4. $y \ge 2$;

5. $g < -8$;

6. $b \le -5$;

7a. yes **b.** no **c.** yes **d.** no **8a.** no **b.** no **c.** no
d. yes **9a.** $m + 38 + 50 \ge 180$ **b.** $m \ge 92$
10a. $1.50p \le 20$ **b.** 13 plants

Lesson 7-4 — pp. 395–397

Check Skills You'll Need **1.** −2 **2.** no solution **3.** $-3\frac{1}{3}$
4. identity **5.** $1\frac{2}{9}$ **6.** −11 **7.** 40 cm **8.** 13 in.

Quick Check **1a.** $x \ge -6$ **b.** $t < 1$ **c.** $n > 3$
2. $2(12) + 2w \le 40$, so the banner's

width must be 8 feet or less. **3a.** $p < -1$
b. $m \le -3$ **c.** $b > 3$ **4.** $b > 3$ **5.** $x \le 2\frac{1}{4}$

Lesson 7-5 — pp. 403–405, 408

Check Skills You'll Need **1.**

2.

3.

4. 6 **5.** −3 **6.** 14 **7.** 3

Quick Check **1a.** $n > -2$ and $n < 9$ or
$-2 < n < 9$;

b. $3.50 \le b \le 6$;

2a. $-2 \le x < 5$;

b. $-1 < x < 4$;

c. $-4 \le n < -2$;

3a. $6.7 \le p \le 8.5$ **b.** $5.2 \le p \le 7$. No; readings in
this range are unlikely if the first readings are high.
4. $n \le -5$ or $n \ge 3$;

5. $x < 2$ or $x \ge 3$;

Checkpoint Quiz 2

1. $d < -3$

2. $n \ge -2$

3. $-2 \le m \le 1$

4. $s < 2$

5. $p > 4$

6. $x \le -4$ or $x > 4$

7. $c < 8$ **8.** $65 \le t \le 75$
9. $2(15) + 2(w) \le 48$, $w \le 9$ **10.** $x \ge -19$

Lesson 7-6 — pp. 411–413

Check Skills You'll Need **1.** 15 **2.** 3 **3.** 6 **4.** −7 **5.** 24
6. 2 **7.** = **8.** > **9.** < **10.** > **11.** > **12.** =

Quick Check **1a.** −1, 1 **b.** −5, 5 **c.** −2, 2
d. No; an absolute value cannot be negative.
2a. −4, 8 **b.** no solution **c.** −2, 2
3a. $w < -7$ or $w > 3$,

b. all real numbers **4.** 33.81 oz to 33.91 oz,
inclusive

Chapter 8

Check Your Readiness   p. 426

1. Let n = number of pens and t = total price; $t = 0.59n$. **2.** Let h = height of house and t = height of tower; $t = h + 200$. **3.** Let s = length of a side and p = perimeter; $p = 3s$. **4.** −7 **5.** −18 **6.** 2 **7.** −1

8–11. 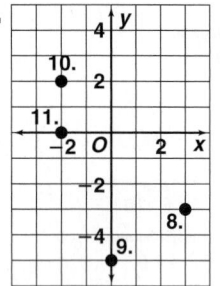   **12.** $6\frac{2}{5}$ **13.** 0.6 **14.** 4.5
15. −58 **16.** −4, 0
17. 3, 7 **18.** no solution

Lesson 8-1   pp. 428–429

Check Skills You'll Need **1.** C **2.** D **3.** E **4.** A **5.** (0, 0) **6.** (−4, −2) **7.** (−3, 3)

Quick Check **1–2.** Labels may vary. Samples are given.

1.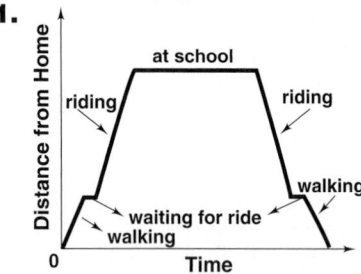

2. 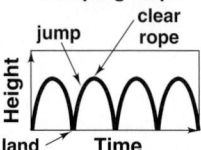   **3.** F

Lesson 8-2   pp. 433–435, 438

Check Skills You'll Need

1–4. 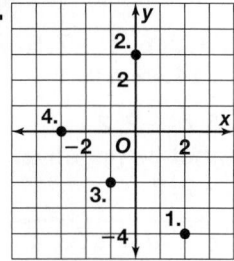   **5.** −17 **6.** −54 **7.** 108

Quick Check **1a.** not a function **b.** function
2a. function **b.** not a function

3.

x	$8 - 3x$	y
1	$8 - 3(1)$	5
2	$8 - 3(2)$	2
3	$8 - 3(3)$	−1
4	$8 - 3(4)$	−10

4a. {−8, −6, −1} **b.** {−20, 0, 8}
  c. {1, 5, 26}

Checkpoint Quiz 1 **1–3.** Graphs may vary. Samples are given. **1.**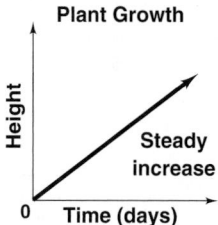

2. 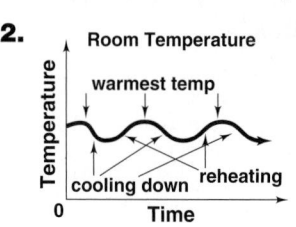   **3.**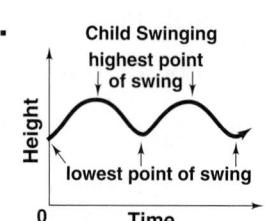

4. Yes; it passes the vertical line test.

5.

x	$-5x$	$f(x)$
1	$-5(1)$	−5
2	$-5(2)$	−10
3	$-5(3)$	−15
4	$-5(4)$	−20

6.

x	$x + 1.4$	$g(x)$
1	$1 + 1.4$	2.4
2	$2 + 1.4$	3.4
3	$3 + 1.4$	4.4
4	$4 + 1.4$	5.4

7.

n	$3n^2$	$f(n)$
1	$3(1)^2$	3
2	$3(2)^2$	12
3	$3(3)^2$	27
4	$3(4)^2$	48

8.

x	$2 - 0.5x$	y
1	$2 - 0.5(1)$	1.5
2	$2 - 0.5(2)$	1
3	$2 - 0.5(3)$	0.5
4	$2 - 0.5(4)$	0

9. function **10.** not a function

Lesson 8-3   pp. 439–441

Check Skills You'll Need

1. ind: time; dep: distance
2. ind: number of apples; dep: price

Quick Check **1a.** They would be the same.

b. Tables may vary. Sample:

x	$f(x)$
0	4
1	7
−1	1
−2	−2

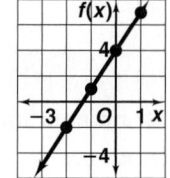

Lesson 10-4   pp. 572–575

Check Skills You'll Need 1. 3.25 h **2.** 275 mi

Quick Check 1. 32 kg 50% alloy; 8 kg 25% alloy **2.** 3850 copies **3.** 440 mi/h; 40 mi/h

Lesson 10-5   pp. 580–582, 586

Check Skills You'll Need 1. never **2.** always
3. sometimes **4.** $y = \frac{2}{3}x - 3$ **5.** $y = -3x + 6$
6. $y = \frac{3}{4}x + \frac{1}{4}$

Quick Check

1. 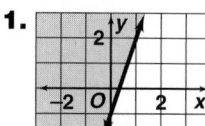 **2.**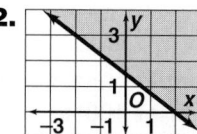

3. Answers may vary. Sample: 6 lb hamburger and 2 lb chicken, 3 lb hamburger and 6 lb chicken, 5 lb hamburger and 3 lb chicken

Checkpoint Quiz 2 1. $(11, -4)$ **2.** $(-9, 1)$ **3.** $(3.5, 10)$
4. no solution **5.** $\left(15, -\frac{1}{2}\right)$ **6.** $n + d = 21$,
$0.05n + 0.10d = 1.70$; 8 nickels, 13 dimes
7. $y = 200 + 0.35x, y = 1.20x$;
about 236 ice cream cones
8. $x + y = 4, x - y = 3$; 3.5 mi/h, 0.5 mi/h

9. 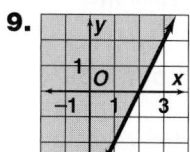 **10.**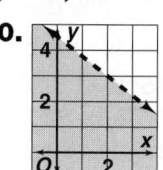

Lesson 10-6   pp. 587–590

Check Skills You'll Need 1. (2, 0);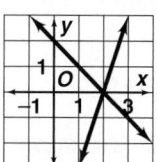

2. no solution; 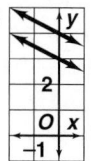 **3.** (4, 0);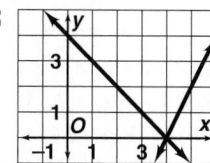

4. 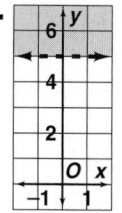 **5.** 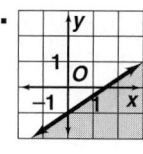 **6.**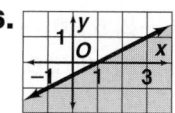

Quick Check

1. 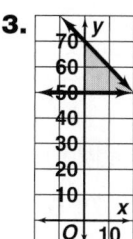 **2a.** $y \geq \frac{1}{2}x - 1$ and $y < 2$
b. $y \leq -\frac{2}{3}x$ and $x > -3$

3. [graph] **4a.** Answers may vary. Sample: 2 20¢ stamps and 6 34¢ stamps; 4 20¢ stamps and 5 34¢ stamps **b.** no **c.** You cannot have a negative or fractional number of stamps.

Chapter 11

Check Your Readiness   p. 604

1. 0.7 **2.** 6.4 **3.** 0.008 **4.** 3.5 **5.** $0.\overline{27}$ **6.** 49
7. 5.027 **8.** 0.75 **9.** 4 **10.** 100 **11.** 49 **12.** 17
13. -31 **14.** $33\frac{1}{3}\%$ **15.** 25% **16.** $\{-24.5, -8, 0\}$
17. $\{-32.875, 10, 18\}$ **18.** $\{-11, -1, 16.5\}$
19. 9, 11 **20.** 14, 20 **21.** 31, 37

Lesson 11-1   pp. 606–608

Check Skills You'll Need 1. 8 **2.** $\frac{1}{16}$ **3.** 4 **4.** -27 **5.** -27
6. 3 **7.** $\frac{1}{2}$ **8.** -1 **9.** 4

Quick Check 1a. $\frac{1}{81}$ **b.** 1 **c.** $-\frac{1}{64}$ **d.** $\frac{1}{7}$ **e.** $-\frac{1}{9}$
2a. $\frac{11}{m^5}$ **b.** $\frac{7t^2}{s^4}$ **c.** $2a^3$ **d.** $\frac{1}{n^5v^2}$ **3a.** $-\frac{1}{8}$ **b.** $-\frac{1}{50}$ **c.** $\frac{1}{16}$
d. $-12\frac{1}{2}$ **4.** 600; 5400; for $x = -2$, the population is 600, 2 months before the population is 5400. For $x = 0$, it is the population when time is 0.

Lesson 11-2   pp. 612–614

Check Skills You'll Need 1. 60,000 **2.** 0.07 **3.** 820,000
4. 0.003 **5.** 34 **6.** 524 **7.** 367.8

Quick Check 1a. yes **b.** No; $52 > 10$. **c.** No;
$0.04 < 1$. **2a.** 2.67×10^5 **b.** 4.6205×10^7
c. 3.25×10^{-5} **d.** 9.0×10^{-9} **e.** 436 is 436 times greater than 1, and $436 = 4.36 \times 10^2$.
Then $(4.36 \times 10^2) \cdot 10^9 = 4.36 \times 10^{11}$.
3a. 3,200,000,000,000 **b.** 50,700 **c.** 0.00056
d. 0.083 **4.** electron, proton, neutron
5. $60.2 \times 10^{-5}, 61 \times 10^{-2}, 0.067 \times 10^3, 63 \times 10^4$
6a. 1.5×10^4 **b.** 8×10^{-10}

Lesson 11-3 — pp. 617–619

Check Skills You'll Need **1.** t^7 **2.** $(6 - m)^3$ **3.** $(r + 5)^5$ **4.** $5^3 s^3$ **5.** -625 **6.** 625 **7.** 1 **8.** $\frac{1}{625}$

Quick Check **1a.** 5^9 **b.** 2^1 **c.** 7^5 **2a.** $7n^6$ **b.** $28x^2 y^7$ **c.** $\frac{7m^3}{n^2}$

3a. 1.5×10^{12} **b.** 4.5×10^2 **c.** 6.3×10^{-14} **4.** about 2.56×10^{13} red blood cells

Lesson 11-4 — pp. 623–625, 628

Check Skills You'll Need **1.** 3^6 **2.** 2^{12} **3.** 5^{28} **4.** 7^3 **5.** x^6 **6.** a^6 **7.** $\frac{1}{y^6}$ **8.** $\frac{1}{n^6}$

Quick Check **1.** a^{28}; $\frac{1}{a^{28}}$ **2a.** $\frac{1}{t^{12}}$ **b.** a^{18}

3a. $16z^4$ **b.** $\frac{1}{16g^{10}}$ **4a.** $81c^{26}$ **b.** $864a^{18}b^6$

c. $\frac{5400n^3}{m^3}$ **5a.** 5.22×10^5 joules

b. about 1.7×10^8 h

Checkpoint Quiz 1 **1.** $\frac{1}{45}$ **2.** r^{20} **3.** $6x^{17}$ **4.** $\frac{mq^2}{n^4}$ **5.** $\frac{1}{a}$

6. $\frac{64m^6}{9}$ **7.** $6m^9$ **8.** $\frac{27t^6}{8}$ **9.** 500; 2000; 16,000

10a. 6.8×10^3 km **b.** about 1.45×10^8 km^2 **c.** 145,000,000 km^2

Lesson 11-5 — pp. 629–631

Check Skills You'll Need **1.** $\frac{1}{4}$ **2.** 5 **3.** $\frac{3}{5}$ **4.** 31 **5.** $\frac{2}{5}$ **6.** $\frac{4}{15}$ **7.** $\frac{2}{7}$ **8.** $\frac{2}{7}$ **9.** $\frac{y}{3}$ **10.** $\frac{2y^2}{x}$ **11.** $\frac{c}{4}$ **12.** $\frac{4}{n^2}$

Quick Check **1a.** $\frac{1}{b^5}$ **b.** z^5 **c.** $\frac{1}{a^2 b^2}$ **d.** $\frac{n}{m^4}$ **e.** $\frac{xz^7}{y^5}$ **2a.** 2.5×10^{-6} **b.** 3.0×10^{16} **c.** $3.\overline{3} \times 10^2$

d. about 9.59×10^{-3} tons **3a.** $\frac{9}{x^4}$ **b.** $\frac{x^3}{y^6}$

4a. $\frac{64}{27}$ **b.** -32 **c.** $\frac{s}{2r}$ **d.** $\frac{m^2}{49a^2}$

Lesson 11-6 — pp. 636–639

Check Skills You'll Need **1.** 2 **2.** -2 **3.** -1.2 **4.** 3.5 **5.** 32, 64 **6.** 108, 324 **7.** 3.2, 6.4 **8.** 12.5, 6.25

Quick Check **1a.** $\frac{1}{5}$ **b.** 2 **c.** $\frac{3}{2}$ **2a.** 81, 243, 729 **b.** 7.5, -3.75, 1.875 **c.** 17.6, 35.2, 70.4
3a. arithmetic **b.** geometric **c.** arithmetic
4a. 4; 972; 708,588 **b.** -2; -6250; $-97,656,250$
5. $A(n) = 200 \cdot 0.56^{n-1}$; 35.1 cm

Lesson 11-7 — pp. 644–646, 649

Check Skills You'll Need

1. 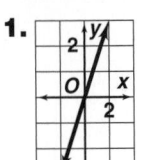 **2.** 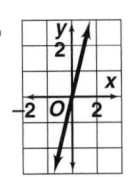 **3.**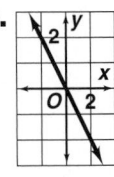

4. 9 **5.** $\frac{1}{125}$ **6.** 162 **7.** $\frac{2}{9}$ **8.** $\frac{3}{2}$ **9.** 90

Quick Check **1a.** $\frac{1}{16}$, 1, 64 **b.** $\frac{2}{5}$, 10, 1250 **c.** $-\frac{2}{9}$, -2, -54 **2.** 40,960 animals

3a. 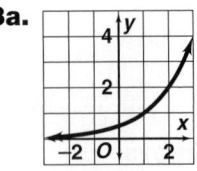 **b.**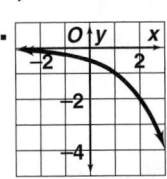

4a.

b. $f(0) = 1$, so copies are made at the same size of the original, or at 100%.

CheckPoint Quiz 2 **1.** 3^{12} **2.** $\frac{y^{15}}{x^{10}}$ **3.** $\frac{4n^{12}}{25m^6}$ **4.** $\frac{1}{t^{10}}$
5. geometric **6.** geometric **7.** arithmetic
8a. -100 **b.** $-\frac{1}{5}$ or -0.2
c. $A(n) = -100 \cdot (-0.2)^{n-1}$ **d.** -0.16; -0.0064
9a. $A(n) = 40 \cdot (0.85)^{n-1}$ **b.** 209 mm
10a. 1.08×10^8 **b.** 2.49×10^8 **c.** about \$2.31

Lesson 11-8 — pp. 651–655

Check Skills You'll Need **1.** 12% decr. **2.** 20% incr. **3.** 6% incr. **4.** 31% decr. **5.** 36% incr.

Quick Check **1a.** $y = 4512 \cdot 1.025^x$ **b.** about 4859 students **2a.** \$3038.72 **b.** \$3038.72
c. $(1 + r)$ is the same as 100% + 100r% written as a decimal. **3a.** \$2813.83 **b.** \$210.23; \$220.99; \$256.67 **4a.** 4 half-lives **b.** 25 mCi; 12.5 mCi
c. 15 mCi; 3.75 mCi **5a.** 604,000 **b.** 0.982
c. $y = 604,000 \cdot (0.982)^x$ **d.** about 420,017 people

Chapter 12

Check Your Readiness — p. 668

1. 40 **2.** -32 **3.** 17 **4.** 28 **5.** 0.64 **6.** 25 **7.** 2 **8.** 7
9. $3d - 12$ **10.** $15x + 5$ **11.** $3u - 24$ **12.** $8y + 28$
13. $-12d + 4$ **14.** $50 - 30s$ **15.** $-21 + 6w$
16. $27 - 6b$ **17.** $11a - 4$ **18.** $5b$ **19.** $-g + 4$
20. $10t + 5s$ **21.** $7b + 4d$ **22.** $-45c$
23. $-10, -4, 2$ **24.** $6, 0, -6$
25. $-10, -2, 6$ **26.** $-6\frac{1}{5}, -5, -3\frac{4}{5}$, **27.** 10, 6, 2
28. $-7\frac{1}{2}, -8, -8\frac{1}{2}$ **29.** $-1, 0, 1$ **30.** $5, -1, -7$

Lesson 12-1 pp. 670–672

Check Skills You'll Need **1.** Start with 60 and subtract 12 repeatedly.
2. Start with 7 and add 5 repeatedly.
3. Start with 6 and multiply by 3 repeatedly.
4. Start with 60 and divide by 2 repeatedly.

Quick Check **1a.** 5 **b.** -3 **2a.** 7, 3, -1; start with 23 and add -4 repeatedly. **b.** $-\frac{2}{3}, \frac{2}{3}, 2$; start with -6 and add $1\frac{1}{3}$ repeatedly. **3a.** 3; 324, 972, 2,916; start with 4 and multiply by 3 repeatedly. **b.** 0.5; 0.25, 0.125, 0.0625; start with 4 and multiply by 0.5 repeatedly. **4a.** geometric; 243, 729, 2,187
b. neither; 34, 45, 58 **c.** geometric; -12, 12, -12
d. arithmetic; 650, 800, 950

Lesson 12-2 pp. 676–677

Check Skills You'll Need **1.** -11, -1, 9 **2.** 2, 3, 4
3. -4, 2, 8 **4.** $-5\frac{1}{2}$, -5, $-4\frac{1}{2}$

Quick Check

1a.

x	$-2x^2 = y$	(x, y)
-2	$-2(-2)^2 = -8$	$(-2, -8)$
-1	$-2(-1)^2 = -2$	$(-1, -2)$
0	$-2(0)^2 = 0$	$(0, 0)$
1	$-2(1)^2 = -2$	$(1, -2)$
2	$-2(2)^2 = -8$	$(2, -8)$

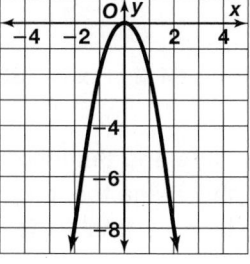

b.

x	$-x^2 + 3 = y$	(x, y)
-2	$-(-2)^2 + 3 = -1$	$(-2, -1)$
-1	$-(-1)^2 + 3 = 2$	$(-1, 2)$
0	$-0^2 + 3 = 3$	$(0, 3)$
1	$-1^2 + 3 = 2$	$(1, 2)$
2	$-2^2 + 3 = -1$	$(2, -1)$

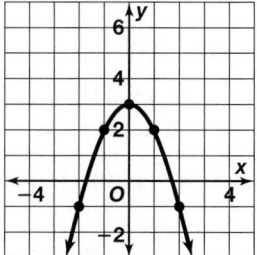

2a.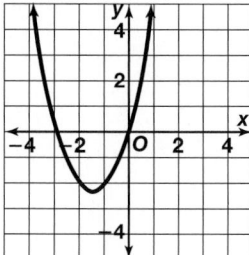

b.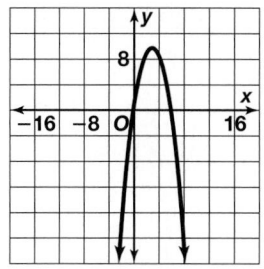

3a.

b.

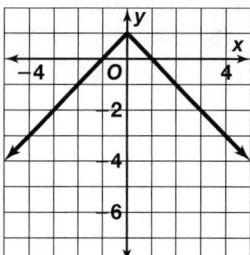

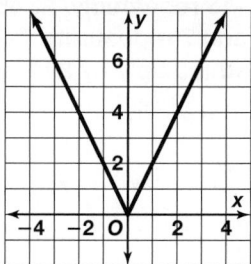

Lesson 12-3 pp. 681–682

Check Skills You'll Need **1.** 25 **2.** 64 **3.** 243 **4.** 256

Quick Check

1.

x	3^x	y	(x, y)
1	3^1	3	$(1, 3)$
2	3^2	9	$(2, 9)$
3	3^3	27	$(3, 27)$
4	3^4	81	$(4, 81)$

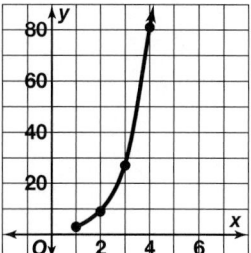

2.

x	$0.5(2)^x$	y	(x, y)
0	$0.5(2)^0$	0.5	$(0, 0.5)$
1	$0.5(2)^1$	1	$(1, 1)$
2	$0.5(2)^2$	2	$(2, 2)$
3	$0.5(2)^3$	4	$(3, 4)$
4	$0.5(2)^4$	8	$(4, 8)$
5	$0.5(2)^5$	16	$(5, 16)$

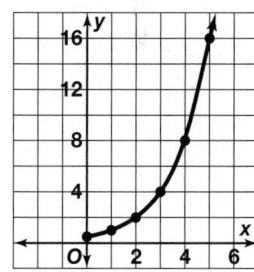

3.

x	$90(\frac{1}{3})^x$	y	(x, y)
0	$90(\frac{1}{3})^0$	90	$(0, 90)$
1	$90(\frac{1}{3})^1$	30	$(1, 30)$
2	$90(\frac{1}{3})^2$	10	$(2, 10)$
3	$90(\frac{1}{3})^3$	$3\frac{1}{3}$	$(3, 3\frac{1}{3})$
4	$90(\frac{1}{3})^4$	$1\frac{1}{9}$	$(4, 1\frac{1}{9})$
5	$90(\frac{1}{3})^5$	$\frac{10}{27}$	$(5, \frac{10}{27})$

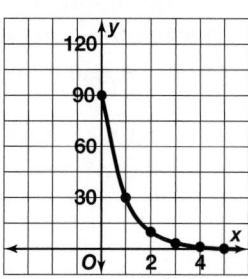

Checkpoint Quiz 1 **1.** 40, 25, 10; start with 100 and

add –15 repeatedly. **2.** 45, 52, 59; start with 17 and add 7 repeatedly. **3.** 208, 416, 832; start with 13 and multiply by 2 repeatedly. **4.** 3, 6, 12, 24, 48

5.

x	$\frac{1}{4}x^2$	y	(x, y)
-2	$\frac{1}{4} \cdot (-2)^2$	1	$(-2, 1)$
-1	$\frac{1}{4} \cdot (-1)^2$	$\frac{1}{4}$	$(-1, \frac{1}{4})$
0	$\frac{1}{4} \cdot 0^2$	0	$(0, 0)$
1	$\frac{1}{4} \cdot 1^2$	$\frac{1}{4}$	$(1, \frac{1}{4})$
2	$\frac{1}{4} \cdot 2^2$	1	$(2, 1)$

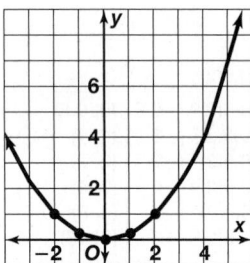

6.

x	$\frac{1}{4}|x|$	y	(x, y)
-2	$\frac{1}{4} \cdot |-2|$	$\frac{1}{2}$	$(-2, \frac{1}{2})$
-1	$\frac{1}{4} \cdot |-1|$	$\frac{1}{4}$	$(-1, \frac{1}{4})$
0	$\frac{1}{4} \cdot |2|$	0	$(0, 0)$
1	$\frac{1}{4} \cdot |1|$	$\frac{1}{4}$	$(1, \frac{1}{4})$
2	$\frac{1}{4} \cdot |2|$	$\frac{1}{2}$	$(2, \frac{1}{2})$

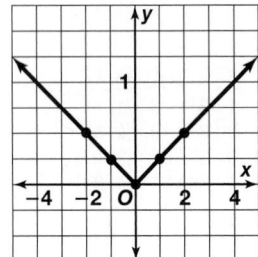

7.

x	$0.5(3)^x$	y	(x, y)
0	$0.5(3)^0$	0.5	$(0, 0.5)$
1	$0.5(3)^1$	1.5	$(1, 1.5)$
2	$0.5(3)^2$	4.5	$(2, 4.5)$
3	$0.5(3)^3$	13.5	$(3, 13.5)$
4	$0.5(3)^4$	40.5	$(4, 40.5)$

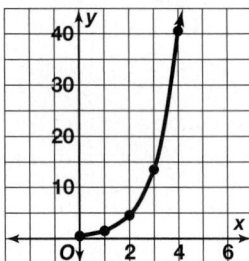

Lesson 12-4 pp. 686–687

Check Skills You'll Need 1. -40 **2.** -24 **3.** -2 **4.** 28

Quick Check 1a. No; the denominator contains a variable. **b.** Yes; it is the product of the variable m and the real number $\frac{1}{6}$. **c.** Yes, it is a real number. **d.** No, it is a sum. **2a.** monomial **b.** binomial **c.** binomial **d.** trinomial **3a.** -50 **b.** 13 **c.** 13 **4.** 264 ft

Lesson 12-5 pp. 692–693

Check Skills You'll Need 1. $2x - 7$ **2.** $5a - 4b$ **3.** $m - 12n$ **4.** $-6x + 3y - 5$

Quick Check 1a. $9d^2 + 10d$ **b.** $4x^2 + 3x + 17$ **2a.** $7x + 4y$ **b.** $9a^2 - 2a - 4$ **c.** $6g^2 - 2g - 1$ **d.** $-2t^2 + 3t + 9$ **3a.** $2a^2 - 5a$ **b.** $9z^2 + 14z - 2$ **c.** $-2w^2 + 11 + 8v$

Lesson 12-6 pp. 697–698

Check Skills You'll Need 1. $7v + 21$ **2.** $3u - 24$ **3.** $-30 + 15t$ **4.** $9p + 72$

Quick Check 1a. $3x^2 + 12x$ **b.** $-2x^2 + 3x$ **2a.** $x^3 + 2x^2 + 4x$ **b.** $4a^5 - 6a^4 + 6a^2$ **3a.** $x(2x + 1)$ **b.** $2b(b^2 + 3b - 6)$

Lesson 12-7 pp. 701–702

Check Skills You'll Need 1. $-4x - 2$ **2.** $21 + 12y$ **3.** $10a - 5b$ **4.** $12m - 8n$

Quick Check 1a. $x^2 + 5x + 6$ **b.** $y^2 + 5y + 4$ **2a.** $x^2 - 3x - 10 + 4x$ **b.** $2m^2 + 7m + 6$

Checkpoint Quiz 2 1. monomial **2.** binomial **3.** monomial **4.** trinomial **5.** -8 **6.** 8 **7.** 10 **8.** 9 **9.** $7a - 6b$ **10.** $2x^2 + 7x + 5$ **11.** $g^2 + 10g + 24$ **12.** $-18m^2 - 6m^3p - 30mp$ **13.** Answers may vary. Sample: $x + 3$; $x^2 + 6x + 9$

Lesson 12-8 pp. 706–707

Check Skills You'll Need 1. $7(-12) = -84$ **2.** $11x = 132$ **3.** $\frac{x}{45} = 3$ **4.** $x^2 = 64$

Quick Check 1. the length of the kite and the length of the tail **2.** The tail is 12 ft plus twice the length of the kite. Together, the two lengths total 21 ft. **3.** $18 = 12 + 2 \cdot 3$ **4.** $3 + 18 = 21$

Selected Answers

Chapter 1

Lesson 1-1   pp. 6–7

EXERCISES 3. Variable expression; *n* is the variable. **5.** Variable expression; *x* is the variable. **11.** 3*b* **15.** 2 − *x* **17.** 2 · 12 **21.** 4 · 3 **23.** Variable expression; *d* is the variable. **25.** Variable expression; *g* is the variable. **29.** $\frac{160}{16}$ **31.** $\frac{100}{12}$ **35.** 70*a* + 100*b* **37.** C **39.** A

Lesson 1-2   pp. 11–12

EXERCISES 15. 49 **23.** We must agree on an order of operations to ensure that everyone gets the same value for an expression. **25.** 24 **31.** 22 **33.** > **37.** > **39.** (7 + 4) · 6 = 66 **41.** (3 + 8 − 2) · 5 = 45 **43.** 4 · 9 + 5; 41 **45.** 17 − (25 ÷ 5); 12

Lesson 1-3   pp. 16–17

EXERCISES 1. 35 **5.** 1 **9.** 4 **13.** 14 **15a.** 55*m* **b.** 1,100 words **23.** 99 **29.** Answers may vary. Sample: You did not work within the grouping symbols first.

Lesson 1-4   pp. 20–22

EXERCISES 3. −45 **5.** −50 **11.** 5 **13.** −9, −2, 8 **15.** −6, 0, 6 **17.** 2, 2 **21.** 4, 4 **23.** 9 **27.** 2 **29.** Answers may vary. Sample: 28 golf strokes over par **31.** 6 **33.** 2 **37.** −13 **39.** −23 **43.** < **45.** < **47.** C **49.** *r* + *n* **51.** Answers may vary. Sample: My friend did not take into account the signs of the numbers. **53.** negative **55.** negative

Lesson 1-5   pp. 27–29

EXERCISES 1. −4 + 7; 3 **3.** −4 + (−2); −6 **7.** 3 **11.** −1 **15.** −13 **19.** 100 **23.** 23 **25.** −61 **27.** Negative; both numbers are negative. **29.** Zero; the numbers are opposites. **31.** 15 **35.** B **39.** > **41.** > **43.** −8 **45.** −20 + 18; −2 **47.** 120 + (−25); 95 **49.** 1 **53.** $158

Lesson 1-6   pp. 32–34

EXERCISES 1. −9 − (−2) = −7 **5.** 1 **13.** −6 **21.** 2 + (−6); −4 **31.** −15 **35.** 170 **39.** −68 **41.** −30 **43.** 10 **45–47.** Answers may vary. Samples are given. **45.** 3 − 3 = 0; (−4) − (−4) = 0 **47.** 1 − 7 = −6; −10 − (−4) = −6 **51.** It decreases. **53.** C **55.** −60 **59.** 66 **61.** −40

Lesson 1-7   pp. 38–39

EXERCISES 1. 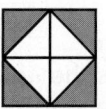 a square with four shaded corners

5. Start with 2 and add 5 repeatedly; 22, 27 **7.** Start with 1 and add 3 repeatedly; 13, 16 **11.** correct **13.** an eight-sided figure with bottom right eighth shaded

15. Start with 1 and add 0.5 repeatedly; 3.5, 4, 4.5 **17.** Start with 6 and add −2 repeatedly; −2, −4, −6 **19.** Incorrect; 8 + (−6) is 2, 2 < 8.

Lesson 1-8   pp. 42–43

EXERCISES 1. 36 laps/day **3.** $10.23 **5.** 11 pieces; 16 pieces **7a.** $59; $21 **b.** 10 people

Lesson 1-9   pp. 47–49

EXERCISES 1. 5 · (−2) = −10 **3.** 5(−5); −25 **9.** −18 **17.** −360 **23.** −7 **27.** −12 **29.** −2°C **31.** 0 **33.** Positive; the integers have the same sign. **35.** Negative; the integers have opposite signs. **37.** *A* **39.** C **43.** 4,661 **47.** −76 **53.** > **55.** = **57.** 12 **59.** −27

Lesson 1-10   pp. 54–56

EXERCISES 1. III **5.** II **9.** (−2, 4) **11.** (−8, 3) **15, 18.**

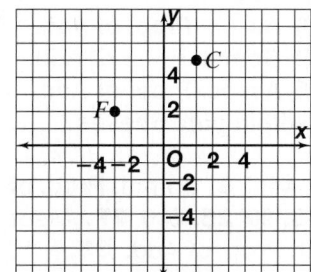

33. *P* **37.** (6, 6) **39.** (0, −4) **41.** IV **43.** II **47.** III **49.** *y*-axis

51. triangle   **53.** parallelogram

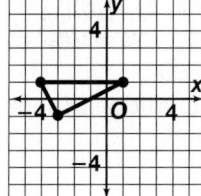 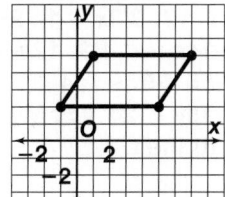

Selected Answers

55. (0, −5) **57.** about 90° W, 32° N
59. Frankfort, Kentucky **61.**

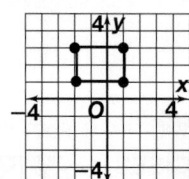

63. Answers may vary.
Sample: 62a flips the figure
across the *y*-axis. 62b flips the figure across the
x-axis. 62c flips the figure across one axis and then
the other. 62d doubles the lengths of the sides.

Chapter 1 Review   pp. 59–61

1. origin **2.** variable **3.** *y*-axis **4.** quadrants
5. integers **6.** *x*-coordinate **7.** absolute value
8. $x - 25$ **9.** $3n$ **10.** $10 - t$ **11.** $\frac{x}{4}$ **12.** $n + 5$
13. $y + 2$ **14.** 24 **15.** 12 **16.** 37 **17.** 19 **18.** 17
19. 20 **20.** 40 **21.** 450 **22.** 16 **23.** −17
24. 1,000 **25.** 9 **26.** −12 **27.** > **28.** > **29.** <
30. = **31.** −30 **32.** −7 **33.** 12 **34.** 14 **35.** −15
36. −27 **37.** −11 **38.** −1 **39.** −20 ft **40.** Start
with 0 and add 6 repeatedly; 24, 30, 36 **41.** Start
with −18 and add 9 repeatedly; 18, 27, 36
42. Start with $\frac{1}{2}$ and add $\frac{1}{2}$ repeatedly; $2\frac{1}{2}$, 3, $3\frac{1}{2}$
43. 8 weeks **44.** $112 **45.** −42 **46.** −5 **47.** 72
48. 7 **49.** −3 **50.** −165 **51.** −8 **52.** 35 **53.** 102
54. (1, −3) **55.** (−2, 1) **56.** (−3, −3) **57.** (2, 2)

Chapter 2

Lesson 2-1   pp. 71–72

EXERCISES 1. (1 + 3) + 25; 1 + (3 + 25)
3. $215; Answers may vary.
Sample: 120 + 15 + 80
= 120 + (15 + 80) Assoc. Prop. of Add.
= 120 + (80 + 15) Comm. Prop. of Add.
= (120 + 80) + 15 Assoc. Prop. of Add.
= 200 + 15 Add within parentheses.
= 215 Add.
5. Ident. Prop. of Add. **9.** Comm. Prop. of Mult.
15. 3 **19.** 7.88 **23.** 90 **25.** 800 **27.** Assoc. Prop.
of Mult. **31.** Ident. Prop. of Add. **35.** −10,000
37. $24.20

Lesson 2-2   pp. 76–77

EXERCISES 7. 784 **9.** 1,176 people **11.** −9
13. 21 **17.** 3(3x − 1); 9x − 3 **19.** 4v − 12
21. −14z − 6 **23.** 12a + 36 **27.** −7t + 28
31. −55 **35.** −104 **37.** 1,792 miles
43. −15y − 24 **45.** My friend didn't distribute
the 7 to the *t*.

Lesson 2-3   pp. 80–81

EXERCISES 1. 3, 5; none; −3 **5.** −3; none;
none **7.** 7x + 10 **9.** 4x + 2 **13.** −b **15.** 8r − 5
17. 5g + 15 **19.** −m + 4d **25.** −5a − 12
33. Answers may vary. Sample: My friend added
x + *y* to get *xy*.

Lesson 2-4   pp. 84–85

EXERCISES 5. false; 7 ≠ 8 **7.** true; 20 = 20
11. 25 = v + 15; open; variable **15.** yes **19.** no
21. 140 + d = 192; yes **23.** True; for example
3 + 2 = 7. **25.** True; by definition, an open
sentence is one that contains a variable.
29. open; variable **31.** true; 12 = 12
33. (−20)(9) = −11; false; −180 ≠ −11
35. 48 ÷ 12 = 3; false; 4 ≠ 3 **37.** yes; −9 = −9
39. no; −6 ≠ 6

Lesson 2-5   pp. 91–92

EXERCISES 5. 28 **11.** 5,200 = s + 2,520;
2,680 m/s **13.** 54 **21.** 108 = d − 42;
150 million km **23.** 86; 86; −236 **31.** 23
35. Answers may vary. Sample: This year the
Tigers won 22 games in all. **37.** 100 **39.** The
student subtracted (rather than added) 6 on the
right side.

Lesson 2-6   pp. 96–97

EXERCISES 17. 23 **19.** 36 h **23.** 105 **27.** 40
33. 300 **37.** Dividing by 0 would result in 4 = 5,
which is not a true statement. **39.** no; $\frac{-18}{-3} \neq -6$
41. −20y = 100; −5 **43.** 7k = −168; −24
49. −15,000

Lesson 2-7   pp. 100–101

EXERCISES 1. Answers may vary. Samples:
14 dimes, 2 nickels; 2 quarters, 6 dimes, 8 nickels
3. 11 years and 12 years **5.** 16 ft² **11.** 2 CDs,
3 books

Lesson 2-8   pp. 106–107

EXERCISES 1.
3. **13.** $x \leq -2$
15. $x < 0$ **17.** $t \leq 3$ **23.** $t > 7$ **27.** Use a solid dot
for ≥ and ≤; use an open dot for > and <.
29. $x \leq -10$ **31.** $x < -\frac{1}{2}$

Lesson 2-9 pp. 110–111

EXERCISES **3.** $x \geq 1$

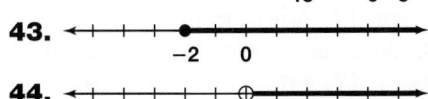

9. 64,000 lb **15.** $c > 14$ **19.** $y \leq 8$ **21.** Add 3 to each side.

23. $y > -13$

29. $b > 5$

31. $13 + n > 15$; $n > 2$ **33.** $\leq$ \$49

Lesson 2-10 pp. 115–116

EXERCISES **7.** $k \leq -8$ **11.** $f \geq -3$ **19.** $q > -18$
25. $h < 80$ **27.** unchanged **29.** reverses

31. $r \leq -21$ **37.** $x \geq 4$ **41.** $7t \leq 21$; $t \leq 3$
45. You have to divide by -4 instead of 4. The direction of each inequality sign is different when you solve each inequality.

Chapter 2 Review pp. 119–121

1. d **2.** b **3.** e **4.** a **5.** c **6.** h **7.** j **8.** f **9.** g **10.** i
11. 80 **12.** 700 **13.** 547 **14.** 6,500 **15.** 300
16. 105 **17.** 864 **18.** 496 **19.** 387 **20.** $4w + 36$
21. $24 + 48a$ **22.** $-42 + 14m$ **23.** You can
write 15 as $5 \cdot 3$. $5x + 5 \cdot 3 = 5(x + 3)$ by the
Distributive Property. **24.** $-3a + 7$ **25.** $7w + 9$
26. $9 - 3x$ **27.** $15 - 24n$ **28.** k **29.** $-17r + 31$
30. They have the same variable or no variable
and are separated by addition or subtraction
signs. **31.** $32 + 5 = 6 \cdot 6$; false **32.** $\frac{t}{17} = -3$;
open **33.** $4 \cdot 20 = 80$; true **34.** $p + 1.75 = 6.50$
35. 11 **36.** 8 **37.** -5 **38.** 27 **39.** 128 **40.** -8
41. \$6.50 **42.**

43.

44.

45.

46. $t < 0$ **47.** $h > 12$ **48.** $n > 14$ **49.** $k \geq 2$
50. $s \leq 3$ **51.** $m < -6$ **52.** $d < -14$ **53.** $c \leq 36$

Chapter 3

Lesson 3-1 pp. 132–133

EXERCISES **1.** hundredths; 27.39 **3.** ones; 1,046
5. 345.7 **7.** 215 **11.** about 40 **13.** about \$30
15. about \$13.90 **19.** about 7.10 miles **21.** about
\$27 **23.** about 80 **27.** about 400 **33.** about
22,000 mi^2 **37, 39.** Answers may vary. Samples
are given. **37.** about 30; rounding **39.** about 90.5;
front-end

Lesson 3-2 pp. 136–137

EXERCISES **1.** about 35 **5.** about 180
7. about \$18 **9.** about 2 **15.** about \$2.00 per
pound **19.** about 380 **23.** about \$6 **25.** Answers
may vary. Samples: elem. school teacher: about
\$45.50/h in Detroit, about \$32.50/h in Lincoln;
secretary: about \$18/h in Detroit, about \$12.75/h
in Lincoln; truck driver: about \$17.50 in Detroit,
about \$15.75 in Lincoln **27.** about \$5
29. reasonable; $72 \div 12 = 6$

Lesson 3-3 pp. 142–143

EXERCISES **1.** 58.9, 56, 56, 45 **5.** 1.8 h, 1.8 h, 1.5 h
7. 1 mode **9.** 1 mode **11.** 115; lowers mean by
about 1.9 **13.** Mean; there likely are no outliers.
15. Mean; there likely are no outliers. **17.** Mean,
median, or mode since they are all about equal.
19. 5.8, 6.5, 6.5, 6.7; median (or mode); the outlier
(1.2) affects the mean too much. **21.** 7.8, 8, none,
14; there is no mode and the mean and median are
nearly the same. **23.** Mode; the data are not
numerical. **25.** Median; there could easily be
outliers.

Lesson 3-4 pp. 147–148

EXERCISES **1.** $d = 481.25$ m **3.** $t = 259.3$ s
5. 67°F **7.** 60°F **9.** 55.4 mm **11.** 136.4°F
13. 161.6°F **17.** 74 cm; 288.96 cm^2

Lesson 3-5 pp. 152–153

EXERCISES **3.** 26.1 **7.** $s + 599.01 = 686.98$;
87.97 days **9.** 23.7 **15.** $x - 13.50 = 26.50$; \$40
17. 1.2, 1.2; 13.8 **19.** $r - 23.86 = 19.32$; 43.18 s
21. 7.285 **25.** -10.5 **27.** 1.2 **31.** Add -1.8 to
each side.

Lesson 3-6 pp. 156–157

EXERCISES **5.** -25.1 **11.** $2.5m = 5.30$; \$2.12
13. -1.94 **21.** 179 hits **23.** 2.3 **27.** -5.4
29. $-7.3n = 30.66$; -4.2 **31.** $\frac{n}{-2.35} = 400.9$;
-942.115

Lesson 3-7 pp. 161–163

EXERCISES **1.** C **5.** A **7.** 5 kg; the mass of a dog
is much greater than the mass of 5 paper clips.
9. 350 g; 350 mg is less than the mass of a paper
clip. **13.** 3,010 **19.** 5.18 m **23.** Centimeter; the
length is much less than a meter and much more
than a millimeter, so meters are too large and
millimeters are too small. **27.** Camille multiplied
6,392 g by 1,000, so she changed grams to
milligrams. To change grams to kilograms she
should have *divided* 6,392 by 1,000 to get 6.392 kg.

29. mm **31.** cm **33.** 150 cm; 150 m is greater than the length of a football field. **35.** 1 g; 1 mg is closer to the mass of a speck of sawdust. **43.** 301,000,000 **45.** 3.068 kg **51.** A **53a.** 33,580 mm **b.** 0.03358 km

| Extension | p. 165 |

1. 5.2 m **3.** 8.7 m **5.** Answers may vary. Sample: You ignored the units of length. **7.** 14.6 kg **9.** 7 cm **11.** 4 significant digits **13.** 5 significant digits **15.** 15.9 ft^2 **17.** 5,720 cm^2

| Lesson 3-8 | pp. 168–169 |

EXERCISES 1. 66 matches **3.** 12 ways **5.** 3.25 ft **7.** 80 sketches

| Chapter 3 Review | pp. 171–173 |

1. mean **2.** compatible numbers **3.** mode **4.** outlier **5.** median **6.** formula **7.** measures of central tendency **8.** perimeter **9–18.** Answers may vary. Samples are given. **9.** about 10; front-end **10.** about 4; rounding **11.** about 24; rounding **12.** about 10; rounding **13.** about 60; clustering **14.** about 7; rounding **15.** about 11.7; front-end **16.** about 6; rounding **17.** about 18; clustering **18.** about 6; rounding **19.** Answers may vary. Sample: You use rounding when only a rough answer is needed and the numbers are not clustered. You use front-end estimation when you need a better estimate of a sum. You use clustering when there are 3 or more numbers and there is one number that they are all close to. **20.** about 40 feet **21.** about 48 **22.** about 4 **23.** about 10 **24.** about 5 **25.** about 12 **26.** about 5 **27.** about −8 **28.** about −6 **29.** about 12 **30.** 5.4, 5, 2 and 5; no outliers **31.** 16.1, 16.2, 16.3; no outliers **32.** 36, 33, none; outlier: 57 **33.** 1.0, 0.2, 0.1; outlier: 7.9 **34–36.** Answers may vary. Samples are given. **34.** Mode; the data are not numerical. **35.** Median; there could easily be outliers. **36.** Mean; there likely are no outliers. **37.** 70 mi **38.** 384 mm^2 **39.** 37.68 in. **40.** 52 cm **41.** 7.1 **42.** 9.25 **43.** −2.01 **44.** 26.2 **45.** −9.1 **46.** 10.6 **47.** 2.5 **48.** 40.817 **49.** 11.3 **50.** 968.75 **51.** −19.4 **52.** −185.0125 **53a.** 3.2 + x = 2.64 **b.** −$.56 **54.** Meter; a kilometer is too large unless you use fractional parts of a kilometer; centimeters are too small. **55.** Kilogram; a bicycle is heavy, so grams are too small. **56.** Milliliter; a liter is about the same as a quart, so liters are too large. **57.** 85 **58.** 0.16 **59.** 230 **60.** 1,600 **61.** 620 **62.** 0.08 **63.** A mature oak tree would be a number of meters tall. Centimeters is too small a unit. **64.** 24 **65.** 24

Chapter 4

| Lesson 4-1 | pp. 182–184 |

EXERCISES 1. p + 4 **3.** 12 − m **9–11.** Choice of variable for the number may vary. **9.** 2n + 2 **11.** 9 − n **17.** c = total cost, n = number of cans, c = 0.70n **19.** ℓ = total length in feet, n = number of tents, ℓ = 60n **21–23.** Choices of variables may vary. Samples are given. **21.** w = number of workers, r = number of radios, r = 13w **23.** n = number of sales, t = total earnings, t = 0.4n **25.** 9 + k − 17 **27.** 37t − 9.85 **35–37.** Answers may vary. Samples are given. **35.** the difference of 3 and t **37.** the quotient of y and 5 **39.** Choices of variables may vary. Sample is given. n = number of days, c = change in height (m), c = 0.165n

| Lesson 4-2 | pp. 188–191 |

EXERCISES 1. 59 **3.** 7 **7.** 21 **9.** 124

13.

Original Price P	P −0.15 P	Sale Price S
$ 12	12−0.15(12)	$ 10.20
$ 16	16−0.15(16)	$ 13.60
$ 20	20−0.15(20)	$ 17.00
$ 25	25−0.15(25)	$ 21.25

15. 22 **17.** 44 **21.** 704 **23.** 185 **29.** 18 **31.** 0 **35.** 8 cm^3 **37.** 21 ft^3 **41.** 15 **43.** 111 **51.** 17 **53.** 143 **59.** $.16 **63a.** 23.89 in.^{3} **b.** 2.0 in.^{3} **c.** 47.38 in.^{2}

| Lesson 4-3 | pp. 196–199 |

EXERCISES 1. integers, rational numbers **3.** rational numbers **11.** Answers may vary. Sample: −17 **13.** Answers may vary. Sample: 0.3 **15.** whole numbers **17.** whole numbers **19.** true **21.** False; answers may vary. Sample: 6 **25.** < **27.** = **29.** $-9\frac{3}{4}$, $-9\frac{2}{3}$, $-9\frac{7}{12}$ **31.** −1.01, −1.001, −1.0009 **35.** 9 **37.** 0.5 **43.** Answers may vary. Sample: $\frac{5}{1}$ **45.** Answers may vary. Sample: $\frac{1034}{1000}$ **47.** natural numbers, whole numbers, integers, rational numbers **49.** rational numbers **51.** = **53.** < **57.** 6 **59.** a **67.** sometimes **69.** always

| Lesson 4-4 | pp. 205–208 |

EXERCISES 1. s = 4c **3.** c = 40 + 25h **5.** number of minutes; cost **7.** number of gallons of gas; distance traveled; 10 to 12 gallons; 250 to 300 miles **9.** w = 125m **11.a.** Yes; there is one range value for each domain value **b.** year, number of students

Lesson 4-5
pp. 211–213

EXERCISES 3. negative correlation
5. no correlation **17.** Answers may vary. Sample: ages of adults and the number of hours they sleep.

Lesson 4-6
pp. 219–221

EXERCISES 1. 12; 11; 10; median
3. 63; 52; none; median
5. $\frac{3.8 + 4.2 + 5.3 + x}{4} = 4.8$; 5.9
7. $\frac{100 + 121 + 105 + 113 + 108 + x}{6} = 112$; 125
9. 18 **11.** 20 **21.** −3.1, −2, −1, and −2, 15
25.a. A—5.7875, 5.75, 5.4, 1.2
    B—5.5625, 5.45, none, 2.9
b. A—mean. There are no outliers.
   B—median. The mean is thrown off by high outliers
c. Plant A has better quality control because there is a smaller range.

Chapter Review
pp. 223–225

1. median **2.** evaluate **3.** algebraic expression
4. rational **5.** absolute value **6.** rational number
7. *x*-coordinate **8.** scatter plot **9.** negative correlation **10.** power **11.** origin **12.** function
13. Let $n =$ the number; $5 + 3n$. **14.** Let $n =$ the number; $30 − n$. **15.** Let $n =$ the number; $\frac{7}{n}$.
16. Let $n =$ the number; $n(12)$. **17.** 9 **18.** 64
19. 4 **20.** 8 **21.** real numbers, rational numbers
22. real numbers, irrational numbers **23.** real numbers, rational numbers **24.** real numbers, rational numbers, natural numbers, whole numbers, integers **25.** real numbers, rational numbers, natural numbers, whole numbers, integers **26.** money spent; number of oranges bought; $0 to $8.00; 0 to 10 oranges **27.** hours worked; money earned; 0 to 18 hours; $0 to $117
28. $y = 7x$ **29.** $y = 3x + 3$ **30.** $y = 24 − 4x$

31.a.
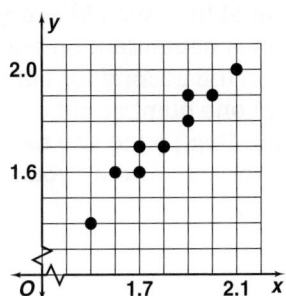
b. positive correlation

32. 85, 85, 87 **33.** 30.6, 27, 24 **34.** 2.3, 2.3, 2.3
35. 42, 42, 37 **36.** 18, 18.4, 19.9, 3.8 **37.** 6 **38.** 7

Chapter 5
Lesson 5-1
pp. 235–239

EXERCISES 1. 6 + (−3); 3 **3.** −5 + 7; 2 **5.** 15
7. −19 **25.** −47 + 12 = −35, 35 ft
27. −6 + 13 = 7, 7°F **29.** −1.7 **31.** −8.7
37. Choices of variable may vary. $c =$ change in amount of money, 74 + c **a.** $92 **b.** $45 **c.** $27
d. $1.94 **39.** $\begin{bmatrix} -18.2 \\ 11.6 \\ 19.1 \end{bmatrix}$ **41.** $\begin{bmatrix} 1.8 & 22 \\ -\frac{1}{2} & 7 \end{bmatrix}$

43. −5, −3, $-1\frac{1}{2}$, 9 **45.** 13.8 million people
47. Weaving; add the numbers in each column.
49. 0 **51.** 1 **57.** The sum of −227 and 319; the sum of −227 and 319 is positive, while the sum of 227 and −319 is negative. **59.** −0.3 **61.** −0.6
65. D **67.** The matrices are not the same size, so they can't be added.

Lesson 5-2
pp. 242–244

EXERCISES 1. −1
(number line: −2 0 2)
3. −6
(number line: −6 −4 −2 0)
9. −4 **11.** −10 **21.** 3 **23.** 6
29. −10 **31.** 1 **37.** $50.64 **39.** −1.5 **41.** 5.5
53. false; 2 − (−1) = 3, 3 ≮ 2 or −1 **57.** $[-\frac{1}{4} \ 0 \ -3]$

Lesson 5-3
pp. 249–252

EXERCISES 1. −15 **3.** 15 **13.** −12 **15.** −15
25. −64 **27.** 4 **33.** 8 **35.** 81 **41.** −4 **43.** 6 **49.** −7
51. 0 **55.** −15 **57.** $-\frac{6}{25}$ **59.** −8, $-7\frac{1}{4}$, $-3\frac{1}{2}$, 4
63. −6 **65.** $-\frac{1}{10}$ **75.** 0.1 is the multiplicative inverse of 10 because 0.1(10) = 1. (−10 is the opposite of 10.)
77. $\begin{bmatrix} -22 & 10 \\ 18 & -12 \\ 8 & -6 \end{bmatrix}$

Lesson 5-4
pp. 258–261

EXERCISES 1. 2412 **3.** 5489 **9.** $3.96 **11.** $29.55
15. $7t − 28$ **17.** $3m + 12$ **27.** $−x − 3$ **29.** $−3 − x$
35. $−3t$ **37.** $7x$ **43.** $3(m − 7)$ **45.** $2(b + 9)$
47. 44,982 **49.** 14.021 **53.** −28; −18; −3; 4
55. −18; −6; 0; 5 **57.** $6\frac{7}{100}$ $\left(8 + \frac{4}{3}p\right)$ **59.** $\frac{17}{z - 34}$
65. $4.78d$ **67.** $−6.1t^2 + 13.7t$ **75.** terms: −7t, 6v, 7, −19y, coefficients: −7, 6, −19, constant: 7
77. 10 pennies, 7 nickels, 4 quarters, 1 dime

Lesson 5-5 pp. 264–266

EXERCISES 1. Ident. Prop. of Add.; 0, the identity for addition, is added. **3.** Ident. Prop. of Mult.; 1, the identity for multiplication, is multiplied. **11.** 7400 **13.** 4200 **17a.** def. of subtr. **b.** Dist. Prop. **c.** addition

19. $25 \cdot 1.7 \cdot 4$

$= 25 \cdot 4 \cdot 1.7$	Comm. Prop. of Mult.
$= (25 \cdot 4) \cdot 1.7$	Assoc. Prop. of Mult.
$= 100 \cdot 1.7$	mult.
$= 170$	mult.

21. $8 + 9m + 7$

$= 9m + 8 + 7$	Comm. Prop. of Add.
$= 9m + (8 + 7)$	Assoc. Prop. of Add.
$= 9m + 15$	add.

25. $2 + g\left(\frac{1}{g}\right) = 2 + 1$ Inv. Prop. of Mult.
        $= 3$ add.

27. $(3^2 - 2^3)(8759) = (9 - 8)(8759)$ mult.
        $= [9 + (-8)](8759)$ def. of subtr.
        $= 1(8759)$ add.
        $= 8759$ Ident. Prop. of Mult.

33. no **35.** yes **41.** No; $(5 - 3) - 1 = 2 - 1 = 1$, while $5 - (3 - 1) = 5 - 2 = 3$. **43.** No; $16 \div (4 \div 2) = 16 \div 2 = 8$, while $(16 \div 4) \div 2 = 4 \div 2 = 2$.

Lesson 5-6 pp. 272–275

EXERCISES 1. $\frac{1}{2}$ **3.** $\frac{1}{6}$ **11.** $\frac{5}{6}$ **13.** 1 **15.** 2 : 4 or 1 : 2 **17.** 5 : 1 **21.** 24% **23.** 15% **29.** $\frac{1}{6}$ **31.** $\frac{1}{3}$ **33.** $\frac{1}{2}$ **35.** $\frac{1}{450}$ **43.** C **45.a.** 14% **b.** 15% **47.** $\frac{3}{16}$ **49.** $\frac{7}{16}$ **51.** 1 : 3 **53.** 4 : 4 or 1 : 1

Lesson 5-7 pp. 280–282

EXERCISES 1. $\frac{1}{36}$ **3.** $\frac{1}{18}$ **9.** $\frac{4}{81}$ **11.** $\frac{1}{9}$ **15.** $\frac{2}{11}$ **17.** $\frac{1}{55}$ **21.** $\frac{2}{7}$ **23.** $\frac{1}{6}$ **25.** $\frac{1}{9}$ **31.** Indep.; the data set hasn't changed. **33.a.** 0.58 **b.** 0.003248 **35.** D **43.a.** 8% **b.** 4 customers

Chapter Review pp. 285–287

1. term **2.** matrix **3.** reciprocal **4.** Distributive Property **5.** Commutative **6.** an outcome **7.** complement of an event **8.** independent **9.** sample space **10.** additive inverse **11.** −17 **12.** −5 **13.** 9.9 **14.** 24.9 **15.** −12 **16.** 0 **17.** 10 **18.** −40 **19.** $-\frac{5}{9}$ **20.** 2 **21.** $-\frac{5}{4}$ **22.** $\frac{15}{8}$ **23.** $4m + 3$ **24.** $b + 10$ **25.** $-5w + 20$ **26.** $36 - 27j$ **27.** $-3 + 30y$ **28.** $-2r + 1$ **29.** $35b + 5$ **30.** $7 - 25v$ **31.** $9t - \frac{6}{5}$ **32.** $-18 + 9m$ **33.** $-4 + x$ **34.** $10g + 1.5$ **35.** Assoc. Prop. of Add. **36.** Indent. Prop. of Add. **37.** Comm. Prop. of Mult. **38.** Dist. Prop.

39. $19 + 56\left(\frac{1}{56}\right)$
    $= 19 + 1$ Inv. Prop. of Mult.
    $= 20$ add.

40. $-12p + 45 - 7p$

$= -12p + 45 + (-7p)$	def. of subtr.
$= -12p + (-7p) + 45$	Comm. Prop. of Add.
$= [-12 + (-7)]p$	Dist. Prop.
$= -19p + 45$ add.	

41. $2(7 - v) - 3v$

$= (14 - 2v) - 3v$	Dist. Prop.
$= 14 + (-2v) + -(3v)$	def. of. subtr.
$= 14 + (-2v + -3v)$	Assoc. Prop. of Add.
$= 14 + [(-2) + (-3)]v$	Dist. Prop.
$= 14 + (-5v)$	add.
$= 14 - 5v$	def. of subtr.

42. $24\,abc - 24\,bac$

$= 24\,abc - 24\,abc$	Comm. Prop of Mult.
$= 24\,abc + (-24\,abc)$	def. of subtr.
$= 0$	Inv. Prop. of Add.

43. $4 \cdot 13 \cdot 25 \cdot 1$

$= 4 \cdot 13 \cdot (25 \cdot 1)$	Assoc. Prop. of Mult.
$= 4 \cdot 13 \cdot 25$	Ident. Prop. of Mult.
$= 4 \cdot 25 \cdot 13$	Comm. Prop. of Mult.
$= (4 \cdot 25) \cdot 13$	Assoc. Prop. of Mult.
$= 100 \cdot 13$	Mult.
$= 1300$	Mult.

44. $4[m - 2(2m + 3)]$

$= 4(m - 4m - 6)$	Dist. Prop.
$= 4[m + (-4m) + (-6)]$	def. of subtr.
$= 4[1m + (-4m + (-6)]$	Ident. Prop. of Mult.
$= 4[m(1 + (-4)) - 6]$	Dist. Prop. of Mult.
$= 4[(-3m) - 6]$	add
$= -12m - 24$	Dist. Prop.

45. 0 **46.** $\frac{5}{6}$ **47.** $\frac{1}{3}$ **48.** $\frac{1}{6}$ **49.** $\frac{5}{6}$ **50.** $\frac{1}{2}$ **51.** 1 : 7 **52.** 1 : 1 **53.** 3 : 5 **54.** 3 : 1 **55.** 1 : 3 **56.** 1 : 1 **57a.** $\frac{1}{4}$ **b.** Sample: P(not 3 heads) means the probability of getting 0, 1, 2, or 4 heads. **58.** $\frac{11}{14}$ **59.** dependent; $\frac{2}{45}$ **60.** independent; $\frac{1}{20}$ **61.** Dep.; $\frac{5}{18}$ **62.** Indep.; $\frac{1}{4}$ **63.** Dep.; $\frac{1}{18}$ **64.** Answers may vary. Sample: In probability, two events are dependent if the outcome of one influences the outcome of the other. In everyday language, if one person is dependent on another, the first person relies on the second for support. **65.** Indep.; the result of one number cube does not affect the other. **66.** Dep.; once you select one sock, there are fewer socks when you make the second selection.

Chapter 6

Lesson 6-1 pp. 298–300

EXERCISES 1. −10 **3.** −1 **21.** $2n + 4028 = 51,514$; 23,743 books **23.** $c = 39.95 + 0.35m$; 85

878 Selected Answers

min **25.** Add. Prop. of Eq., Simplify., Mult. Prop. of Eq., Simplify. **27.** Subtr. Prop. of Eq., Simplify., Div. Prop. of Eq., Simplify. **29.** 75 **31.** 1

41. $7 - 3k - 7 = -14 - 7$ Subtr. Prop. of Eq.
$\qquad -3k = -21$ Simplify.
$\qquad \dfrac{-3k}{-3} = \dfrac{-21}{-3}$ Div. Prop. of Eq.
$\qquad k = 7$ Simplify.

43. $\dfrac{-y}{2} + 14 - 14 = -1 - 14$ Subtr. Prop. of Eq.
$\qquad \dfrac{-y}{2} = -15$ Simplify.
$\qquad \dfrac{-y}{2}(-2) = -15(-2)$ Mult. Prop. of Eq.
$\qquad y = 30$ Simplify.

45. $P = 0.8c - 500$; $4437.50 **47.** 43 **49.** 2
55. 15.5 **57.** 31.5 **59.** The neg. sign was dropped in the term $-3y$; -1. **63.** 100°; 98.6°; 20°; 32°; −40°

Lesson 6-2   pp. 305–308

EXERCISES 1. 9 **3.** $5\frac{4}{7}$ **11.** $x + 9 + x = 25$; 8 ft by 9 ft **13.** 8 **21.** 11 **23.** 46 **31.** 21 **33.** 3.5 **39.** 2 **41.** 5 **55.** $4\frac{2}{3}$ **57.** 92 mi

Lesson 6-3   pp. 312–315

EXERCISES 1. 3 **11.** $16.95 + 0.05m = 22.95 + 0.02m$ 200 min **13.** 4.25
17a. Answers may vary. Sample:
    0:   $9 = 9$
    3:   $-9 = -9$
    −4: $33 = 33$
    −6: $45 = 45$ **b.** identity
19. no solution **21.** identity **25.** 0 **27.** 10
33. $1200 + 9b = 25b$; 75 bags **35.** $a = 3, b = 6, c = 5, d = \frac{1}{3}$ **37.** The student subtracted y from both sides instead of adding y to both sides; 5.3.

Lesson 6-4   pp. 321–324

EXERCISES 1. $9.50/h **3.** 131 cars/week **9.** A
11. B **13.** 480 **15.** 10,800 **17.** 11.25 **19.** 25.2
25. 105.6 km **27.** $8\frac{11}{12}$ **29.** $-3\frac{1}{2}$ **33.** 18.75
35. 18.25 **39.** 15 mi/h **41.** 1 mi/h **45.** $5.\overline{3}$
49. about 646 students **57.** 48 V

Lesson 6-5   pp. 328–331

EXERCISES 1. $\overline{AB} \cong \overline{PQ}, \overline{BC} \cong \overline{QR}, \overline{CA} \cong \overline{RP}$;
$\angle A \cong \angle P, \angle B \cong \angle Q, \angle C \cong \angle R$ **3.** 3.125 ft
5. 80 in. **11.** 10.8 in. **13.** 145.25 mi
15. 350 mi **19.** $2\frac{2}{3}$ in. by 4 in. **27.** 3 ft **33.** C

Lesson 6-6   pp. 338–341

EXERCISES 1a. Let w = width **b.** $\ell = w + 3$
c. $2w + 2(w + 3) = 30$; 6 **d.** 9 in. **3.** 9 cm; 18 cm
5. 304, 305, 306 **7.** −148, −150
11a. x; $2\frac{1}{4} - x$ **b.** $22x = 72 - 3x$, $1\frac{1}{3}$ h **15.** −31, −29, −27 **17.** 12:30 P.M. **21.** 175 mi/h; 375 mi/h
23. 1993, 1994, 1995 **27.** 6 6-*V*; 4 12-*V*

Lesson 6-7   pp. 347–349

EXERCISES 1. 50%; increase **3.** 25%; increase
13. 39% **15.** 0.5 ft **17.** 0.005 g **19.** 19.25 cm², 29.25 cm² **21.** 46.75 in.², 61.75 in.² **25.** 25%
27. 12.5% **29a.** 48 cm³ **b.** 74.375 cm³
c. 28.125 cm³ **d.** 26.375 cm³ **e.** 55%
31. 22%; decrease **33.** 175%; increase **39.** 2%
41. 1 mm **45.** 24.5 cm², 25.5 cm² **47.** 54.1 in.², 54.3 in.² **51.** 11%

Lesson 6-8   pp. 354–356

EXERCISES 1. 13 **3.** $\frac{1}{3}$ **13.** irrational
15. irrational **17.** 5 and 6 **19.** −12 and −11
21. 3.46 **23.** 107.47 **25.** 0.93 **27.** 0 **29.** $\pm\frac{3}{7}$
41. $-\frac{2}{5}$ **43.** 1.26

Lesson 6-9   pp. 360–363

EXERCISES 1. 10 **3.** 17 **17.** no
19. yes **23.** no **25.** yes **27.** $\frac{4}{15}$ **29.** 1.25
33. C **35.** 559.9 **37.** 9.7 **41.** 12.8 ft **45.** A figure is a square; the figure is a rectangle; if a figure is a rectangle then the figure is a square; false.
47. An angle is a right angle; its measure is 90°; if the measure of an angle is 90°, then it is a right angle; true. **49.** 6 in.

Chapter Review   pp. 367–369

1. inverse operations **2.** Solutions of equivalent equations **3.** rate **4.** cross products **5.** greatest possible error **6.** 4 **7.** 3 **8.** 5 **9.** 3 **10.** 2

11. 11 **12.** Let p = number of people; $6p + 3 = 27$; 4 people
13. $\qquad 314 = -n + 576$
$314 - 576 = -n + 576 - 576$ Subtr. Prop. of Eq.
$\qquad -262 = -n$ Simplify.
$-1(-262) = -1(-n)$ Mult. Prop. of Eq.
$\qquad 262 = n$ Simplify.

14. $-\frac{1}{4}w - 1 = 6$

$-\frac{1}{4}w - 1 + 1 = 6 + 1$	Add. Prop. of Eq.
$-\frac{1}{4}w = 7$	Simplify.
$-4(-\frac{1}{4}w) = -4(7)$	Mult. Prop. of Eq.
$w = -28$	Simplify.

15. $3h - 4 = 5$

$3h - 4 + 4 = 5 + 4$	Add. Prop. of Eq.
$3h = 9$	Simplify.
$\frac{3h}{3} = \frac{9}{3}$	Div. Prop. of Eq.
$h = 3$	Simplify.

16. -18 **17.** 4 **18.** $-\frac{1}{2}$

19. $\frac{3}{2}$ **20.** 2 **21.** 0 **22.** no solution **23.** identity
24. 20 **25.** 10 **26.** $2x + 2(x - 6) = 72$; width =
15 cm, length = 21 cm **27.** 150 mi/h **28.** 3.4 mi/h
29. 0.2 mi/h **30.** 2 **31.** 2.3 **32.** -6 **33.** 20
34. 6 **35.** 5 **36.** 7.5 **37.** 19.5 **38.** 36 ft
39. $4r = 7.6$; 1.9 h or 1 h 54 min **40.** $n + (n + 1) +$
$(n + 2) = 582$; 193, 194, 195 **41.** $10t + 18(t - 2) =$
209; 6.75 h or 6 h 45 min **42.** 13%; increase
43. 25%; decrease **44.** 33.3%; decrease
45. 5.4% **46.** irr.; 9.27 **47.** rat.; -11
48. irr.; ±0.71 **49.** irr.; 1.60 **50.** rat.; $-\frac{2}{5}$ **51.** 5.8
52. 17.8 **53.** 14.8 **54.** 9.8 **55.** yes **56.** yes

Chapter 7

Lesson 7-1   pp. 378–381

EXERCISES 1. yes **3.** yes **5.** no **9a.** no **b.** no **c.**
yes **11a.** no **b.** no **c.** no **15.** C **17.** D
19. (number line: $-1\ 0\ 1\ 2\ 3$, open dot at 1) **21.** (number line: $-7\ -6\ -5\ -4\ -3\ -2$, closed dot at -3)
27–35. Choice of variable may vary. **27.** $x > -3$
29. $x \geq 1$ **33.** Let s = number of students. $s \leq 48$
35. Let w = safe number of watts. $w \leq 60$
39. b is greater than 0. **41.** z is greater than or
equal to -5.6.
53. (number line: $-1\ 0\ 1\ 2\ 3$, open dot at 2) **55.** (number line: $-2\ -1\ 0\ 1\ 2$, closed dot at 1)
57. (number line: $-2\ -1\ 0\ 1\ 2$, closed dot at -1) **59.** (number line: $0\ 1\ 2\ 3\ 4\ 5$, closed dot at 3)
65. Since $1231 < 1513$, Option A $<$ Option B.
67. Put an open dot at 3 and color the rest of the
number line.

Lesson 7-2   pp. 384–387

EXERCISES 1. 5 **3.** 4.3 **5.** $t < 1$ (number line: $-2\ -1\ 0\ 1\ 2$, open dot at 1)
7. $d \geq 10$ (number line: $8\ 9\ 10\ 11\ 12\ 13$, closed dot at 10)

21. $\frac{5}{3}$ **23.** $w \leq 5$; (number line: $3\ 4\ 5\ 6\ 7\ 8$, closed dot at 5)
25. $b > -7$; (number line: $-8\ -6\ -4\ -2\ 0\ 2$, open dot at -7)
39. $s + 637 \qquad \leq 2000$, \$1363 **41.**
$r + 17 + 12 \geq 50$, 21 reflectors **43.** Subtract 9
from each side.
45. $w \geq 11$ **47.** $y < 3.1$ **63.** nearly 51.2 MB
67. $x \geq 1$ **69.** $t \leq -3$

Lesson 7-3   pp. 391–393

EXERCISES 1. $t \geq -4$; (number line: $-6\ -4\ -2\ 0\ 2$, closed dot at -4)
3. $w \leq -2$; (number line: $-3\ -2\ -1\ 0\ 1$, closed dot at -2)
17. $t < -3$; (number line: $-5\ -4\ -3\ -2\ -1\ 0\ 1$, open dot at -3)
19. $w \leq -5$; (number line: $-8\ -6\ -4\ -2\ 0\ 2$, closed dot at -5)
29. $4.5c \geq 300$, 67 cars **31–33.** Answers may
vary. Samples are given. **31.** $-2, -3, -4, -5$
33. $-3, -4, -5, -6$ **39.** Multiply each side by -4
and reverse the inequality symbol. **41.** Divide
each side by 5. **45.** -2 **47.** 4 **51.** x and y are
equal. **53–55.** Estimates may vary. **53.** $j > -6$
55. $s \geq 28$ **59.** $d \leq -7$ **61.** $s < -\frac{1}{4}$ **75.** Yes; in
each case, y is greater than 6.

Lesson 7-4   pp. 398–401

EXERCISES 1. $d \leq 4$ **3.** $x > -2\frac{1}{2}$
11. $27 \geq 2s + 8$ and $s \leq 9.5$, so the two equal
sides must be no longer than 9.5 cm. **13.** $j \geq 1$
15. $h > 5$ **23.** $t \leq -1$ **25.** $n \geq 2$ **31.** $v \geq -4$
33. $r \geq -1\frac{4}{5}$ **37.** Subtract 8 from each side.
39. Add 5 and subtract y from each side. **43.** for
x = the number of guests, $(0.75)200 + 1.25x \geq$
250, $x \geq 80$, so at least 80, guests must attend.
45. B **47.** F **53.** $m \geq 2$ **55.** $n \geq -2\frac{5}{8}$
73. Distribute 4 to 2 as well as n, so $n > -7$.

Lesson 7-5   pp. 405–408

EXERCISES 1. $-4 < x$ and $x < 6$ or $-4 < x < 6$;
(number line: $-6\ -4\ -2\ 0\ 2\ 4\ 6\ 8$, open dots at -4 and 6)
3. $23 < c < 23.5$; (number line: $22\ 23\ 24$, open dots at 23 and 23.5)
5. $-5 < j < 5$; (number line: $-10\ -5\ 0\ 5\ 10$, open dots at -5 and 5)
7. $2 < n \leq 6$; (number line: $-2\ 0\ 2\ 4\ 6\ 8$, open dot at 2, closed dot at 6)
17. $n \leq -3$ or $n \geq 5$; (number line: $-4\ -2\ 0\ 2\ 4\ 6$, closed dots at -3 and 5)

19. $h < 1$ or $h > 3$; [number line: 0 1 2 3 4 5]

21. $b < -2$ or $b > 2$; [number line: −3 −2 −1 0 1 2 3]

23. $c < 2$ or $c \geq 3$; [number line: −1 0 1 2 3 4]

29. $-2 < x < 3$ **31.** $x \leq 0$ or $x > 2$ **33.** $q \leq -2\frac{2}{3}$ or $q > 4$ **35.** $4 \leq t \leq 14$ **39.** D **43.** $6 < x < 30$
45. $11 < x < 21$ **47.** $15 \leq D \leq 30$

Extension — p. 409

1. $A \cup B = \{2, 5, 7, 8, 9\}$, $A \cap B = \{5\}$

3. $C \cup D = \{2, 4, 6, 7, 8\}$, $C \cap D = \{2,8\}$

5. $B \cup D = \{2, 4, 5, 6, 7, 8, 9\}$, $B \cap D = \{\ \}$ or $\emptyset$

7a. $P \cap Q = \{x | x,$ is a multiple of $12\}$,

b. Yes; since $40 \in Q$, $40 \in P \cup Q$

Lesson 7-6 — pp. 413–416

EXERCISES 1. $-2, 2$ **3.** $-\frac{1}{2}, \frac{1}{2}$ **13.** $3, 13$ **15.** $-3, 1$
23. $k < -2.5$ or $k > 2.5$; [number line: −4 −3 −2 −1 0 1 2 3 4]

25. $-8 < x < 2$; [box with y]

35. between 12.18 mm and 12.30 mm, inclusive
37. $-9, 9$ **39.** $-1\frac{1}{2}, 1\frac{1}{2}$ **53.** $|n| > 7.5$
55. $|n + 1| \geq 3$ **57.** 39%, 45% **63.** $|x - 2| = 4$
65. $|x - 12\frac{1}{2}| = 3\frac{1}{2}$

Extension — p. 417

1. Symmetric Prop. of Equality **7.** Add. Prop. of Ineq., Add. Prop. of Ineq., Transitive Prop. of Ineq.

Chapter Review — pp. 419–421

1. C **2.** B **3.** A **4.** C **5.** D **6.** [number line: −1 0 1 2 3 4]

7. [number line: −6 −5 −4 −3 −2 −1 0 1]
8. [number line: 5 6 7 8 9 10 11 12]
9. [number line: −2 −1 0 1 2 3 4]
10. $n < -2$ **11.** $n \geq -3.5$ **12.** $n > -6$ **13.** $n \geq 2$
14. Let p = number of people, $p \geq 600$.
15. Let n = number of people, $n \leq 15$. **16.** Let t = temperature in degrees Fahrenheit, $t < 32$.
17. $h > -1$; [number line: −3 −2 −1 0 1 2]

18. $t < -5$; [number line: −8 −7 −6 −5 −4 −3]
19. $m \geq -3$; [number line: −4 −3 −2 −1 0 1]
20. $w \geq -2$; [number line: −4 −3 −2 −1 0 1]
21. $q > -2.5$; [number line: −4 −3 −2 −1 0 1]
22. $y > -14$; [number line: −15 −10 −5 0 5]
23. $n \leq 15$; [number line: −5 0 5 10 15 20]
24. $d \geq 4$; [number line: −2 0 2 4 6]
25. $-2 \leq t$; [number line: −6 −4 −2 0 2 4 6]
26. $0 < c$; [number line: −2 −1 0 1 2]
27. $2.5 \geq u$; [number line: −1 0 1 2 3 4]
28. $-9 < p$; [number line: −10 −8 −6 −4 −2 0 2]
29. $3.50 + 2.75 + x \leq 12.00,$
$x \leq 5.75$
30. $7.25h \geq 200$, $h \geq 27.586$
You must work at least 28 h.
31. $n > -2$ **32.** $k \leq -\frac{1}{2}$ **33.** $b < 40$ **34.** $c \leq -2$
35. $m < -6$ **36.** $t > 3$ **37.** $x \geq 2$ **38.** $y \leq -56$
39. $x < \frac{8}{3}$ **40.** $190 + 0.04x \geq 500$, $x \geq 7750$
41. [number line: −4 −2 0 2 4] **42.** [number line: −4 −3 −2 −1 0 1 2 3]
43. [number line: −4 −2 0 2 4 6]
44. $-2 \leq z < 4$, [number line: −4 −2 0 2 4 6]
45. $-\frac{5}{2} \leq d < 4$, [number line: −3 −2 −1 0 1 2 3 4 5]
46. $-\frac{3}{2} \leq b < 0$, [number line: −4 −3 −2 −1 0 1]
47. $t \leq -2$ or $t \geq 7$, [number line: −2 0 2 4 6 8]
48. $2 \leq a < 5$, [number line: 1 2 3 4 5 6]
49. $2 \leq a < 4$, [number line: 1 2 3 4 5 6] **50.** $75 \leq t \leq 89$
51. $|n + 2| > 3$
52. $|n - 12| \leq 5$ **53.** 5 or −5
54. $n \leq -6$ or $n \geq 2$ **55.** $-3 \leq x \leq 3$
56. $-9.6 < m < 9.6$ **57.** $x < 3$ or $x > 4$
58. 6.5 or −12.5 **59.** 8 **60.** all real numbers
61. no solution **62.** $k < -7$ or $k > -3$
63. −5 or 1 **64.** $z \leq -0.25$ or $z \geq 0.25$
65. $2.74 \leq d \leq 2.86$ **66.** $19.6 \leq \ell \leq 20.4$

Chapter 8

EXERCISES 1. Labels may vary. Sample is given.

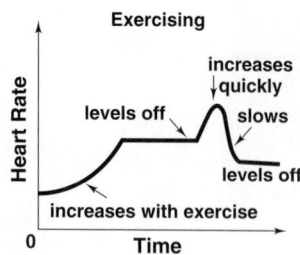

5.

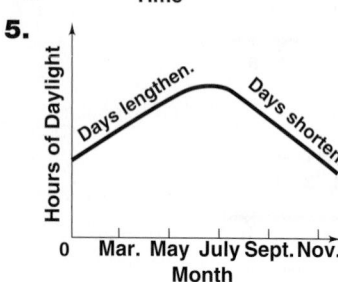

9. C; the temperature increases steadily and then alternates cooling and warming as the oven turns off and on during a cooking cycle.

11a. Bottom to Top   **b.** Top to Bottom

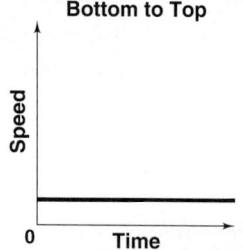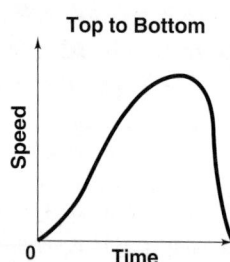

No; the graphs are different because you have a constant speed traveling up but not down.

15a.

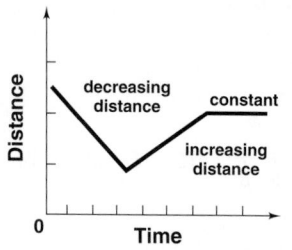

b. section showing the distance decreasing
c. first 2 sections

EXERCISES 1. no **3.** yes **5.** yes **7.** no

9.

x	x + 7	f(x)
1	1 + 7	8
2	2 + 7	9
3	3 + 7	10
4	4 + 7	11

11.

x	x^2	f(x)
1	1^2	1
2	2^2	4
3	3^2	9
4	4^2	16

17. {0.5, 53} **19.** {−27, −7, −2, 8, 48}

21. no **23.** yes; {−4, −1, 0, 3}; {−4}
27. {−3, 3, 15.8} **29.** {−0.5, 0, 2.7}
33. no **35.** yes **37.** yes **39.** no

EXERCISES
1–3. Tables may vary. Samples are given.

1.

x	f(x)
−1	3
0	0
1	−3

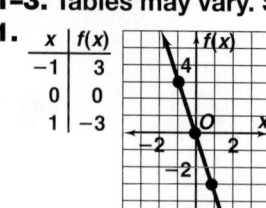

3.

x	f(x)
−2	4
−1	1
0	−2
1	−5

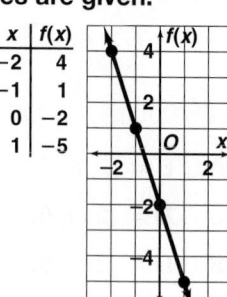

11a.

ℓ	P(ℓ)
1	5
2	10
3	15
4	20

11b.

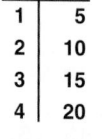

13a. continuous **13b.**

n	A(n)
1	2
2	4
3	6
4	8

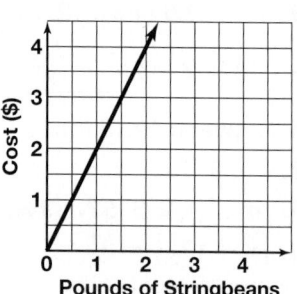

15. **17.**

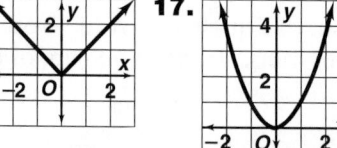

27. **29.**

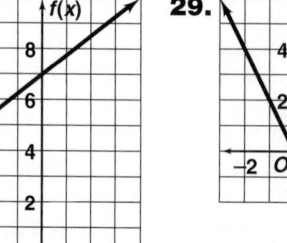

37a.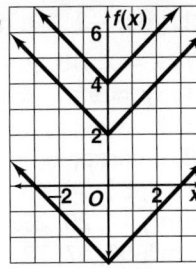

39a.

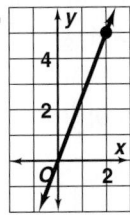

Lesson 8-4   pp. 448–451

EXERCISES 1. B **3.** C **11.** $d(n) = 45n$
13. $e(n) = 6.37n$ **17a.** $f(x) = 0.19x$ **b.** $1.52
19. $f(x) = 1000x$ **21a.** $C(a) = 10a + 1$ **b.** $31
c. 61; the total cost of 12 books
27–29. Tables may vary. Samples are given.

27.

x	y
−1	3
0	2
1	1
2	0
3	−1

$y = -x + 2$

29.

x	f(x)
−2	−1
0	0
2	1

$y = x + 3$

Lesson 8-5   pp. 456–459

EXERCISES 1. no **3.** yes; −2 **11.** $y = \frac{1}{5}x$
13. $y = \frac{9}{5}x$ **23.** Choices of variables may vary.
$E(h) = 7.10h$ **25.** no **27a.** $\frac{20}{50}$ or 0.4 **b.** $f = 0.4w$,
52 lb **29.** $y = \frac{1}{6}x$ **31.** $y = -\frac{36}{25}x$ **33.** $y = 9x$
41.

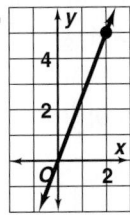

$y = \frac{5}{2}x$

45a. $\frac{1}{32}$ **b.** $b = \frac{1}{32}w$

Lesson 8-6   pp. 464–466

EXERCISES 1. $xy = 18$ **3.** $xy = 56$ **11.** 15 **13.** 7
23. 13.3 mi/h **25.** inverse variation; $xy = 60$
27. Direct variation; the ratio $\frac{\text{cost}}{\text{pound}}$ is constant at
$1.79. **29.** Inverse variation; the product of the
length and width remains constant with an area
of 24 square units. **31.** 1.1; $rt = 1.1$ **33.** 1; $ab = 1$
37. Inverse variation; the product of the rate and
the time is always 150. **39.** 121 ft **41.** direct
variation; $y = 0.4x$; 8 **43.** inverse variation;
$xy = 48$; 0.5 **47.** A

Lesson 8-7   pp. 470–473

EXERCISES 1. "Add 2 to the previous term"; 12,
14. **3.** "Add 2 to the first term, 3 to the second
term and continue, adding 1 more each time"; 18,
24. **13.** 3 **15.** −11 **23.** −3, 15, 39 **25.** 17, 44, 80
35. $3\frac{1}{4}$, $3\frac{1}{2}$ **37.** $\frac{4}{27}$, $\frac{4}{81}$ **47.** $4500, $4350, $4200,
$4050, $3900; the balance after 4 payments
49. No; there is no common difference. **51.** No;
there is no common difference. **57.** 4.5, −4.5,
−22.5 **59.** 1, $2\frac{3}{5}$, $5\frac{4}{5}$ **63.** value of new term =
value of previous term + 6 **65.** value of new
term = value of previous term − 2.5

Chapter Review   pp. 475–477

1. C **2.** D **3.** A **4.** E **5.** B **6.** G **7.** F
8. Answers may vary. Sample: A computer rental
costs $2.50/h. If you start with a fixed amount of
money, the longer you work on the computer, the
less money you will have left.
9. Answers may vary. Sample: A residential
thermostat senses when the temperature in the
room falls below the set level. The heater is turned
on until the temperature is 3°F above the set level.
The heater is then turned off. The graph shows the
air temperature rising while the heater is working,
and falling after the heater is turned off.
10. Answers may vary. Sample: An elevator is on
the second floor. Someone gets in, goes to the
11th floor, and gets off.
11–14. Answers may vary. Samples are given.
11.

Height of a Sunflower
Over a Summer

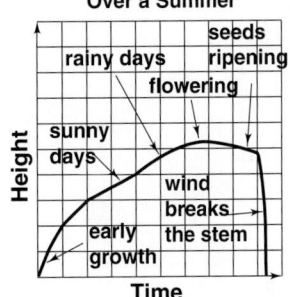

12.

Number of People in
a Restaurant

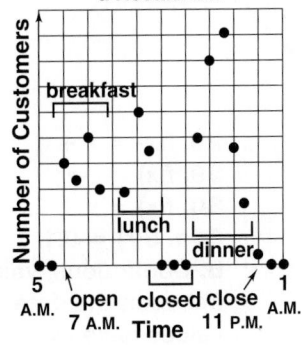

13.

Number of Vehicles that Enter the School Parking Lot

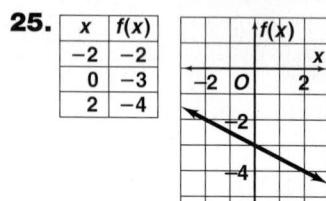

14.

Bags of Peanuts Sold During a Baseball Game

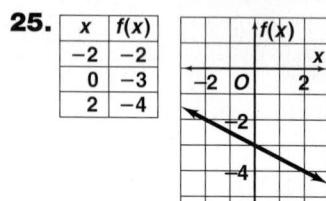

15. {−23, −7, −3, 13} **16.** {1, 3, 3.5, 5.5}
17. {1, 2, 17, 26} **18.** {−10, 2, 5, 17} **19.** no
20. yes **21.** yes **22.** no **23.** A relation is a function when each value of the domain corresponds to exactly one value of the range.
24–27. Tables may vary. Samples are given.

24.

x	f(x)
−1	−2
0	−3
1	−2

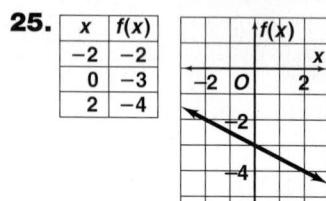

25.

x	f(x)
−2	−2
0	−3
2	−4

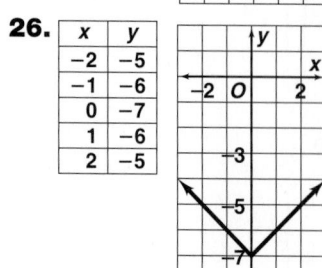

26.

x	y
−2	−5
−1	−6
0	−7
1	−6
2	−5

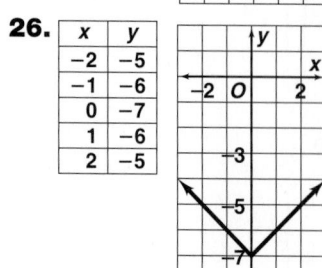

27.

x	y
−2	−3
−1	−1
0	1
1	3

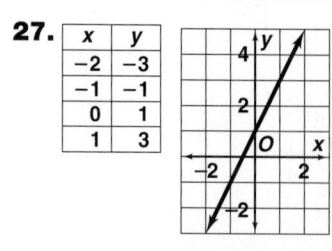

28. $f(x) = x + 1$
29. $f(x) = -x$
30. $f(x) = x + 3.5$
31a. $S(r) = 0.1r$
b. Continuous; values between the data values have meaning for inches of snow.

32. yes; −3 **33.** no **34.** no **35.** yes; $\frac{2}{5}$ **36.** $y = \frac{1}{5}x$
37. $y = x$ **38.** $y = 2x$ **39.** $y = -3x$ **40.** $xy = 6$
41. $xy = 9$ **42.** $xy = 4.4$ **43.** 4 **44.** 2.5 **45.** 18.75
46. inverse; $xy = 70$ **47.** direct; $y = 8.2x$
48. inverse; $xy = 3$ **49.** "Add −9 to the previous term"; 63, 54, 45. **50.** "Add 3 to the previous term"; 17, 20, 23. **51.** "Add 11 to the previous term"; 56, 67, 78. **52.** 3, 13, 17 **53.** 10, 25, 31
54. 4.5, 12, 15 **55.** −2, −17, −23
56. yes; 42, 49, 56 **57.** no

Chapter 9

Lesson 9-1　　　　　　　　　　　　pp. 488–491

EXERCISES 1. 3; the temperature increases 3°F each hour. **3.** $-\frac{1}{15}$ gal/mi; the amount of fuel consumed each month is $\frac{1}{15}$ gal. **7.** $\frac{1}{2}$ **9.** $\frac{2}{3}$ **11.** 2
13. $-\frac{3}{2}$ **23.** undefined **25.** undefined
27. $\frac{9}{10}$ in./month **29.** 30 mi/h **31.** $\frac{1}{6}$ **33.** −20
37.

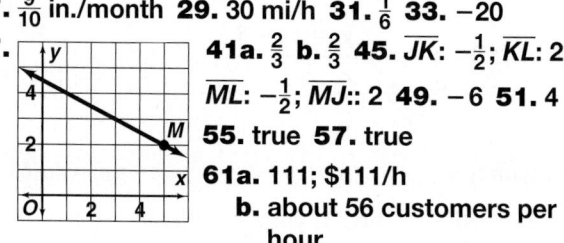

41a. $\frac{2}{3}$ **b.** $\frac{2}{3}$ **45.** $\overline{JK}$: $-\frac{1}{2}$; $\overline{KL}$: 2; $\overline{ML}$: $-\frac{1}{2}$; $\overline{MJ}$: 2 **49.** −6 **51.** 4
55. true **57.** true
61a. 111; $111/h
b. about 56 customers per hour

Lesson 9-2　　　　　　　　　　　　pp. 496–499

EXERCISES 1. −2; 1 **3.** 1; $-\frac{5}{4}$ **11.** $y = 3x + \frac{2}{9}$
13. $y = 1$ **23.** $y = \frac{3}{4}x + 2$ **25.** $y = \frac{1}{2}x + \frac{1}{2}$

29.

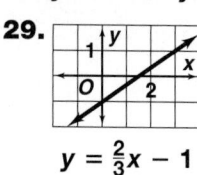

$y = \frac{2}{3}x - 1$

31.

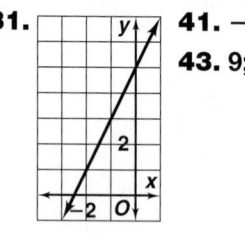

$y = 2x + 5$

41. −3; 2
43. 9; $\frac{1}{2}$

51.

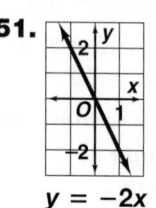

$y = -2x$

53.

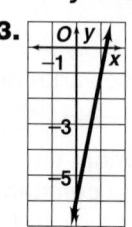

$y = 5x - 6$

59. no **61.** no
67. $y = -4x + 7$
69. $y = -\frac{1}{4}x + 5$

884　Selected Answers

Lesson 9-3   pp. 501–504

1. $y = 1.2x$

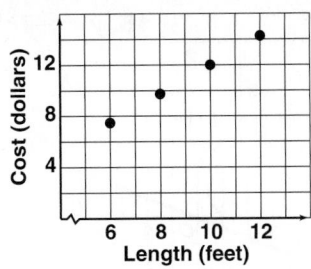

3. $y = 25 - 3w$

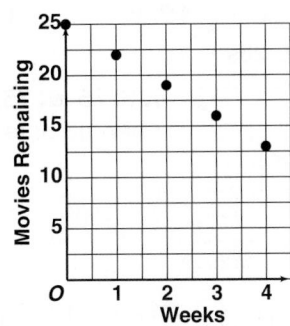

5a. Yes; the candle burns continuously.
b. h = height of candle in inches and t = time in hours the candle has burned; $h = 8 - 2t$
c. The graph of the line would be steeper but the y-intercept would be the same. **9a.** yes; both time and distance are continuous. **b.** The line will be less steep because the kayakers are going more slowly. Since the kayakers are heading back to camp, the slope is negative. **11.** C

Lesson 9-4   pp. 509–511

EXERCISES 1. 18; 9 **3.** −6; 30 **11.** C

13. 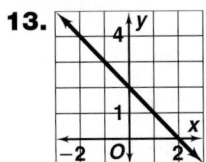   **15.**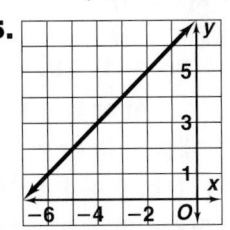

19. horizontal **21.** horizontal

23. 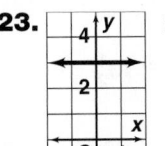   **25.** 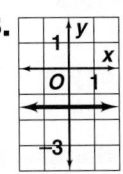   **27.** $-3x + y = 1$
29. $x - 2y = 6$

37a. Answers may vary. Sample: x = time walking; y = time running **b.** $3x + 8y = 15$

39. 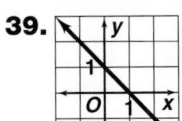   **41.**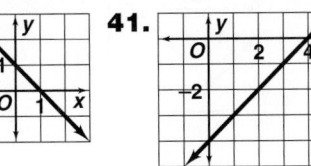

47a. $3x + 7y = 28$
49. $y = \frac{4}{5}x + 10$

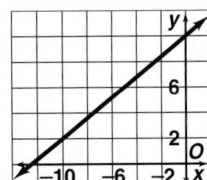

51. $y = -\frac{4}{5}x - 3$
57. $-3x$ instead of $3x$
59. $y = -2$ **61.** $x = -2$

Lesson 9-5   pp. 515–517

EXERCISES 1. 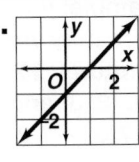   **3.**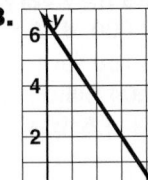

11. $y - 2 = -\frac{5}{3}(x - 4)$ **13.** $y + 7 = -\frac{3}{2}(x + 2)$
19–21. Answers may vary for the point indicated by the equation. **19.** $y = 1(x + 1); y = x + 1$
21. $y + 2 = -\frac{6}{5}(x - 4); y = -\frac{6}{5}x + \frac{14}{5}$ **31.** Yes; answers may vary. Sample: $y - 9 = -2(x + 4)$
33. no **37–39.** Answers may vary for point indicated by the equation. **37.** $y + 3 = \frac{2}{5}(x - 1)$ **39.** $y - 4 = \frac{3}{2}(x - 1); -3x + 2y = 5$
55. $y = -2.6x + 315.6$ **57.** y-intercept changes

Lesson 9-6   pp. 522–525

EXERCISES 1. $\frac{1}{2}$ **3.** 1 **7.** no, different slopes
9. yes, same slopes and different y-intercepts
13. $y = 6x$ **15.** $y = -2x - 1$ **19.** $-\frac{1}{2}$ **21.** $-\frac{5}{7}$
25. $y = -\frac{1}{2}x$ **27.** $y = 3x - 10$ **31.** $y = \frac{5}{4}x + 1$
33. parallel **35.** neither **41.** $y = -\frac{4}{5}x - \frac{19}{5}$;
$y = -\frac{4}{5}x + \frac{3}{5}$ **43.** $y = -\frac{1}{2}x; y = 2x$ **47.** about $\frac{5}{4}$
49. Answers may vary. Sample: $\frac{5}{4} \cdot \left(-\frac{1}{2}\right) \neq -1$
53. No; the slopes are not neg. reciprocals.
55. False; the product of two positive numbers can't be −1. **59.** The slope of $\overleftrightarrow{JK}$ is $\frac{1}{5}$. The slope of $\overleftrightarrow{KL}$ is −2. The slope of $\overleftrightarrow{LM}$ is $\frac{1}{6}$. The slope of $\overleftrightarrow{JM}$ is −4. The quadrilateral is not a parallelogram.

Lesson 9-7   pp. 528–532

EXERCISES 1–3. Trend lines may vary. Samples are given. **1.** $y - 52.5 = 2(x - 91)$
3. $y - 16.4 = 0.64 (x - 69.9)$
7. $y = -1.06x + 92.31; -0.970$
9. $y = -1.63x + 556.76; -0.725$

13a.

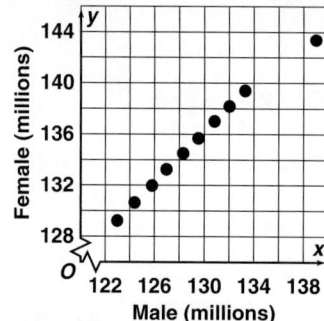

b. Answers may vary. Sample: $y = 0.939x + 13.8$
c. 154,650,000 **d.** Answers may vary. Sample: No, the year is too far in the future. **17.** $y = 0.37x - 28.66$; $12.04 billion **19a.** (2, 3) and (6, 6); $y = 0.75x + 1.5$ **b.** $y = 0.75x + 1.21$

Lesson 9-8   pp. 537–539

EXERCISES 1. Answers may vary. Sample: same shape, shifted 3 units up **3.** Answers may vary. Sample: same shape, shifted 7 units down

5. 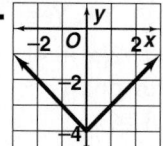   **7.**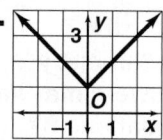

11. $y = |x| - 6$ **13.** $y = |x| + \frac{5}{2}$

17. 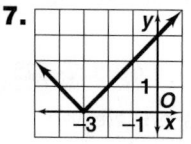 **19.**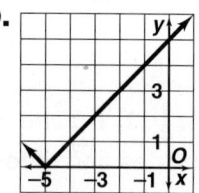

23. $y = |x - 9|$ **25.** $y = |x + \frac{3}{2}|$

29. 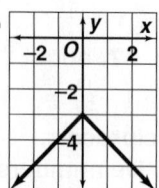   **33.** $y = -|x + 2.25|$
35. $y = -|x - 4|$

37. 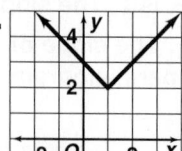   **39.**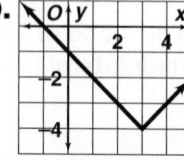

Chapter Review   pp. 541–543

1. perpendicular lines **2.** parallel lines
3. translation **4.** slope **5.** y-intercept **6.** 8 oz/mo
7. 3.375 in./wk **8.** 5; the speed is 5 mi/h. **9.** −1.25; gasoline decreases 1.25 gal for each hour of driving time. **10.** 0; the height is at a constant

level of 150 ft. **11.** $\frac{1}{4}$ **12.** undefined **13.** 1

14. $y = -3$ 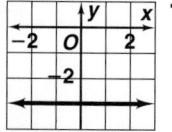 **15.** $y = -7x + \frac{1}{2}$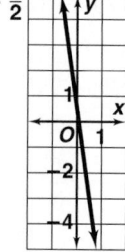

16. $y = \frac{2}{5}x$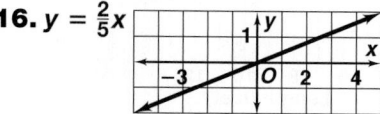

17. $y = -\frac{1}{2}x - \frac{1}{2}$ **18.** $y = \frac{1}{4}x - 3$
19a. $p = 0.25s + 75$

b. 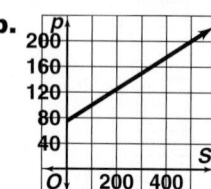   **c.** $275 **d.** 75; weekly salary when no sales are made

20. 2; 5 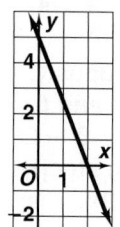   **21.** 8; −13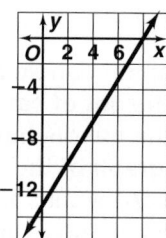

22. −1; −$\frac{1}{3}$ 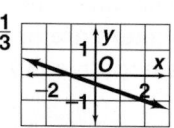   **23.** $3x - 5y = -35$
24. $x + 3y = -6$

25. $4x - 3y = 15$
26. $y + 2 = 2(x - 1)$
27. $y + 2 = \frac{3}{4}(x - 1)$
28. $y + 2 = -3(x - 1)$ **29.** $y + 2 = 0$
30. $y - 3 = \frac{1}{3}(x - 4)$ or $y - 1 = \frac{1}{3}(x + 2)$
31. $y + 4 = -\frac{6}{5}(x - 5)$ or $y - 2 = -\frac{6}{5}x$
32. $y = \frac{1}{2}(x + 1)$ or $y + 1 = \frac{1}{2}(x + 3)$
33. $y + 1 = 5(x - 2)$ or $y = 5x - 11$
34. $y - 5 = \frac{1}{3}(x - 3)$ or $y = \frac{1}{3}x + 4$
35. $y + 5 = 9x$ or $y = 9x - 5$
36. $y - 10 = -\frac{1}{8}(x - 4)$ or $y = -\frac{1}{8}x + 10\frac{1}{2}$
37. $l = 3.5w$
38a. Answers may vary. Sample: $y = 1.28x - 60.2$
b. For sample in (a): 80.6 lb/person

39. 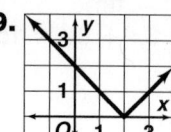   **40.**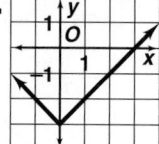

Chapter 10

EXERCISES 1. Yes, (−1, 5) makes both equations true. **3.** Yes, (−1, 5) makes both equations true.

5. (0, 2); 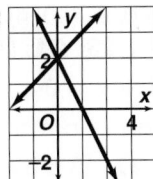   **13a.** 3 weeks **b.** $35

15. no solution;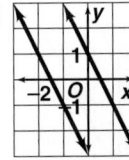

19. no solution; same slope, different y-int.
21. one solution; different slopes **23.** A

25. (20, 60); 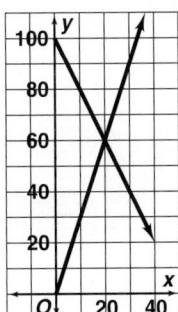   **35.** (−2, 10)
     37. (−0.9, 1.6)

EXERCISES 1. D **3.** B **5–13.** Coordinates given in alphabetical order. **5.** (9, 28) **7.** $\left(6\frac{1}{3}, -\frac{1}{3}\right)$

11. (2, 0) **13.** (6, −2) **17.** 4 cm by 13 cm
19. (15, 15) **21.** (−4, 4) **23.** 15 video rentals
25. D **27.** estimate: (2,3); (−2, 3) **29.** estimate:
(−3.5, −3.5); $\left(-\frac{10}{3}, -\frac{11}{3}\right)$ **35.** $\left(-\frac{1}{2}, -\frac{1}{2}\right)$ **37.** $\left(2, -\frac{1}{2}\right)$

EXERCISES 1. (1, 3) **3.** (5, −17) **7a.** $x + y = 20$, $x − y = 4$ **b.** 12 and 8 **9.** (−5, 1) **11.** $\left(-2, -\frac{5}{2}\right)$
15a. $30w + \ell = 17.65$, $20w + 3\ell = 25.65$
b. $.39 for a wallet size, $5.95 for an 8 × 10
17. (−1, −3) **19.** (2, −2) **23–25.** Choice of method may vary. Samples are given. **23.** (−1, −2); substitution; both solved for y **25.** (10, 2); substitution; one eq. solved for x **33.** (10, −6)
35. (−15, −1) **39.** 9

EXERCISES 1a. $4a + 5b = 6.71$
b. $5a + 3b = 7.12$ **c.** pen: $1.19, pencil: $.39

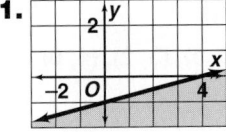

3a*a*	b	24
0.04a	0.08b	0.05(24)

b. $a + b = 24$; $0.04a + 0.08b = 1.2$ **c.** 18 kg A, 6 kg B **5.** 600 games **7a.** $s + c = 2.75$
b. $s − c = 1.5$ **c.** 2.125 mi/h **d.** 0.625 mi/h
9–11. Answers may vary. Samples are given.
9. Substitution; one eq. is solved for t.
11. Elimination; subtract to eliminate m.
15a. $t = 99 − 3.5m$; $t = 0 + 2.5m$; $t = 41.25°C$, $m = 16.5$ min **b.** After 16.5 min, the temp. of either piece will be 41.25°C. **19a.** 42 mi/h
b. 12mi/h

EXERCISES 1. no **3.** yes **7.** A **9.** B

11.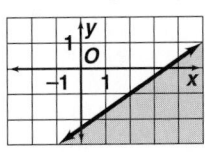

19. $y \le \frac{2}{3}x − \frac{7}{3}$;   **21.** $y \le \frac{2}{3}x − \frac{8}{3}$;

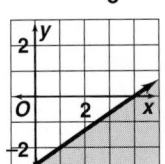

23a. $3x + 5y \le 48$
b. 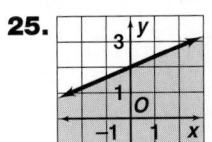   **c.** Answers may vary. Sample: 8 blue and 4 gold, 2 blue and 8 gold, 12 blue and 2 gold **d.** No; you cannot buy −2 rolls of paper.

25. 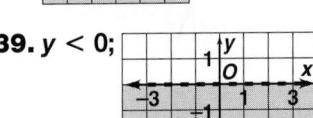   **35.** $x \le −3$

39. $y < 0$;   **43.** $y < x + 2$

Selected Answers

Lesson 10-6 pp. 590–594

EXERCISES 1. no **3.** no **5.**
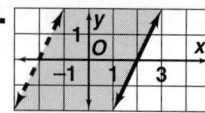

17. $y \geq -\frac{1}{2}x - 2$ and $y \leq \frac{1}{2}x + 2$

19. $y \leq -\frac{2}{3}x - 4$ and $y \geq \frac{1}{5}x - 3$

21.
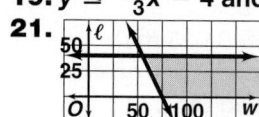

23. $x + y \geq 50, 4x + 3y \leq 180$

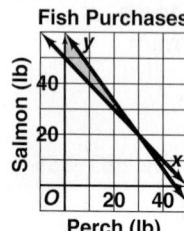
Fish Purchases
Salmon (lb)
Perch (lb)

25. $x \leq 3, x \geq -3, y \leq 3, y \geq -3$
27. $y \geq \frac{2}{3}x - 2, y < \frac{2}{3}x + 2$
31a. triangle **b.** $(2, 2), (-4, -1), (-4, 2)$ **c.** 9 units^2

35a. $x \geq 1, 10.99x + 4.99y \leq 45$

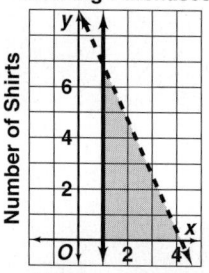
Clothing Purchases
Number of Shirts
Number of Pants

b. $(3, 0), (3, 1), (3, 2), (4, 0)$

Chapter Review pp. 597–599

1. elimination **2.** solution of the system of linear equations **3.** system of linear inequalities
4. solution of the inequality **5.** substitution
6. A **7.** No; $(2, 5)$ only satisfies one equation.
8. Infinitely many; the equations are equivalent.
9. Answers may vary. Sample: systems with noninteger solutions

10.
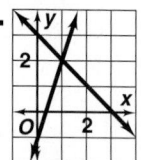
$(1, 2)$ **11.**
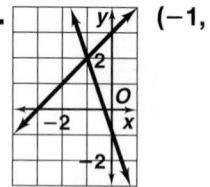
$(-1, 2)$

12.
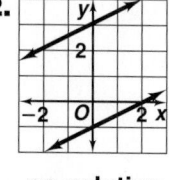
13.
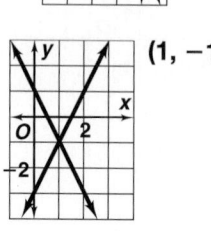
$(1, -1)$

no solution

14. $(-2, 5)$ **15.** $\left(-4\frac{1}{2}, -6\right)$ **16.** $\left(-1\frac{1}{9}, -\frac{5}{9}\right)$ **17.** $(2, 2)$
18. Answers may vary. Sample: There is no solution when you get a false equation such as $0 = 2$. There are infinitely many solutions when you get a true equation such as $5 = 5$.
19a. $x + y = 24, 4x + 5y = 100$ **b.** $(20, 4)$
c. 20 4-point, 4 5-point **20.** $(-6, 23)$ **21.** $(1, -1)$
22. $(6, 4)$ **23.** $\left(5\frac{5}{11}, 1\frac{7}{11}\right)$ **24.** $x + y = 34,$
$2x + 4y = 110$; 13 chickens and 21 cows
25. $10\frac{2}{3}$ fl oz **26.** 63° and 27° **27.** 18 ft by 39 ft
28. \$1.29 **29.** 154 km/h

30.
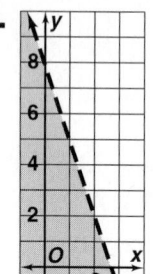
31.
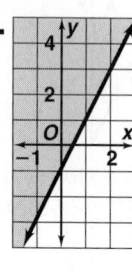

32.
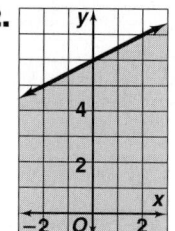
33.
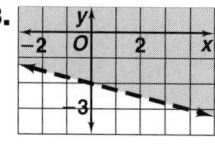
34. $x \geq 4$

35. $y \leq 3x + 3$ **36.** $2x + 3y \geq -6$

37.
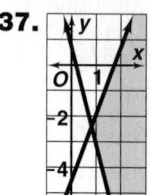
38.
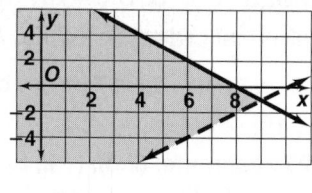

39.
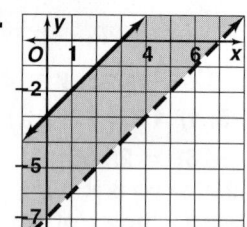
40.
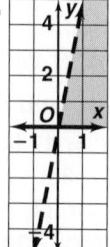

41. $y \leq 3, y > x$ **42.** $y > -2x + 2, y > \frac{4}{5}x - 4$
43. $x > -1, y \leq x + 5$ **44.** $y \leq -\frac{3}{2}x + 3,$
$y \geq -\frac{1}{2}x - 1$

Chapter 11

Lesson 11-1 p. 609–611

EXERCISES 1. -1 **3.** $\frac{1}{25}$ **13.** -2 **15.** 0; -3
17. $3a$ **19.** x^7 **33.** $\frac{1}{25}$ **35.** $-\frac{1}{9}$ **45a.** \$20.48; \$.32

b. No; the value of the allowance rapidly
becomes very great. **47.** pos. **51.** 10^{-1} **53.** 10^{-3}
57. 0.000001 **59.** 0.03 **61a.** $5^{-2}, 5^{-1}, 5^0, 5^1, 5^2$
b. 5^4 **c.** $\frac{a^n}{1}$ **63.** 45 **65.** 40 **69.** $\frac{2}{9}$ **71.** $\frac{1}{16}$

73.

a	4	$\frac{1}{3}$	6	$\frac{7}{8}$	2
a^{-1}	$\frac{1}{4}$	3	$\frac{1}{6}$	$\frac{8}{7}$	0.5

75. A, B, D

77. No; $3x^{-2} \cdot 3x^2 = 9 \cdot x^0 = 9$. The product of
reciprocals should be 1. **79a.** 1 correct, 0.4096; 2
correct, 0.1536; 3 correct, 0.0256; 4 correct,
0.0016 **b.** 0 or 1

Lesson 11-2 pp. 614–616

EXERCISES 1. No; $55 > 10$. **3.** No; $0.9 < 1$.
7. 9.04×10^9 **9.** 9.3×10^6 **15.** 500 **17.** 2040
27. C,A,B, **29.** 2.4×10^{15} **31.** 3.18×10^{-3}
35. 7×10^1 **37.** 4.6×10^{-2}

Lesson 11-3 pp. 619–622

EXERCISES 1. 2^{10} **3.** 1 **7.** c^5 **9.** $\frac{10}{t^7}$
23. 6×10^9 **25.** 3.4×10^{-5} **29.** 1.08×10^{21}
dollars **31.** 9 **33.** -3 **41.** $4x^4$ **43.** $4c^4$ **45.** $12a^7$
47. $3^4 \cdot 2^2$ **49.** 8.0×10^5 **51.** 1.2×10^{-4}
59. 7.65×10^{14} **61.** 7.039305×10^{-7} **63.** about
6.7×10^{33} molecules **65.** x^3 **67.** $5c^3$

Lesson 11-4 pp. 625–628

EXERCISES 1. c^{10} **7.** $\frac{1}{t^{14}}$ **9.** $625y^4$ **11.** $49a^2$
23. 1.6×10^{11} **25.** 8×10^{-30} **31.** $8.57375 \times$
$10^{-10}\,\text{m}^3$ **33.** -4 **35.** -3 **41.** The student who
wrote $x^5 + x^5 = 2x^5$ is correct; x^5 times x^5 is x^{10}.
43. $243x^3$ **45.** $30x^2$ **51a.** $24x^2; 96x^2$ **b.** 4 times
c. $8x^3; 64x^3$ **d.** 8 times **53.** $(ab)^5$ **55.** $\left(\frac{2x}{y}\right)^2$

59a. about $5.15 \times 10^{14}\,\text{m}^2$ **b.** about $3.60 \times 10^{14}\,\text{m}^2$
c. about $1.37 \times 10^{18}\,\text{m}^3$

Lesson 11-5 pp. 632–635

EXERCISES 1. 7 **3.** -3 **5.** $\frac{1}{4}$ **7.** $\frac{1}{c^3}$ **13.** 5×10^7
15. 6×10^2 **19a.** 3.86×10^{11} h; 2.65×10^8 people
b. about 1457 h **c.** about 4.0 h **21.** $\frac{9}{25}$ **23.** $\frac{32x^5}{y^5}$
37. 5^3 simplifies to 125. **39.** Each term should be
raised to the 4th power and simplified. **43.** $\frac{1}{16m^{12}}$

45. a^6 **53.** $\frac{a^5c^5}{b^3}$ **55.** 5 **63a.** The student treated
$\frac{5^4}{5}$ as $\left(\frac{5}{5}\right)^4$. **b.** 125 **65.** $\left(\frac{m}{n}\right)^7$ **67.** 10^{10} **75.** dividing
powers with the same base, def. of neg. exponent
77. mult. powers with the same base

Lesson 11-6 pp. 639–641

EXERCISES 1. 4 **3.** 0.1 **7.** 40, 80, 160 **9.** 20.25,
30. 375, 45.5625 **13.** geometric **15.** geometric
19. 5; 135; 10,935 **21.** 5; -135; $-10,935$
25. $A(n) = 6 \cdot 0.5^{n-1}$; 0.375 **27.** $A(n) = 7 \cdot (1.1)^{n-1}$;
9.317 **29a.** $A(n) = 100 \cdot (0.64)^{n-1}$
b. about 10.74 cm **31.** 1, 0.2, 0.04;
$A(n) = 625 \cdot (0.2)^{n-1}$ **33.** 1, -0.5, 0.25;
$A(n) = 16 \cdot (-0.5)^{n-1}$ **37.** arithmetic; 3, 1, -1
39. geometric; 1.125, 0.5625, 0.28125
41a. $A(n) = 36 \cdot (0.9)^{n-1}$ **b.** 6; $n = 1$ corresponds
to the first swing, because $A(1) = 36$. **c.** 21.3 cm

Lesson 11-7 pp. 646–649

EXERCISES 1. 216 **3.** 2.5 **9.** \$160,000; \$320,000
11. \$16,000, \$32,000 **13.** C **15.** B **17.** C

19. 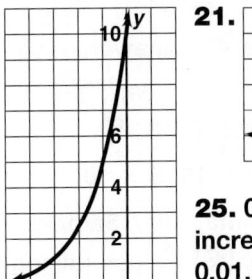 **21.**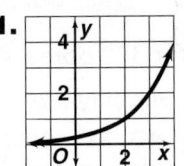

25. 0.04, 0.2, 1, 5, 25, 125;
increase **27.** 100, 10, 1, 0.1,
0.01, 0.001; decrease

37a.

x	y
1	-2
2	4
3	-8
4	16
5	-32

39. $f(t) = 200 \cdot t^2$
41. $f(x) = 100x^2$

Lesson 11-8 pp. 655–658

EXERCISES 1. 20; 2 **3.** 10,000; 1.01 **7.** 1.05
9. 1.0875 **11.** 0.75%, 0.25% **13.** 1.125%; 0.375%
17. \$16,661.35 **19.** \$28,338.18 **21a.** 3 half-lives
b. 3.125 mCi **23.** 0.1 **25.** 0.9 **27.** exp. decay
29. exp. decay **31.** $y = 130,000 \cdot (1.01)^x$; about
142,179 people **33.** $y = 2400 \cdot (1.07)^x$; \$4721.16
35a. $y = 584 \cdot (1.065)^x$; \$3862.79 **37.** Neither; it is
not just one straight line. **39.** Neither; it
decreases and and then increases, unlike an
exponential function. **41.** exponential function

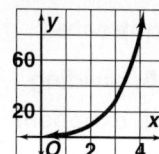

45. 4 half-lives
47a. $y = 6,284,000 \cdot (1.01)^x$
b. 7,667,674 people **49.** 88%
51. 46.1%

Chapter Review pp. 661–663

1. exponential growth **2.** growth factor
3. Scientific notation **4.** exponential decay
5. decay factor **6.** Compound interest
7. common ratio **8.** interest period **9.** geometric
sequence **10.** exponential function **11.** $\frac{d^6}{b^4}$ **12.** $\frac{y^8}{x^2}$
13. $\frac{7h^3}{k^8}$ **14.** $\frac{q^4}{p^2}$ **15.** $\frac{625}{16}$ or $39\frac{1}{16}$ **16.** $-\frac{1}{8}$ **17.** $-\frac{1}{8}$
18. $\frac{1}{49y^4}$ **19.** $\frac{9x^2}{w^4y^7}$ **20.** 36 **21.** $\frac{4}{9}$ **22.** $\frac{9}{8}$ or $1\frac{1}{8}$ **23.** 1
24. 108 **25.** C **26.** No; for values other than 0,
$(-3b)^4 = 81b^4 \neq -12b^4$. **27.** No; $950 > 10$.
28. No; $72.35 > 10$. **29.** yes **30.** No; $0.84 < 1$.
31. 2.793×10^6 mi **32.** 1.89×10^8 cars and
trucks **33.** $2d^5$ **34.** $q^{12}r^4$ **35.** $-20c^4m^2$ **36.** 1.34^2
or 1.7956 **37.** $\frac{243x^2y^{14}}{64}$ **38.** $-\frac{4}{3r^{10}z^8}$
39. about 7.8×10^3 pores **40.** Answers may
vary. Sample: Simplify $(2a^{-2})^{-2}(-3a)^2$; $\frac{9a^6}{4}$.
41. $\frac{1}{w^3}$ **42.** $\frac{1}{64}$ **43.** $7x^2$ **44.** $\frac{n^{35}}{v^{21}}$ **45.** $\frac{c^3}{e^{11}}$
46. 2×10^{-3} **47.** 2.5×10^1 **48.** 5×10^{-5}
49. 3×10^3 **50.** Answers may vary. Sample:
Simplify and use div. prop.: $\left(\frac{a^2}{2}\right)^{-3}$; use raising a
quot. to a power prop.: $\frac{a^{-6}}{2^{-3}}$; use the def. of neg.
exp.: $\frac{2^3}{a^6}$ or $\frac{8}{a^6}$ **51.** 0.1 **52.** 3 **53.** $-\frac{1}{2}$
54. geometric; $\frac{25}{4}, \frac{25}{16}, \frac{25}{64}$ **55.** neither; $-30, -25,$
-19 **56.** arithmetic; 42, 49, 56 **57.** 6, 12, 24, 48
58. 7.5, 5.625, 4.21875 **59a.** 2430 bacteria
b. about 180 min **60.** $a = 100$, $b = 1.025$
61. $a = 32$, $b = 0.75$ **62.** $a = 0.4$, $b = 2$
63. growth; 3 **64.** growth; 1.5 **65.** decay; 0.32
66. decay; $\frac{1}{4}$

67. 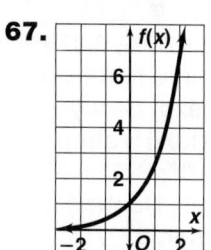 **68.**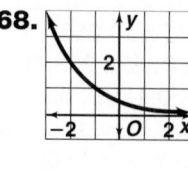

69. 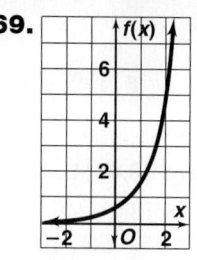 **70.**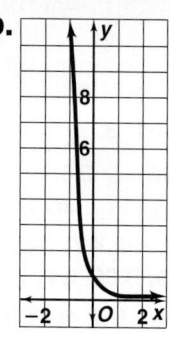

71. about 8.2 mg

Chapter 12

Lesson 12-1 pp. 673–674

EXERCISES 1. -1 **3.** -6 **7.** 20, 25, 30; start with
0 and add 5 repeatedly. **9.** 1, 4, 7; Start with -11
and add 3 repeatedly. **11.** 2; 48, 96, 192; start with
3 and multiply by 2 repeatedly. **13.** 2; 720, 1440,
2880; start with 45 and multiply by 2 repeatedly. **17.** geometric; 81, 243, 729 **21.** geometric;
$-81, 243, -729$ **23.** B **25.** geometric; 5
31. $-5, -7, -9$; start with 3 and add
-2 repeatedly **33.** 144, 288, 576; start with 9
and multiply by 2 repeatedly **37.** neither; 3, 30, 4
39. arithmetic; 7.12, 7.15, 7.18

Lesson 12-2 pp. 678–679

EXERCISES

1.

x	$4(x)^2$	y	(x, y)
-2	$4(-2)^2$	16	$(-2, 16)$
-1	$4(-1)^2$	4	$(-1, 4)$
0	$4(0)^2$	0	$(0, 0)$
1	$4(1)^2$	4	$(1, 4)$
2	$4(2)^2$	16	$(2, 16)$

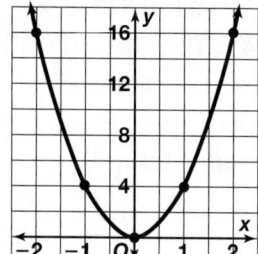

7.

x	$x^2 + 4$	y	(x, y)
-2	$(-2)^2 + 4$	8	$(-2, 8)$
-1	$(-1)^2 + 4$	5	$(-1, 5)$
0	$0^2 + 4$	4	$(0, 4)$
1	$1^2 + 4$	5	$(1, 5)$
2	$2^2 + 4$	8	$(2, 8)$

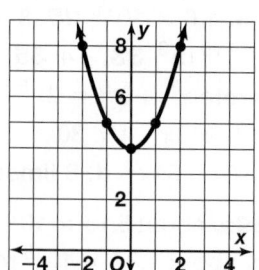

15.

x	$\lvert x \rvert + 3$	y	(x, y)
-2	$\lvert -2 \rvert + 3$	5	$(-2, 5)$
-1	$\lvert -1 \rvert + 3$	4	$(-1, 4)$
0	$\lvert 0 \rvert + 3$	3	$(0, 3)$
1	$\lvert 1 \rvert + 3$	4	$(1, 4)$
2	$\lvert 2 \rvert + 3$	5	$(2, 5)$

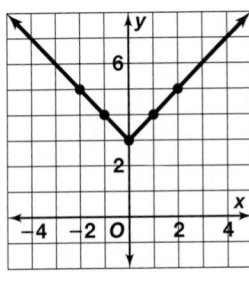

21. U shape

x	$x^2 - 8$	y	(x, y)
-2	$(-2)^2 - 8$	-4	$(-2, -4)$
-1	$(-1)^2 - 8$	-7	$(-1, -7)$
0	$(0)^2 - 8$	-8	$(0, -8)$
1	$(1)^2 - 8$	-7	$(1, -7)$
2	$(2)^2 - 8$	-4	$(2, -4)$

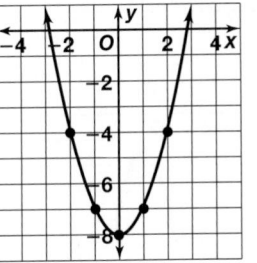

Lesson 12-3   pp. 683–684

EXERCISES

1.

x	4^x	y	(x, y)
0	4^0	1	$(0, 1)$
1	4^1	4	$(1, 4)$
2	4^2	16	$(2, 16)$
3	4^3	64	$(3, 64)$
4	4^4	256	$(4, 256)$

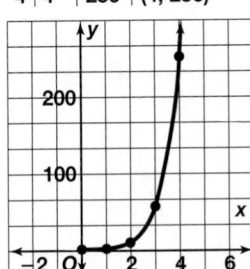

11. B **13.** C

9.

x	$30(\frac{1}{3})^x$	y	(x, y)
0	$30(\frac{1}{3})^0$	30	$(0, 30)$
1	$30(\frac{1}{3})^1$	10	$(1, 10)$
2	$30(\frac{1}{3})^2$	$3\frac{1}{3}$	$(2, 3\frac{1}{3})$
3	$30(\frac{1}{3})^3$	$1\frac{1}{9}$	$(3, 1\frac{1}{9})$
4	$30(\frac{1}{3})^4$	$\frac{10}{27}$	$(4, \frac{10}{27})$
5	$30(\frac{1}{3})^5$	$\frac{10}{81}$	$(5, \frac{10}{81})$

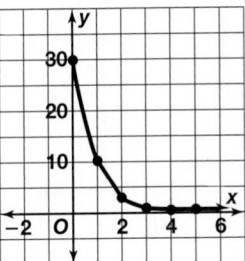

15.

x	$\frac{1}{5} \cdot 5^x$	y	(x, y)
0	$\frac{1}{5} \cdot 5^0$	$\frac{1}{5}$	$(0, \frac{1}{5})$
1	$\frac{1}{5} \cdot 5^1$	1	$(1, 1)$
2	$\frac{1}{5} \cdot 5^2$	5	$(2, 5)$
3	$\frac{1}{5} \cdot 5^3$	25	$(3, 25)$
4	$\frac{1}{5} \cdot 5^4$	125	$(4, 125)$

21. yes; $2^4 = 16$
23. no; $\left(\frac{1}{2}\right)^4 \neq 16$

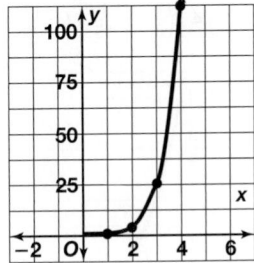

Lesson 12-4   pp. 688–689

EXERCISES 1. No; it is a sum. **3.** Yes; it is a product of the real number $\frac{1}{3}$ and the variable a. **9.** binomial **15.** monomial **19.** 32 **23.** 37 **29.** Yes; it is a real number. **31.** No; it is a sum. **33.** binomial **37.** binomial **43.** -4 **47.** 12

Lesson 12-5   pp. 694–696

EXERCISES 1. $(2x^2 + x + 2) + (x^2 + 4) = 3x^2 + x + 6$ **3.** $2x^2 + 4x + 7$ **5.** $-x + 5$ **7.** $2a + 9b$ **11.** $2x^3 + 5x^2 + x + 4$ **13.** $3x + 8$ **17.** $-2ab + 2$ **19.** $x^2 - 8x - 5$ **23.** $w^2 + 7w - 6$ **29.** $m^2 + 5m$ **33.** $5y - 2$ **35.** $4b - 1$ **37.** $2a + 2$

Lesson 12-6   pp. 699–700

EXERCISES 1. $3x^2 + 3x$ **5.** $6x^2 + 2x$ **13.** $5x^3 + x^2 - 4x$ **15.** $6b^3 - 3b^2 + 12b$ **21.** $d^2(3d^2 + 1)$ **25.** $7(2a^2 + a - 1)$ **31.** $a^3 + 3a$ **35.** $6y^4 - 12y^3 - 2y^2$ **41.** D **43.** $4x^2(x^3 - x^2 + 2)$ **45.** $2a(a^2 - 3a - 2)$

Lesson 12-7   pp. 703–704

EXERCISES 1. $x^2 + 3x + 2$ **5.** $x^2 + 9x + 20$ **11.** $c^2 + 16c + 63$ **17.** $x^2 + x - 6$ **19.** C **21.** $9x^2 - 9$ **23.** $n^2 + 4n - 320$ **25.** $b^2 + 2b + 1$

Lesson 12-8   pp. 708–709

EXERCISES 1a. 4:30 P.M. **b.** 180 mi **3.** 30 ft **7.** Sandy 101 g, White Ears 108 g, Sport 115 g **9.** 64 choices

---

Chapter 12 Review   pp. 711–713

EXERCISES 1. d **2.** e **3.** a **4.** f **5.** b **6.** h **7.** g **8.** i **9.** c **10.** 17, 21, 25; start with 1 and add 4 repeatedly. **11.** $-3.75, -1.875, -0.9375$; start with -60 and multiply by 0.5 repeatedly. **12.** 128, 135, 142; start with 100 and add 7 repeatedly. **13.** $-20, -25, -30$; start with 0 and add -5 repeatedly. **14.** $-18, -29, -40$; start with 26 and add -11 repeatedly. **15.** $62\frac{1}{2}, 312\frac{1}{2}, 1{,}562\frac{1}{2}$; start with $\frac{1}{10}$ and multiply by 5 repeatedly. **16.** arithmetic; 25, 29, 33 **17.** geometric; $-\frac{1}{2}, -\frac{1}{4}, -\frac{1}{8}$ **18.** arithmetic; 7, 8, 9 **19.** arithmetic; 22, 33, 44 **20.** neither; 30, 3, 40 **21.** geometric; $\frac{2}{25}, \frac{4}{25}, \frac{8}{25}$ **22.** Sample: A club starts with 10 members and adds 1 new member every week; 10, 11, 12, . . .; 1

23.

x	$\frac{1}{2}x^2$	y	(x, y)
-2	$\frac{1}{2} \cdot (-2)^2$	2	$(-2, 2)$
-1	$\frac{1}{2} \cdot (-1)^2$	$\frac{1}{2}$	$(-1, \frac{1}{2})$
0	$\frac{1}{2} \cdot (0)^2$	0	$(0, 0)$
1	$\frac{1}{2} \cdot (1)^2$	$\frac{1}{2}$	$(1, \frac{1}{2})$
2	$\frac{1}{2} \cdot (2)^2$	2	$(2, 2)$

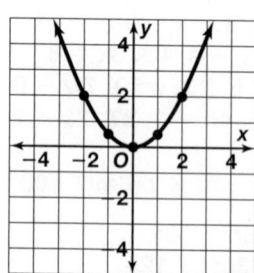

24.

x	$2|x|$	y	(x, y)
-2	$2|-2|$	4	$(-2, 4)$
-1	$2|-1|$	2	$(-1, 2)$
0	$2|0|$	0	$(0, 0)$
1	$2|1|$	2	$(1, 2)$
2	$2|2|$	4	$(2, 4)$

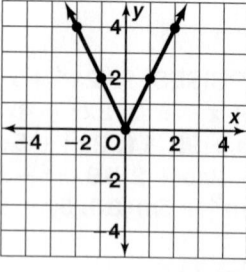

25.

x	$|x| + 1$	y	(x, y)
-2	$|-2| + 1$	3	$(-2, 3)$
-1	$|-1| + 1$	2	$(-1, 2)$
0	$|0| + 1$	1	$(0, 1)$
1	$|1| + 1$	2	$(1, 2)$
2	$|2| + 1$	3	$(2, 3)$

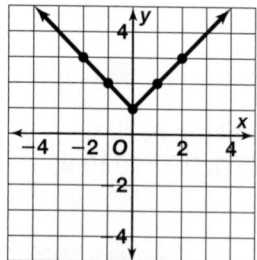

26.

x	$x^2 + 5$	y	(x, y)
-2	$(-2)^2 + 5$	9	$(-2, 9)$
-1	$(-1)^2 + 5$	6	$(-1, 6)$
0	$0^2 + 5$	5	$(0, 5)$
1	$1^2 + 5$	6	$(1, 6)$
2	$2^2 + 5$	9	$(2, 9)$

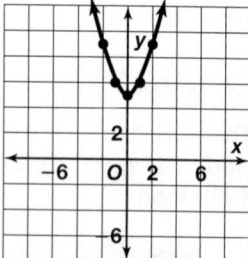

27.

x	$-|x|$	y	(x, y)
-2	$-|-2|$	-2	$(-2, -2)$
-1	$-|-1|$	-1	$(-1, -1)$
0	$-|0|$	0	$(0, 0)$
1	$-|1|$	-1	$(1, -1)$
2	$-|2|$	-2	$(2, -2)$

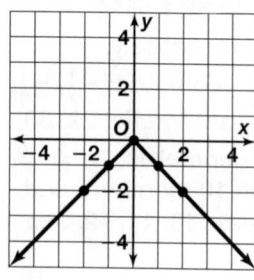

28.

x	$\frac{1}{2}|x|$	y	(x, y)
-2	$\frac{1}{2}|-2|$	1	$(-2, 1)$
-1	$\frac{1}{2}|-1|$	$\frac{1}{2}$	$(-1, \frac{1}{2})$
0	$\frac{1}{2}|0|$	0	$(0, 0)$
1	$\frac{1}{2}|1|$	$\frac{1}{2}$	$(1, \frac{1}{2})$
2	$\frac{1}{2}|2|$	1	$(2, 1)$

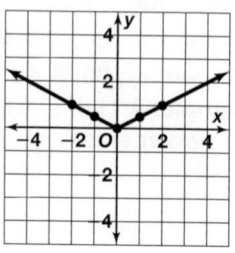

29.

x	$-x^2 - 3$	y	(x, y)
-2	$-(-2)^2 - 3$	-7	$(-2, -7)$
-1	$-(-1)^2 - 3$	-4	$(-1, -4)$
0	$-(0)^2 - 3$	-3	$(0, -3)$
1	$-(1)^2 - 3$	-4	$(1, -4)$
2	$-(2)^2 - 3$	-7	$(2, -7)$

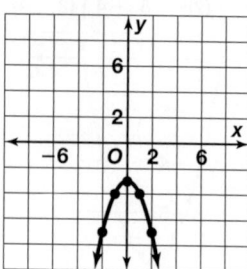

30.

x	$-x^2 + 4$	y	(x, y)
-2	$-(-2)^2 + 4$	0	$(-2, 0)$
-1	$-(-1)^2 + 4$	3	$(-1, 3)$
0	$-(0)^2 + 4$	4	$(0, 4)$
1	$-(1)^2 + 4$	3	$(1, 3)$
2	$-(2)^2 + 4$	0	$(2, 0)$

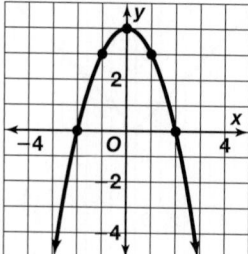

31.

x	$\left(\frac{1}{4}\right)^x$	y	(x, y)
0	$\left(\frac{1}{4}\right)^0$	1	$(0, 1)$
1	$\left(\frac{1}{4}\right)^1$	$\frac{1}{4}$	$(1, \frac{1}{4})$
2	$\left(\frac{1}{4}\right)^2$	$\frac{1}{16}$	$(2, \frac{1}{16})$
3	$\left(\frac{1}{4}\right)^3$	$\frac{1}{64}$	$(3, \frac{1}{64})$
4	$\left(\frac{1}{4}\right)^4$	$\frac{1}{256}$	$(4, \frac{1}{256})$

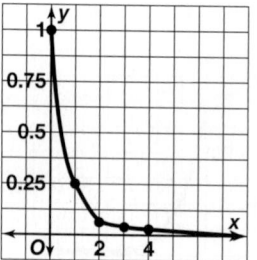

32.

x	$\frac{1}{2} \cdot 2^x$	y	(x, y)
0	$\frac{1}{2} \cdot 2^0$	$\frac{1}{2}$	$(0, \frac{1}{2})$
1	$\frac{1}{2} \cdot 2^1$	1	$(1, 1)$
2	$\frac{1}{2} \cdot 2^2$	2	$(2, 2)$
3	$\frac{1}{2} \cdot 2^3$	4	$(3, 4)$
4	$\frac{1}{2} \cdot 2^4$	8	$(4, 8)$

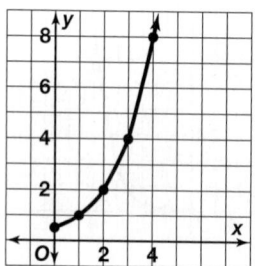

33.

x	3^x	y	(x, y)
0	3^0	1	$(0, 1)$
1	3^1	3	$(1, 3)$
2	3^2	9	$(2, 9)$
3	3^3	27	$(3, 27)$
4	3^4	81	$(4, 81)$

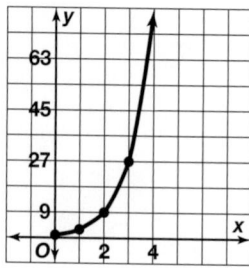

34.

x	$\left(\frac{1}{2}\right)^x$	y	(x, y)
0	$\left(\frac{1}{2}\right)^0$	1	$(0, 1)$
1	$\left(\frac{1}{2}\right)^1$	$\frac{1}{2}$	$(1, \frac{1}{2})$
2	$\left(\frac{1}{2}\right)^2$	$\frac{1}{4}$	$(2, \frac{1}{4})$
3	$\left(\frac{1}{2}\right)^3$	$\frac{1}{8}$	$(3, \frac{1}{8})$
4	$\left(\frac{1}{2}\right)^4$	$\frac{1}{16}$	$(4, \frac{1}{16})$

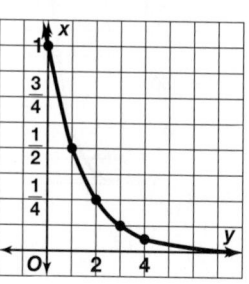

35. monomial **36.** binomial **37.** monomial
38. trinomial **39.** monomial **40.** monomial
41. binomial **42.** binomial **43.** binomial
44. trinomial **45.** 32 **46.** 7 **47.** 6 **48.** −12 **49.** 9
50. $3a^2 + 2a + 8$ **51.** $4m^2 − 2m − 12$
52. $4x^2 − 2x + 2$ **53.** $4p − 7q − 2$
54. $3w^2 + 9w − 5$ **55.** $6x + 6y$ **56.** $2a^2 + 5a$
57. $12c^2 − 28c$ **58.** $−30y^2 − 18y$
59. $3x^3 − 3x^2 − 15x$ **60.** $x^3 + 7x^2$
61. $2x^4 − 6x^3 − 12x^2$ **62.** $x^2 + 7x + 12$
63. $x^2 − 4x − 5$ **64.** $x^2 − 6x + 8$ **65.** $x(x − 1)$
66. $9(p^2 + 3)$ **67.** $3x(x^2 − 3x + 2)$
68. $5(b^5 + 4b^3 − 6)$ **69.** $2x(4x^2 + x + 2)$
70. $4a(7a − b)$ **71.** 2,401 ft^2 **72.** Answers may
vary. Sample: A diagram gives a visual picture
of the problem. A table organizes possible
dimensions and their related areas. Looking
for a pattern leads to the answer.

Extra Practice

Chapter 1   pp. 720–721

1. $x − 6$ **5.** $8p$ **9.** 9 **11.** 5 **13.** 42 **15.** 11
19. = **21.** > **23.** −7 **27.** −32 **31.** Start with
−12, and add 9 to the previous term. 33, 42, 51
33. Add the two previous terms. 21, 34, 55 **37.** 24
41. 9   **42–50.**

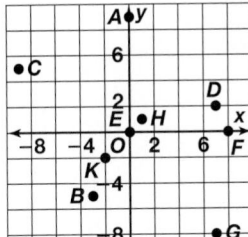

51. $g − 8$
53. $28 ÷ 7 − 2 = 2$
55. $3 + 10p = 33$
57. $t − 4$
59. $1000 − 450 = 550$
61. incorrect; $−5 + 2 = −3$
63. 12
65. (−3, −6)

Chapter 2   pp. 722–723

1. $99 + (−99) + 45 + (−46)$
Commutative Property of Addition
$0 + 45 + (−46)$
additive inverse
$−1$

5. $2 • 50 • 58$
Commutative Property of Multiplication
$100 • 58$
Multiply from left to right.
$5,800$

7. 20 **13.** $−17y + 38$ **17.** $\frac{−3}{−1} = 3$; true **21.** −24
25. 24 **33.**

35.

39. $x > −13$ **43.** $c ≤ −15$
49. Commutative Prop. of Add.
51. 116,800 people **53.** $4d + 7 + 3 = 4d + 10$
55. $15w = 105; 15(6) = 90$; no
57. $15p = 165$; 11 cans **59.** 10 and 12
61. $7p > 42; p > 6$

63. $s + 37 ≥ 100; s ≥ 63$

Chapter 3   pp. 724–725

1. about 13; rounding **5.** about 120; clustering
7. about 120 **11.** about 18 **13.** mean: 12.9;
median: 12; modes: 10 and 12; outlier: 19
15. mean: $27.30; median: $29; mode: $30; outlier:
$15 **17.** 130 yd **19.** 175 mi **25.** 63.6 **33.** 3
37. 0.25 **45.** 0.036 **49.** about $21 **51.** about $27
53. $31.20; $30; $25; $17; mean **55.** about 0.65
mi/min **57.** 52.5 mi **59.** $1.5c = 5.64$; $3.76/lb
61. 10,000 m

Chapter 4   pp. 726–727

1. S = edge length; ℓ = total length of edges; ℓ =
$12s$ **3.** e = length of rectangle,
A = area of rectangle; $A = 12e$ **17.** < **19.** <
25. $C = 0.20E$ **27.** $C = 9n$
29. mean = 39.375
    median = 38
    mode = 35
31. mean = 6.3
    median = 6
    mode = 5,8
33. c = cost of gas
    g = gallons
    $c = 2.25g$
35. a = available tickets
    s = tickets sold
    $a = 4200 − s$

37. 7725 ft^2 **39.** Answer may vary Sample: false;
$1 ÷ 2 = \frac{1}{2}$ **41.** number of people; total charge
43. acres plowed; time **45.** no correlation;
The length of a town's name is not likely to affect
its population. **47.** negative; The lower the price,
the more likely people are to buy it.

Chapter 5   pp. 728–729

1. −11 **3.** $\frac{−32}{15}$ **25.** $−16x + 12$
27. $8 − 4t$ **37.** $\frac{5}{54}$ **39.** 0 **45.** $\frac{1}{12}$ **47.** $\frac{1}{6}$ **51.** $\frac{5}{72}$
53. 75°C **55.** $16 **59.** $27.65 **61.** $48.60
63. Comm. Prop. of Mult. **65.** $\frac{1}{2}$ **67.** $\frac{1}{4}$ **69.** $\frac{5}{87}$

Chapter 6   pp. 730–731

1. 2 **3.** −5.7 **13.** t = test score;
$\frac{87 + 84 + 85 + t}{4} = 90$; no **15.** 1 **17.** −40 **25.** 1
27. 26 **33.** bus: 5h; car: 4h **35.** 16% increase
37. 200% increase **41.** $\pm\frac{2}{3}$ **43.** $\pm\frac{5}{6}$
47. no; $3^2 + 7^2 \neq 10^2$ **49.** no; $3 + 4 \neq 5$
51. 10.3 **53.** 9.1 **55.** 7h **57.** $340; $510
61. about 16.9 ft/sec **63.** 1.25 mi **65.** 12.5%
increase **67.** about 19.4 ft

Chapter 7   pp. 732–733

1. $w > -3$;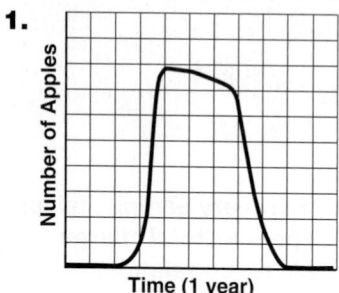
3. $r > -4$;
25. $18x \leq 102$, 5 balls **27.** $5 < w < 7$
29. $m \leq 4$ or $m > 8.4$ **37.** $|x| < 2$ **39.** $|x + 4| < 1$
43. $t > 1$ or $t < -1$;
45. $m > 3\frac{2}{3}$ or $m < -3$;
51. $|x - 2.5| < 0.5$
53. c is the number of cars sold; $c \geq 35$
55. y is age in years; $y \geq 18$
57. $375 + c \geq 500$, $c \geq 125$ **59.** $25c \geq 200$, $c \geq 8$
63. $32 \leq t \leq 212$
67. $|r - 4.25| \leq 0.005$; $4.245 \leq r \leq 4.255$

Chapter 8   pp. 734–735

1.

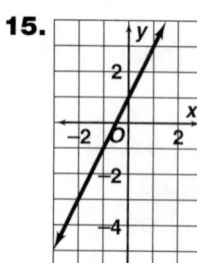

5. {−29, −11, −5, 13} **7.** {5, −1, 1, 19} **11.** yes
13. yes

15.

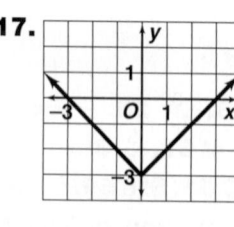

17.

19. $f(x) = 2x$ **21.** $f(x) = \frac{1}{2}x$
23.

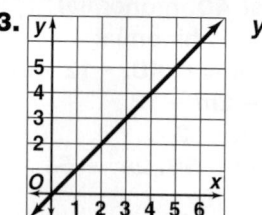

$y = x$

27. 70 **29.** 0.8 **31.** 7.5
33. 8 **37.** −4, −10 **39.** 5, 17 **43.** {19, 16, 11}
45. {8, 32, 72} **49.** $A(w) = 100w$
51. $P(n) = \frac{n}{16}$ **53.** $P = 4s$; 53.6 in.
55. $rt = 12$; about 6.9 mi/h
57. $9020, $8840, $8660

CHAPTER 9   pp. 736–737

1. 0.2 m/yr **3.** 1.6 mm/s
5. slope = 6, y-intercept = 8
7. slope = 0, y-intercept = 4
13. x-intercept = 2, y-intercept = 12
15. x-intercept = −6, y-intercept = 3
17. $y - 6 = -5(x - 4)$ **19.** $y - 5 = \frac{1}{2}(x - 8)$
21.

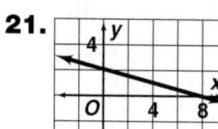

27. $y = \frac{3}{2}x + 2$
29. $y = x + 6$
35. $4x - y = -17$
37. $4x - 3y = 25$

41a–b.

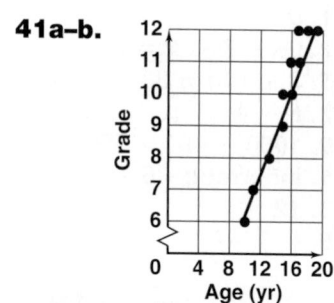

c. grade = 0.720 · age − 1.118

43.

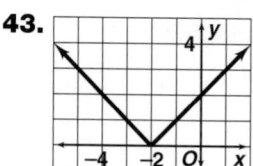

51. −250 ft/s **53.** $y = 6x + 2575$
55. $t = 2n$; even whole numbers
57. $3j + 2c = 25$ **59.** $y - 24 = \frac{3}{4}(x - 32)$
61. False; the slopes of perpendicular lines have
a product of −1, so one must be positive and the
other must be negative. **63.** $y = 50|x - 0.5|$

CHAPTER 10 pp. 738–739

1. $(4, -3)$;

1.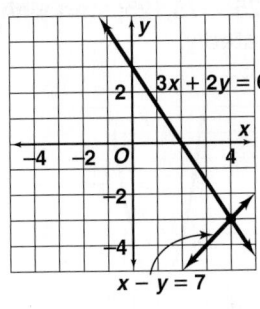

5. $x = 1, y = -1$
7. $x = 6, y = 13$
9. $x = 4, y = -9$
13. $x + y = 12$,
$5x + y = 32$, 5 nickels,
7 pennies
15. $2x + 2y = 74$,
$7x + 2y = 159$,
length:
20 ft, width: 17 ft

19. 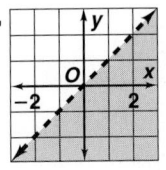 **25.**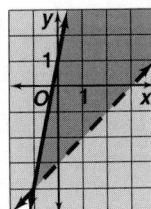

31. $y = 0.5 + 0.02x$
$y = 0.25 + 0.03x$
25 minutes

33. $c + s = 300, s = c + 110$; corn: 95 acres;
soybeans: 205 acres

35. $4h + 7c = 34.50, 8h + 3c = 30.50$; h: \$2.50,
c: \$3.50 **37.** $b = \frac{4}{5}g, b + g = 3321$; 1476 boys,
1845 girls

CHAPTER 11 pp. 740–741

1. $\frac{1}{64t^6}$ **3.** 20.25 **17.** 9 **19.** 144
25. 3.4×10^7 **27.** 1.5×10^3 **33.** 8,050,000
35. 900,000,000 **41.** 1.5; 40.5, 60.75
43. 0.2; −0.008, −0.0016
49. $\left\{\frac{1}{3}, 1, 3, 9\right\}$; increase **51.** $\left\{\frac{2}{3}, 1, \frac{3}{2}, \frac{9}{4}\right\}$; increase
61. exponential growth; growth factor = 8
63. exponential decay; decay factor = $\frac{1}{2}$
69. $y = 200(1.04)^x$; \$243.33
71. $y = 3000(0.92)^x$; \$2336.06
73. 7.5×10^9 **75.** about 9.5×10^{12} km
77. about 9.5×10^{-11} m² **79.** 36 min
81. $A(n) = 60 \cdot (0.4)^{n-1}$; 0.6144
83. $f(x) = 15 \cdot 3^x$; 10,935 **85.** \$987.61

Chapter 12 pp. 742–743

1. 20, 0, −20; start with 100 and add −20
repeatedly **5.** −3,125, 15,625, −78,125; start with
−5 and multiply by −5 repeatedly.

9. 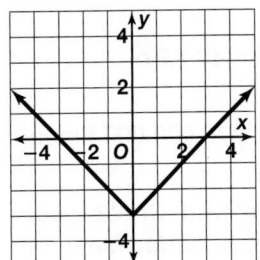 **13.**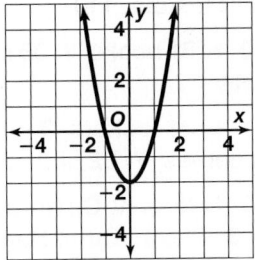

15.

x	y
0	1
1	4
2	16
3	64
4	256

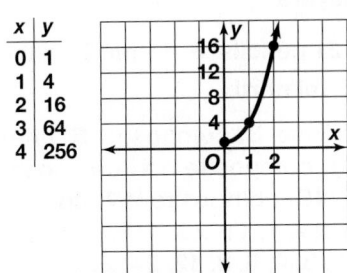

17.

x	y
0	10
1	5
2	2.5
3	1.25
4	0.625

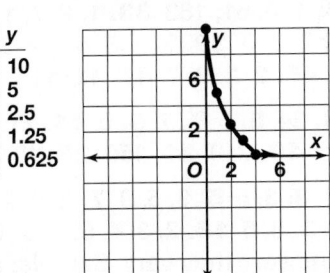

19. trinomial **23.** monomial **27.** $7y - 2$
31. $6x^2 + 5x - 12$ **35.** $10x^3 + 12x$
39. $2y^2 + 16y + 24$ **43.** $2(a^2b - 2a + 3b)$
45. $x(6y + 2 + 3xy)$ **47.** 25, 30, 35 **49.** 6 ft
51. **53.** 144 m²
55. $(8x^2 + 48x)$ m²
57.

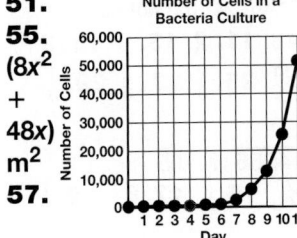

Number of Cells in a
Bacteria Culture

$(50.24c^2 - 50.24c + 12.56)$ ft²

Algebra Skills Handbook

p. 748 1. 10 games **3.** 9 tacks

p. 749 1. 17 and 19, or –19 and –17 **3.** 33, 34, 35, and 36 **5.** 24 years old **7.** mother: 38 yr; son: 16 yr; daughter: 7 yr **9.** regular tickets: 80; student tickets: 110

p. 750 1. 81 books **3.** 36 stories **5.** 7.2 m **7.** 6 ways

p. 751 1. 21 lockers **3.** about 370,000,000 times **5.** 63 games **7.** 32 and 33

p. 752 1. dog: K. C.; horse: Bo; bird: Cricket; cat: Tuffy **3.** Alexa, Karin, Heather, Annette, Tanya, Garo **5.** 126 players

p. 753 1. 6 **3.** 21 pencils **5.** 11 mi **7.** 290 mi **9.** $4\frac{3}{4}$ mi east, 2 mi north

p. 754 1. composite **3.** composite **5.** prime **7.** composite **9.** composite **11.** composite **13.** composite **15.** composite **17.** composite **19.** 1, 2, 23, 46 **21.** 1, 11 **23.** 1, 3, 9, 27 **25.** 1, 5, 41, 205 **27.** 1, 2, 3, 4, 6, 8, 12, 24 **29.** 1, 2, 4, 8, 11, 22, 44, 88 **31.** 1, 3, 61, 183 **33.** 1, 2, 7, 14, 49, 98 **35.** 1, 59 **37.** $2 \cdot 3 \cdot 3$ **39.** $3 \cdot 3 \cdot 3$ **41.** $2 \cdot 2 \cdot 2 \cdot 2 \cdot 2 \cdot 2$ **43.** $2 \cdot 2 \cdot 5 \cdot 5$ **45.** $2 \cdot 2 \cdot 3 \cdot 7$ **47.** $11 \cdot 11$

p. 755 1. 2 **3.** 24 **5.** 3 **7.** 7 **9.** 5 **11.** 21 **13.** 80 **15.** 33 **17.** 60 **19.** 240 **21.** 150 **23.** 40

p. 756 1. 2, 4 **3.** 3, 5 **5.** 3, 5, 9 **7.** 2 **9.** 2, 3, 4, 6, 8, 9 **11.** none **13.** 3, 5 **15.** 2, 3, 4, 6, 8, 9 **17.** 2, 4 **19.** 15 **21.** Answers may vary. Sample: $a + 1$ is not divisible by 2. Dividing by 2 will leave a remainder of 1.

p. 757 1. $350 **3.** $300 **5.** $17.00 **7.** 7.10 **9.** 7.00 **11.** $30.80

p. 758 1. $\frac{8}{14}, \frac{12}{21}, \frac{16}{28}, \frac{20}{35}, \frac{24}{42}$ **3.** $\frac{6}{16}, \frac{9}{24}, \frac{12}{32}, \frac{15}{40}, \frac{18}{48}$ **5.** $\frac{10}{12}, \frac{15}{18}, \frac{20}{24}, \frac{25}{30}, \frac{30}{36}$ **7.** 9 **9.** 48 **11.** 2 **13.** 9 **15.** 3 **17.** no **19.** no **21.** no **23.** $\frac{1}{2}$ **25.** $\frac{2}{3}$ **27.** $\frac{2}{5}$ **29.** $\frac{1}{3}$ **31.** $\frac{2}{5}$ **33.** $\frac{3}{4}$

p. 759 1. 0.3 **3.** 0.2 **5.** $0.\overline{714285}$ **7.** $0.\overline{5}$ **9.** $0.\overline{285714}$ **11.** 0.16 **13.** $\frac{7}{100}$ **15.** $\frac{7}{8}$ **17.** $6\frac{1}{3}$ **19.** $\frac{7}{9}$ **21.** $\frac{3}{8}$ **23.** $6\frac{12}{25}$

p. 760 1. $\frac{5}{7}$ **3.** 3 **5.** $10\frac{7}{15}$ **7.** $6\frac{2}{9}$ **9.** $6\frac{7}{33}$ **11.** $9\frac{2}{3}$ **13.** $13\frac{7}{16}$ **15.** $56\frac{11}{15}$ **17.** $\frac{3}{5}$ **19.** $1\frac{2}{7}$ **21.** $2\frac{3}{8}$ **23.** $3\frac{1}{3}$ **25.** $9\frac{4}{63}$ **27.** $2\frac{1}{6}$ **29.** $7\frac{5}{6}$

1. 20, 0, –20; start with 100 and add –20 repeatedly **5.** –3,125, 15,625, –78,125; start with –5 and multiply by –5 repeatedly.

9. 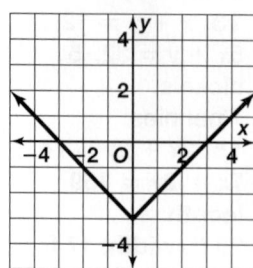   **13.**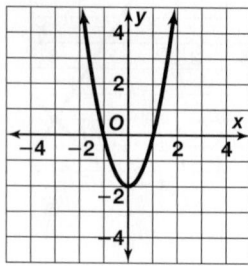

15.

x	y
0	1
1	4
2	16
3	64
4	256

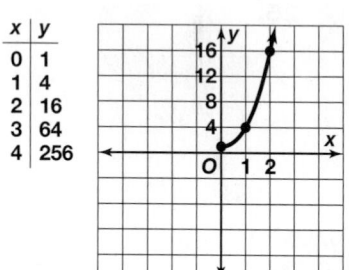

17.

x	y
0	10
1	5
2	2.5
3	1.25
4	0.625

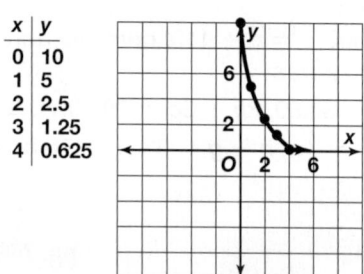

19. trinomial **23.** monomial **27.** $7y - 2$ **31.** $6x^2 + 5x - 12$ **35.** $10x^3 + 12x$ **39.** $2y^2 + 16y + 24$ **43.** $2(a^2b - 2a + 3b)$ **45.** $x(6y + 2 + 3xy)$ **47.** 25, 30, 35 **49.** 6 ft

51.

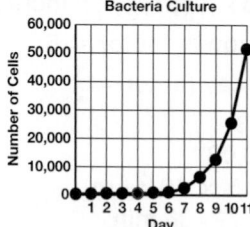

Number of Cells in a Bacteria Culture

    53. 144 m²

55. $(8x^2 + 48x)$ m² **57.** $(50.24c^2 - 50.24c + 12.56)$ ft²

Skills Handbook

PAGE 779 **1.** > **3.** > **11.** 3,347; 3,474; 3,734; 3,747; 3,774 **13.** 30,256,403; 30,265,403; 32,056,403; 302,056,403

PAGE 780 **3.** 670 **5.** 7,030 **15.** 82,000 **17.** 35,000 **23.** 71,230,000 **25.** 400,000

PAGE 781 **17.** 9,214 **19.** 492

PAGE 782 **37.** 26 R 8 **39.** 7 R 32

PAGE 783 **1.** 9 hundred-thousandths **3.** 5 hundredths **9.** 0.000008 **11.** 0.013 **15.** eleven hundred-thousandths **17.** twelve thousandths

PAGE 784 **1.** < **3.** > **13.** 0.23, 0.231, 2.31, 3.21, 23.1 **15.** 0.002, 0.02, 0.22, 0.222, 2.22

PAGE 785 **1.** 105,000 **5.** 4,312,000 **7.** 3 **9.** 101 **11.** 82.0 **13.** 20.4 **17.** 96.40 **19.** 4.23 **33.** 2.58 **35.** 19

PAGE 786 **41.** 12.403 **43.** 747.1109

PAGE 787 **9.** 1.1424 **11.** 2.07828

PAGE 788 **31.** 0.01812 **33.** 0.007

PAGE 789 **23.** 2.551 **25.** 3.9

PAGE 790 **15.** 0.47 **17.** 0.236

PAGE 791 **15.** 16 **17.** 44

PAGE 792 **1.** 0.046 **3.** 0.075

PAGE 793 **9.** 3 **11.** 16 **17.** $\frac{5}{6}$ **19.** $\frac{3}{4}$

PAGE 794 **9.** $3\frac{2}{5}$ **11.** $4\frac{1}{4}$ **39.** $\frac{24}{7}$ **41.** $\frac{31}{10}$

PAGE 795 **7.** $\frac{3}{8}$ **9.** $\frac{3}{5}$

PAGE 796 **13.** $7\frac{1}{2}$ **15.** $43\frac{3}{4}$ **19.** $\frac{7}{8}$ **21.** $1\frac{3}{8}$

PAGE 797 **5.** 3 **7.** 12 **11.** < **15.** >

Index

Distance-rate-time problems
  formula for, 318, 335
  solving, 335–338, 574

Distributive Property, 73–75, 120, 254,
    255–257, 823
  Addition, 73–74, 693
  area of rectangle, 73–74
  defined, 73, 255, 263, 286
  like terms in, 79, 302
  multiplication, 73–74, 697, 701
  multiplying polynomials, 713
  solving equations using, 303–305
  solving inequalities using, 397
  substitution and, 559
  using, 255–256, 264
  variable expressions, 75, 120

Divisibility, 788

Division
  decimals, 135, 154–155, 771, 773
  estimating quotients, 135, 172
  fractions, 778, 793
  integers, 46, 56, 61
  numbers with different signs, 248, 286
  numbers with same sign, 248, 286
  order of operations, 8–10, 46
  powers, 629–631, 772
  rational numbers, 248–249, 286
  solving equations, 94–95, 154–155, 294
  solving inequalities, 112–113, 121,
    390–391
  using reciprocal, 249
  by zero, 249

Division Property
  Equality, 94, 294, 309, 823
  Inequality, 112, 390, 823

Divisor, 135

Domain
  of function, 205, 224
  reasonable, 205, 206, 500, 501, 502,
    503, 642

Dorling Kindersley Activity Lab. *See*
  Activity Lab

Double-bar graph, 199

Draw a Diagram, 540, 780

Drawing, scale, 327, 368

E

Earth, geometry of, 371

EDIT feature, on graphing calculator,
  527, 531

Einstein, Albert, 625

Element
  in matrix, 235
  in set, 409

Elimination method, 563–566, 572, 598

Endpoint, 389

Enrichment. *See also* Extensions
  algebraic expressions and integers, 7,
    12, 17, 21, 28, 33, 39, 43, 56
  decimals and fractions, 133, 137, 143,
    147, 153, 157, 162, 168
  exponents and exponential functions,
    611, 616, 621, 627, 634, 640, 648, 657

graphs and functions, 432, 437, 443, 450,
  458, 466, 472
linear equations and graphs, 491, 498,
  503, 510, 517, 524, 531, 538
nonlinear functions and polynomials,
  674, 678, 684, 689, 695, 700, 709
one-step equations and inequalities, 72,
  77, 81, 85, 92, 97, 107, 110, 116
rational numbers, 238, 244, 251, 252,
  260, 266, 274, 282
solving equations, 300, 307, 314, 324,
  330, 341, 349, 355, 362
solving inequalities, 380, 386, 392, 400,
  407, 415
systems of equations and inequalities,
  555, 561, 568, 577, 585, 593
variables, function patterns, and graphs,
  184, 190, 198, 207, 212, 221

Equality
  Addition Property of, 90, 151, 294, 309,
    563, 823
  Division Property of, 94, 294, 309, 823
  Multiplication Property of, 95, 294, 320,
    823
  Reflexive Property of, 417, 823
  Subtraction Property of, 88, 294, 297,
    309, 563, 564, 823
  Symmetric Property of, 417, 823
  Transitive Property of, 417, 823

Equations. *See also* Function(s)
  classifying, 82
  combining like terms, 692
  decimals, 150–151, 154–155, 173, 304
  defined, 82, 181
  direct variation, 453–455
  equivalent, 294
  fractions, 304
  grouping symbols, 303, 305
  identity, 312, 313, 341, 368, 399
  inverse variation, 461
  linear. *See* Linear equations
  literal, 316
  modeling, 86–87, 120, 309
  modeling relationships with, 181–182
  multi-step, 302–305, 374
  with no solution, 312, 313, 341
  one-step, 294, 374
  parallel lines, 520
  perpendicular lines, 521
  problem solving and, 334–338, 369
  quadratic. *See* Quadratic equations
  solution of, 83, 120, 294
  solving, 217, 294
  solving by adding, 90, 109, 121, 151, 294
  solving by dividing, 94–95, 154–155, 294
  solving by inverse operations, 88–90,
    94–95
  solving by multiplying, 95, 155, 294
  solving by subtracting, 88–89,
    150–151, 294
  solving using Distributive Property,
    303–305
  solving using graphs, 301, 445
  solving using properties of equality, 294
  solving using tables, 301, 310, 336
  standard form of, 506–508, 515, 518, 542
  substitution, 83, 145–146

transforming with only variables, 316
trend line, 526–527, 528, 530, 531,
  532, 533
two-step, 295–297, 367, 374
variables on both sides, 310–312
writing, 82–83

Equivalent equations, 294

Equivalent fractions, 790

Equivalent inequalities, 382, 420

Eratosthenes, 371

Error(s), 345–346, 350, 369

Error Analysis, *See also* Mental Math.
  algebraic expressions and integers, 7,
    11, 16, 17, 28
  decimals and equations, 133, 153,
    156, 165
  exponents and exponential functions,
    610, 620, 626, 633
  graphs and functions, 431, 436, 437
  linear equations and graphs, 490,
    497, 510
  nonlinear functions and polynomials,
    170, 695, 703
  one-step equations and inequalities, 77,
    80, 92, 115
  rational numbers, 259, 284
  solving equations, 299, 306, 314, 329,
    348, 366
  solving inequalities, 380, 392, 400, 402
  systems of equations and inequalities,
    568, 584

Estimation, 129. *See also* Mental Math
  of answers, 789
  clustering, 131
  compatible numbers, 135
  decimals, 134–135
  to determine reasonableness, 130, 135
  differences, 130
  exercises that use,
    algebraic expressions and integers,
      33, 64
    decimals and fractions, 132, 136–137,
      143, 148, 156, 159, 162, 163, 169,
      171, 174
    exponents and exponential
      functions, 657, 659, 662
    graphs and functions, 442
    linear equations and graphs,
      490, 531
    solving equations, 300, 391
    solving inequalities, 400
    systems of equations and
      inequalities, 561
    variables, function patterns and
      graphs, 214
  front-end, 130, 131, 171, 789
  metric units, 159
  products, 134, 172
  proportions, 300
  quotients, 135
  reasonableness of, 130, 135, 159
  rounding, 129–131, 171–172
  of square roots, 353–354
  sums, 130
  tables, 138
  units of measurement, 159

Index

Index

exponents and exponential functions, 610, 616, 620, 626, 633, 640, 648, 656

graphs and functions, 431, 436, 443, 449, 465, 472

linear equations and graphs, 490, 497, 502, 510, 517, 523, 531, 538

nonlinear functions and polynomials, 673, 678, 683, 688, 695, 699, 703, 709

one-step equations and inequalities, 71, 77, 80, 85, 92, 96, 100, 107, 110, 115

rational numbers, 236, 243, 250, 260, 265, 273, 281

solving equations, 299, 307, 314, 323, 330, 340, 348, 355, 362

solving inequalities, 380, 386, 391, 399, 407, 415

systems of equations and inequalities, 554, 561, 568, 577, 585, 592

variables, function patterns, and graphs, 183, 189, 197, 206, 212, 220

Online Lesson Quiz

exponents and exponential functions, 611, 615, 621, 627, 635, 641, 649, 657

graphs and functions, 431, 437, 443, 451, 459, 465, 471

linear equations and graphs, 491, 497, 503, 511, 517, 525, 531, 539

rational numbers, 237, 243, 251, 261, 265, 275, 281

solving equations, 299, 307, 315, 323, 341, 349, 355, 363

solving inequalities, 381, 385, 393, 401, 407, 415

systems of equations and inequalities, 555, 561, 569, 577, 585, 593

variables, function patterns, and graphs, 183, 191, 199, 207, 213, 221

Online Point in Time, 239, 473, 499

Online Video Tutor Help

exponents and exponential functions, 624, 629

graphs and functions, 439, 454

linear equations and graphs, 486, 520

rational numbers, 241, 278

solving equations, 335

solving inequalities, 377, 397

systems of equations and inequalities, 566, 588

variables, function patterns, and graphs, 186

Online Vocabulary Quiz, 223, 285, 367, 419, 475, 541, 597, 661

Open-Ended

algebraic expressions and integers, 12, 20, 21, 32, 34, 48, 49, 56

decimals and equations, 133

exponents and exponential functions, 610, 620, 626, 633, 634, 639, 656, 662, 664

graphs and functions, 436, 442, 445, 449, 457, 465, 470, 471, 472, 478

linear equations and graphs, 490, 498, 502, 510, 516, 517, 523, 530, 544

nonlinear functions and polynomials, 678, 685, 688, 699, 704, 712, 714

one-step equations and inequalities, 80, 87, 92, 97, 116, 122, 124

rational numbers, 237, 243, 250, 259, 273, 276, 281, 288

solving equations, 299, 306, 314, 323, 329, 340, 348, 355, 361

solving inequalities, 379, 385, 386, 392, 399, 407, 415, 422

systems of equations and inequalities, 554, 557, 561, 568, 576, 585, 592, 593, 600, 603

variables, function patterns, and graphs, 184, 189, 191, 196, 198, 211, 212, 220, 226

Open sentence, 82, 120, 181

Operations
inverse, 294
matrix, 253
order of, 185, 186, 224

Opposite(s), 196
addition of, 24
defined, 19, 60

Opposite integers, 24

***Or,* compound inequalities joined by,** 405, 421

Order of operations, 185, 186, 224
addition, 8–10, 26, 59
division, 8–10, 46
grouping symbols, 9–10
multiplication, 8–10
subtraction, 8–19
using, 8–9, 26, 59, 60

Ordered pair, 52, 57, 61, 200, 677

Ordering
integers, 18–19
fractions, 195
numbers, 2, 197, 761

Origin, 52, 200

Outcome, 269, 286

Outlier
defined, 140
effect on mean, 140, 141

Outliers, 216

P

Papyrus, Ahmes, 239

Parabolas, 676–677, 712

Parallel lines, 519–520, 542–543

Parallelogram, 524, 822

Parent function, 493, 534

Parentheses, 9, 187, 257, 303, 470, 513, 624

Patterns. *See also* Sequences
Activity Lab, 202
arithmetic, 672, 711
discovering, 670
exercises that use, 33, 45, 49, 148, 157, 245, 250, 468, 609, 617, 640, 648, 674, 703
exponents and, 185
extending, 36, 41
finding, 245, 609, 640, 648
functions and, 203–205
geometric, 671–672, 711

inductive reasoning, 35–37, 61
looking for, 40–41, 61,
multiplying integers, 45
number, 35, 36, 40–41, 61, 468–470, 477
predictions and, 36–37, 202
as problem solving strategy, 782
tables and, 40–41, 447
variable expressions and, 202
visual, 35, 37, 38, 43
writing rules for, 35–36

Pentagon, perimeter of, 442

People and Math
Armstrong, Lance, 319
Acosta Bañuelos, Romana, 473
Cobb, Dr. Jewel Plummer, 628
Einstein, Albert, 625
Eratosthenes, 371
Griffith-Joyner, Florence, 348
Johnson, Lyndon B., 444
Loroupe, Tegla, 324
Matzeliger, Jan, 190
Papyrus, Ahmes, 239
Pythagoras, 357
Reifenstuhl, Rocky, 261
Resnik, Judith A., 499
Takahashi, Naoko, 324
Vermeer, Johannes, 289

Percent(s), 344–345, 369, 794. *See also* Decimals; Fraction(s)

Percent error, 345–346, 350, 369

Percent problems, 342–343

Perfect square(s), 353, 369

Perfect-square trinomial, 705

Perimeter
defined, 146, 797
formulas for, 146, 172, 185, 464, 797, 822
pentagon, 442
rectangle, 185, 303, 306, 334, 396, 559, 560, 562, 589, 591, 822
scale factor and, 332–333
square, 172, 822
triangle, 330, 341, 407, 464

Perpendicular lines, 520–521, 542–543

Pi (π), 194, 197

Place value, 128

Place-value chart, 128

Plane, coordinate, 52, 61, 200, 326

PLOT feature, of calculator, 57

Point(s)
endpoint, 389
finding slope using, 487
graphing, 200–201
midpoint, 201
plotting, 52–53

Point in Time
Romana Acosta Bañuelos, 473
Ahmes Papyrus, 239
Judith A. Resnik, 499

Point-slope form of linear equations, 512–515, 518, 542

Polynomials
adding, 692–693, 713
binomials, 686–687, 701–702, 705, 710, 712

R

Radicand, 352

Random event, 283

Random integer function, on graphing calculator, 276, 283

Random sample, 602

Range
of coordinates, 476
of data, 218, 225
defined, 139
finding, 139
of function, 205, 224
interquartile, 228–229
reasonable, 205, 206, 440, 500, 501, 502, 503

Rate(s). *See also* Distance-rate-time problems
of change, 484–485, 541
converting, 319
defined, 318, 484
ratios and, 318–319
unit, 318

Ratio(s)
common, 636, 637–638, 663, 671–672, 711
defined, 318, 368
direct variation and, 455–456
rates and, 318–319
trigonometric, 781

Rational numbers, 193, 194, 224. *See also* Decimals; Fraction(s); Whole numbers
adding, 232–235
defined, 193, 224
dividing, 248–249, 286
mixed numbers, 793
multiplying, 245–247, 286
other real numbers and, 194
subtracting, 240–242

Rational square roots, 353

Reading Comprehension
Geometry of Earth, 371
Milk and Calcium, 175
Music to Our Ears, 601
Numbers in Nature, 63
Train Math, 479
Travel Math, 227

Real numbers
adding, 232–233
defined, 194, 224
dividing, 248–249
multiplying, 245–247
properties of, 262–263
subtracting, 240–241

Real-World Connections. *See also* Algebra at Work; Interdisciplinary Connections; Point in Time
account balances, 32
agriculture, 281, 345, 560, 598
air travel, 339, 340, 380, 465, 485, 497, 574, 575, 576
amusement parks, 106
animal habitat, 589
art, 237, 289, 315

automobiles, 210, 219, 307, 458, 500, 560, 656, 664
aviation, 339, 340, 380, 465, 485, 497, 574, 575, 576, 577
backpacks, 583
bamboo plants, 551
banking, 288, 385, 415, 664, 700
baseball, 290–291
basketball, 259, 387, 480, 564, 639
batting averages, 155, 156, 157
bicycling, 319, 424–425, 457, 459, 464
birds, 526
birthdays, 273
blood, 276, 619
bone scans, 682
budgeting, 110, 115, 385, 420, 582, 583, 584, 591
business, 311, 313, 485, 490, 568, 575, 576, 586, 592, 593
buying a car, 560
cable service, 600
car sales, 152
carbon dating, 716–717
carousel, 490
carpentry, 447, 594, 595
carpooling, 463
cars, 210, 219, 307, 458, 500, 560, 656, 664
cell phones, 298, 306
charity, 696
checking accounts, 151, 152
cheetah, 319
chess, 708
city property, 699
climate, 421
climbing, 234
coin collections, 100
collections, 100, 133
commission, 400, 420, 495
communication, 553, 610
community service, 390, 422
commuting, 428–429, 649
comparison shopping, 141, 318
computers, 109, 111, 386, 615, 627, 632
concerts, 181
construction and building, 168, 317, 354, 361, 460, 465, 490
consumer decisions, 577
cooking, 298, 430, 514, 582
credit cards, 511, 657
culture, 120
currency, 46, 100
cycling, 319, 424–425, 457, 459, 464
day care, 116
deep-sea exploration, 44
demographics, 323
diving, 362
donations, 298
earnings, 96, 115, 391, 400, 442, 447, 457, 465, 542, 592
ecology, 648
education, 600, 656
elections, 168, 414
electricity, 340, 458, 568
energy, 625, 650
engineering, 324, 336
entertainment, 251, 370

environment, 347, 516
expenses, 399
fables, 554
famous ships, 21
fencing, 122, 168
farming, 281, 345, 560, 598
finance, 28, 152, 173, 307, 343, 633, 646
fire rescue, 358
fireworks, 687
fitness, 313, 509
food, 136, 190, 448
football, 25, 28, 234
freight handling, 400
fulcrum, 462
fund-raising, 139, 385, 391, 501, 509, 510
games, 278, 279
garage sale, 600
gardening, 71, 303, 600, 697
gas mileage, 4, 137, 458
gears, 415, 424–425
giraffes, 433
goat pen, 677
golf, 68
grades, 142
grocery shopping, 130
gymnastics, 385
Habitat for Humanity, 460
hair, 323
hat sales, 611
health care, 89, 137, 399, 615
hiking, 97
hobbies, 368, 706–707
horses, 163
iguanas, 436
in-line skating, 431
income, 84
inductive reasoning, 44, 48
information, 40
insects, 145
insurance, 299
investing, 48, 307
jewelry, 569
jobs, 12, 238, 420, 555
jogging, 709
knot tying, 163
latitude and longitude, 53
laundry, 203
lawn care, 183, 447
Library of Congress, 299
mailing packages, 590
manufacturing, 156, 220, 271, 413, 414, 421, 422, 583
marathon training, 85
marketing, 281
markup, 151
measurement, 6, 135, 157
mechanics, 174
memory, 659
memory stick, 204
metallurgy, 572–573
meteorology, 31, 33, 43, 47, 98, 101, 116, 133, 171, 249, 348, 407, 415, 430, 455, 476
milk consumption, 654–655
modeling, 7, 86, 87
money, 176–177, 236
motorcycles, 206

Index

length of side, 326
perimeter, 330, 341, 407, 464, 822
proportions, 325
right. *See* Right triangles
Sierpinski's, 640
similar, 326
sum of angles, 306
Triangle Inequality Theorem, 386
Trigonometric ratios, 821
Trinomials, 686–687, 705, 712
Try, Check, Revise, 98–99, 121, 781
Two-step equations, 295–297, 367

U

Uniform histogram, 481
Uniform motion problems, 335–338
Union, of two sets, 409
Unit analysis, 319
Unit fractions, 239
Unit rate, 318
Units of measure, 818
Unlike fractions, 792
Upper quartile, 228–229
Use Logical Reasoning, 784

V

Value, absolute. *See* Absolute value
Variable(s)
    both sides of equation, 310–312
    both sides of inequality, 397
    defined, 4, 59, 180, 224
    defining in terms of another, 334–335
    dependent, 205–206, 224
    eliminating, 566, 598
    independent, 205–206, 224
    modeling relationships with, 180–181
    one side of inequality, 395–397
    using, 474
Variable expressions, 202
    binomials, 686–687, 701–702, 705, 710, 712
    coefficient, 78, 79
    constant, 78, 79
    defined, 4, 59
    Distributive Property, 75, 120
    evaluating, 14–15, 57, 60
    identifying, 4–5, 78
    modeling with algebra tiles, 75, 79, 86–87
    monomials, 686, 697–698, 712, 713
    polynomials. *See* Polynomials
    simplifying, 78–79, 120
    terms of, 88–90
    trinomials, 686–687, 705, 712
    writing, 5, 59
Variation
    constant of, 454, 461, 477
    direct, 453–456, 462–463, 477
    linear functions and direct, 493
    inverse, 460–463, 467, 477
Venn diagrams, 215
Vermeer, Johannes, 289

Vertex, 796
Vertical angles, 311
Vertical lines, 487, 507
Vertical-line test, 434, 435, 436, 476
Vertical translations, 535–536, 543, 798
Video Tutor Help Online,
    algebraic expression and integers, 7, 11, 17, 21, 28, 32, 38, 43, 54
    decimals and equations, 133, 137, 142, 147, 152, 156, 162, 168
    exponents and exponential functions, 610, 616, 620, 624, 626, 629, 633, 640, 648, 656
    graphs and functions, 431, 436, 439, 443, 449, 454, 465, 472
    linear equations and graphs, 486, 490, 497, 502, 510, 517, 520, 523, 531, 538
    nonlinear functions and polynomials, 673, 678, 683, 688, 695, 699, 703, 709
    one-step equations and inequalities, 71, 77, 80, 85, 92, 96, 100, 107, 110, 115
    rational numbers, 236, 241, 243, 250, 260, 265, 273, 278, 281
    solving equations, 299, 307, 314, 323, 330, 335, 340, 348, 355, 362
    solving inequalities, 377, 380, 386, 391, 397, 399, 407, 415
    systems of equations and inequalities, 554, 561, 566, 568, 577, 585, 588, 592
    variables, function patterns, and graphs, 183, 186, 189, 197, 206, 212, 220
Visual patterns, 35, 37, 38, 43
Vocabulary
    exercise, 432
    New Vocabulary,
        exponents and exponential functions, 612, 636, 644, 651
        graphs and functions, 433, 439, 453, 460, 468
        linear equations and graphs, 484, 493, 506, 512, 519, 526, 535
        rational numbers, 232, 245, 255, 262, 269, 277
        solving equations, 310, 318, 325, 334, 344, 352, 357
        solving inequalities, 376, 382, 403
        systems of equations and inequalities, 550, 558, 563, 580, 587
        variables, function patterns, and graphs, 180 185, 193, 203, 209, 216
    Vocabulary Builder, 50, 117, 351, 410, 518
    Vocabulary Quiz Online, 59, 119, 171, 223, 285, 367, 419, 475, 541, 597, 661
    Vocabulary Review, 59, 119, 171, 223, 285, 367, 419, 475, 541, 597, 661, 711
    Vocabulary Tips,
        algebraic expressions and integers, 19, 45
        decimals and equations, 130, 141, 146, 159
        exponents and exponential functions, 607, 636
        graphs and functions, 435, 454, 461, 468

linear equations and graphs, 484, 493, 513, 535
    nonlinear functions and polynomials, 671, 672, 677
    one-step equations and inequalities, 69, 75, 82, 83, 105
    rational numbers, 248, 269, 270
    solving equations, 304, 311, 320, 352, 353, 357
    solving inequalities, 376, 377, 383, 399, 403
    systems of equations and inequalities, 552, 558, 563, 569
    variables, function patterns, and graphs, 180 194, 195, 217
Vocabulary Builder
    High-Use Academic Words, 410
    Learning Vocabulary, 351
    Understanding Vocabulary, 518
Vocabulary Quiz Online, 59, 119, 171, 223, 285, 367, 419, 475, 541, 597, 661
Vocabulary Review, 119, 223, 285, 367, 419, 475, 541, 597, 661
Vocabulary Tips,
    exponents and exponential functions, 607, 636
    graphs and functions, 435, 454, 461, 468
    linear equations and graphs, 484, 493, 513, 535
    rational numbers, 248, 269, 270
    solving equations, 304, 311, 320, 352, 353, 357
    solving inequalities, 376, 377, 383, 399, 403
    systems of equations and inequalities, 552, 558, 563, 569
    variables, function patterns, and graphs, 180 194, 195, 217
Volume
    cube, 626
    cylinder, 190
    defined, 797
    finding percent error in calculating, 346, 350
    formulas for, 192, 797
    measures of, 818
    rectangular prism, 350, 621
    scale factor and, 332–333
    sphere, 190, 192, 612

W

Weight, measures of, 818
Whole numbers, 19, 193, 194, 225
    comparing and ordering, 2, 761
    dividing, 764, 771
    multiplying, 763
    rounding, 762, 767
WINDOW feature, of graphing calculator, 312, 445, 492
Word problems, 192, 505, 579
Working backward, 785
Writing in Math,
    algebraic expressions and integers, 5, 7, 11, 17, 21, 28, 33, 39, 48, 55, 56, 62

Index